Art Notebook for

BIOLOGY

Campbell • Reece

Sixth Edition

San Francisco Boston New York
Cape Town Hong Kong London Madrid Mexico City
Montreal Munich Paris Singapore Sydney Tokyo Toronto

Development Editor: Evelyn Dahlgren

Art Editor: Donna Kalal

Production Artist: Karl Miyajima

Cover Photo: Photograph of an agave plant, Hawaii, © 1991 by Brett Weston. Courtesy of the Brett Weston Archive.

ISBN 0-8053-7095-1

3 4 5 6 7 8 9 10—VG—05 04 03
www.aw.com/bc

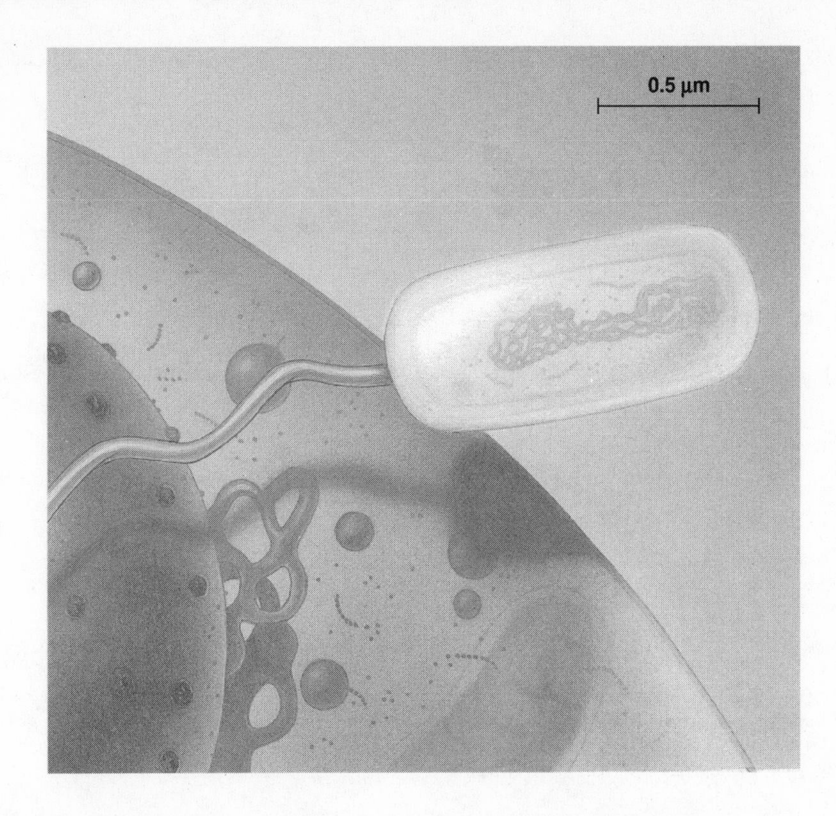

Figure 1.4 Structural organization of eukaryotic and prokaryotic cells, page 6

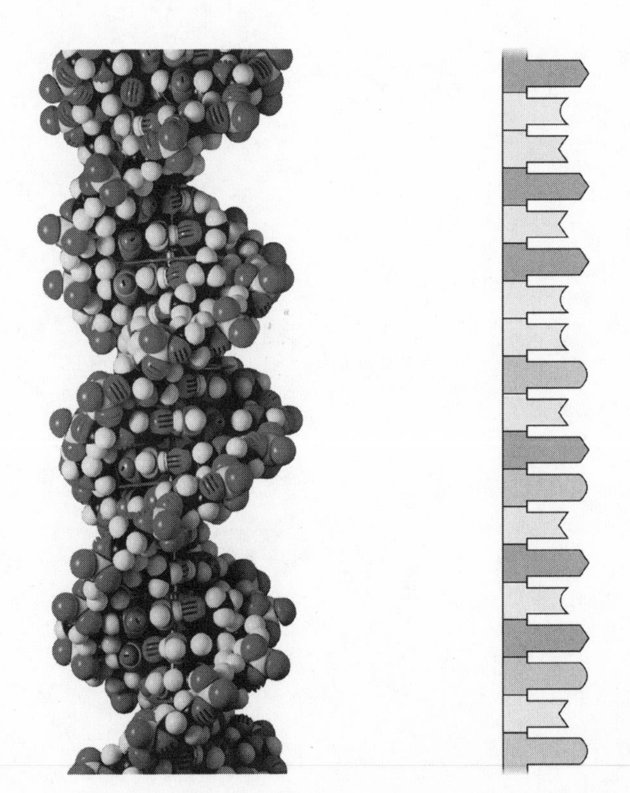

Figure 1.5 The genetic material: DNA, page 6

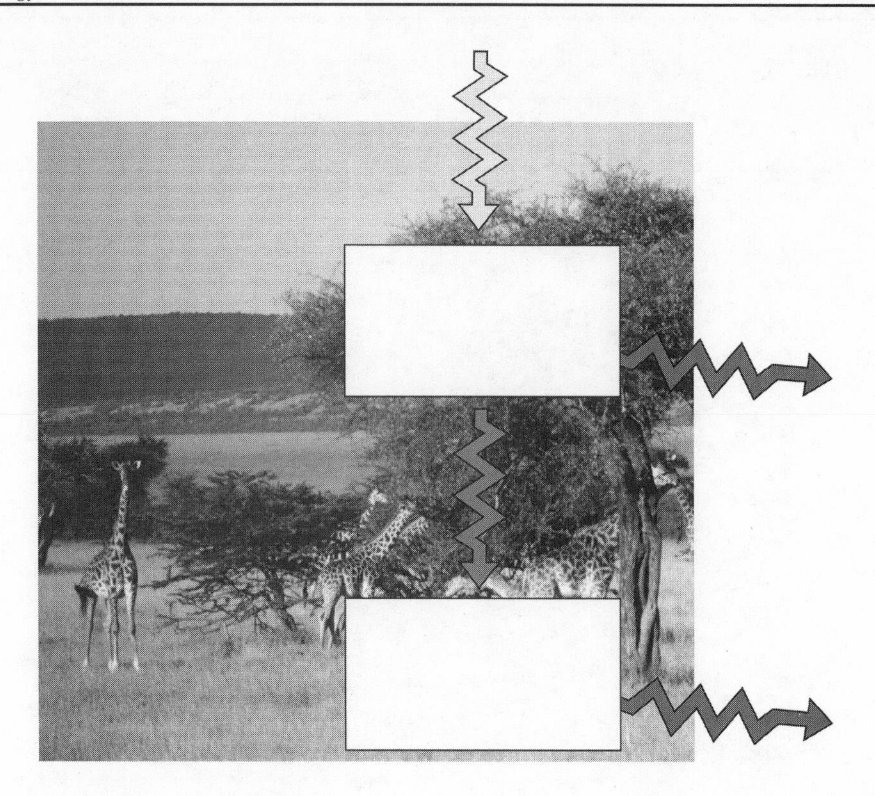

Figure 1.7 An introduction to energy flow and energy transformation in an ecosystem, page 8

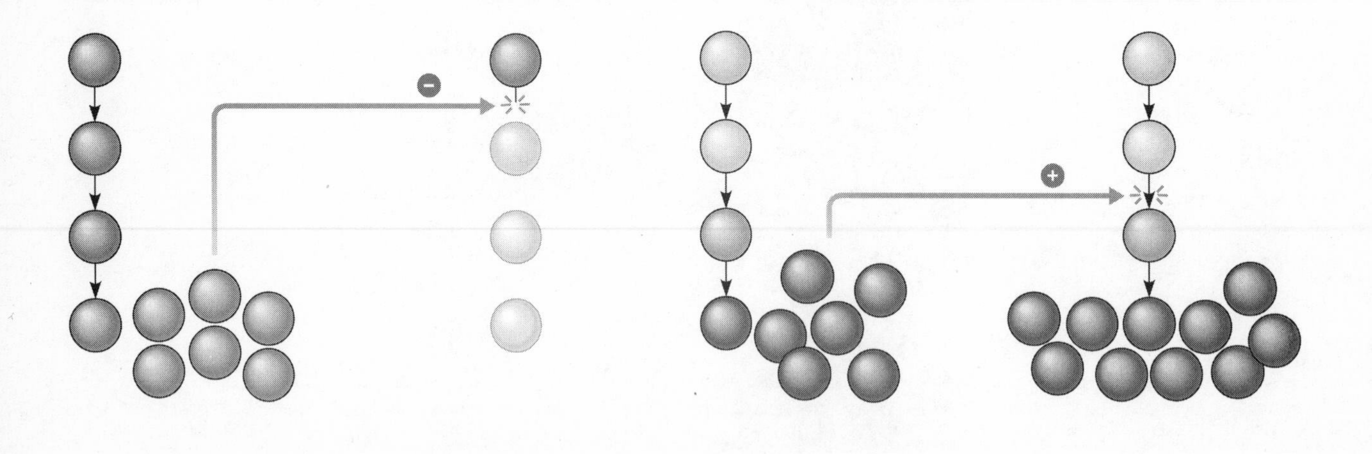

Figure 1.8 Regulation by feedback mechanisms, page 9

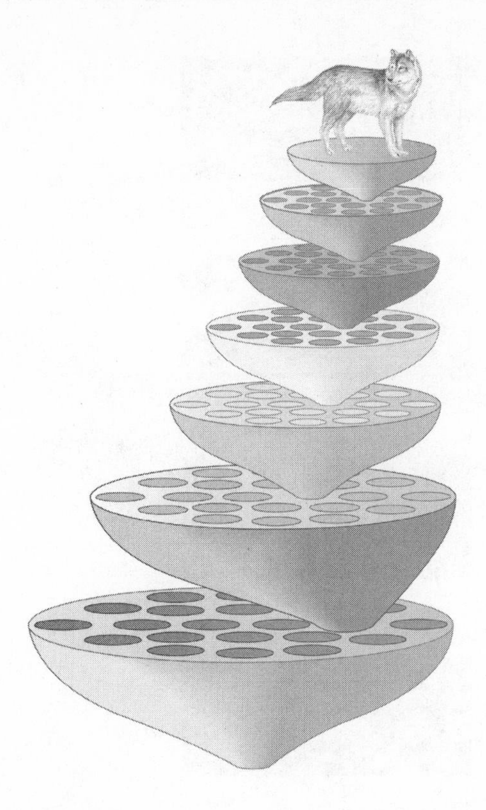

Figure 1.10 Classifying life, page 10

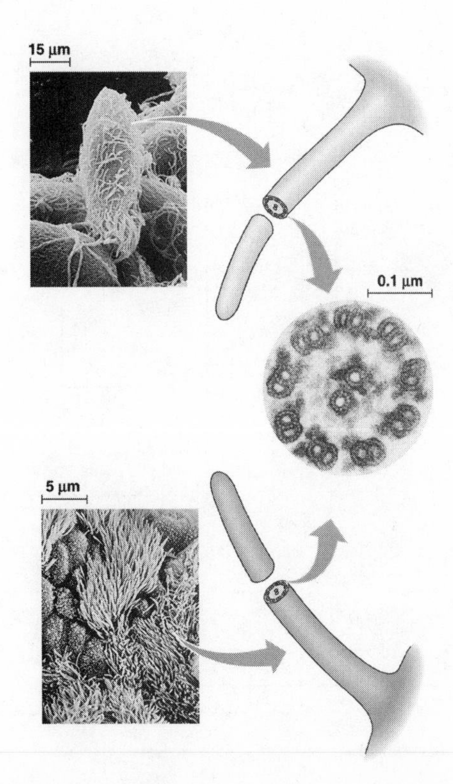

Figure 1.12 An example of unity underlying the diversity of life: the architecture of eukaryotic cilia, page 12

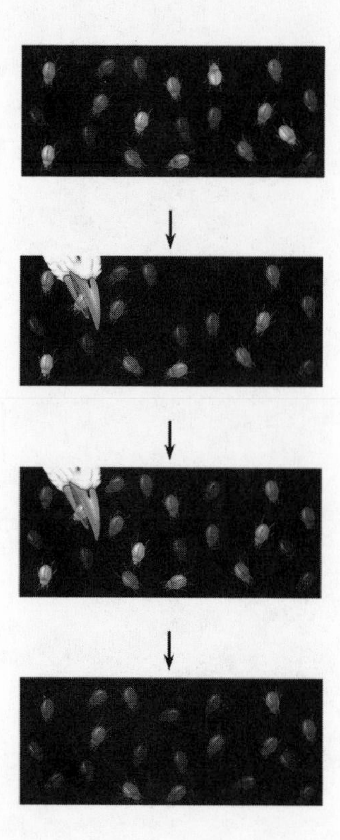

Figure 1.15 Natural selection, page 14

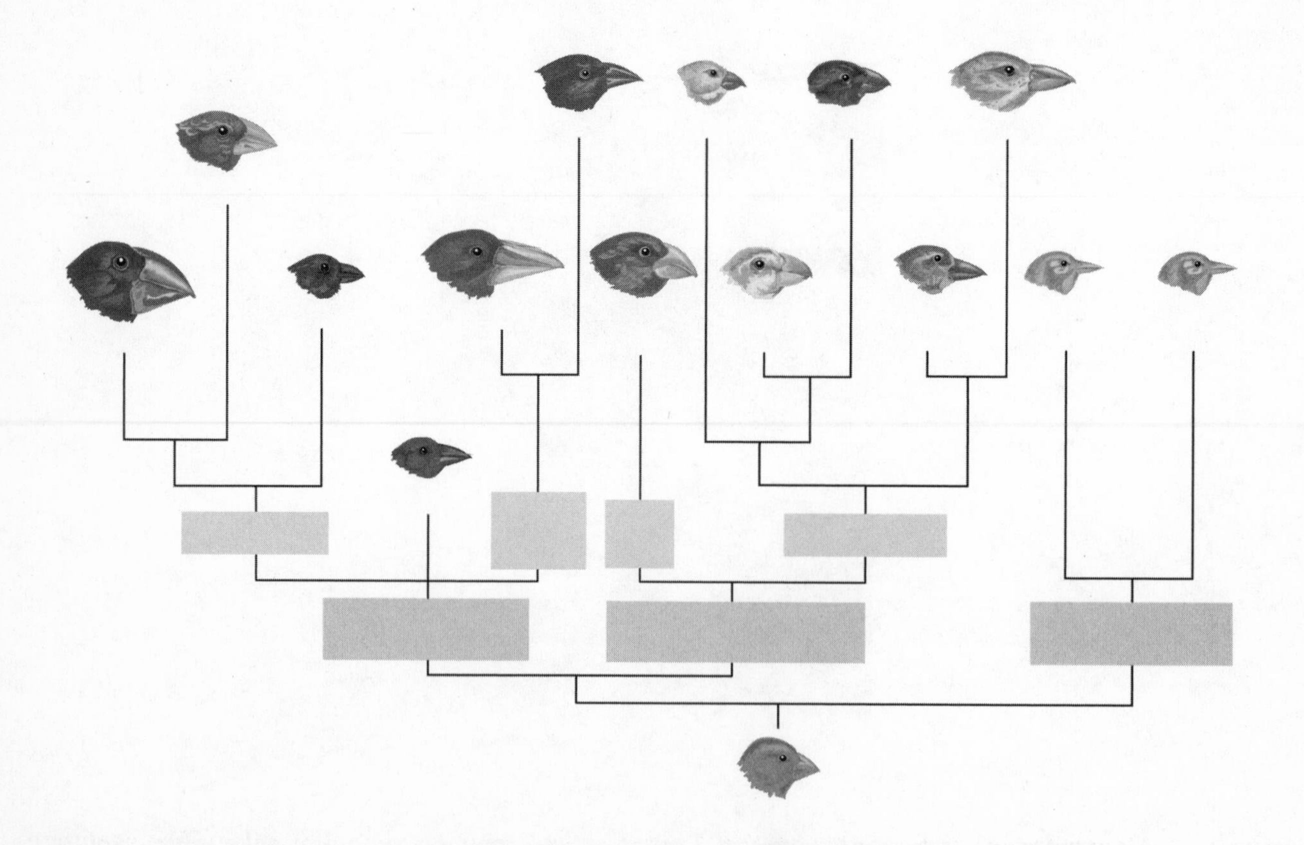

Figure 1.17b Diversification of finches on the Galápagos Islands, page 15

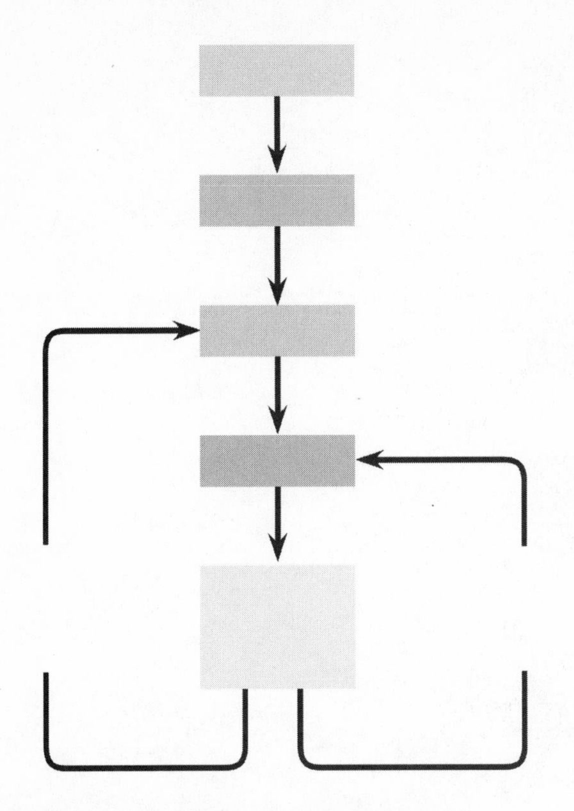

Figure 1.19 Idealized version of the scientific method, page 17

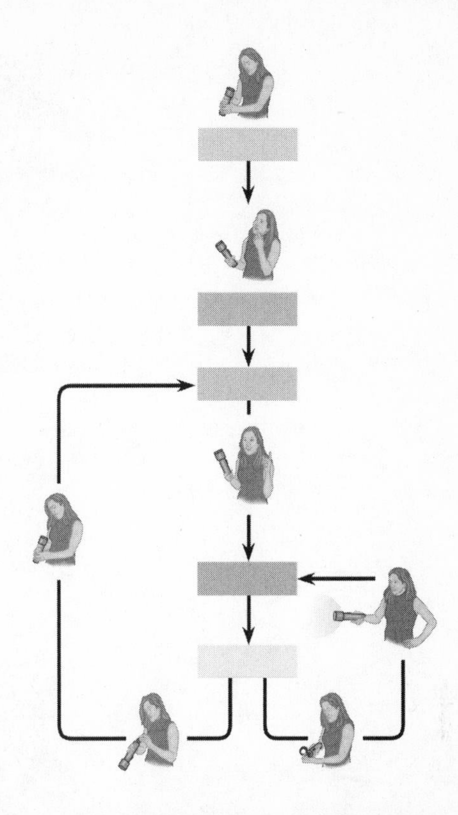

Figure 1.20 Applying hypothetico-deductive reasoning to a campground problem, page 17

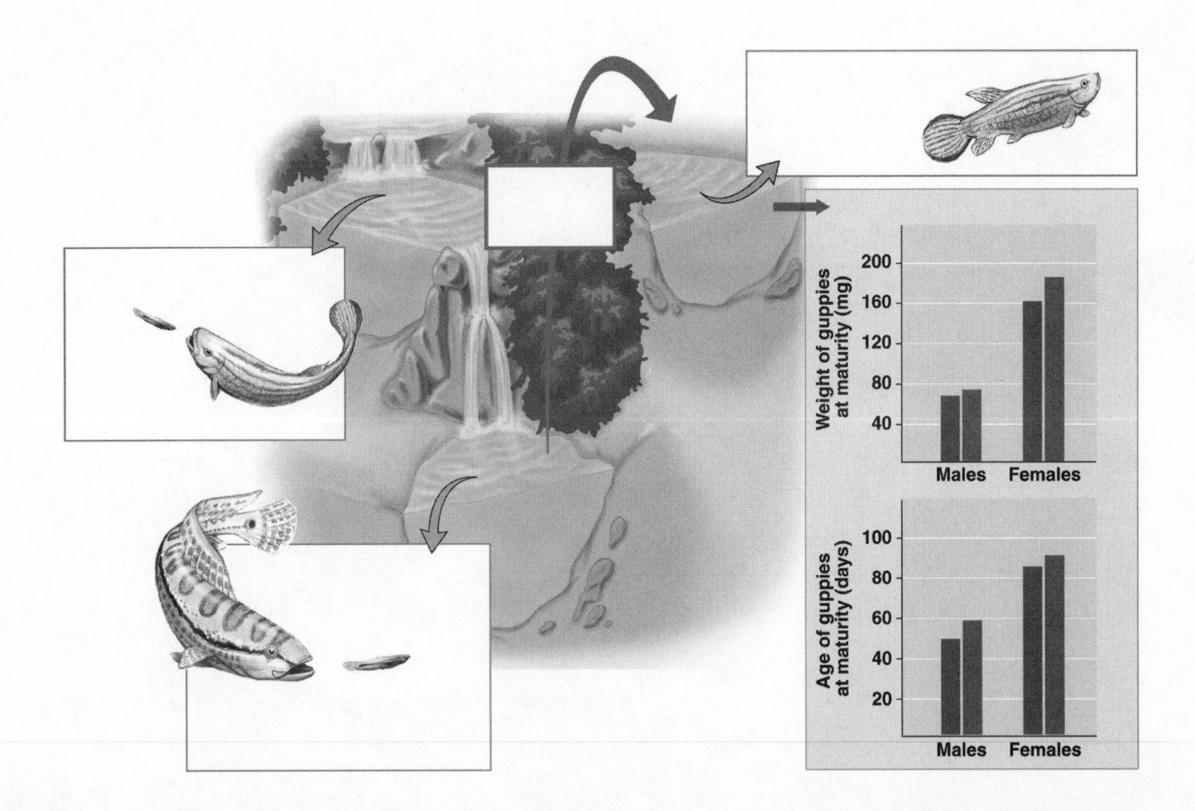

Figure 1.21 Controlled experiments to test the hypothesis that selective predation affects the evolution of guppy populations, page 19

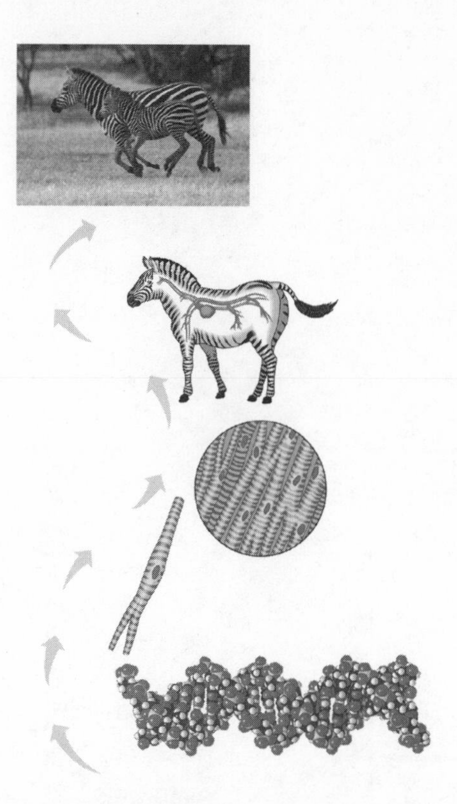

Figure 2.1 The hierarchy of biological order from atom to organism, page 27

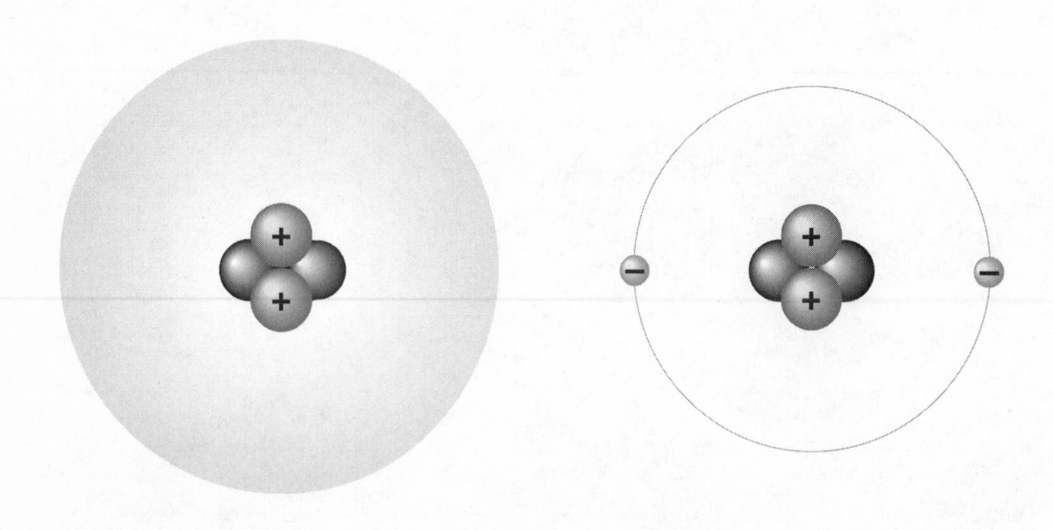

Figure 2.5 Two simplified models of a helium (He) atom, page 29

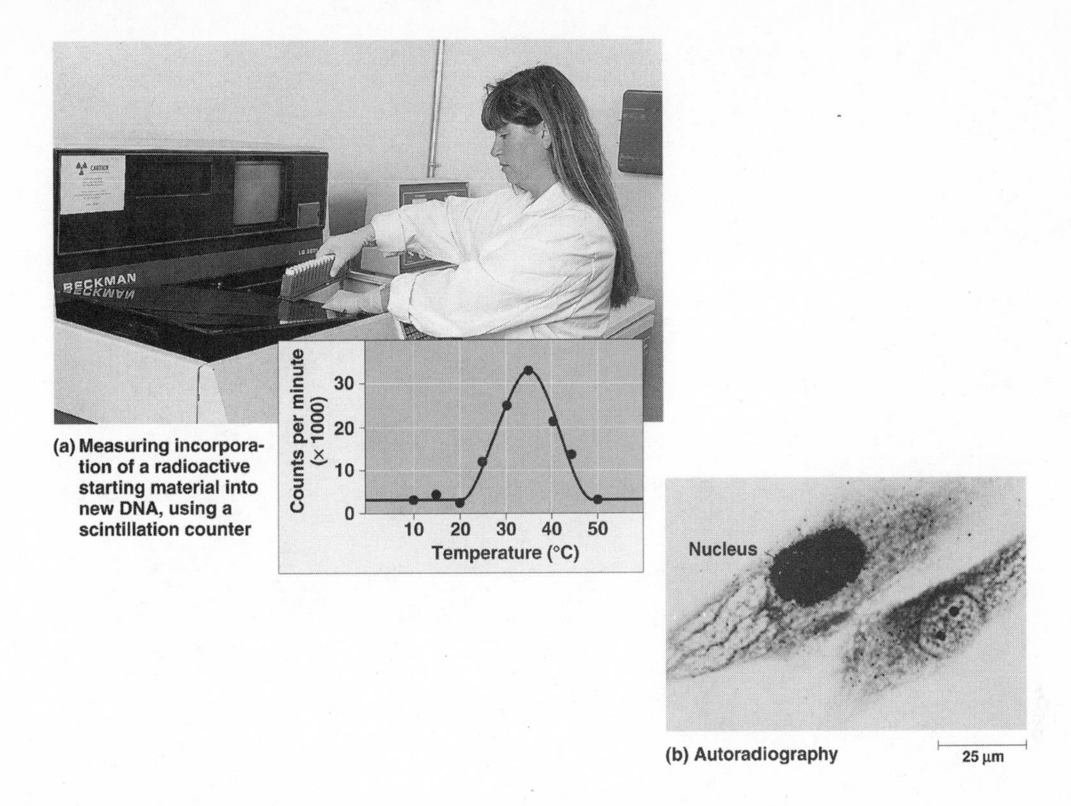

Figure 2.6 Using radioactive isotopes to study cell chemistry, page 30

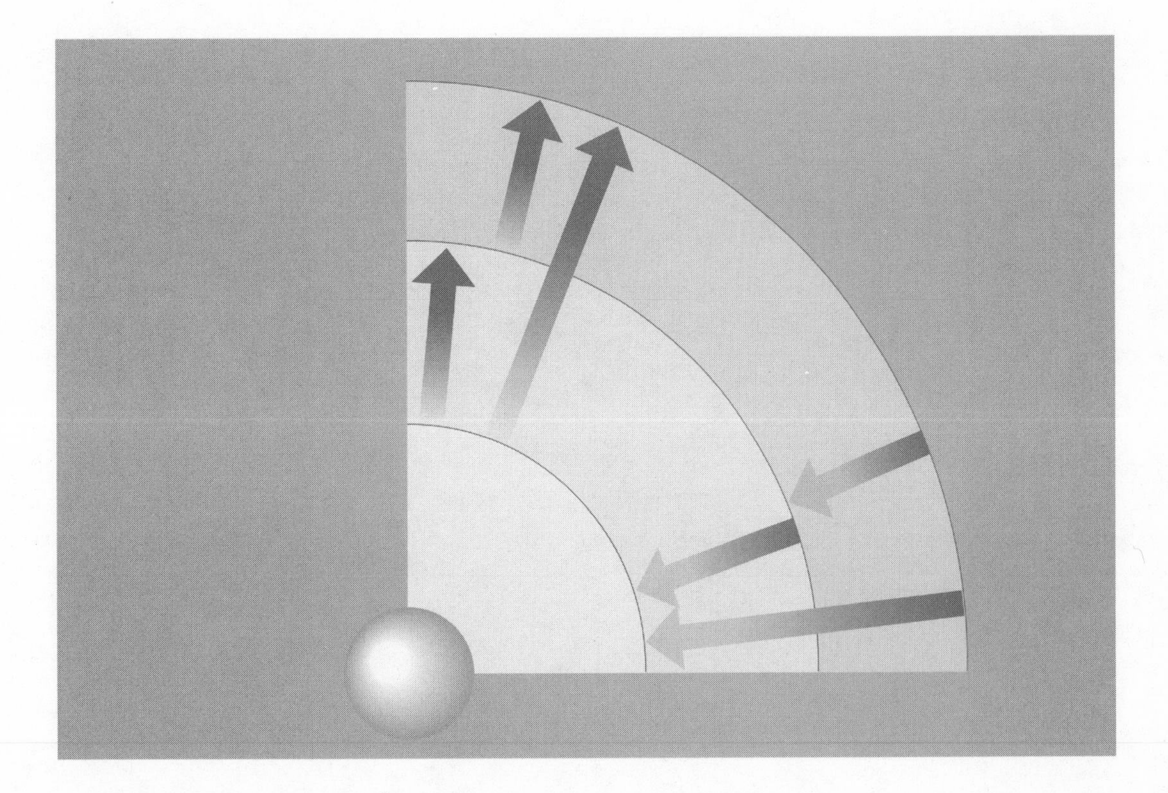

Figure 2.9 Energy levels of an atom's electrons, page 31

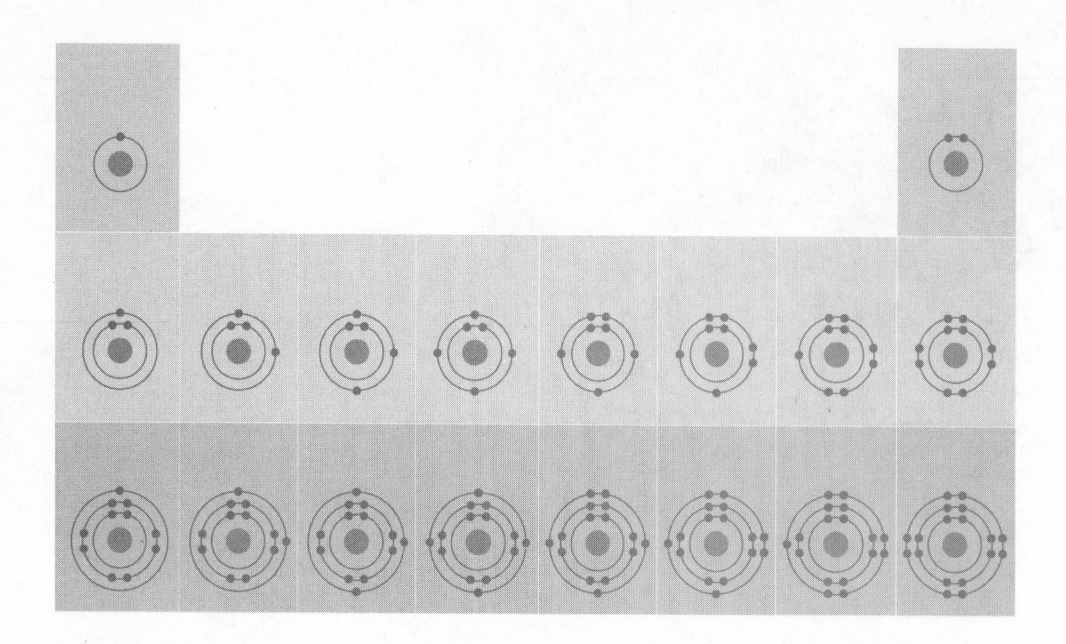

Figure 2.10 Electron configurations of the first 18 elements, page 32

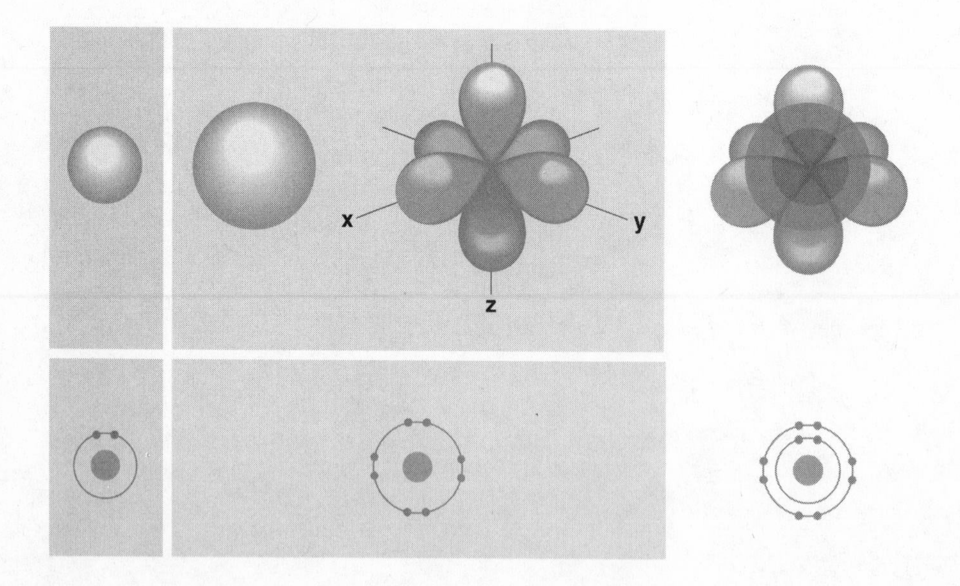

Figure 2.11 Electron orbitals, page 33

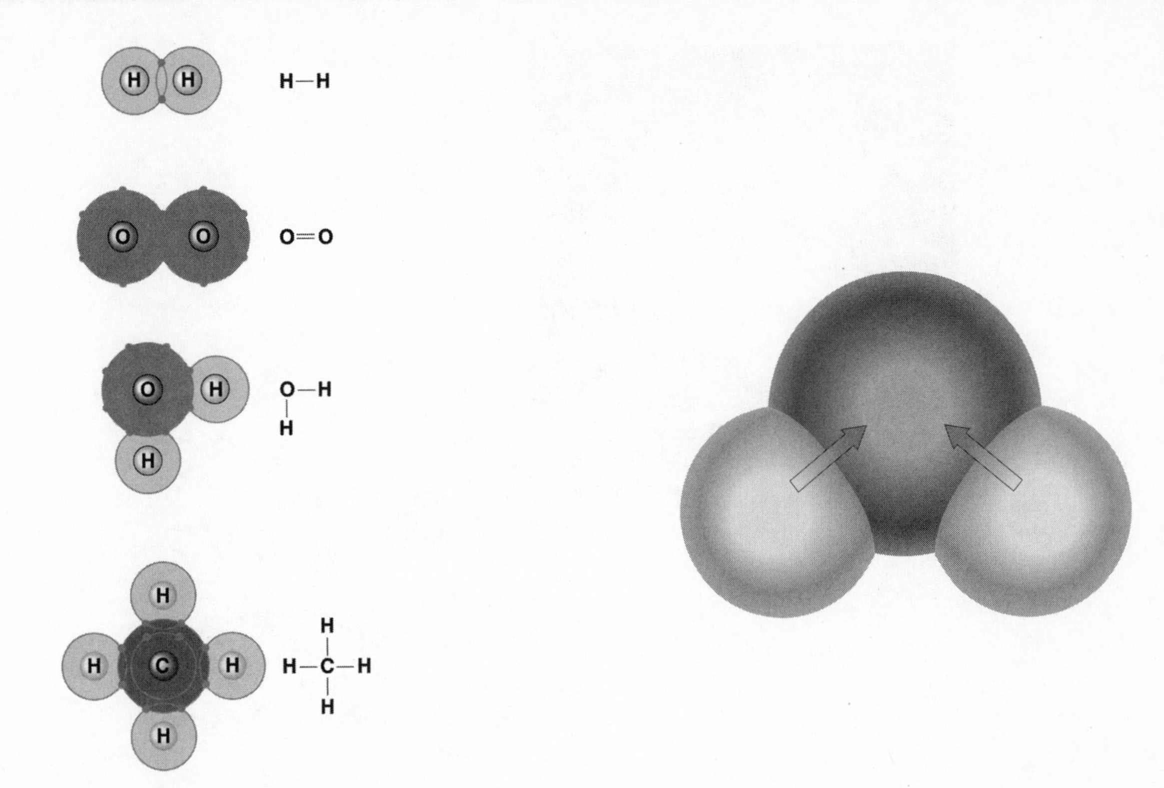

Figure 2.12 Covalent bonding in four molecules, page 34

Figure 2.13 Polar covalent bonds in a water molecule, page 35

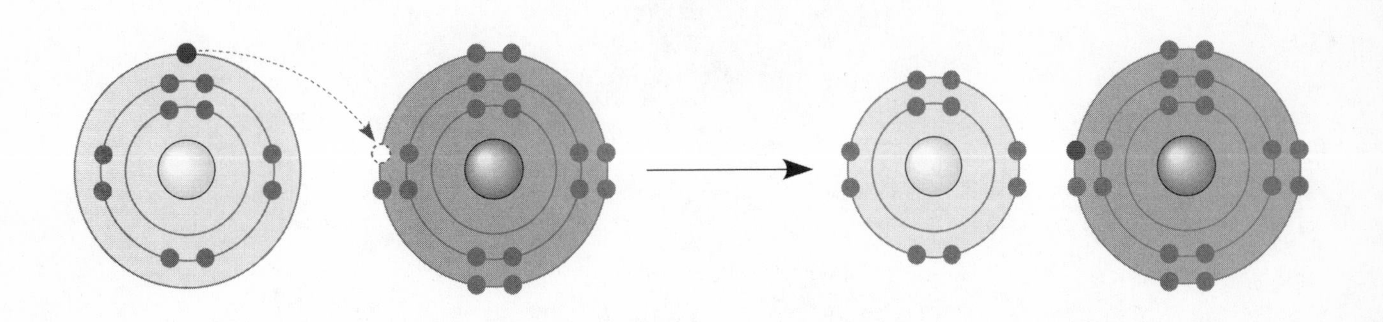

Figure 2.14 Electron transfer and ionic bonding, page 35

Figure 2.15 A sodium chloride crystal, page 35

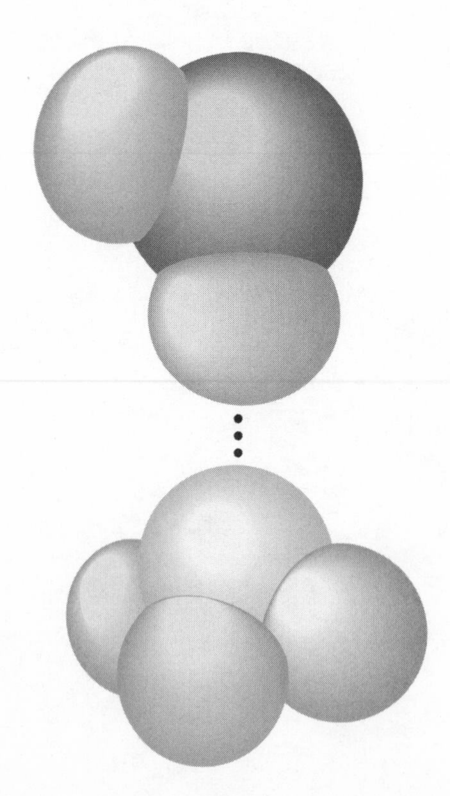

Figure 2.16 A hydrogen bond, page 36

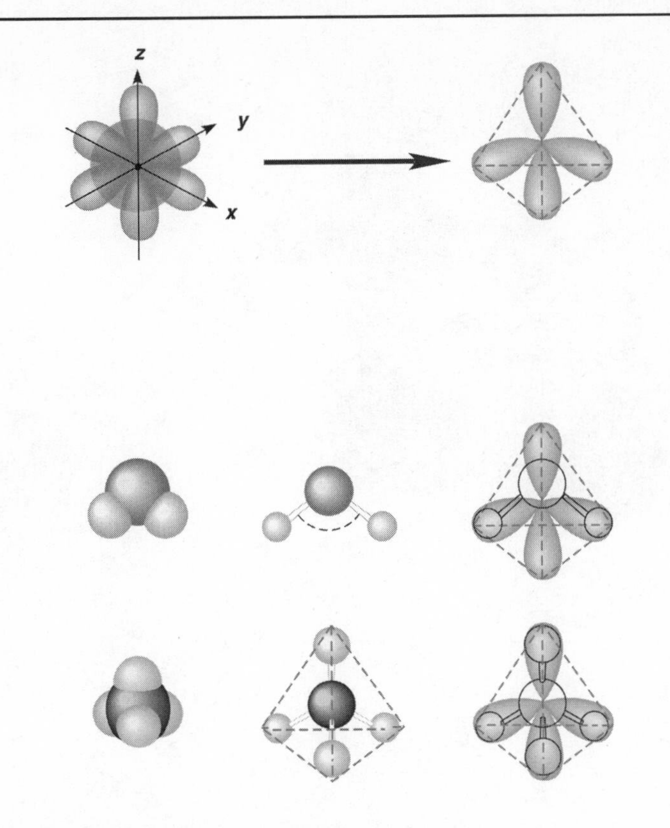

Figure 2.17 Molecular shapes due to hybrid orbitals, page 37

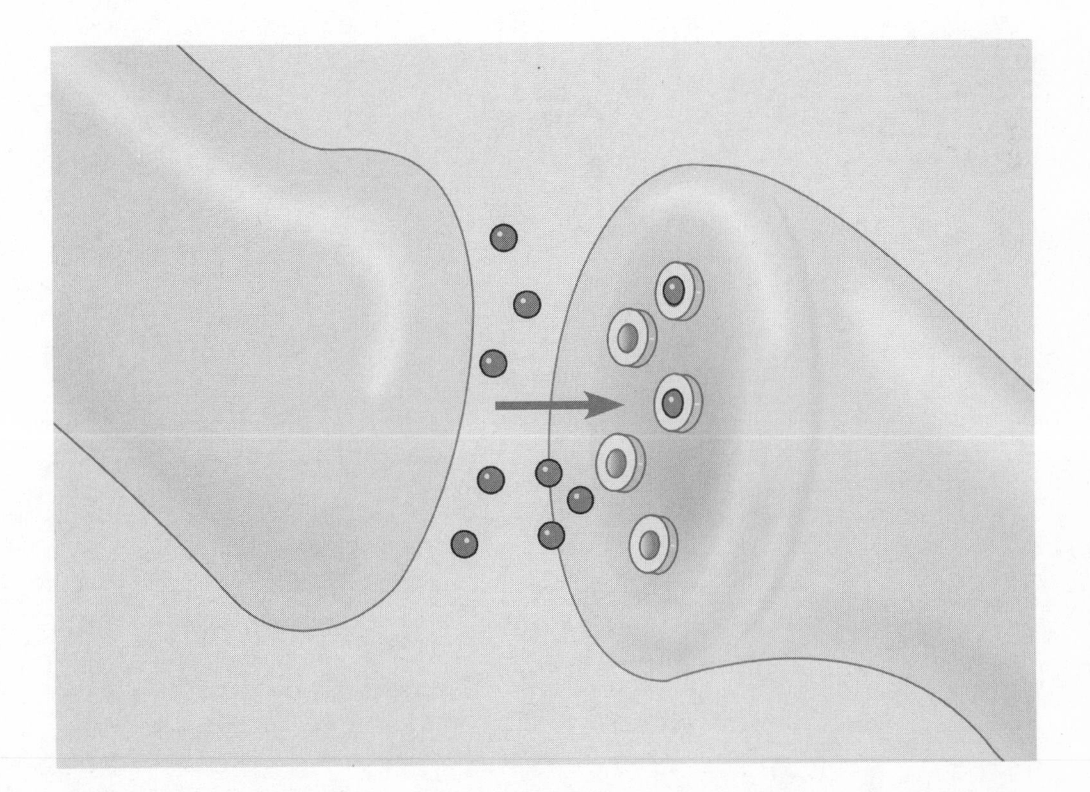

Figure 2.18 Molecular shape and brain chemistry, page 37

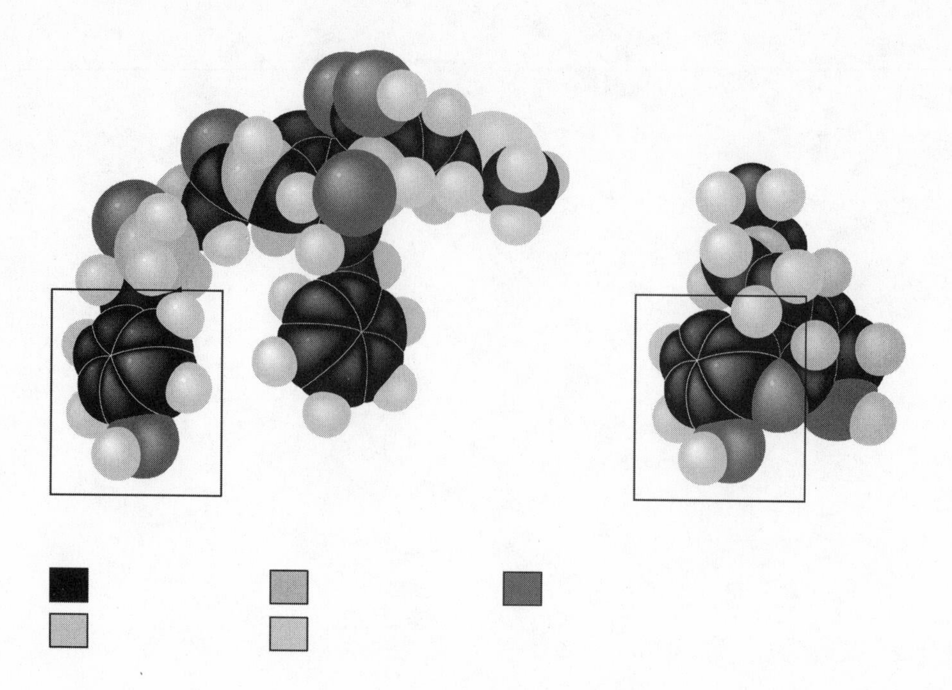

Figure 2.19 A molecular mimic, page 38

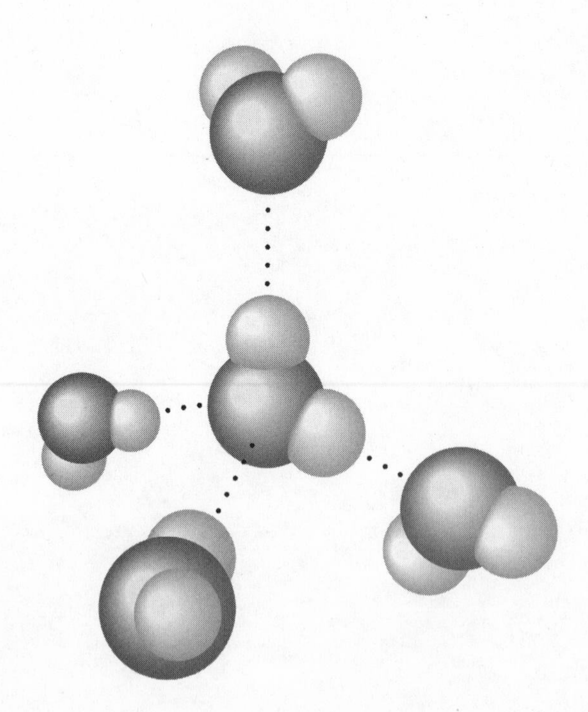

Figure 3.1 Hydrogen bonds between water molecules, page 42

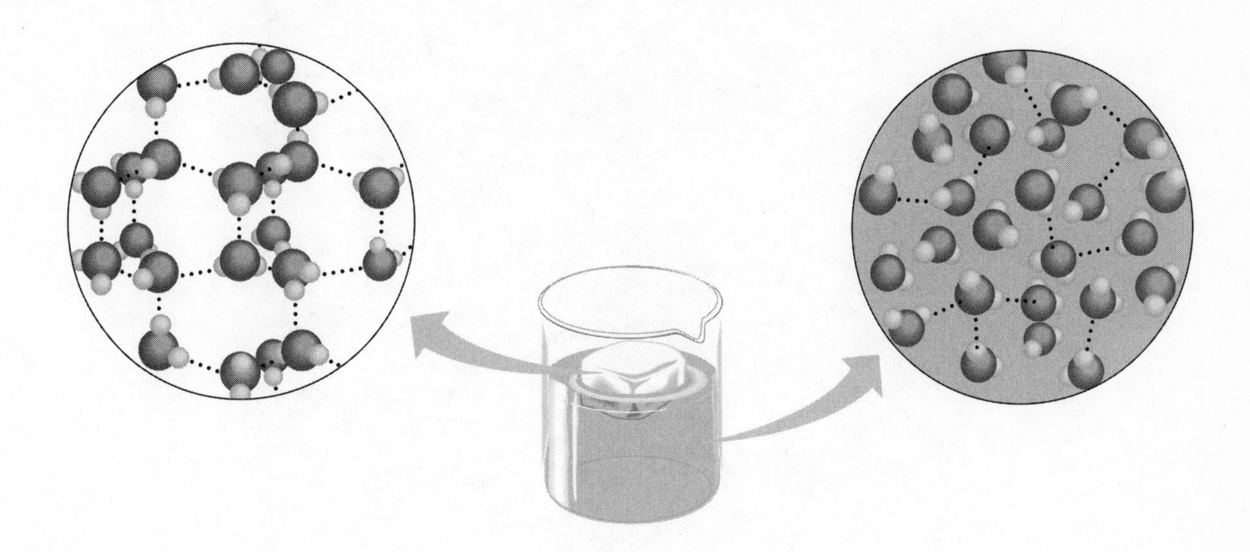

Figure 3.5 The structure of ice, page 45

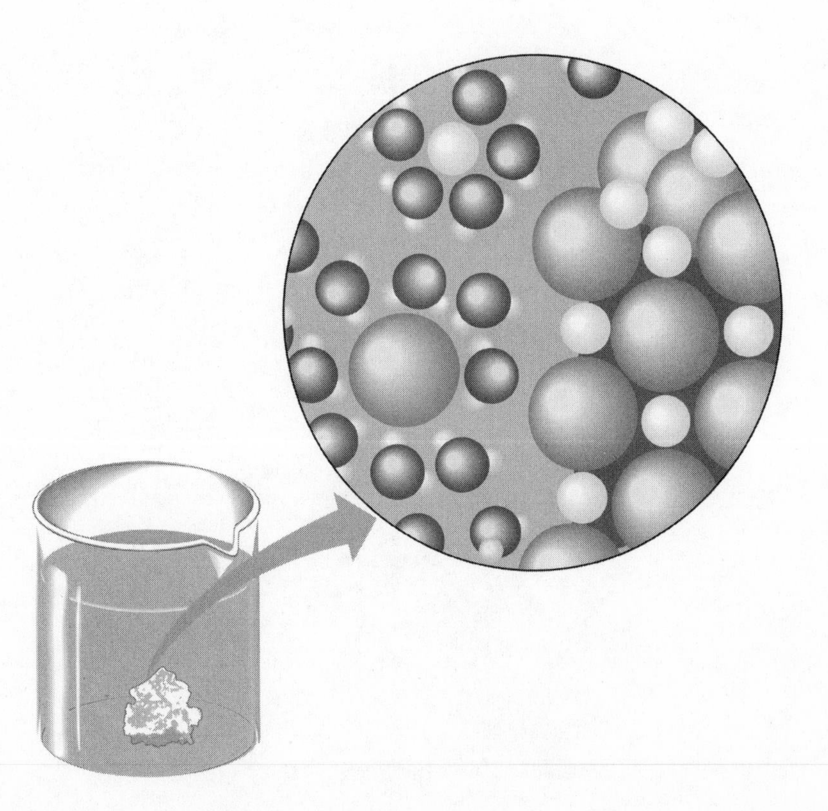

Figure 3.7 A crystal of table salt dissolving in water, page 45

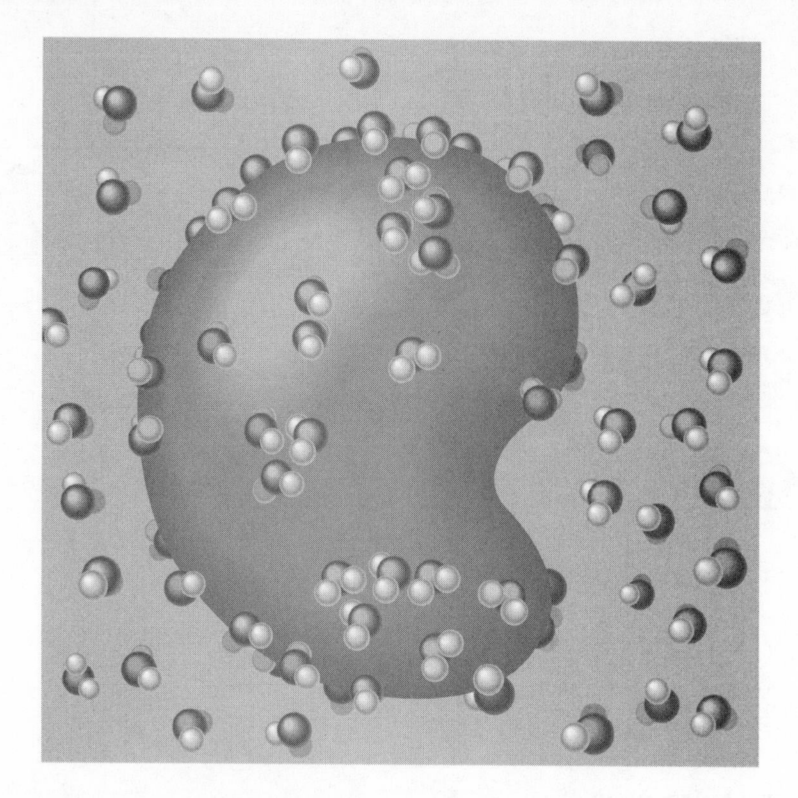

Figure 3.8 A water-soluble protein, page 46

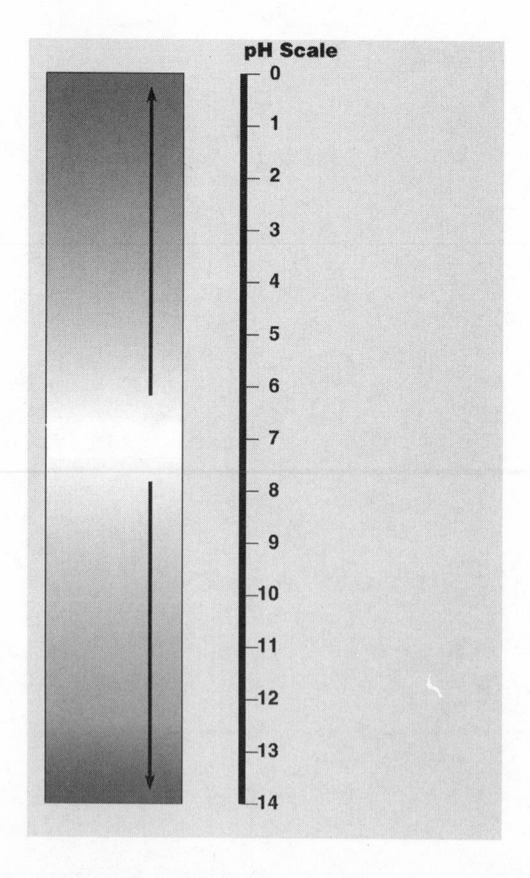

Figure 3.9 The pH of some aqueous solutions, page 48

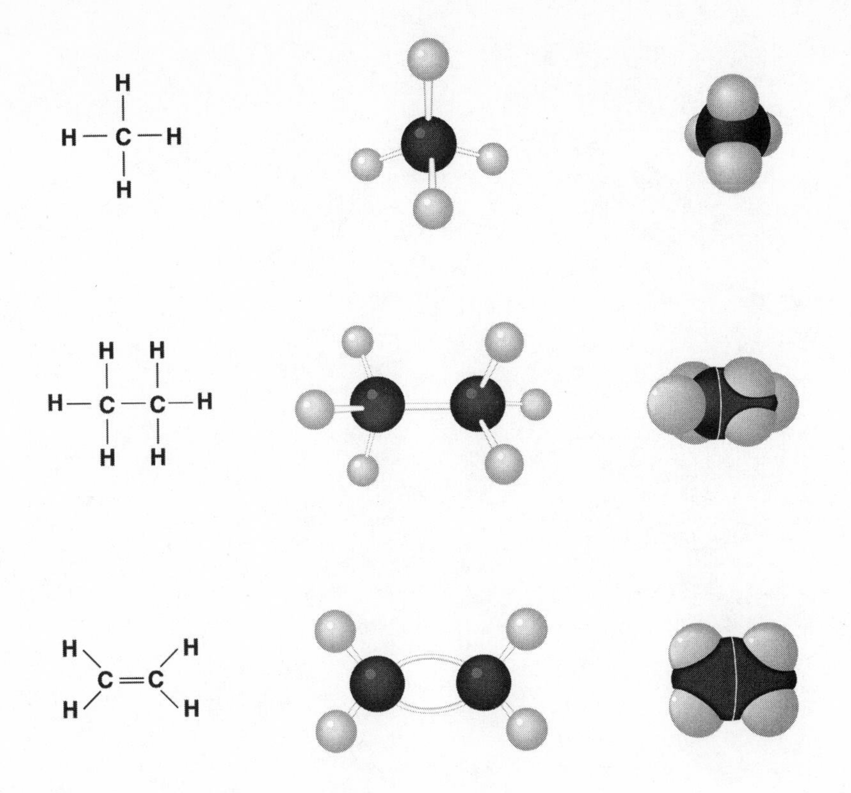

Figure 4.2 The shapes of three simple organic molecules, page 54

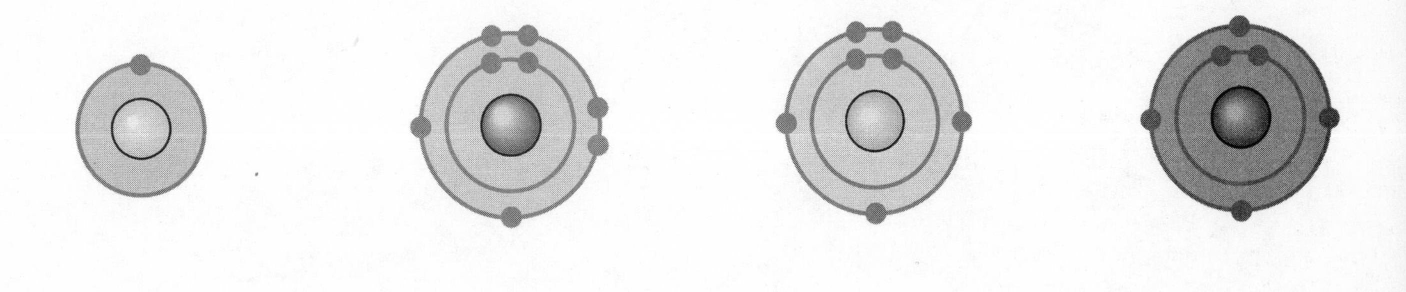

Figure 4.3 Valences for the major elements of organic molecules, page 54

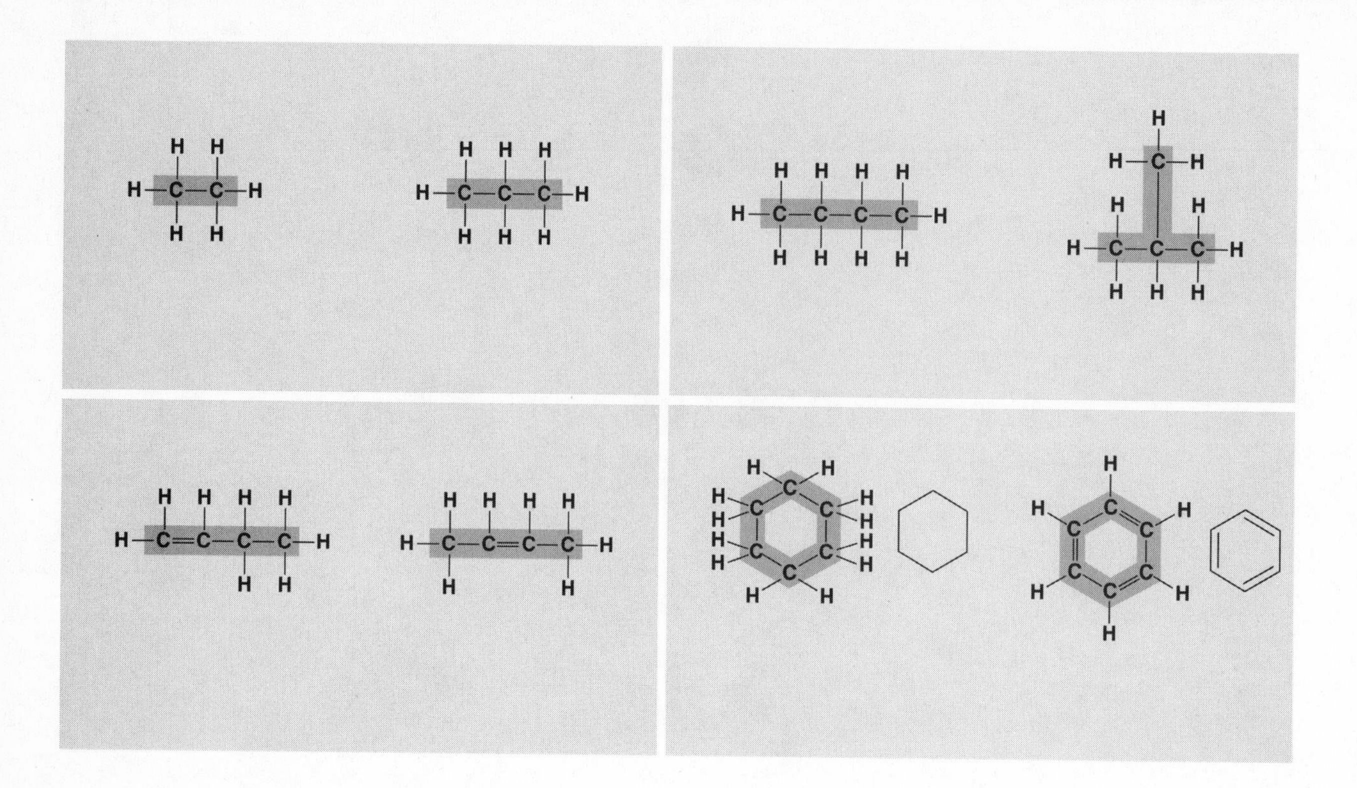

Figure 4.4 Variations in carbon skeletons, page 55

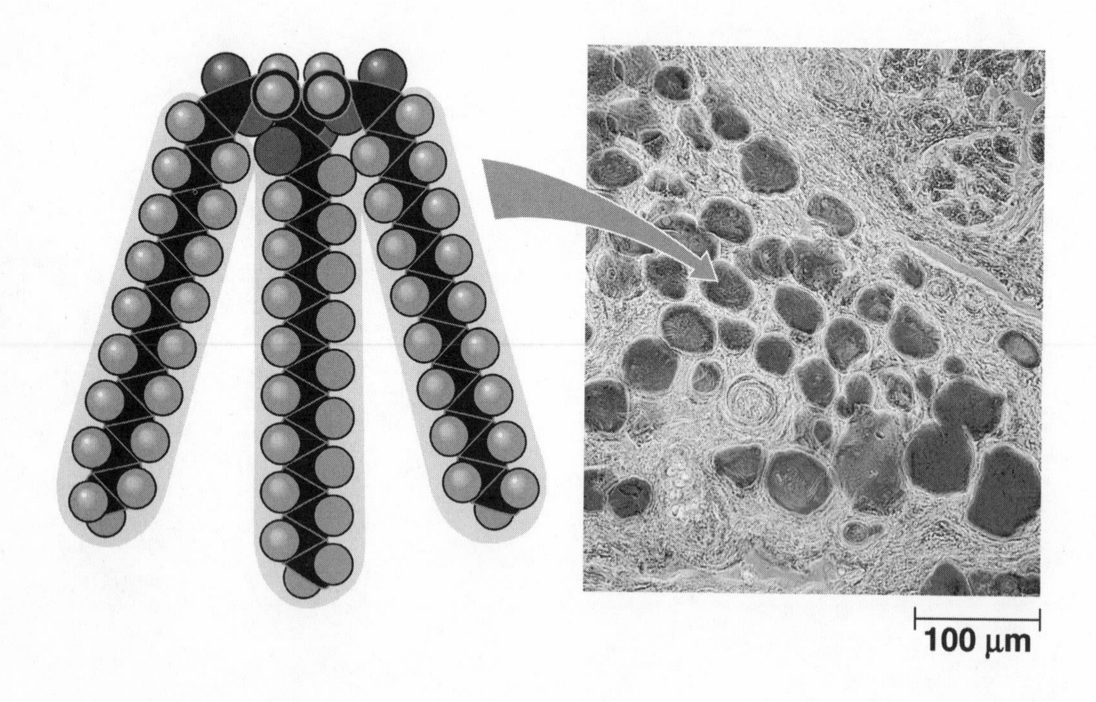

Figure 4.5 The role of hydrocarbons in fats, page 55

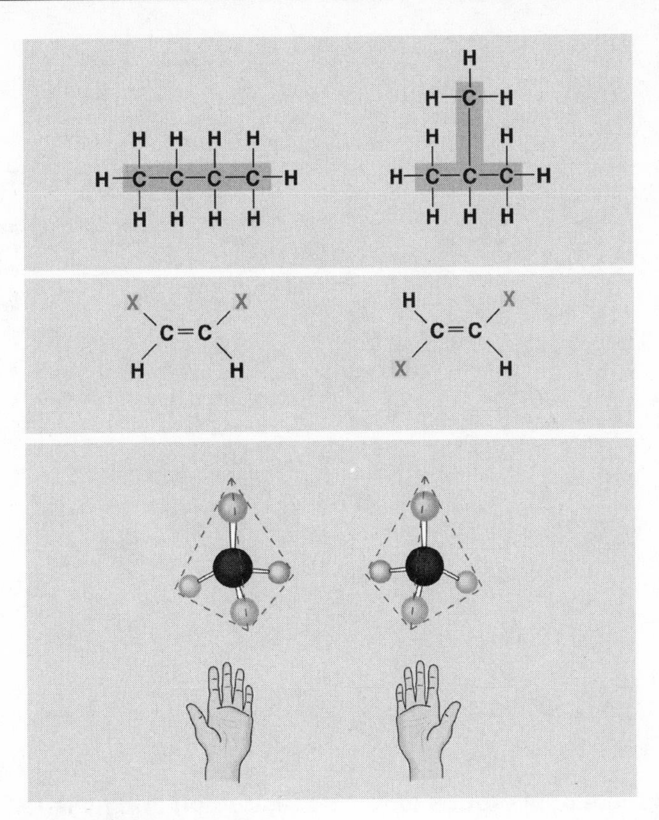

Figure 4.6 Three types of isomers, page 56

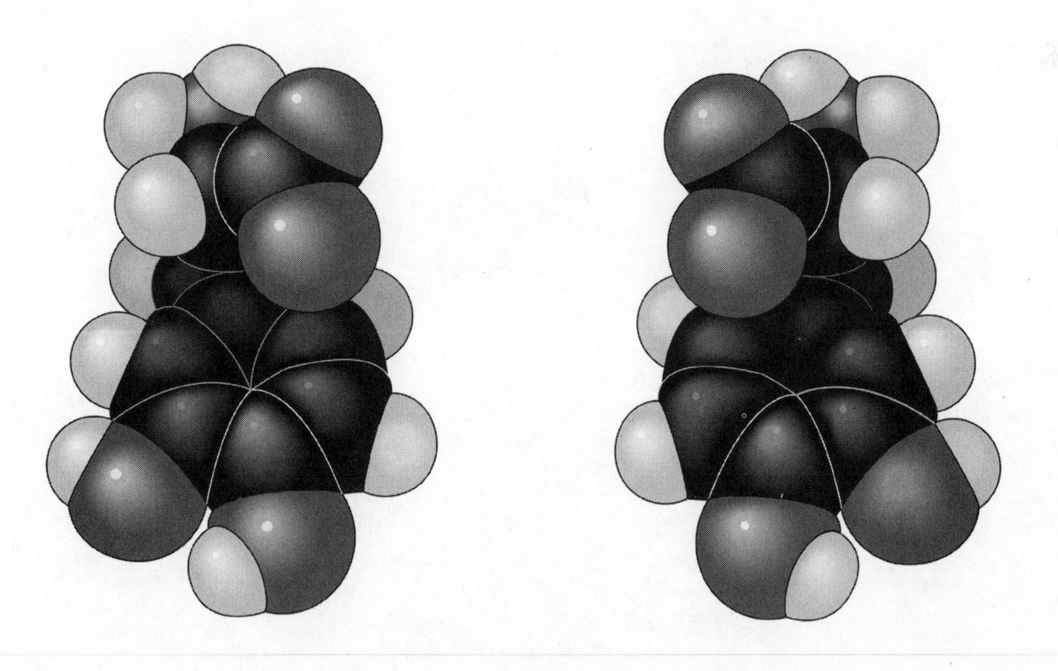

Figure 4.7 The pharmacological importance of enantiomers, page 56

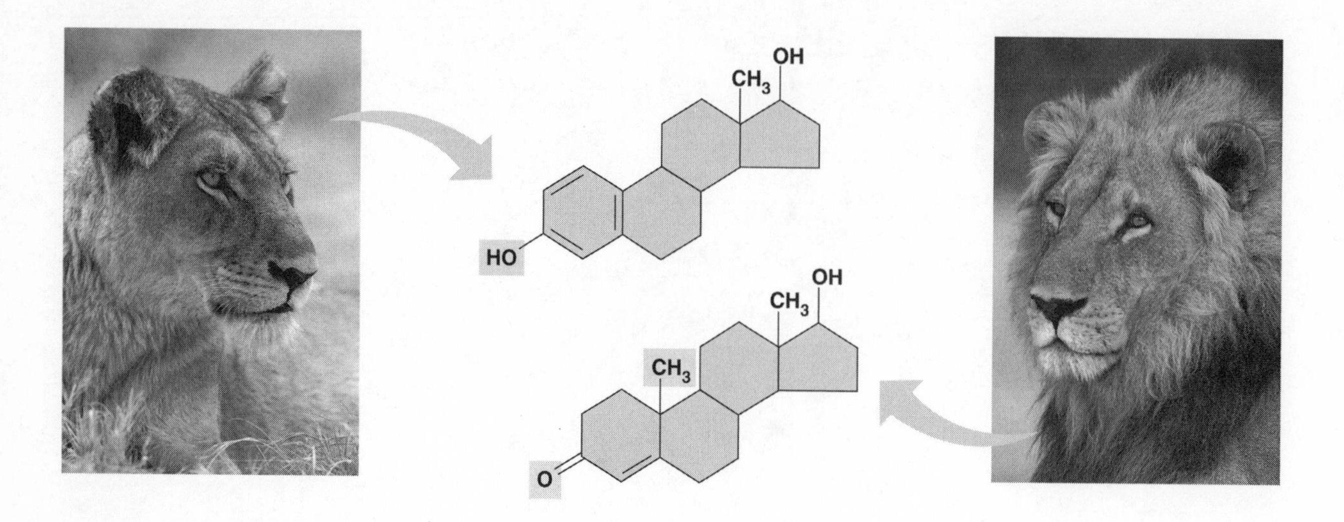

Figure 4.8 A comparison of functional groups of female (estradiol) and male (testosterone) sex hormones, page 57

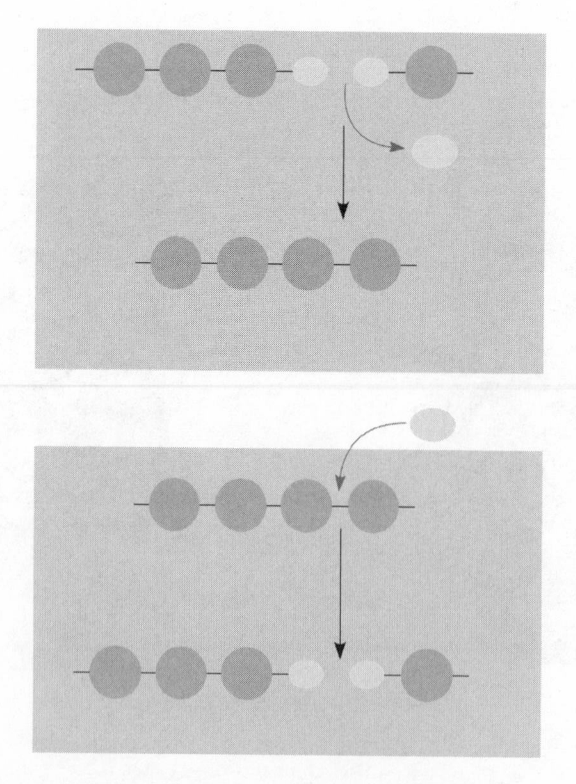

Figure 5.2 The synthesis and breakdown of polymers, page 63

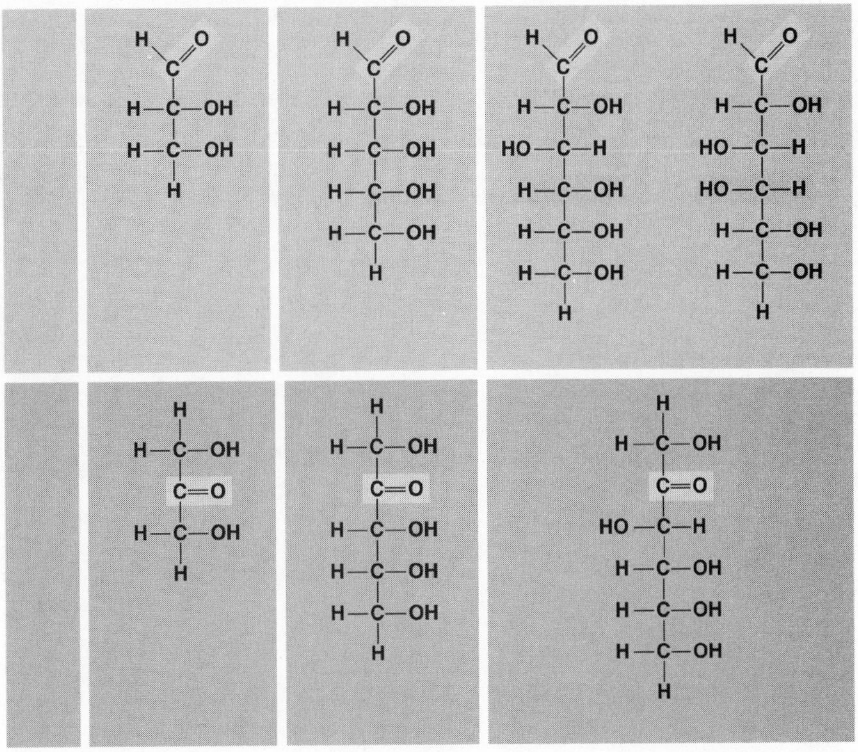

Figure 5.3 The structure and classification of some monosaccharides, page 64

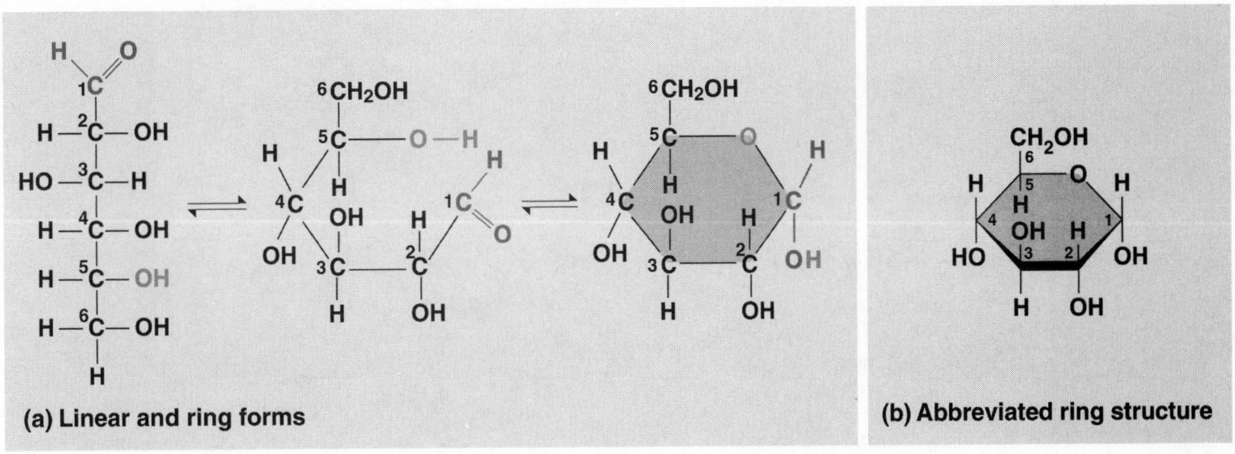

(a) Linear and ring forms

(b) Abbreviated ring structure

Figure 5.4 Linear and ring forms of glucose, page 65

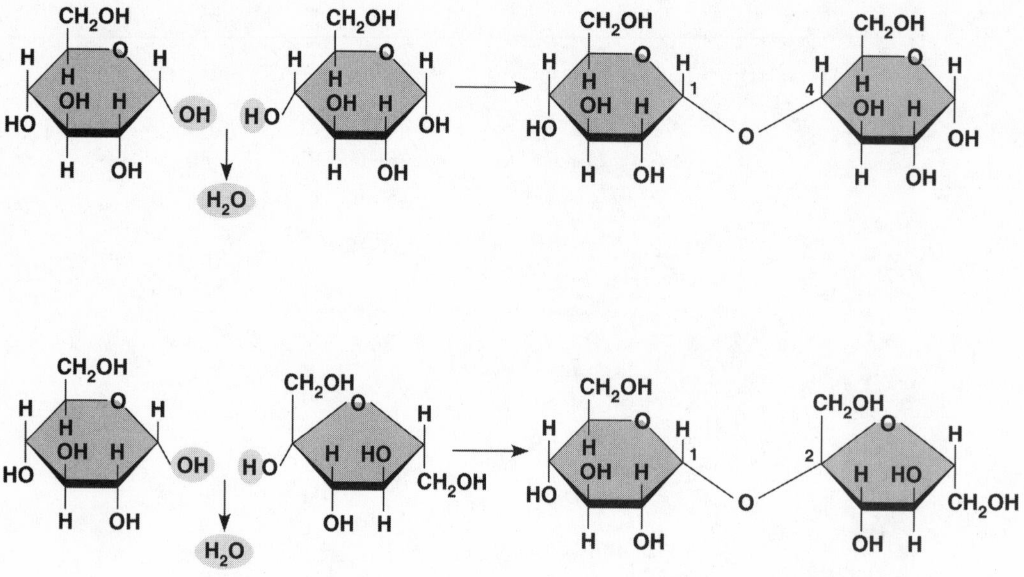

Figure 5.5 Examples of disaccharide synthesis, page 65

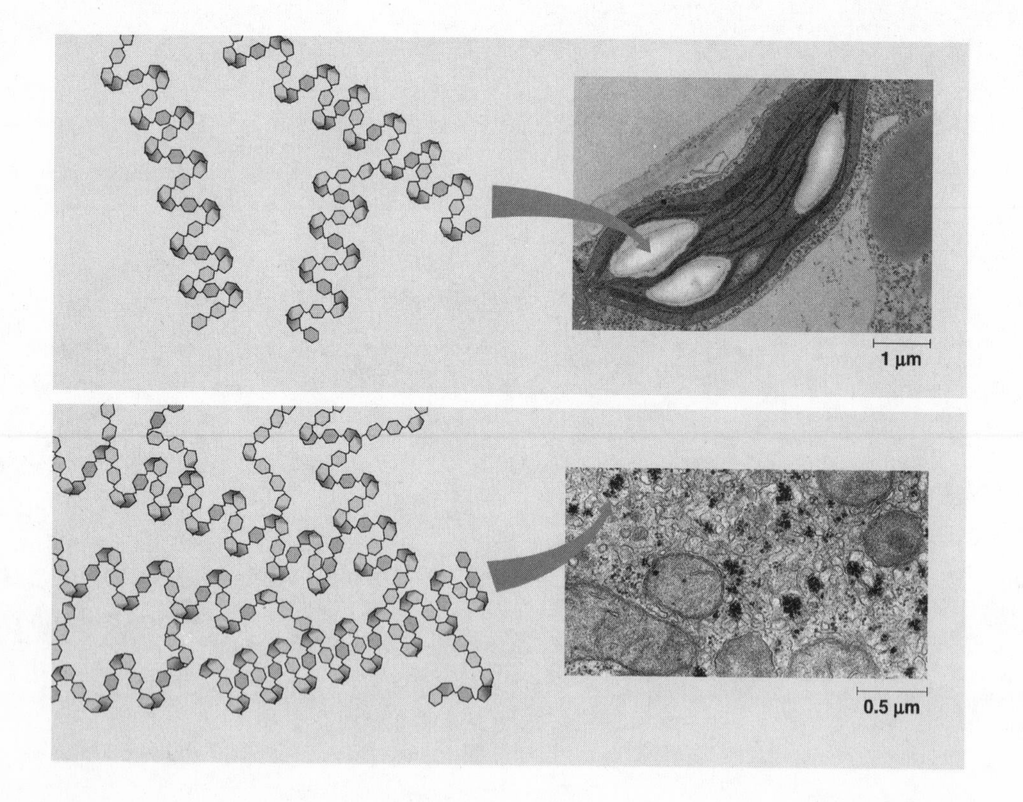

Figure 5.6 Storage polysaccharides, page 66

Figure 5.7 Starch and cellulose structures, page 67

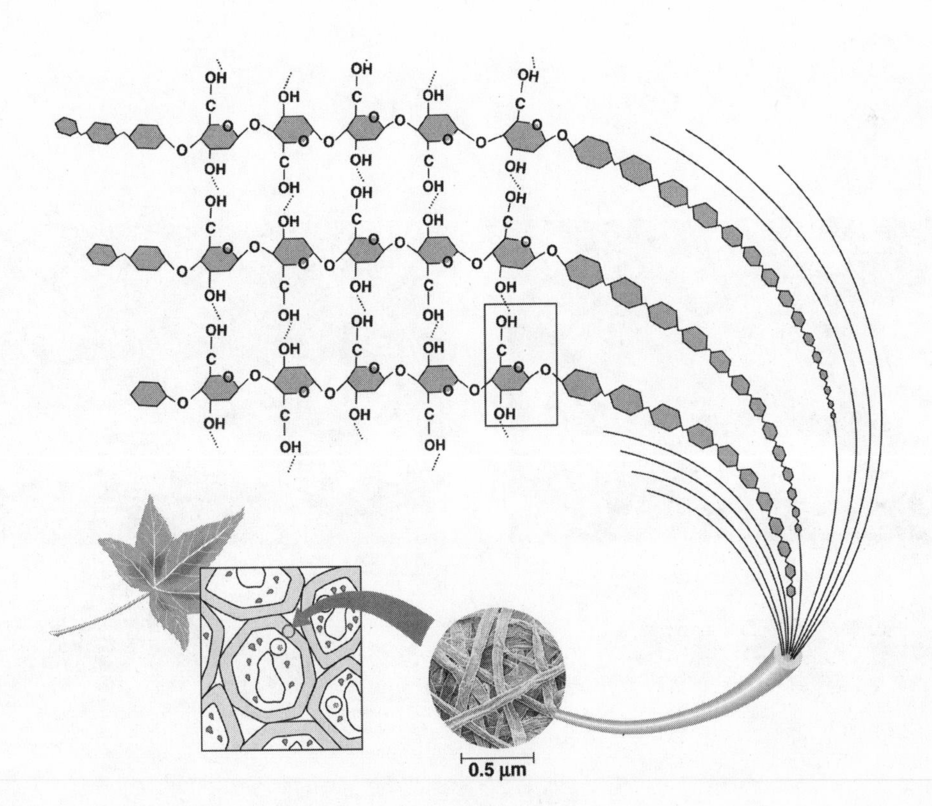

Figure 5.8 The arrangement of cellulose in plant cell walls, page 68

Figure 5.10 The synthesis and structure of a fat, or triacylglycerol, page 69

Figure 5.11 Examples of saturated and unsaturated fats and fatty acids, page 69

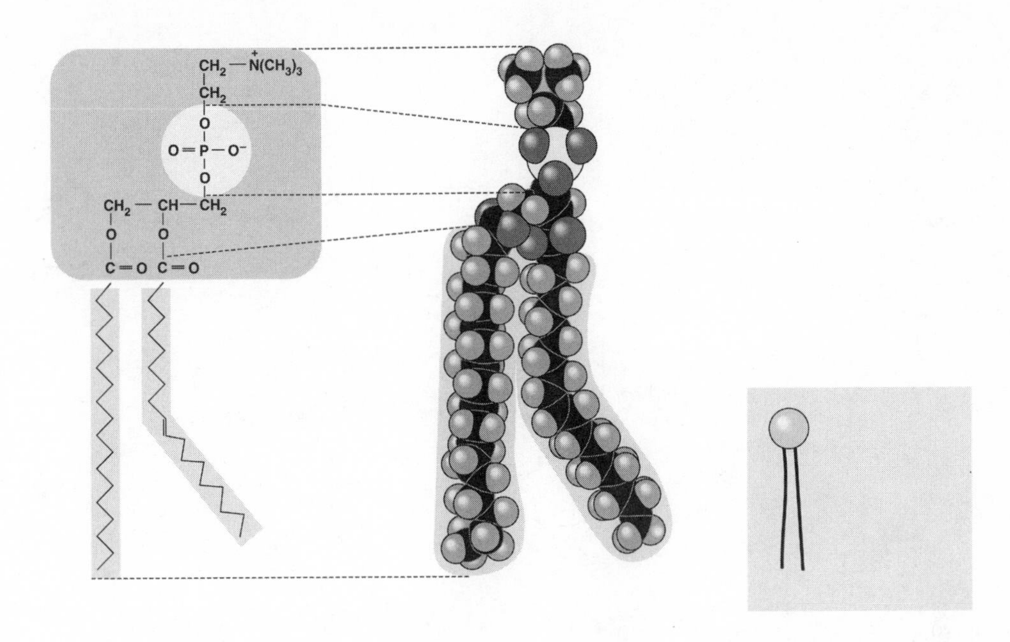

Figure 5.12 The structure of a phospholipid, page 70

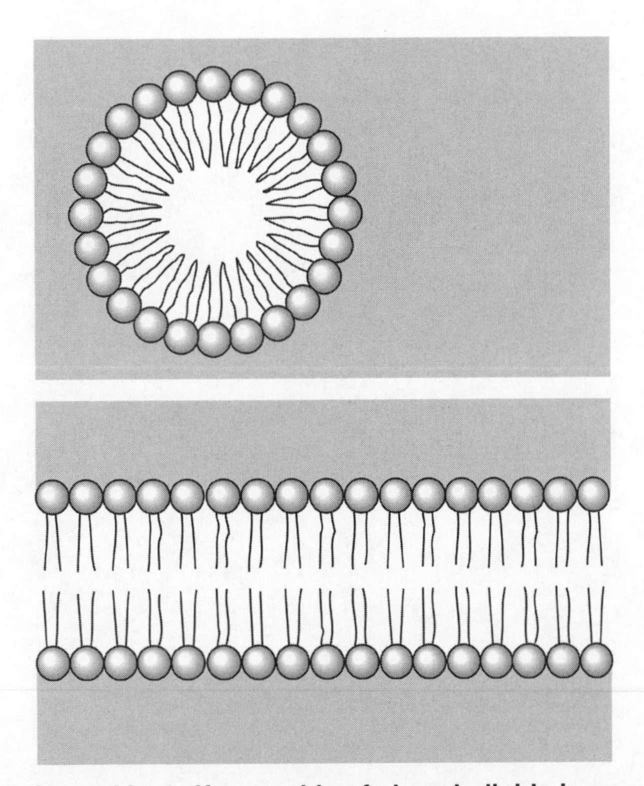

Figure 5.13 Two structures formed by self-assembly of phospholipids in aqueous environments, page 71

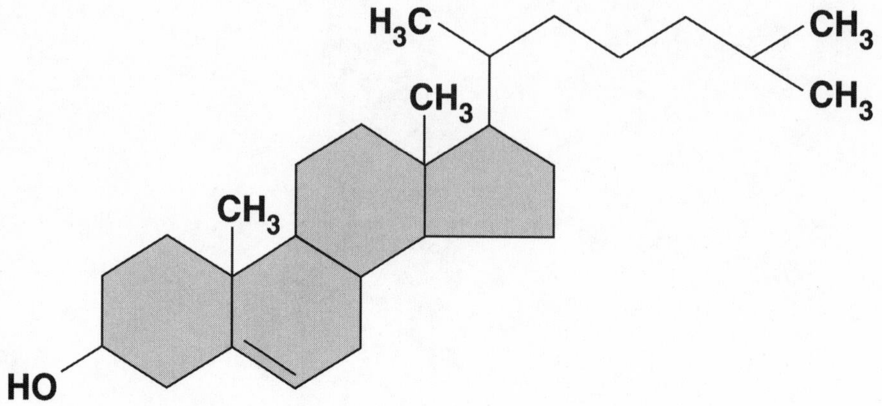

Figure 5.14 Cholesterol, a steroid, page 71

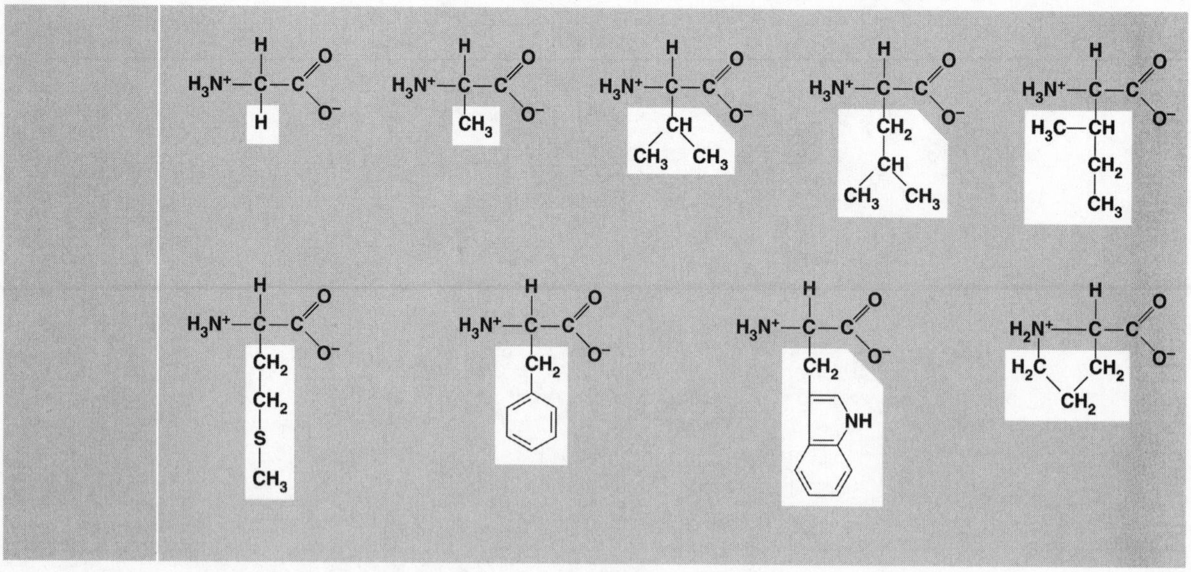

Figure 5.15 The 20 amino acids of proteins: nonpolar, page 72

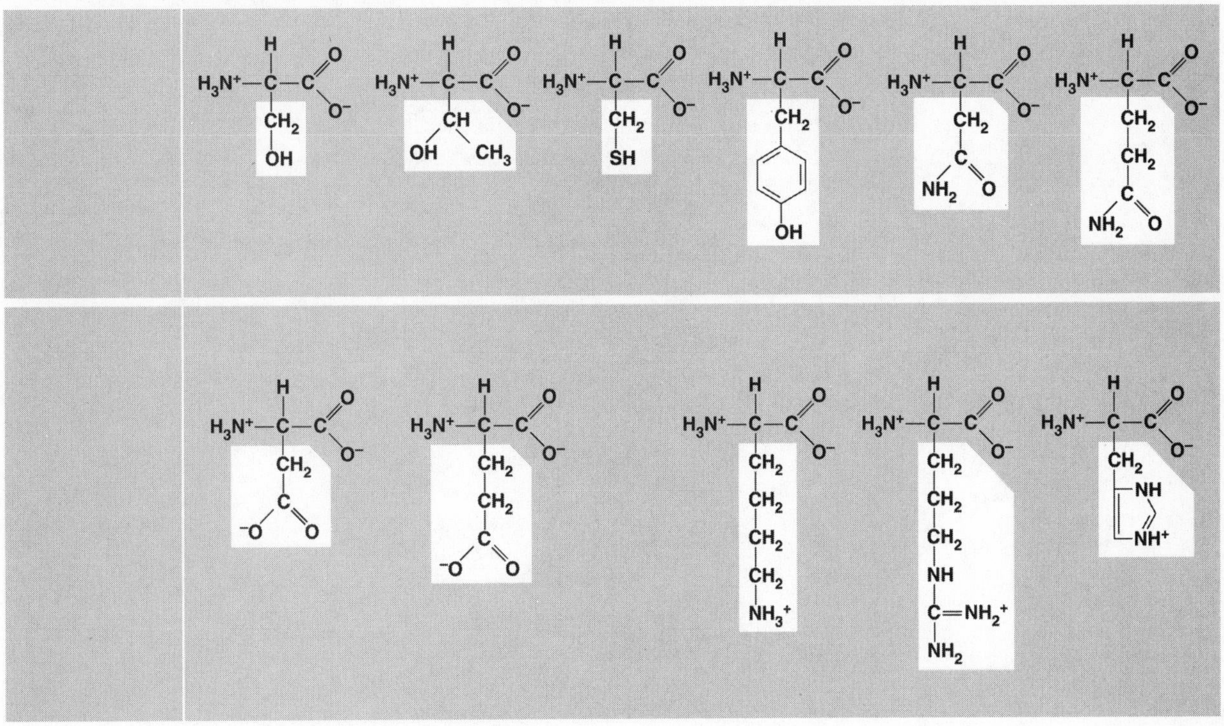

Figure 5.15 The 20 amino acids of proteins: polar and electrically charged, page 73

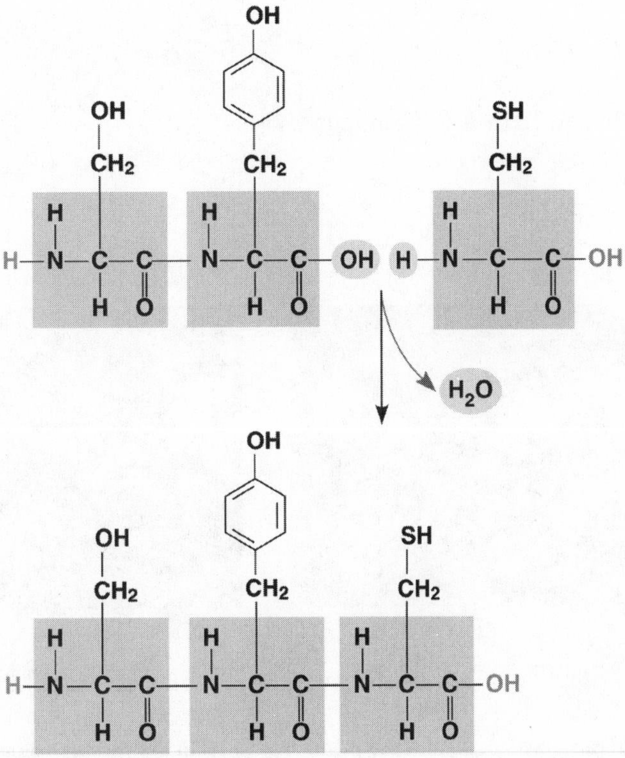

Figure 5.16 Making a polypeptide chain, page 73

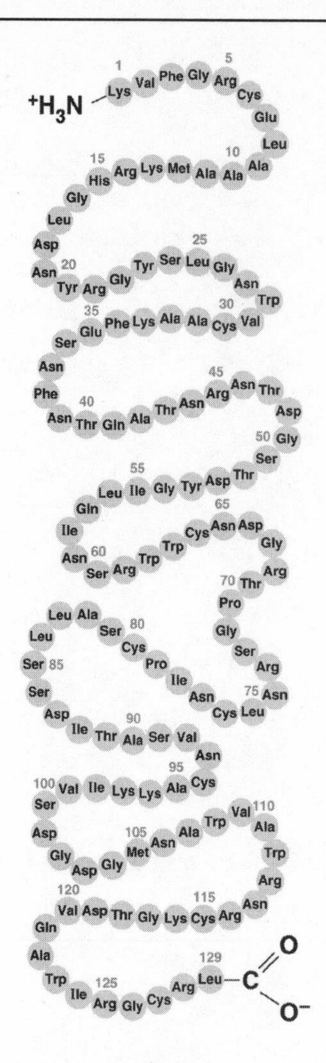

Figure 5.18 The primary structure of a protein, page 75

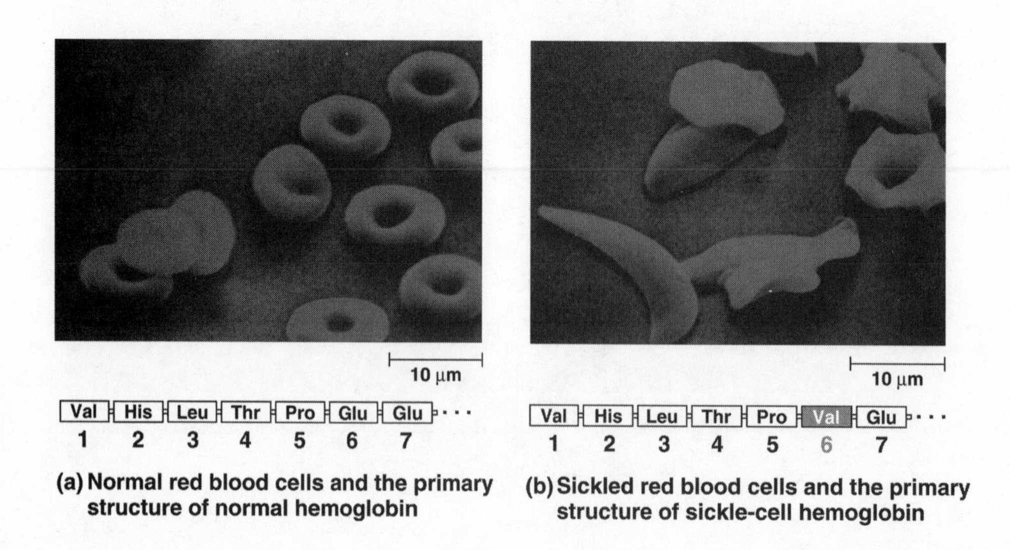

(a) Normal red blood cells and the primary structure of normal hemoglobin

(b) Sickled red blood cells and the primary structure of sickle-cell hemoglobin

Figure 5.19 A single amino acid substitution in a protein causes sickle-cell disease, page 75

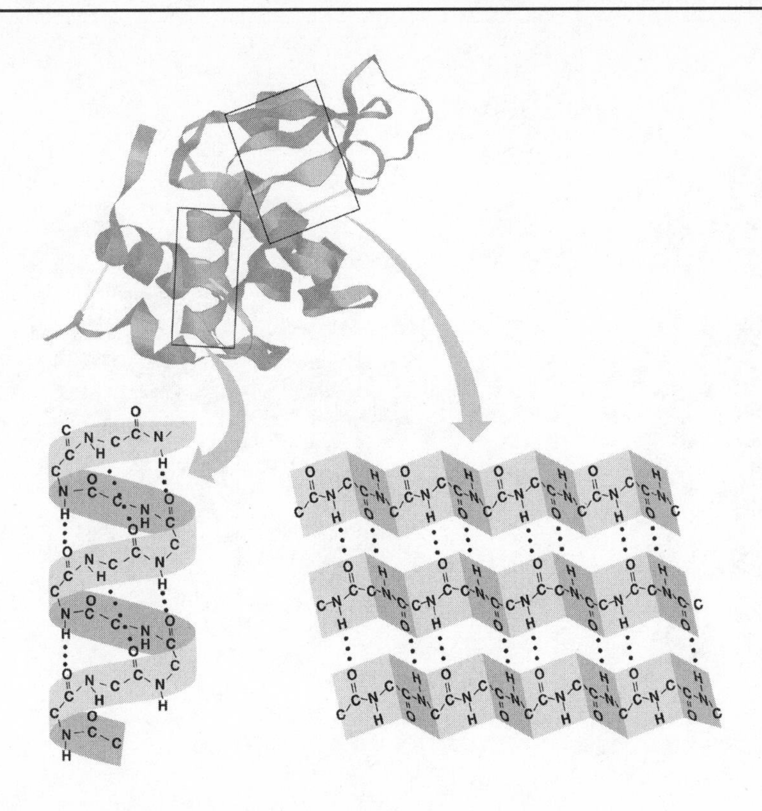

Figure 5.20 The secondary structure of a protein, page 76

Figure 5.22 Examples of interactions contributing to the tertiary structure of a protein, page 77

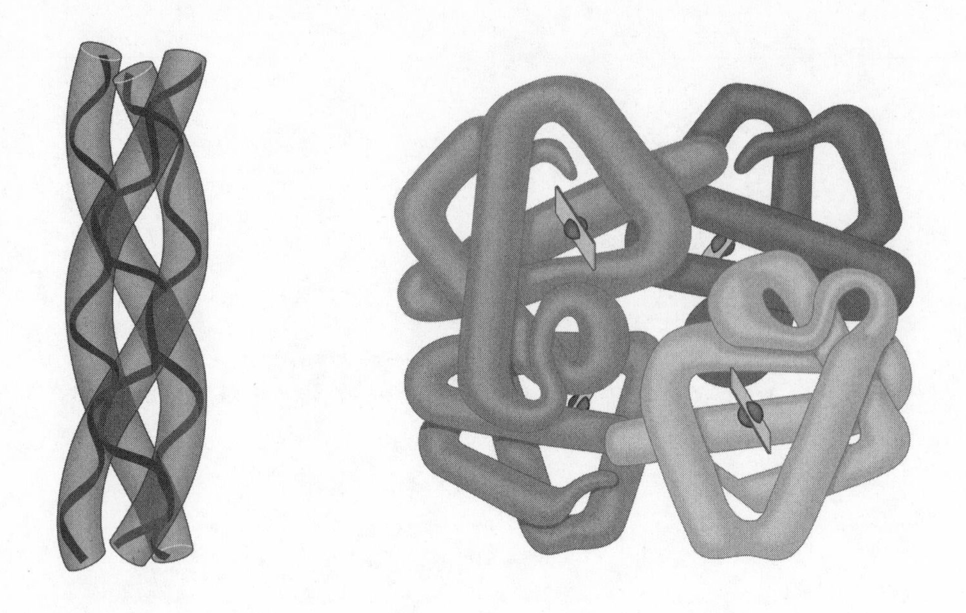

Figure 5.23 The quaternary structure of proteins, page 78

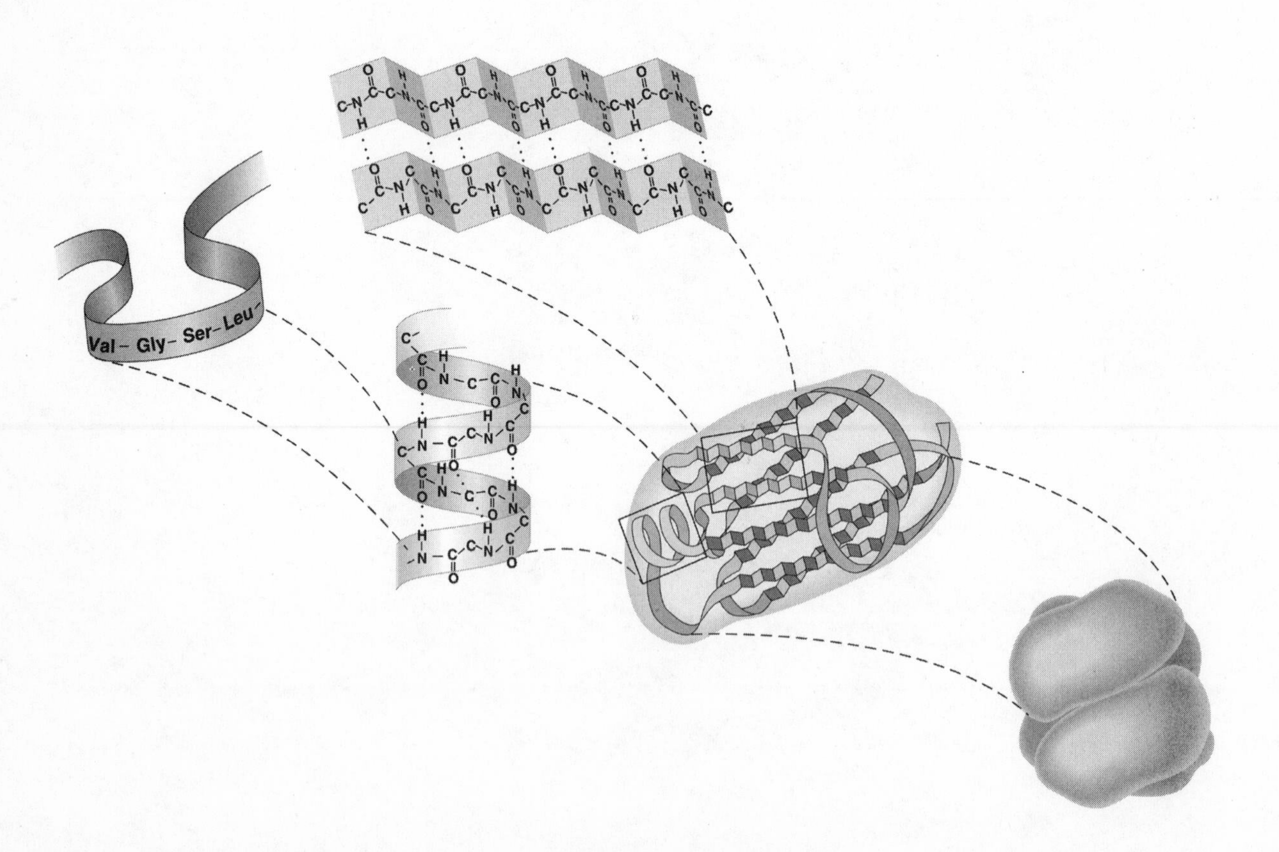

Figure 5.24 Review: the four levels of protein structure, page 79

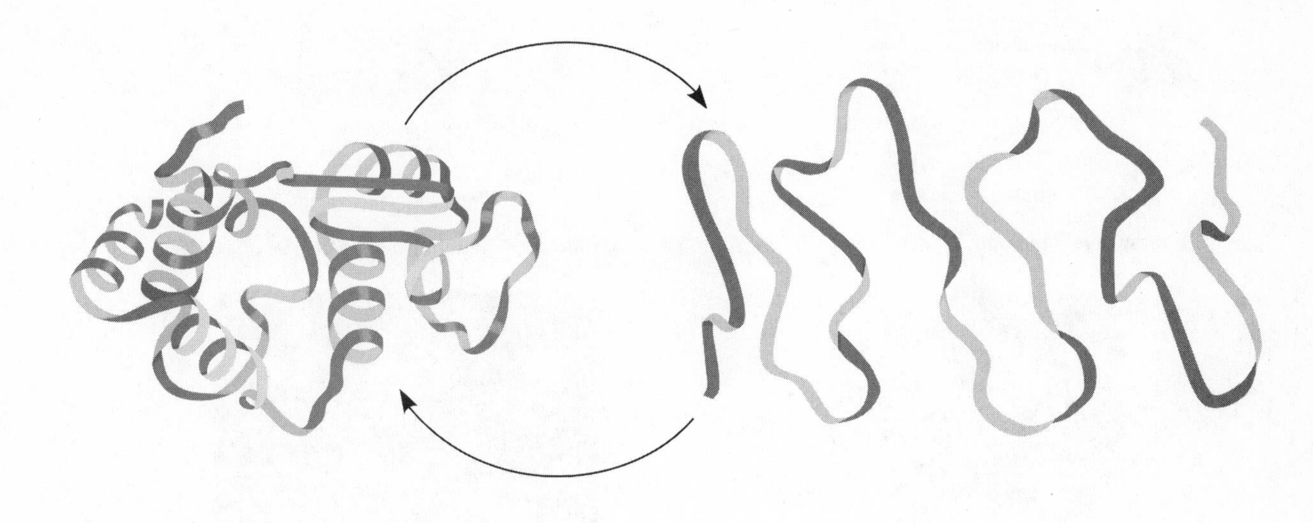

Figure 5.25 Denaturation and renaturation of a protein, page 79

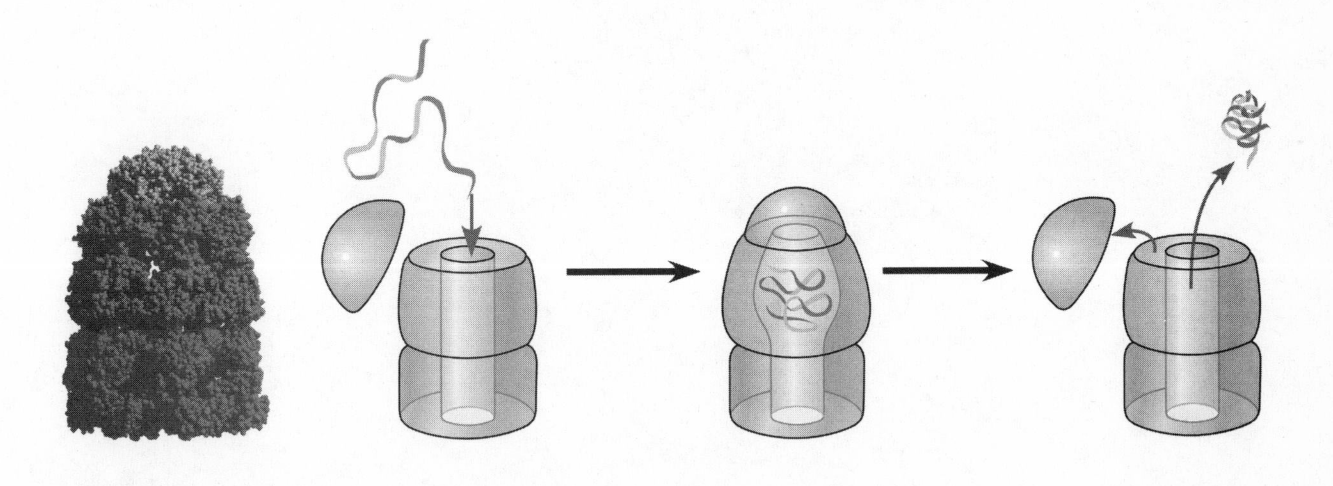

Figure 5.26 A chaperonin in action, page 80

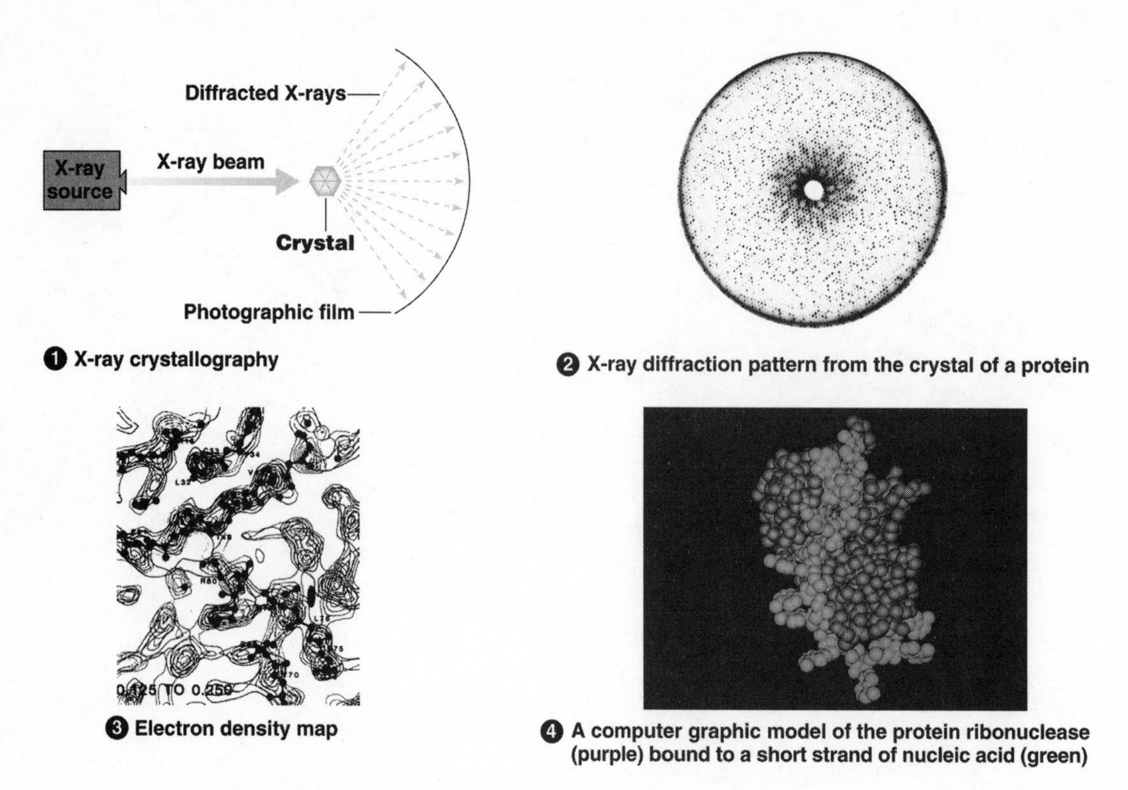

Figure 5.27 X-ray crystallography, page 81

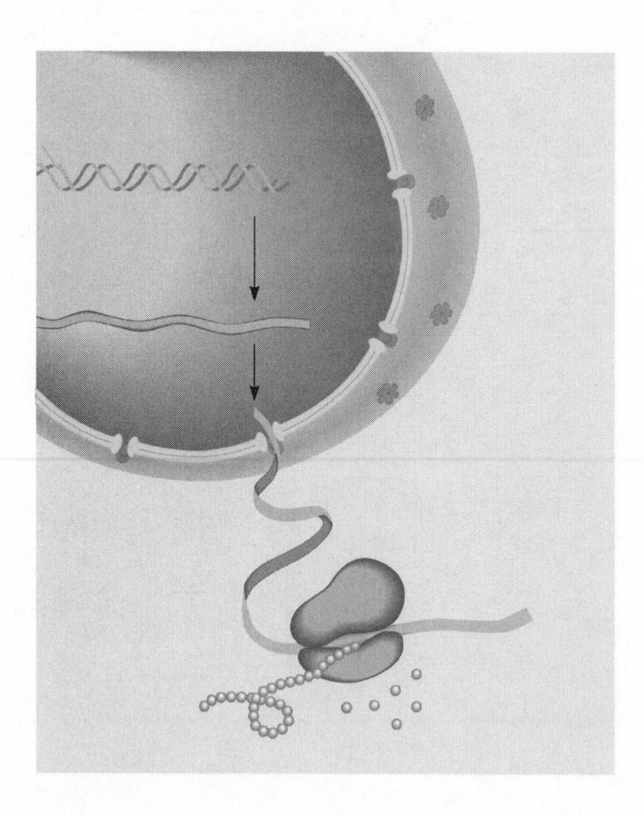

Figure 5.28 DNA → RNA → protein: a diagrammatic overview of information flow in a cell, page 82

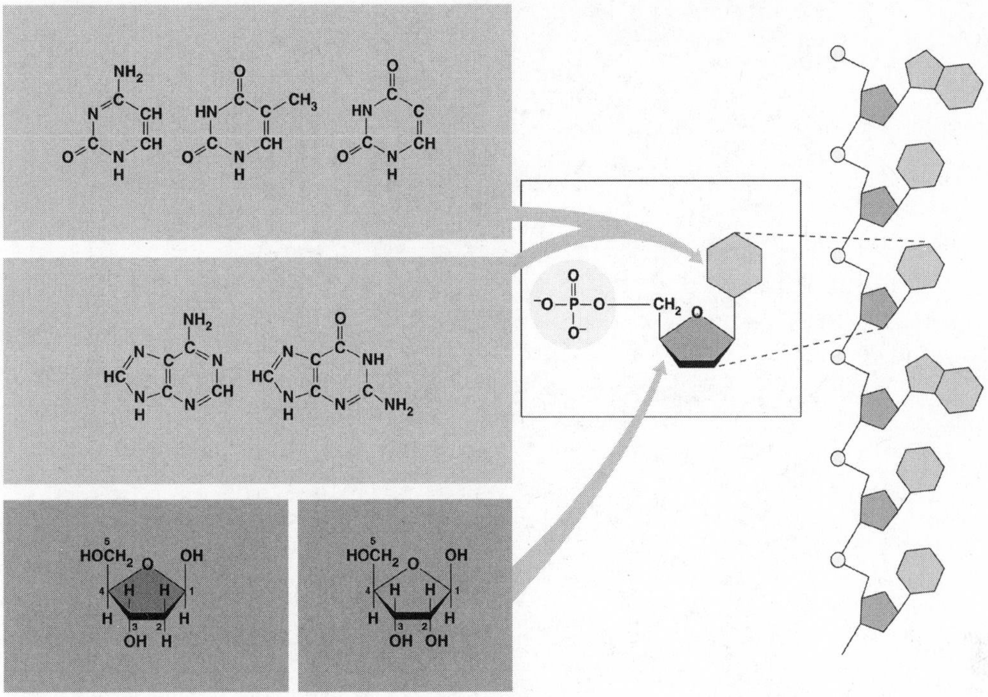

Figure 5.29 The components of nucleic acids, page 83

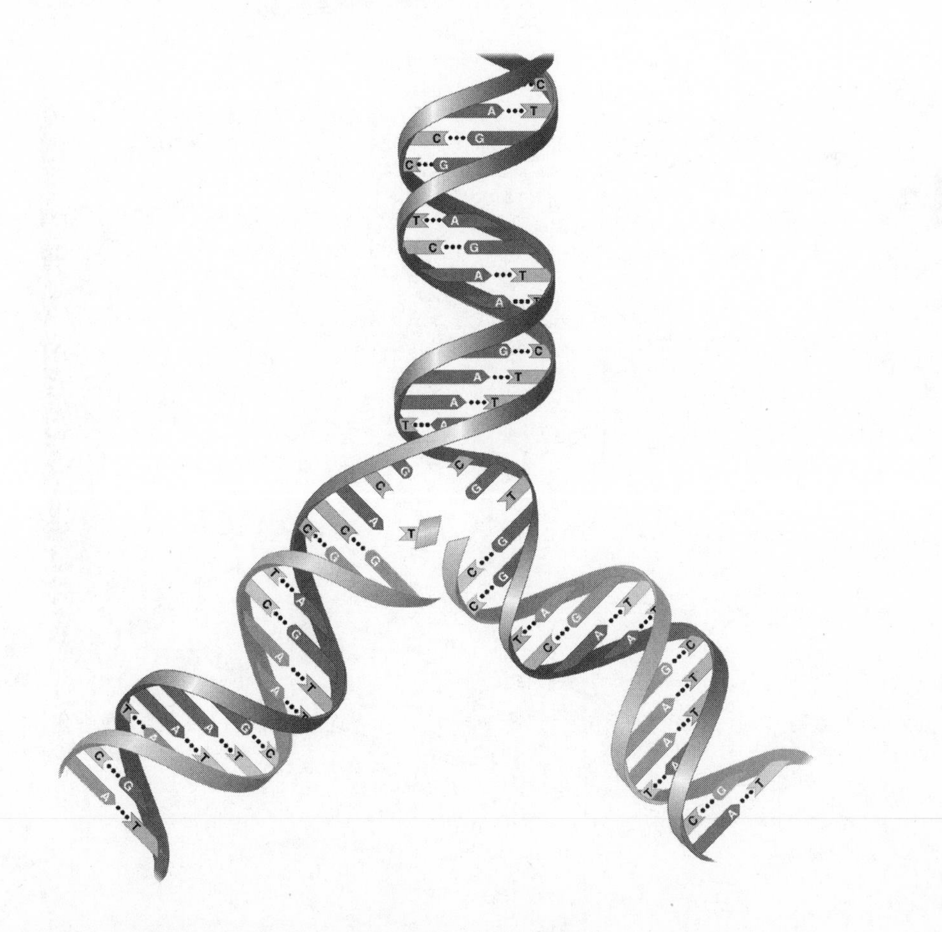

Figure 5.30 The DNA double helix and its replication, page 84

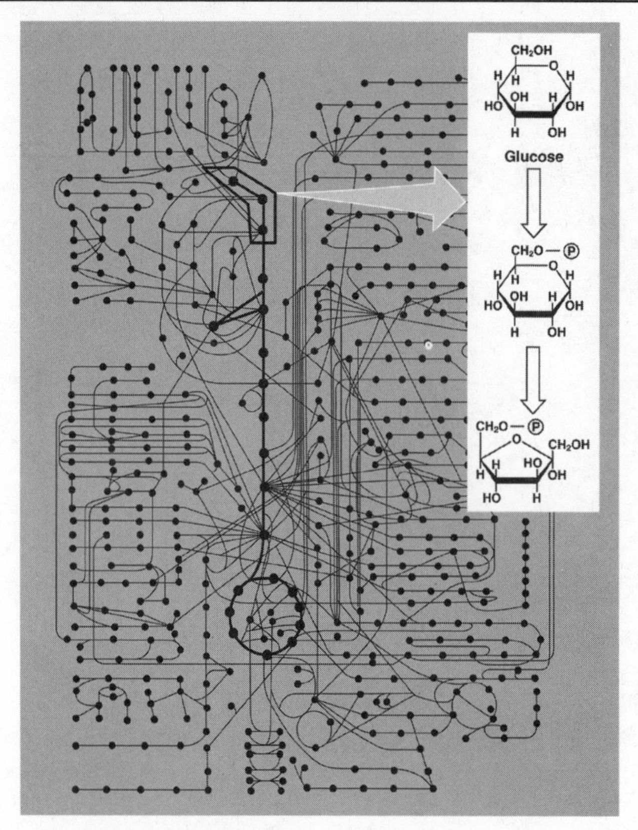

Figure 6.1 The complexity of metabolism, page 88

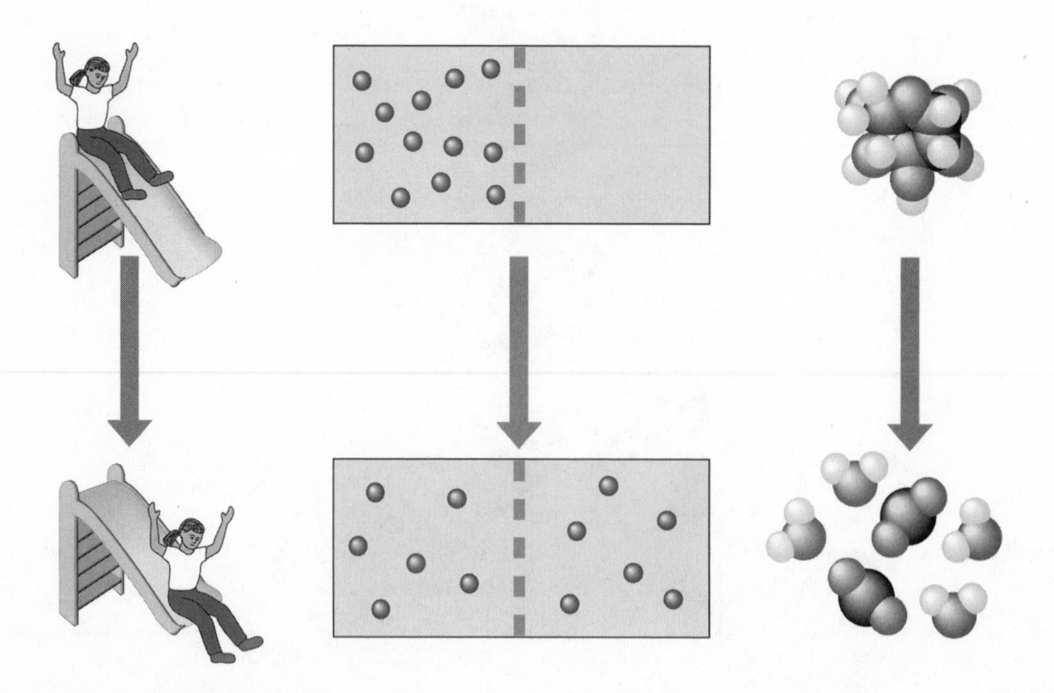

Figure 6.5 The relationship of free energy to stability, work capacity, and spontaneous change, page 91

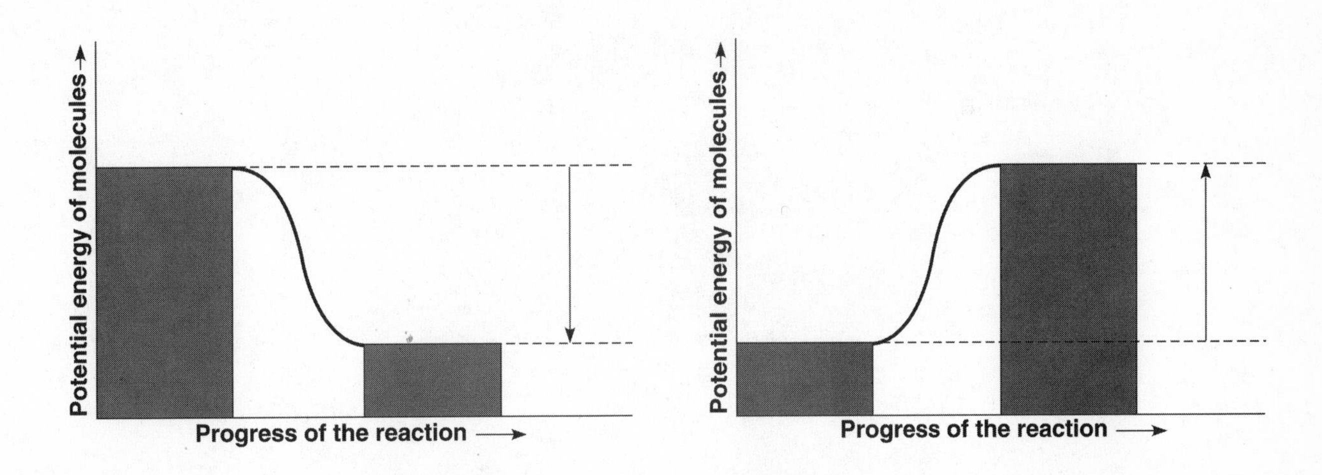

Figure 6.6 Energy changes in exergonic and endergonic reactions, page 93

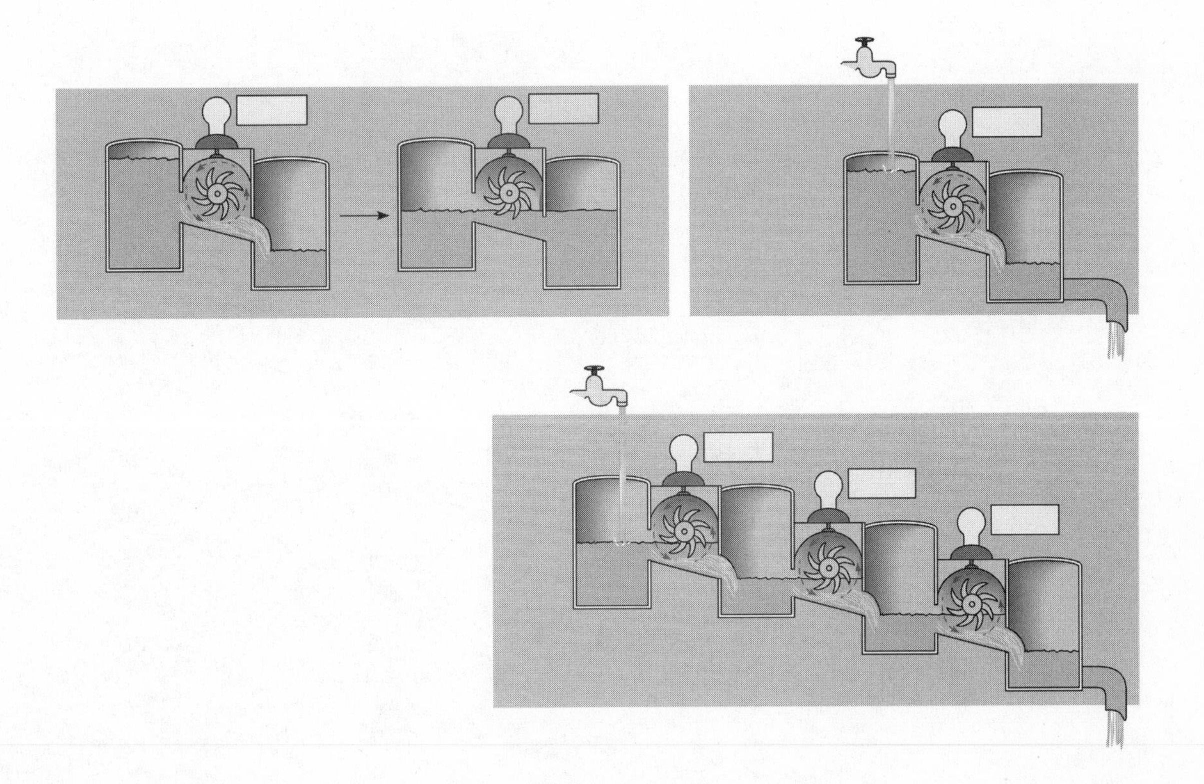

Figure 6.7 Disequilibrium and work in closed and open systems, page 93

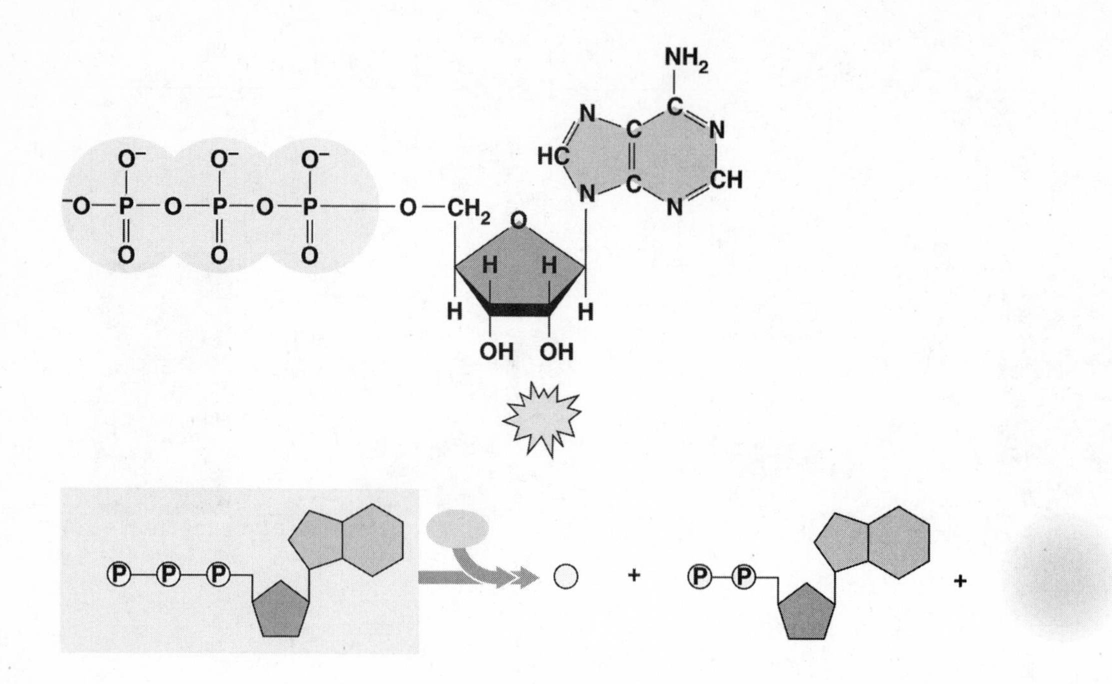

Figure 6.8 The structure and hydrolysis of ATP, page 94

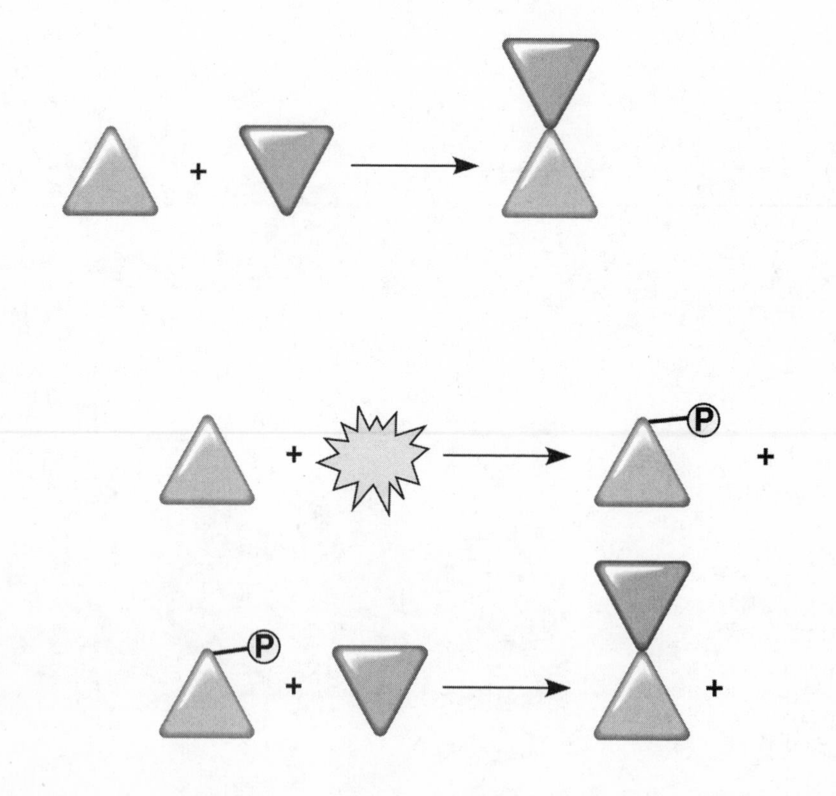

Figure 6.9 Energy coupling by phosphate transfer, page 95

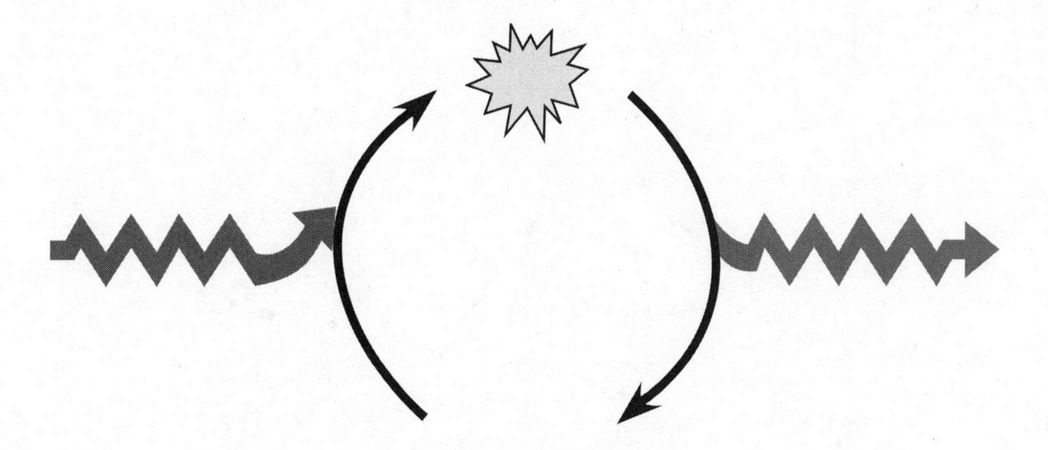

Figure 6.10 The ATP cycle, page 95

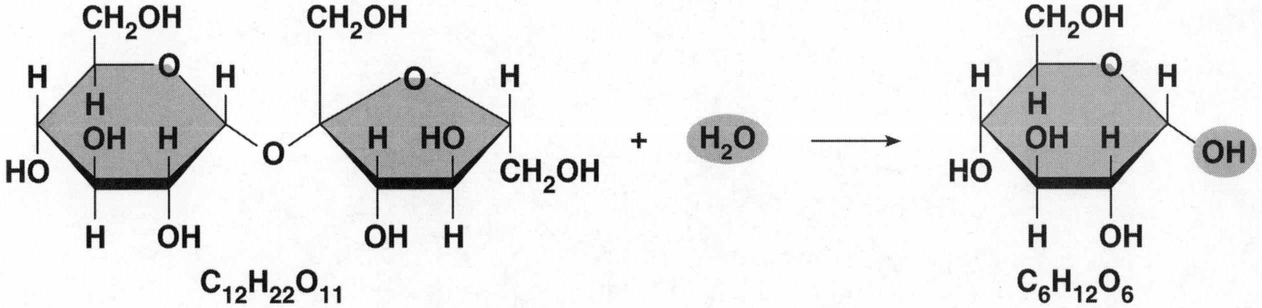

CH_2OH CH_2OH CH_2OH

H H H H H H H H

OH H H HO OH H

HO O CH_2OH + H_2O → HO OH

H OH OH H H OH

$C_{12}H_{22}O_{11}$ $C_6H_{12}O_6$

Figure 6.11 Example of an enzyme-catalyzed reaction: Hydrolysis of sucrose, page 96

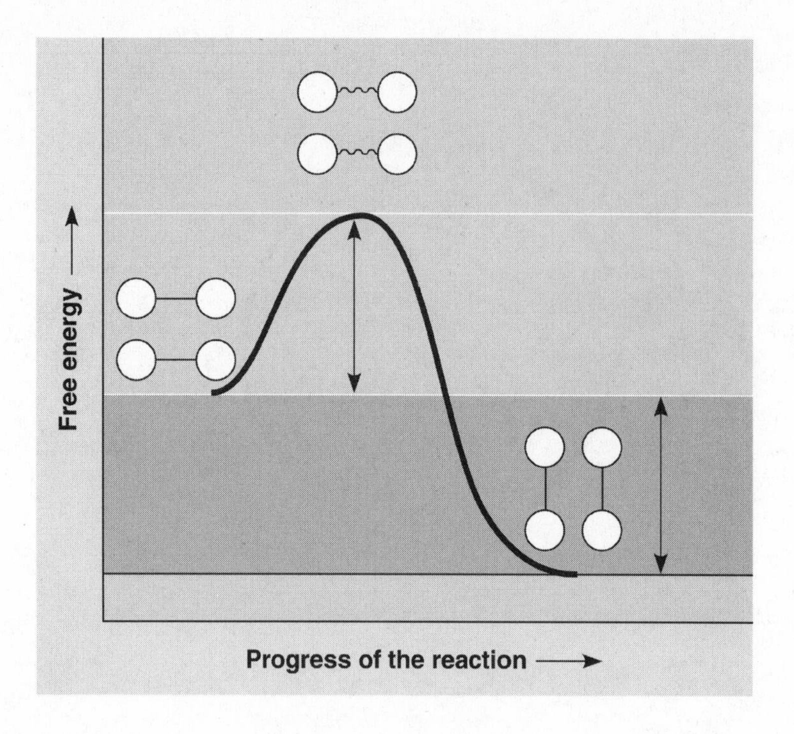

Figure 6.12 Energy profile of an exergonic reaction, page 97

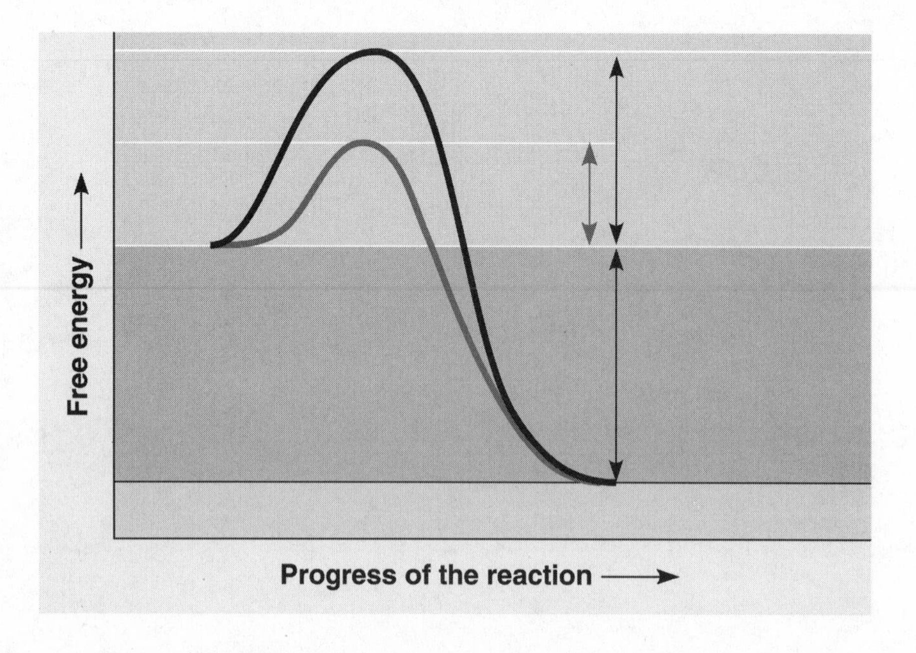

Figure 6.13 Enzymes lower the barrier of activation energy, page 97

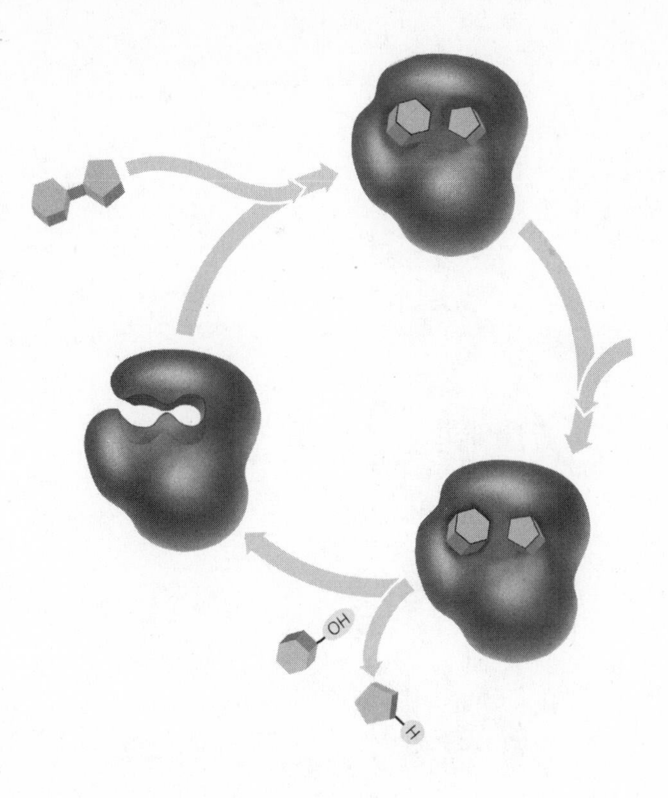

Figure 6.15 The catalytic cycle of an enzyme, page 99

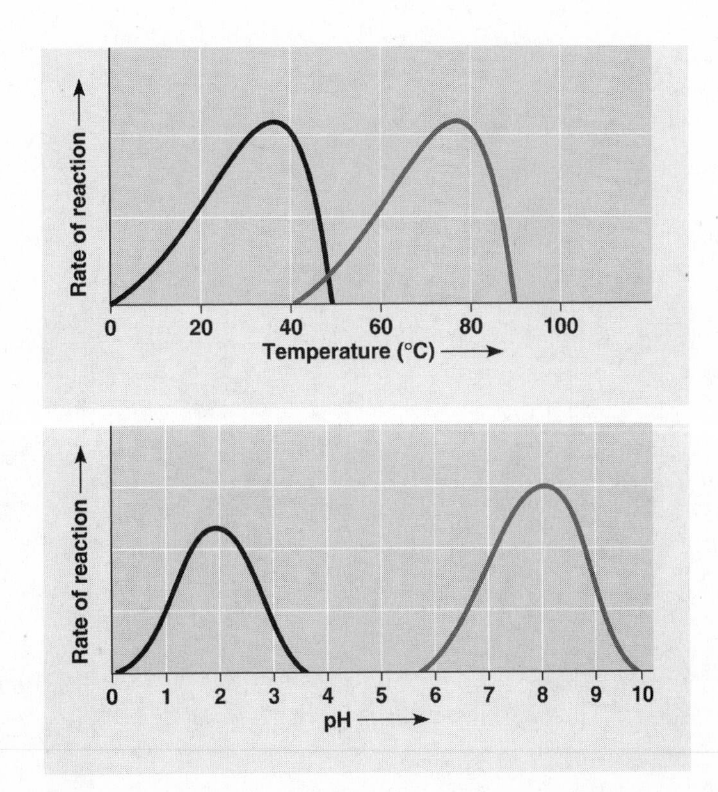

Figure 6.16 Environmental factors affecting enzyme activity, page 100

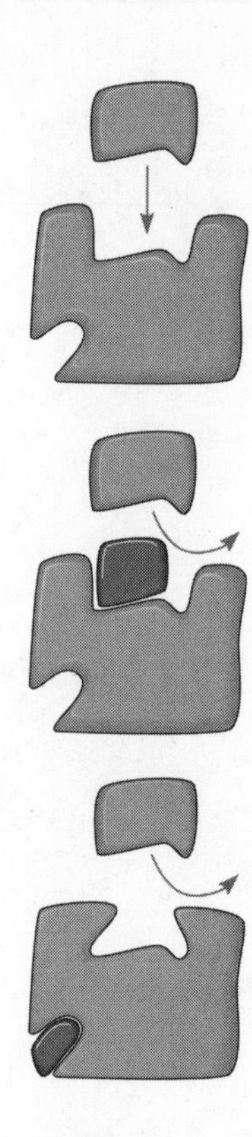

Figure 6.17 Inhibition of enzyme activity, page 101

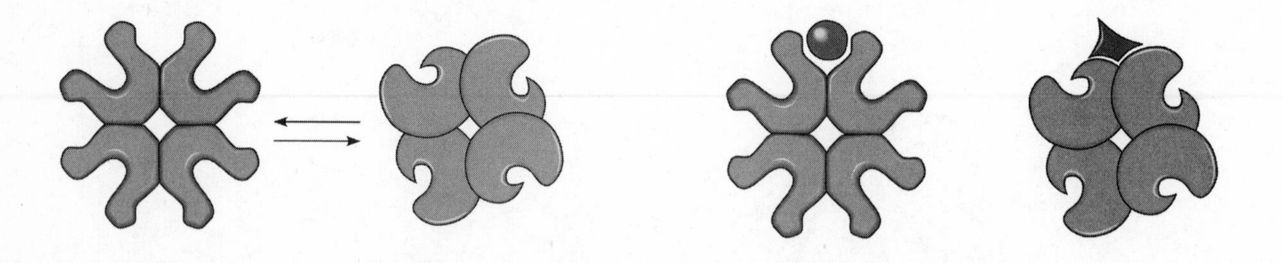

Figure 6.18 Allosteric regulation of enzyme activity, page 101

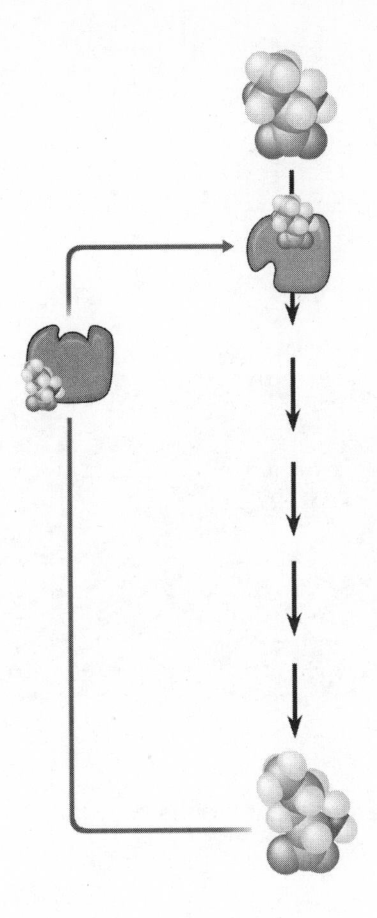

Figure 6.19 Feedback inhibition, page 102

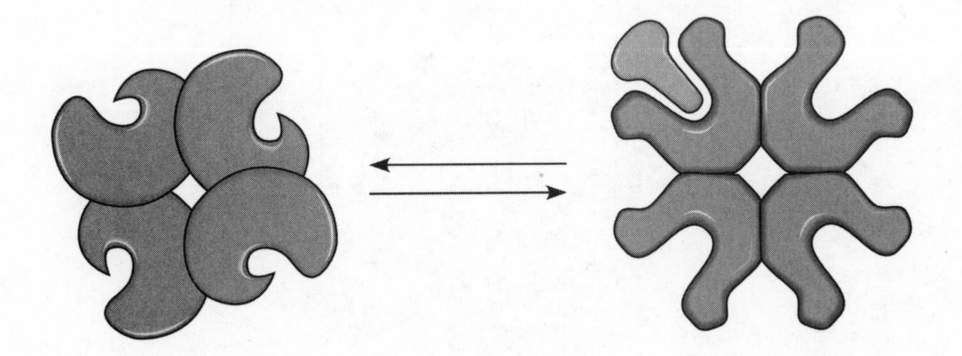

Figure 6.20 Cooperativity, page 103

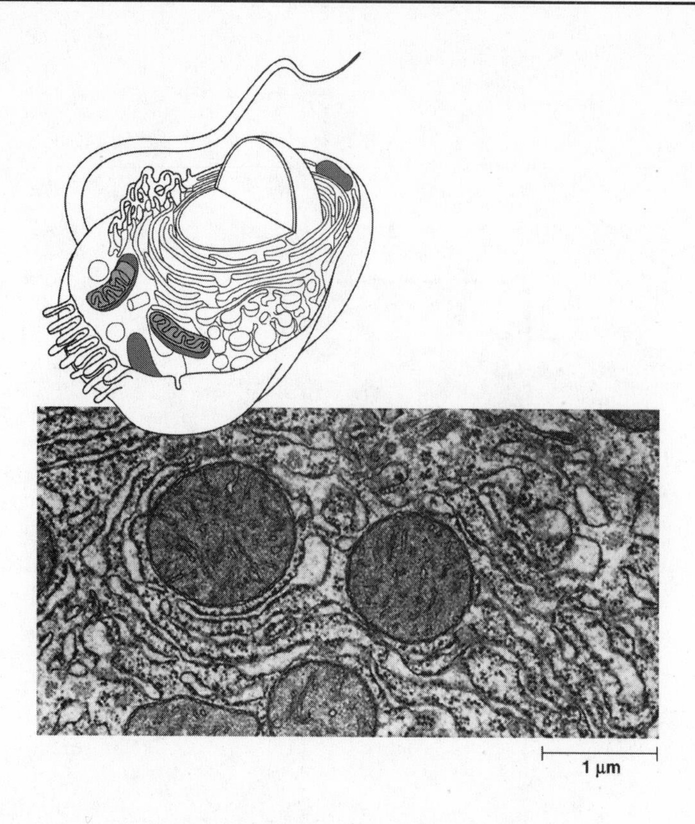

Figure 6.21 Organelles and structural order in metabolism, page 103

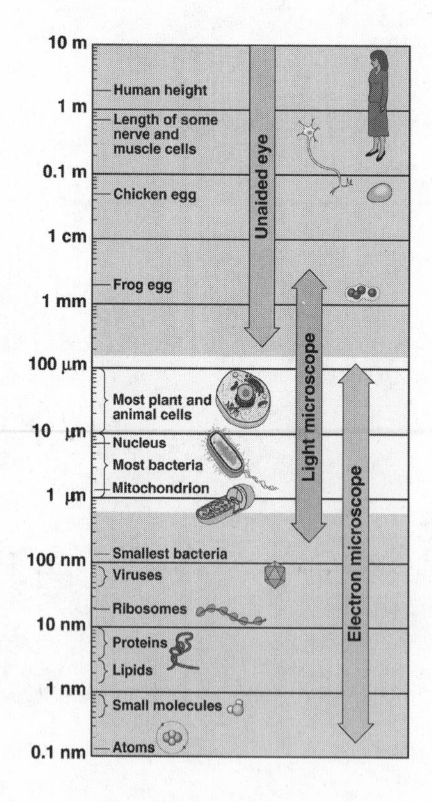

Figure 7.1 The size range of cells, page 109

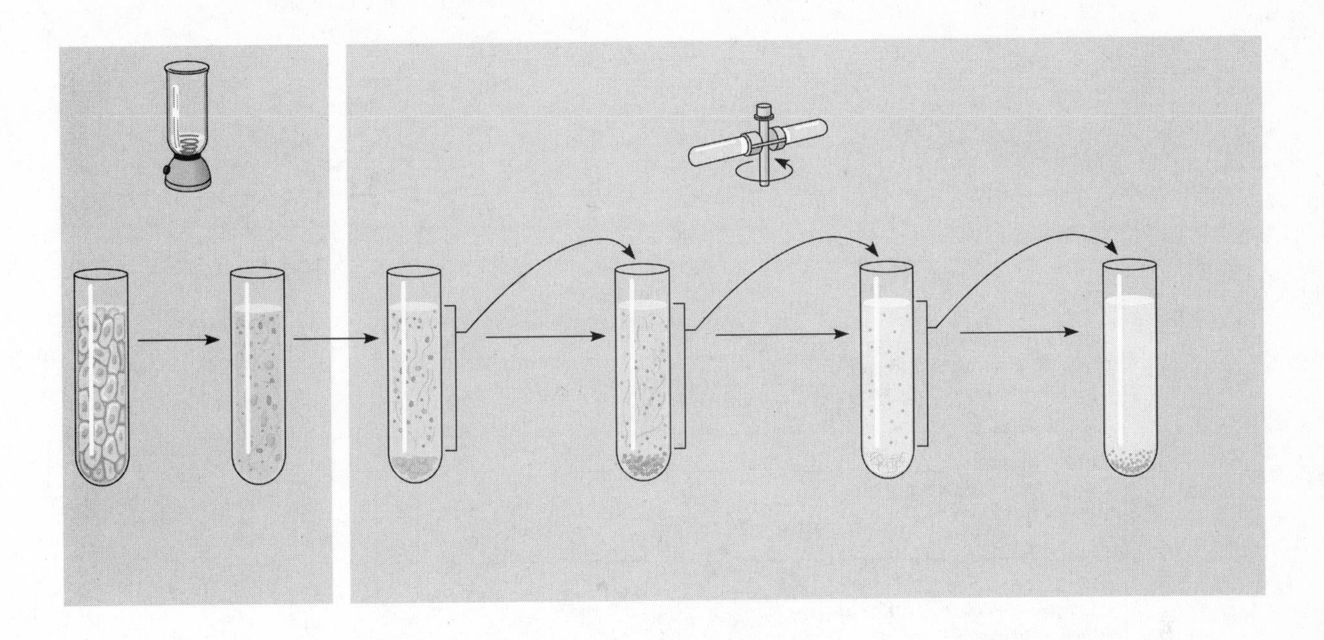

Figure 7.3 Cell fractionation, page 111

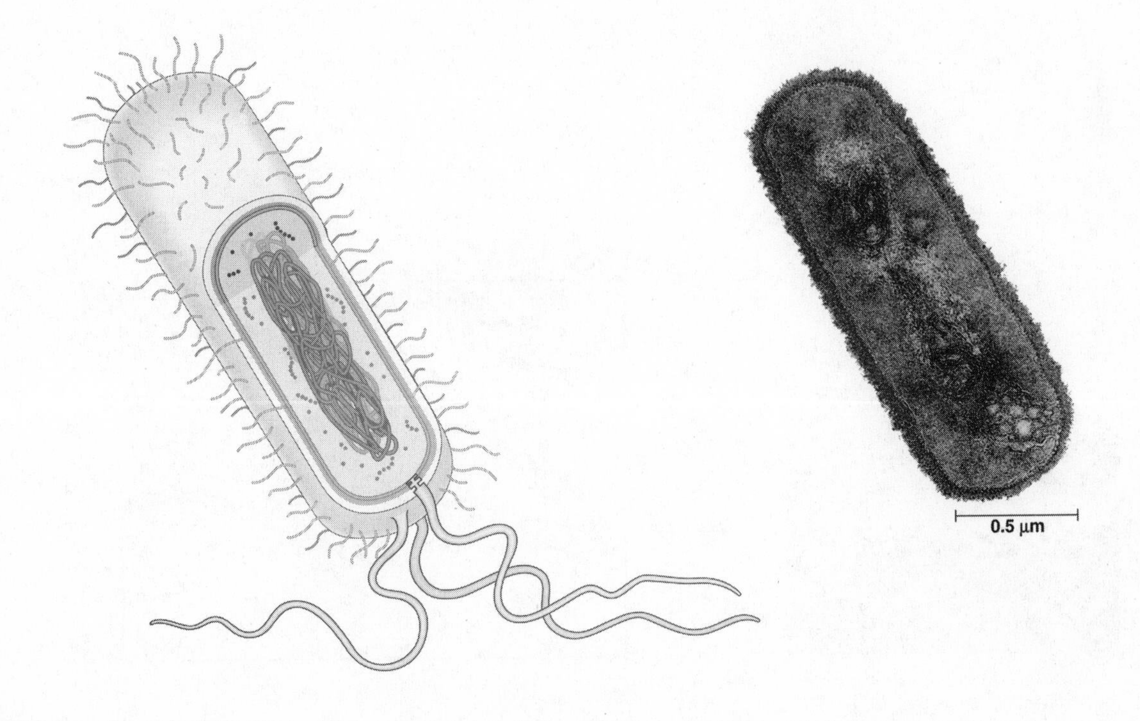

Figure 7.4 A prokaryotic cell, page 112

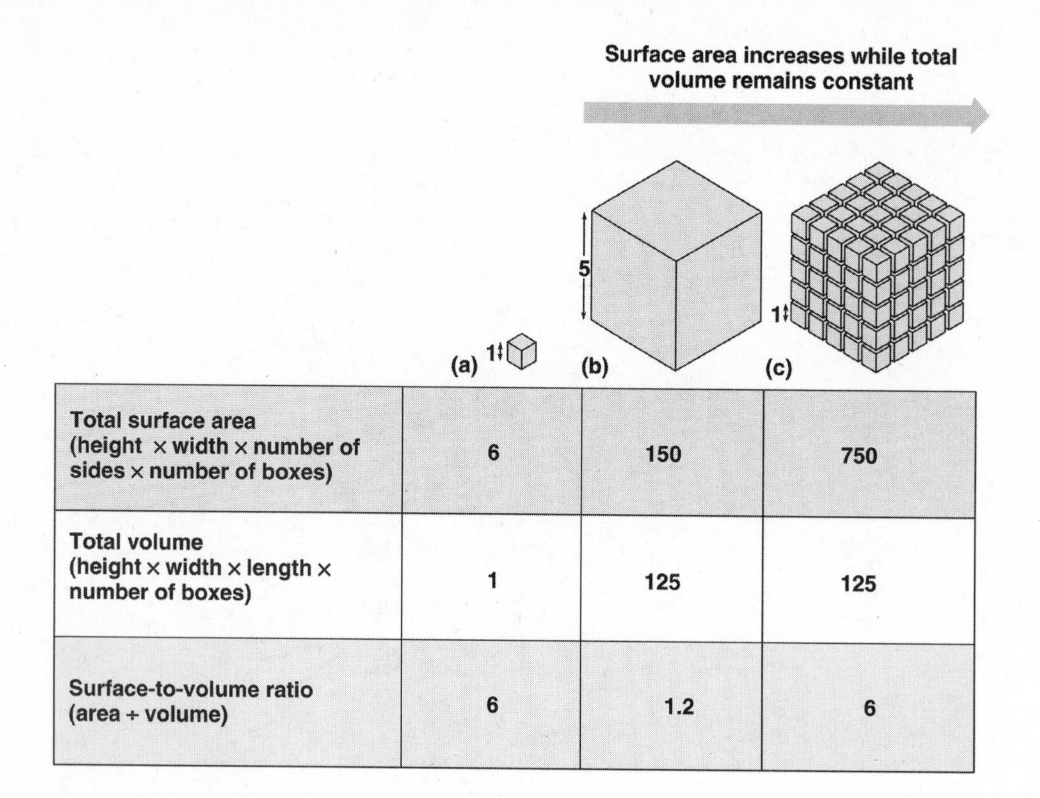

	(a)	(b)	(c)
Total surface area (height × width × number of sides × number of boxes)	6	150	750
Total volume (height × width × length × number of boxes)	1	125	125
Surface-to-volume ratio (area ÷ volume)	6	1.2	6

Figure 7.5 Geometric relationships explain why most cells are microscopic, page 113

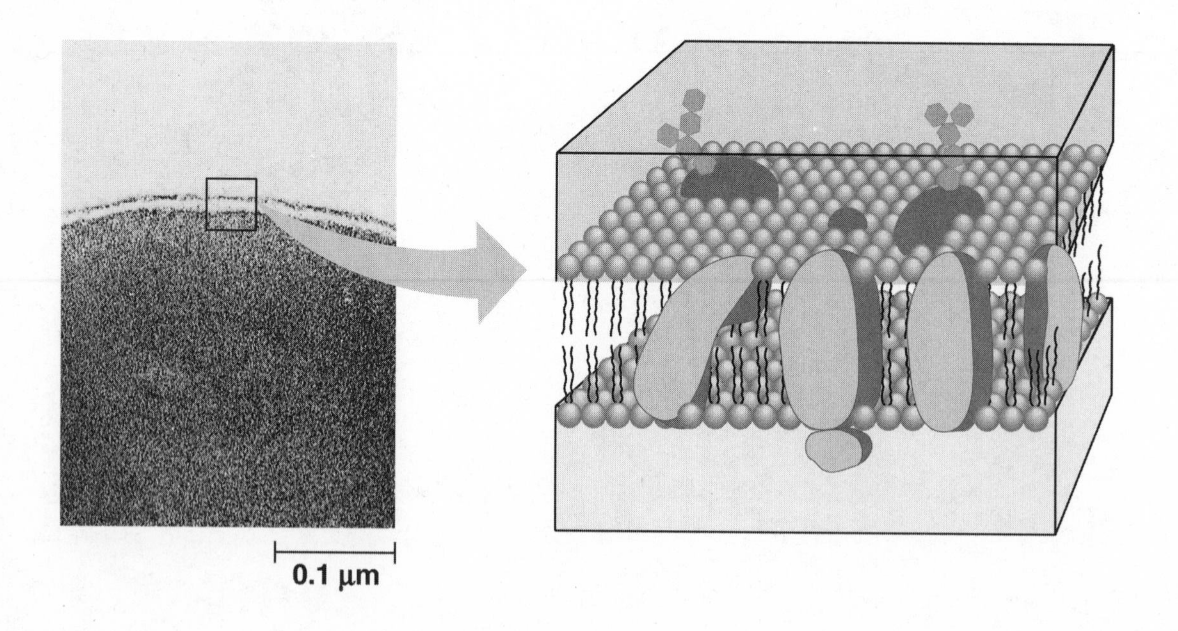

Figure 7.6 The plasma membrane, page 113

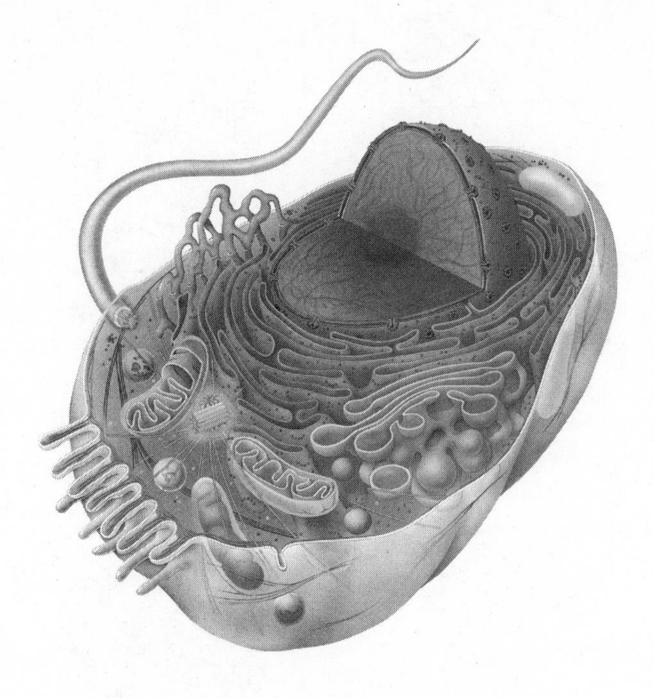

Figure 7.7 Overview of an animal cell, page 114

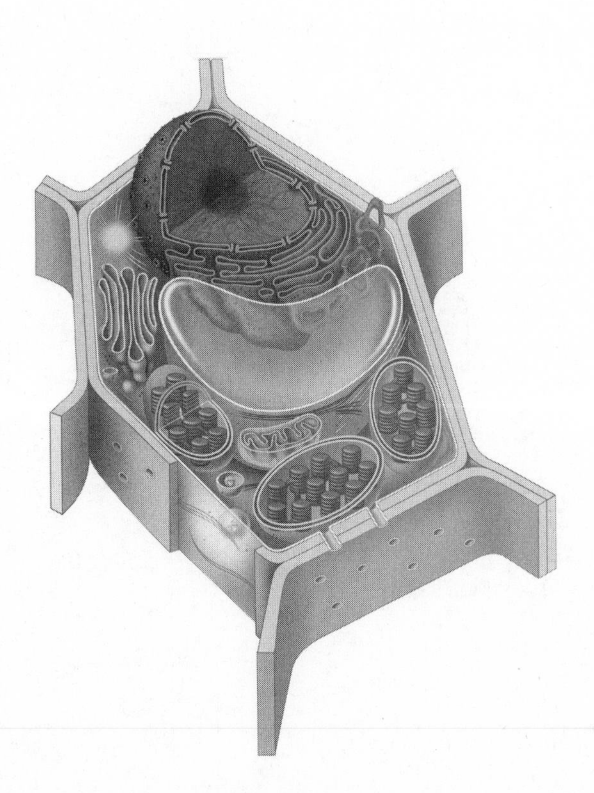

Figure 7.8 Overview of a plant cell, page 115

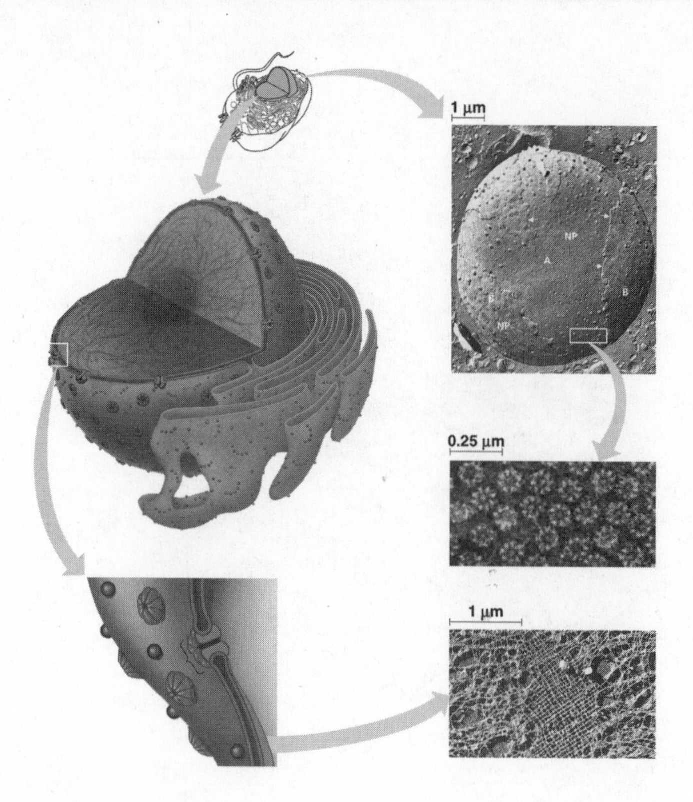

Figure 7.9 The nucleus and its envelope, page 116

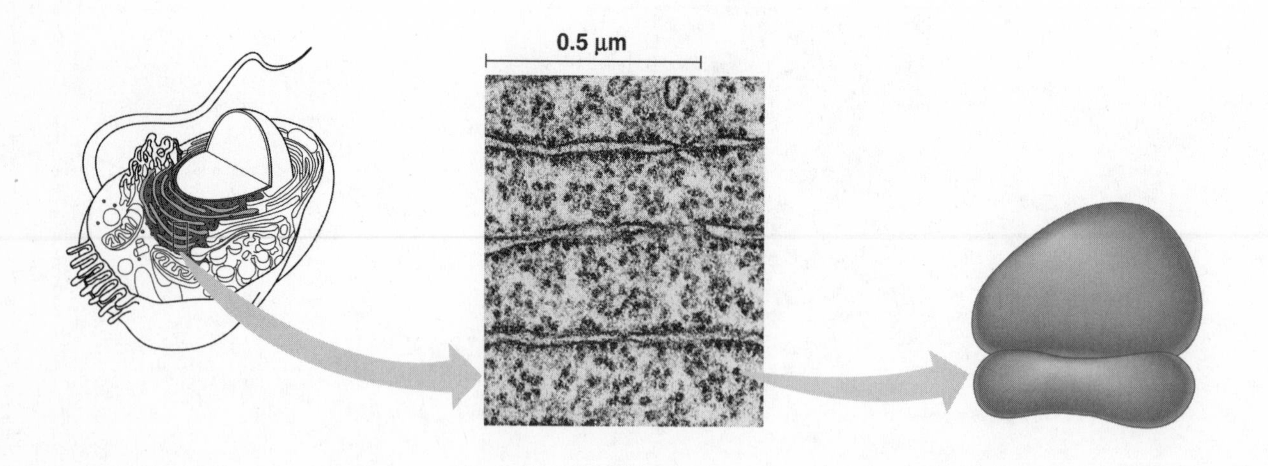

Figure 7.10 Ribosomes, page 117

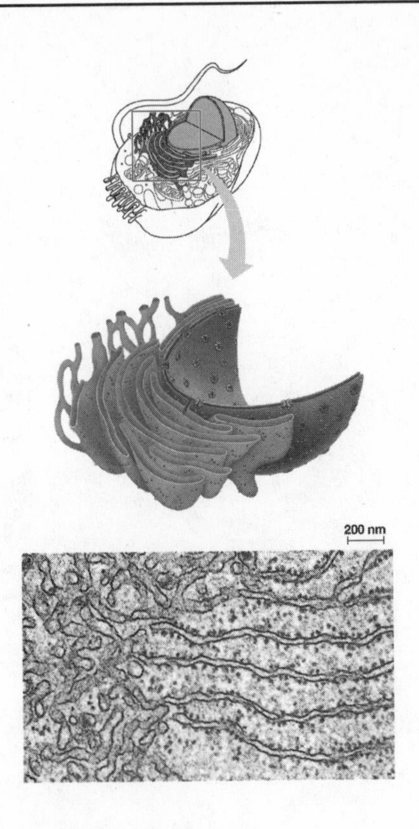

Figure 7.11 Endoplasmic reticulum (ER), page 119

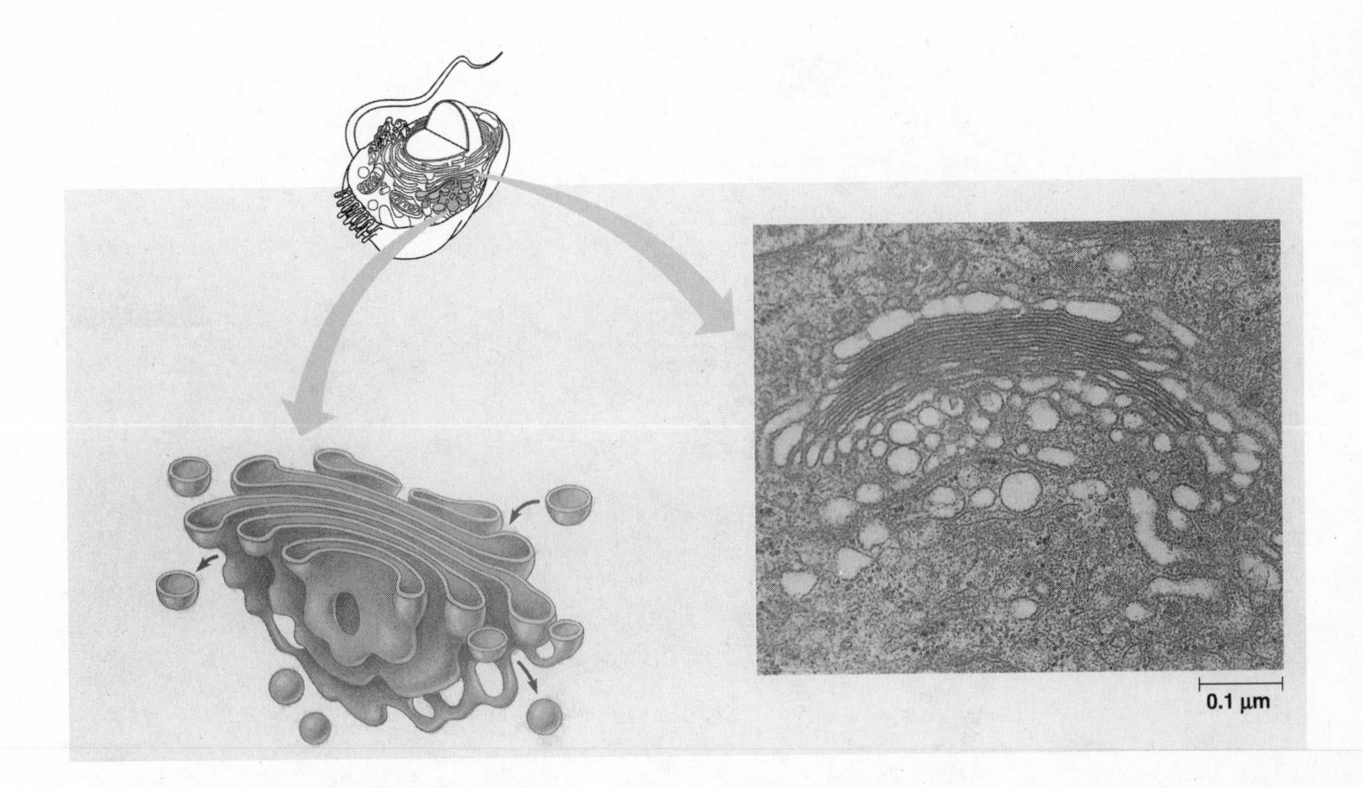

Figure 7.12 The Golgi apparatus, page 120

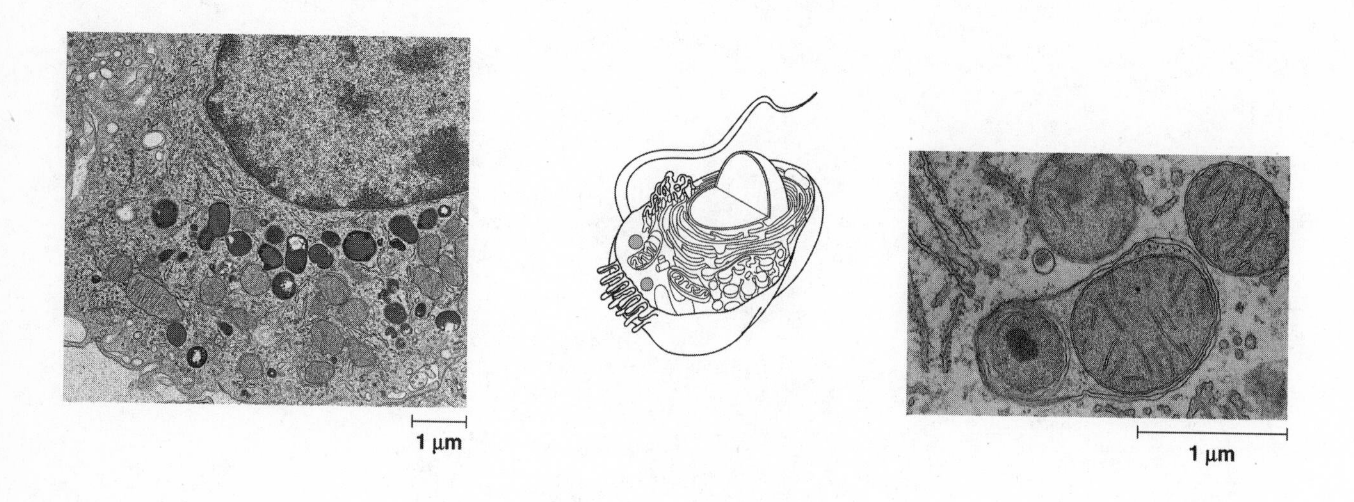

Figure 7.13 Lysosomes, page 121

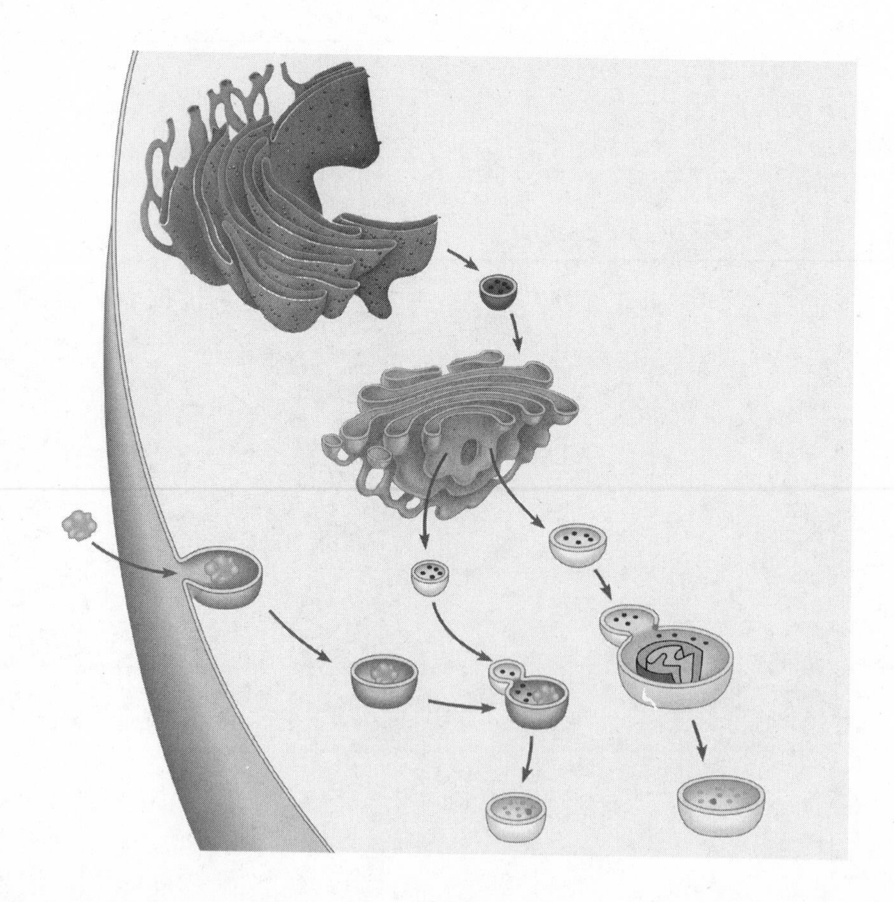

Figure 7.14 The formation and functions of lysosomes, page 122

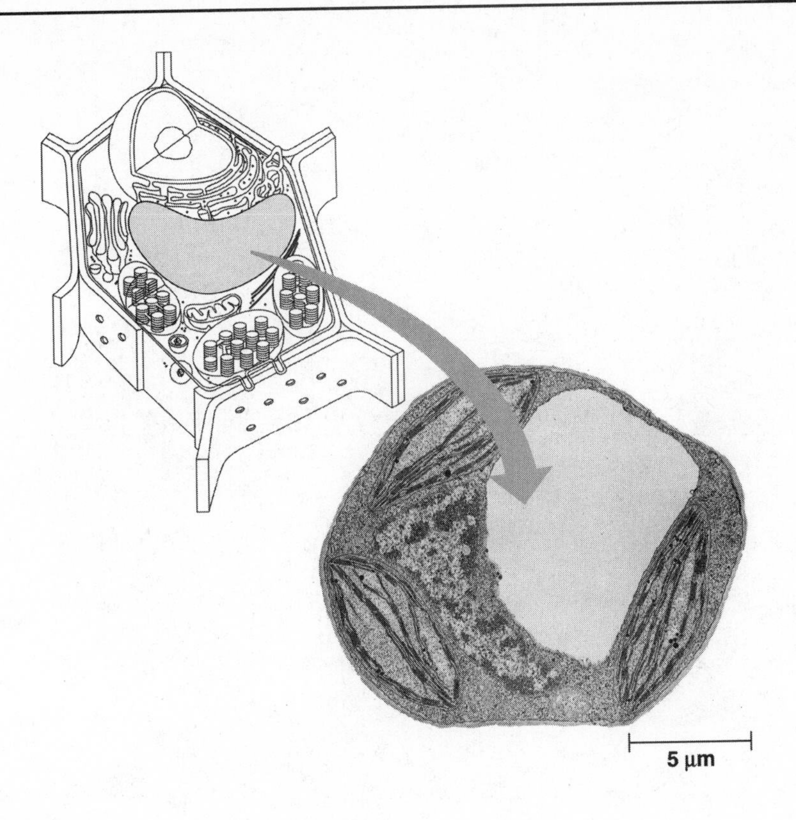

Figure 7.15 The plant cell vacuole, page 123

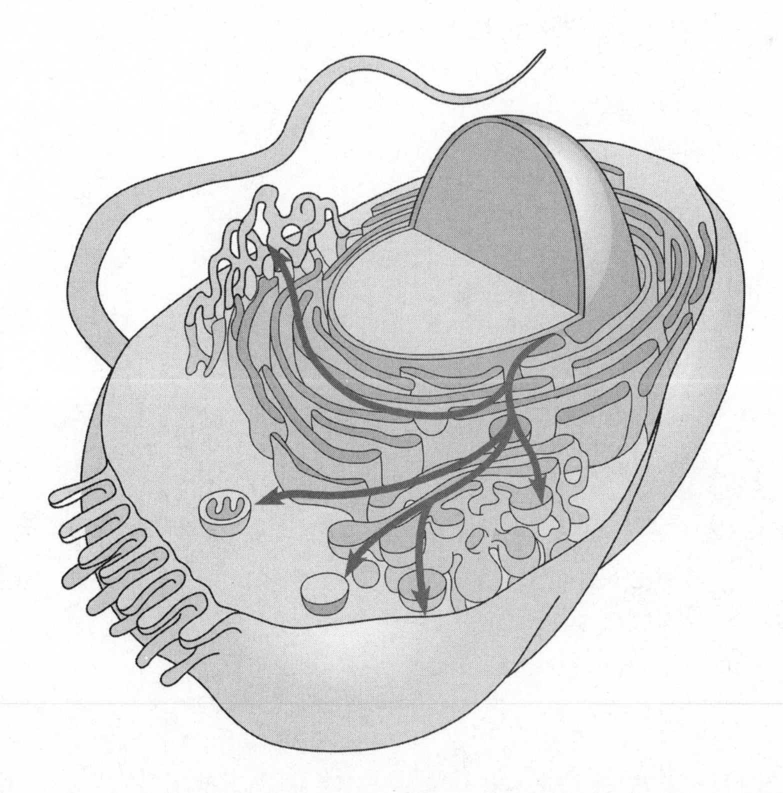

Figure 7.16 Review: relationships among organelles of the endomembrane system, page 123

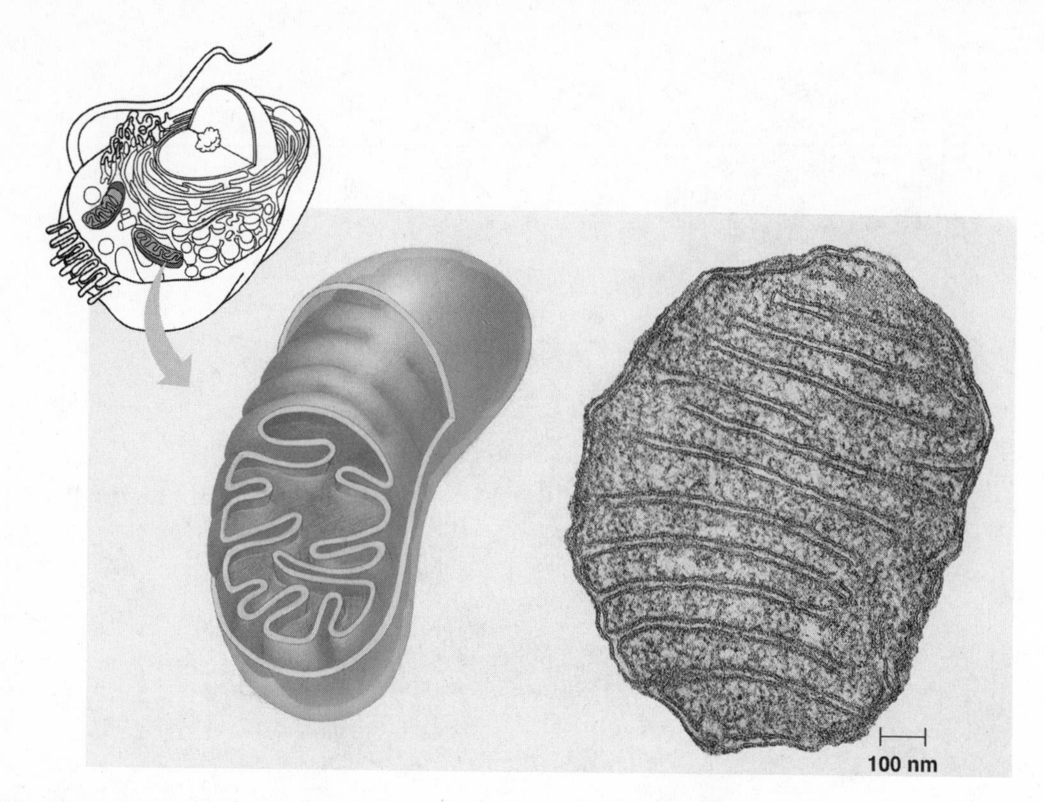

Figure 7.17 The mitochondrion, site of cellular respiration, page 124

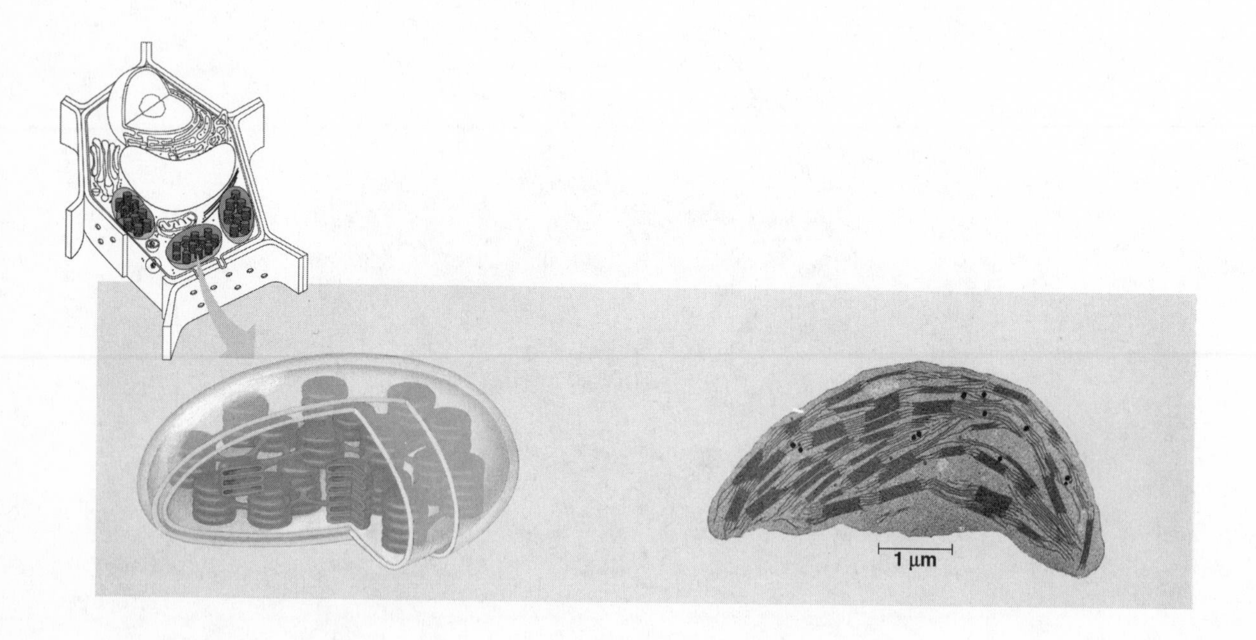

Figure 7.18 The chloroplast, site of photosynthesis, page 125

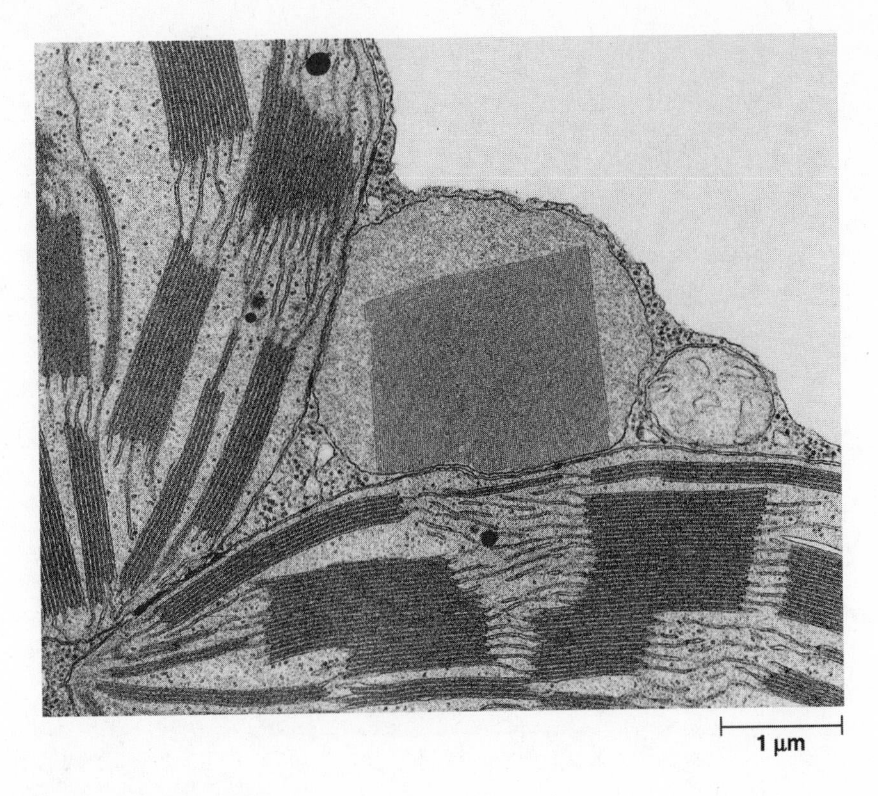

Figure 7.19 Peroxisomes, page 125

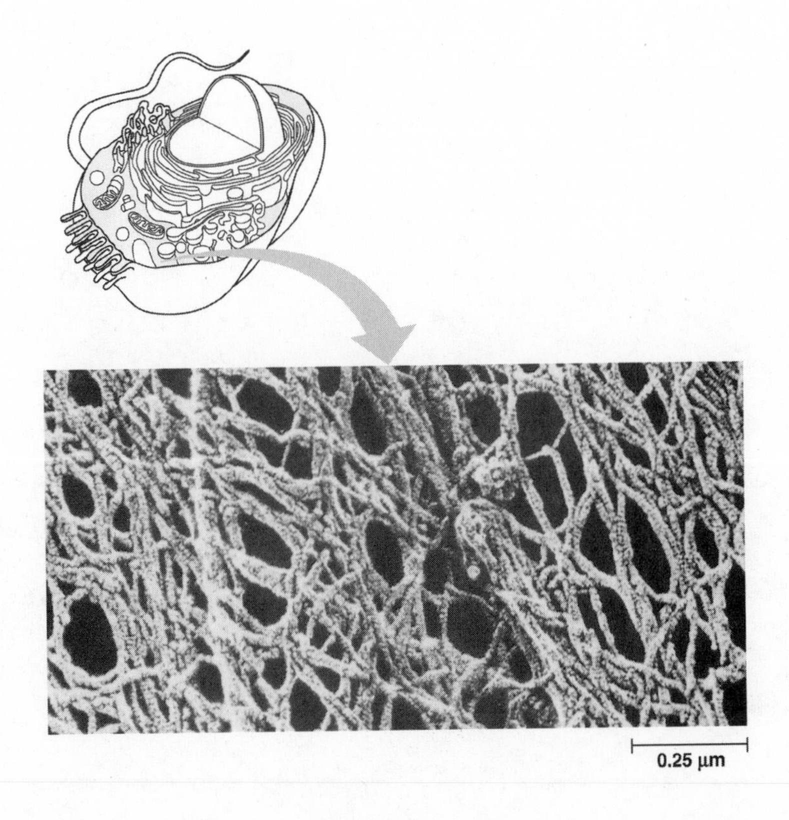

Figure 7.20 The cytoskeleton, page 126

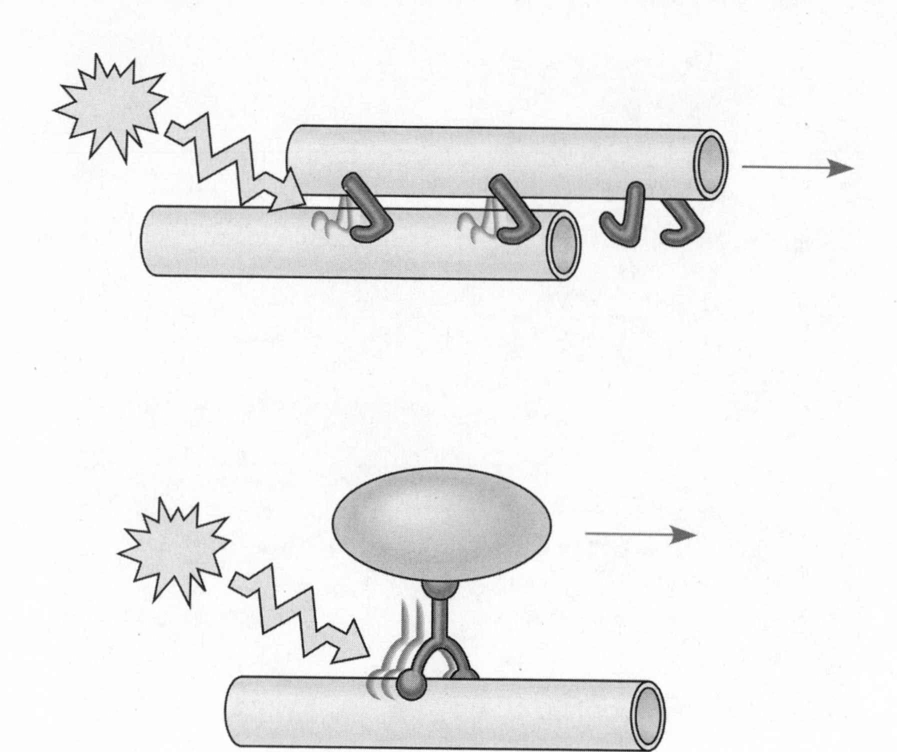

Figure 7.21 Motor molecules and the cytoskeleton, page 126

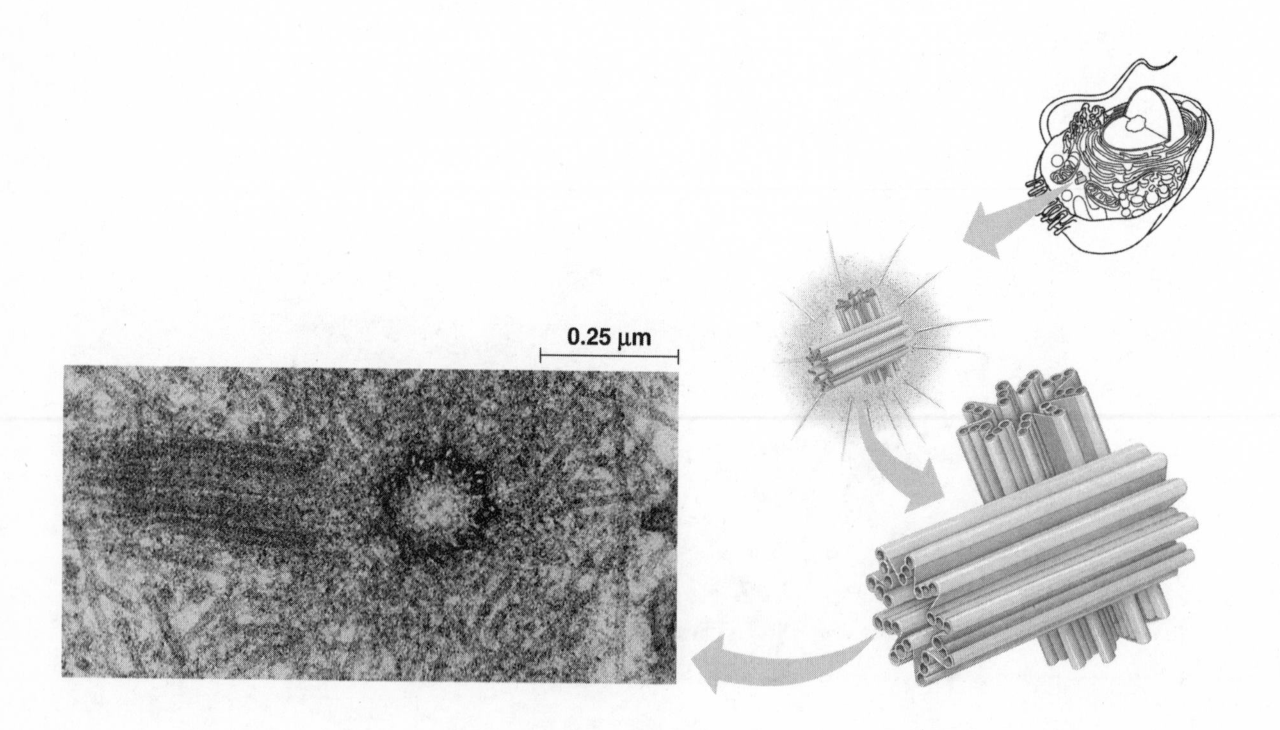

Figure 7.22 Centrosome containing a pair of centrioles, page 128

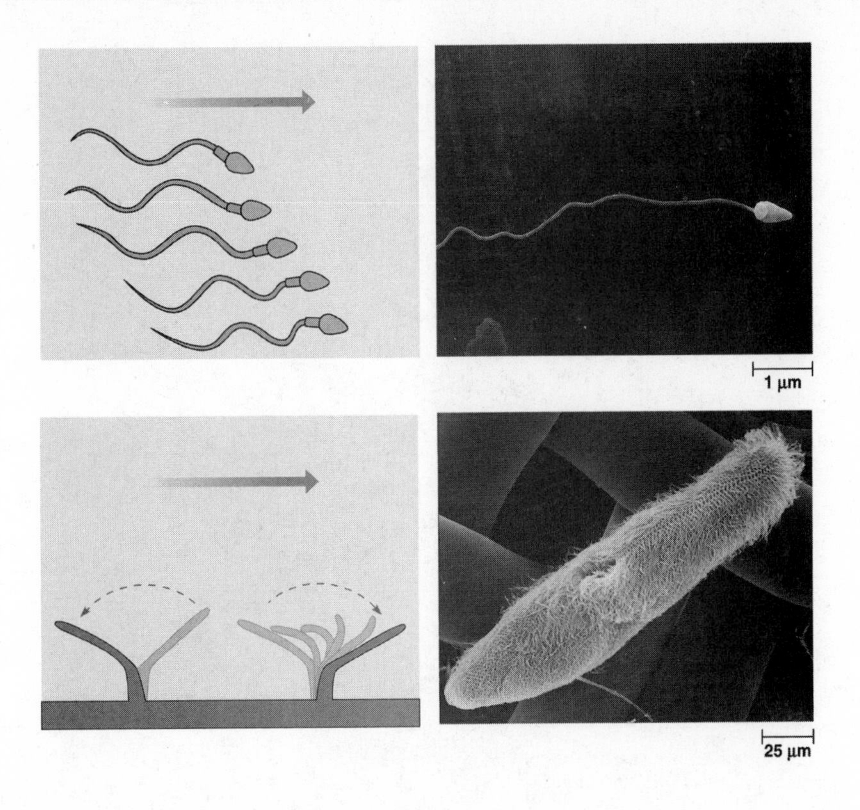

Figure 7.23 A comparison of the beating of flagella and cilia, page 129

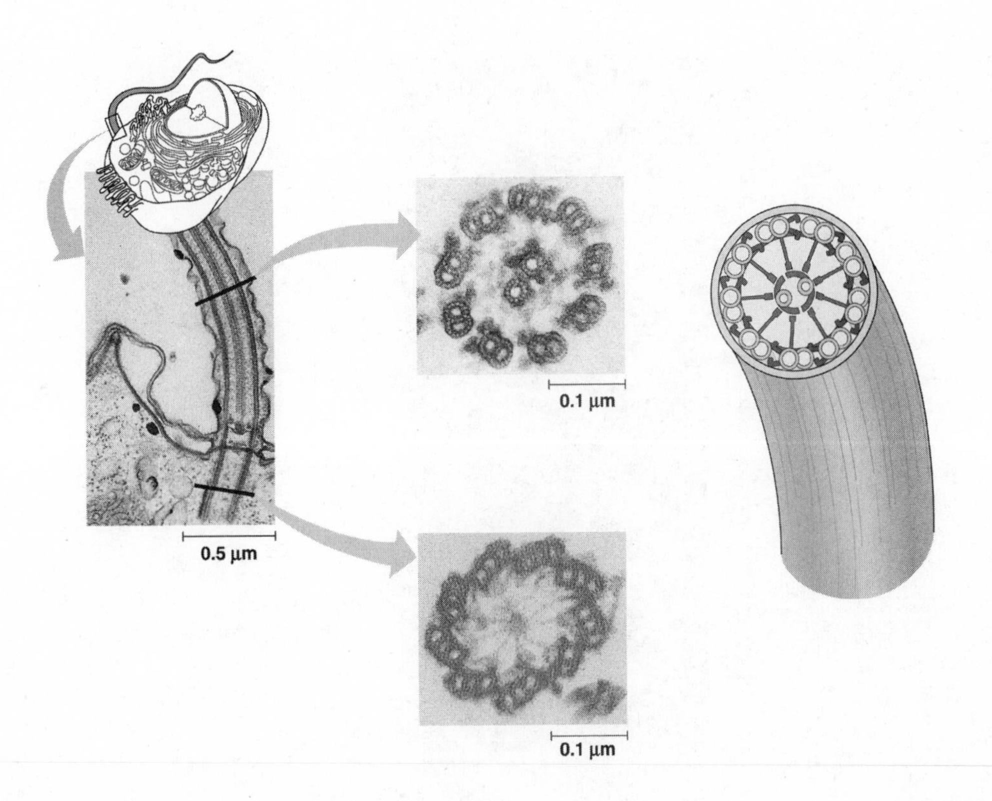

Figure 7.24 Ultrastructure of a eukaryotic flagellum or cilium, page 129

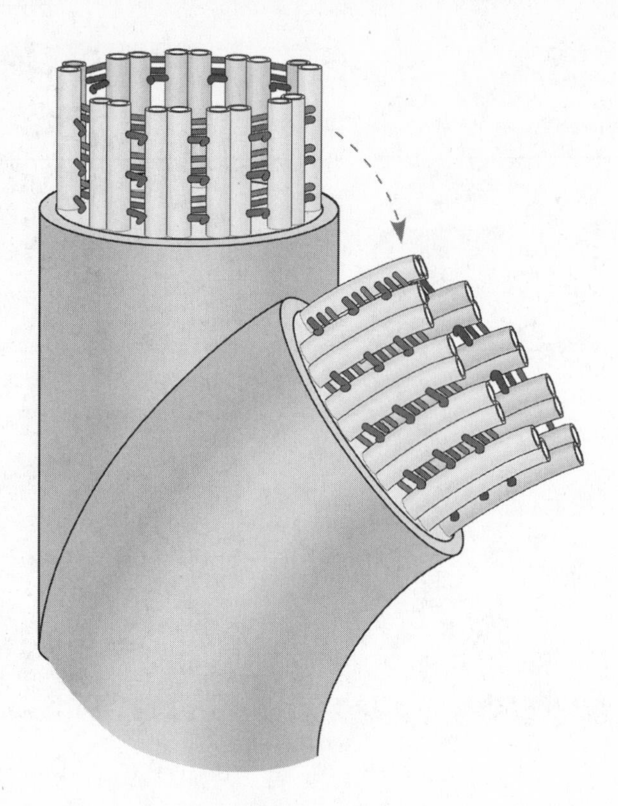

Figure 7.25 How dynein "walking" moves cilia and flagella, page 130

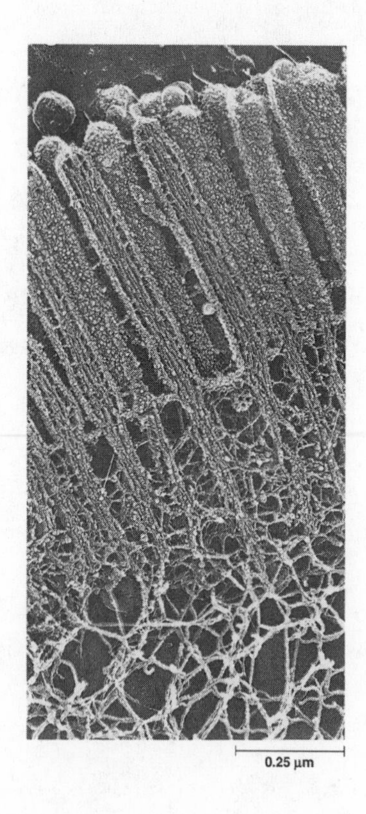

Figure 7.26 A structural role of microfilaments, page 130

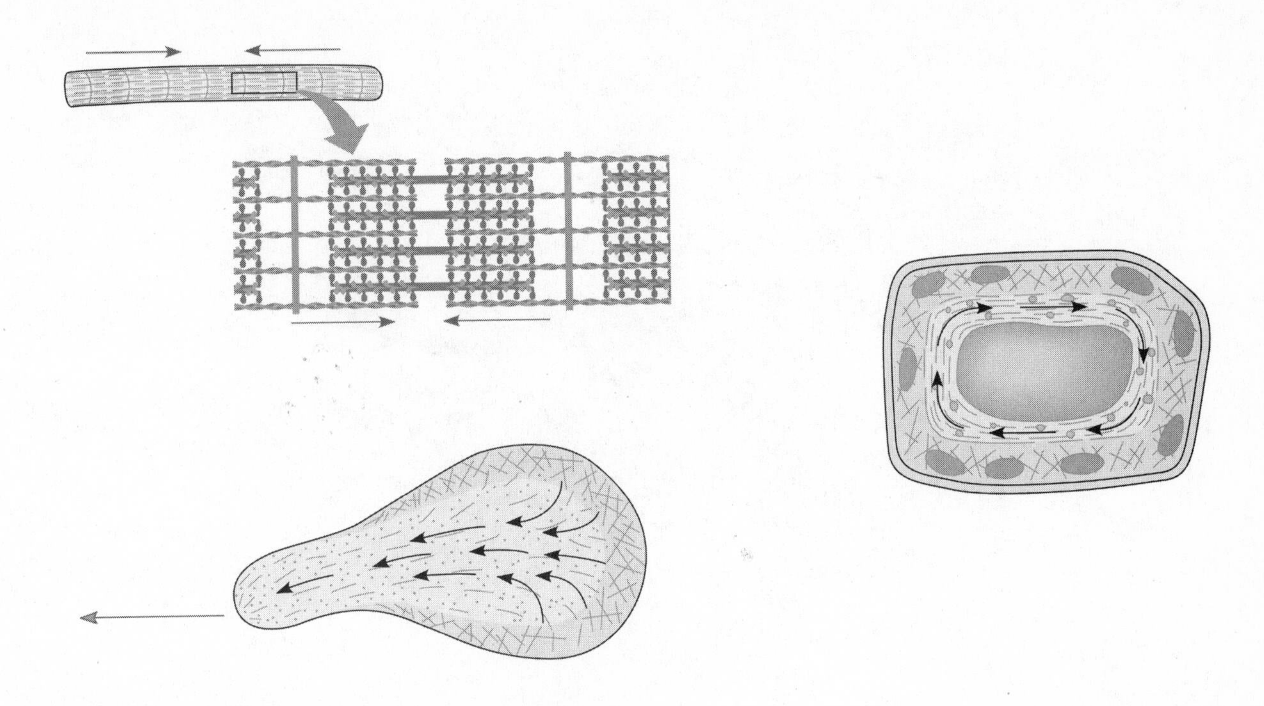

Figure 7.27 Microfilaments and motility, page 131

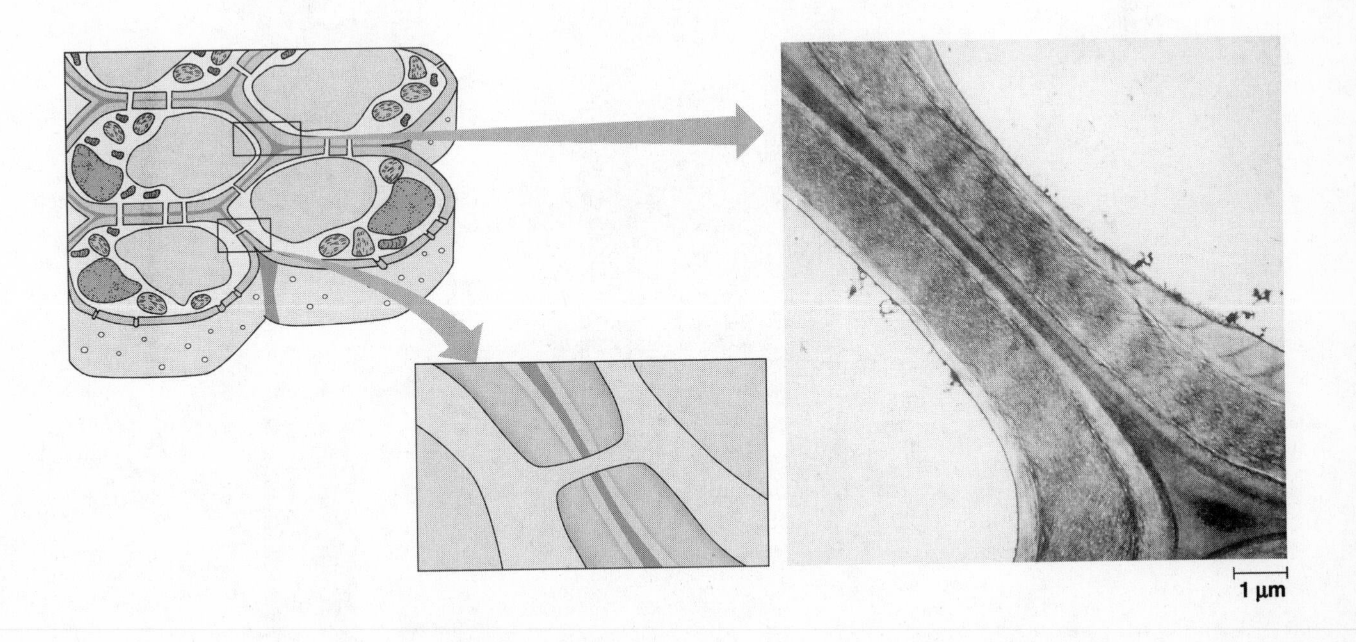

Figure 7.28 Plant cell walls, page 132

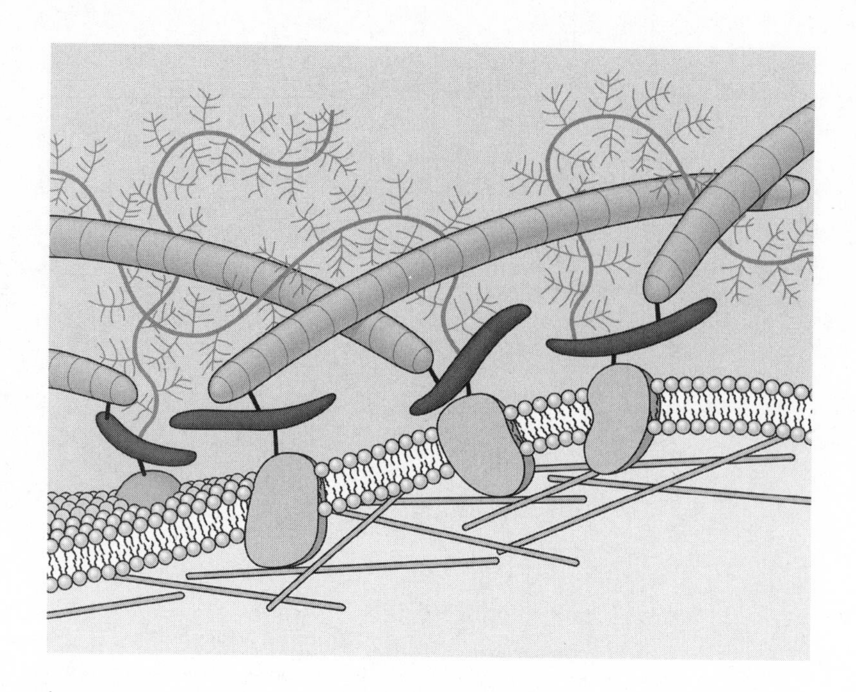

Figure 7.29 Extracellular matrix (ECM) of an animal cell, page 133

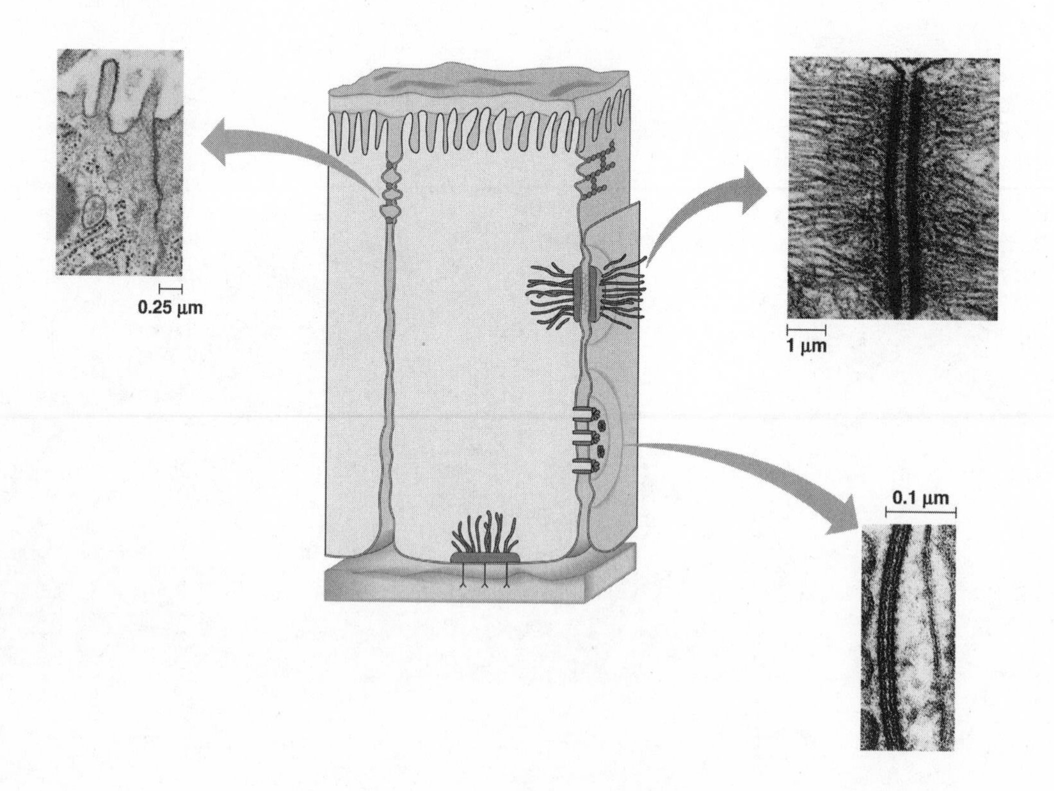

Figure 7.30 Intercellular junctions in animal tissues, page 134

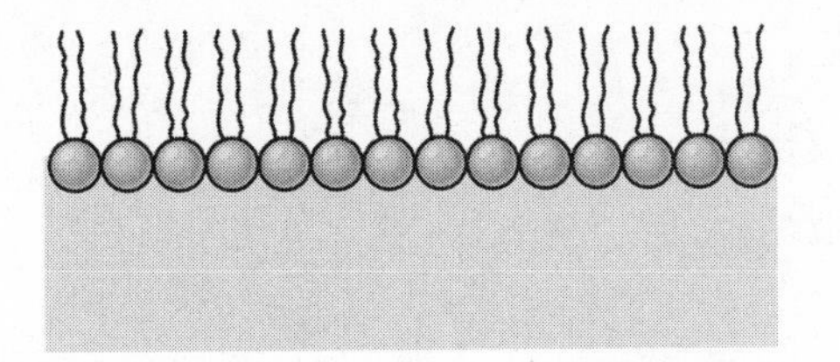

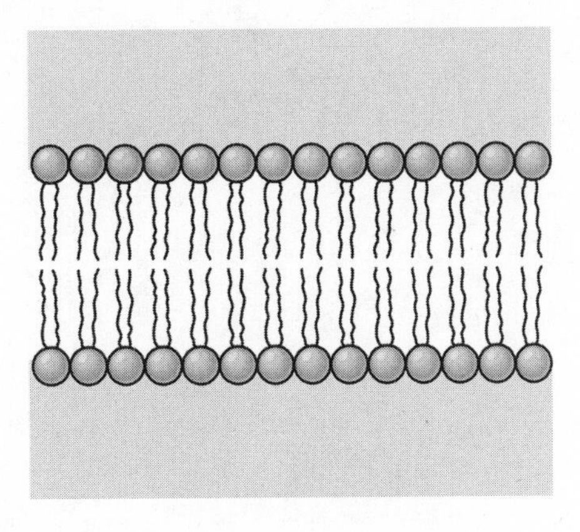

Figure 8.1 Artificial membranes (cross sections), page 139

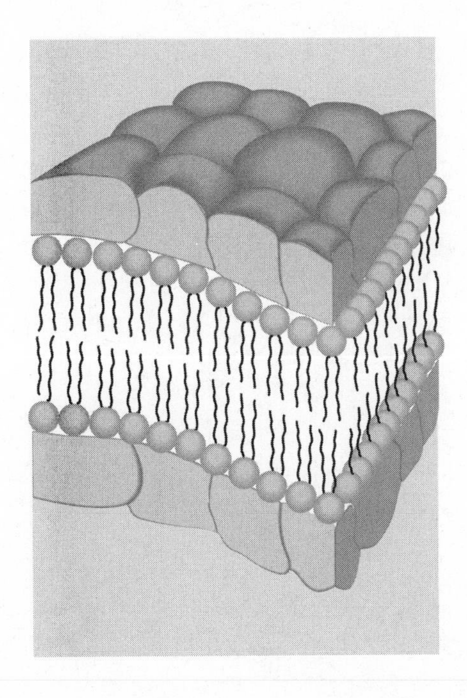

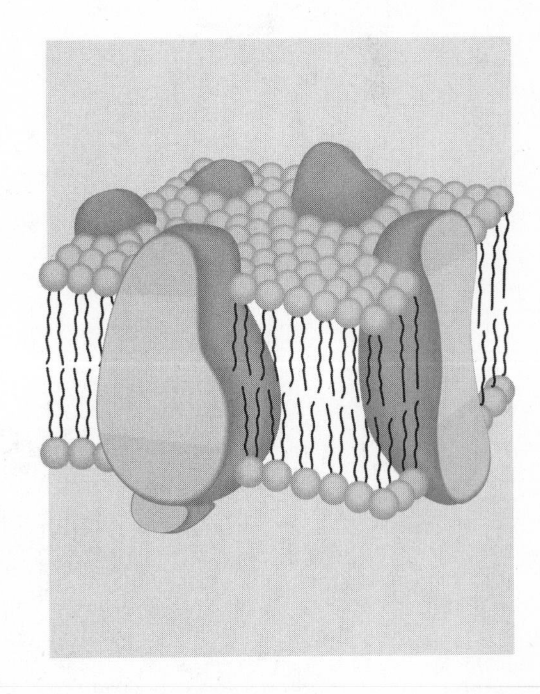

Figure 8.2 Two generations of membrane models, page 139

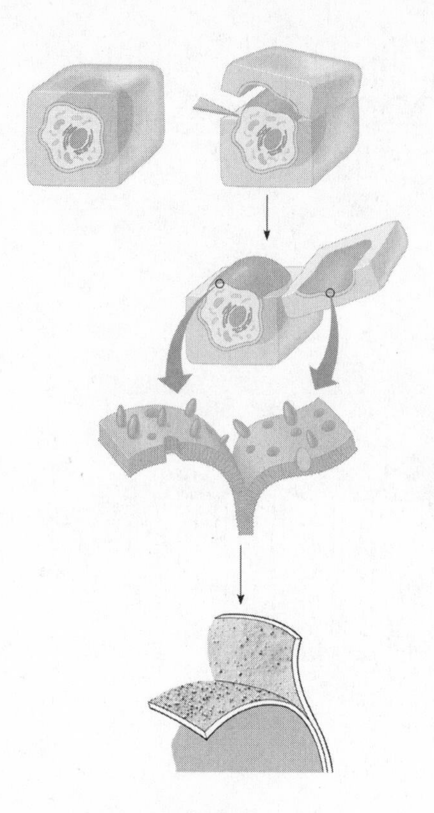

Figure 8.3 Freeze-fracture and freeze-etch, page 140

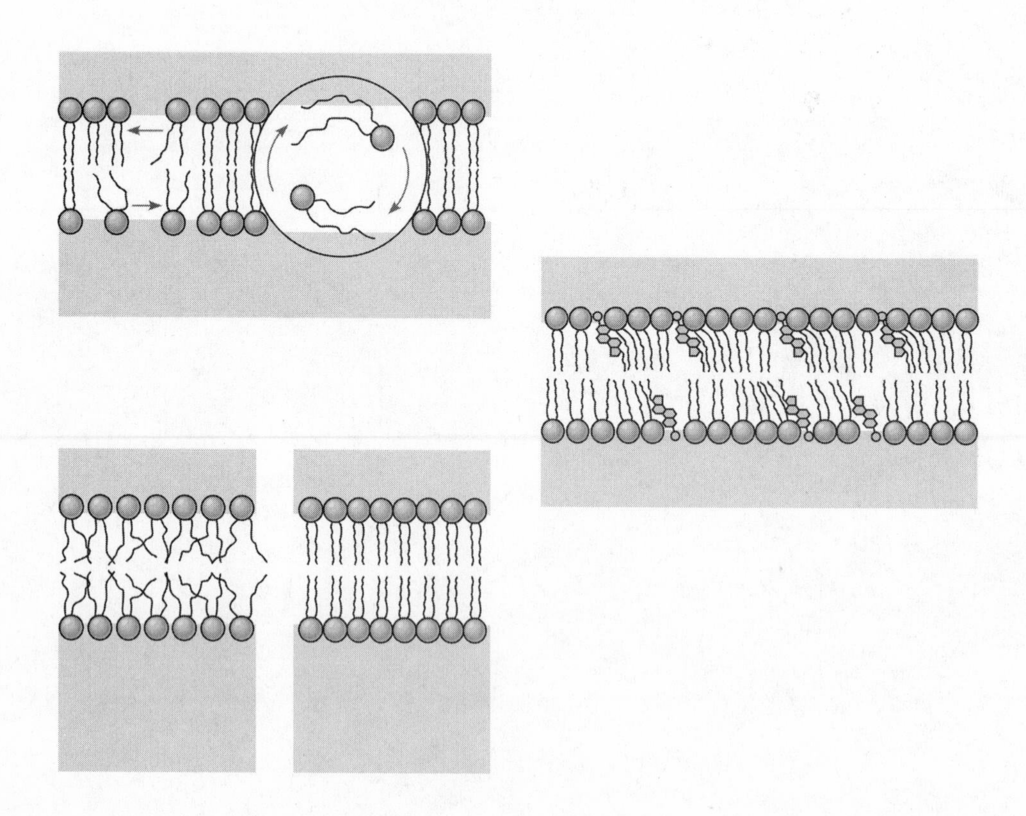

Figure 8.4 The fluidity of membranes, page 141

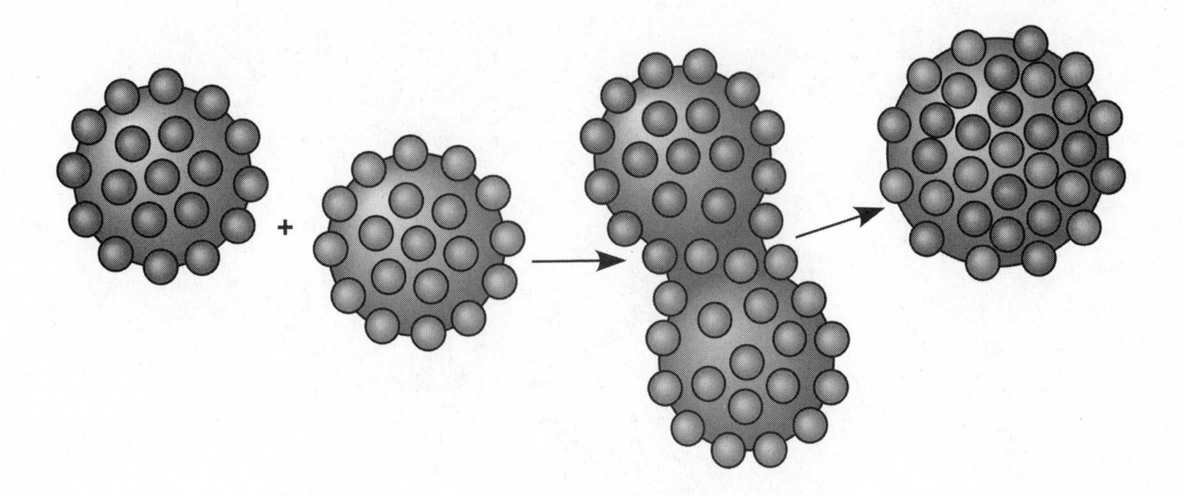

Figure 8.5 Evidence for the drifting of membrane proteins, page 141

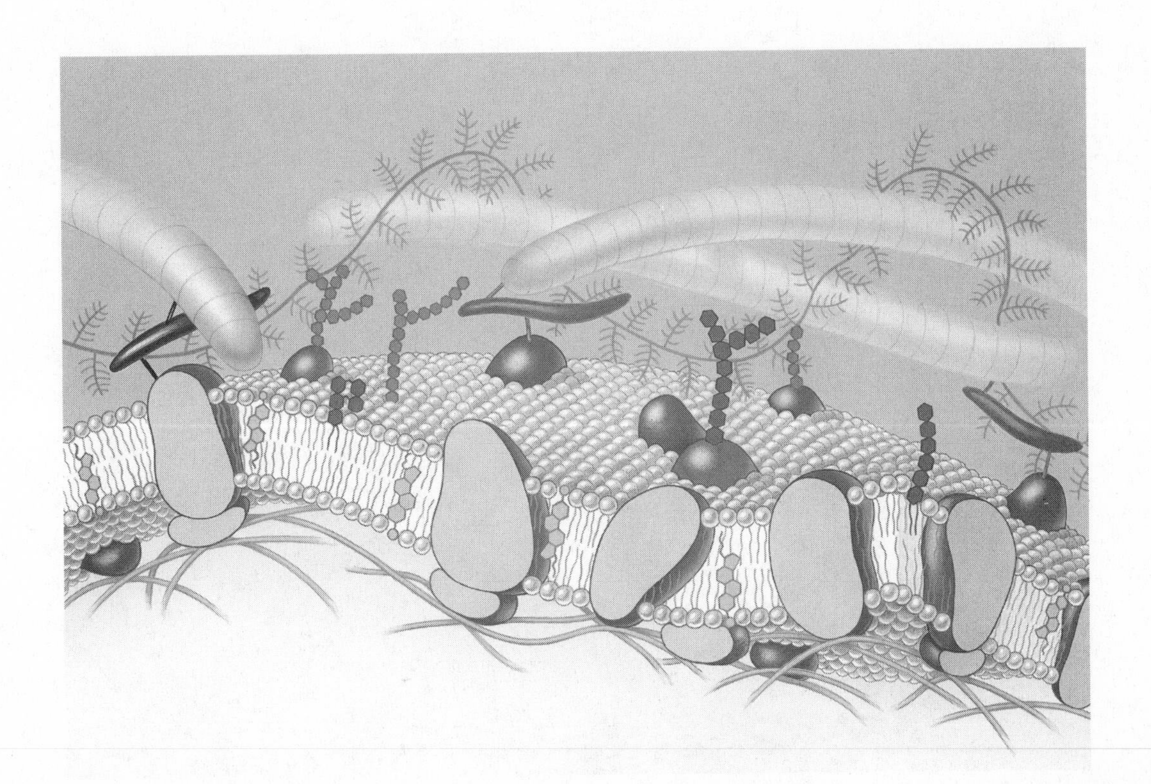

Figure 8.6 The detailed structure of an animal cell's plasma membrane, in cross section, page 142

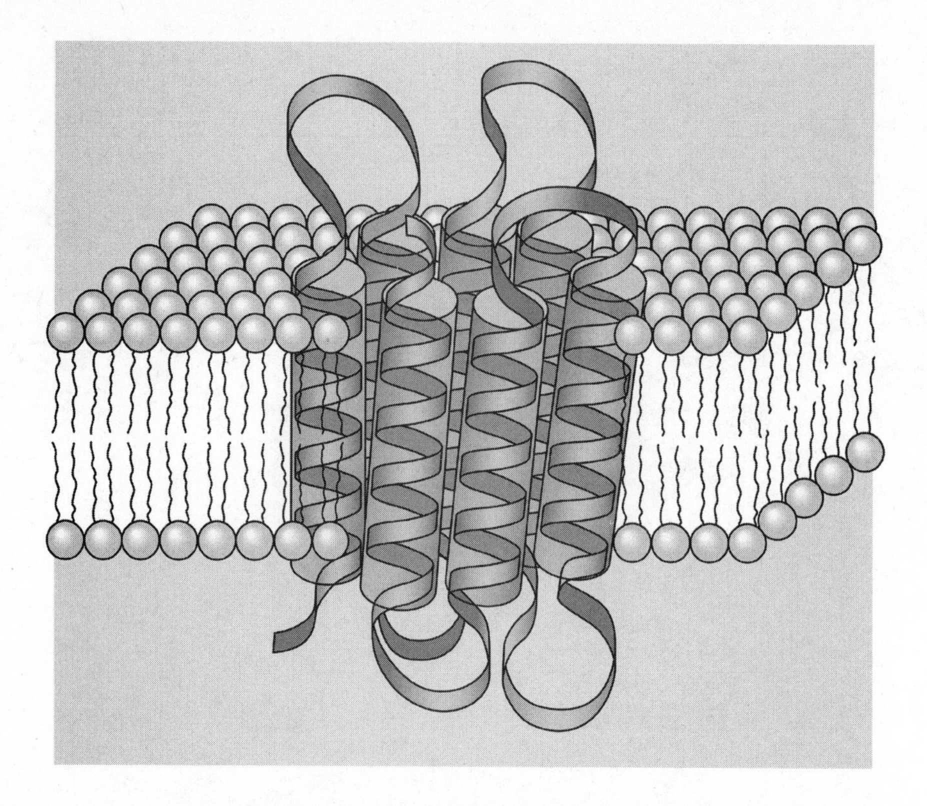

Figure 8.7 The structure of a transmembrane protein, page 143

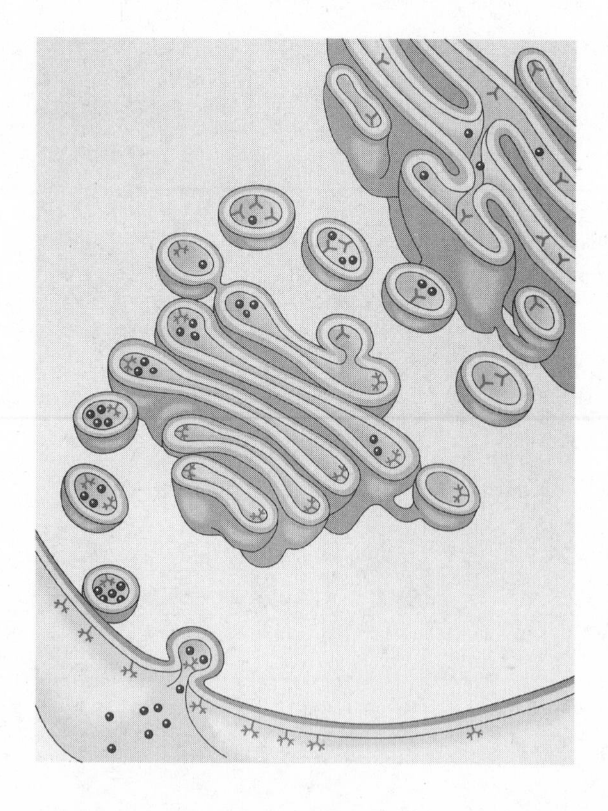

Figure 8.8 Sidedness of the plasma membrane, page 143

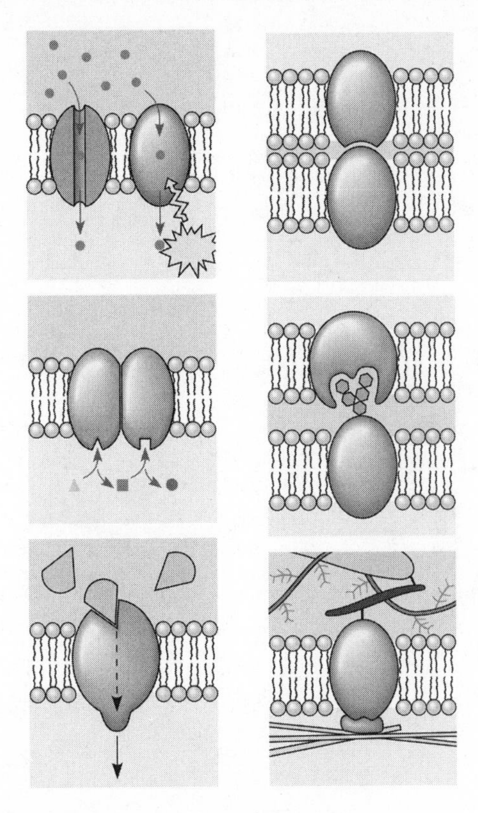

Figure 8.9 Some functions of membrane proteins, page 144

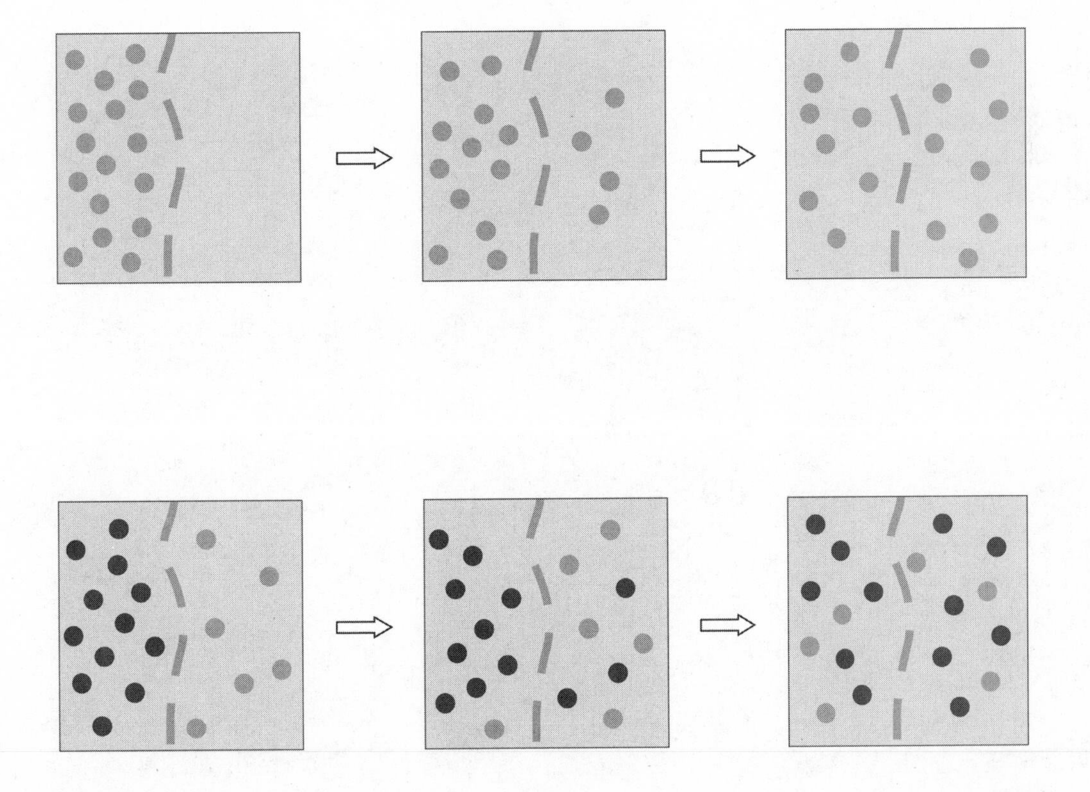

Figure 8.10 The diffusion of solutes across membranes, page 145

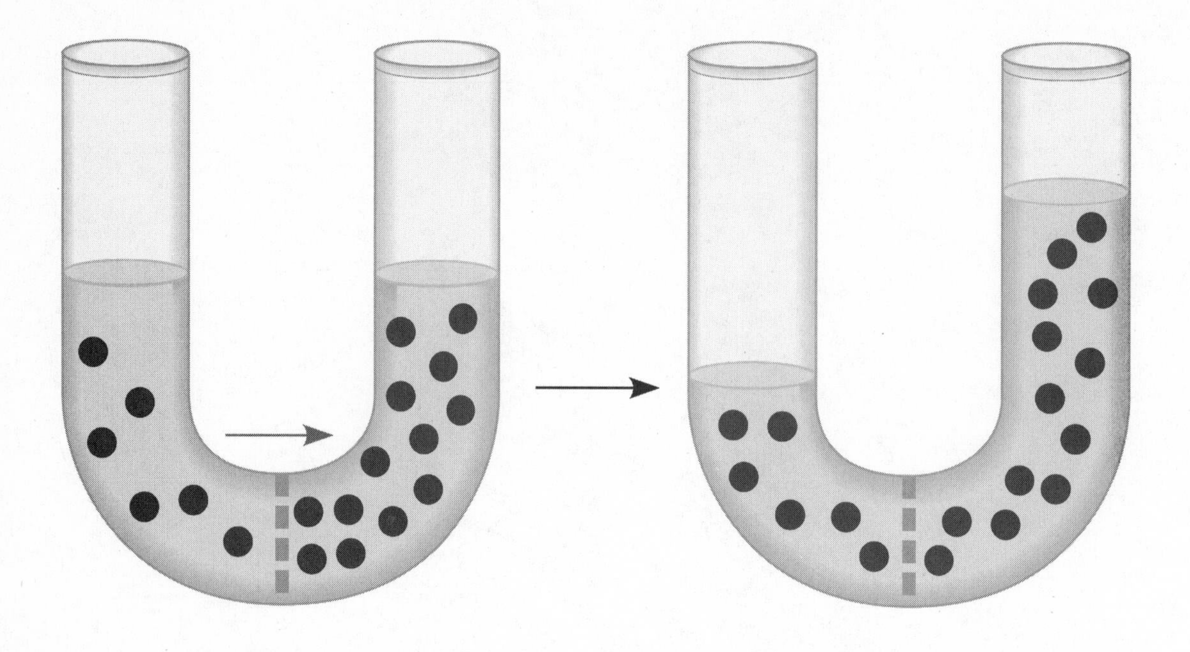

Figure 8.11 Osmosis, page 146

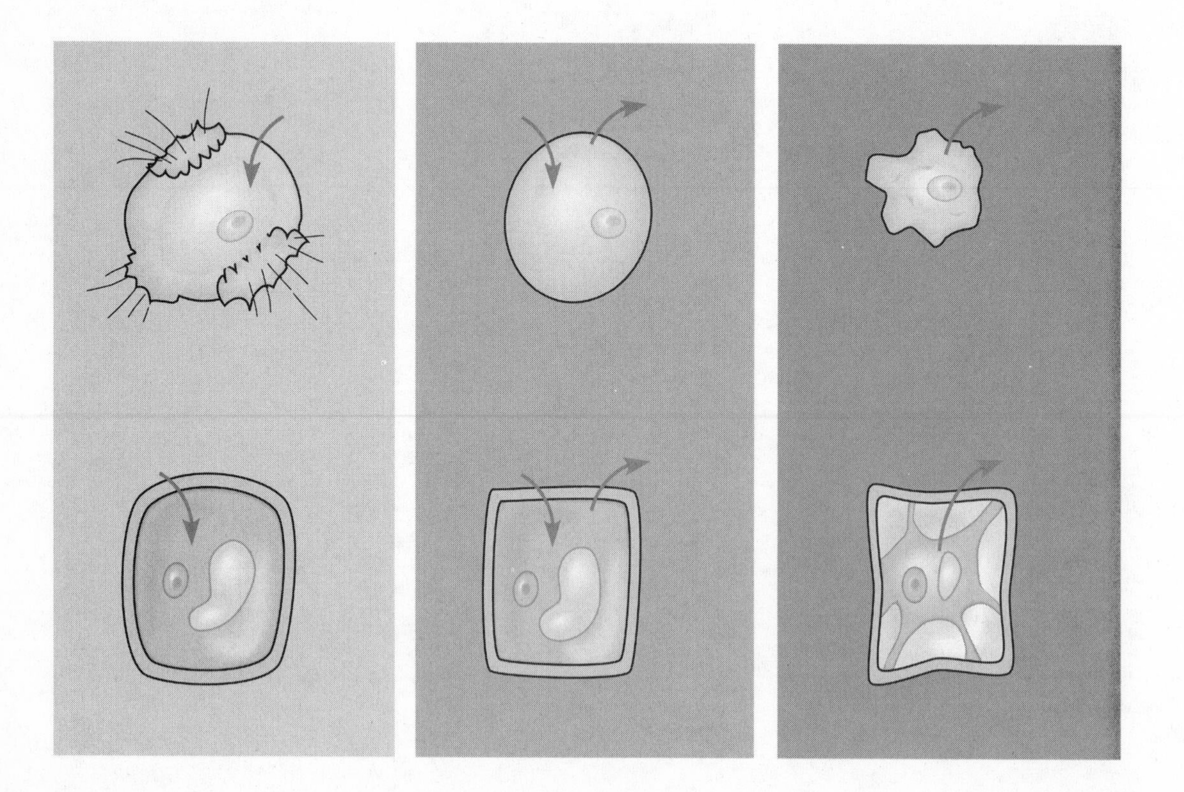

Figure 8.12 The water balance of living cells, page 147

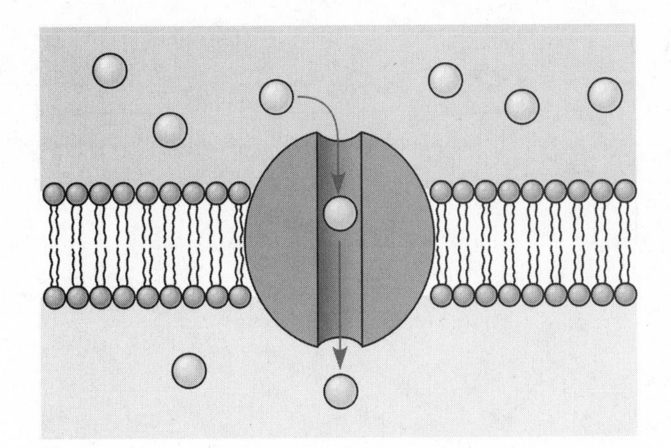

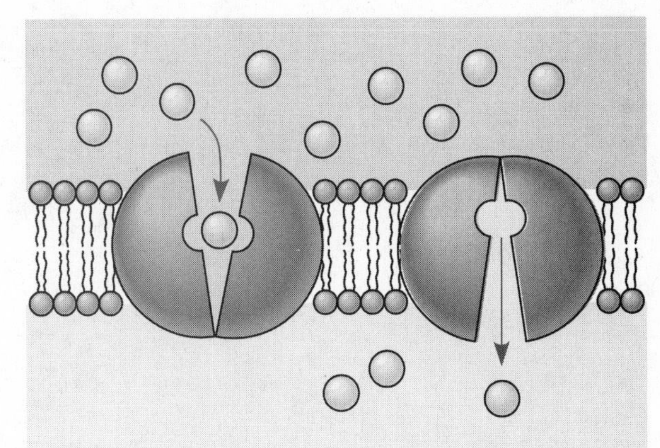

Figure 8.14 Two models for facilitated diffusion, page 148

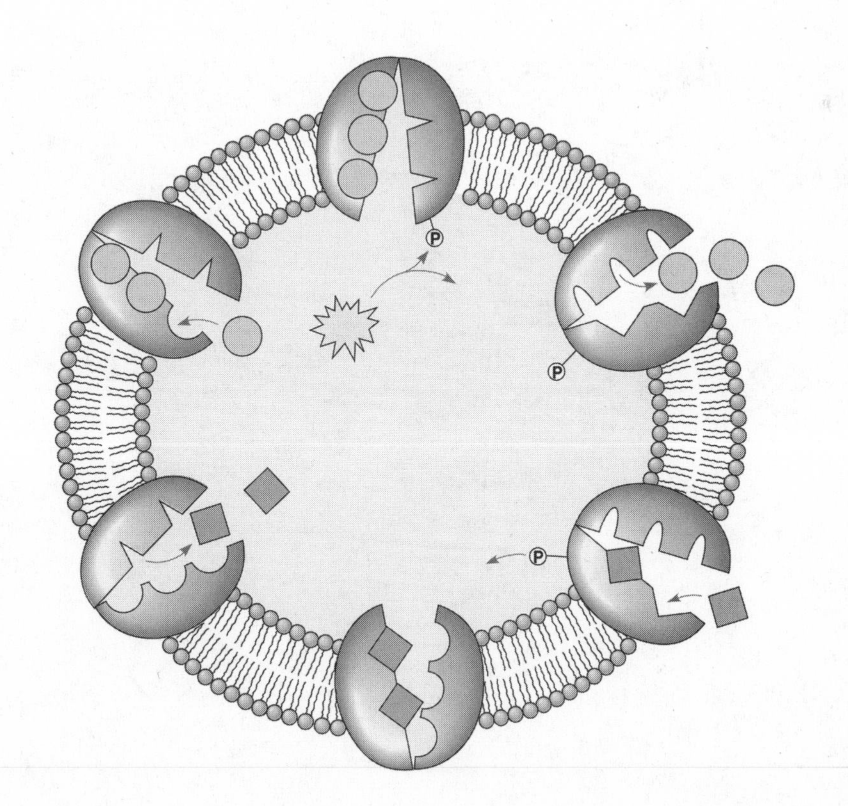

Figure 8.15 The sodium-potassium pump: a specific case of active transport, page 149

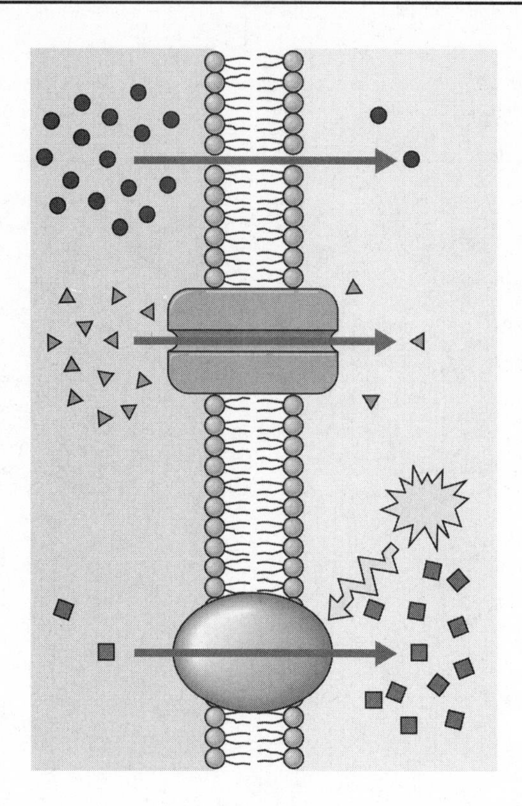

Figure 8.16 Review: passive and active transport compared, page 150

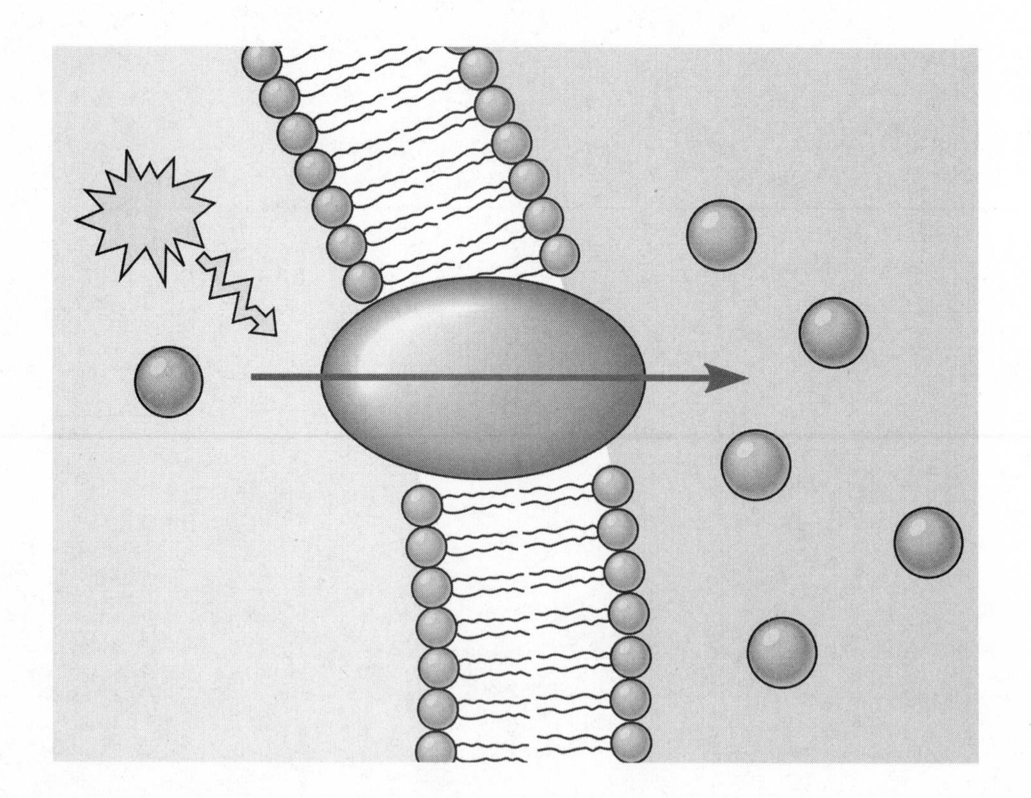

Figure 8.17 An electrogenic pump, page 150

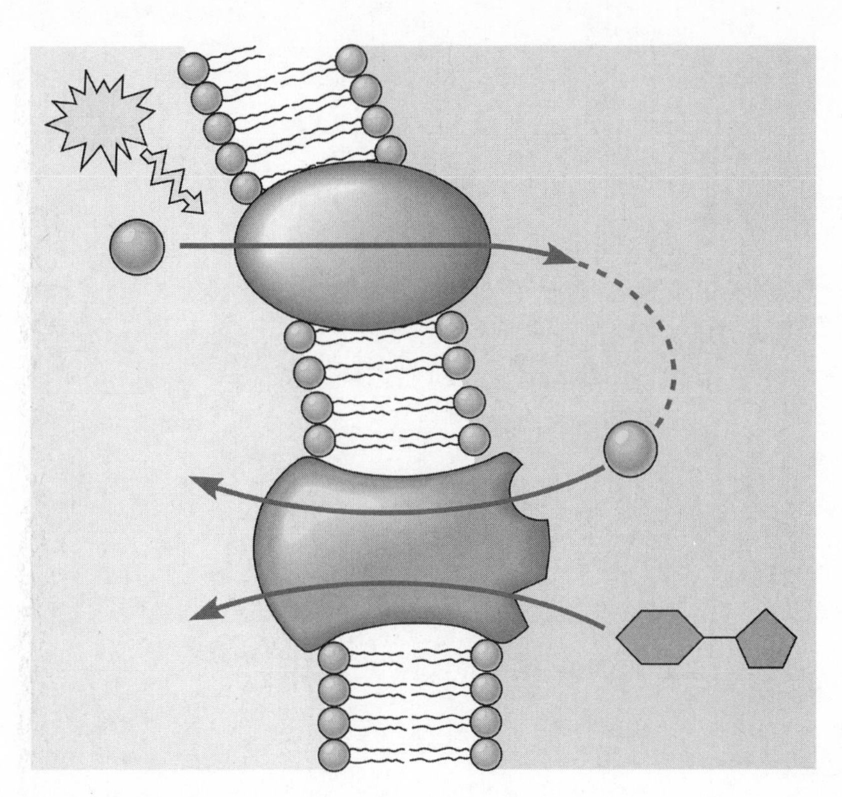

Figure 8.18 Cotransport, page 151

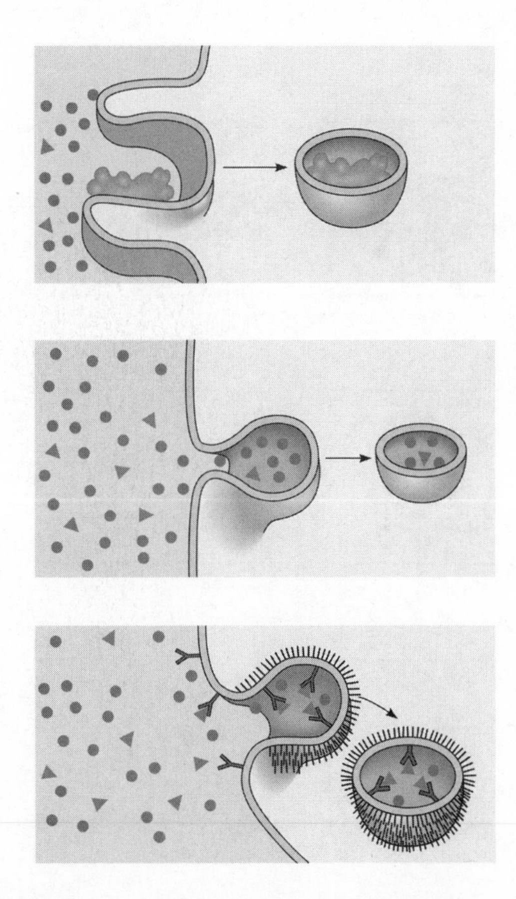

Figure 8.19 The three types of endocytosis in animal cells, page 152

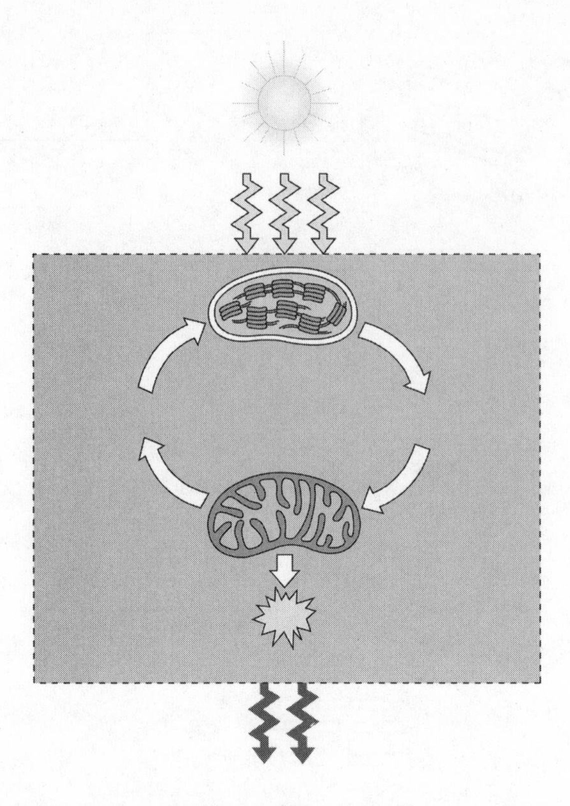

Figure 9.1 Energy flow and chemical recycling in ecosystems, page 156

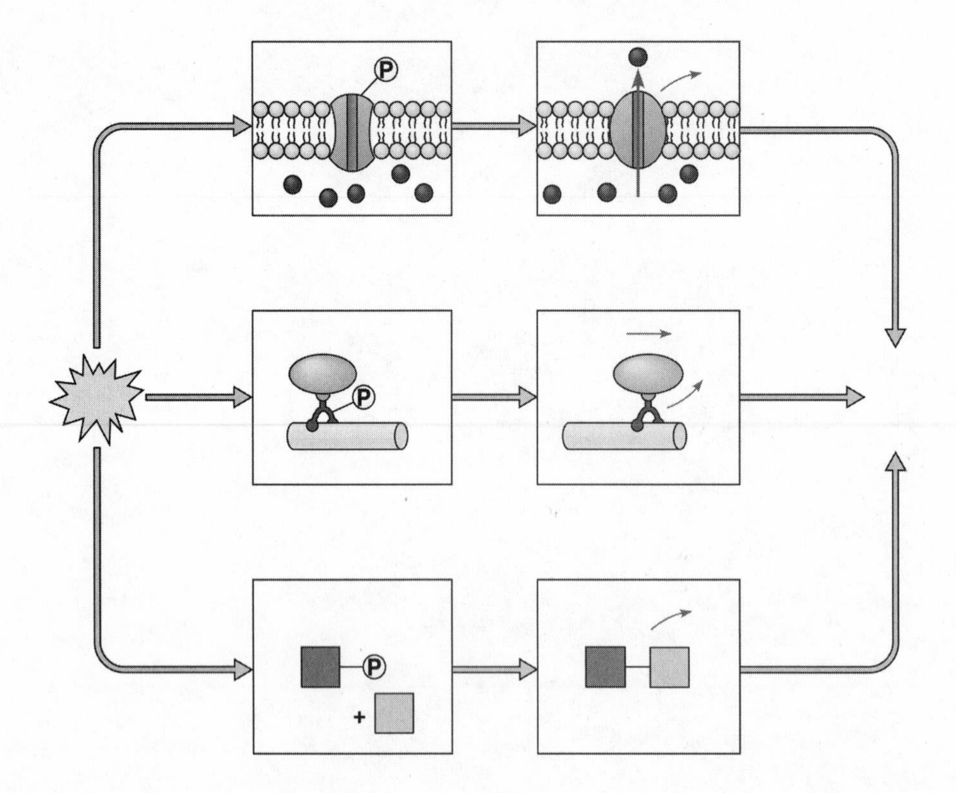

Figure 9.2 A review of how ATP drives cellular work, page 157

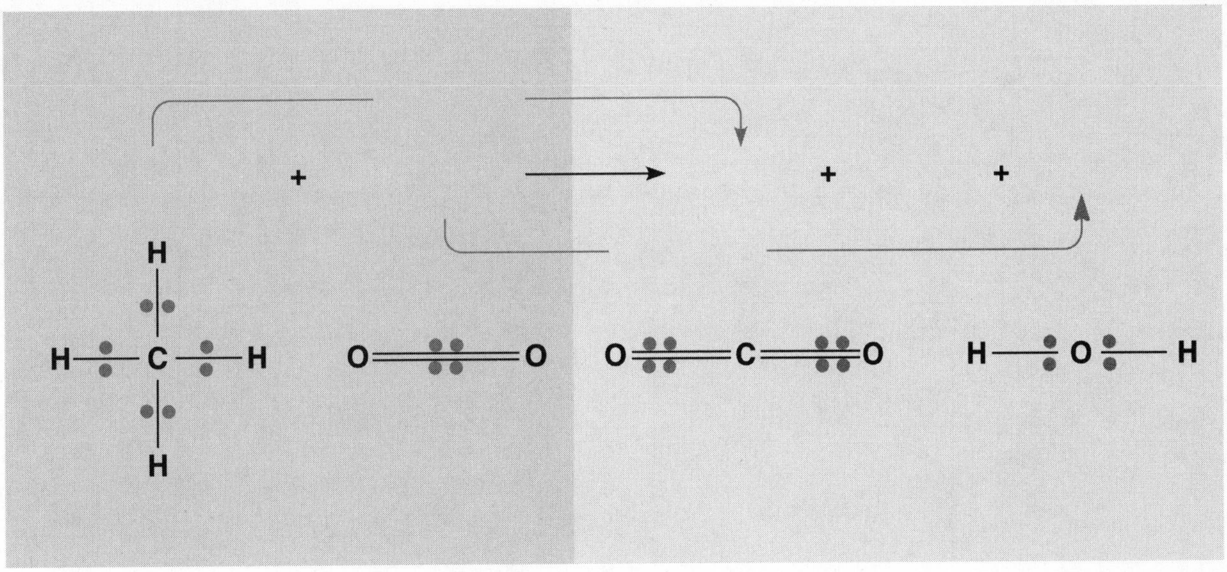

Figure 9.3 Methane combustion as an energy-yielding redox reaction, page 157

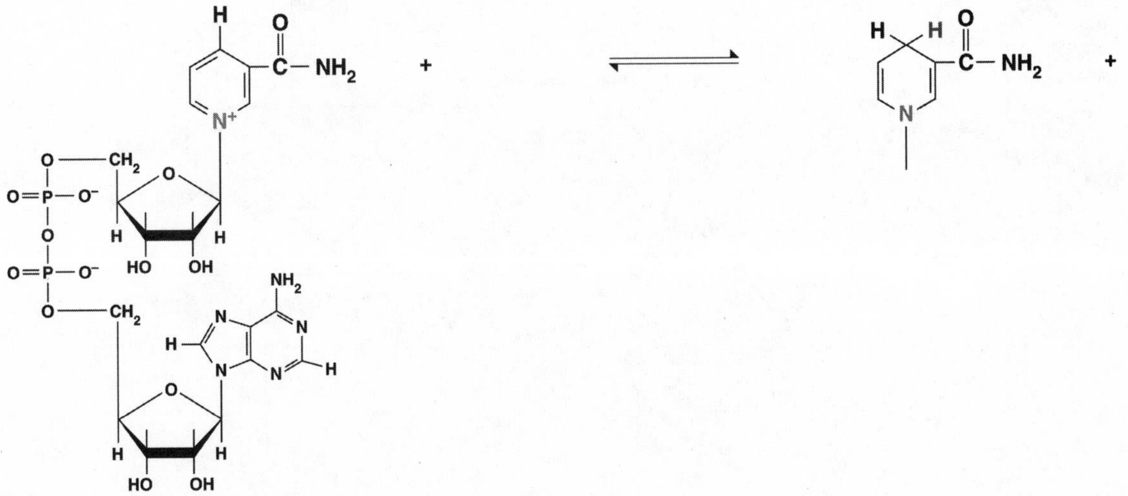

Figure 9.4 NAD+ as an electron shuttle, page 159

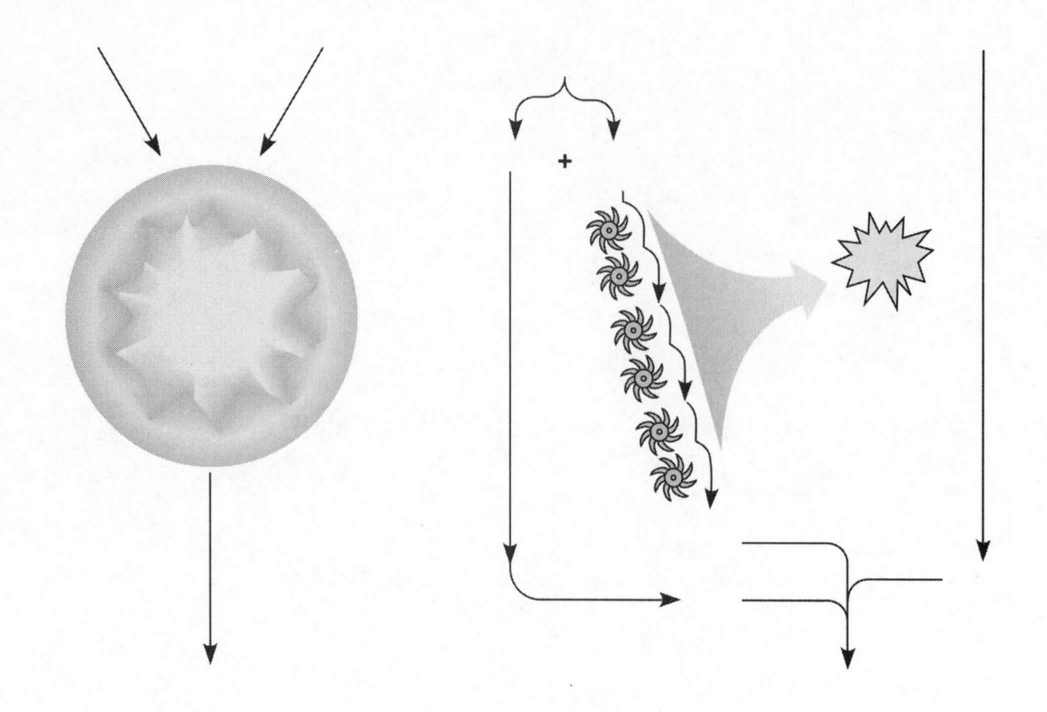

Figure 9.5 An introduction to electron transport chains, page 159

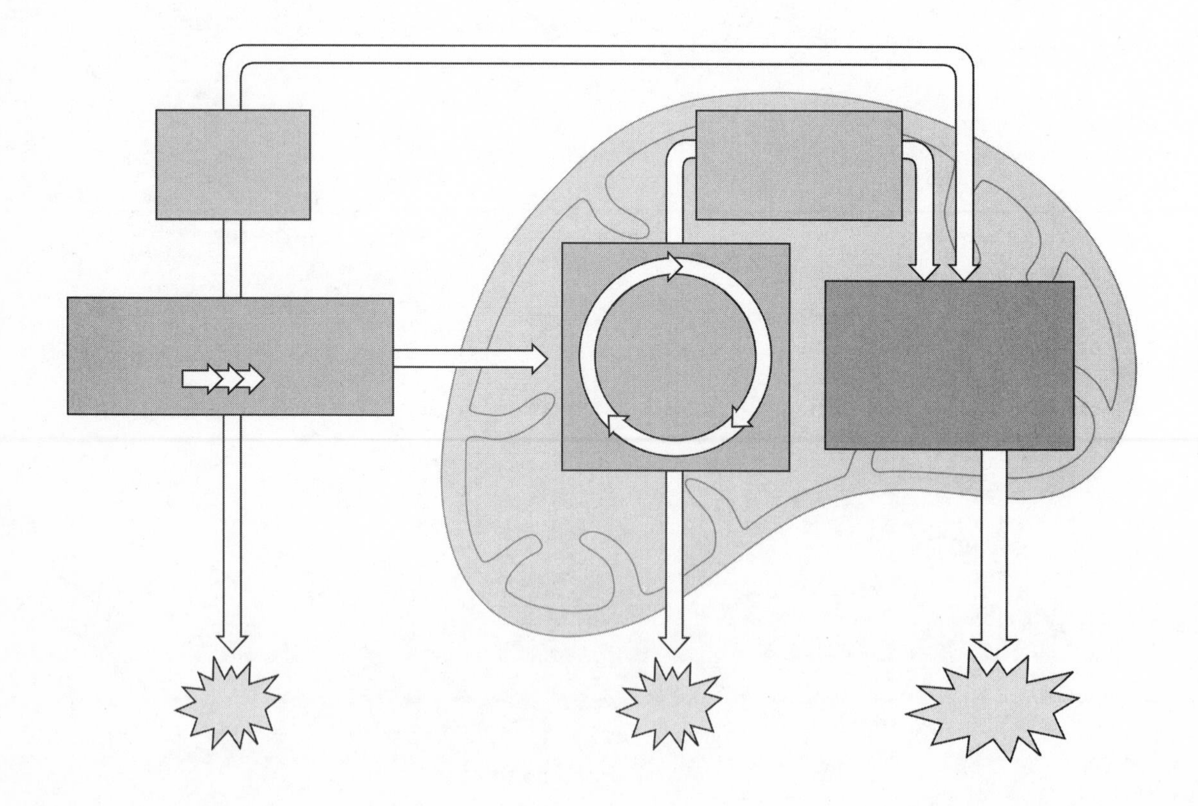

Figure 9.6 An overview of cellular respiration, page 160

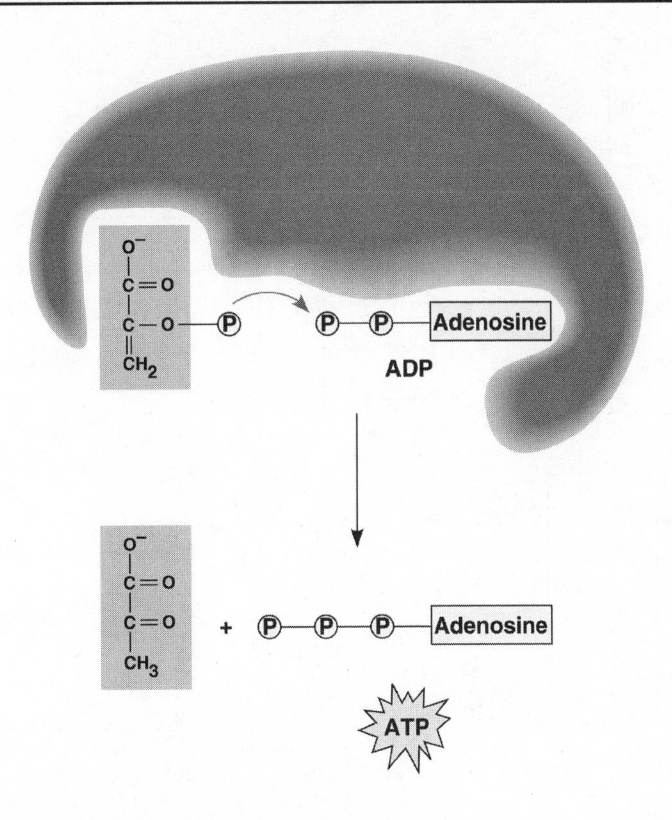

Figure 9.7 Substrate-level phosphorylation, page 161

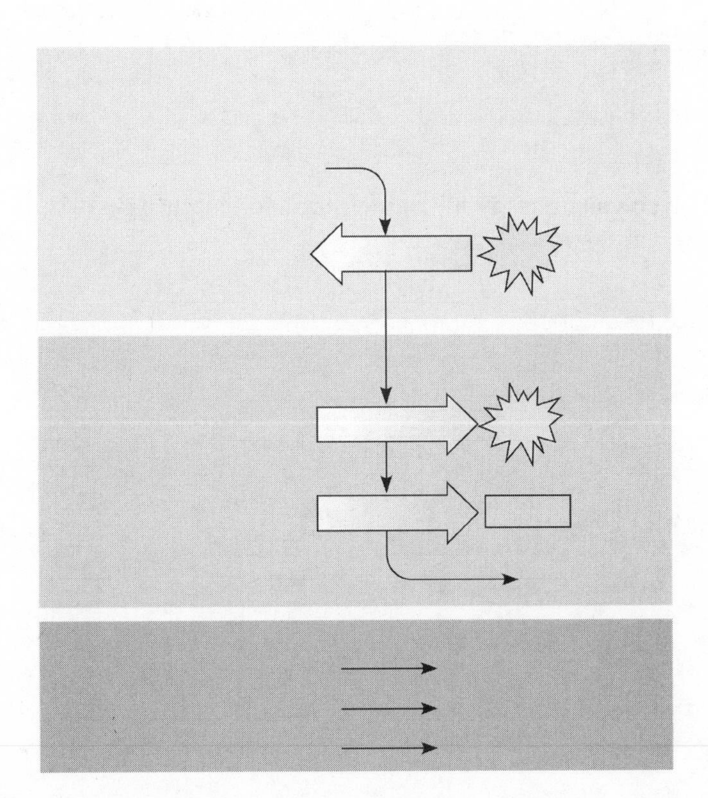

Figure 9.8 The energy input and output of glycolysis, page 161

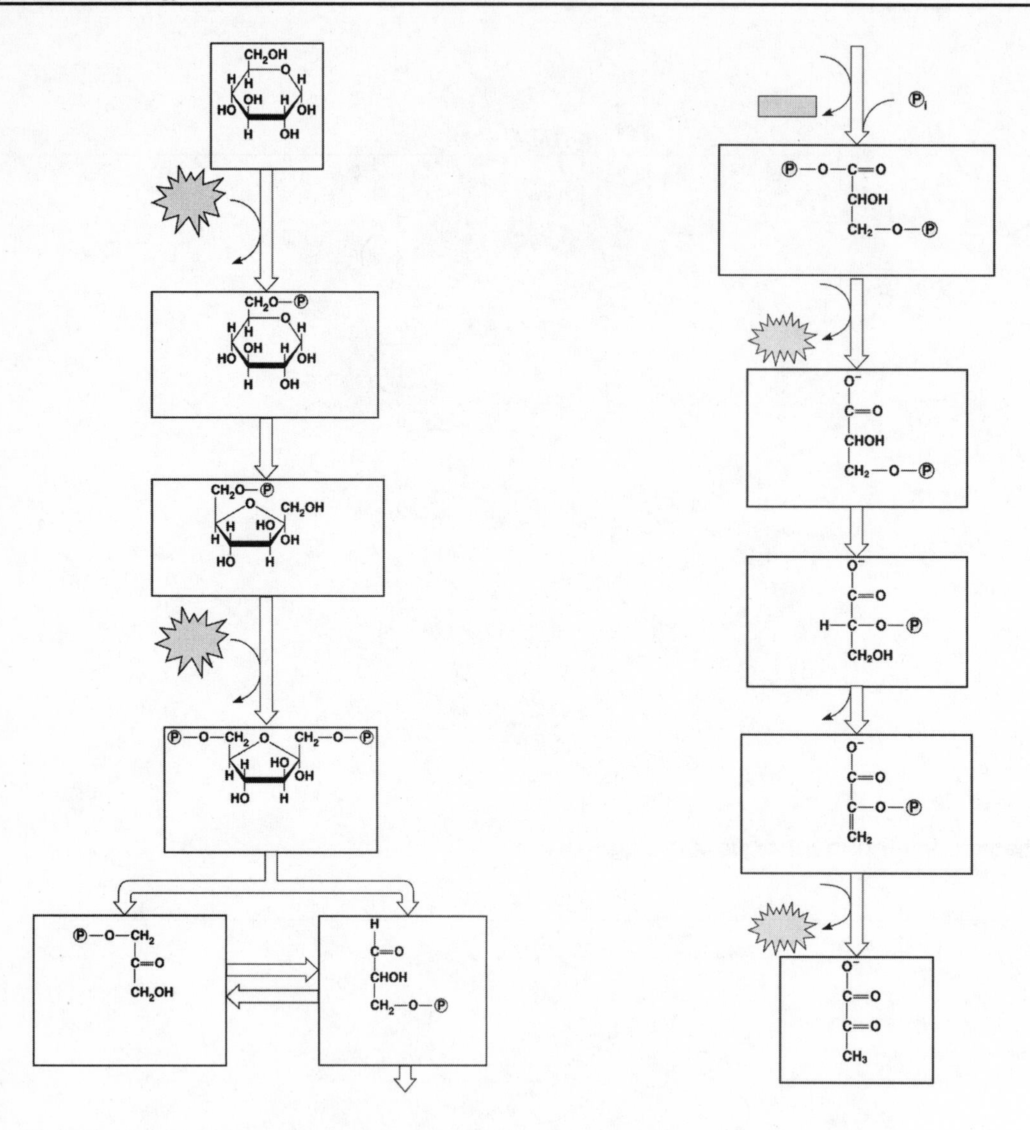

Figure 9.9 A closer look at glycolysis: energy investment phase, pages 162-163

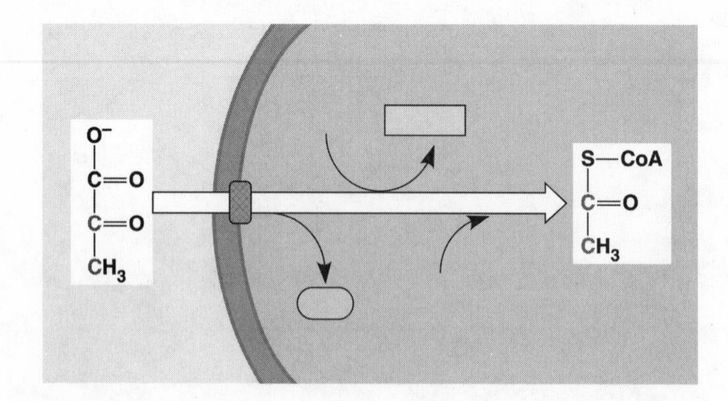

Figure 9.10 Conversion of pyruvate to acetyl CoA, the junction between glycolysis and the Krebs cycle, page 164

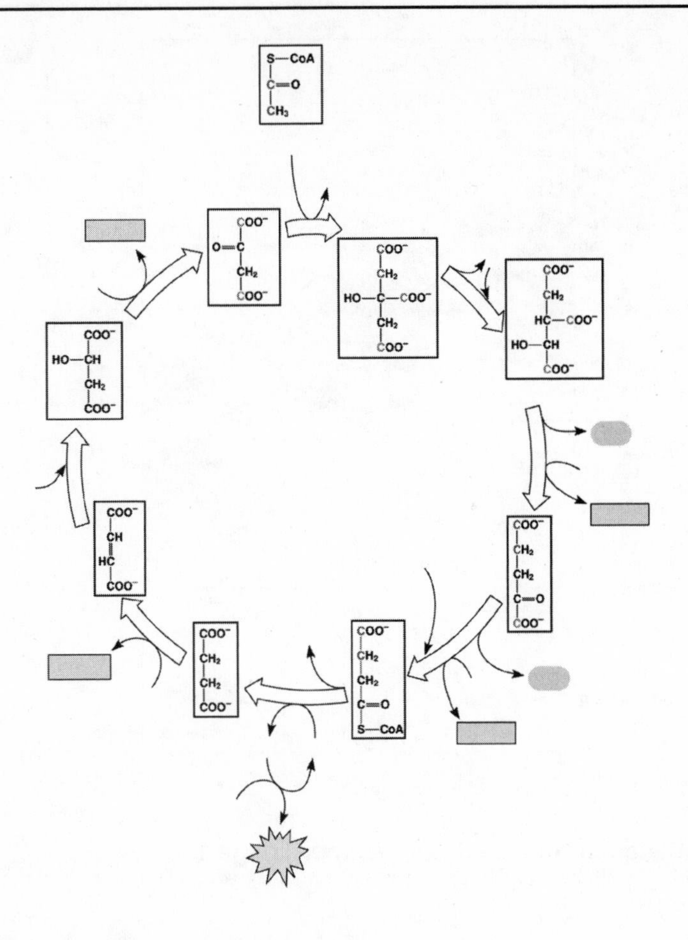

Figure 9.11 A closer look at the Krebs cycle, page 165

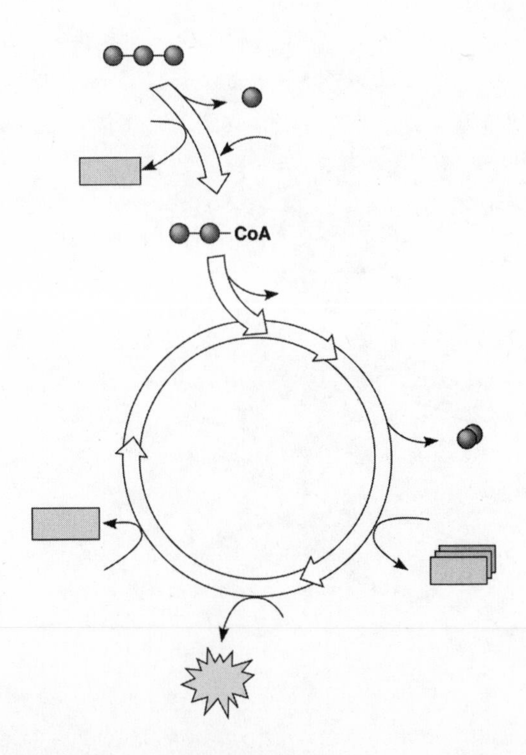

Figure 9.12 A summary of the Krebs cycle, page 166

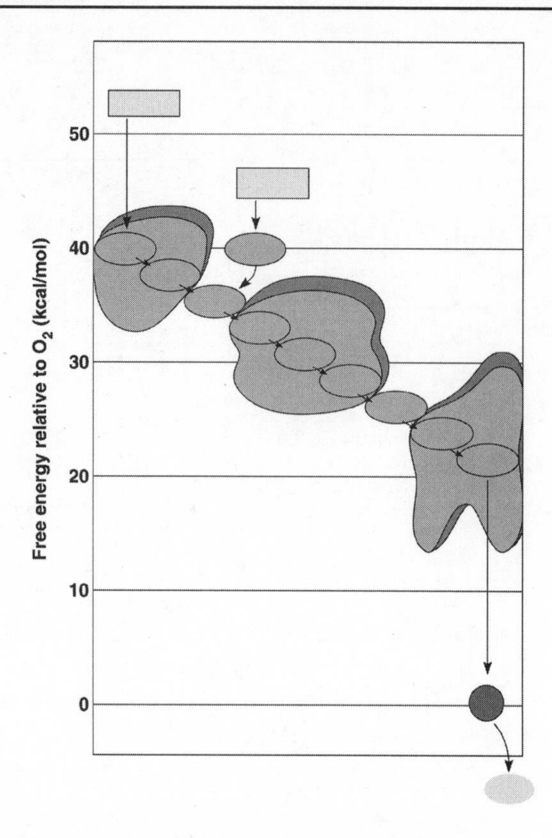

Figure 9.13 Free-energy change during electron transport, page 166

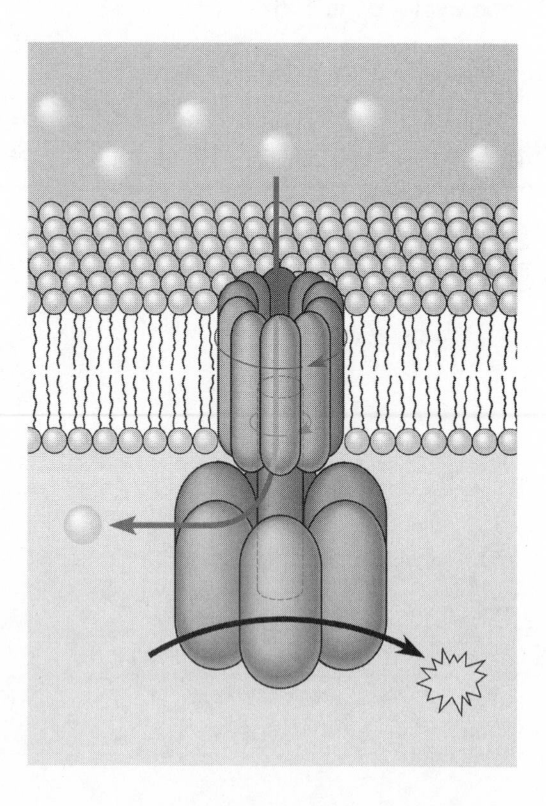

Figure 9.14 ATP synthase, a molecular mill, page 167

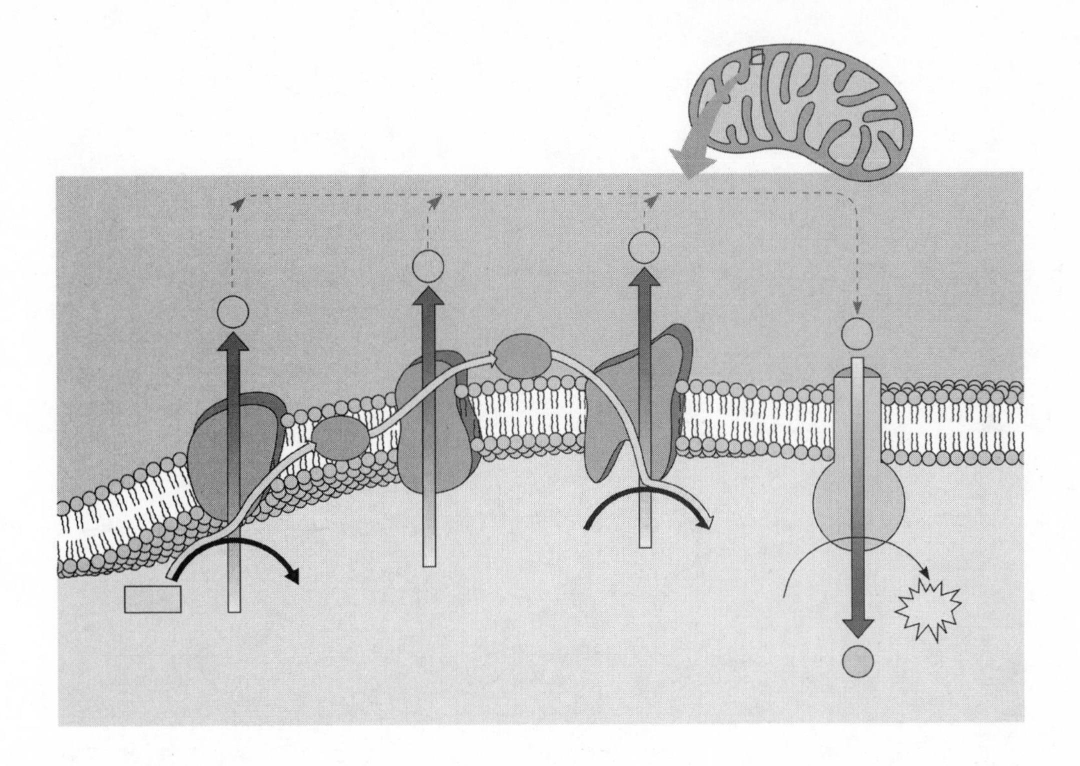

Figure 9.15 Chemiosmosis couples the electron transport chain to ATP synthesis, page 168

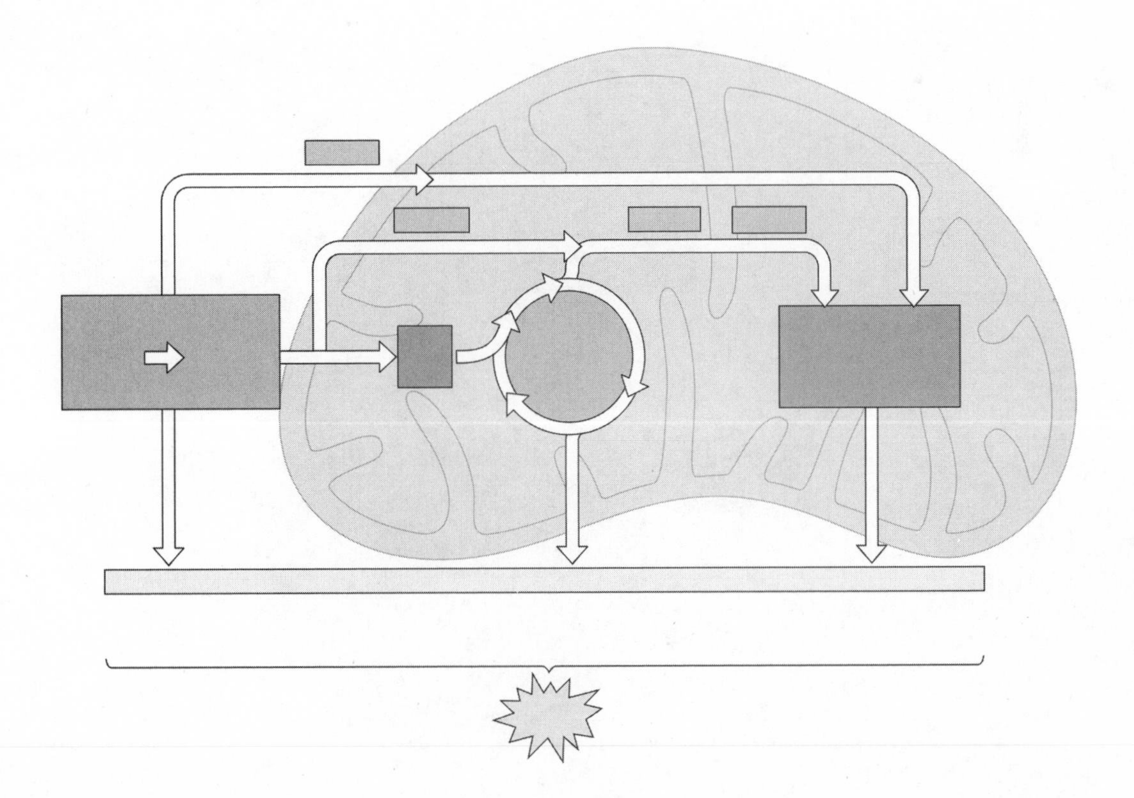

Figure 9.16 Review: how each molecule of glucose yields many ATP molecules during cellular respiration, page 169

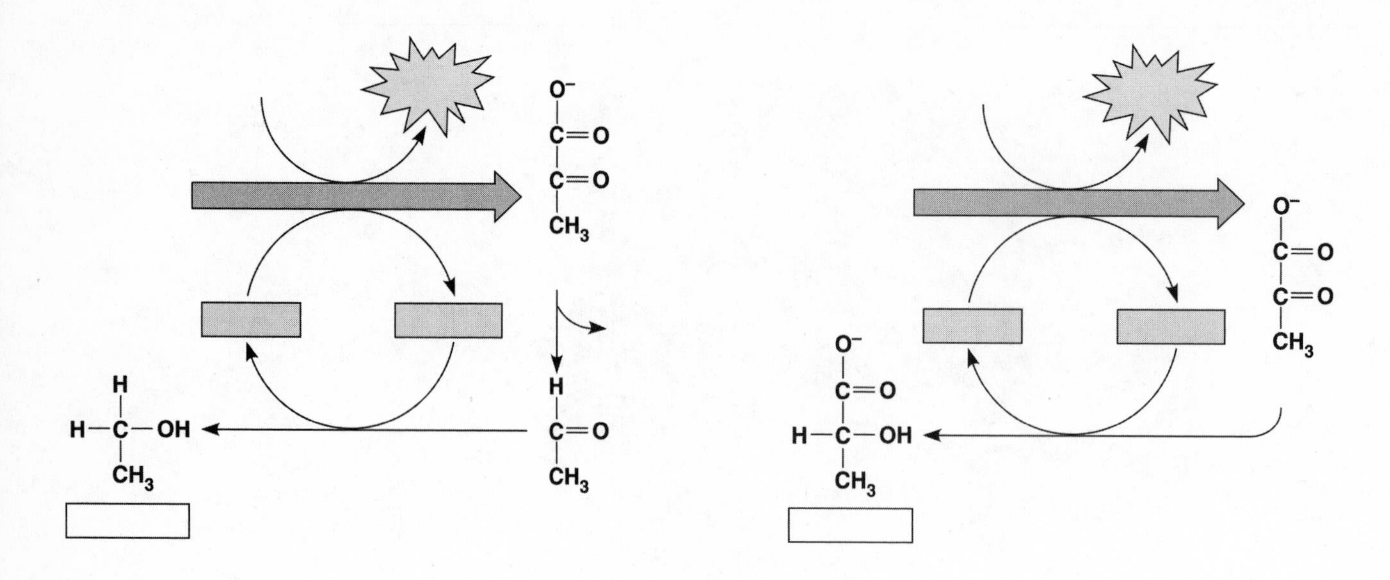

Figure 9.17 Fermentation, page 171

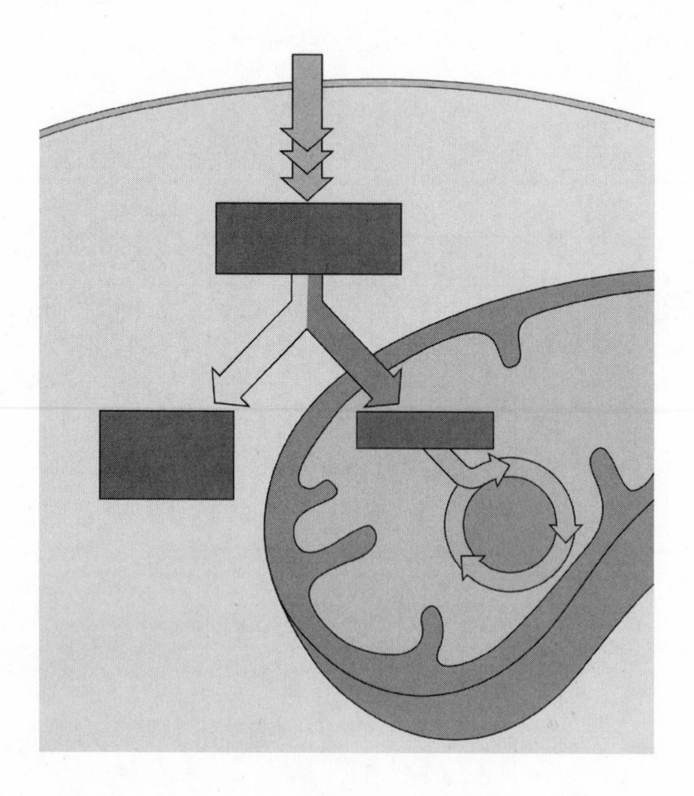

Figure 9.18 Pyruvate as a key juncture in catabolism, page 171

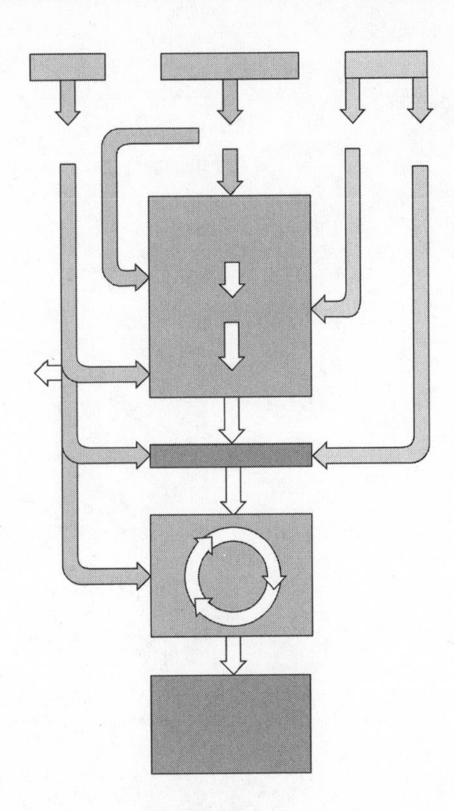

Figure 9.19 The catabolism of various food molecules, page 172

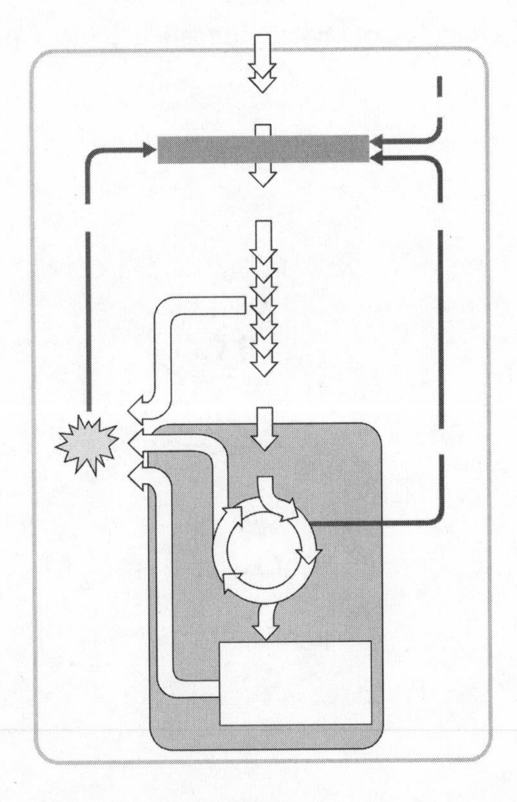

Figure 9.20 The control of cellular respiration, page 173

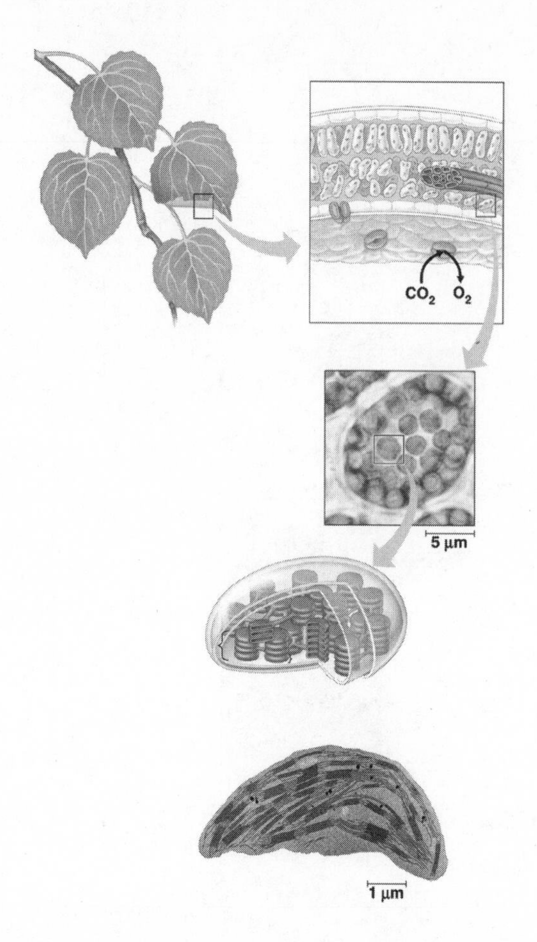

Figure 10.2 Focusing in on the location of photosynthesis in a plant, page 178

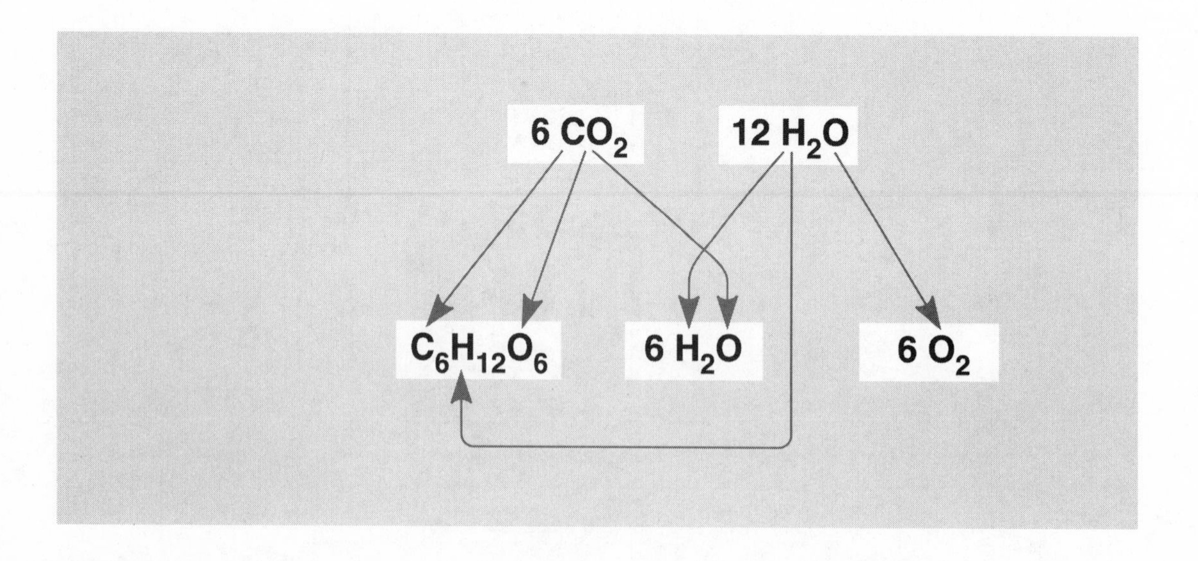

Figure 10.3 Tracking atoms through photosynthesis, page 179

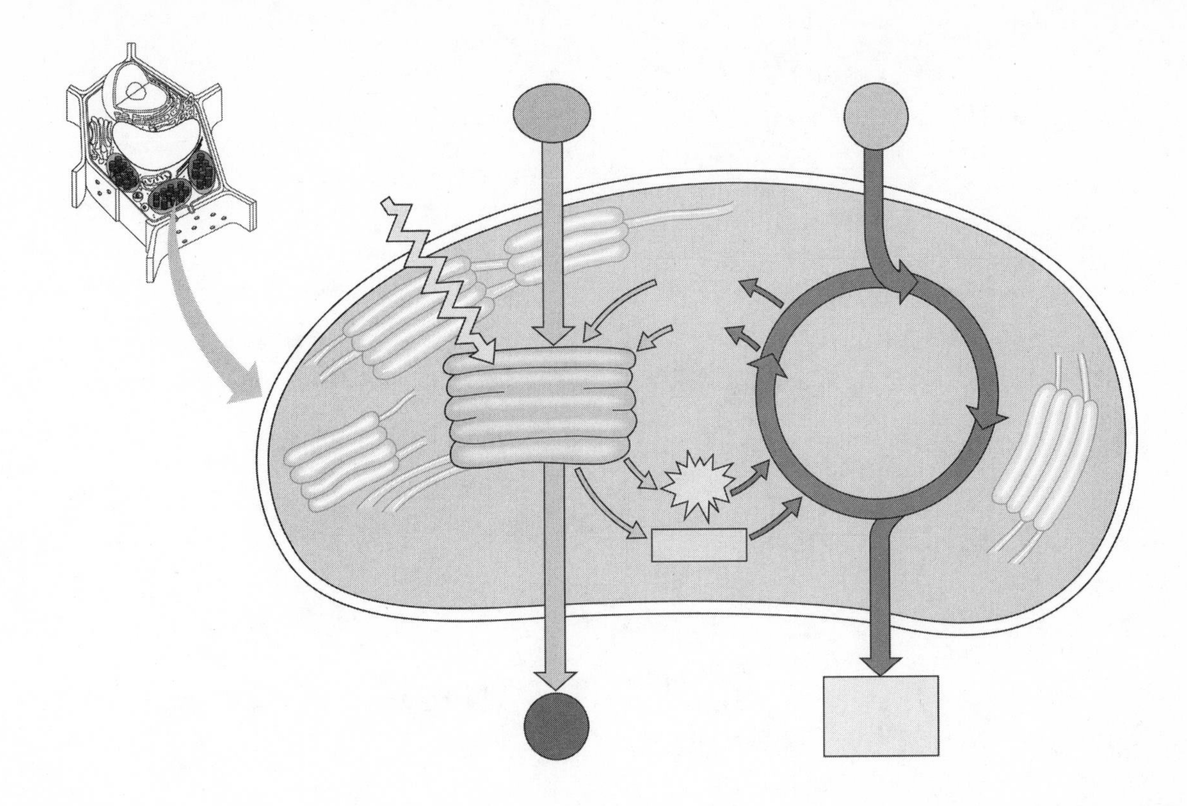

Figure 10.4 An overview of photosynthesis: cooperation of the light reactions and the Calvin cycle, page 180

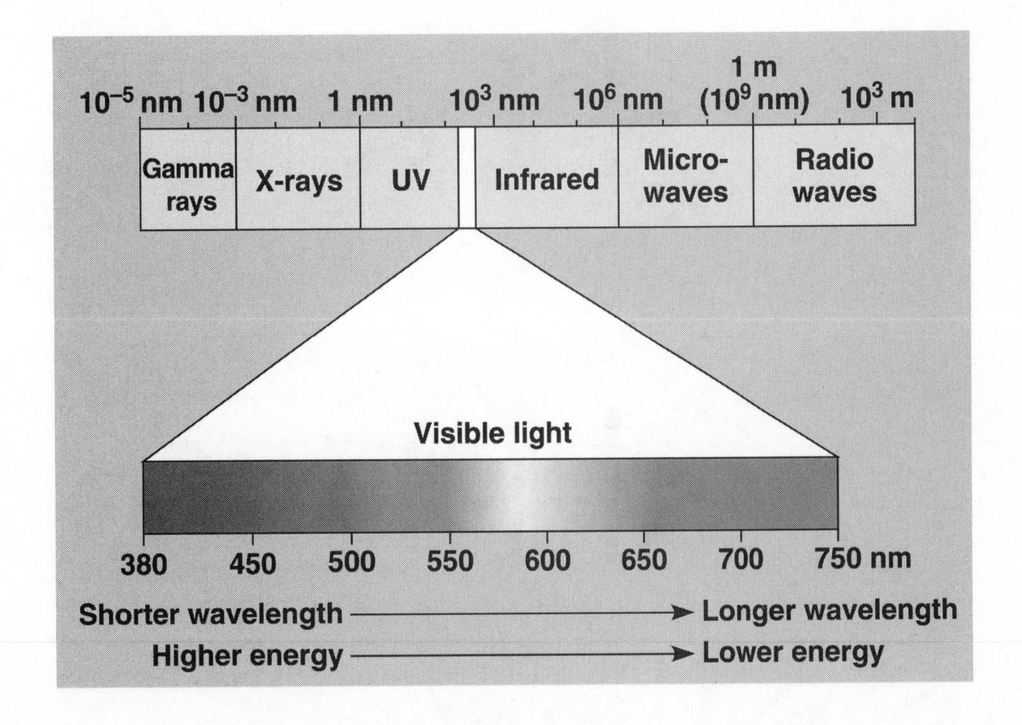

Figure 10.5 The electromagnetic spectrum, page 181

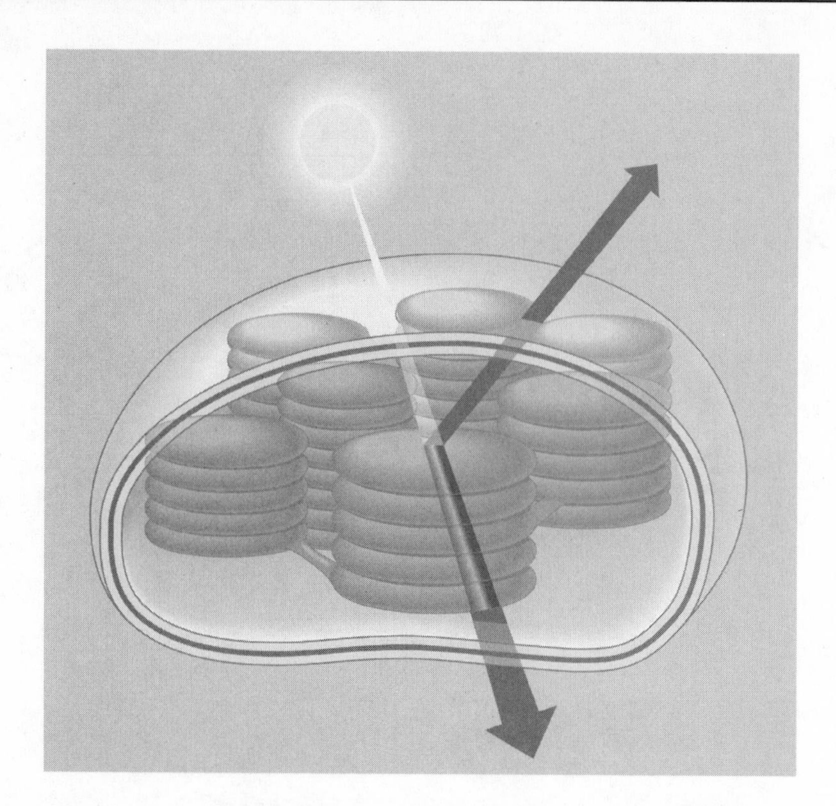

Figure 10.6 Why leaves are green: interaction of light with chloroplasts, page 182

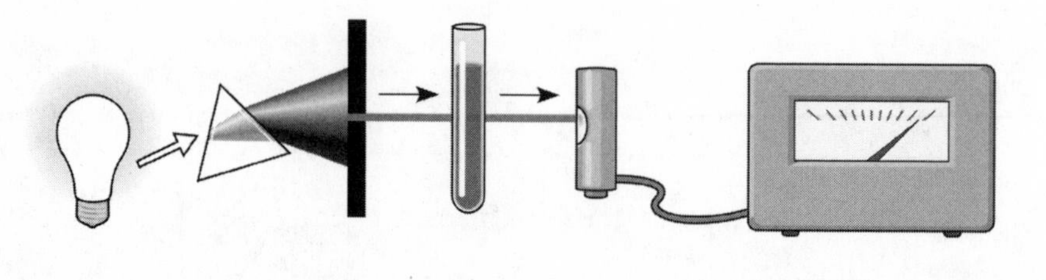

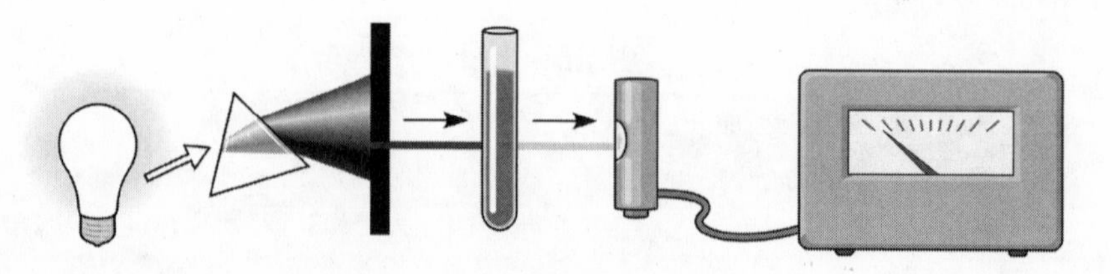

Figure 10.7 Determining an absorption spectrum, page 182

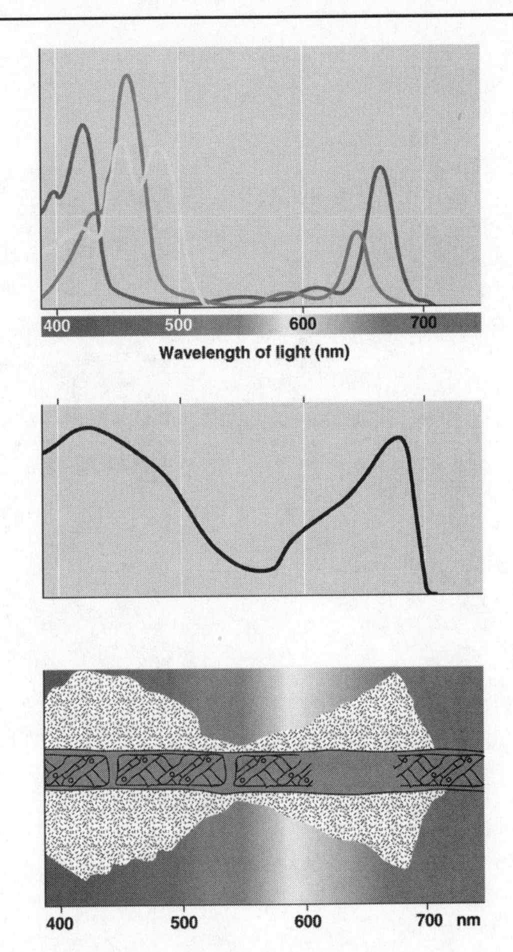

Figure 10.8 Evidence that chloroplast pigments participate in photosynthesis: absorption and action spectra for photosynthesis in an alga, page 183

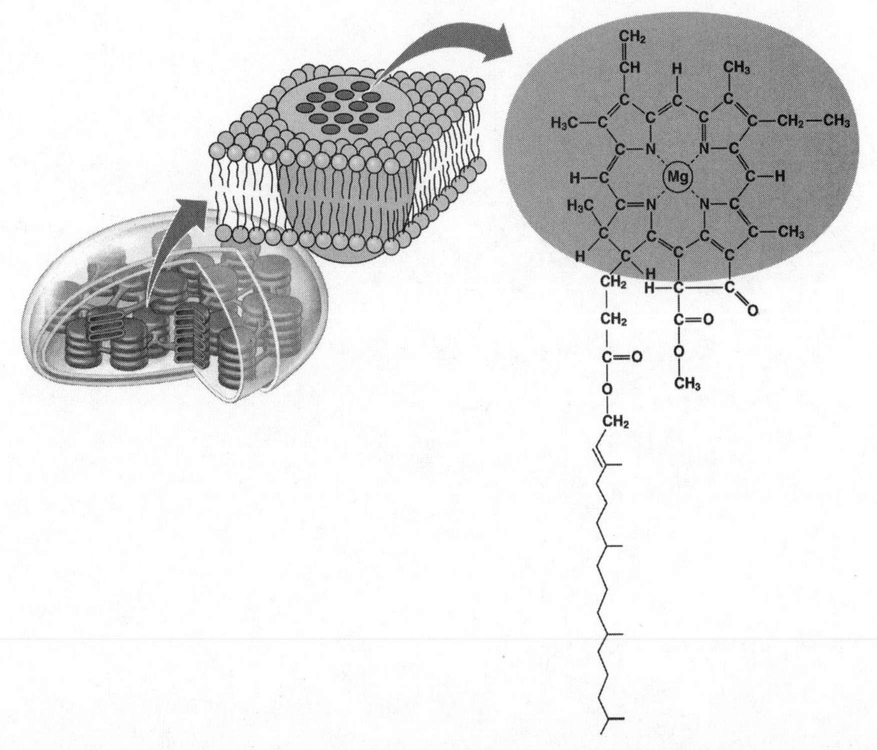

Figure 10.9 Location and structure of chlorophyll molecules in plants, page 184

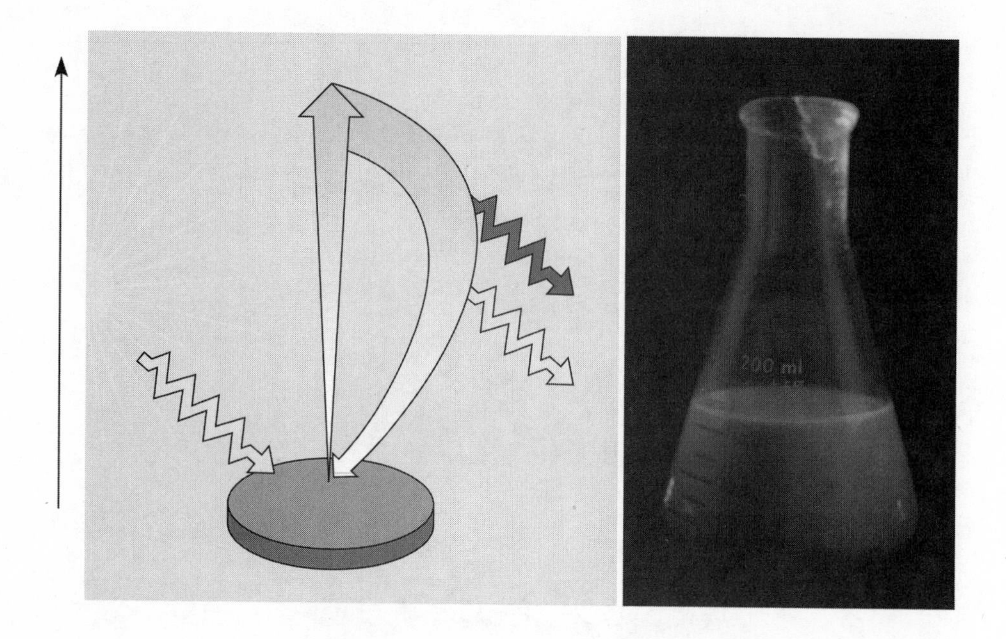

Figure 10.10 Excitation of isolated chlorophyll by light, page 185

Figure 10.11 How a photosystem harvests light, page 185

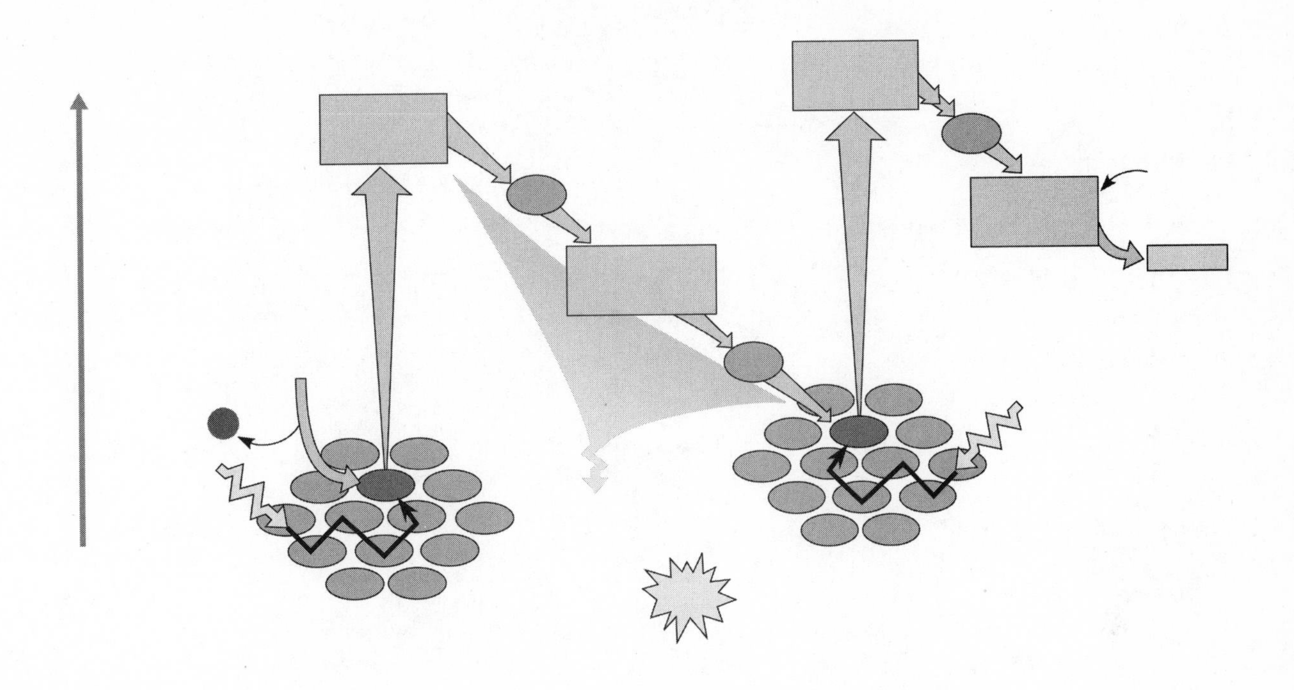

Figure 10.12 How noncyclic electron flow during the light reactions generates ATP and NADPH, page 186

Figure 10.13 A mechanical analogy for the light reactions, page 187

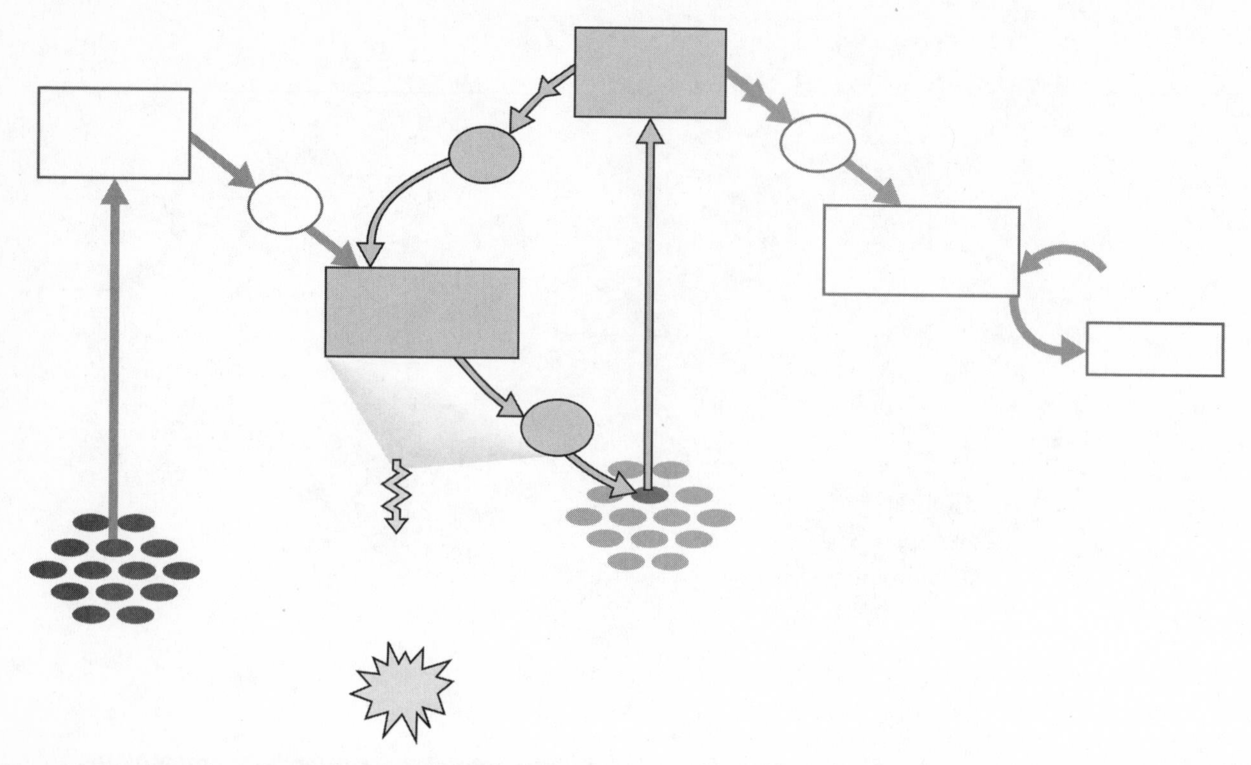

Figure 10.14 Cyclic electron flow, page 187

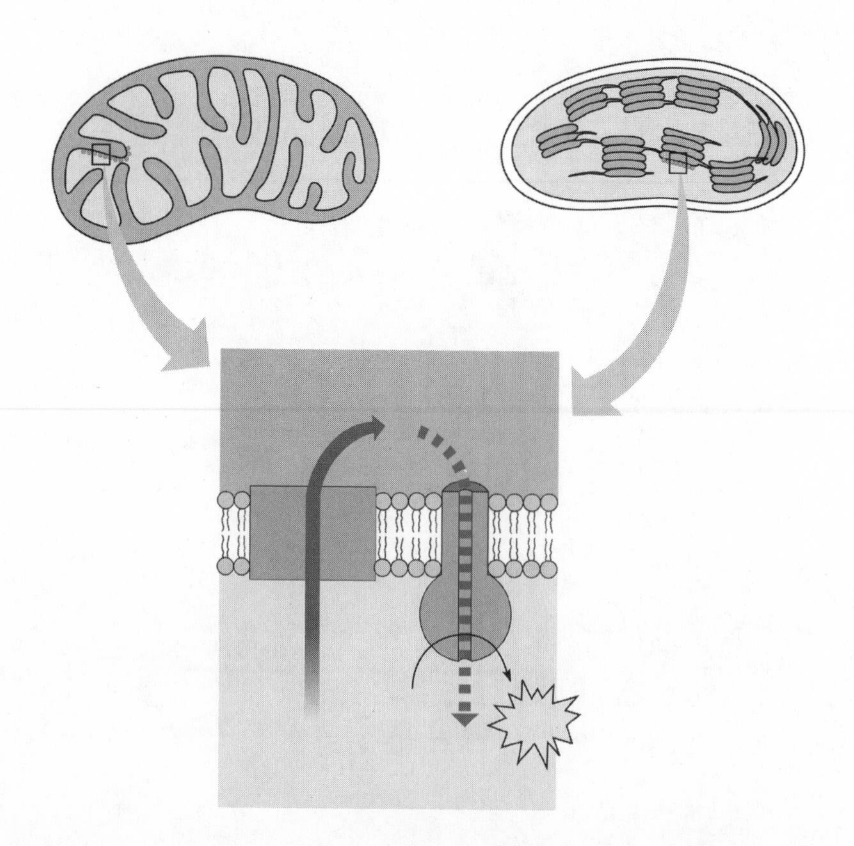

Figure 10.15 Comparison of chemiosmosis in mitochondria and chloroplasts, page 188

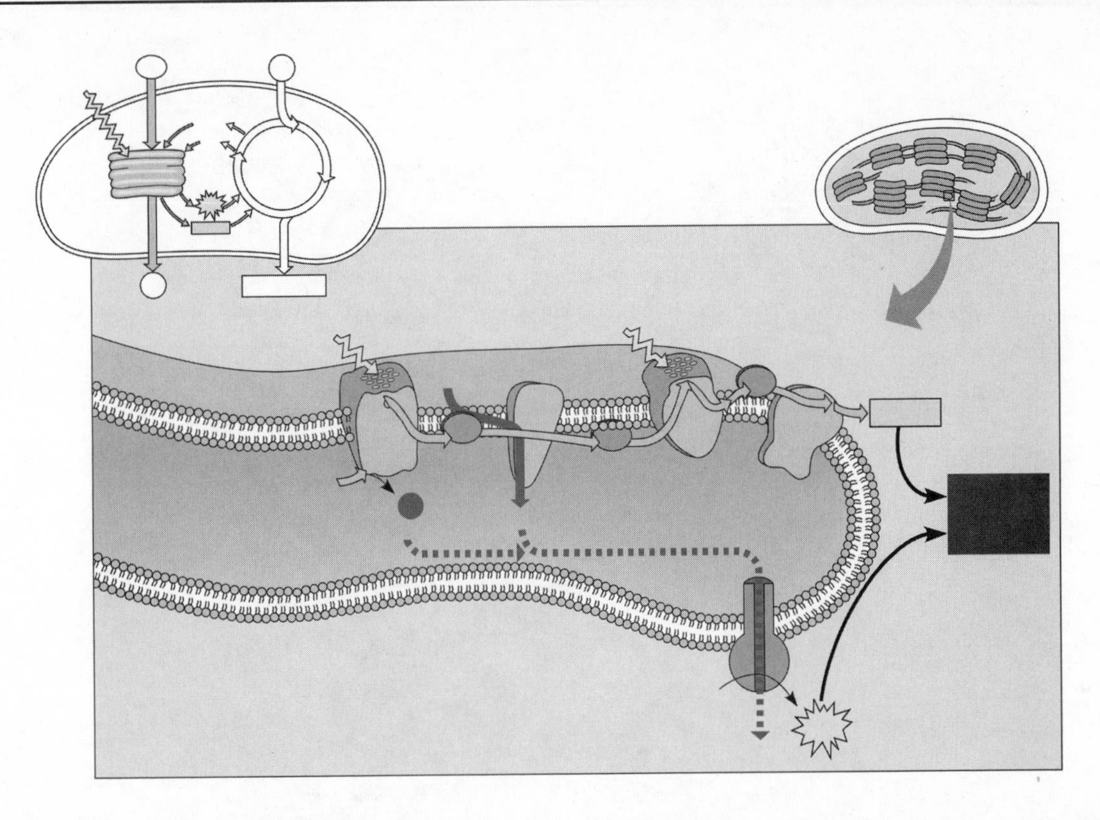

Figure 10.16 The light reactions and chemiosmosis: the organization of the thylakoid membrane, page 189

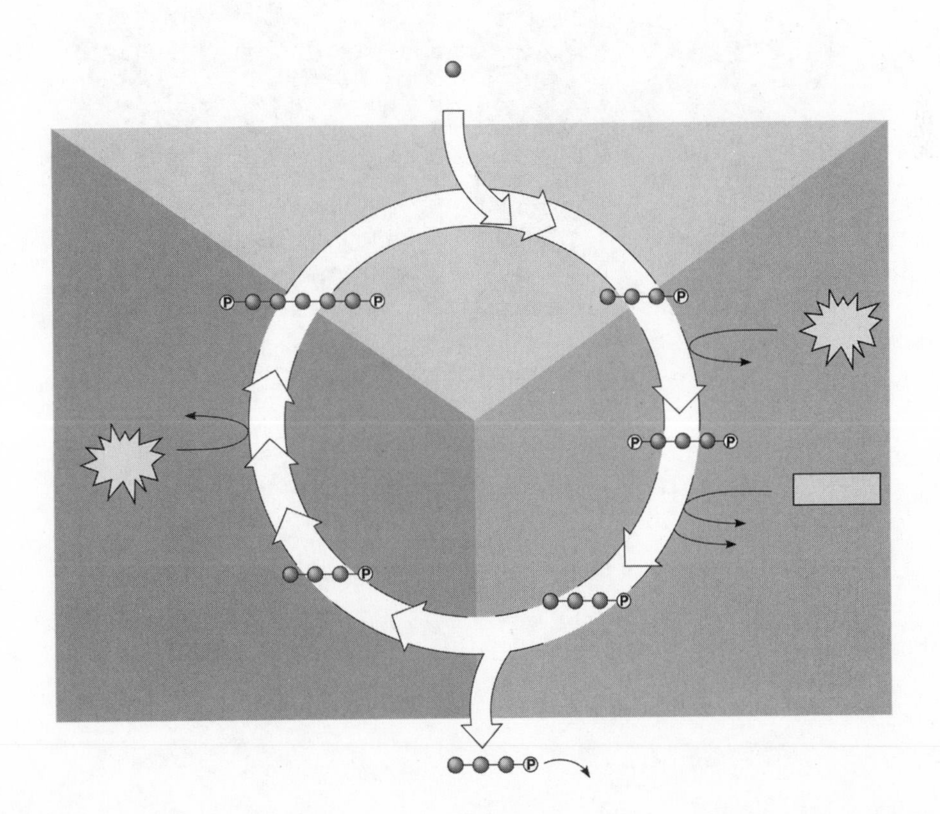

Figure 10.17 The Calvin cycle, page 190

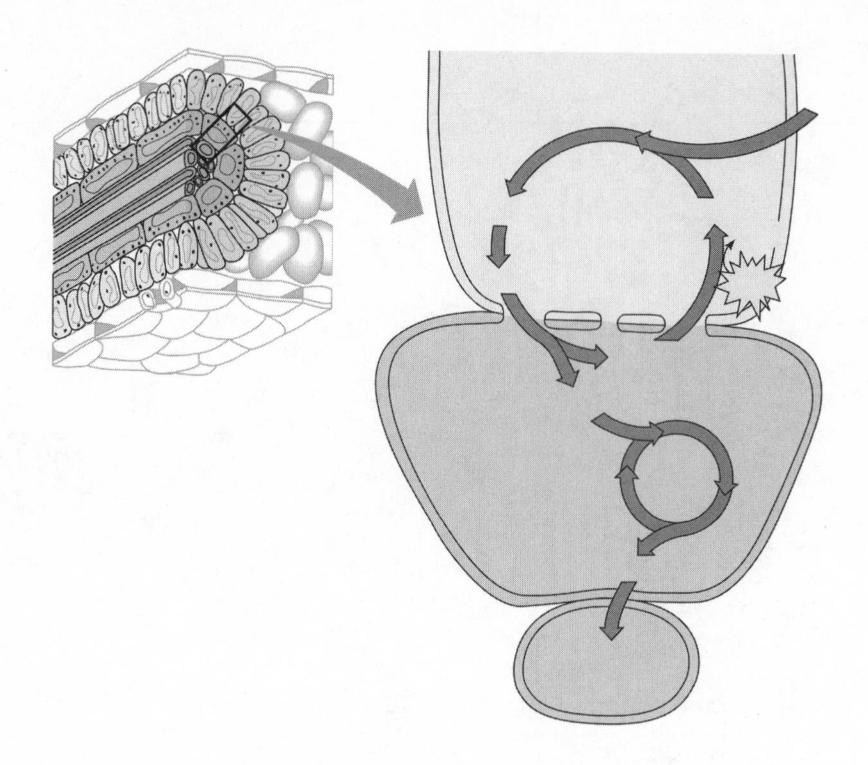

Figure 10.18 C_4 leaf anatomy and the C_4 pathway, page 192

Figure 10.19 C_4 and CAM photosynthesis compared, page 193

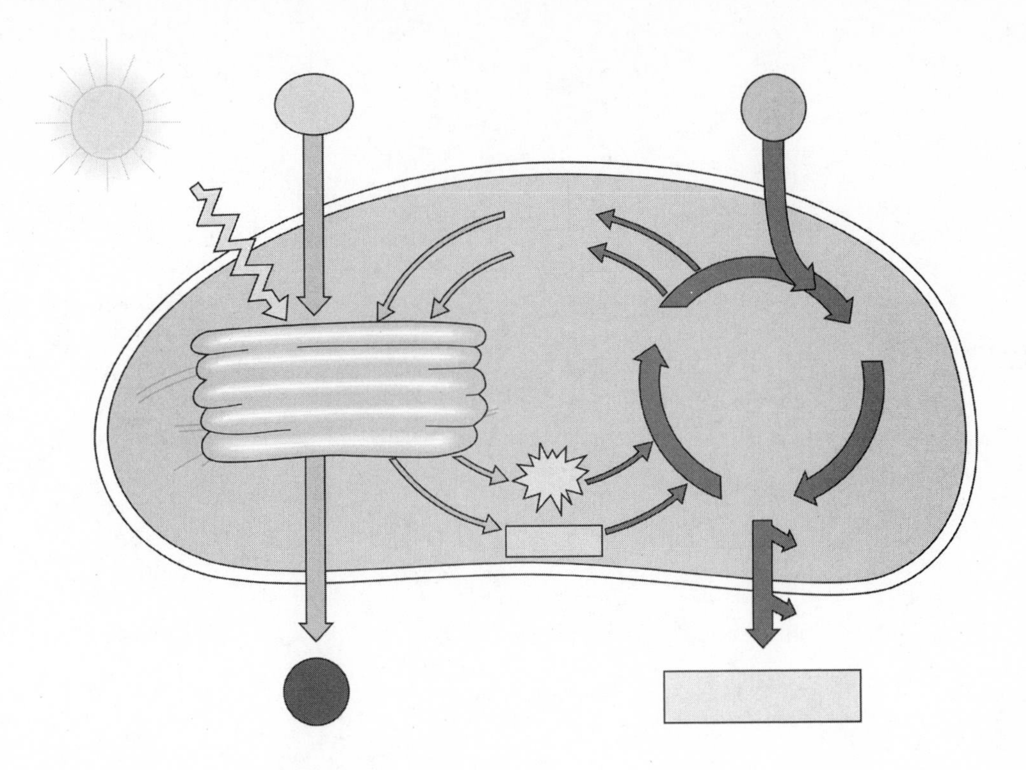

Figure 10.20 A review of photosynthesis, page 194

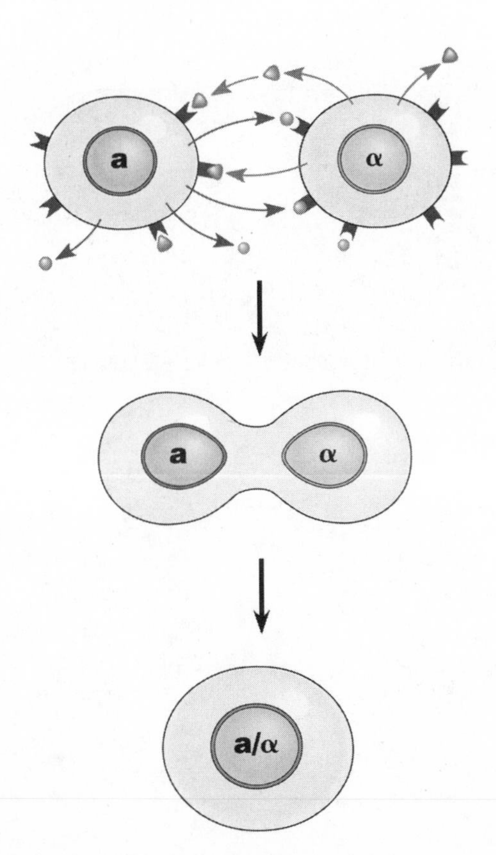

Figure 11.1 Communication between mating yeast cells, page 198

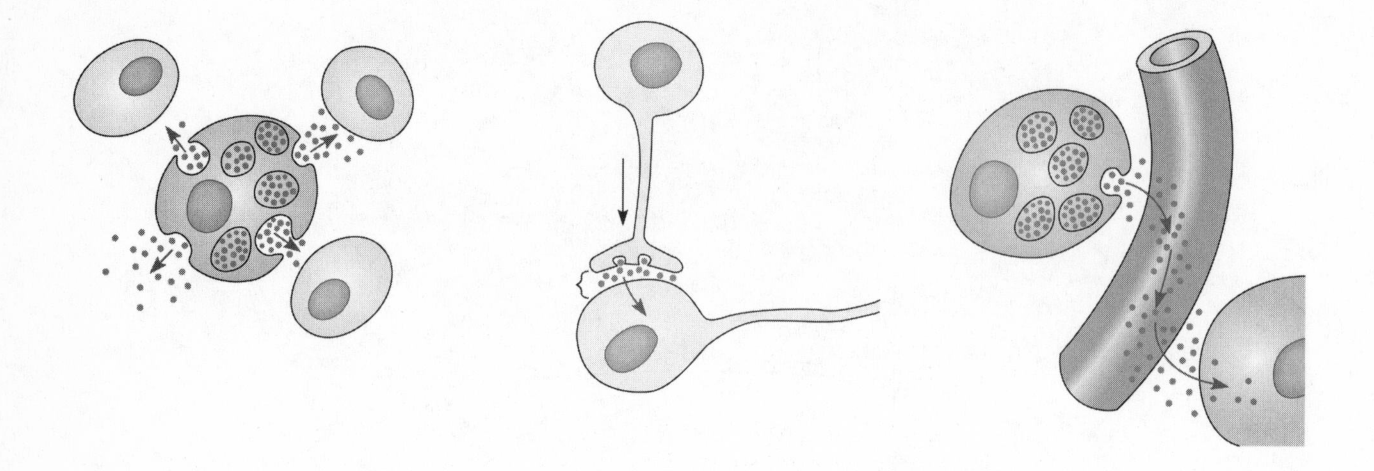

Figure 11.3 Local and long-distance cell communication in animals, page 199

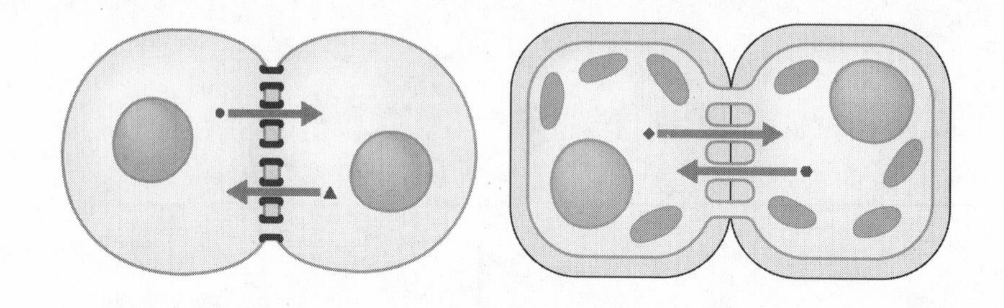

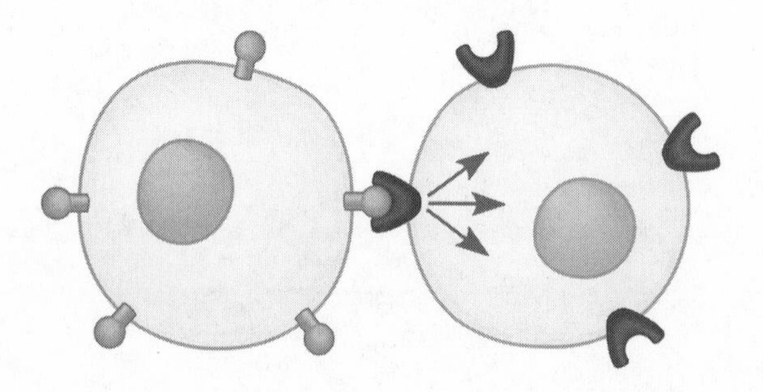

Figure 11.4 Communication by direct contact between cells, page 200

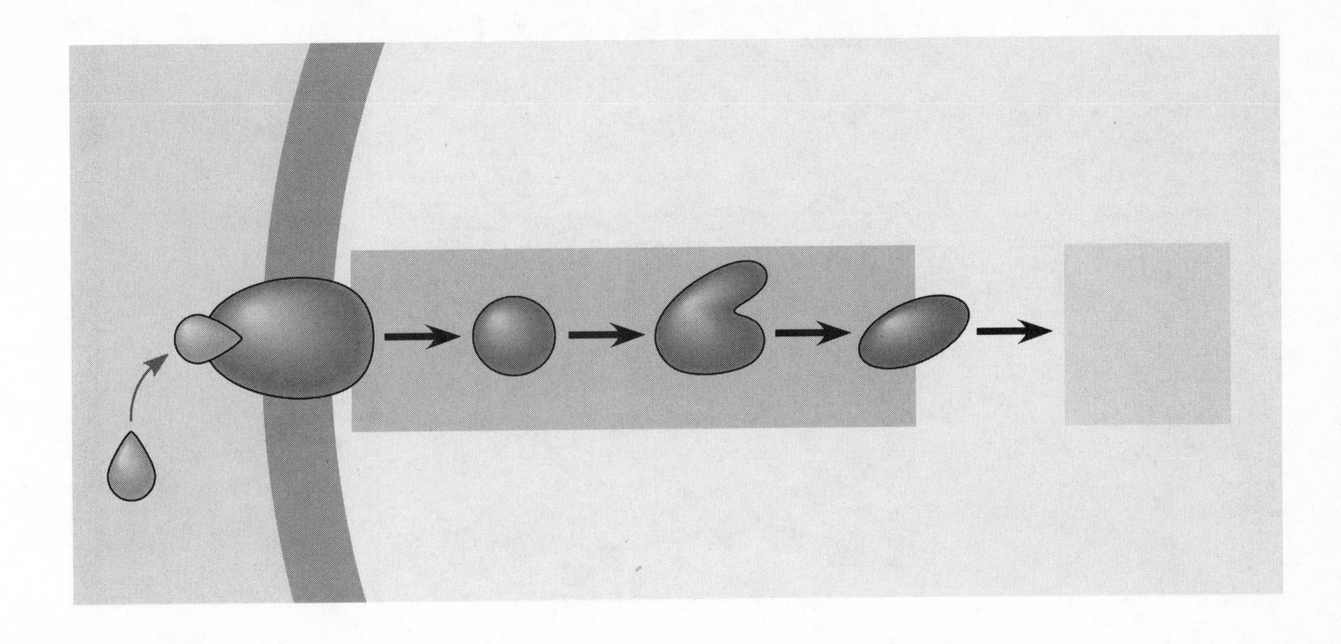

Figure 11.5 Overview of cell signaling, page 200

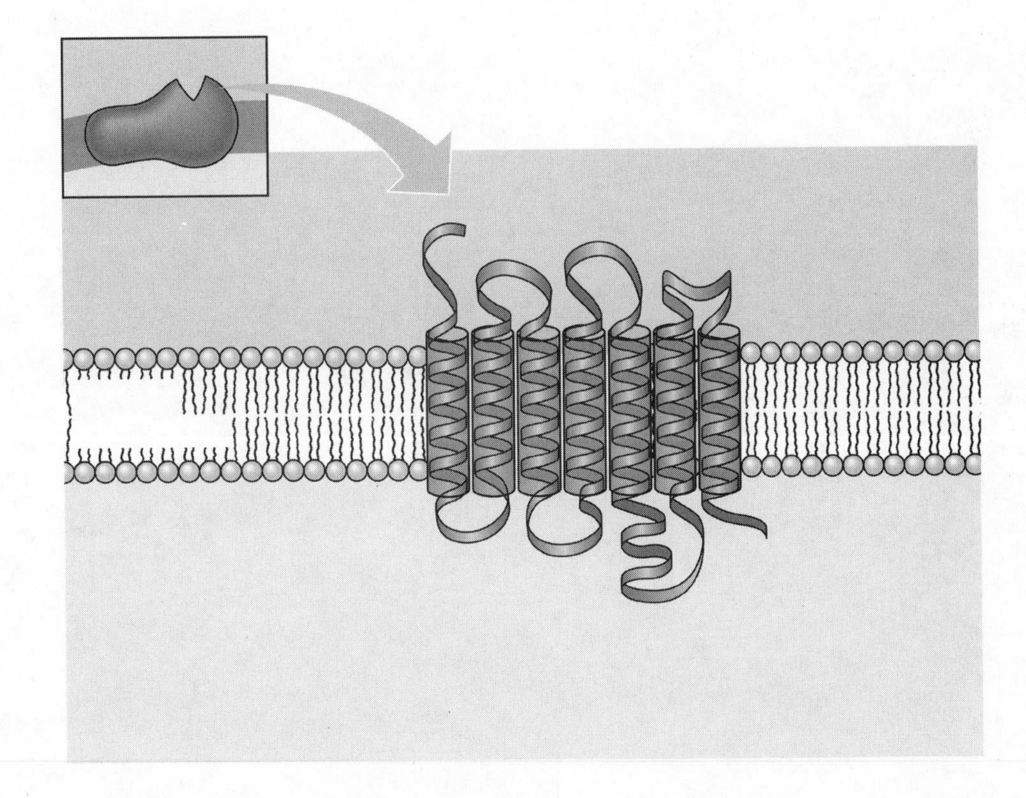

Figure 11.6 The structure of a G-protein-linked receptor, page 201

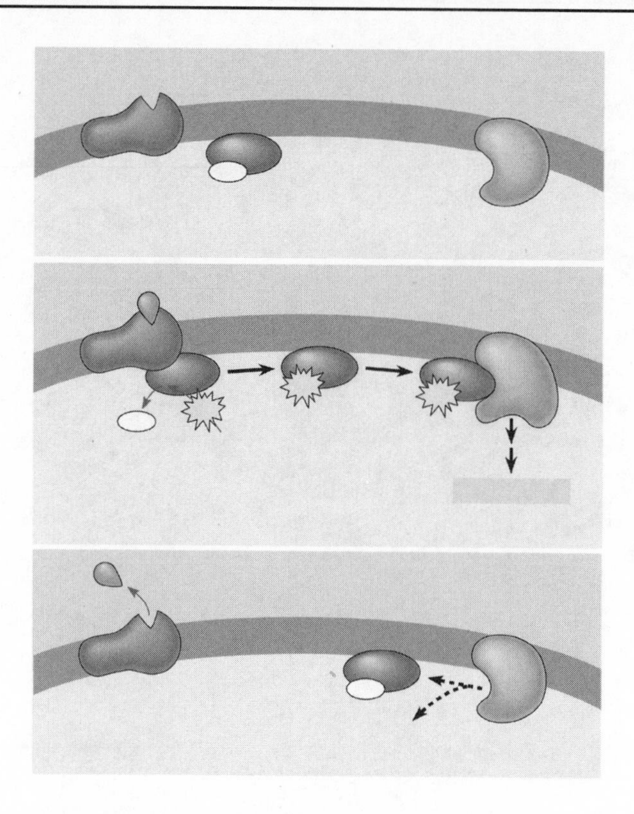

Figure 11.7 The functioning of a G-protein-linked receptor, page 202

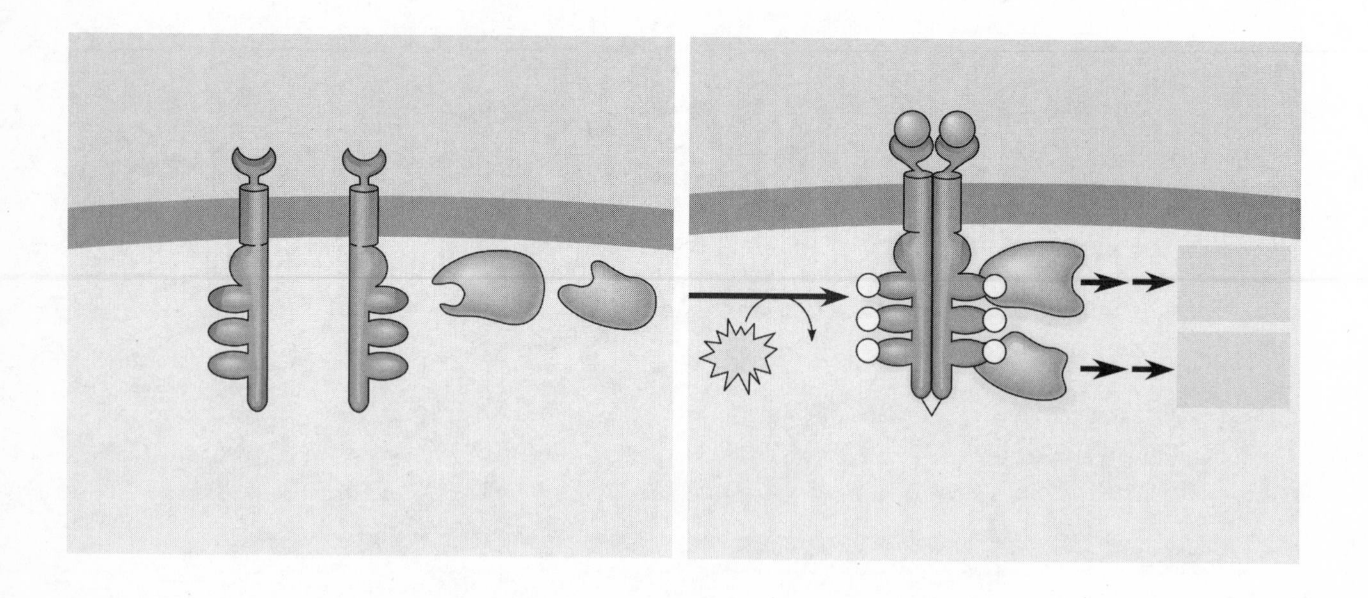

Figure 11.8 The structure and function of a tyrosine-kinase receptor, page 203

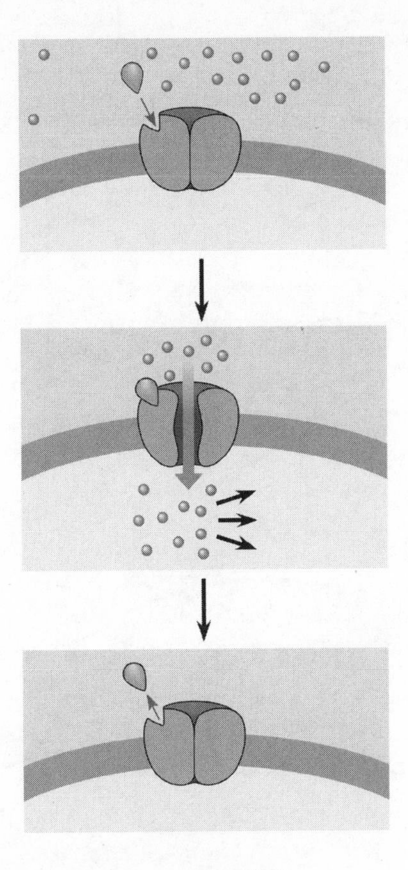

Figure 11.9 A ligand-gated ion-channel receptor, page 204

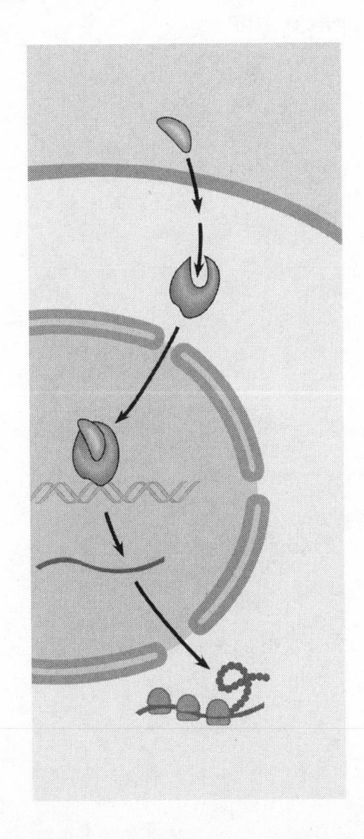

Figure 11.10 Steroid hormone interacting with an intracellular receptor, page 205

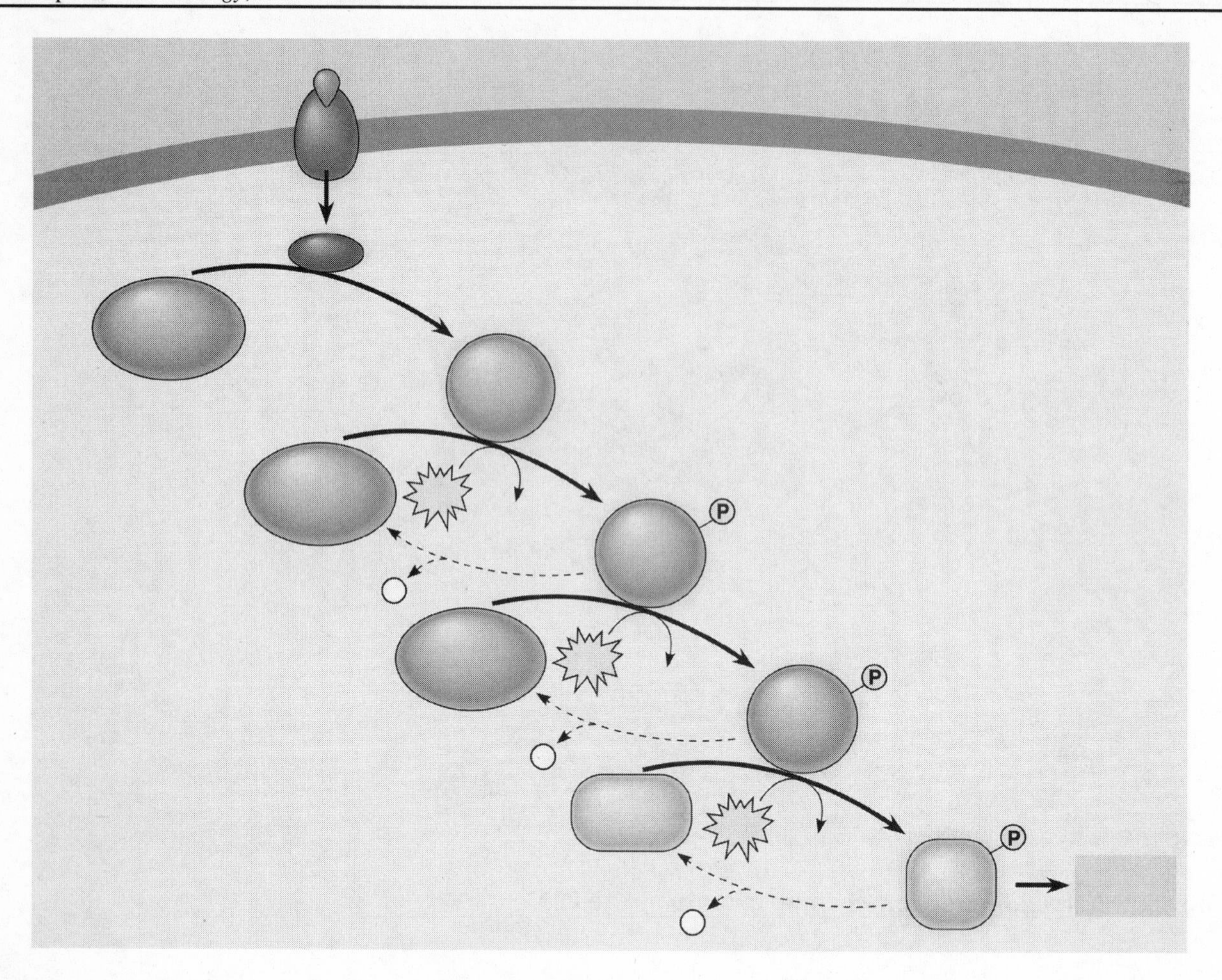

Figure 11.11 A phosphorylation cascade, page 206

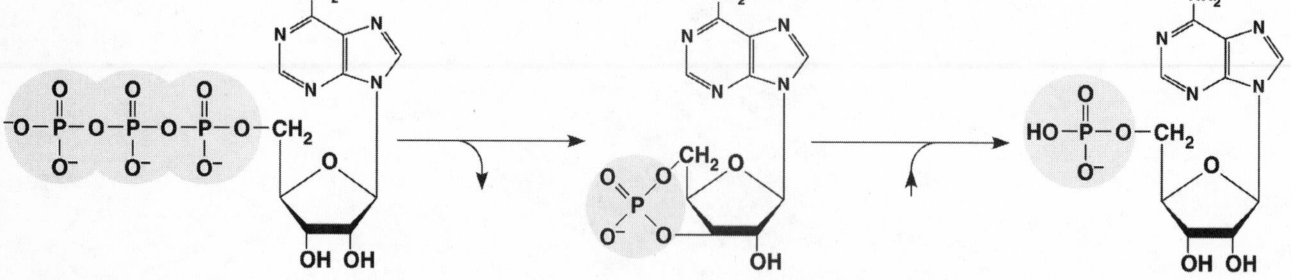

Figure 11.12 Cyclic AMP, page 207

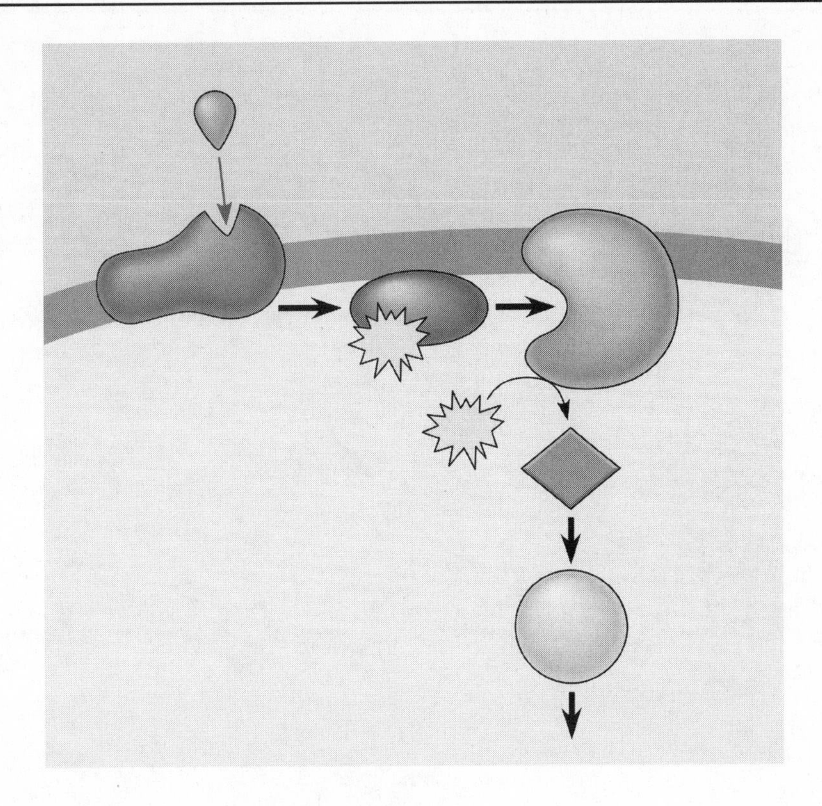

Figure 11.13 cAMP as a second messenger, page 207

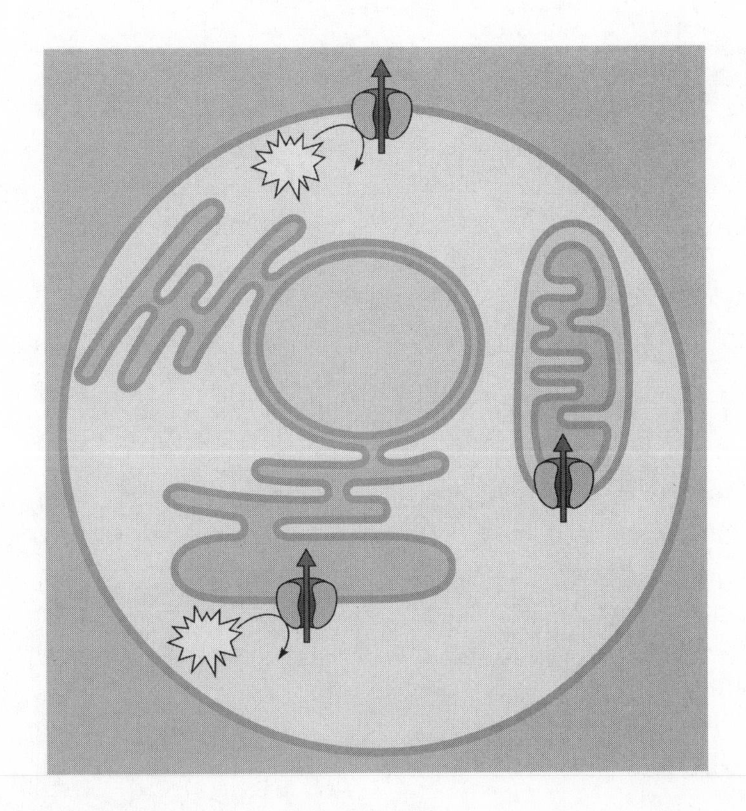

Figure 11.14 The maintenance of calcium ion concentrations in an animal cell, page 208

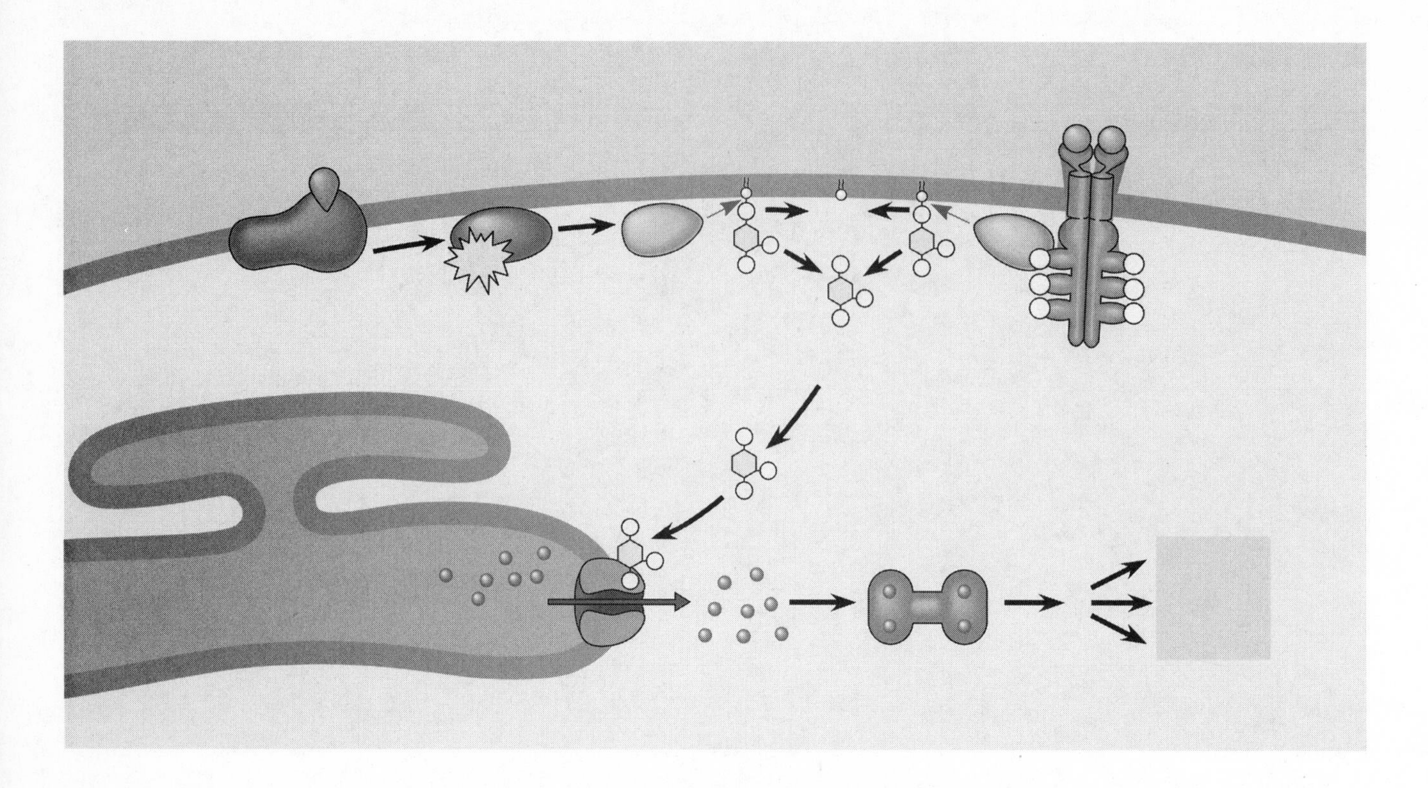

Figure 11.15 Calcium and inositol triphosphate in signaling pathways, page 209

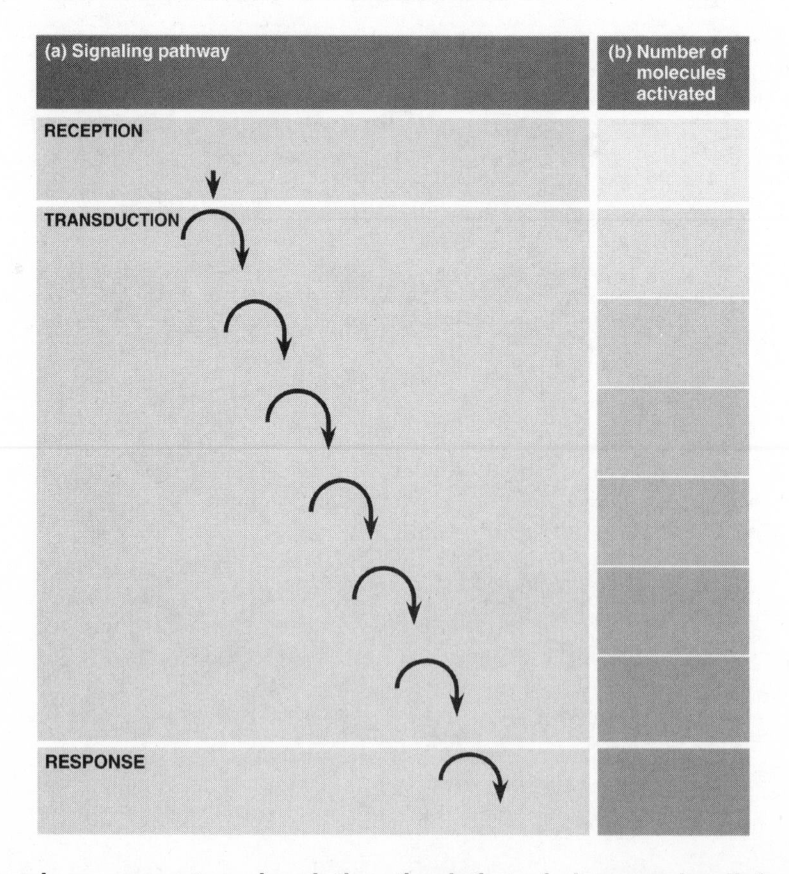

Figure 11.16 Cytoplasmic response to a signal: the stimulation of glycogen breakdown by epinephrine, page 210

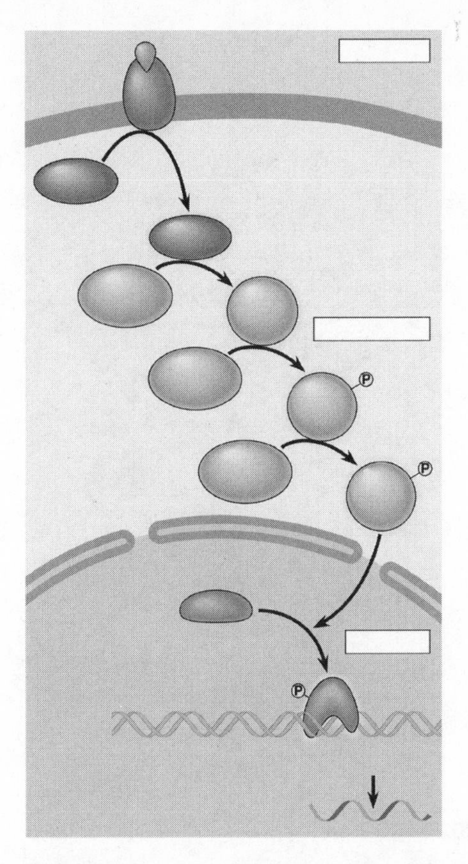

Figure 11.17 Nuclear response to a signal: the activation of a specific gene by a growth factor, page 211

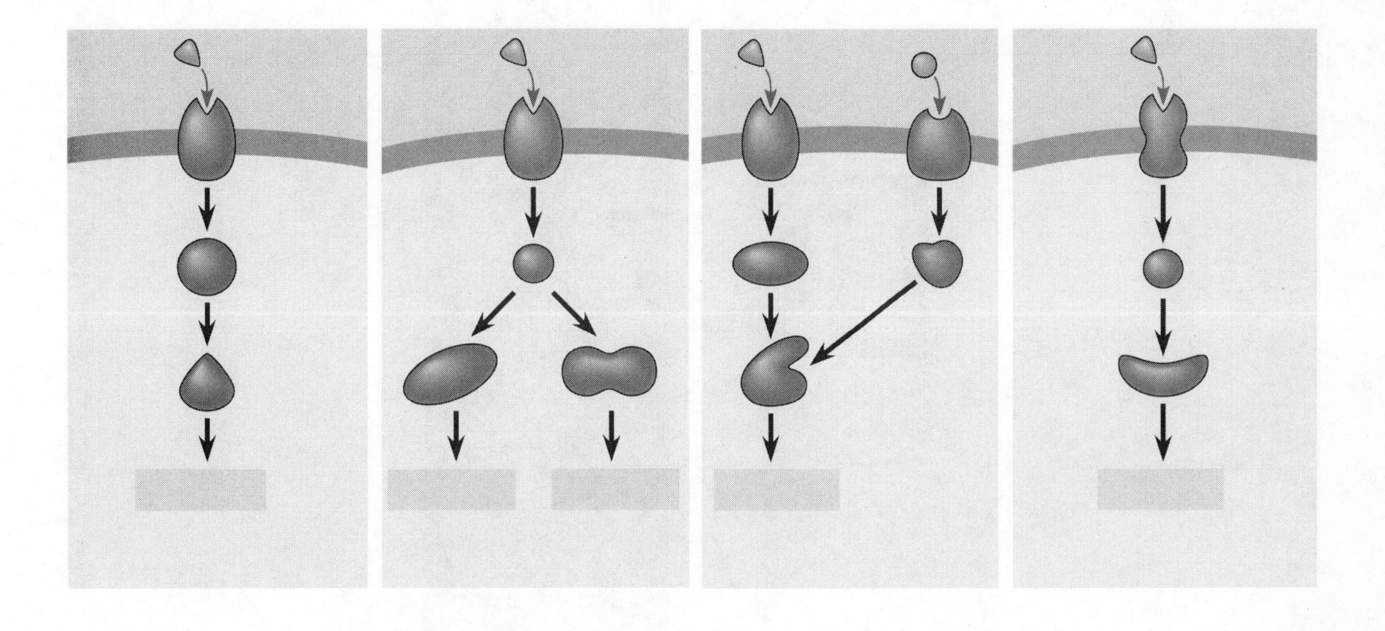

Figure 11.18 The specificity of cell signaling, page 211

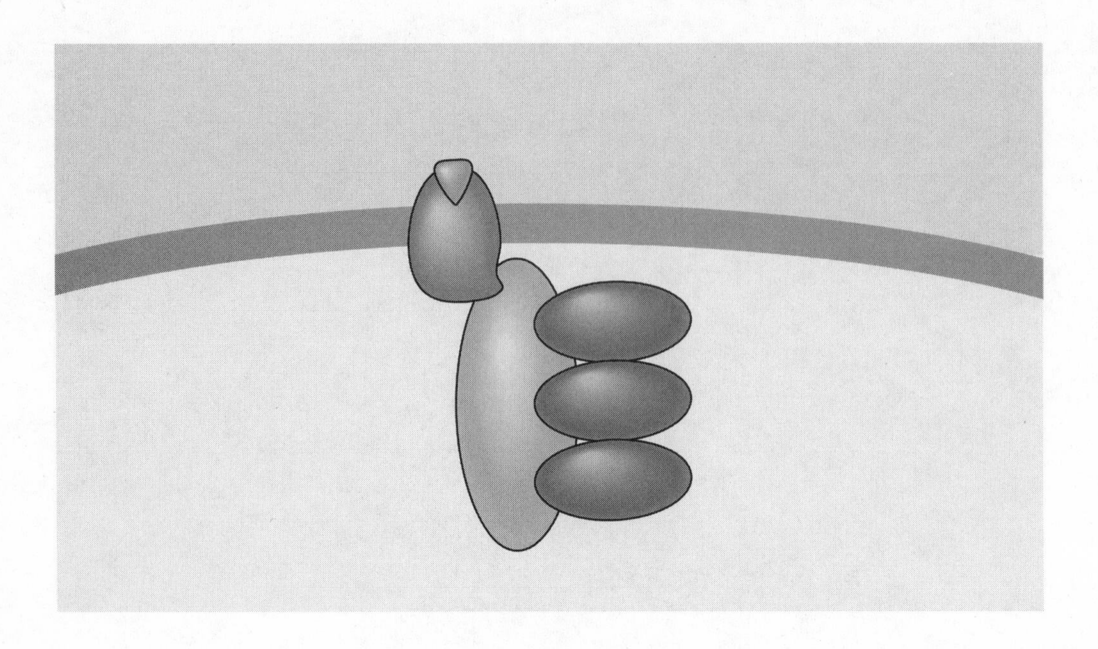

Figure 11.19 A scaffolding protein, page 212

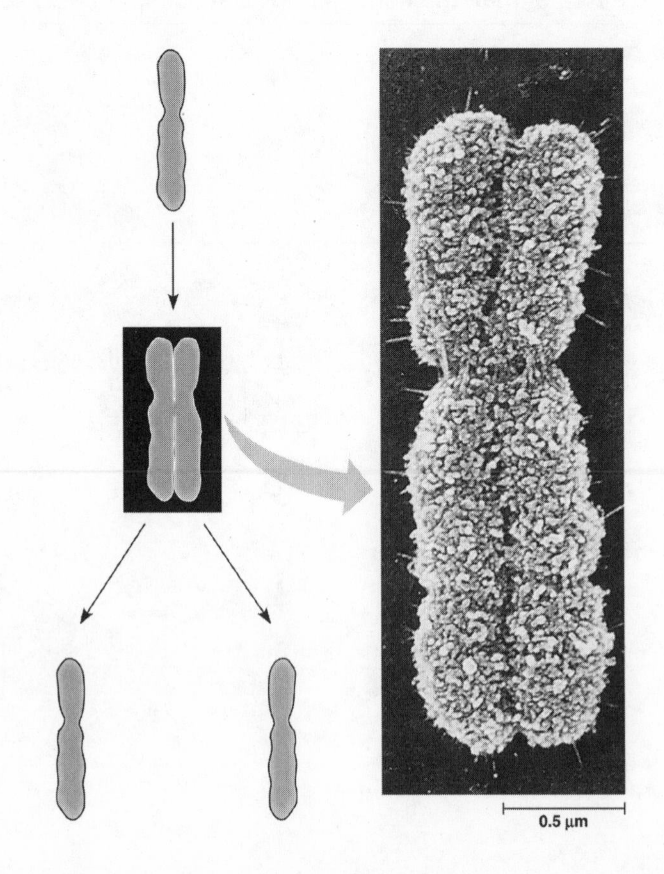

Figure 12.3 Chromosome duplication and distribution during mitosis, page 217

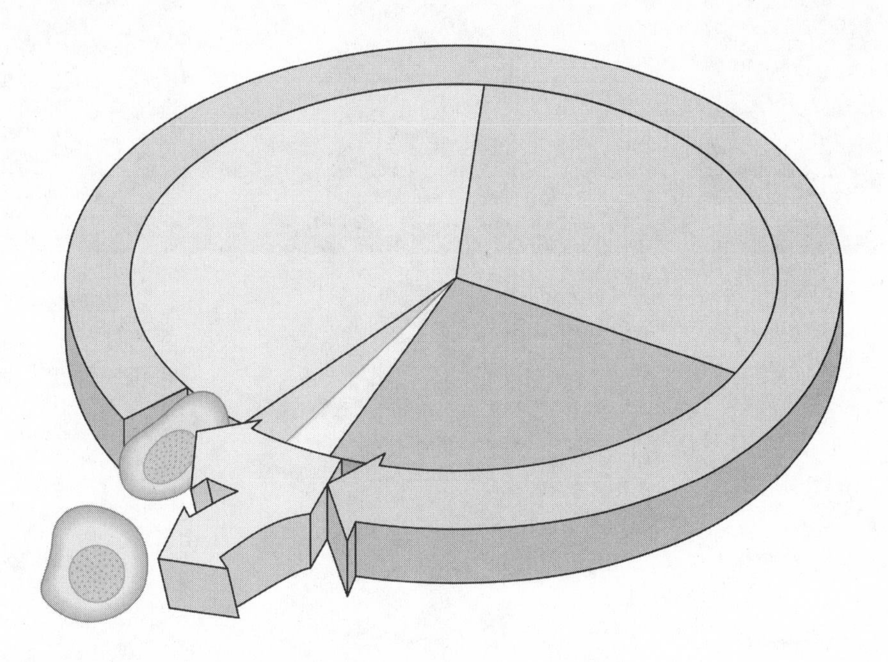

Figure 12.4 The cell cycle, page 217

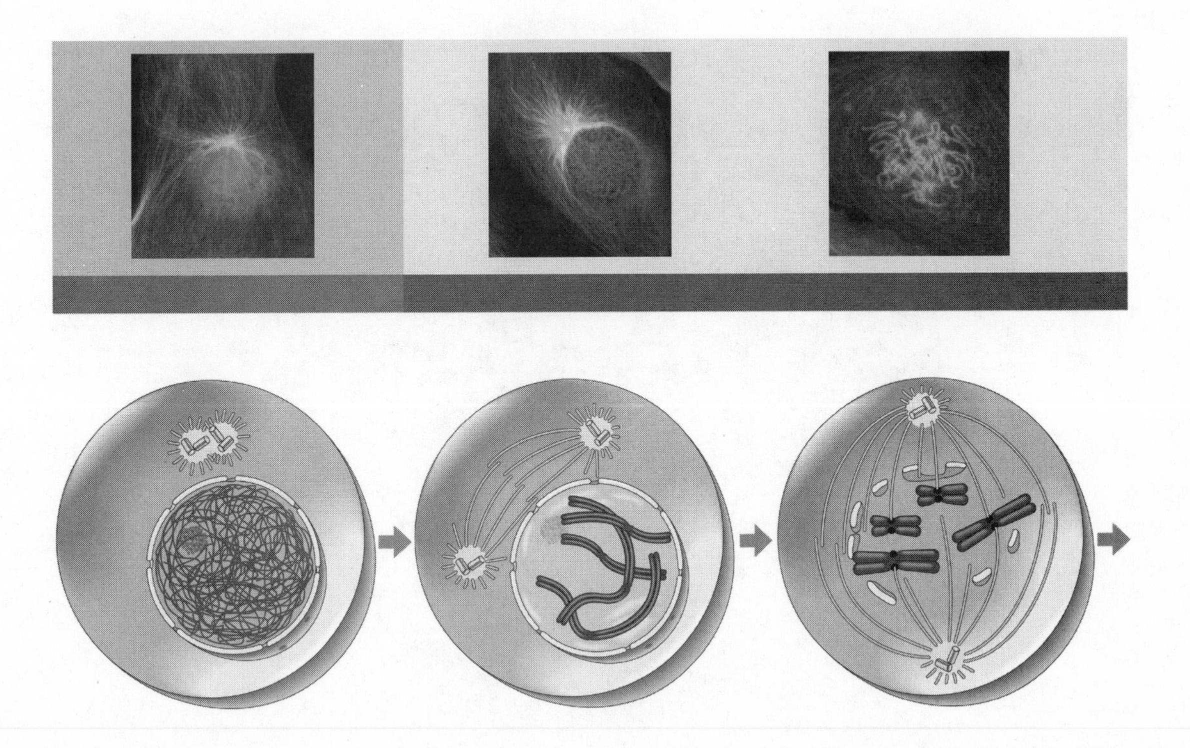

Figure 12.5 The stages of mitotic cell division in an animal cell: G2 phase; prophase; prometaphase, page 218

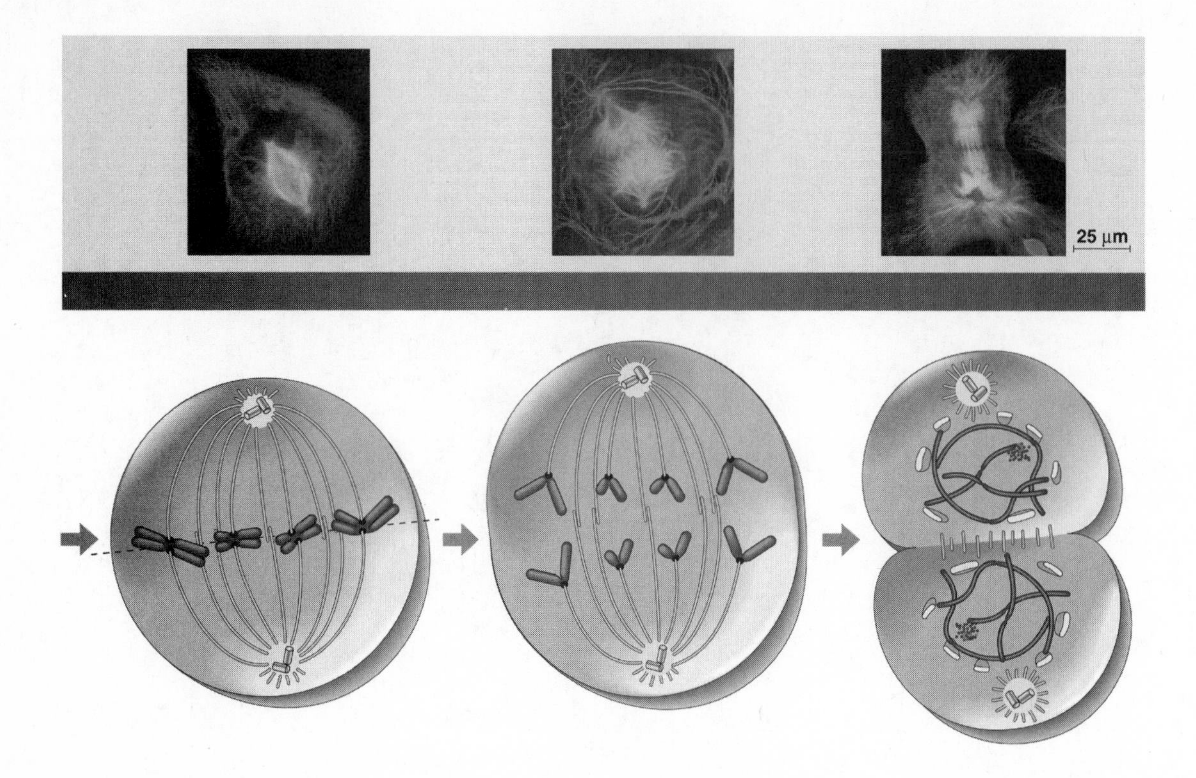

Figure 12.5 The stages of mitotic cell division in an animal cell: metaphase; anaphase; telophase and cytokinesis, page 219

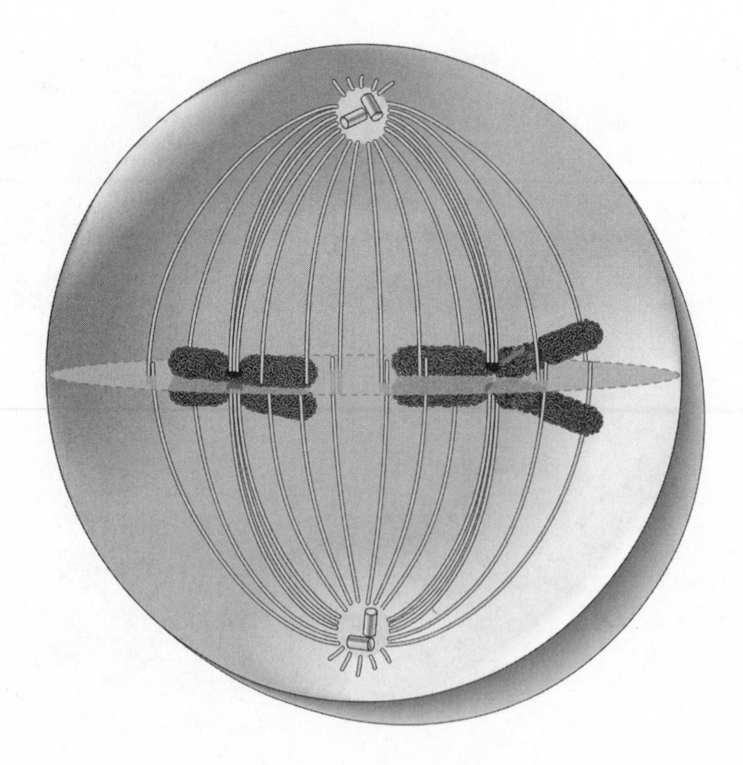

Figure 12.6 The mitotic spindle at metaphase, page 220

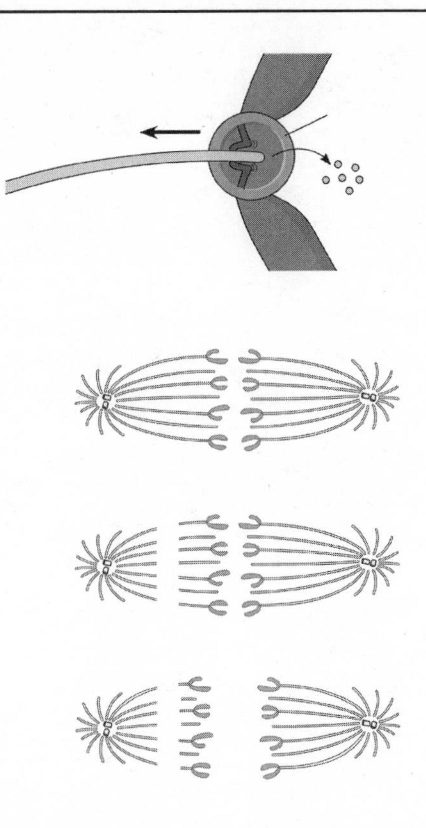

Figure 12.7 Testing a hypothesis for chromosome migration during anaphase, page 221

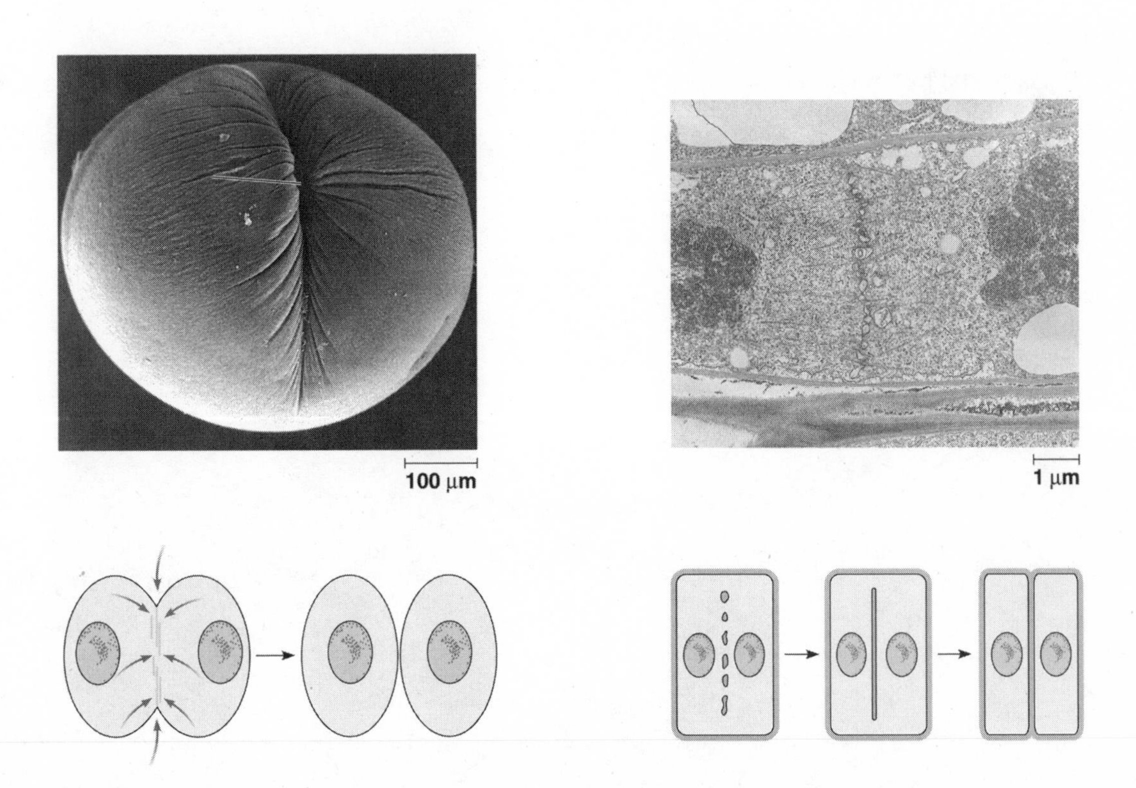

Figure 12.8 Cytokinesis in animal and plant cells, page 222

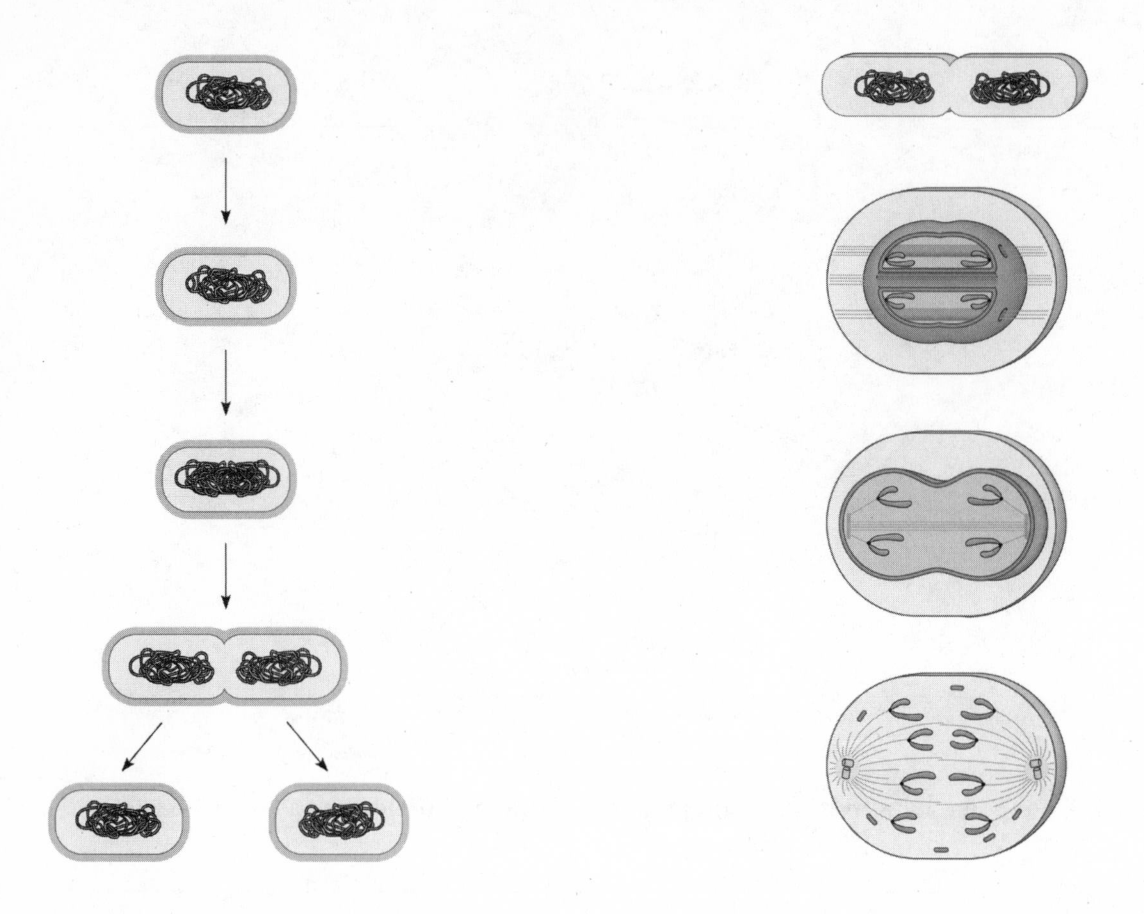

Figure 12.10 Bacterial cell division (binary fission), page 224

Figure 12.11 A hypothesis for the evolution of mitosis, page 225

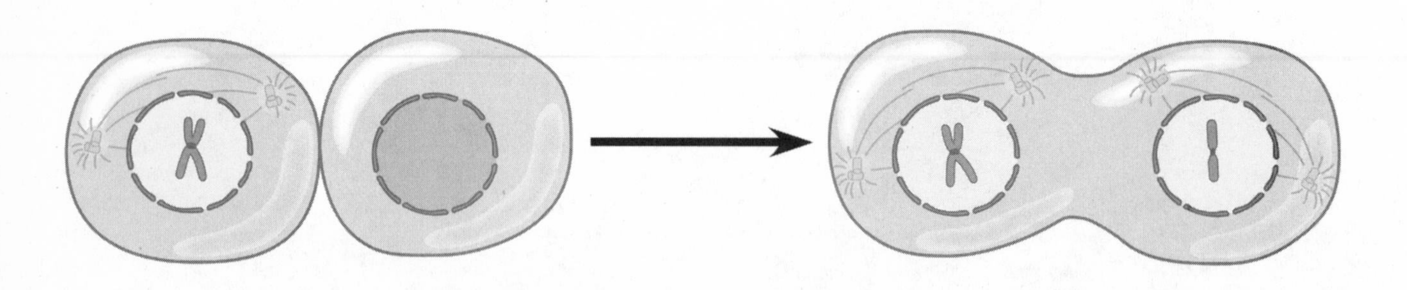

Figure 12.12 Evidence for cytoplasmic chemical signals in cell cycle regulation, page 225

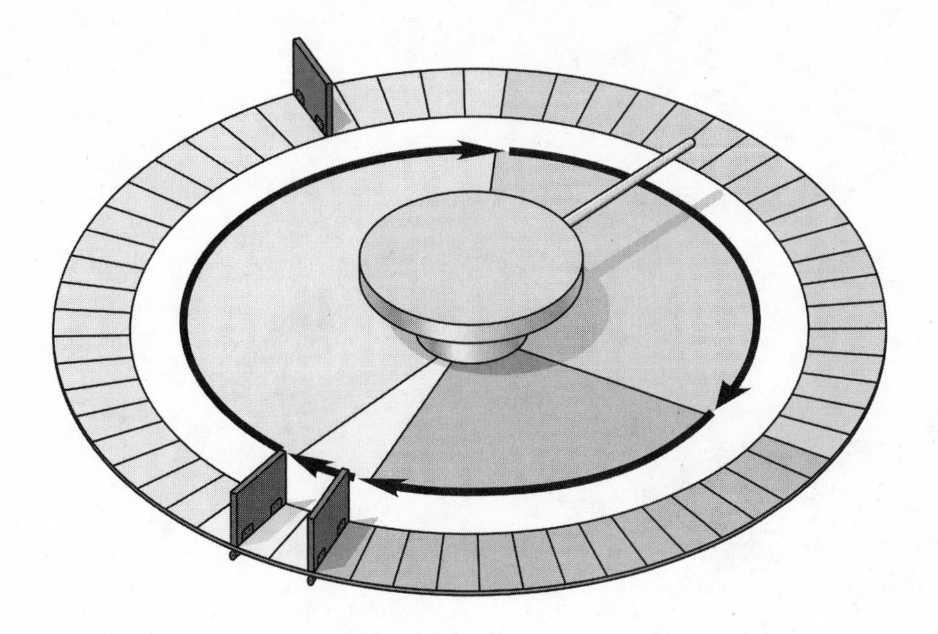

Figure 12.13 Mechanical analogy for the cell cycle control system, page 226

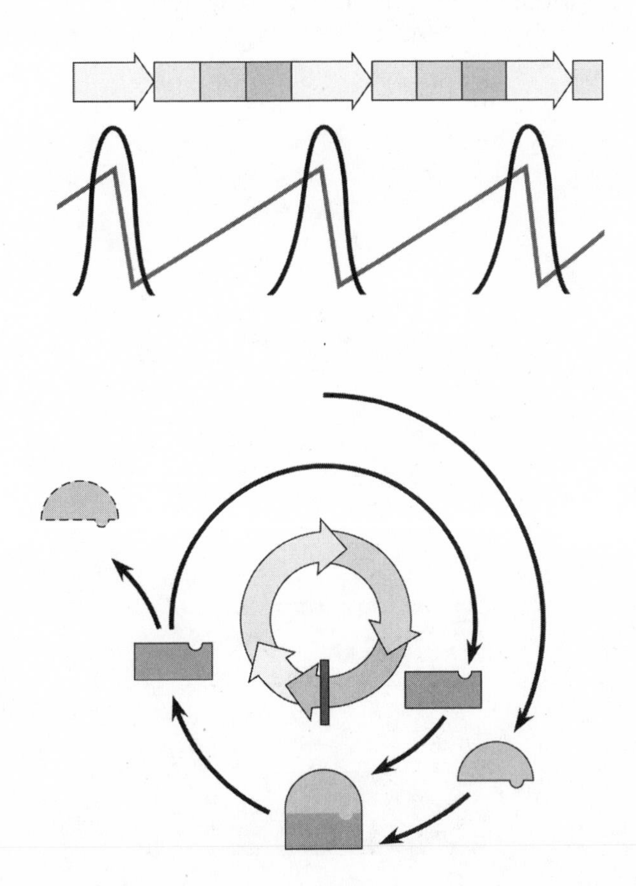

Figure 12.14 Molecular control of the cell cycle at the G2 checkpoint, page 227

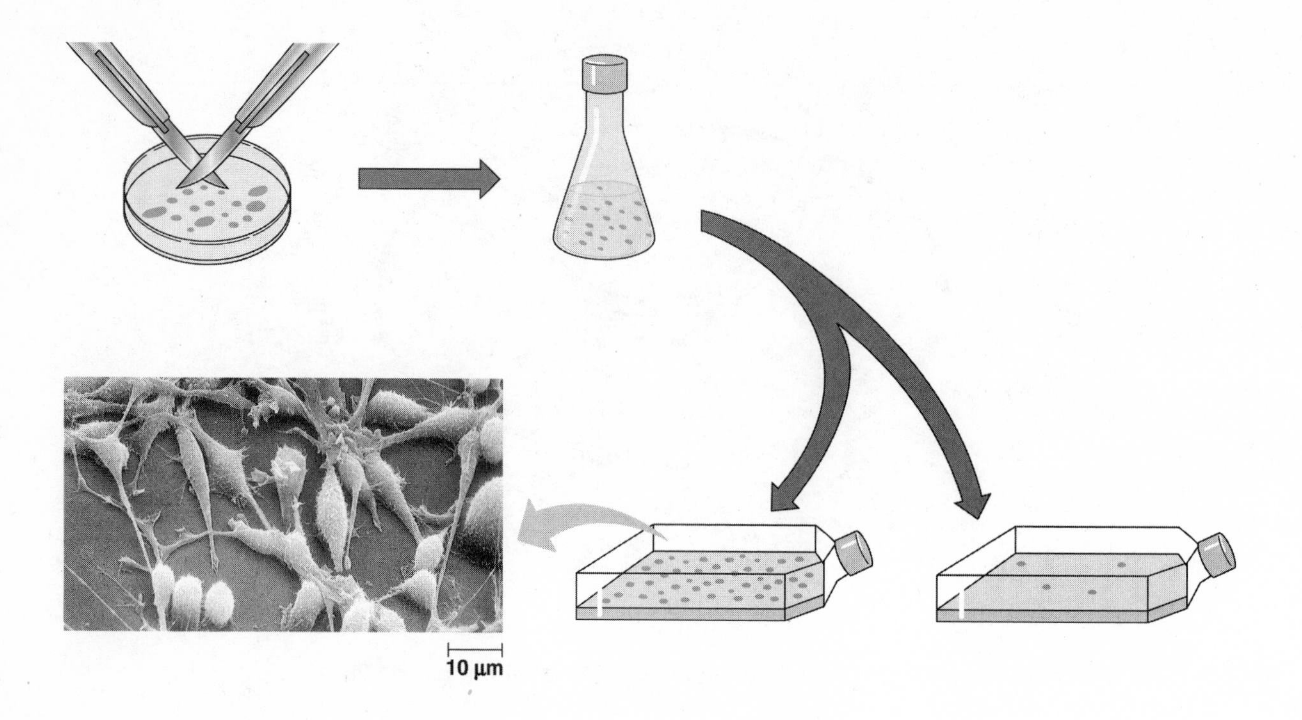

Figure 12.15 The effect of a growth factor on cell division, page 228

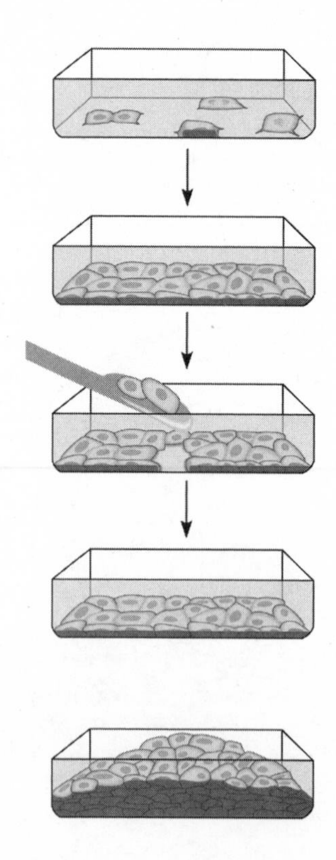

Figure 12.16 Density-dependent inhibition of cell division, page 229

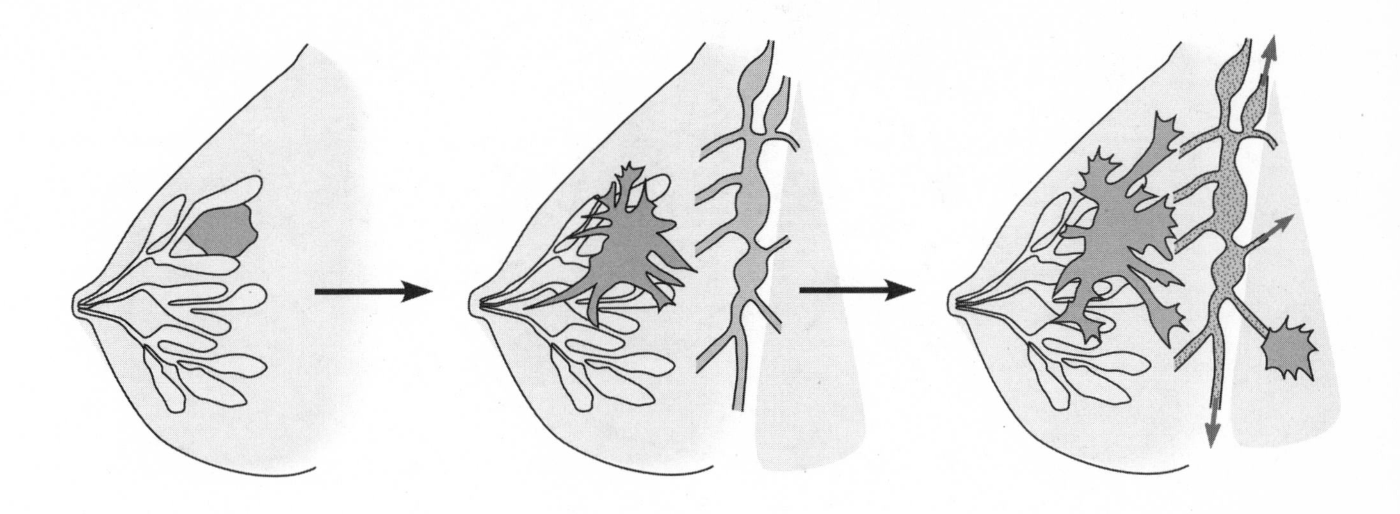

Figure 12.17 The growth and metastasis of a malignant breast tumor, page 229

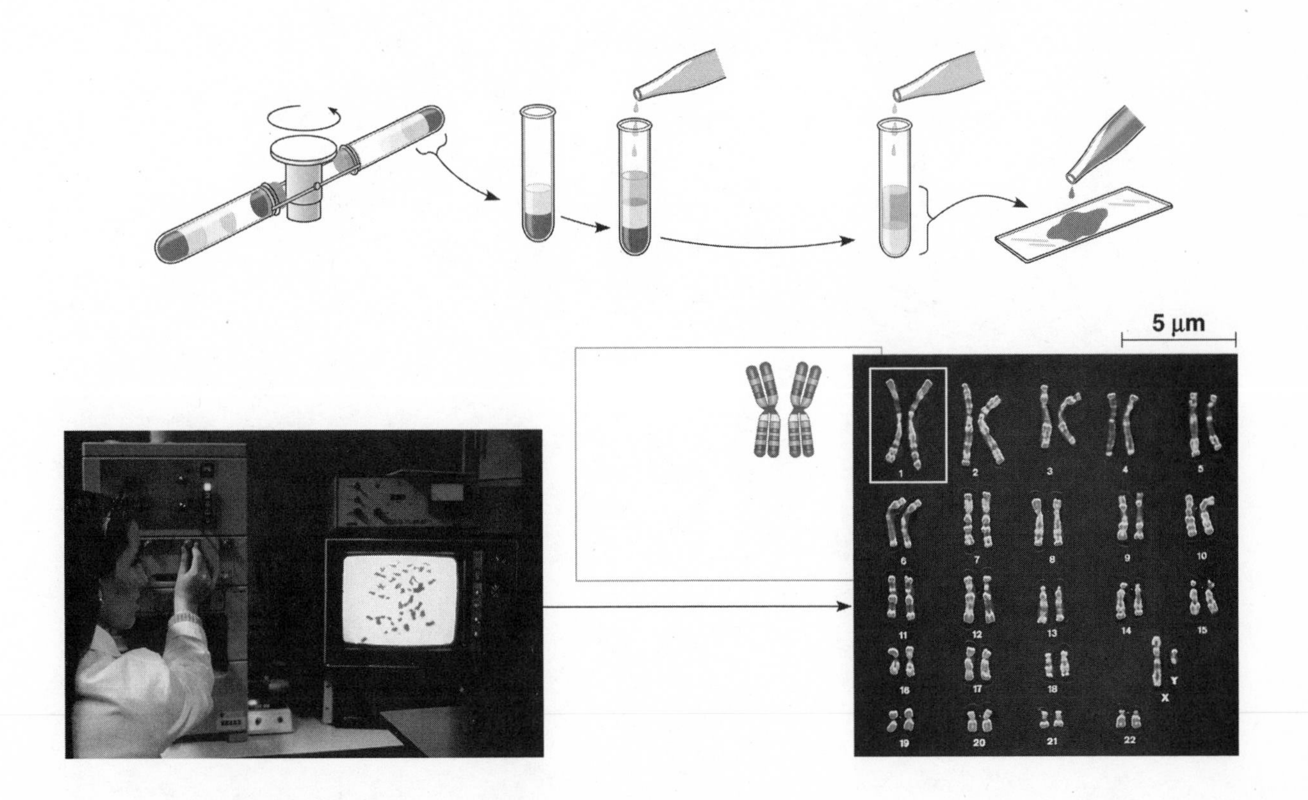

Figure 13.3 Preparation of a human karyotype, page 237

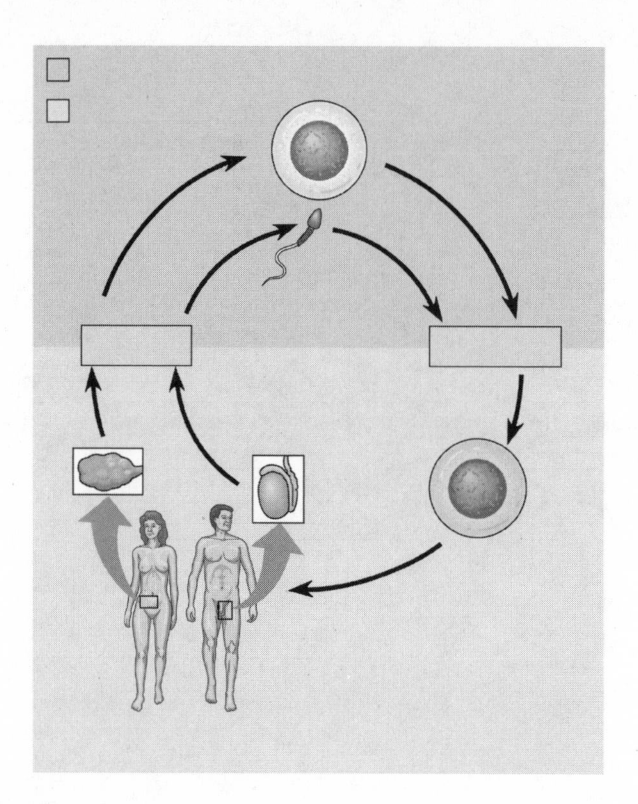

Figure 13.4 The human life cycle, page 238

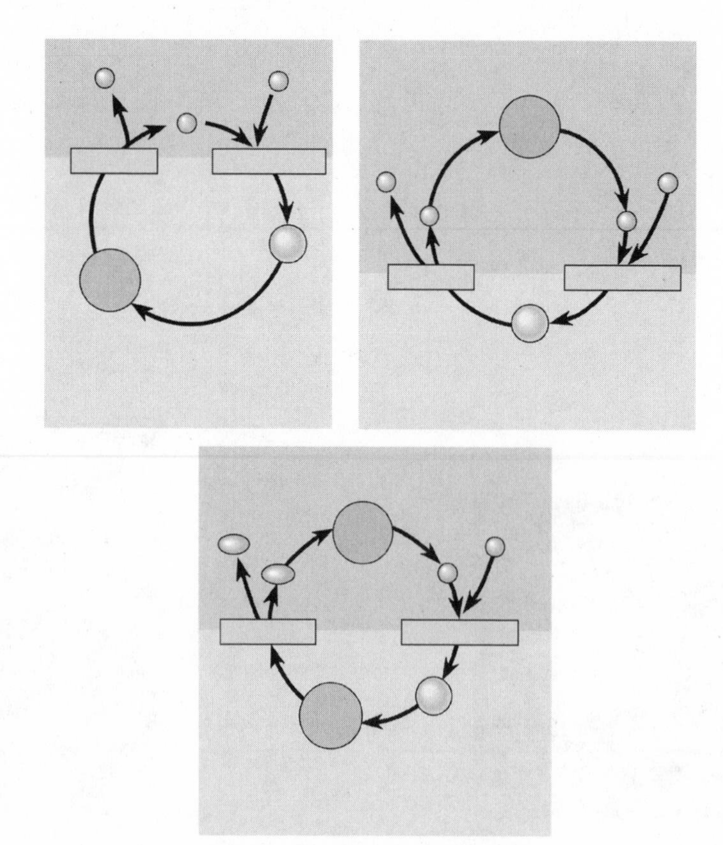

Figure 13.5 Three sexual life cycles differing in the timing of meiosis and fertilization (syngamy), page 238

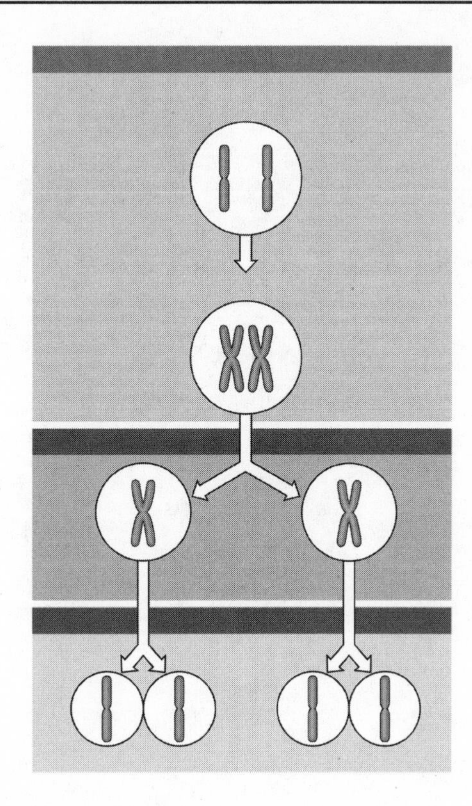

Figure 13.6 Overview of meiosis: how meiosis reduces chromosome number, page 239

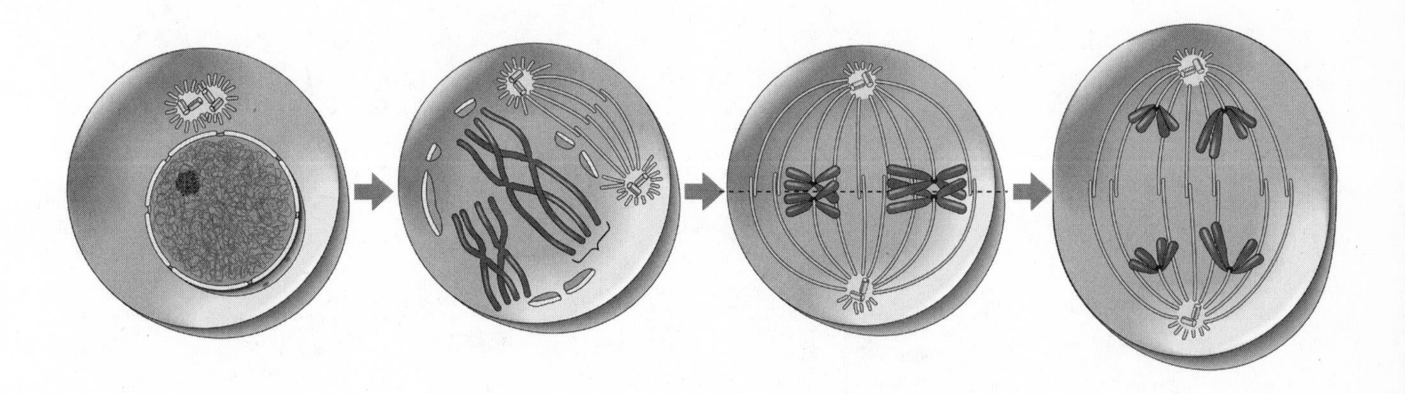

Figure 13.7 The stages of meiotic cell division: Meiosis I, page 240

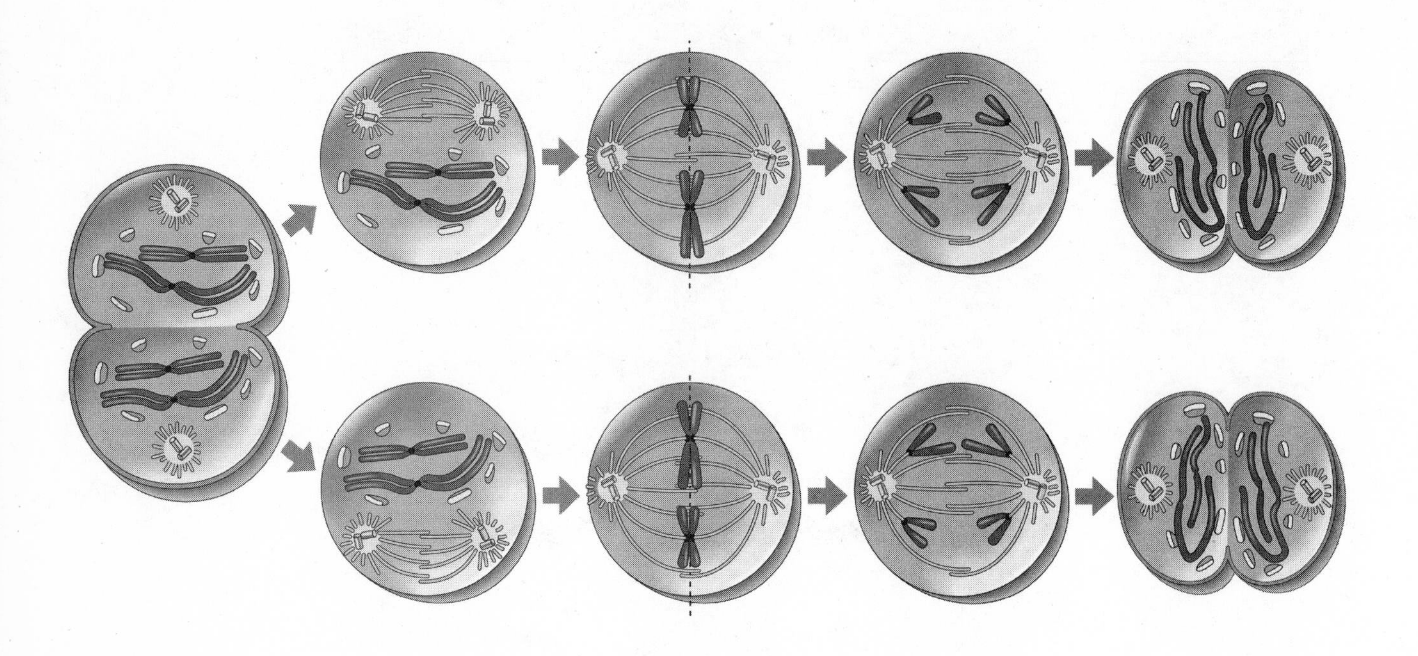

Figure 13.7 The stages of meiotic cell division: Meiosis II, page 241

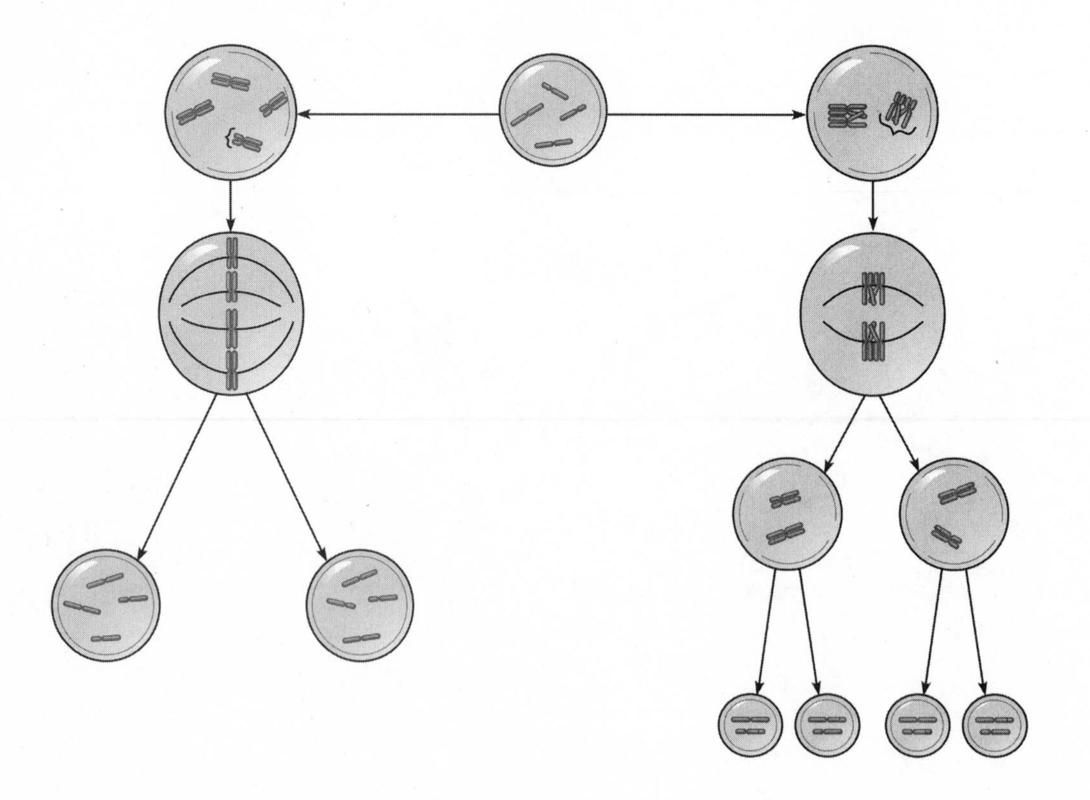

Figure 13.8 A comparison of mitosis and meiosis, page 242

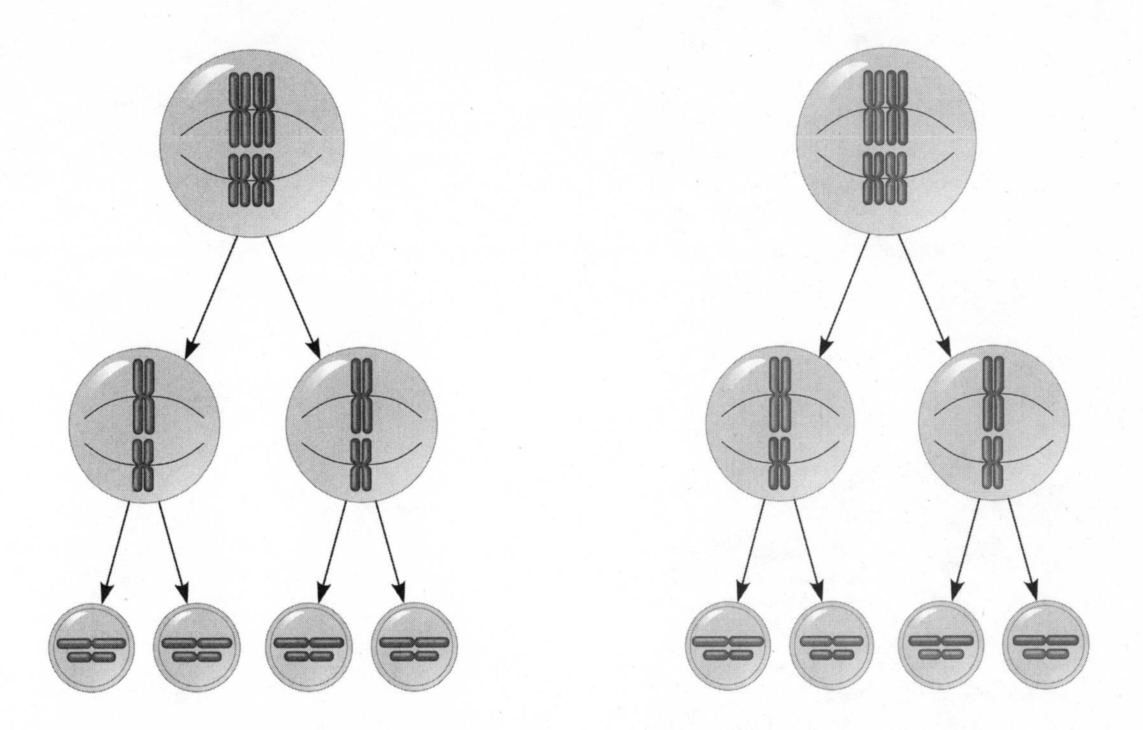

Figure 13.9 The results of alternative arrangements of two homologous chromosome pairs on the metaphase plate in meiosis I, page 243

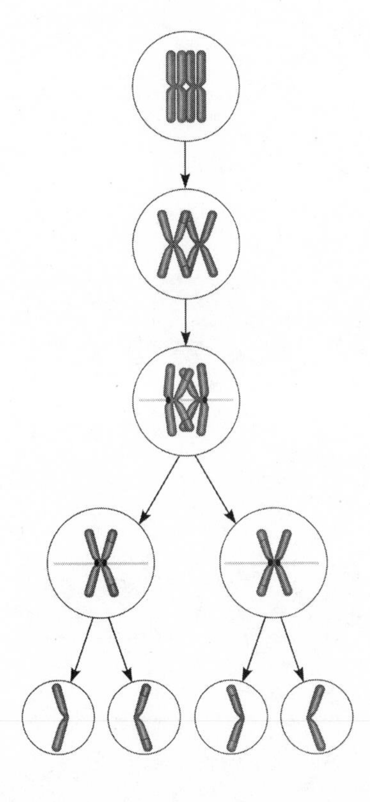

Figure 13.10 The results of crossing over during meiosis, page 244

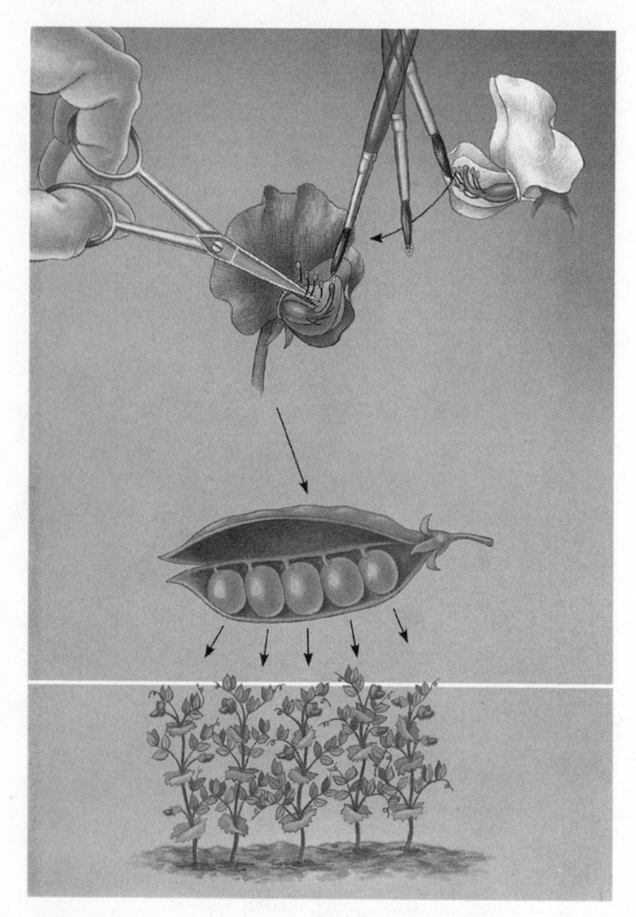

Figure 14.1 A genetic cross, page 248

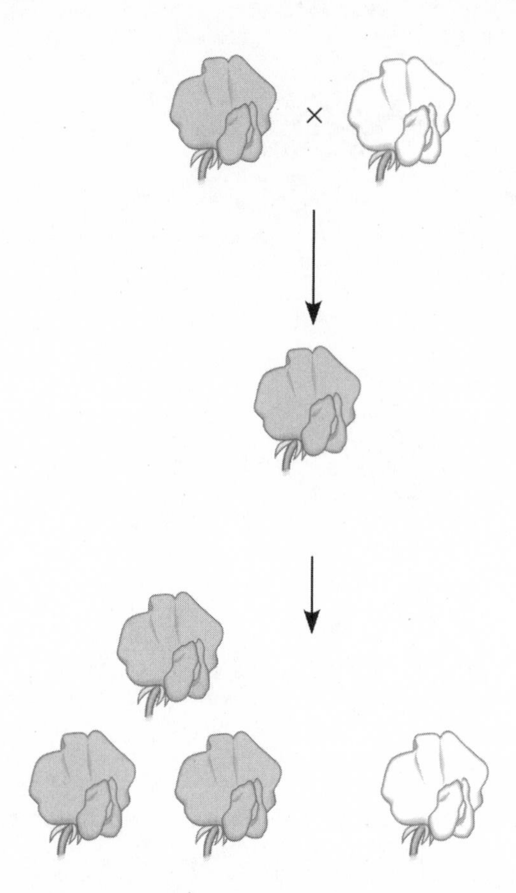

Figure 14.2 Mendel tracked heritable characters for three generations, page 249

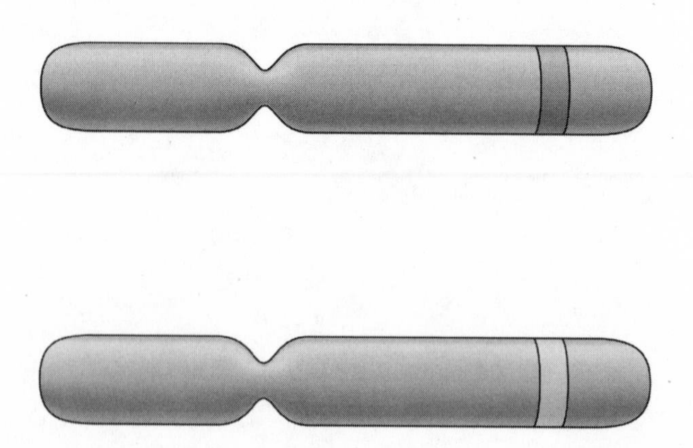

Figure 14.3 Alleles, alternative versions of a gene, page 249

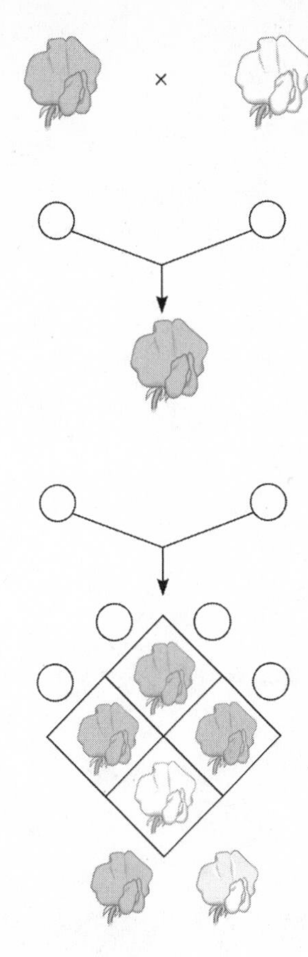

Figure 14.4 Mendel's law of segregation, page 251

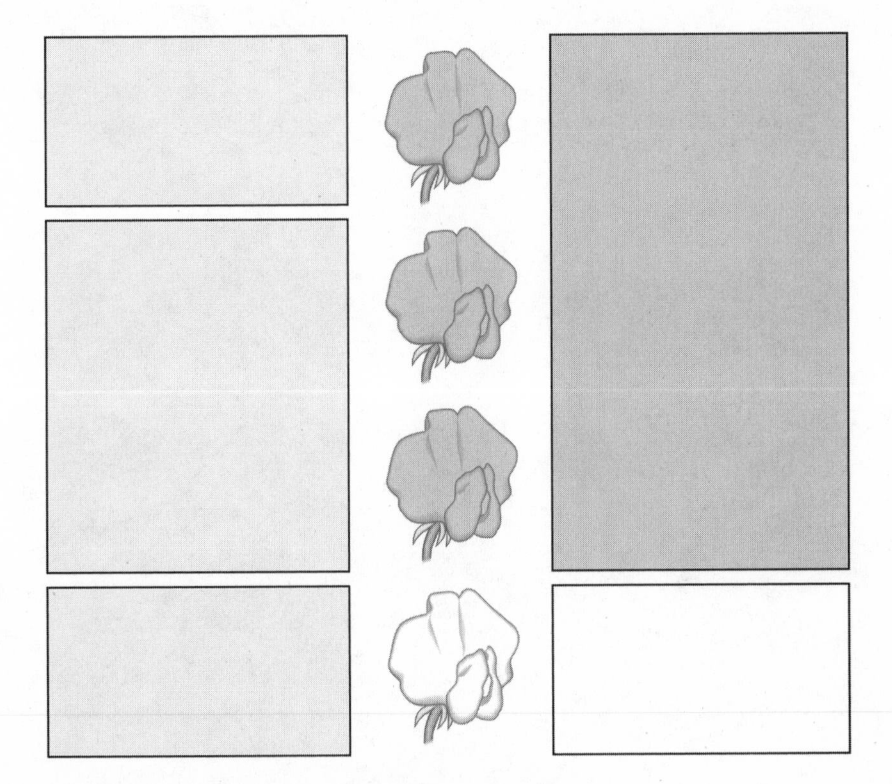

Figure 14.5 Genotype versus phenotype, page 252

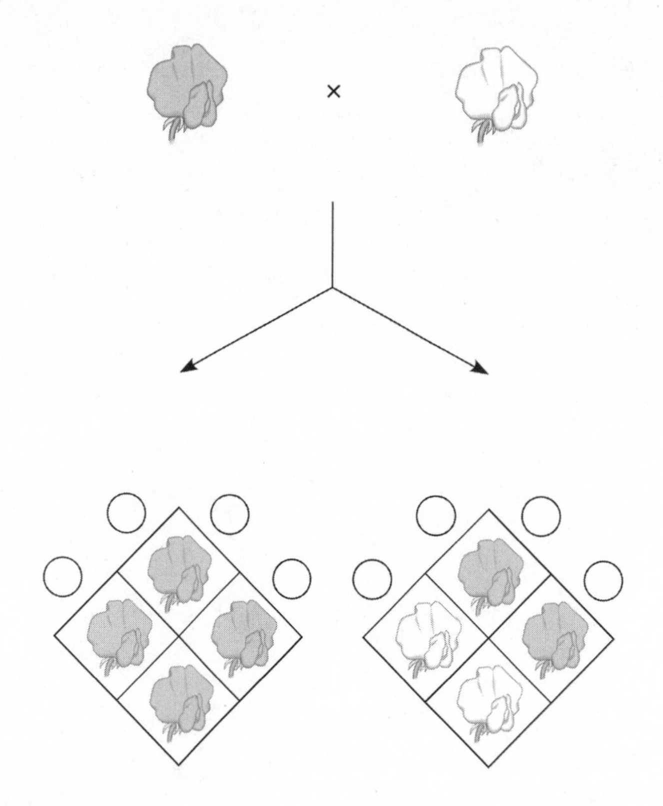

Figure 14.6 A testcross, page 252

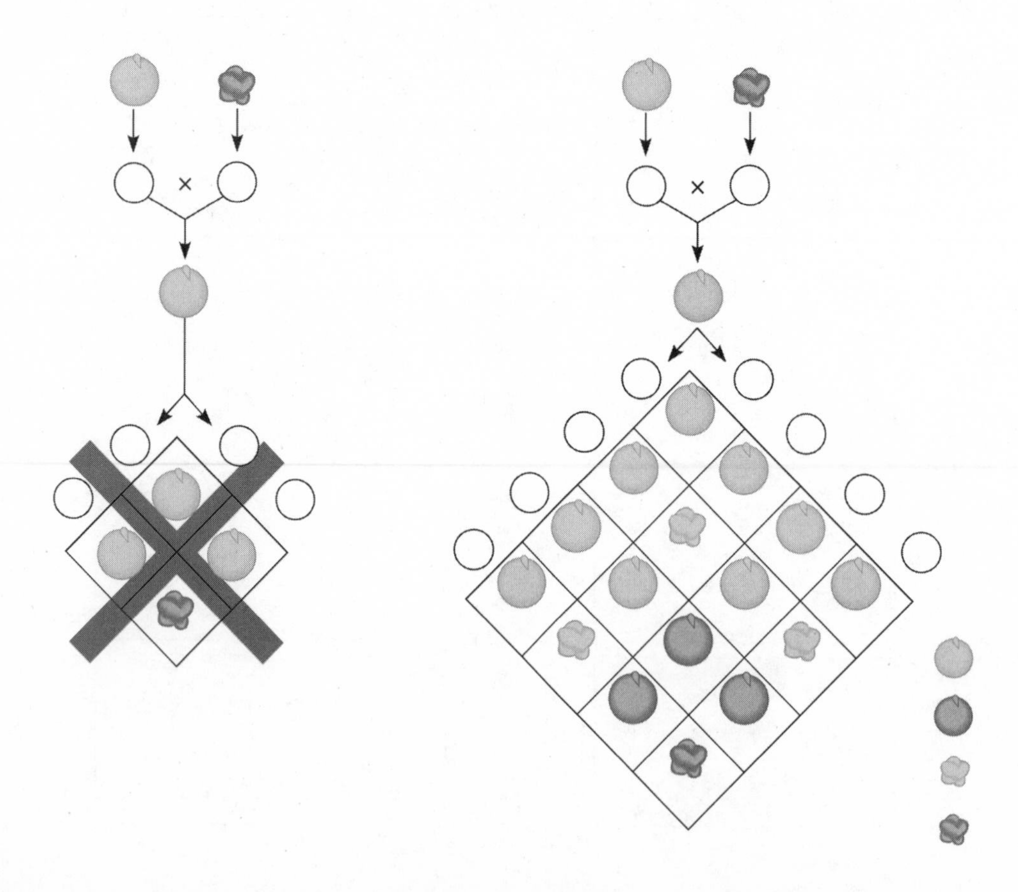

Figure 14.7 Testing two hypotheses for segregation in a dihybrid cross, page 253

Figure 14.8 Segregation of alleles and fertilization as chance events, page 254

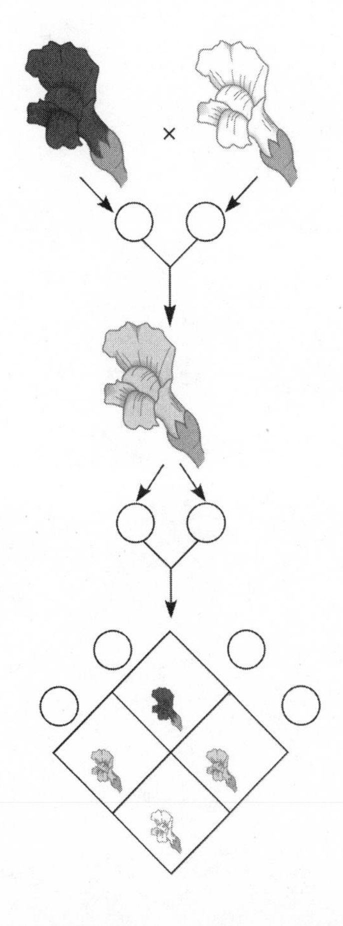

Figure 14.9 Incomplete dominance in snapdragon color, page 256

(a) Phenotype (blood group)	(b) Genotypes (see p.258)	(c) Antibodies present in blood serum	(d) Results from adding red blood cells from groups below to serum from groups at left			
			A	B	AB	O
A	$I^A I^A$ or $I^A i$	Anti-B				
B	$I^B I^B$ or $I^B i$	Anti-A				
AB	$I^A I^B$	—				
O	ii	Anti-A Anti-B				

Figure 14.10 Multiple alleles for the ABO blood groups, page 257

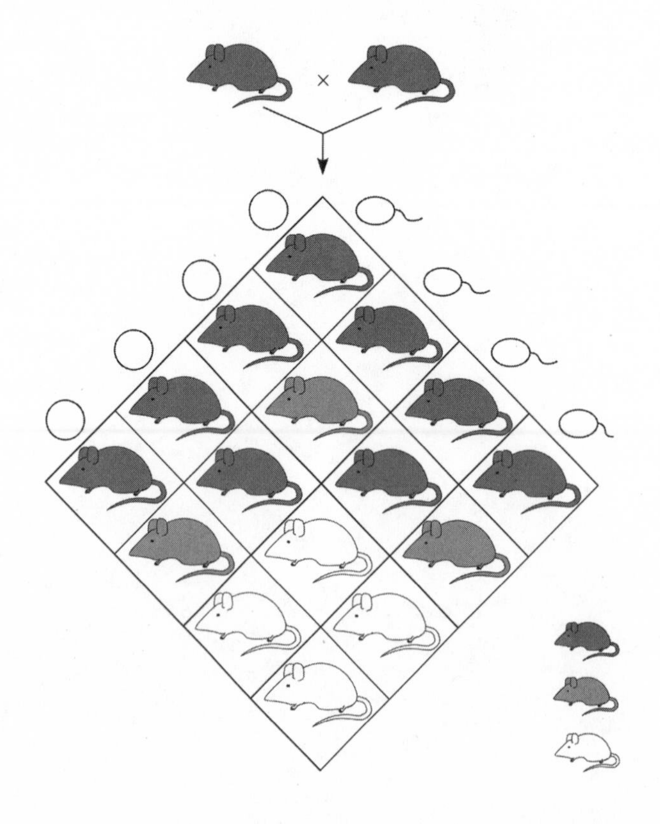

Figure 14.11 An example of epistasis, page 258

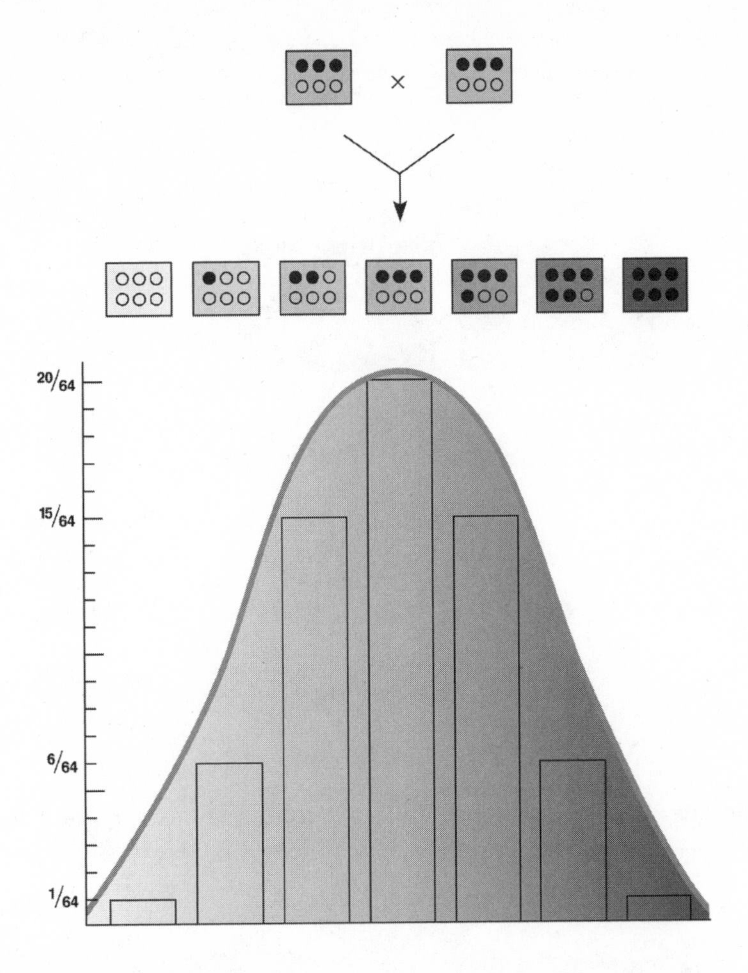

Figure 14.12 A simplified model for polygenic inheritance of skin color, page 259

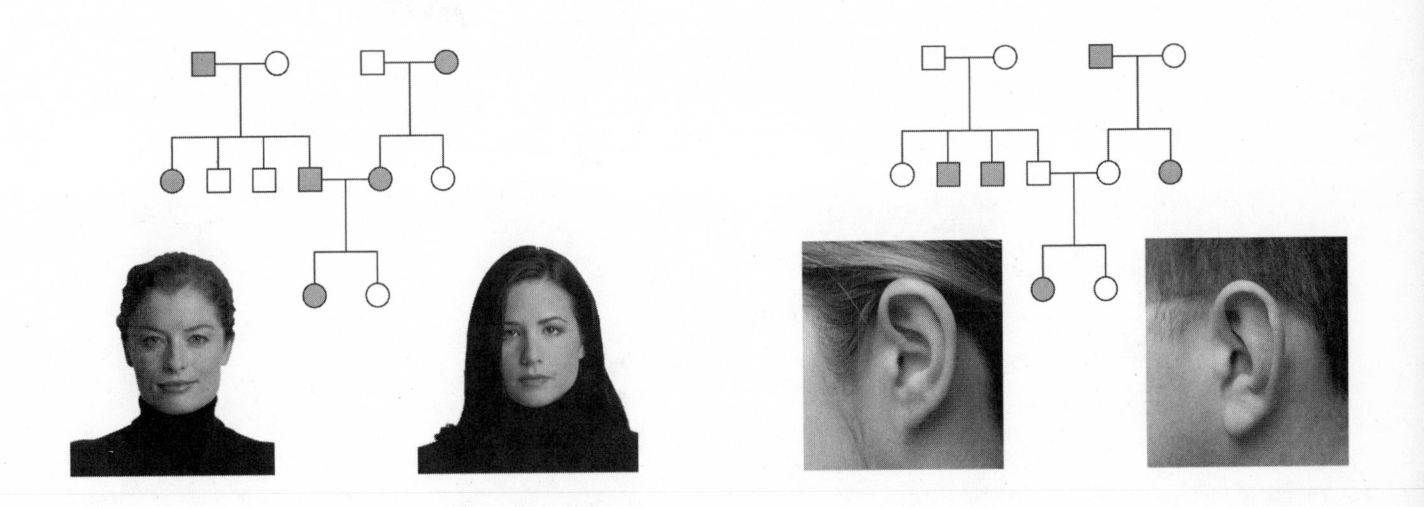

Figure 14.14 Pedigree analysis, page 261

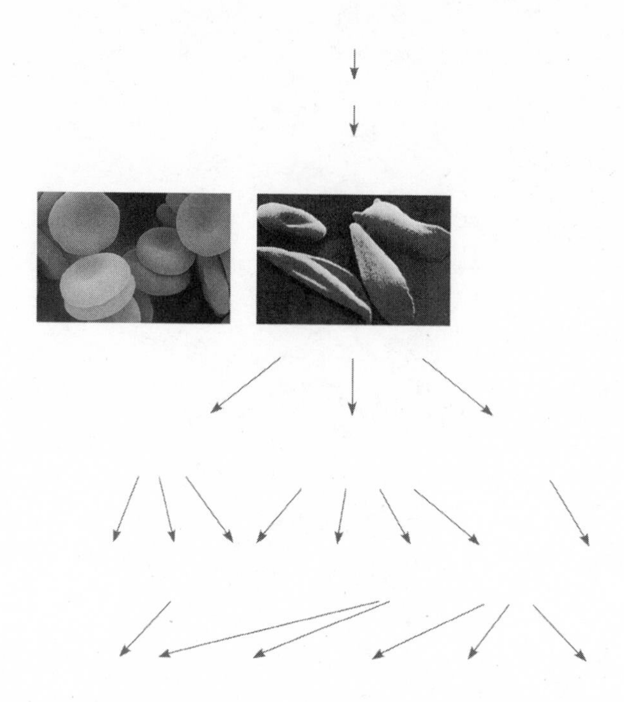

Figure 14.15 Pleiotropic effects of the sickle-cell allele in a homozygote, page 262

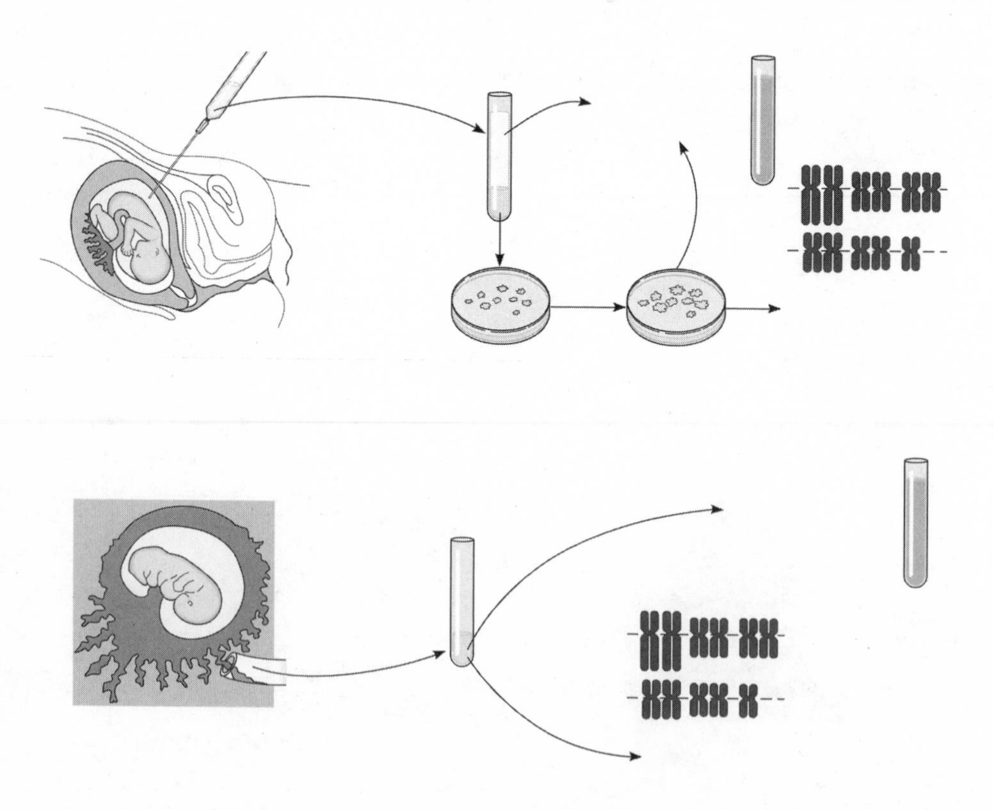

Figure 14.17 Testing a fetus for genetic disorders, page 265

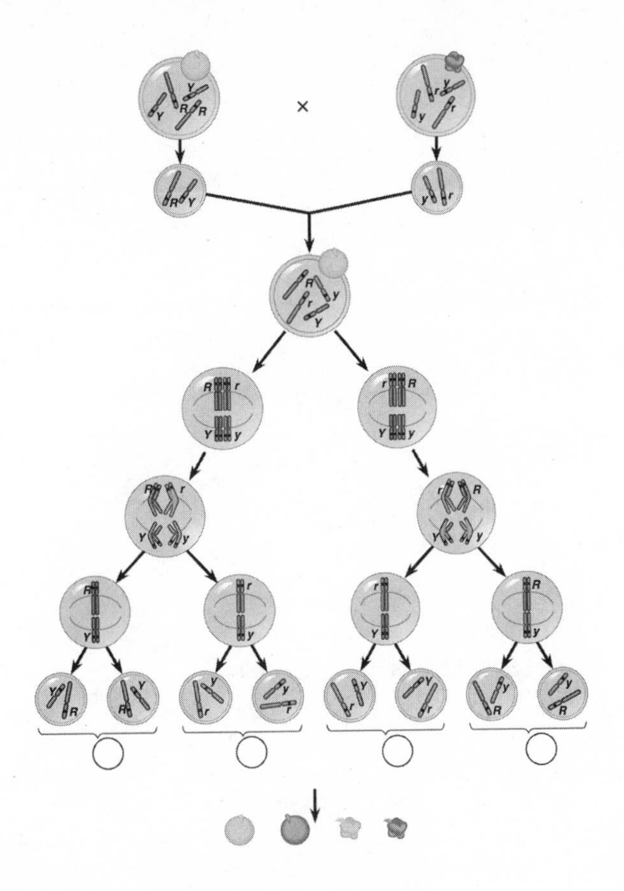

Figure 15.1 The chomosomal basis of Mendel's laws, page 270

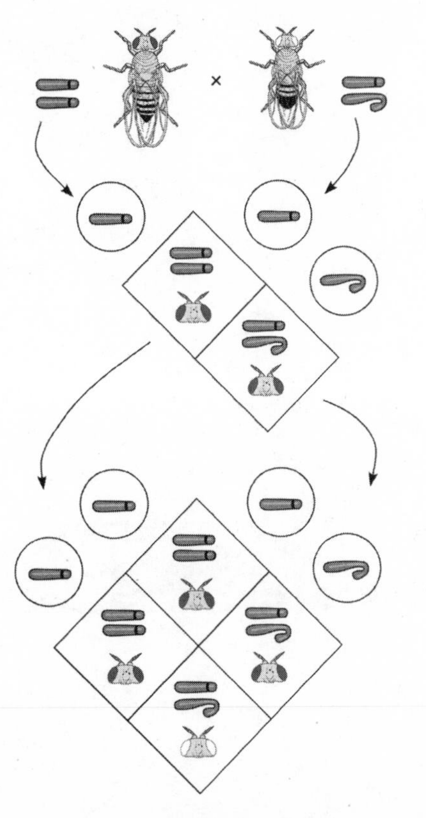

Figure 15.3 Sex-linked inheritance, page 272

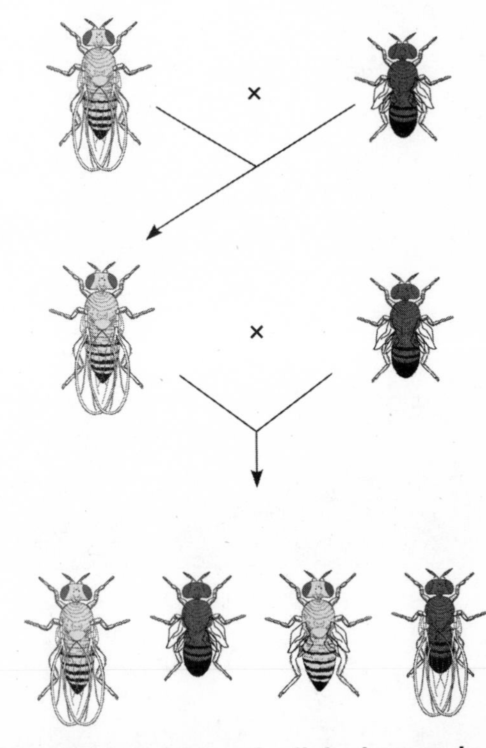

Figure 15.4 Evidence for linked genes in *Drosophila*, page 273

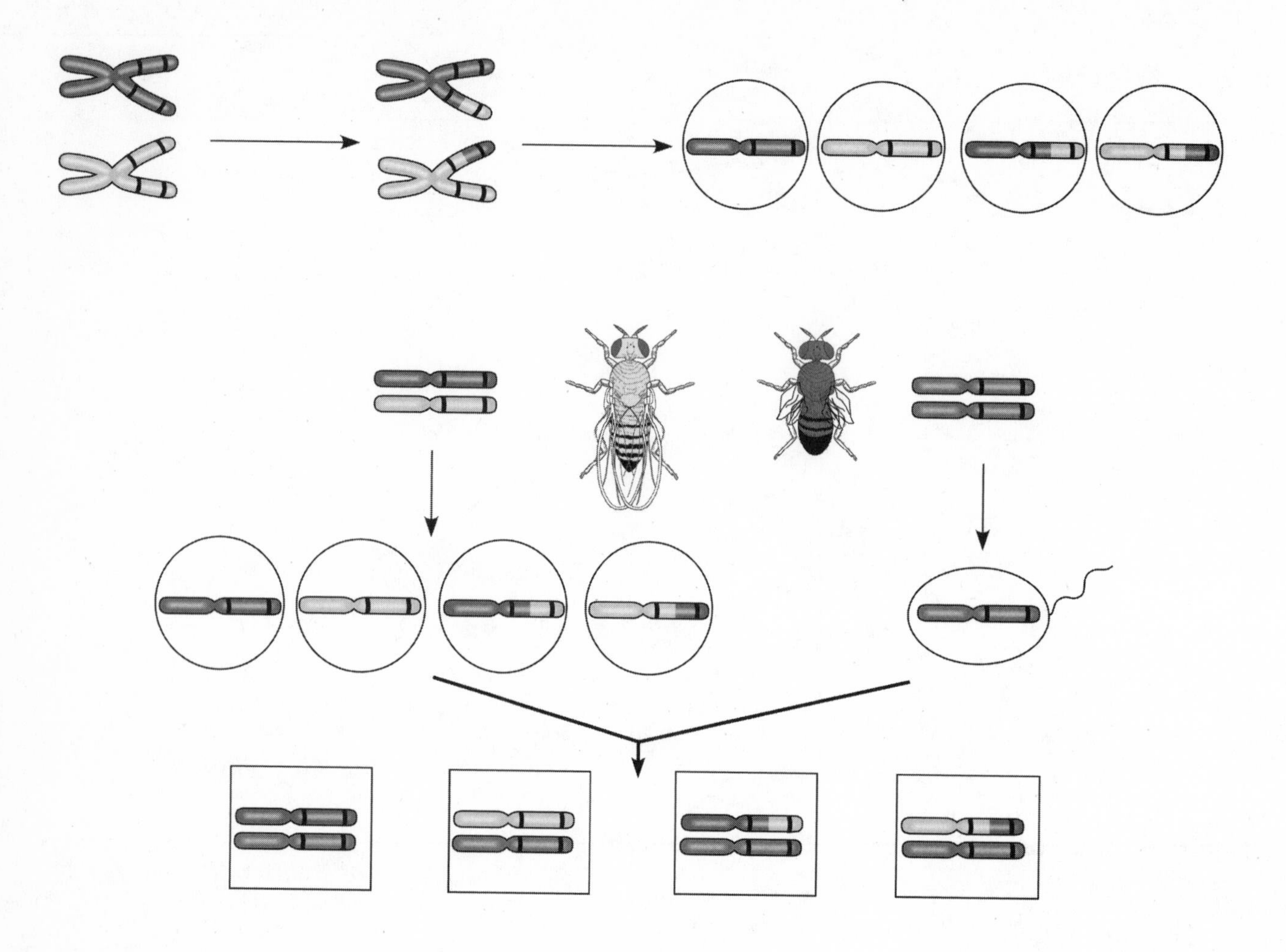

Figure 15.5 Recombination due to crossing over, page 274

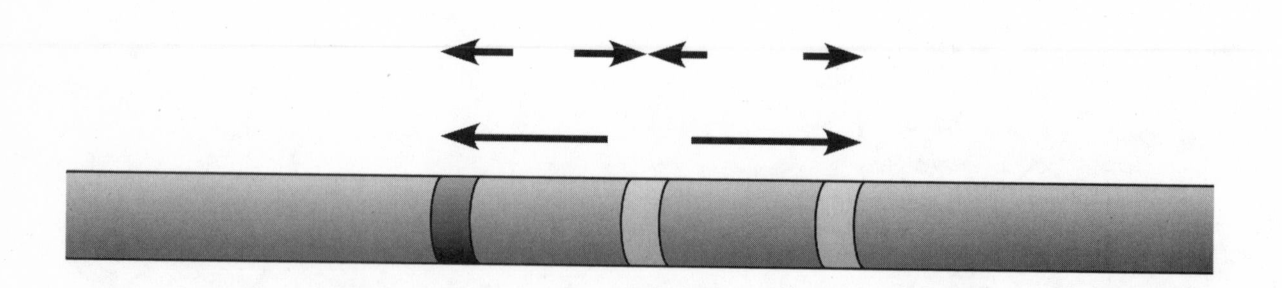

Figure 15.6 Using recombination frequencies to construct a genetic map, page 275

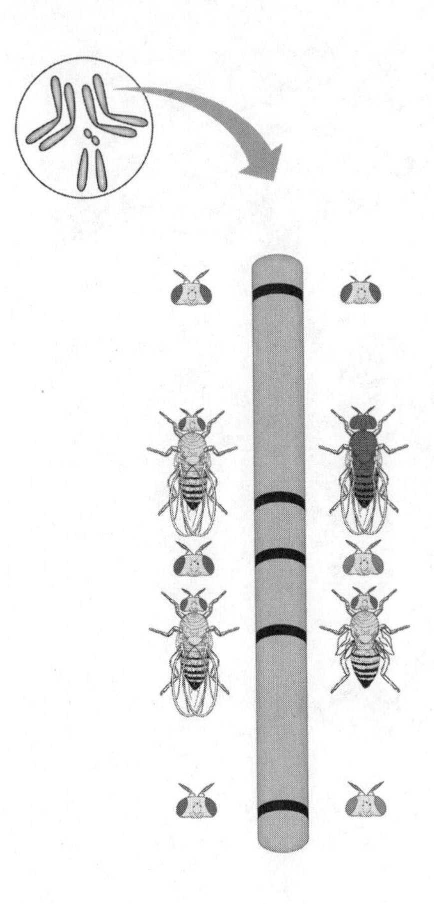

Figure 15.7 A partial genetic map of a *Drosophila* chromosome, page 276

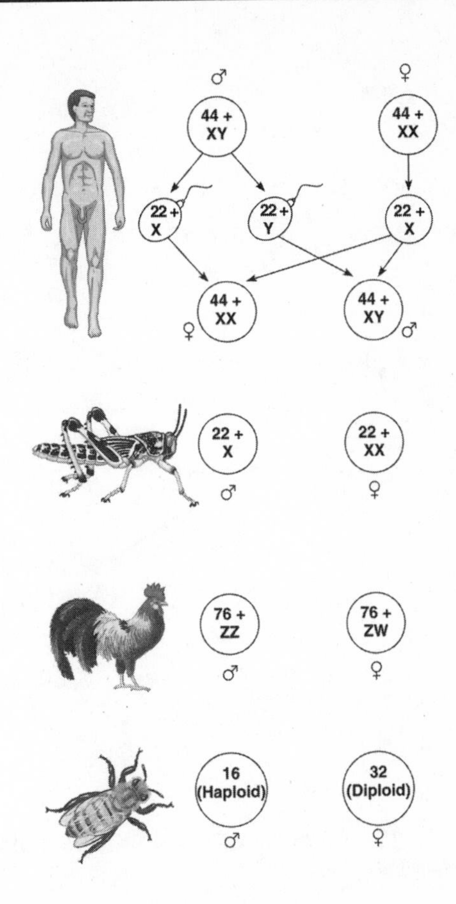

Figure 15.8 Some chromosomal systems of sex determination, page 276

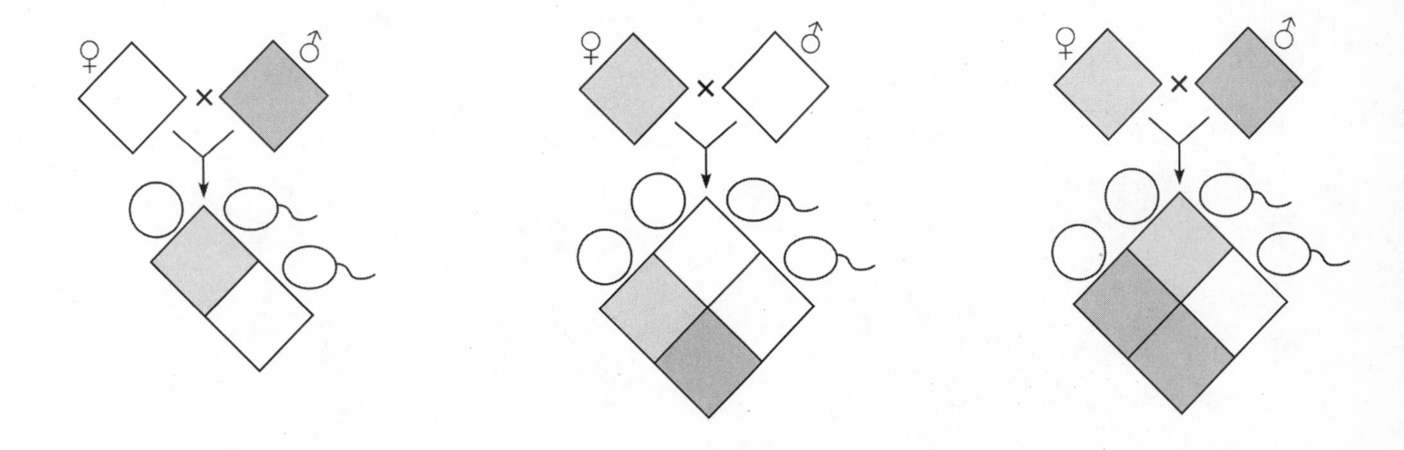

Figure 15.9 The transmission of sex-linked recessive traits, page 277

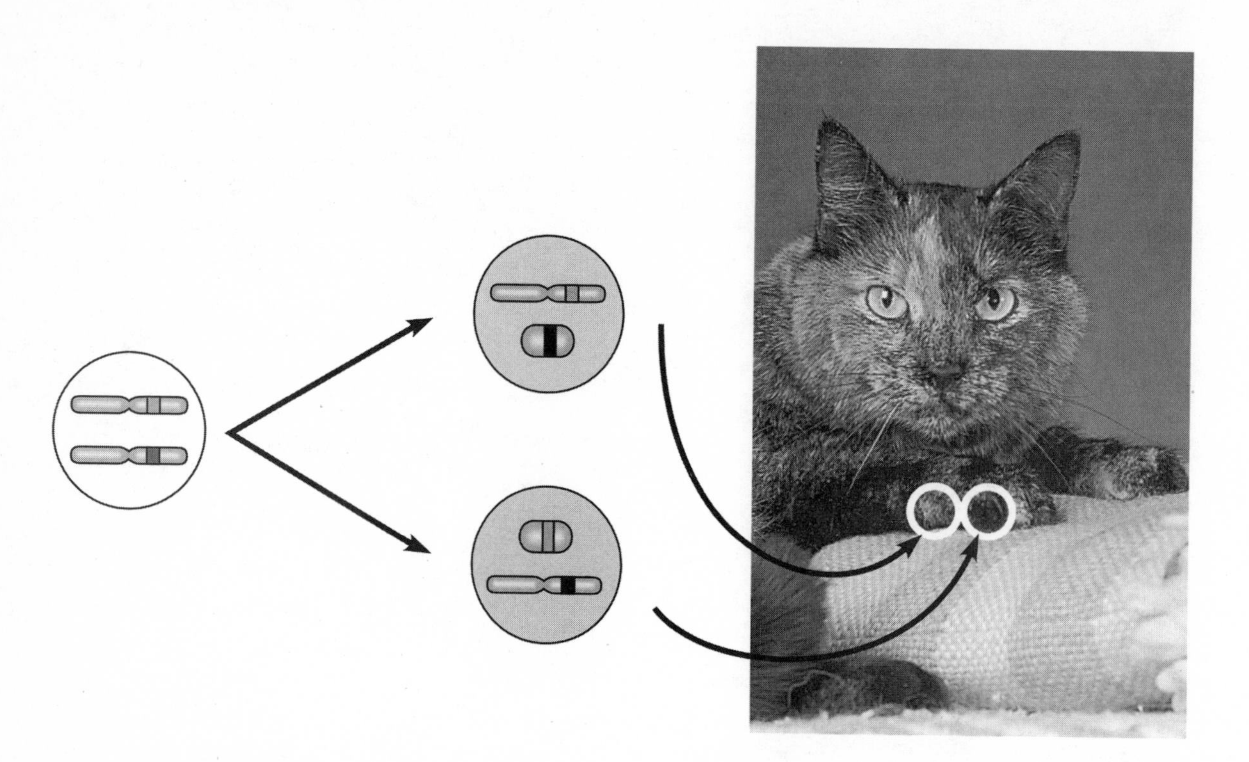

Figure 15.10 X inactivation and the tortoiseshell cat, page 278

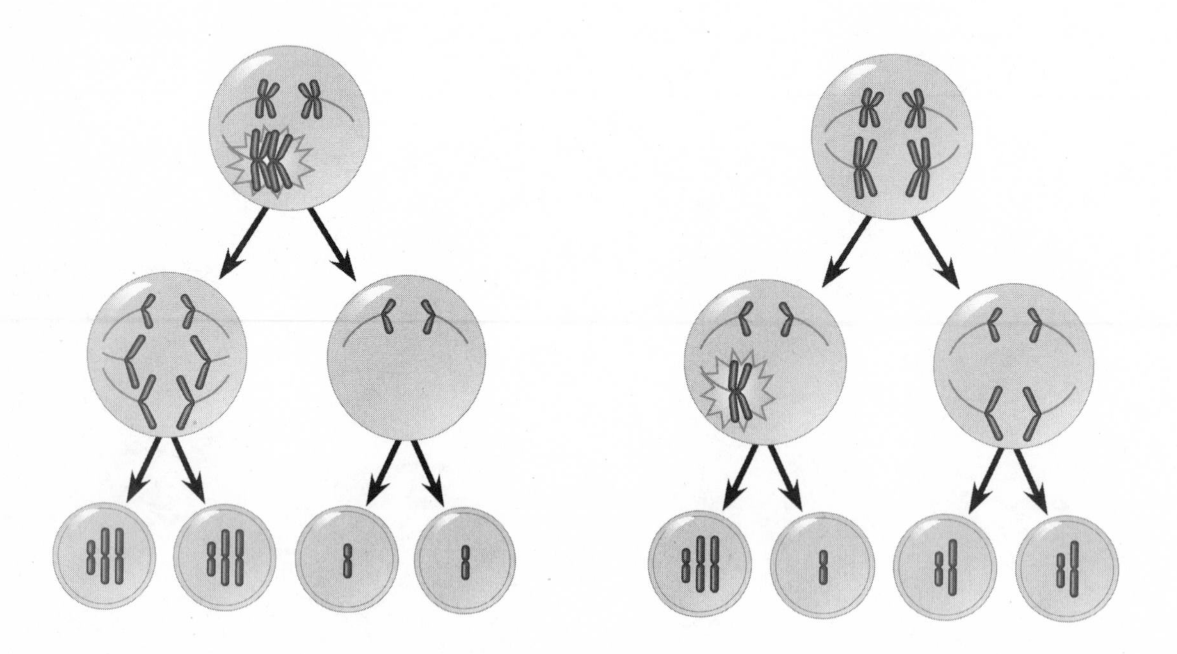

Figure 15.11 Meiotic nondisjunction, page 279

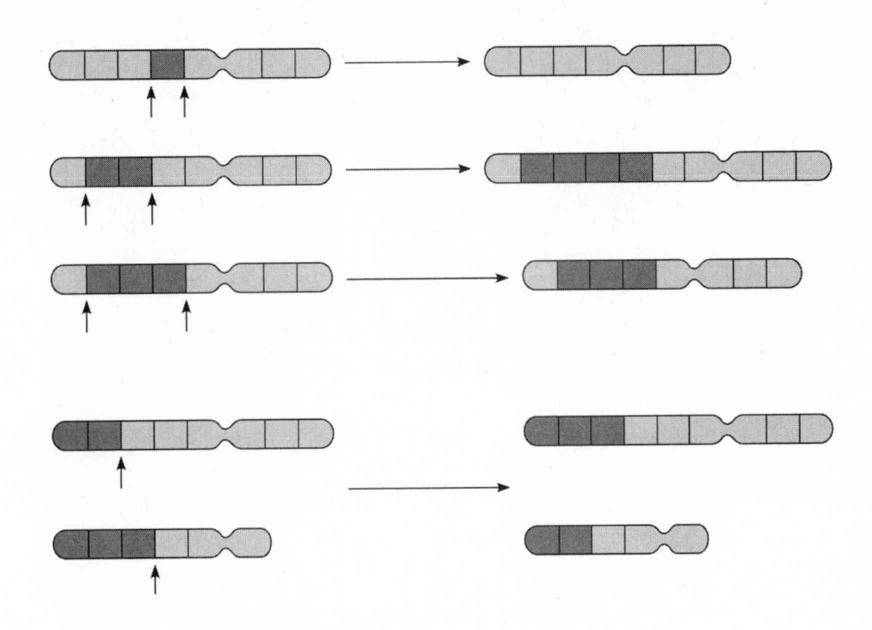

Figure 15.13 Alterations of chromosome structure, page 281

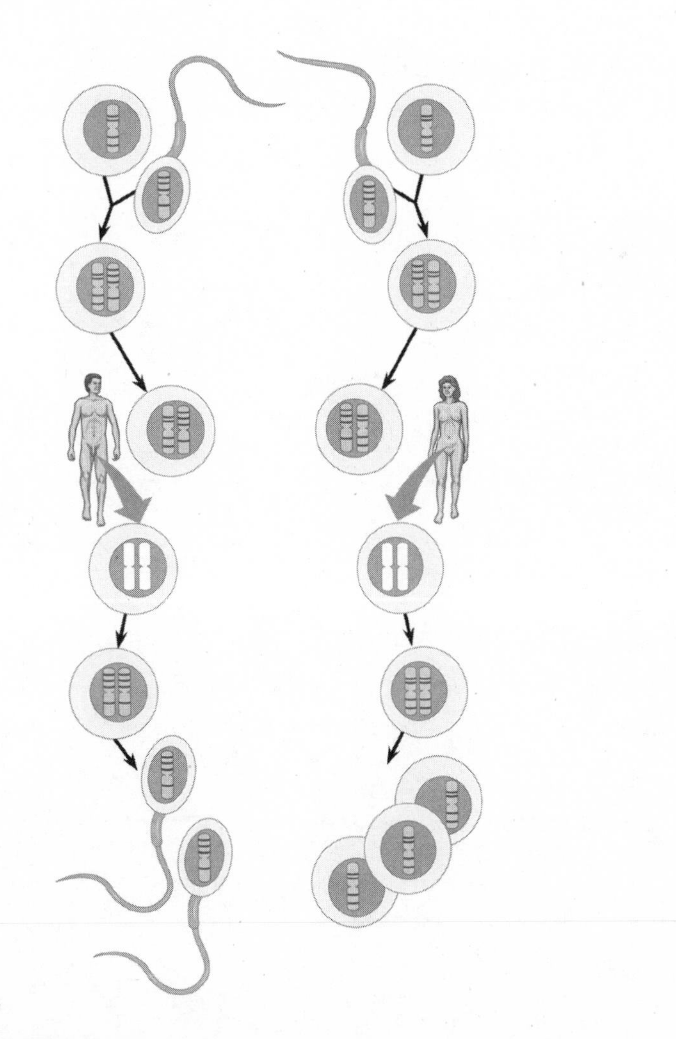

Figure 15.15 Genomic imprinting, page 283

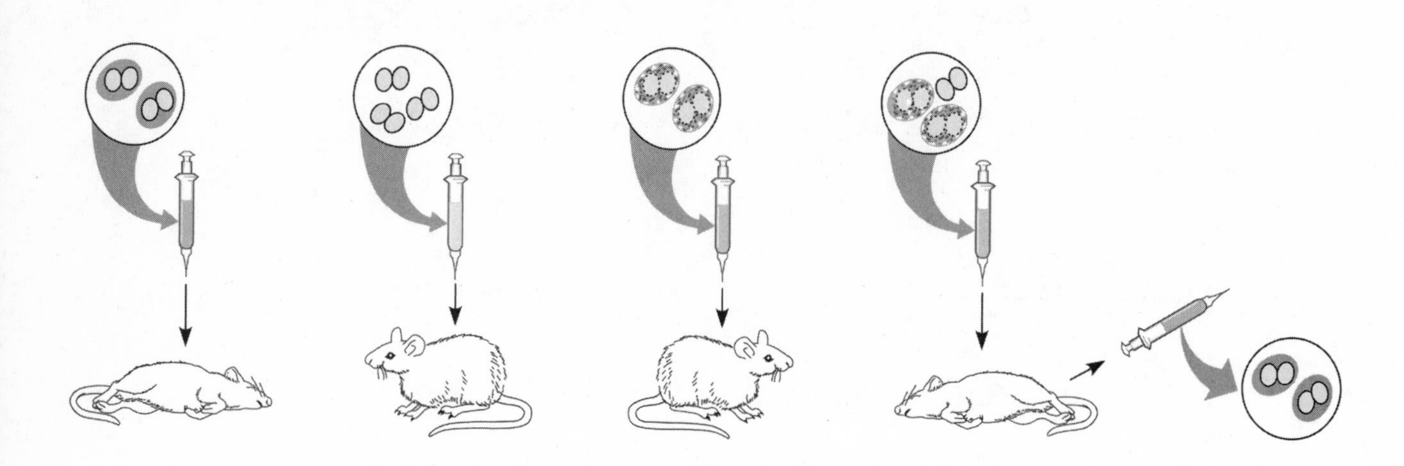

Figure 16.1 Transformation of bacteria, page 288

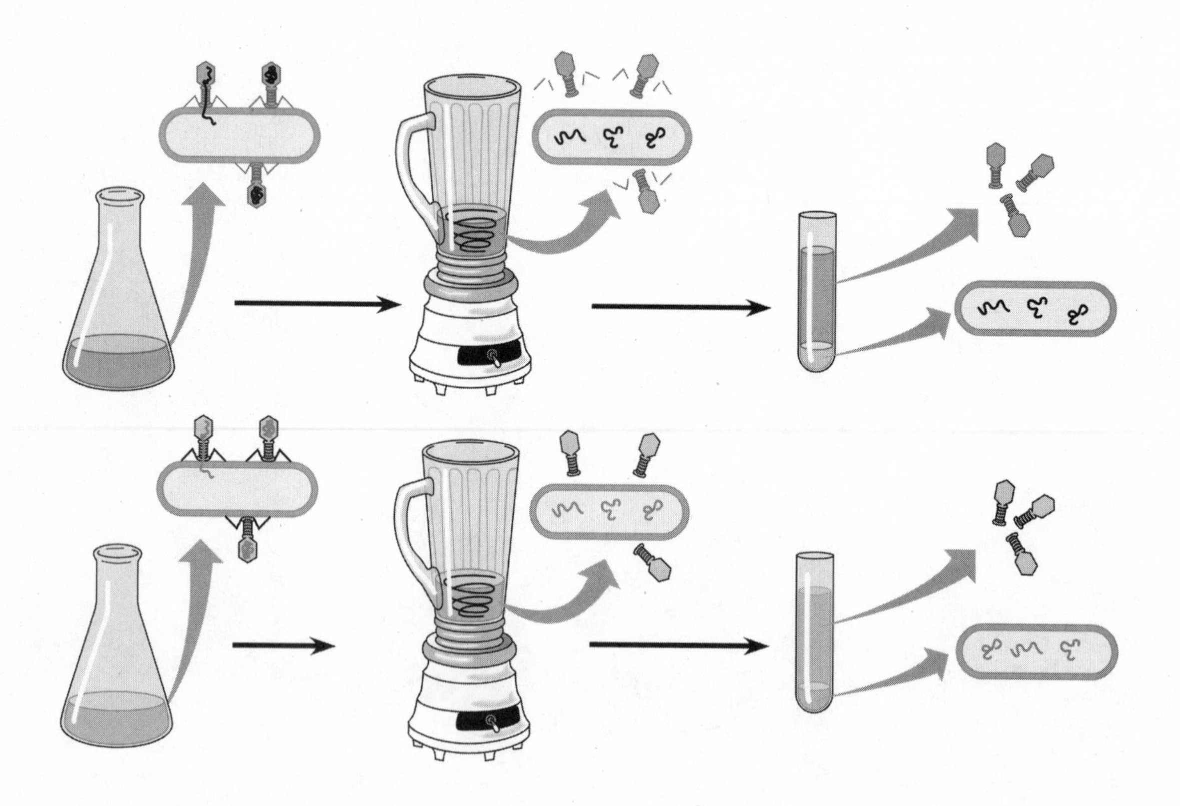

Figure 16.2 The Hershey-Chase experiment, page 289

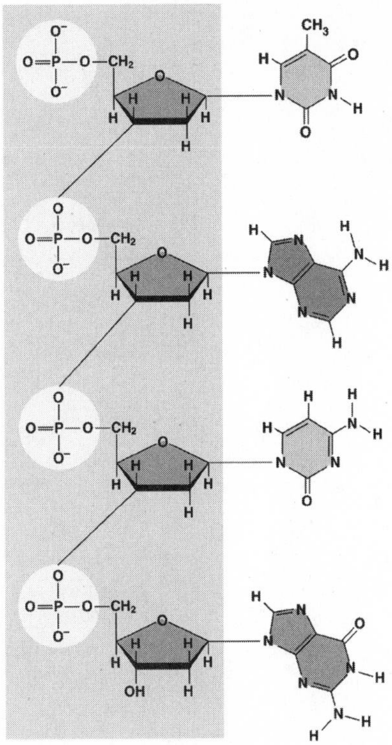

Figure 16.3 The structure of a DNA strand, page 290

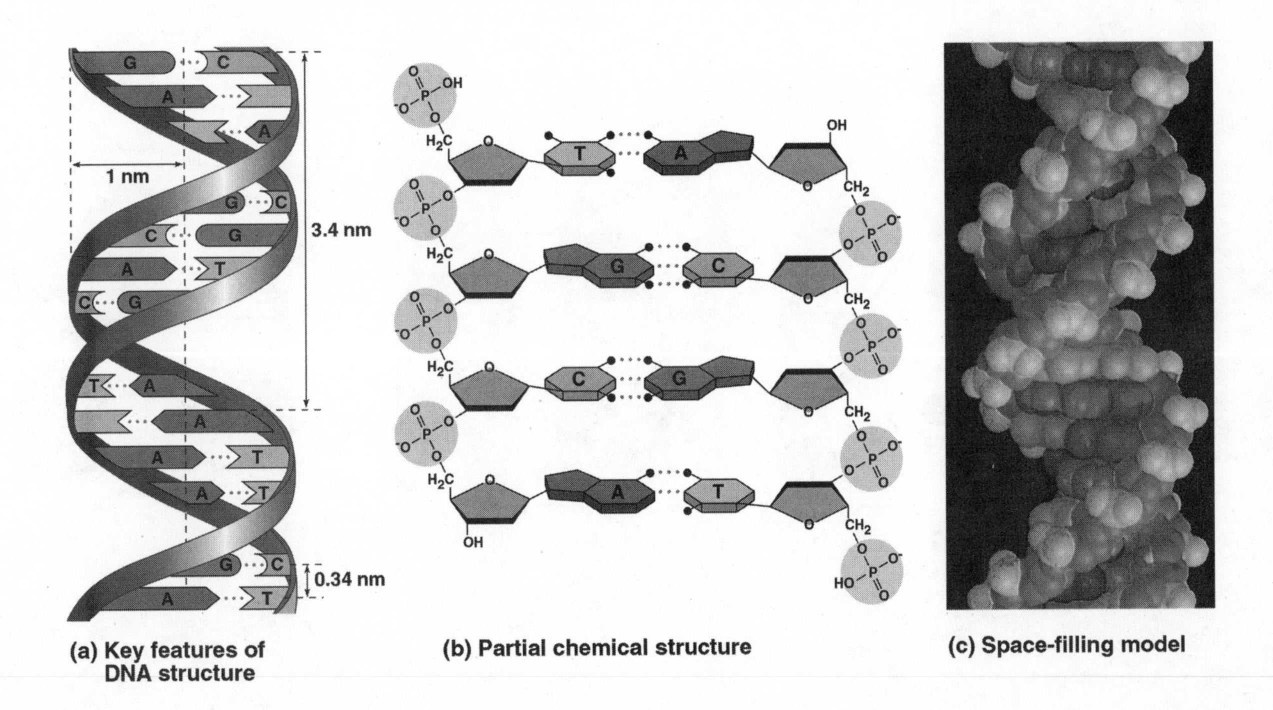

Figure 16.5 The double helix, page 291

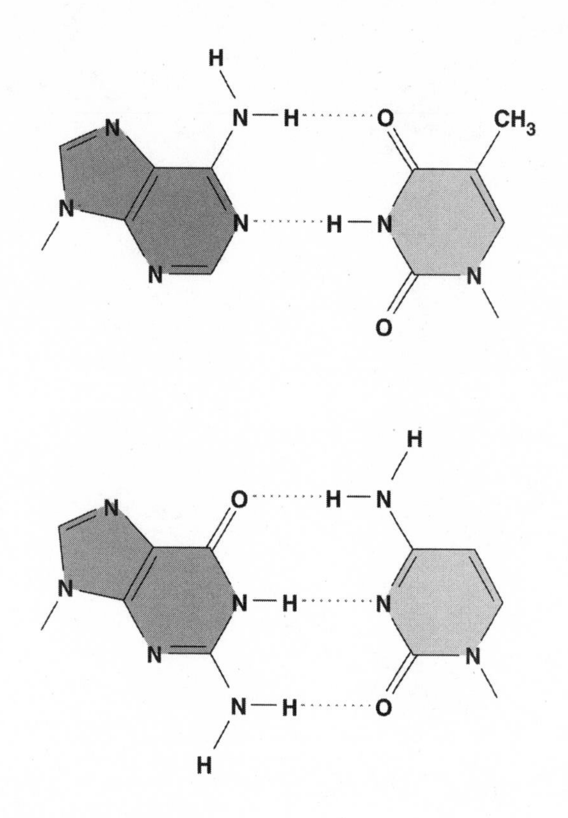

Figure 16.6 Base pairing in DNA, page 292

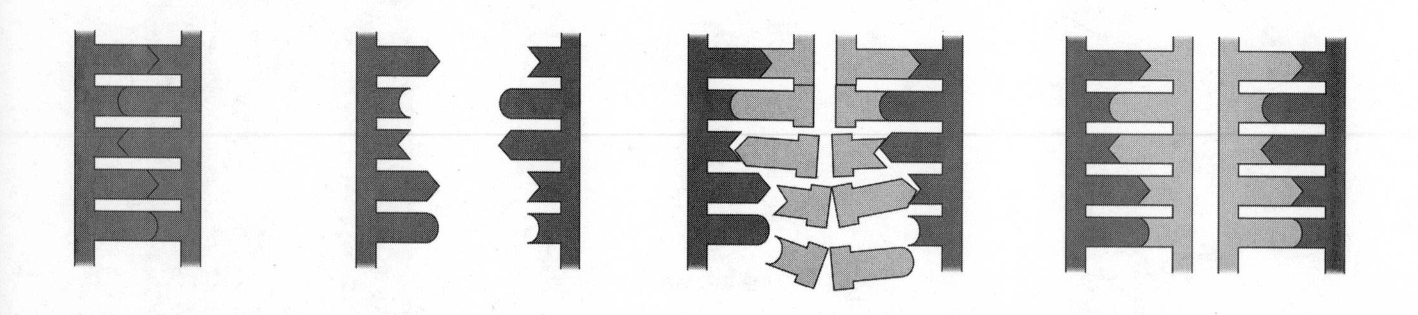

Figure 16.7 A model for DNA replication: the basic concept, page 293

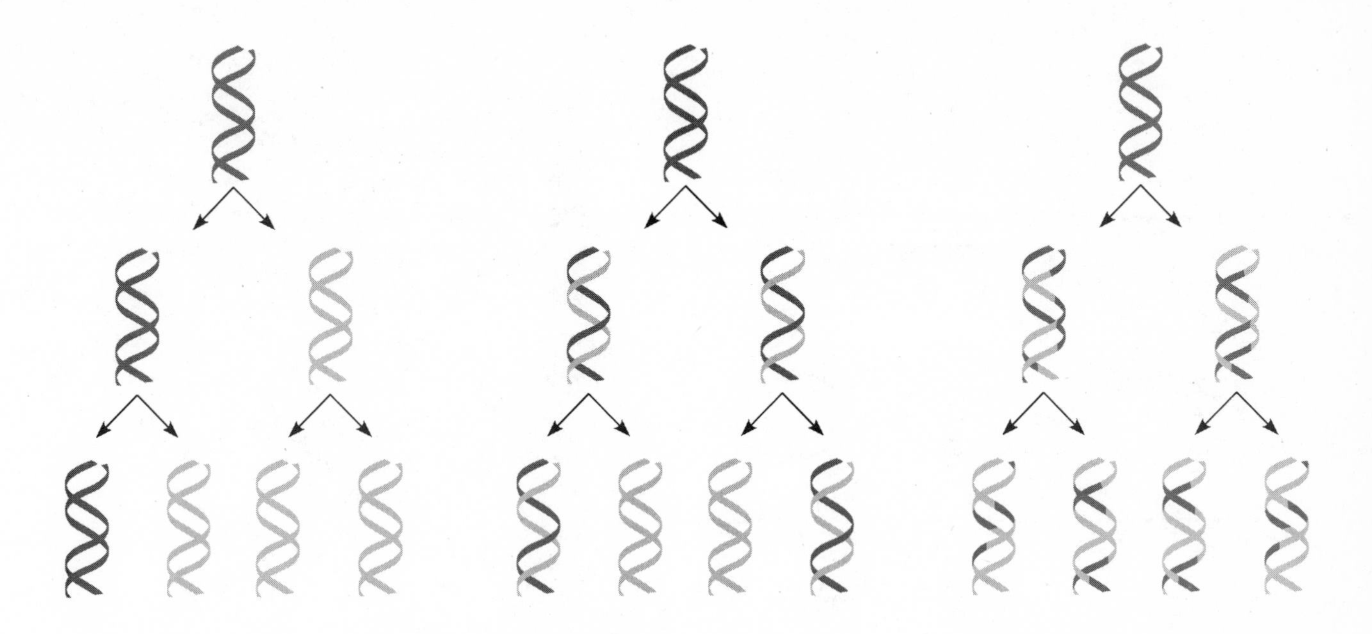

Figure 16.8 Three alternative models of DNA replication, page 294

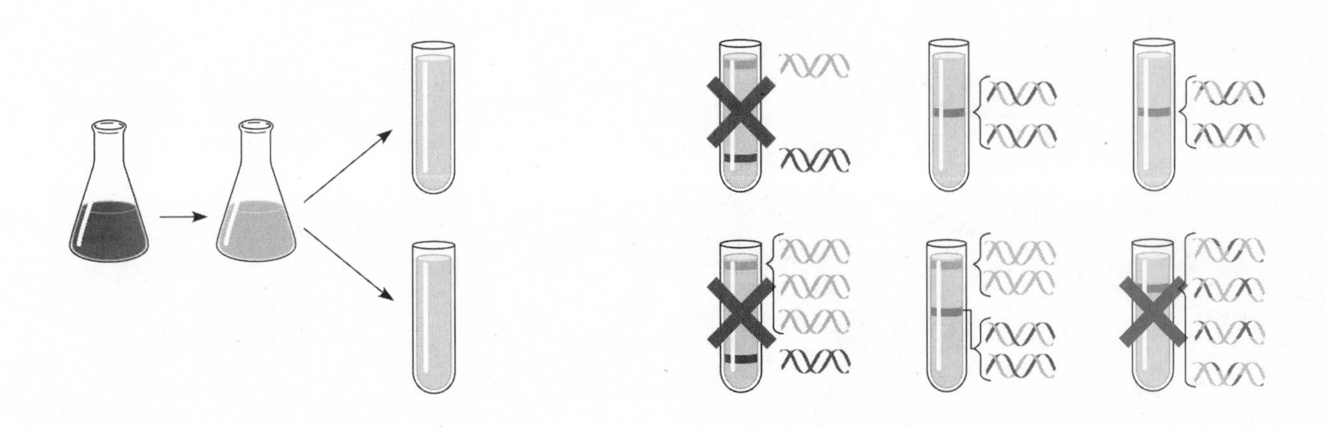

Figure 16.9 The Meselson-Stahl experiment tested three models of DNA replication, page 294

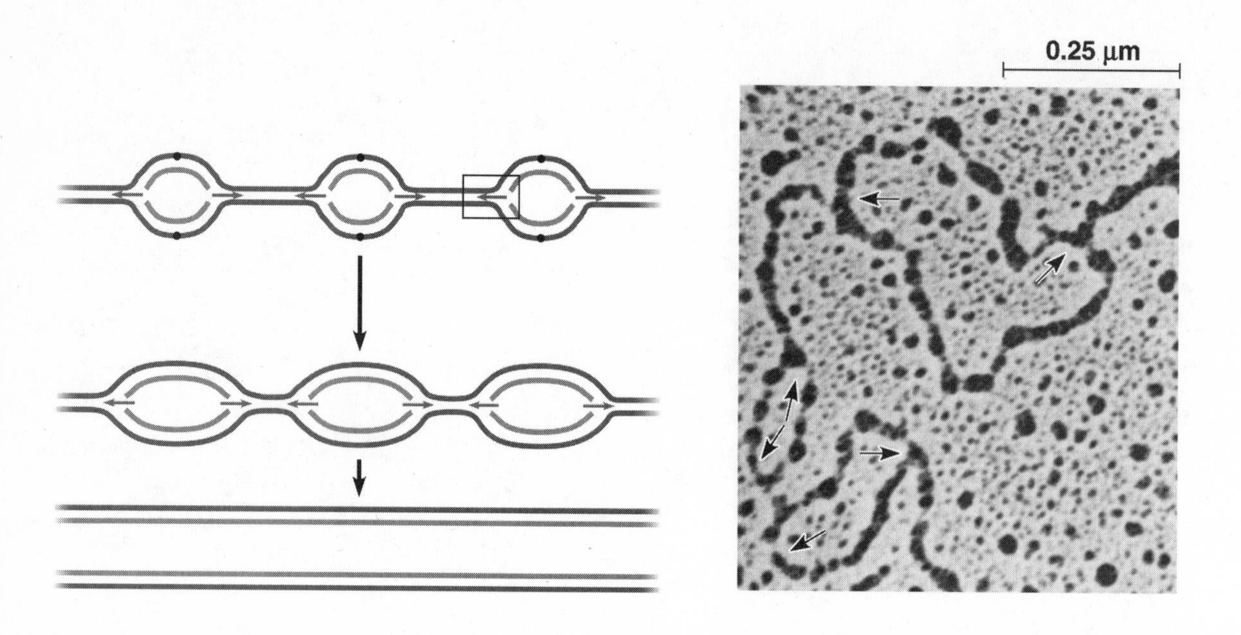

Figure 16.10 Origins of replication in eukaryotes, page 295

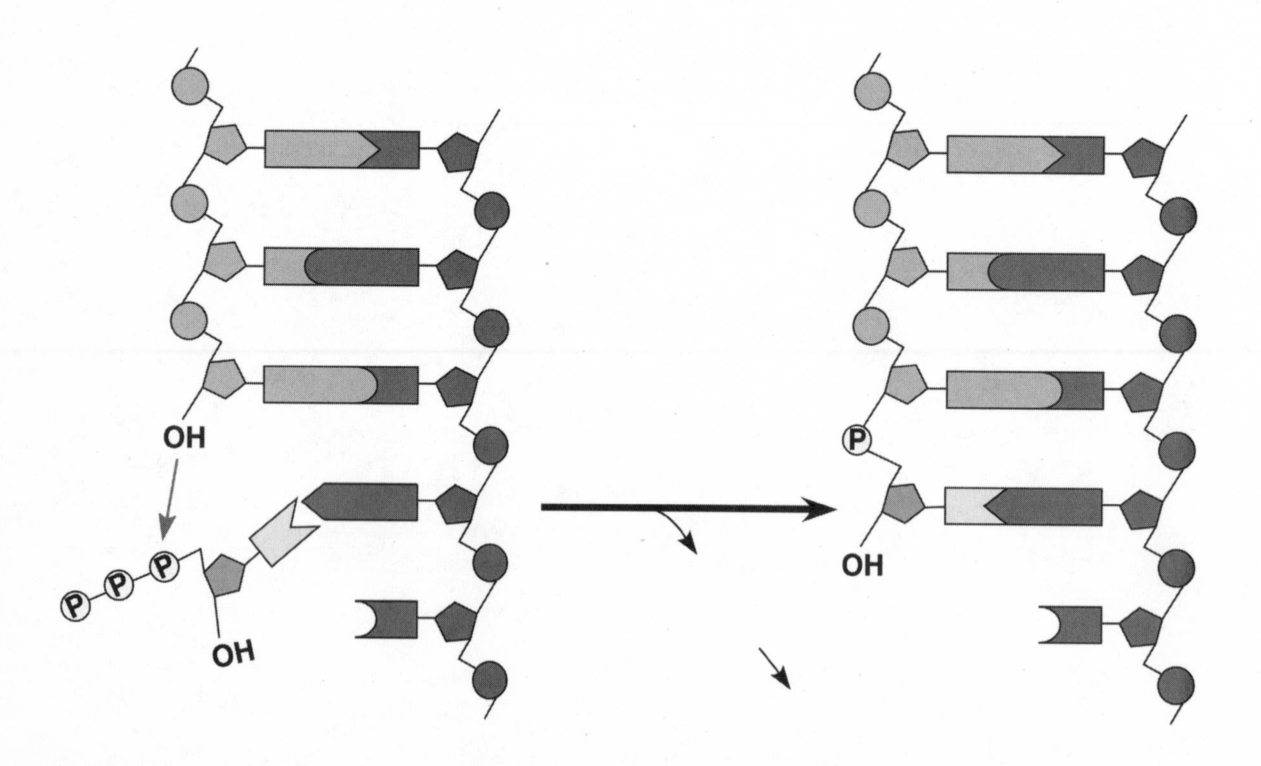

Figure 16.11 Incorporation of a nucleotide into a DNA strand, page 296

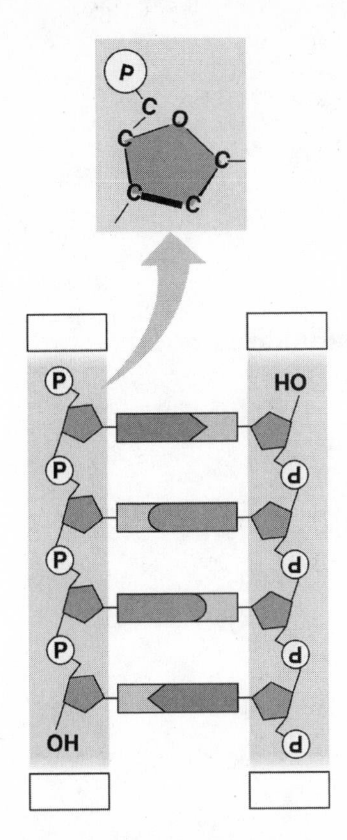

Figure 16.12 The two strands of DNA are antiparallel, page 296

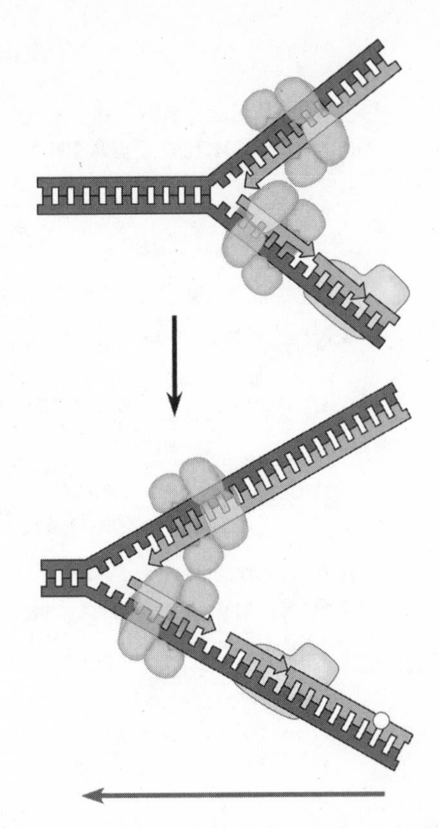

Figure 16.13 Synthesis of leading and lagging strands during DNA replication, page 297

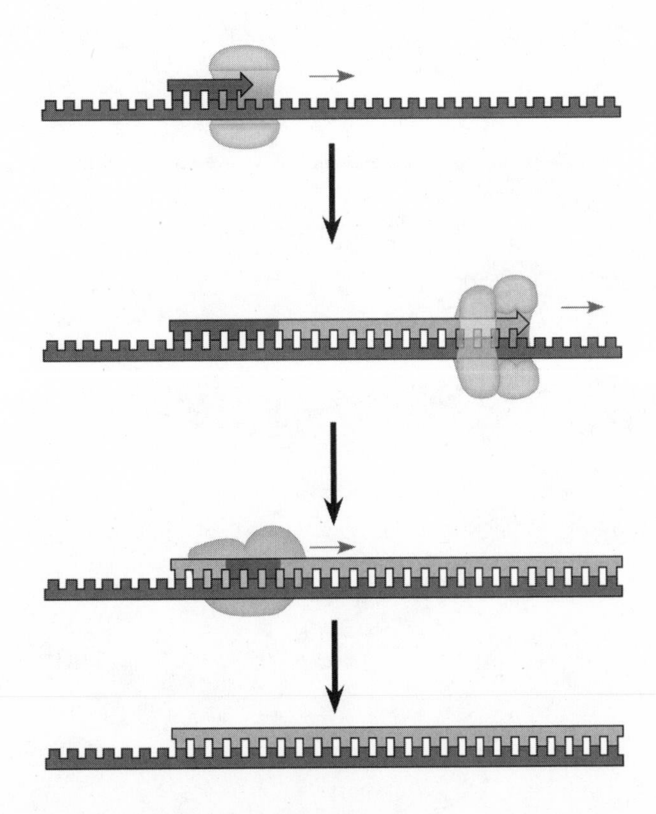

Figure 16.14 Priming DNA synthesis with RNA, page 297

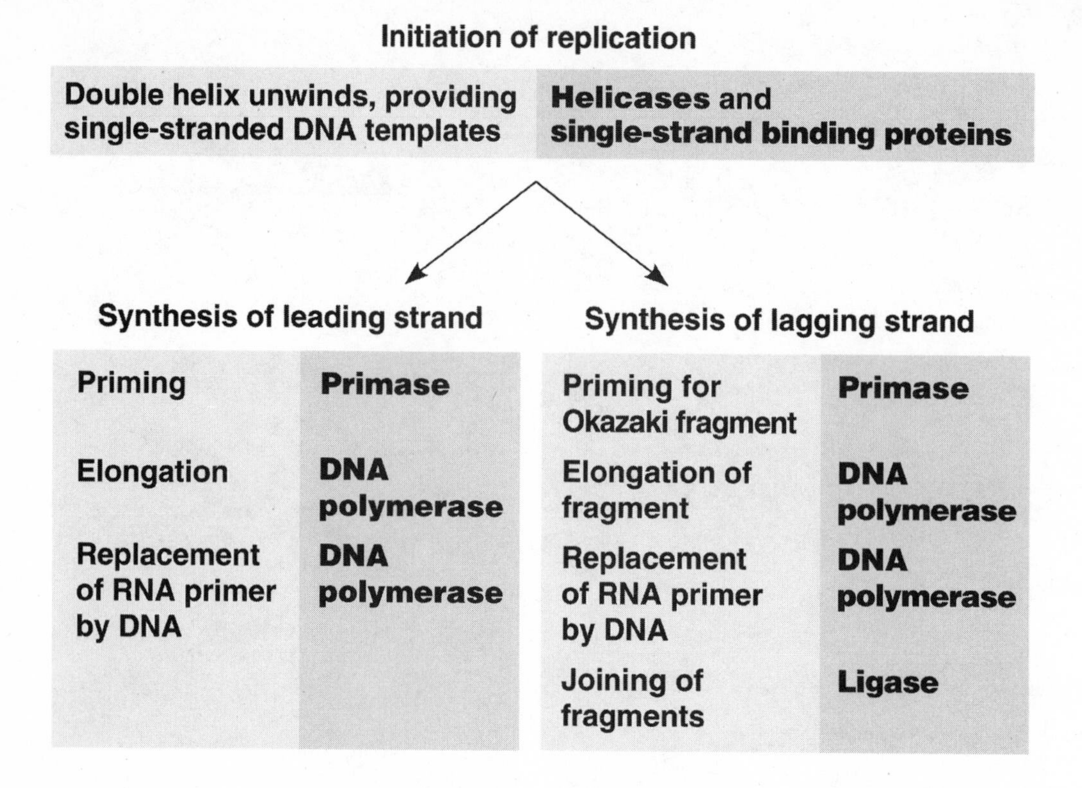

Figure 16.15 The main proteins of DNA replication and their functions, page 298

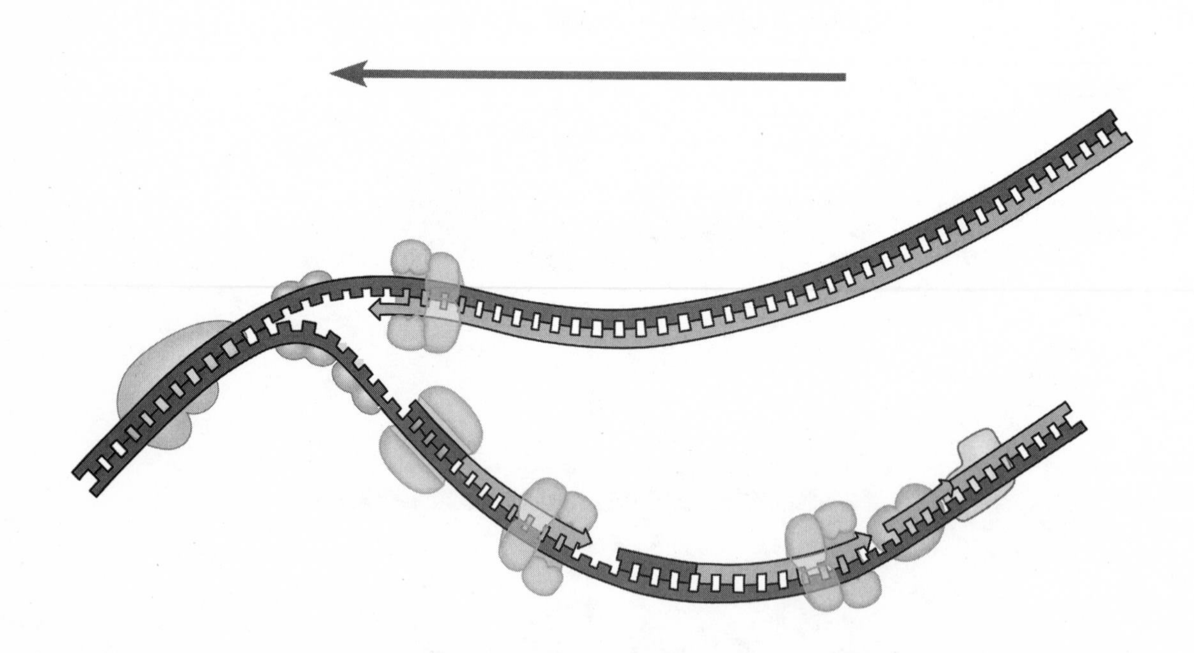

Figure 16.16 A summary of DNA replication, page 298

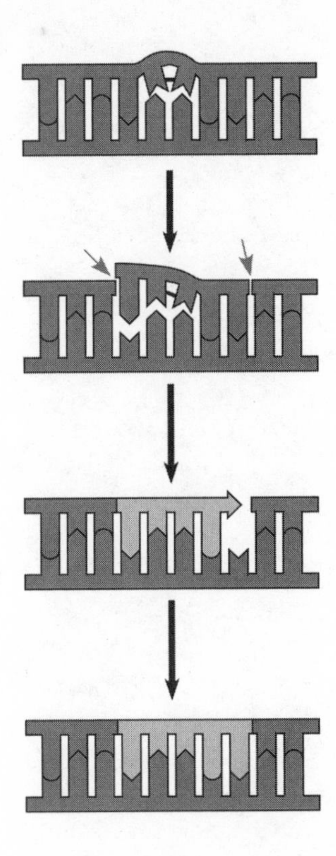

Figure 16.17 Nucleotide excision repair of DNA damage, page 299

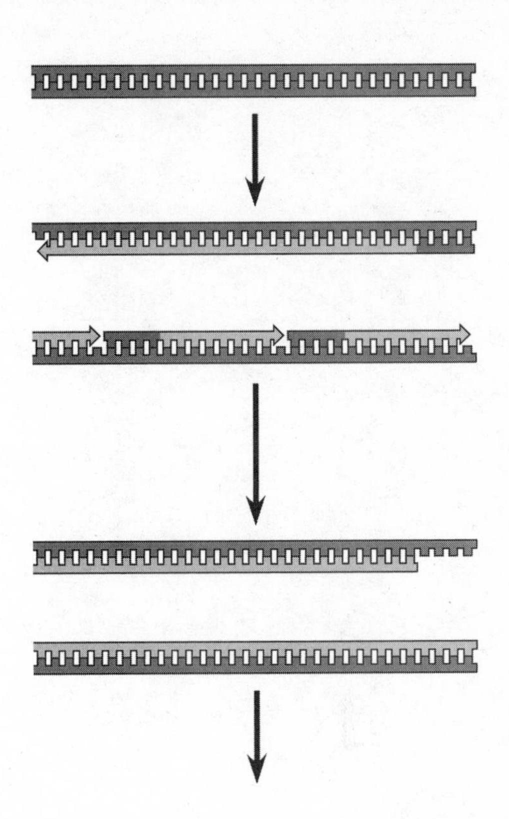

Figure 16.18 The end-replication problem, page 300

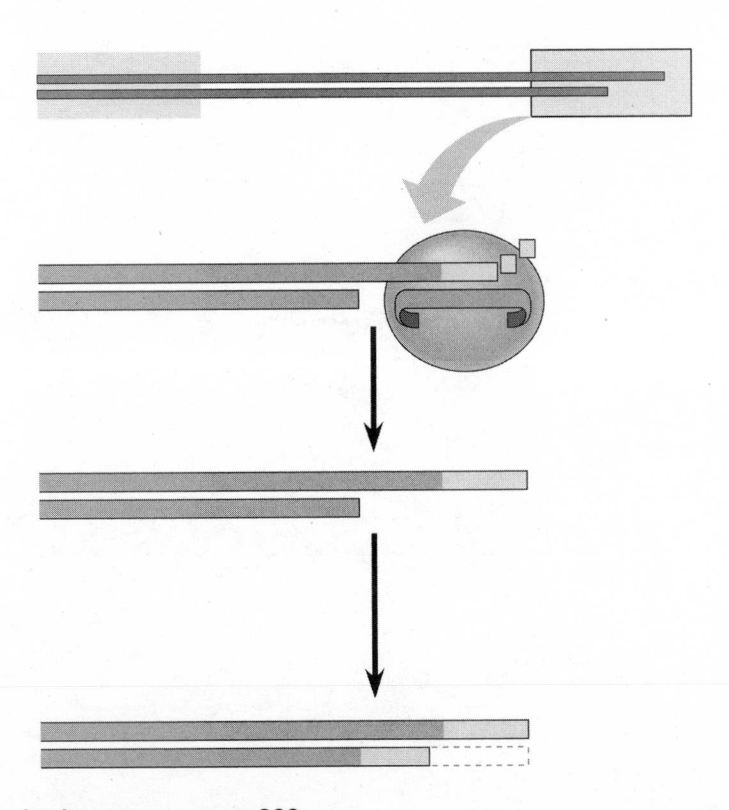

Figure 16.19 Telomeres and telomerase, page 300

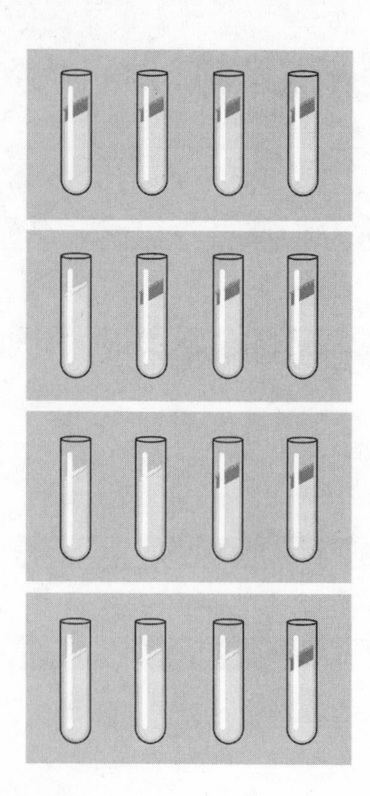

Figure 17.1 Beadle and Tatum's evidence for the one gene–one enzyme hypothesis, page 305

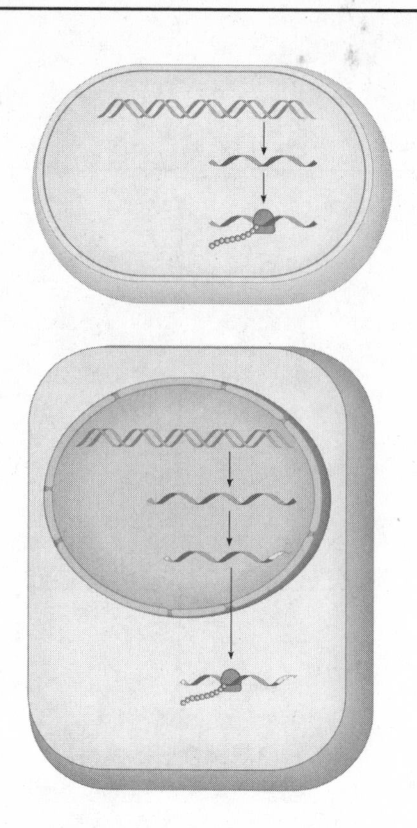

Figure 17.2 Overview: the roles of transcription and translation in the flow of genetic information, page 306

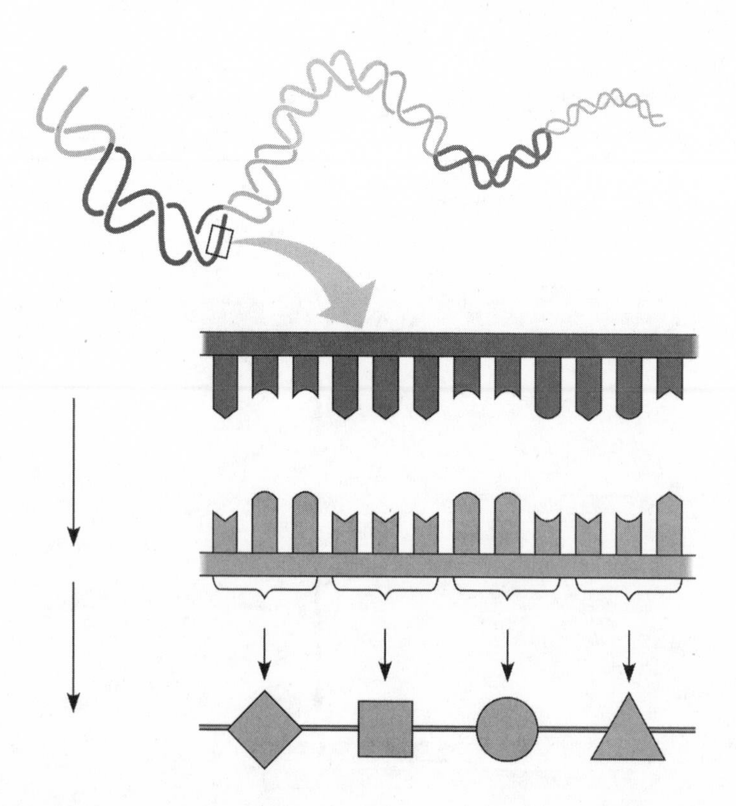

Figure 17.3 The triplet code, page 307

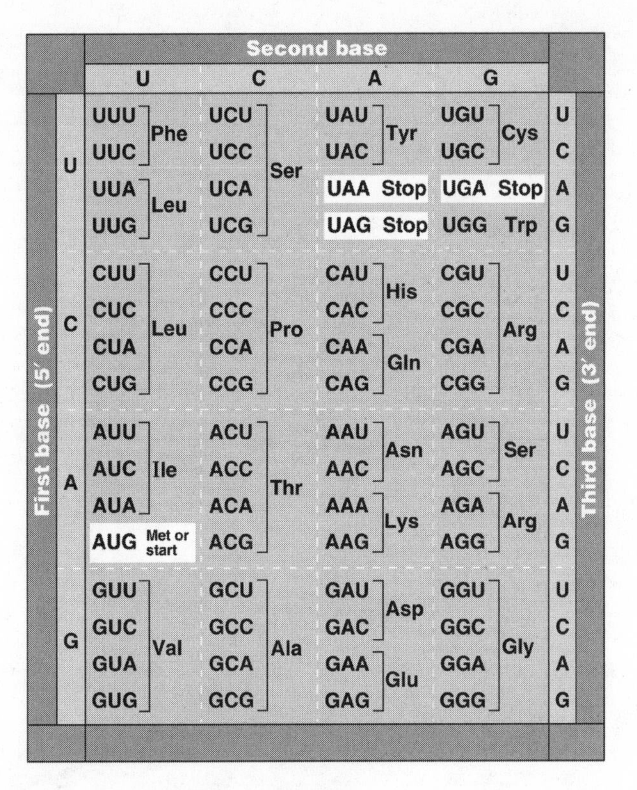

First base (5′ end)	Second base: U	Second base: C	Second base: A	Second base: G	Third base (3′ end)
U	UUU Phe	UCU Ser	UAU Tyr	UGU Cys	U
U	UUC Phe	UCC Ser	UAC Tyr	UGC Cys	C
U	UUA Leu	UCA Ser	UAA Stop	UGA Stop	A
U	UUG Leu	UCG Ser	UAG Stop	UGG Trp	G
C	CUU Leu	CCU Pro	CAU His	CGU Arg	U
C	CUC Leu	CCC Pro	CAC His	CGC Arg	C
C	CUA Leu	CCA Pro	CAA Gln	CGA Arg	A
C	CUG Leu	CCG Pro	CAG Gln	CGG Arg	G
A	AUU Ile	ACU Thr	AAU Asn	AGU Ser	U
A	AUC Ile	ACC Thr	AAC Asn	AGC Ser	C
A	AUA Ile	ACA Thr	AAA Lys	AGA Arg	A
A	AUG Met or start	ACG Thr	AAG Lys	AGG Arg	G
G	GUU Val	GCU Ala	GAU Asp	GGU Gly	U
G	GUC Val	GCC Ala	GAC Asp	GGC Gly	C
G	GUA Val	GCA Ala	GAA Glu	GGA Gly	A
G	GUG Val	GCG Ala	GAG Glu	GGG Gly	G

Figure 17.4 The dictionary of the genetic code, page 308

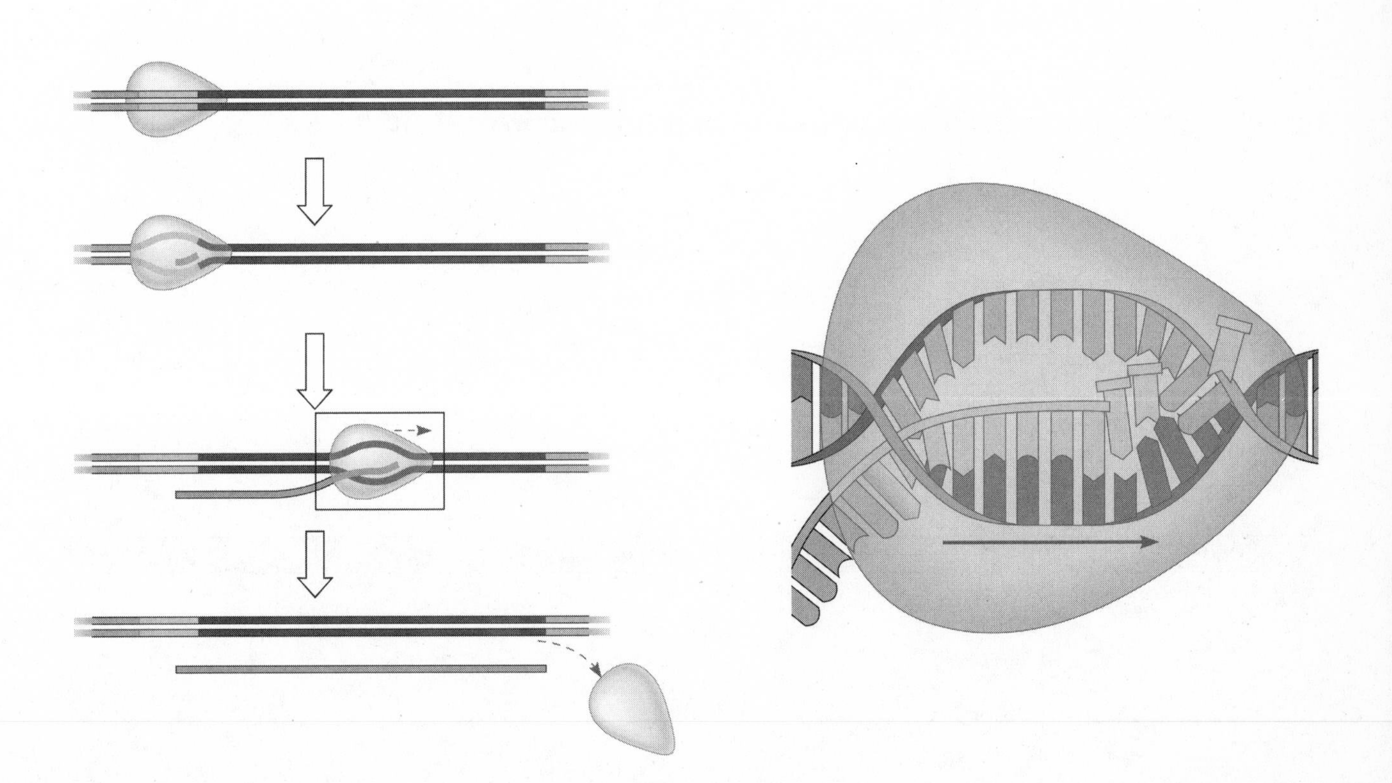

Figure 17.6 The stages of transcription: initiation, elongation, and termination, page 309

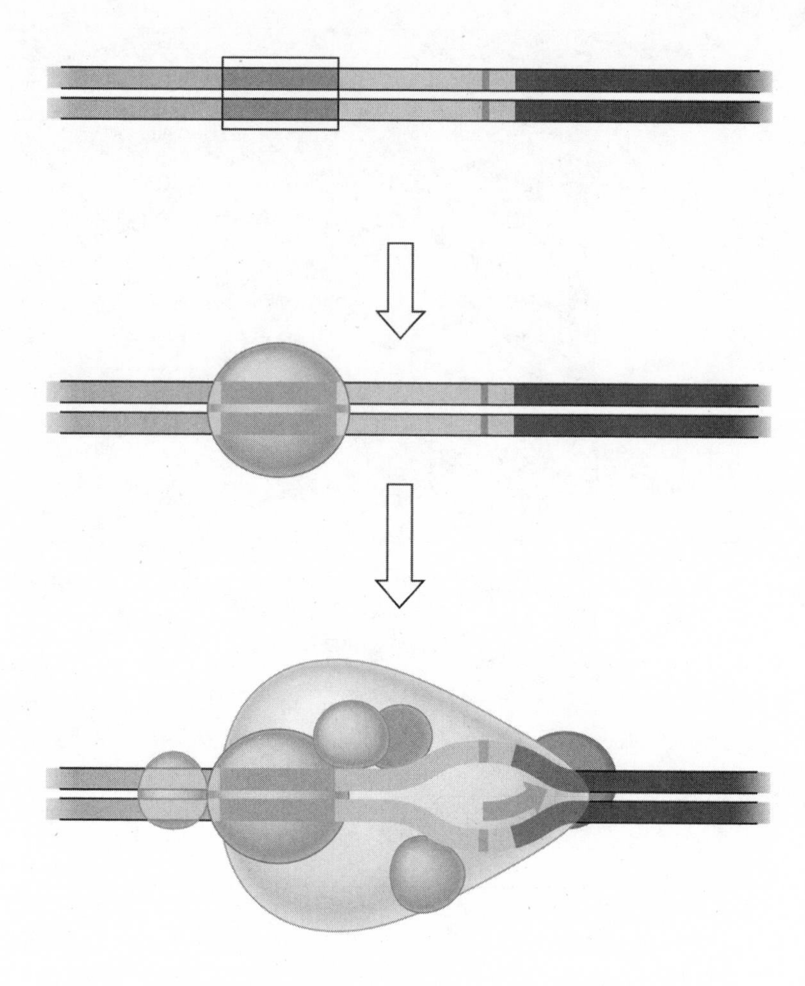

Figure 17.7 The initiation of transcription at a eukaryotic promoter, page 310

G –P–P–P– AAUAAA AAA··AAA

Figure 17.8 RNA processing; addition of the 5' cap and poly(A) tail, page 311

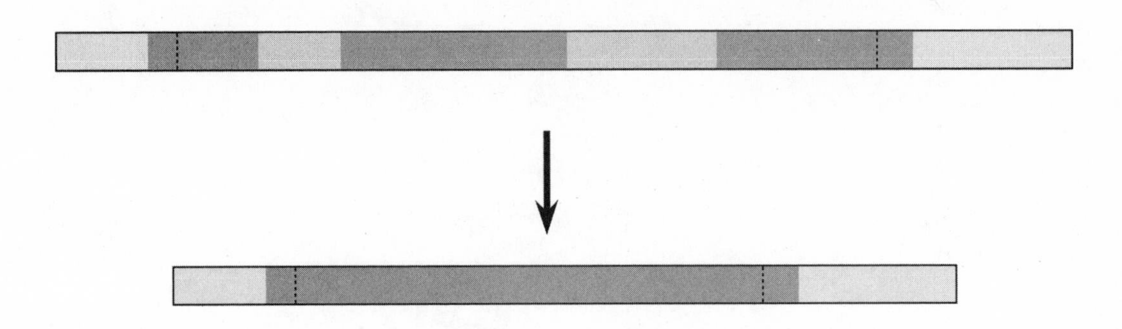

Figure 17.9 RNA processing: RNA splicing, page 312

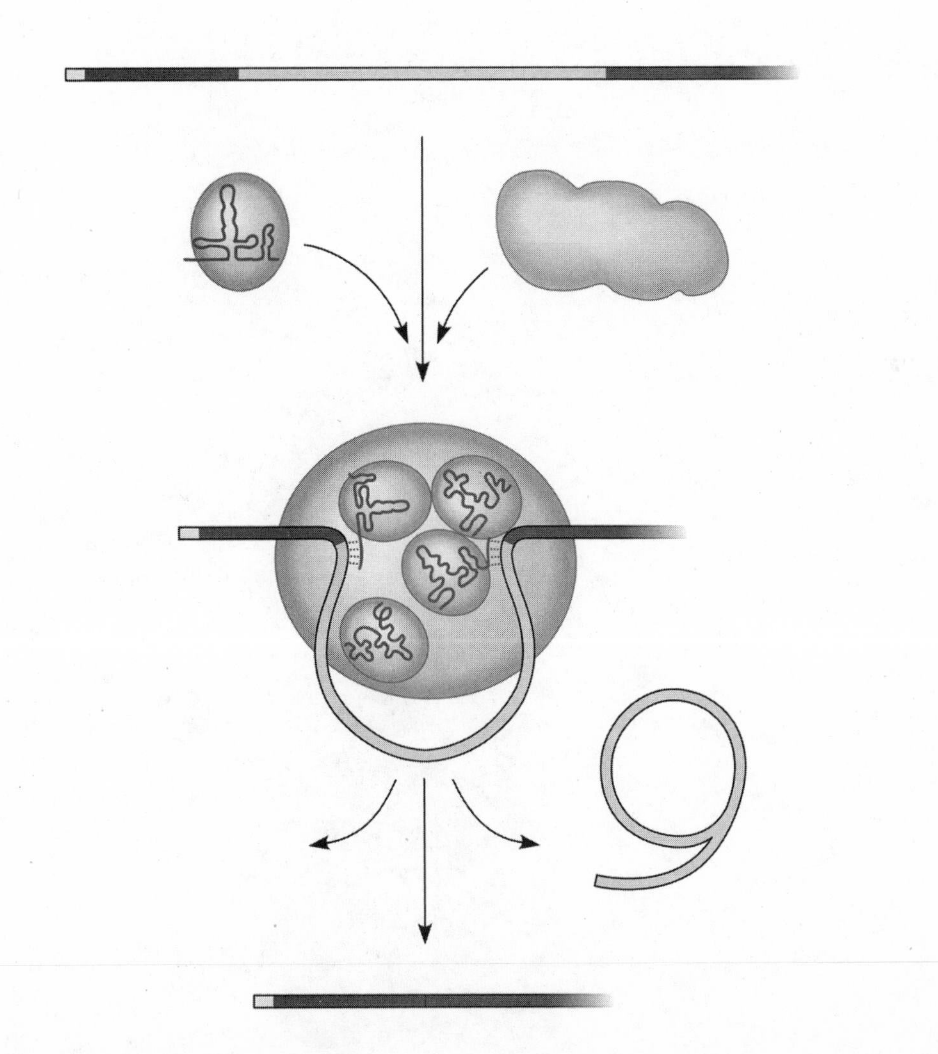

Figure 17.10 The roles of snRNPs and spliceosomes in mRNA splicing, page 312

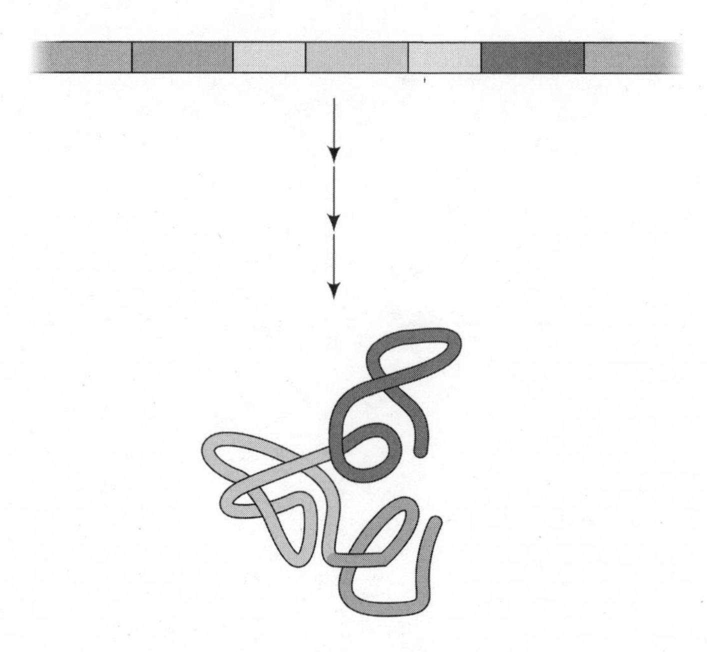

Figure 17.11 Correspondence between exons and protein domains, page 313

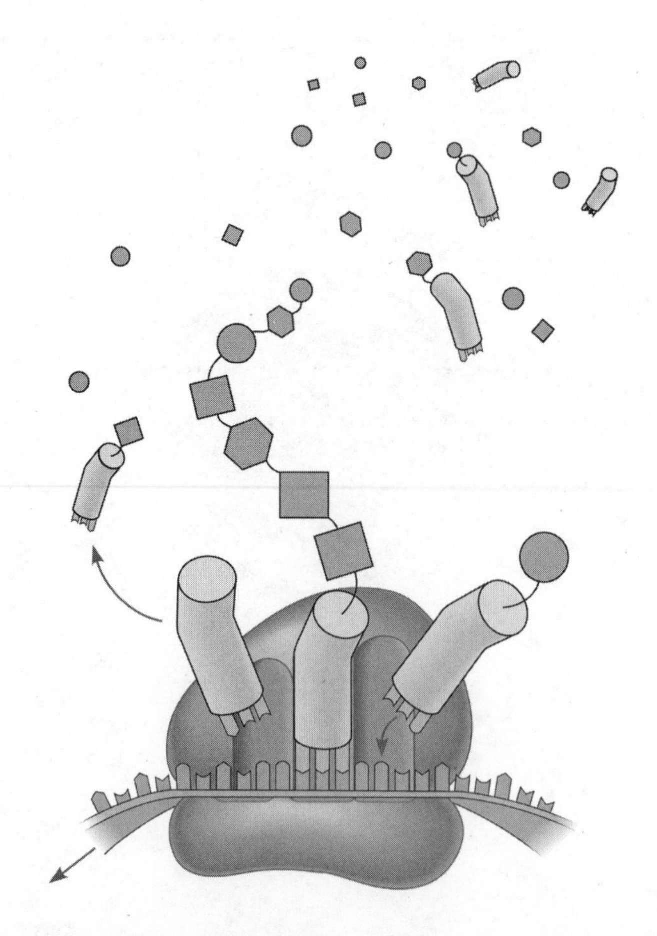

Figure 17.12 Translation: the basic concept, page 314

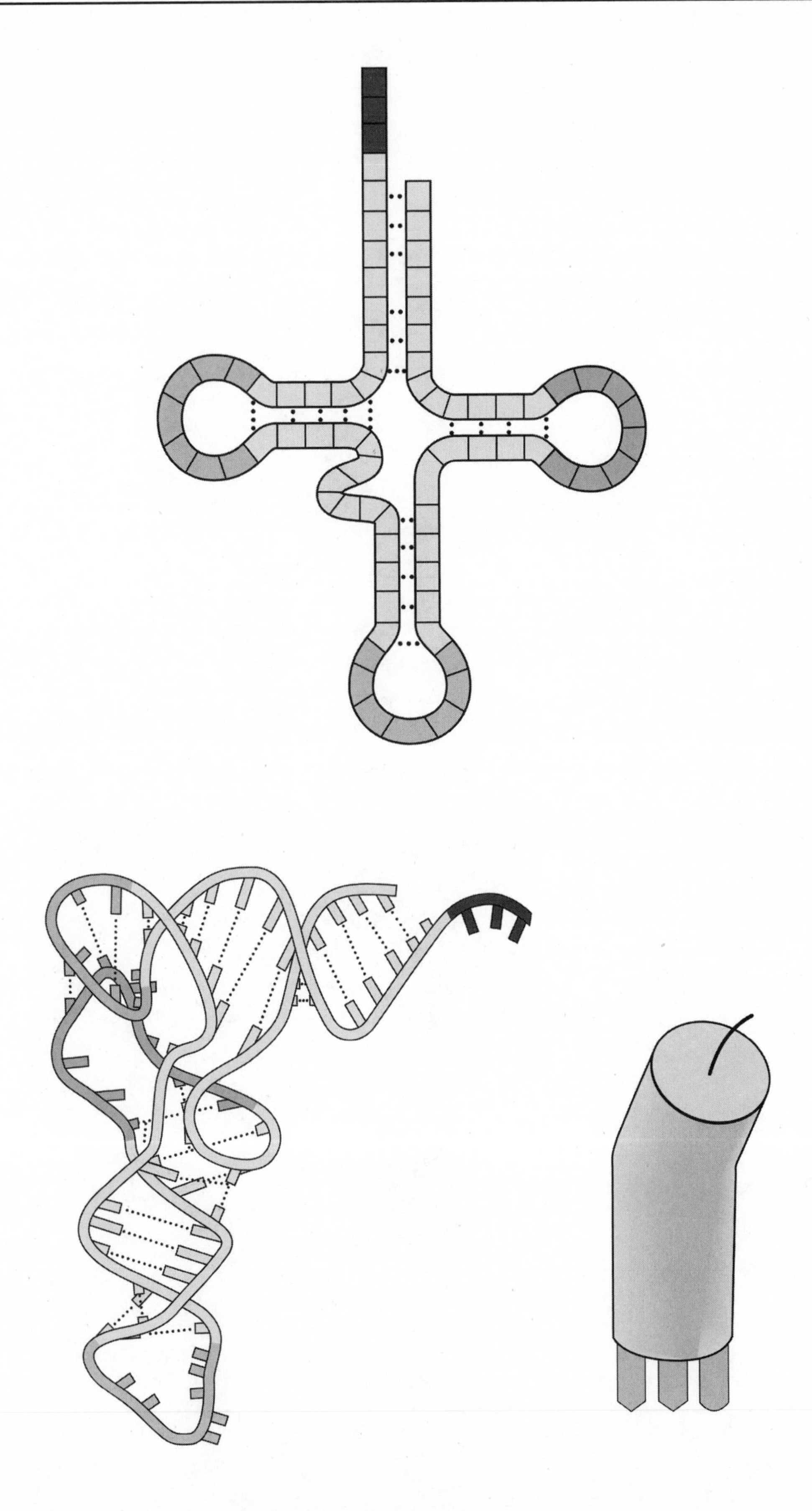

Figure 17.13 The structure of transfer RNA (tRNA), page 315

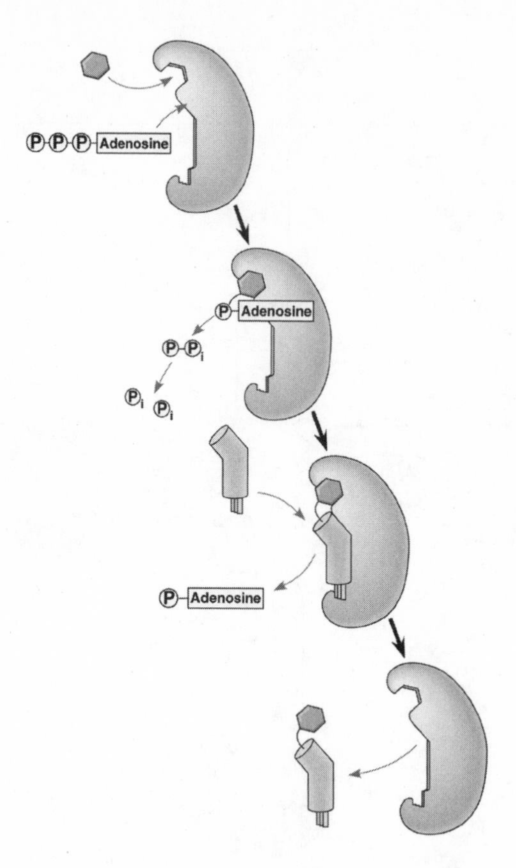

Figure 17.14 An aminoacyl-tRNA synthetase joins a specific amino acid to a tRNA, page 315

Figure 17.15 The anatomy of a functioning ribosome, page 316

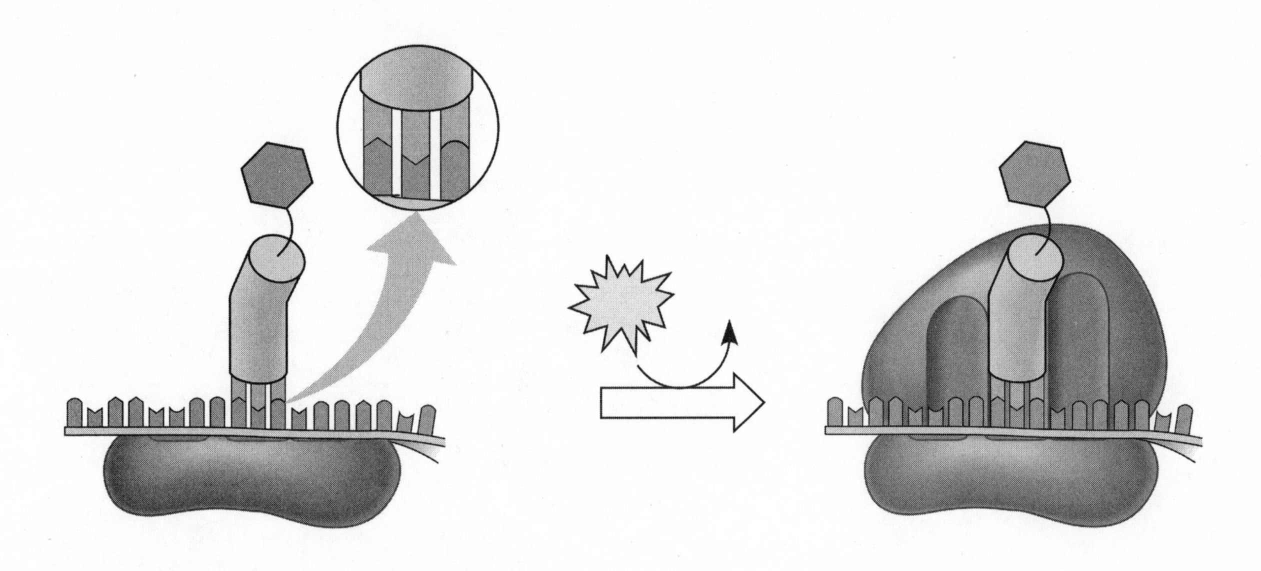

Figure 17.17 The initiation of translation, page 317

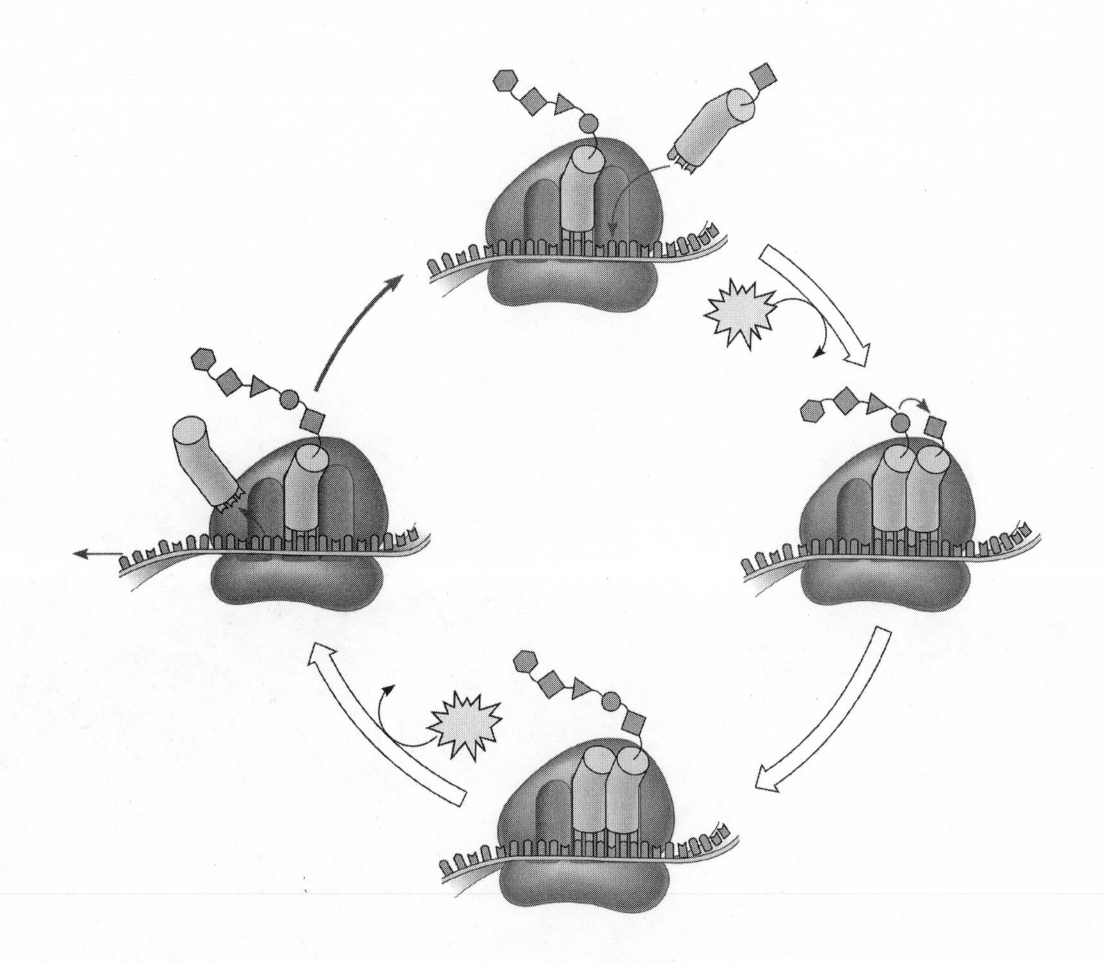

Figure 17.18 The elongation cycle of translation, page 318

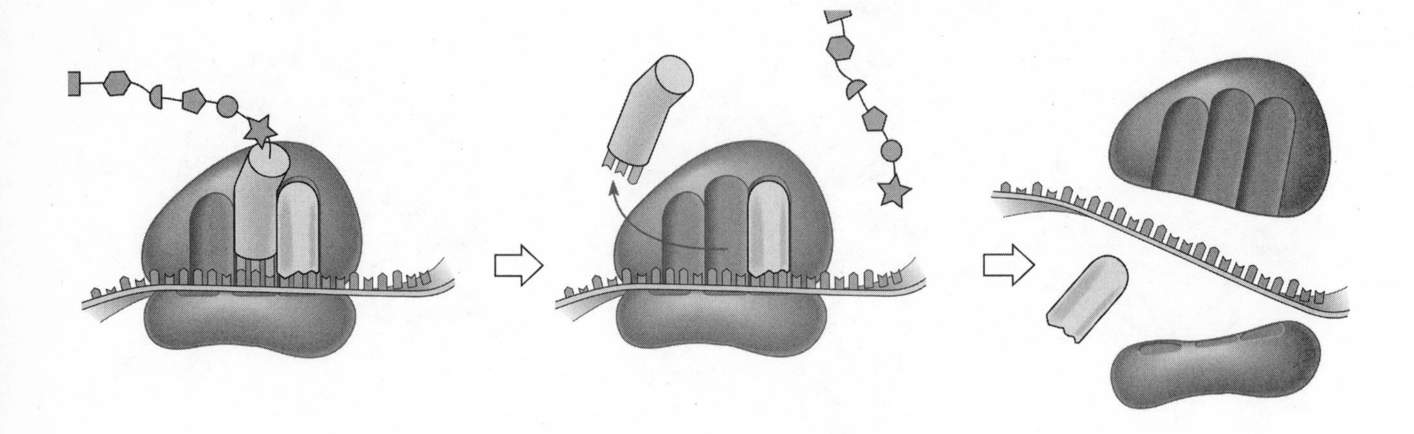

Figure 17.19 The termination of translation, page 319

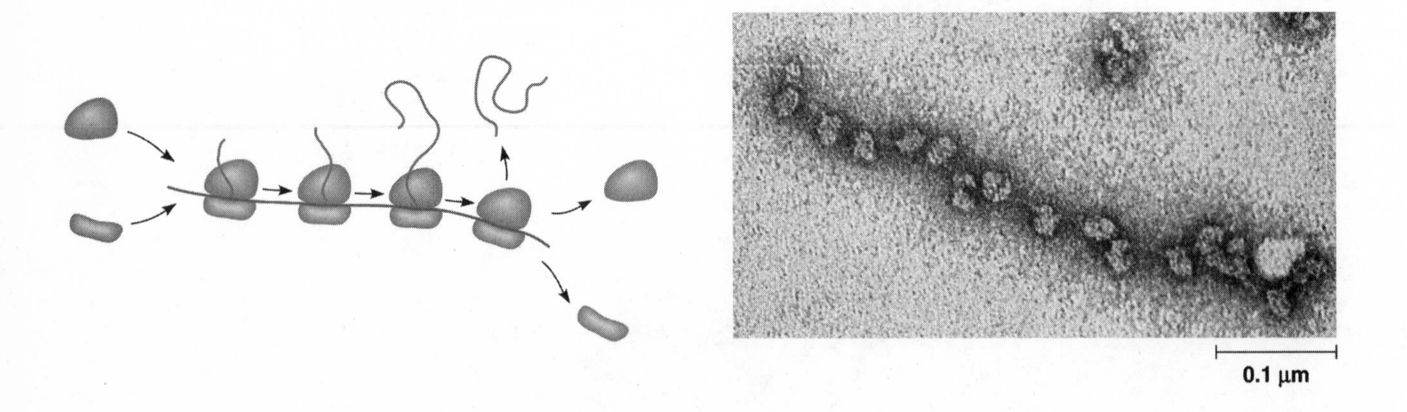

Figure 17.20 Polyribosomes, page 319

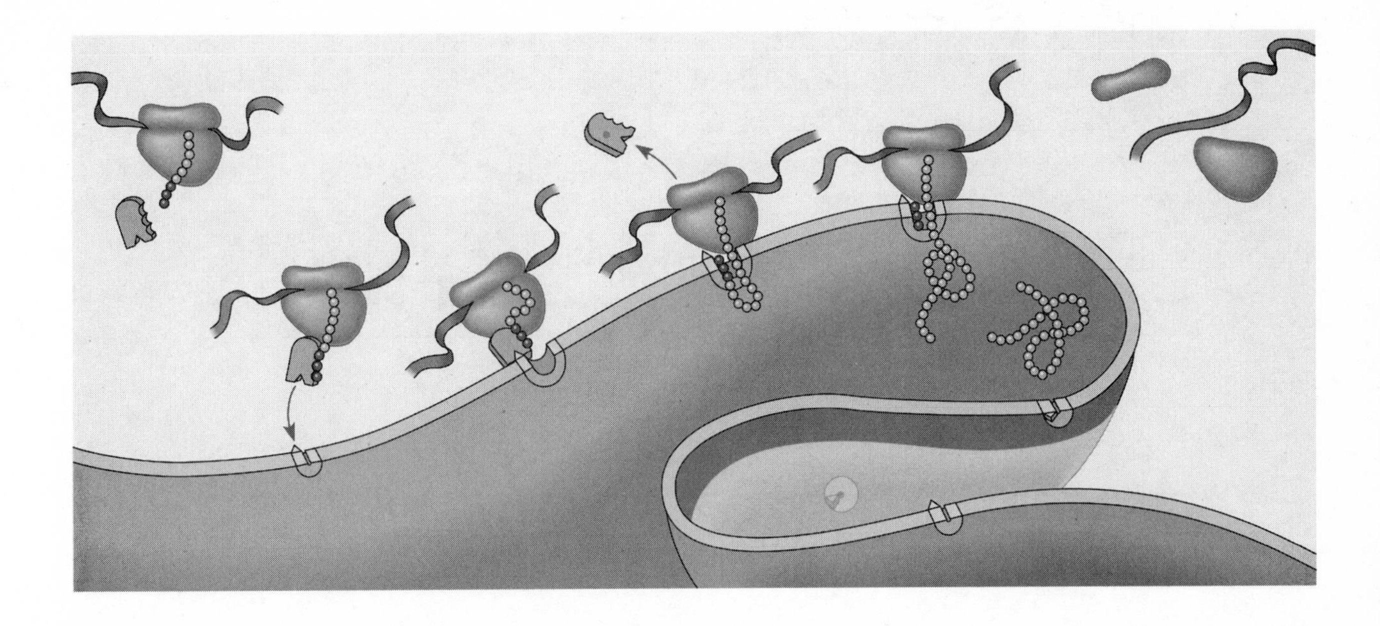

Figure 17.21 The signal mechanism for targeting proteins to the ER, page 320

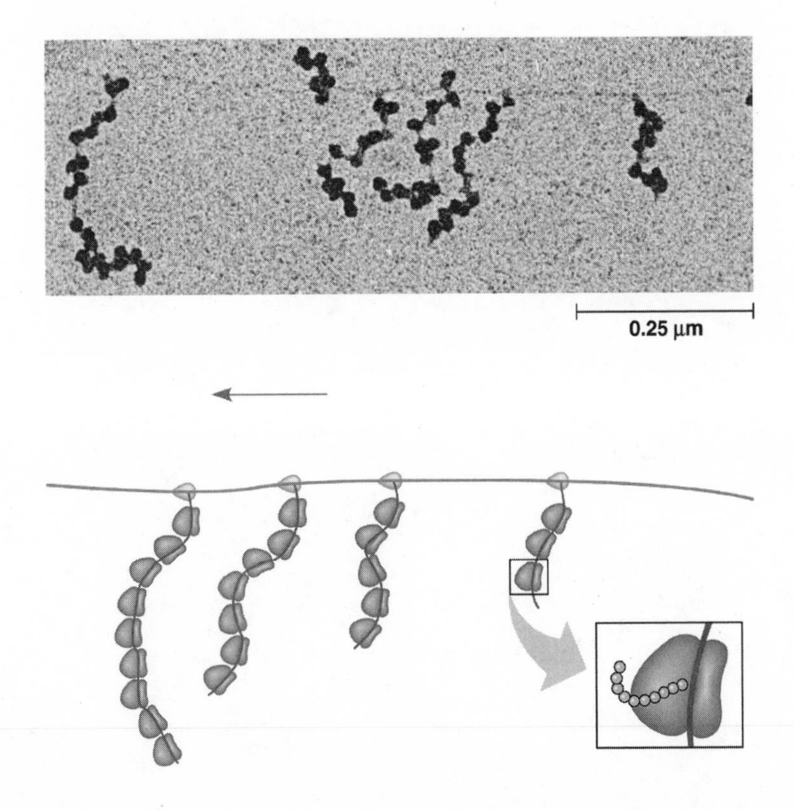

Figure 17.22 Coupled transcription and translation in bacteria, page 321

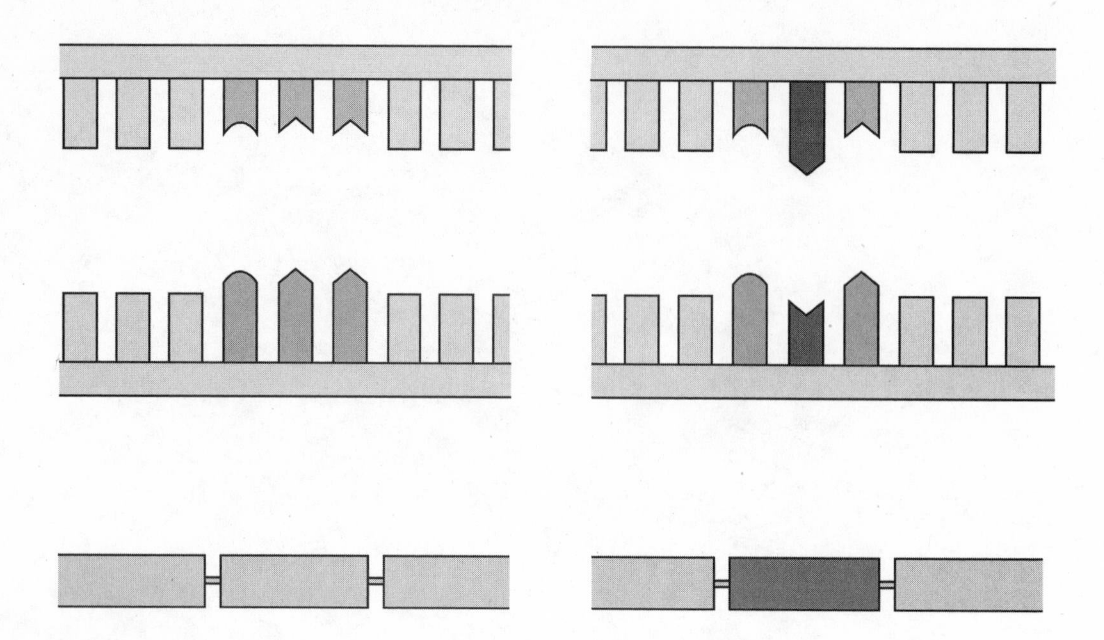

Figure 17.23 The molecular basis of sickle-cell disease: a point mutation, page 322

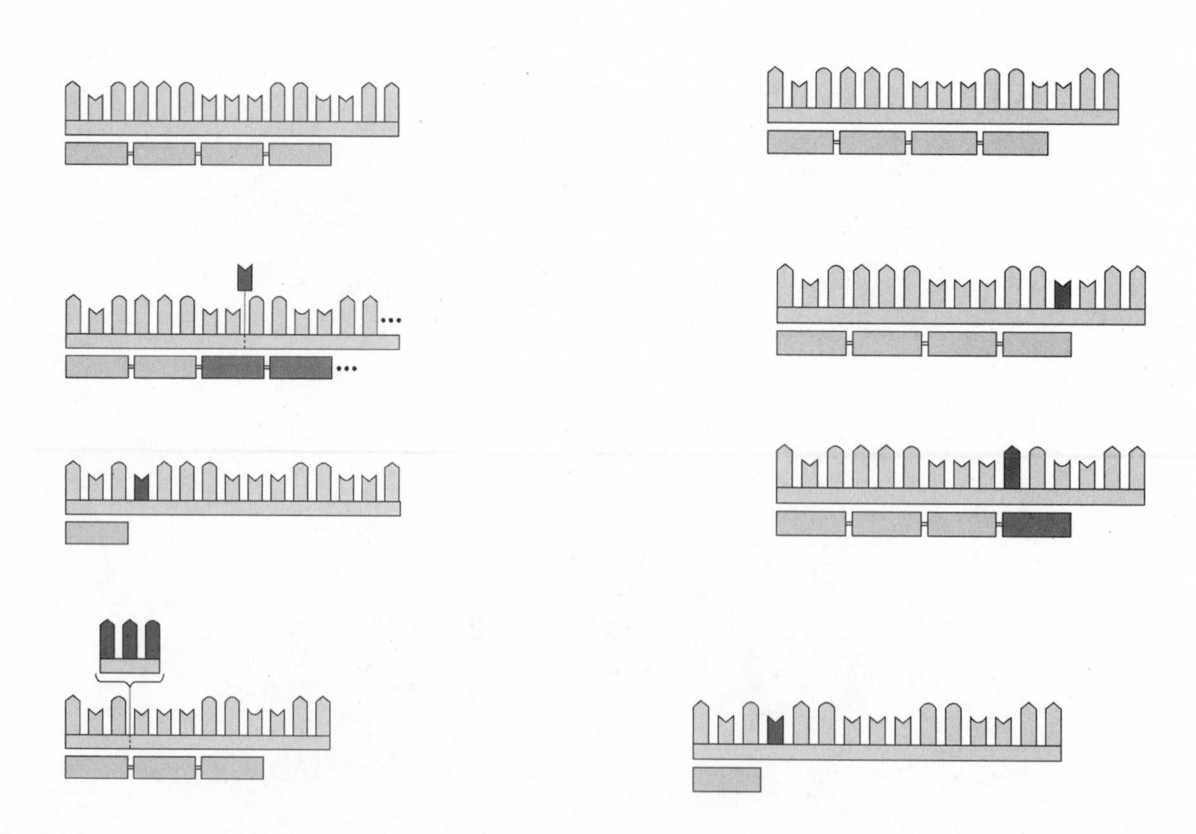

Figure 17.24 Categories and consequences of point mutations, page 323

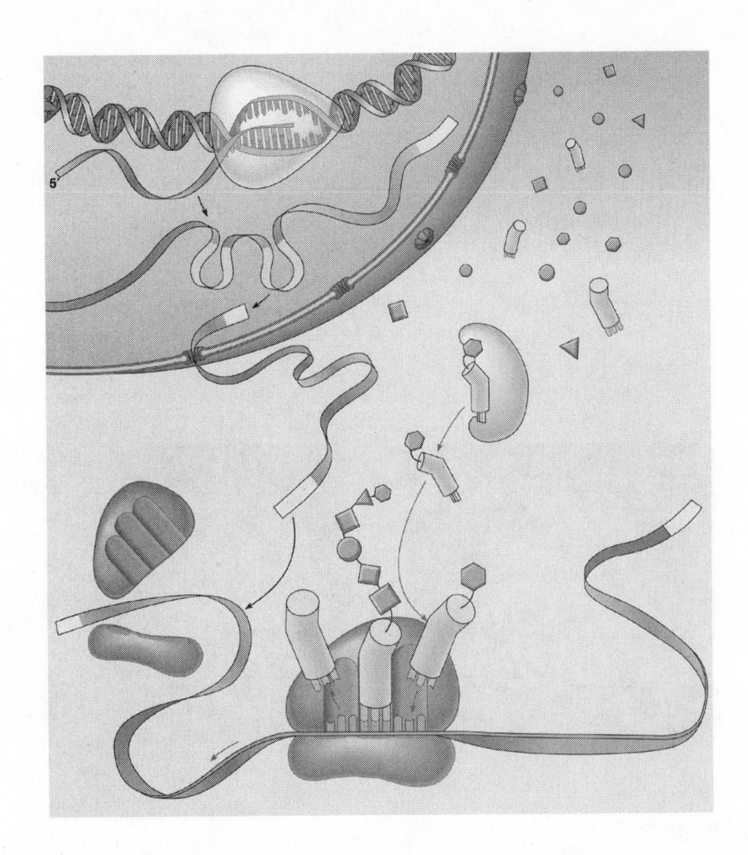

Figure 17.25 A summary of transcription and translation in a eukaryotic cell, page 324

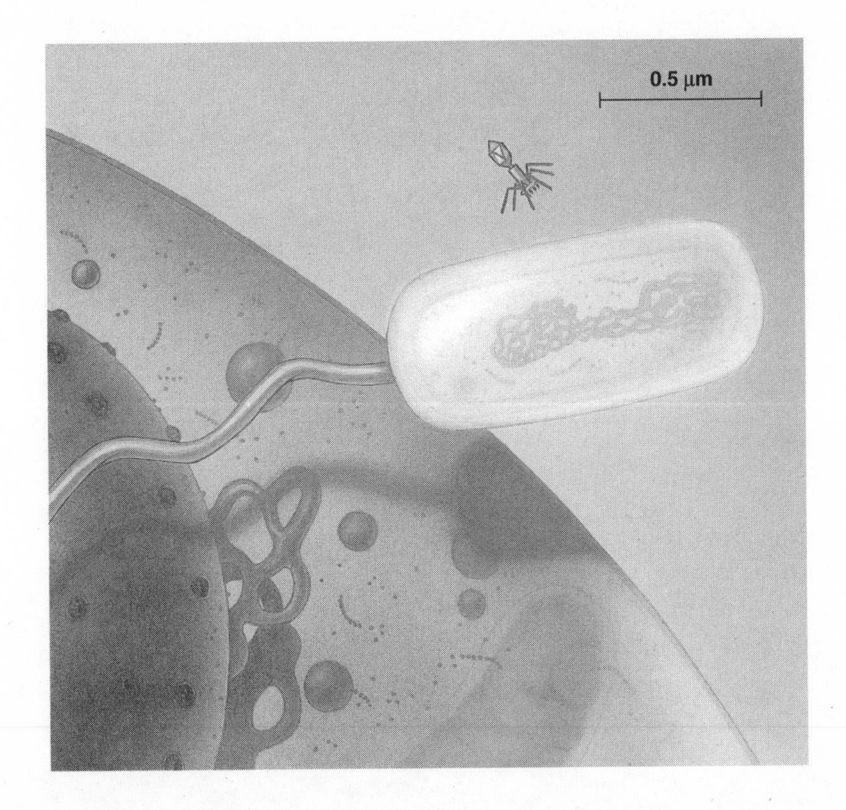

Figure 18.1 Comparing the size of a virus, a bacterium, and a eukaryotic cell, page 329

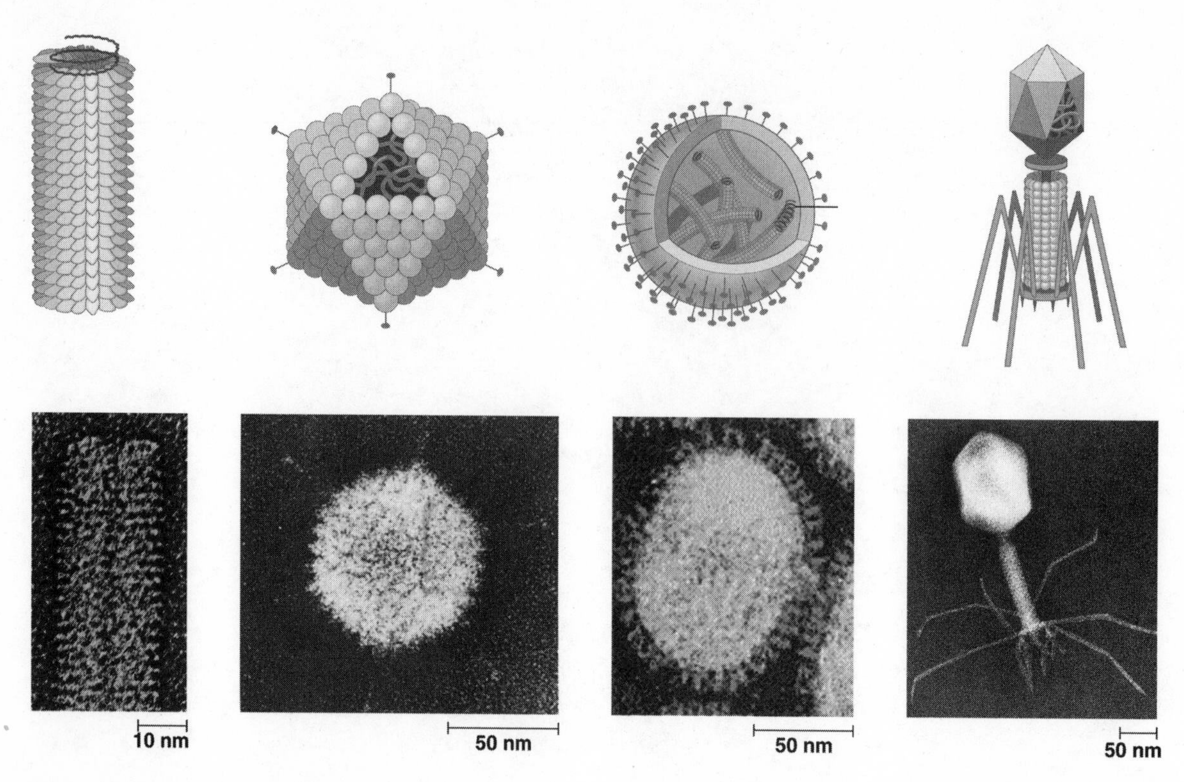

Figure 18.2 Viral structure, page 330

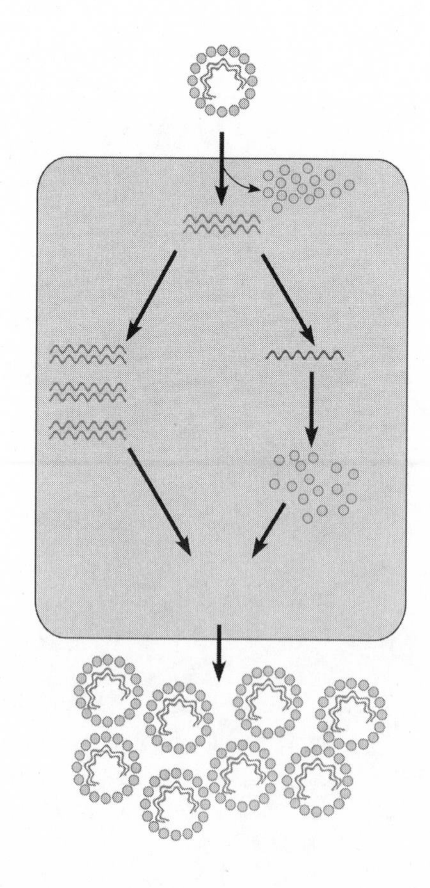

Figure 18.3 A simplified viral reproductive cycle, page 331

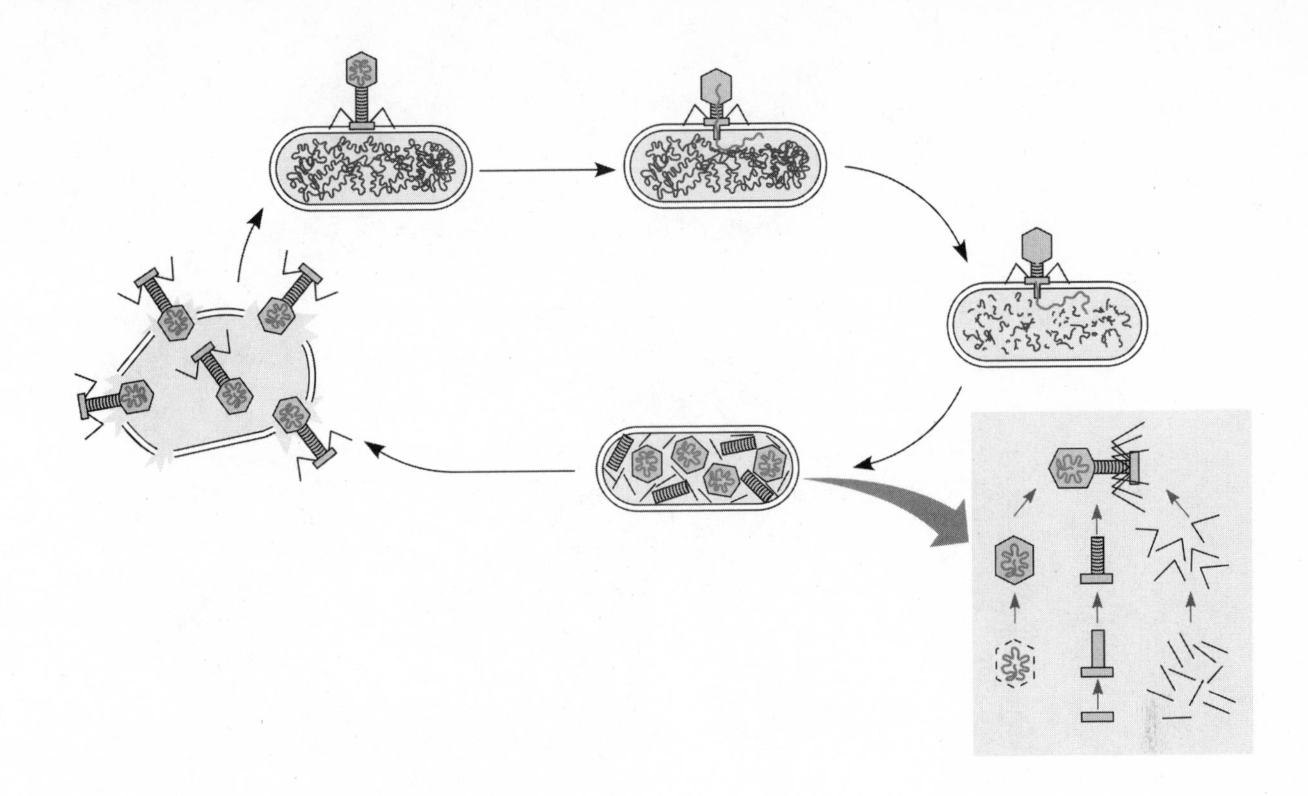

Figure 18.4 The lytic cycle of phage T4, page 332

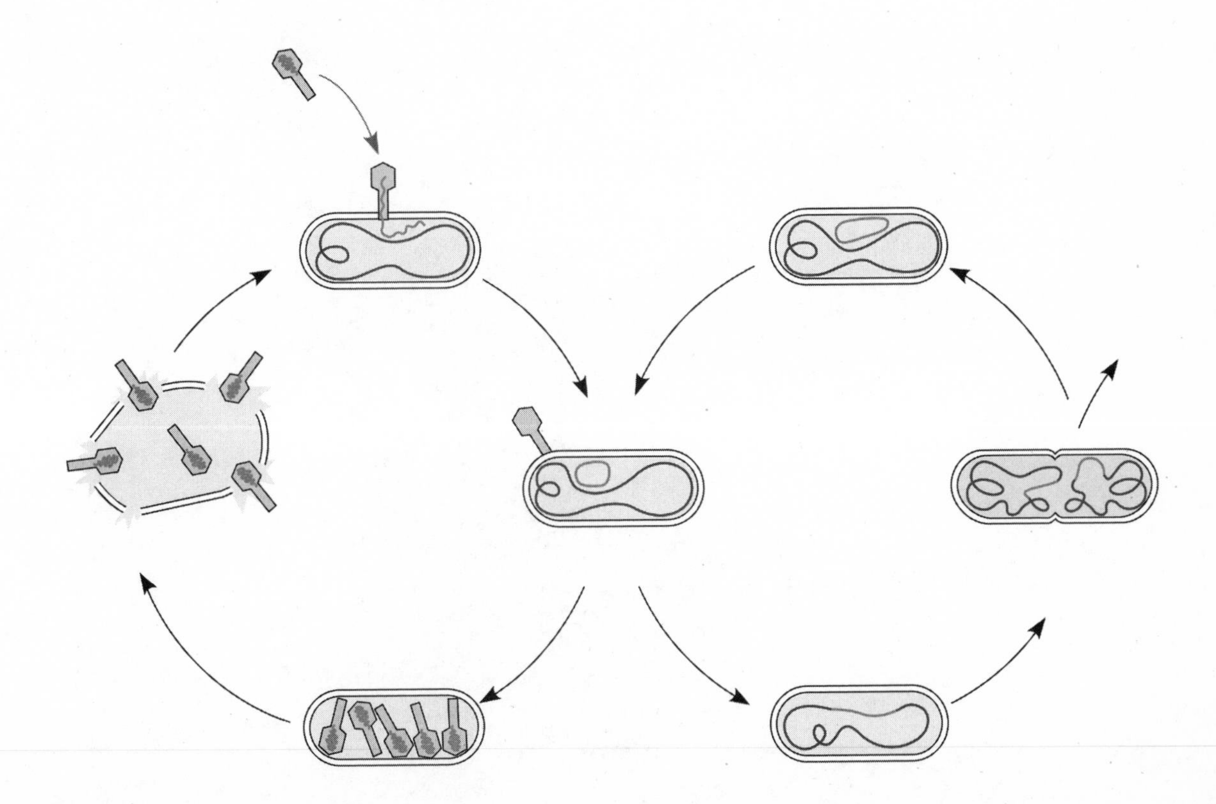

Figure 18.5 The lysogenic and lytic reproductive cycles of phage λ, a temperate phage, page 333

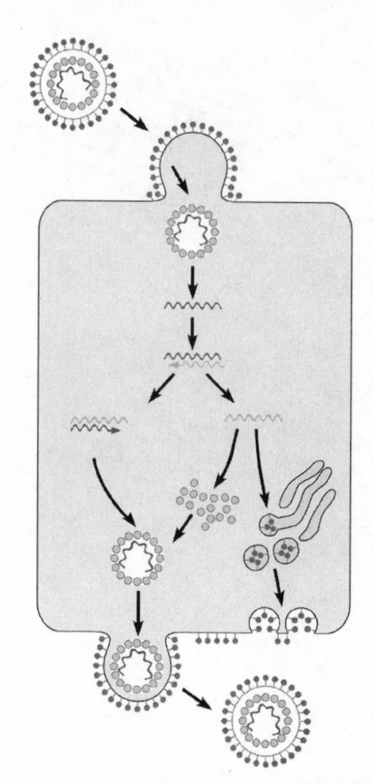

Figure 18.6 The reproductive cycle of an enveloped virus, page 334

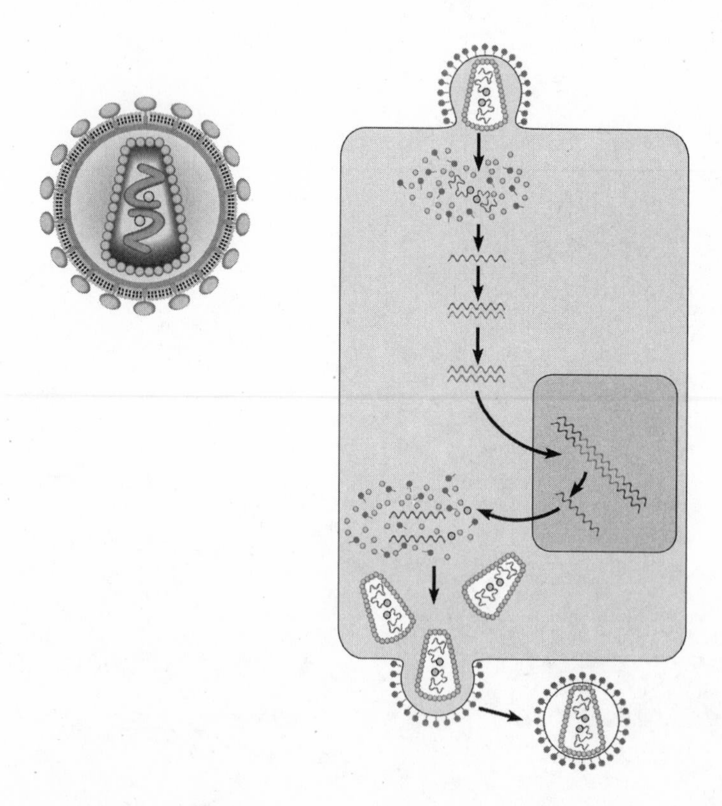

Figure 18.7 HIV, a retrovirus, page 336

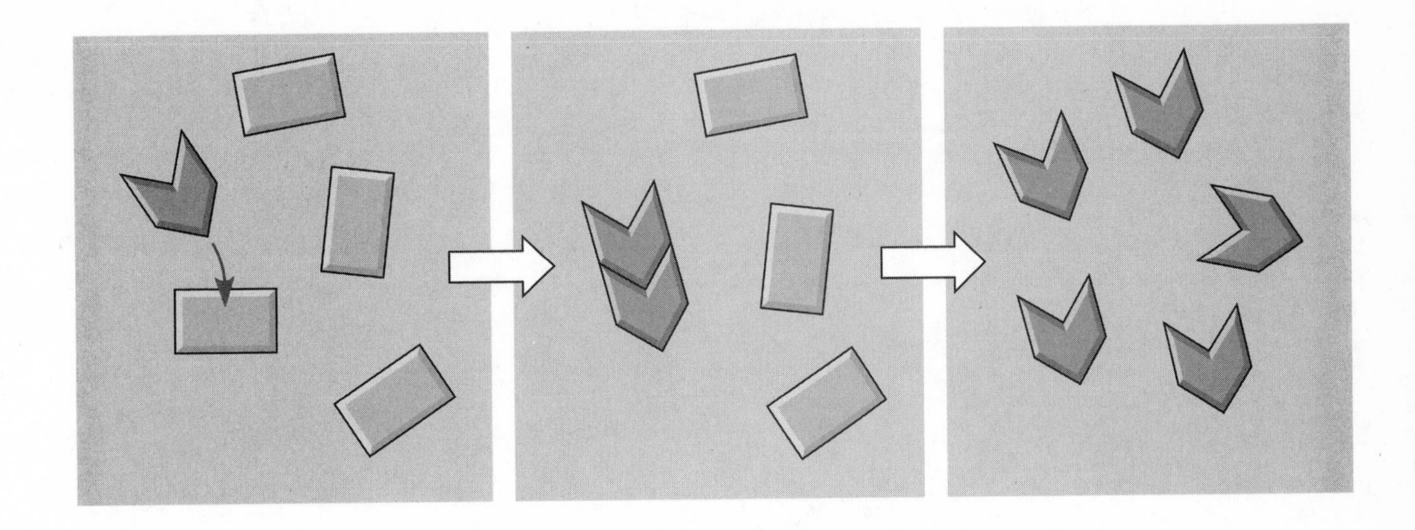

Figure 18.10 A hypothesis to explain how prions propagate, page 339

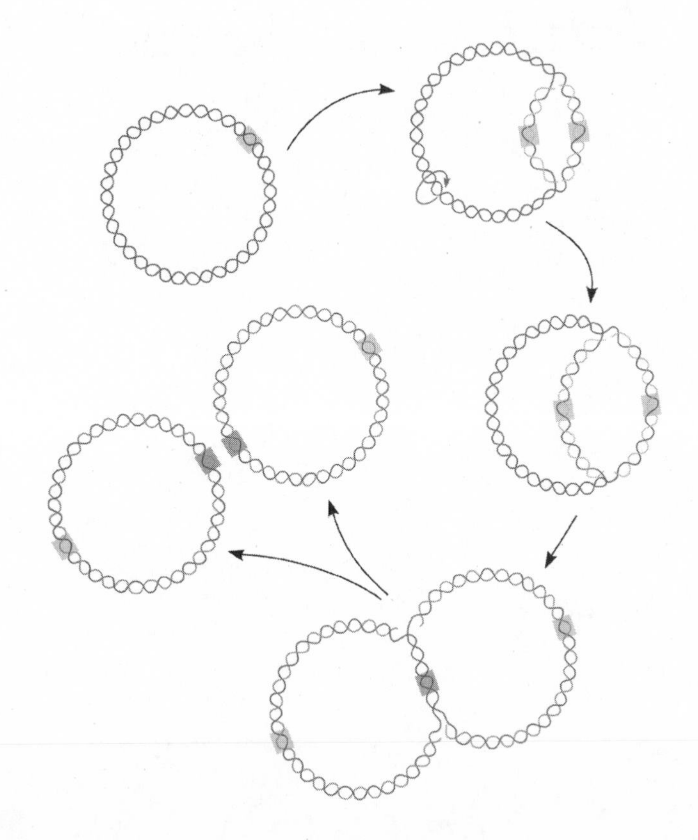

Figure 18.11 Replication of the bacterial chromosome, page 340

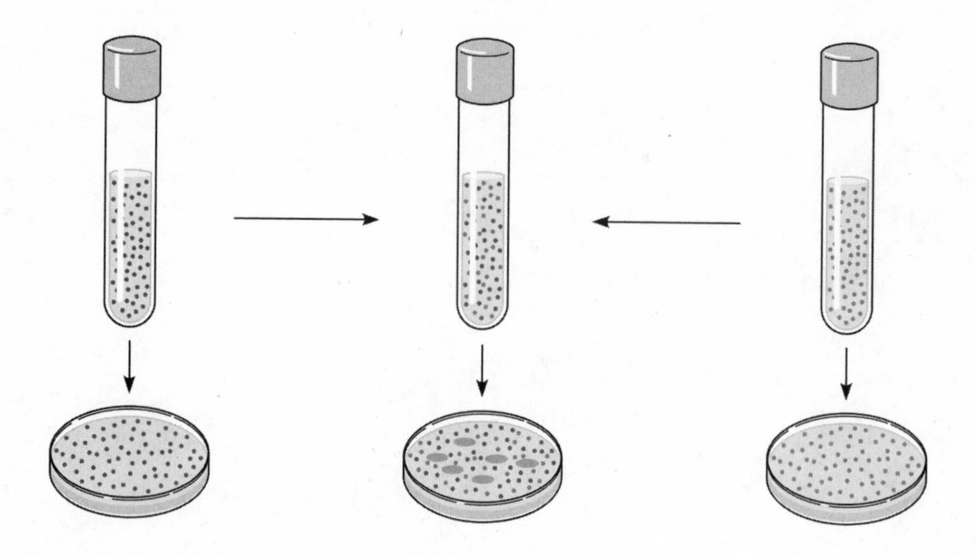

Figure 18.12 Detecting genetic recombination in bacteria, page 341

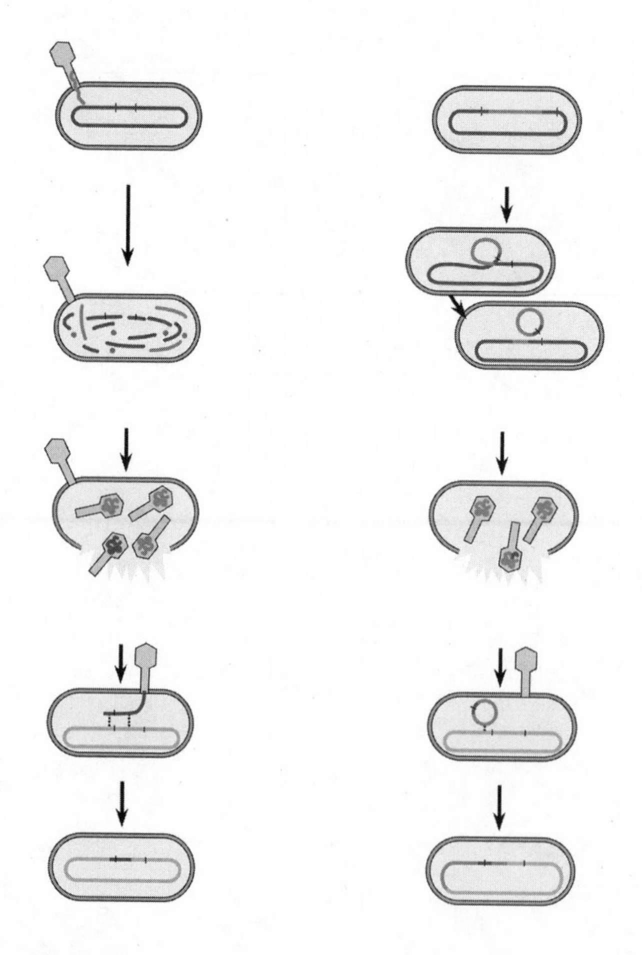

Figure 18.13 Transduction, page 342

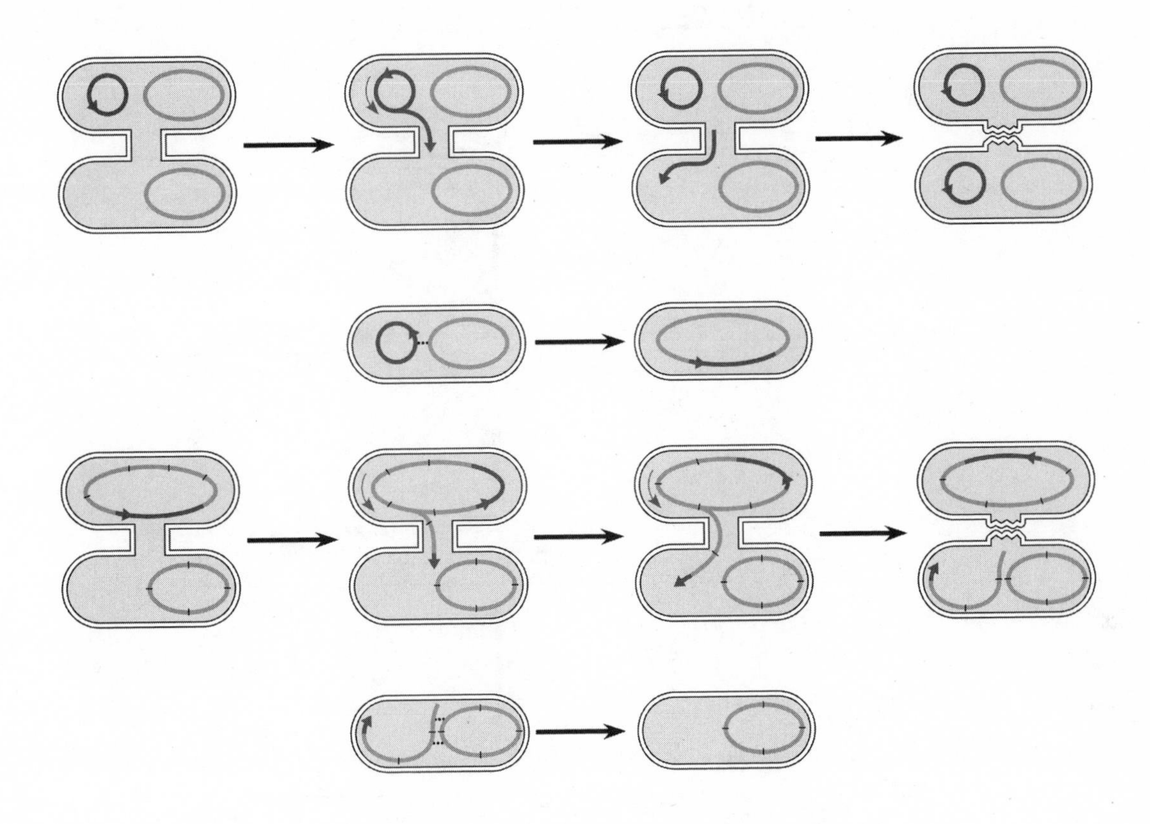

Figure 18.15 Conjugation and recombination in *E. coli*, page 344

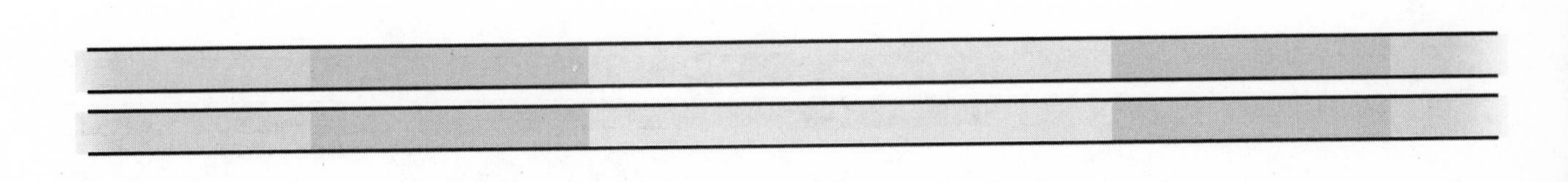

Figure 18.16 Insertion sequences, the simplest transposons, page 345

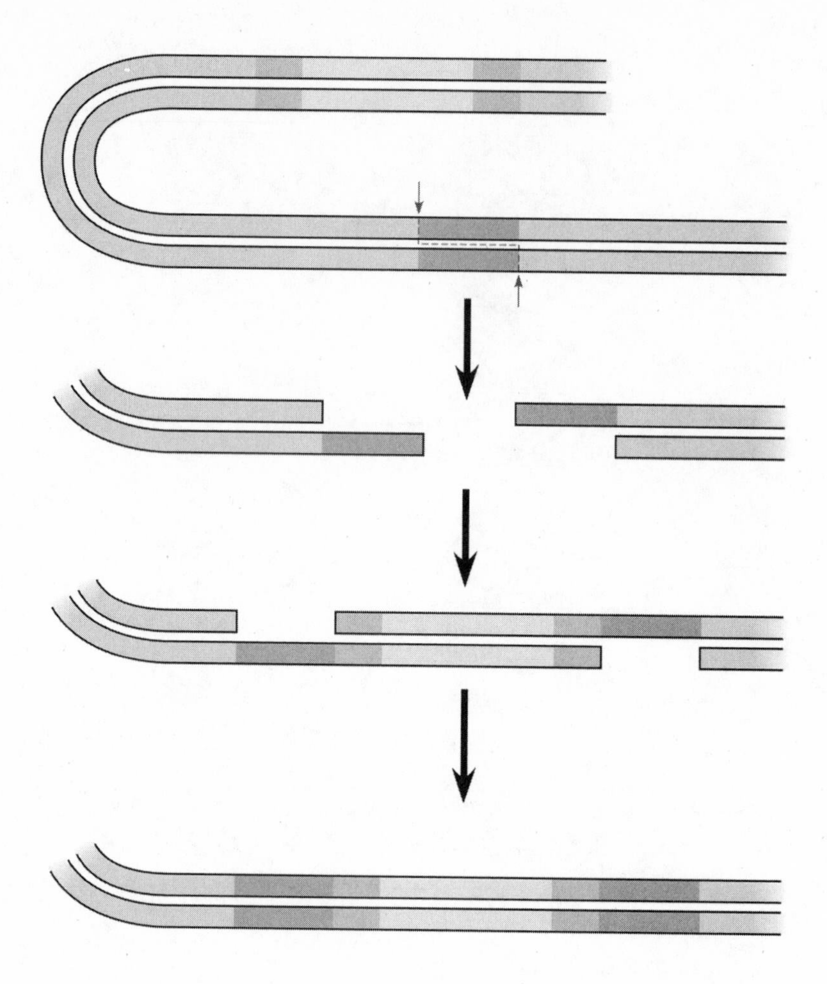

Figure 18.17 Insertion of a transposon and creation of direct repeats, page 346

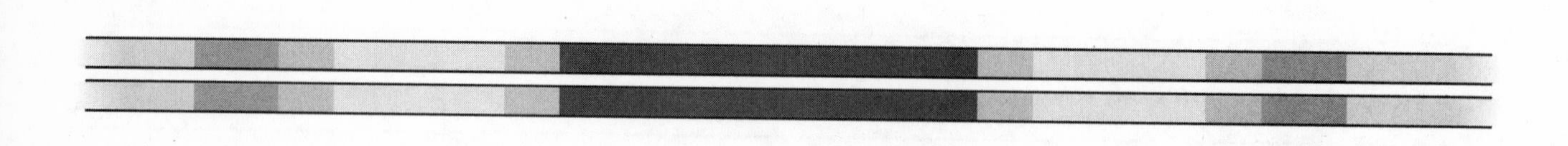

Figure 18.18 Anatomy of a composite transposon, page 346

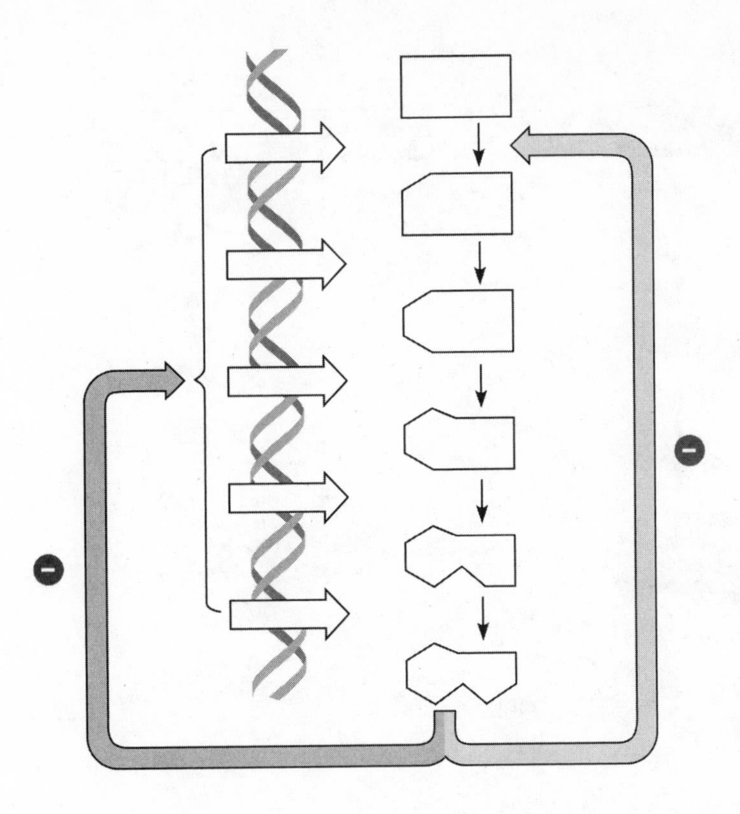

Figure 18.19 Regulation of a metabolic pathway, page 347

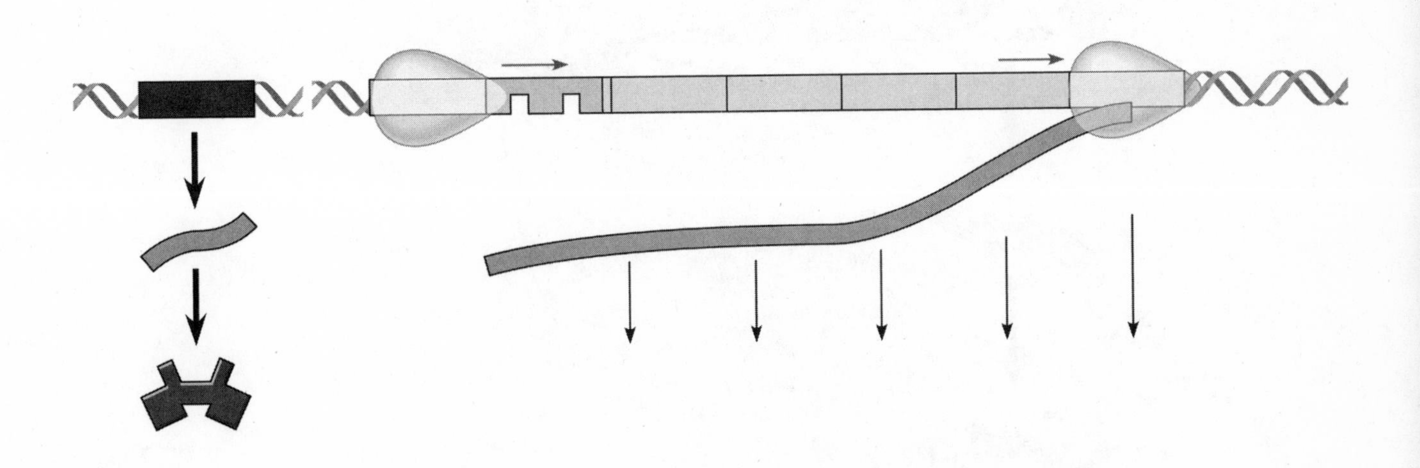

Figure 18.20a The *trp* operon: regulated synthesis of repressible enzymes, page 348

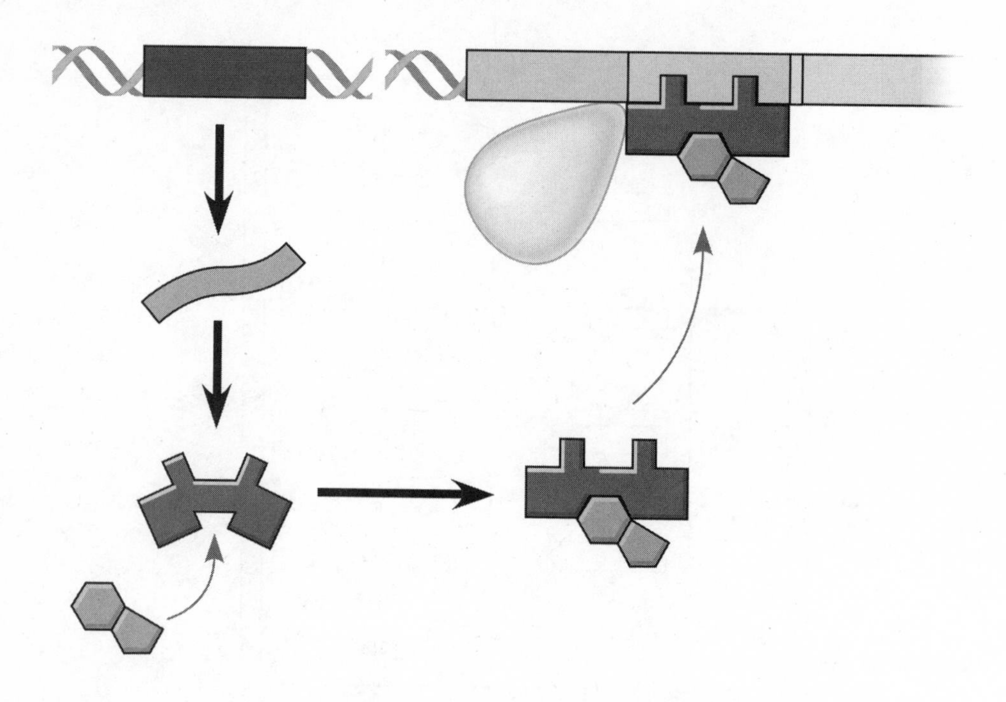

Figure 18.20b The *trp* operon: regulated synthesis of repressible enzymes, page 348

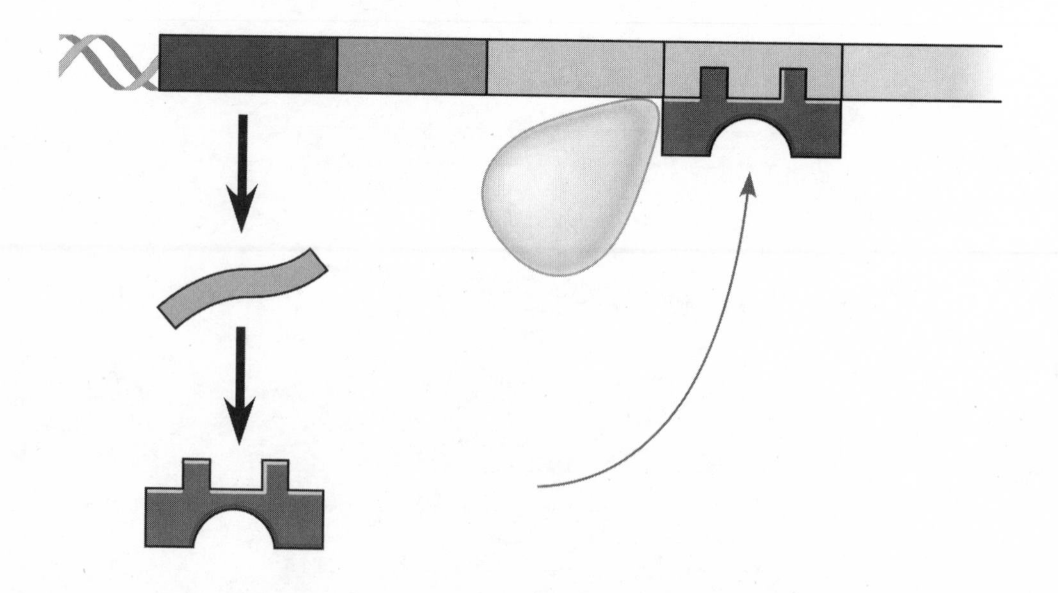

Figure 18.21a The *lac* operon: regulated synthesis of inducible enzymes, page 349

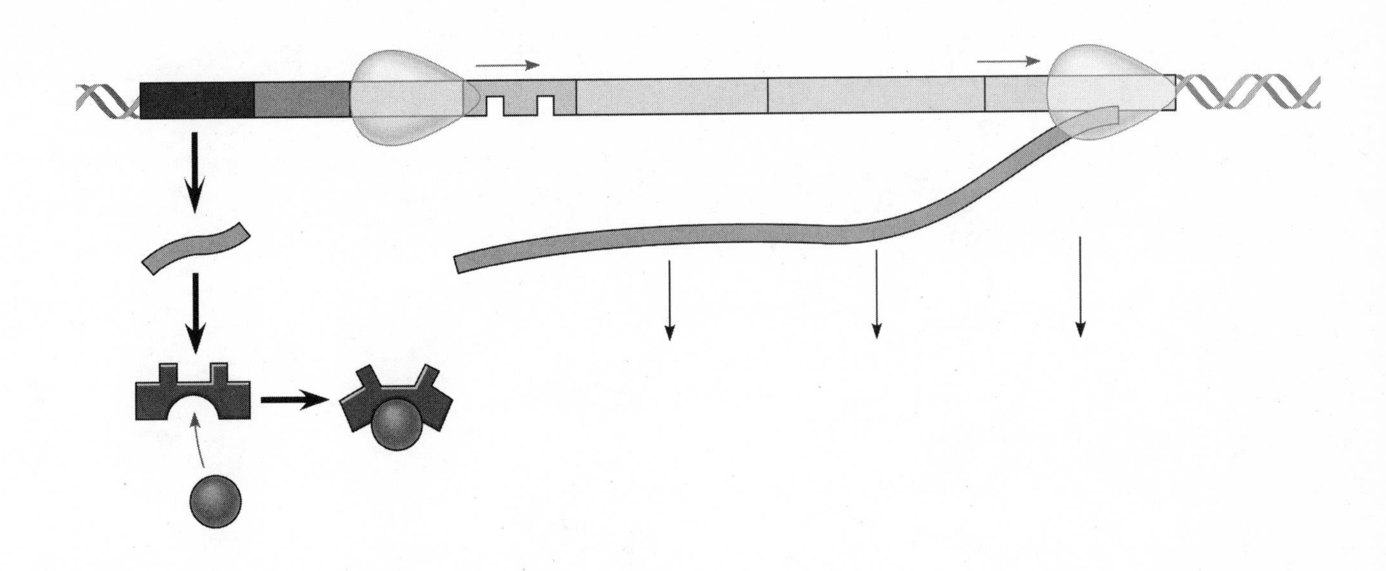

Figure 18.21b The *lac* operon: regulated synthesis of inducible enzymes, page 349

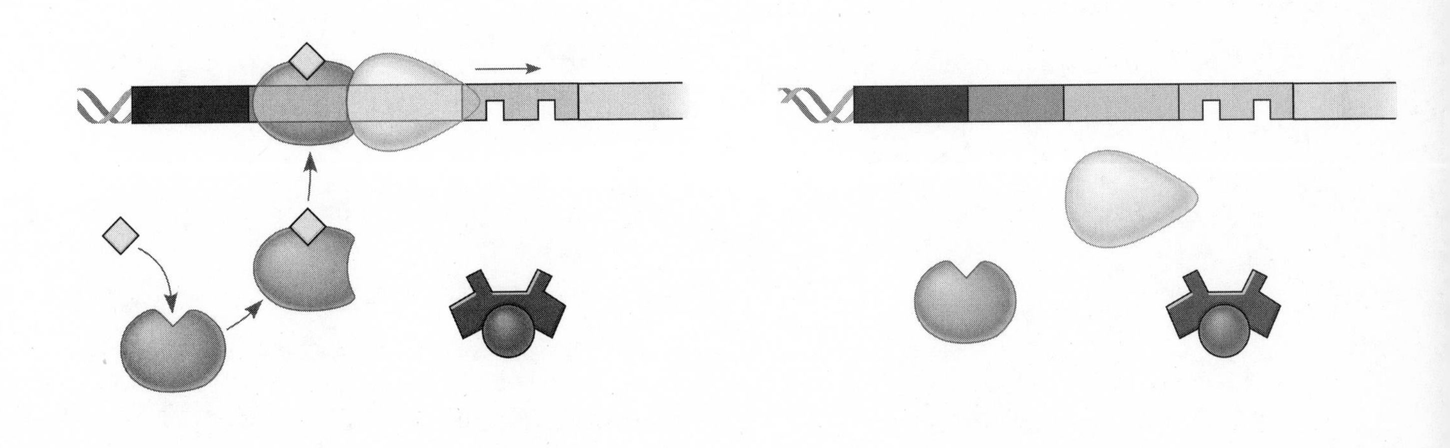

Figure 18.22 Positive control: cAMP receptor protein, page 351

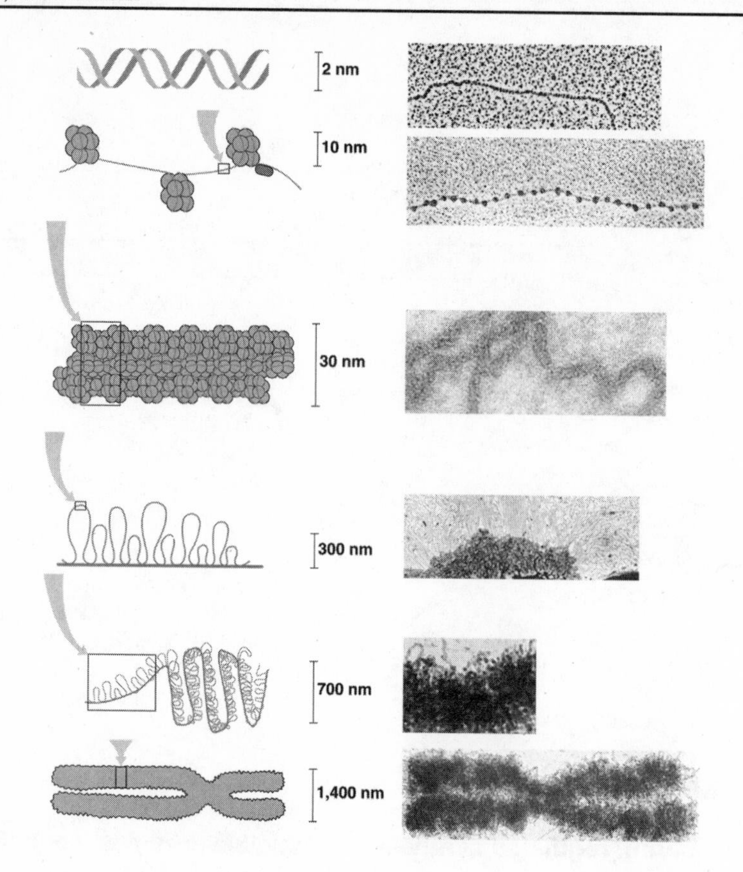

Figure 19.1 Levels of chromatin packing, page 355

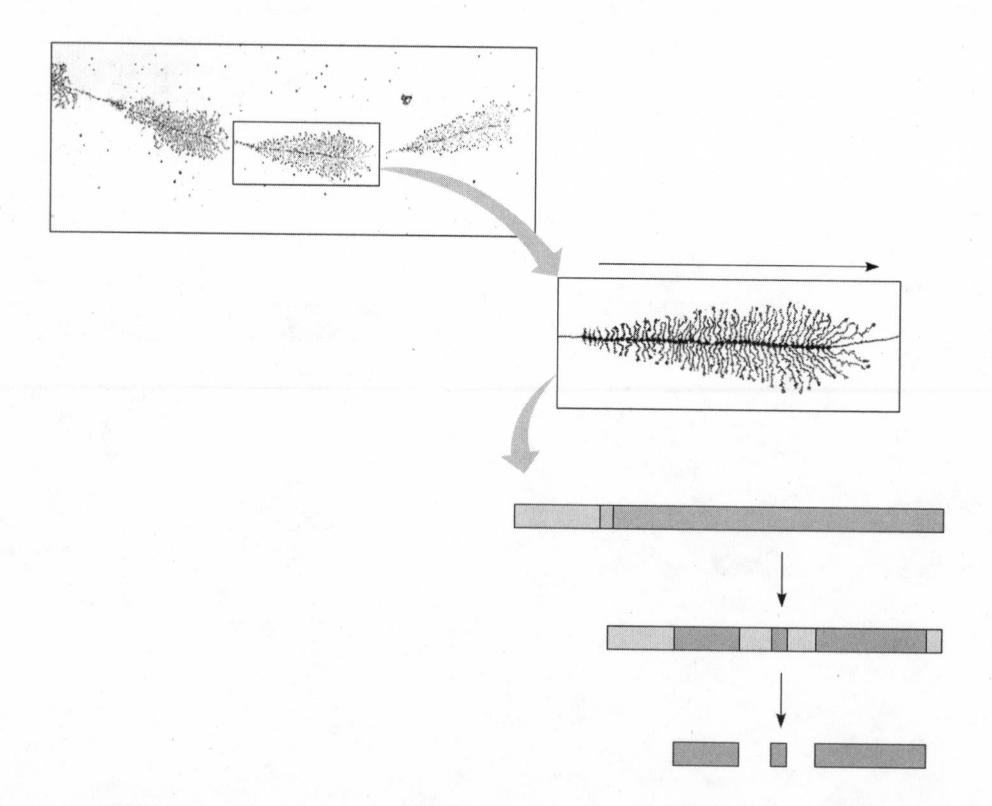

Figure 19.2 Part of a family of identical genes for ribosomal RNA, page 358

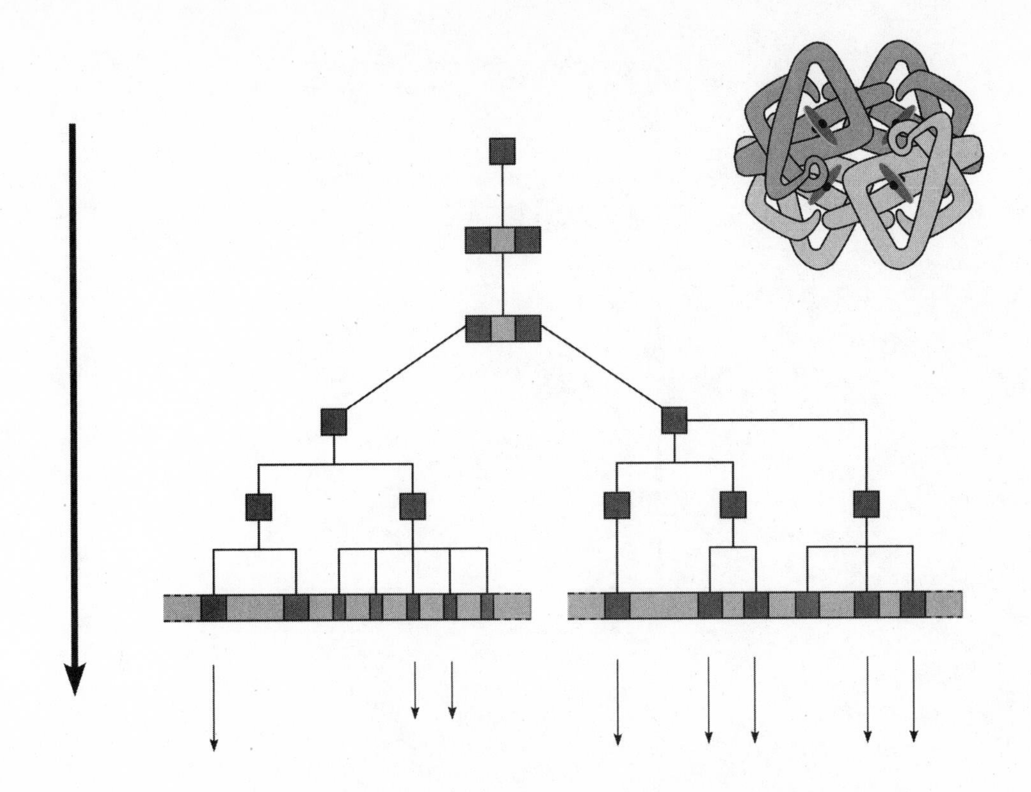

Figure 19.3 The evolution of human α-globin and β-globin gene families, page 359

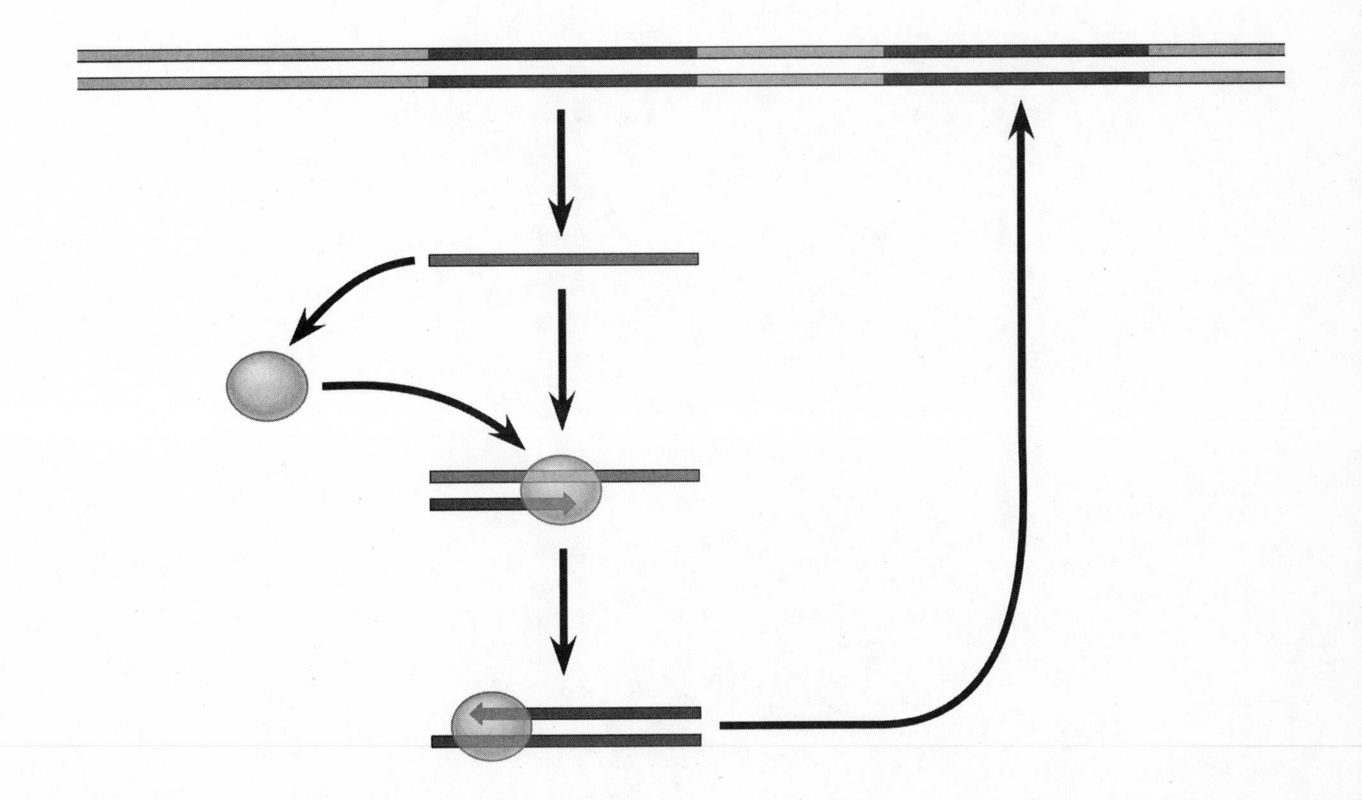

Figure 19.5 Retrotransposon movement, page 360

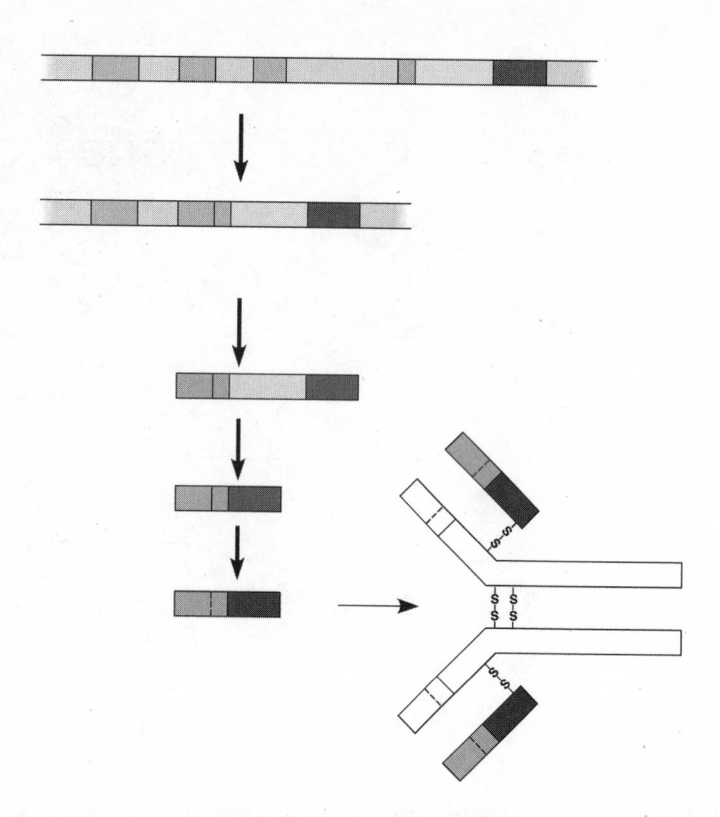

Figure 19.6 DNA rearrangement in the maturation of an immunoglobulin (antibody) gene, page 361

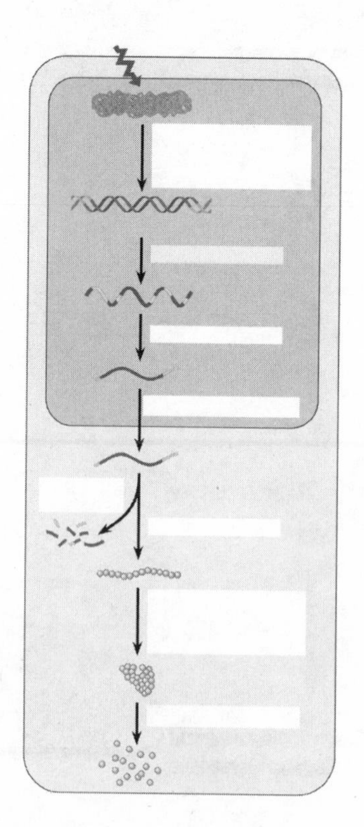

Figure 19.7 Opportunities for the control of gene expression in eukaryotic cells, page 363

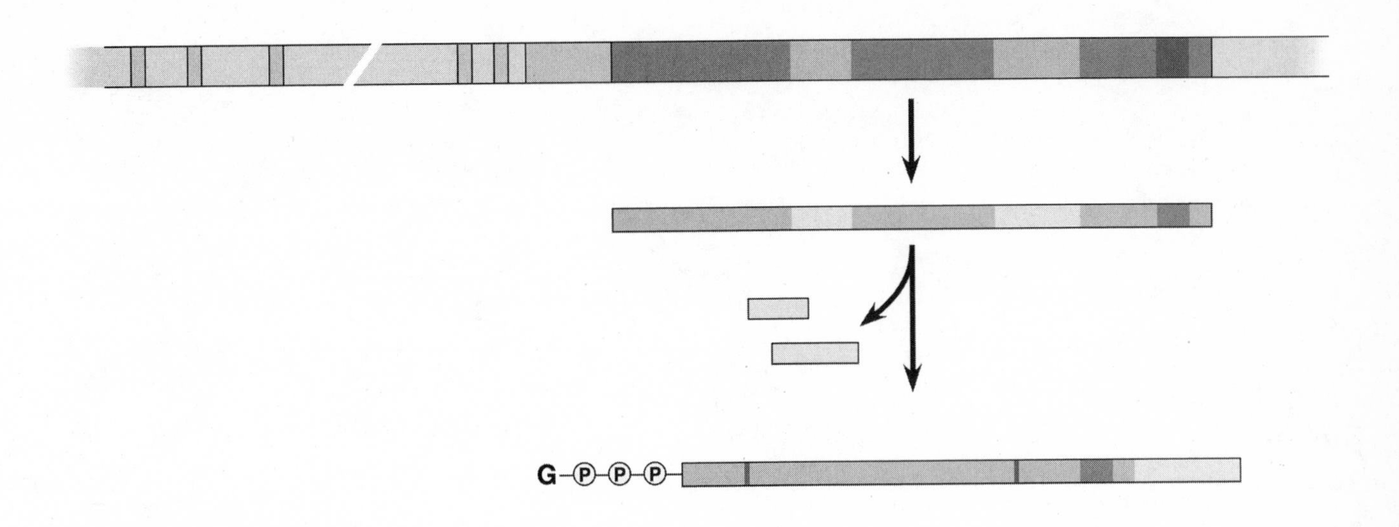

Figure 19.8 A eukaryotic gene and its transcript, page 364

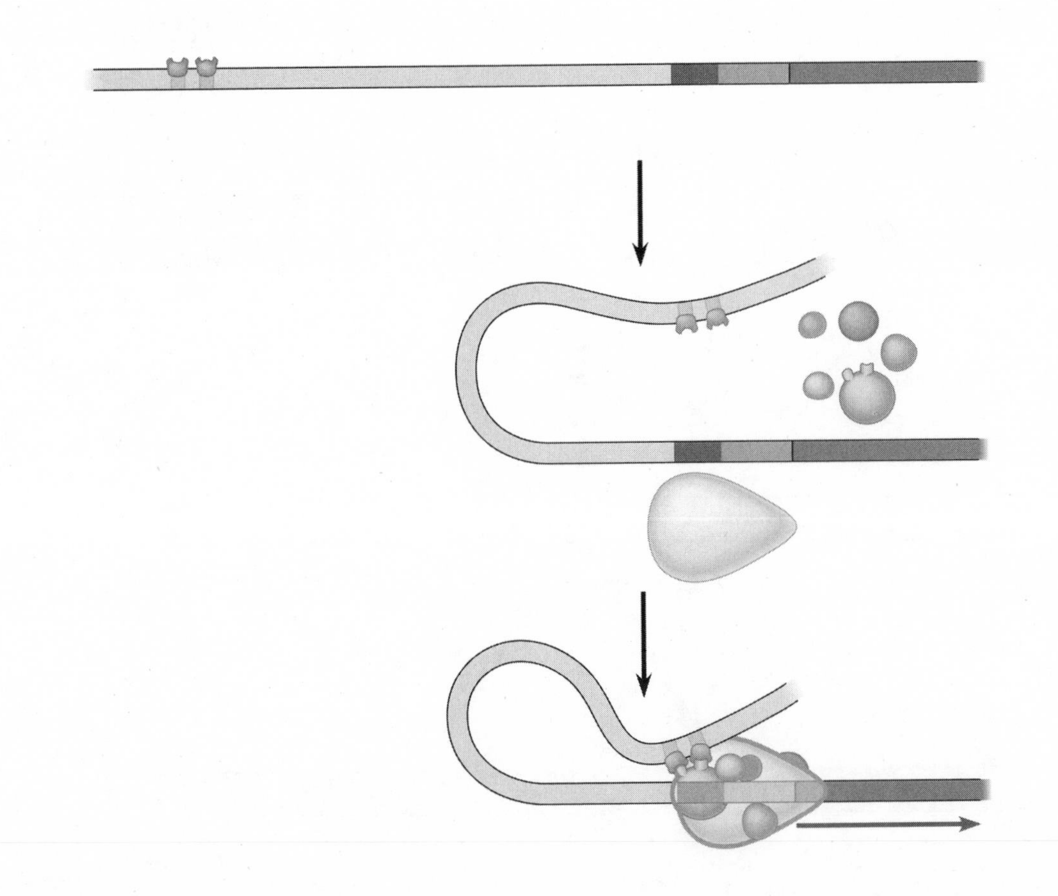

Figure 19.9 A model for enhancer action, page 365

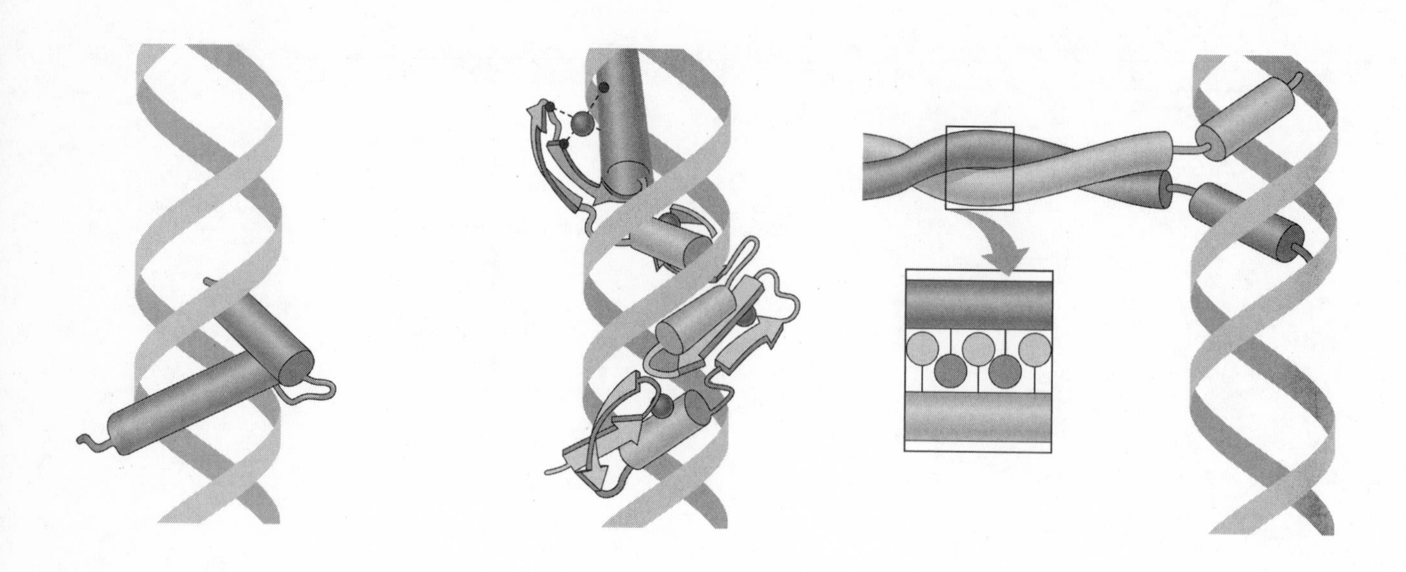

Figure 19.10 Three of the major types of DNA-binding domains in transcription factors, page 366

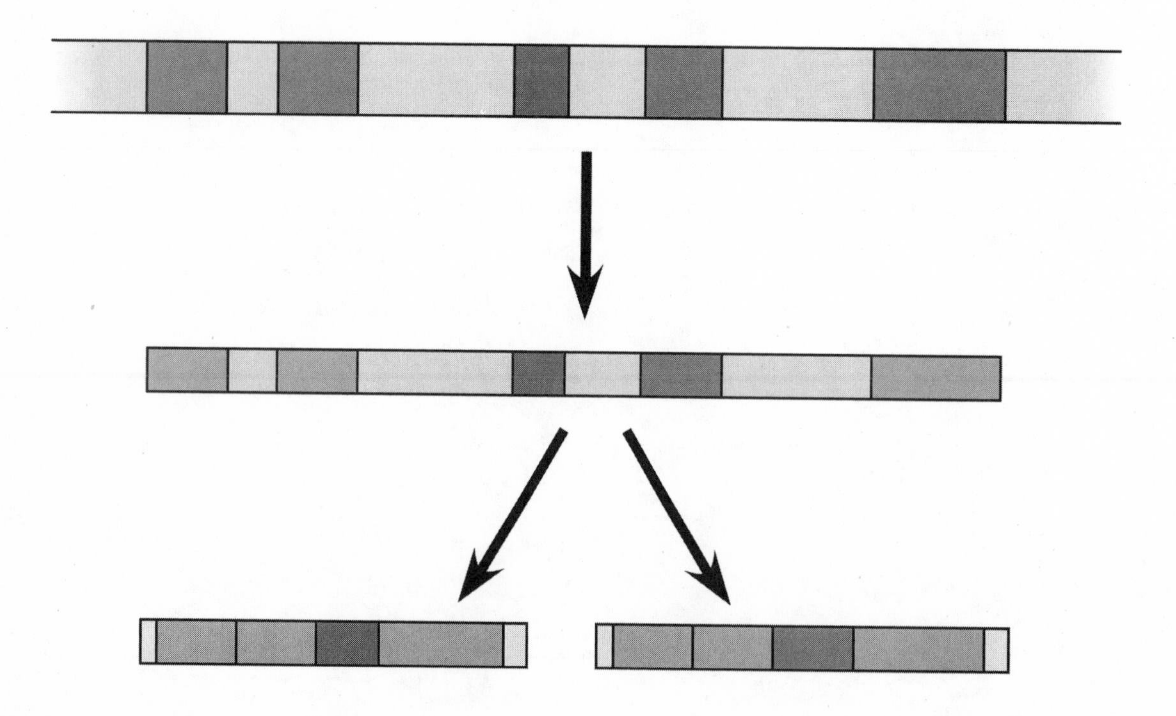

Figure 19.11 Alternative RNA splicing, page 367

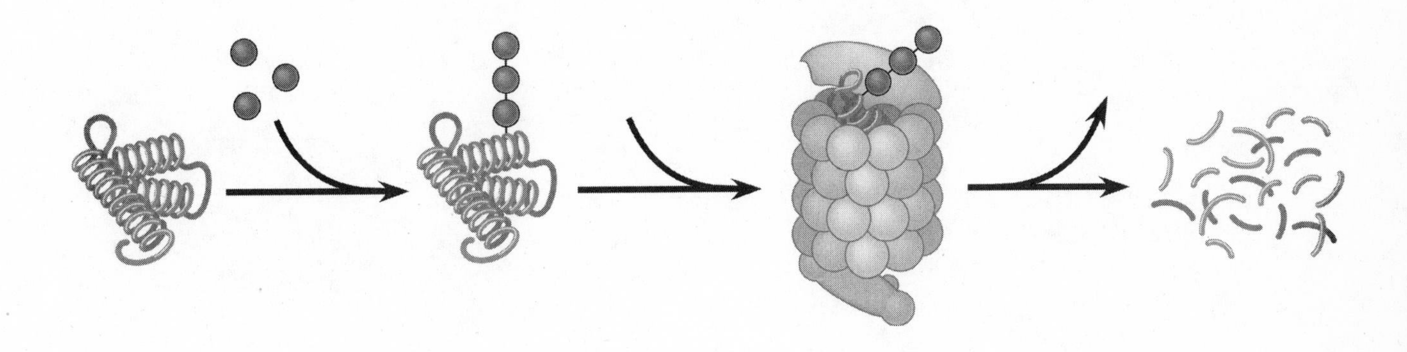

Figure 19.12 Degradation of a protein by a proteasome, page 368

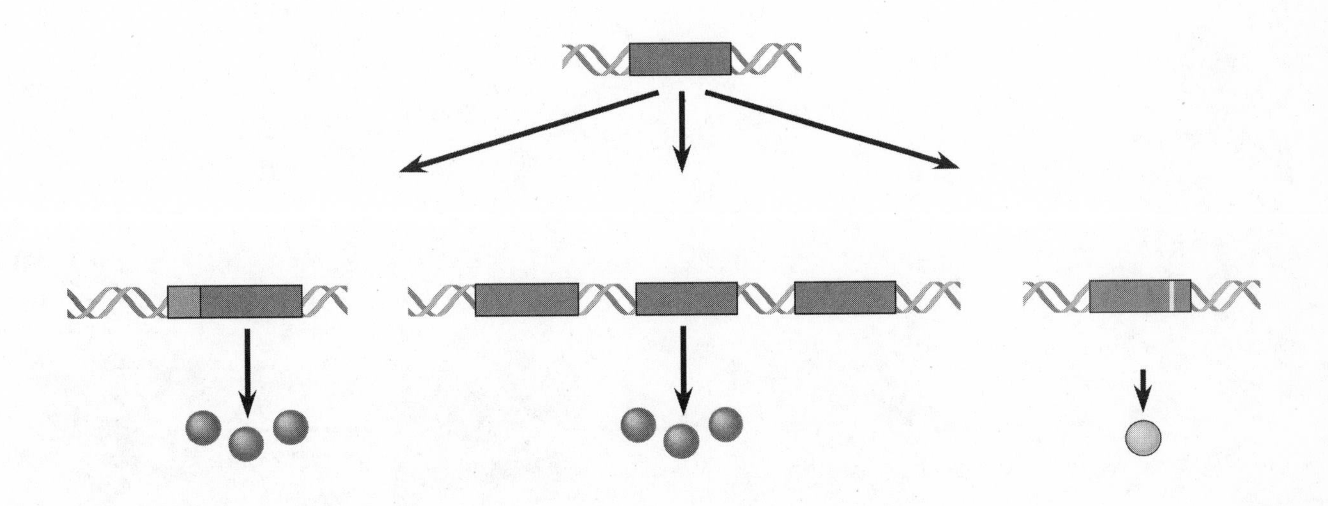

Figure 19.13 Genetic changes that can turn proto-oncogenes into oncogenes, page 369

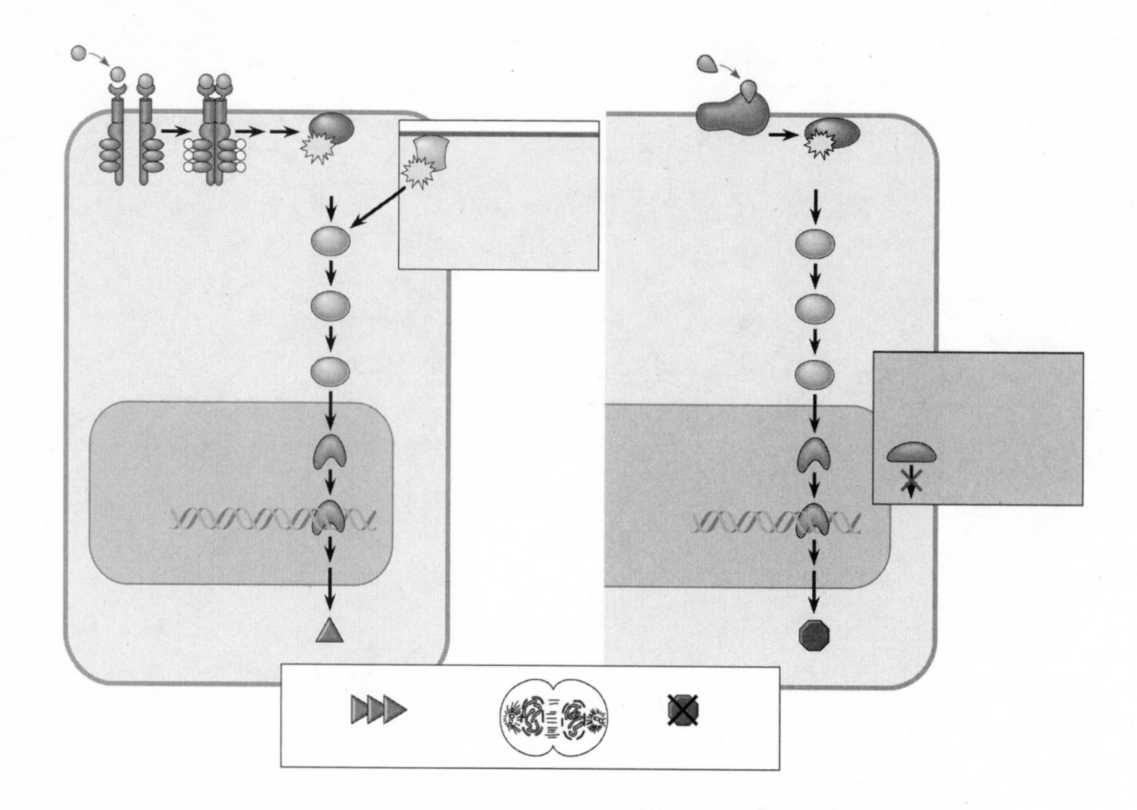

Figure 19.14 Signaling pathways that regulate cell growth, page 370

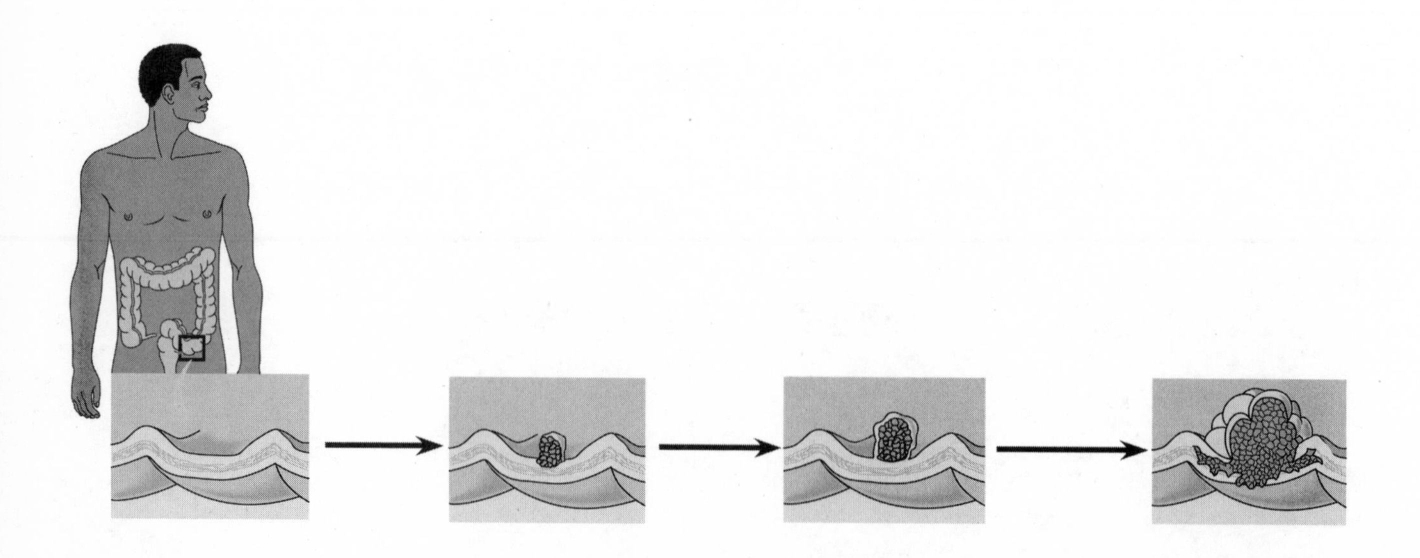

Figure 19.15 A multi-step model for the development of colorectal cancer, page 371

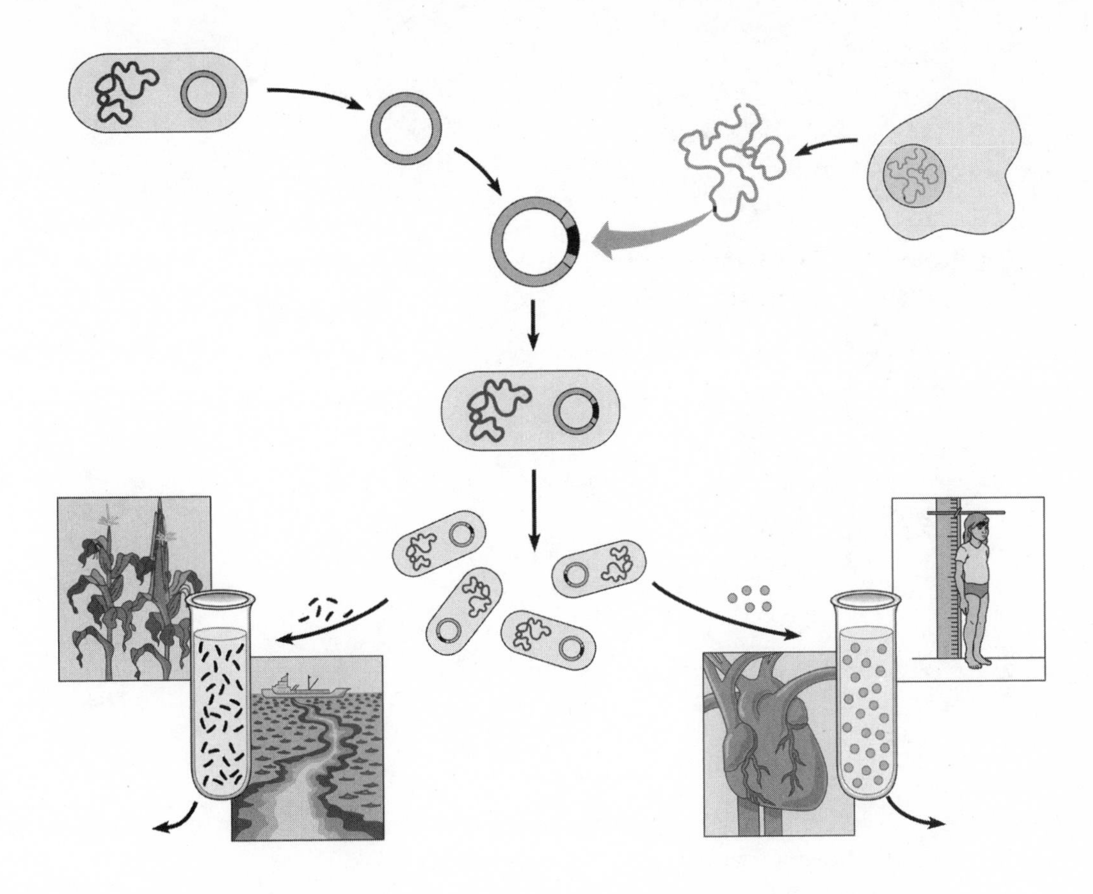

Figure 20.1 An overview of how bacterial plasmids are used to clone genes, page 376

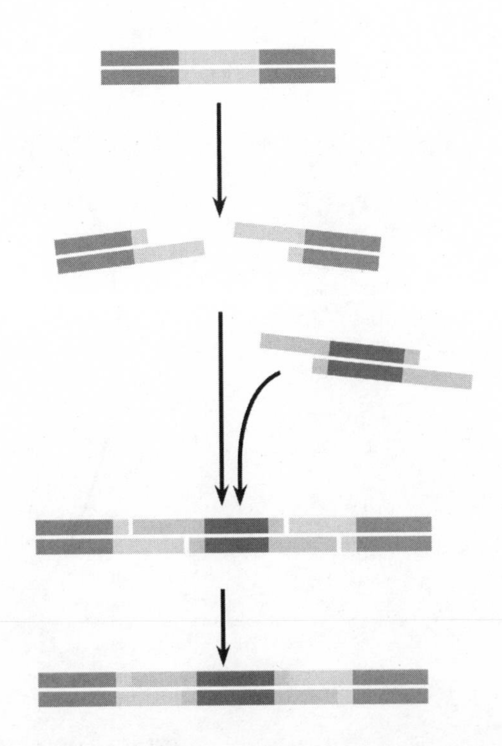

Figure 20.2 Using a restriction enzyme and DNA ligase to make recombinant DNA, page 377

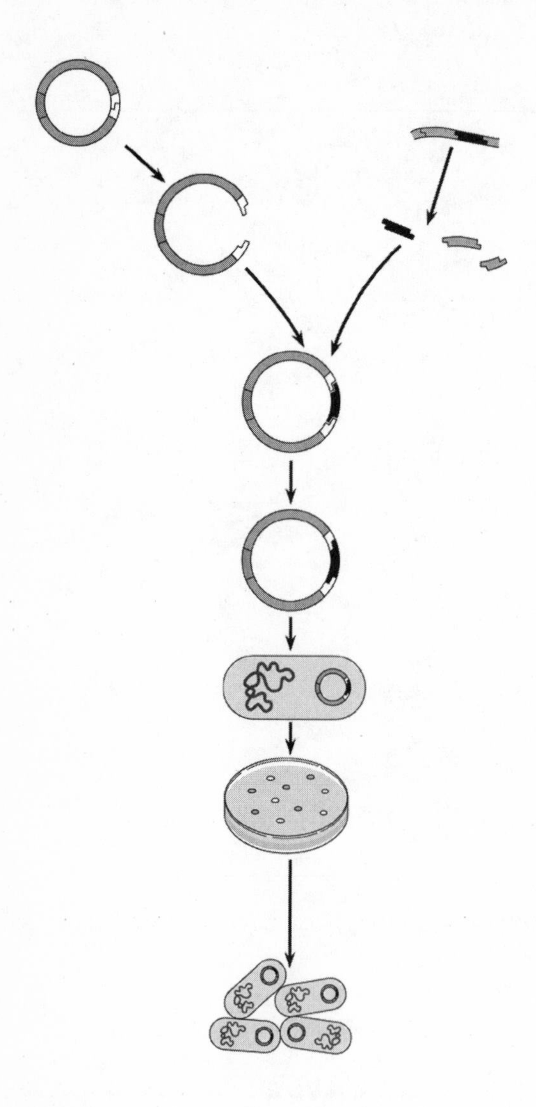

Figure 20.3 Cloning a human gene in a bacterial plasmid: a closer look, page 378

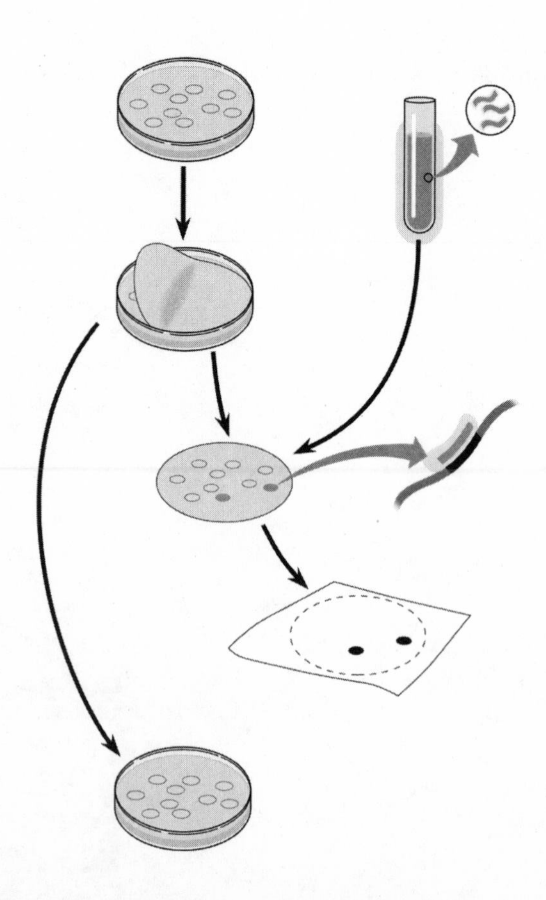

Figure 20.4 Using a nucleic acid probe to identify a cloned gene, page 380

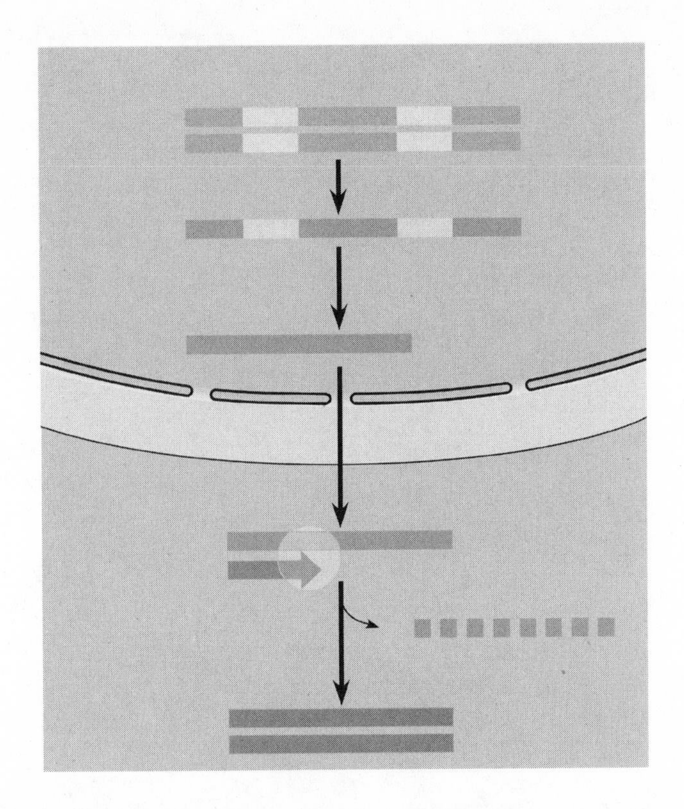

Figure 20.5 Making complementary DNA (cDNA) for a eukaryotic gene, page 380

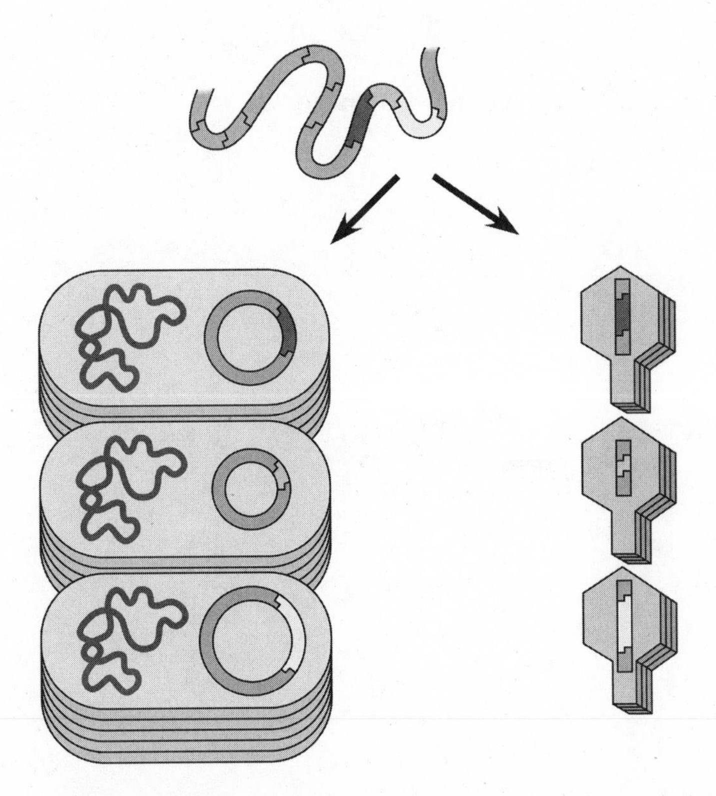

Figure 20.6 Genomic libraries, page 381

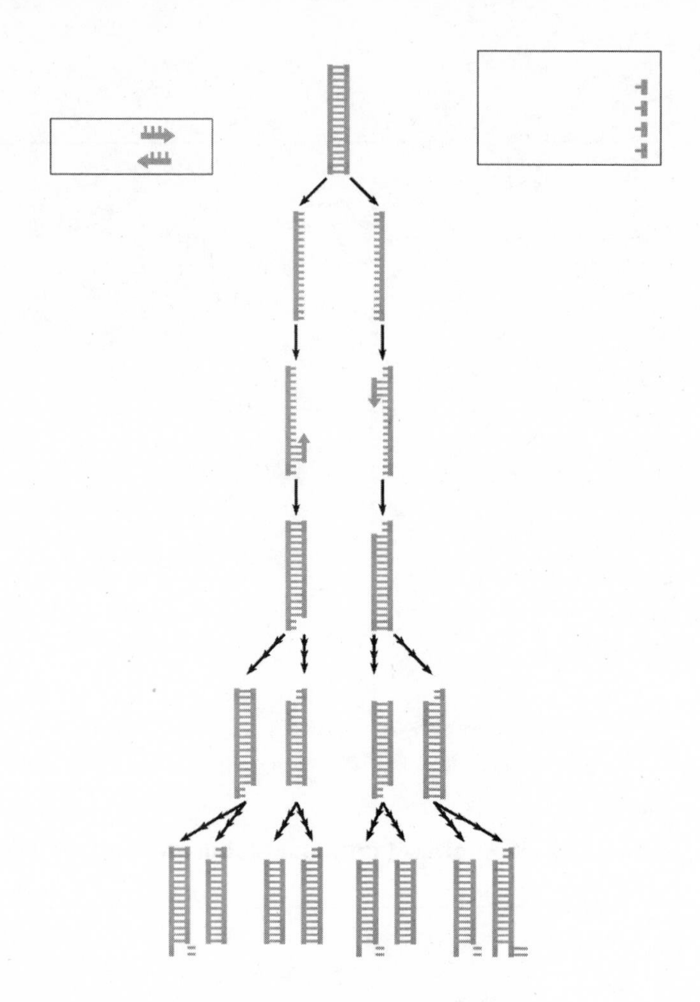

Figure 20.7 The polymerase chain on reaction (PCR), page 382

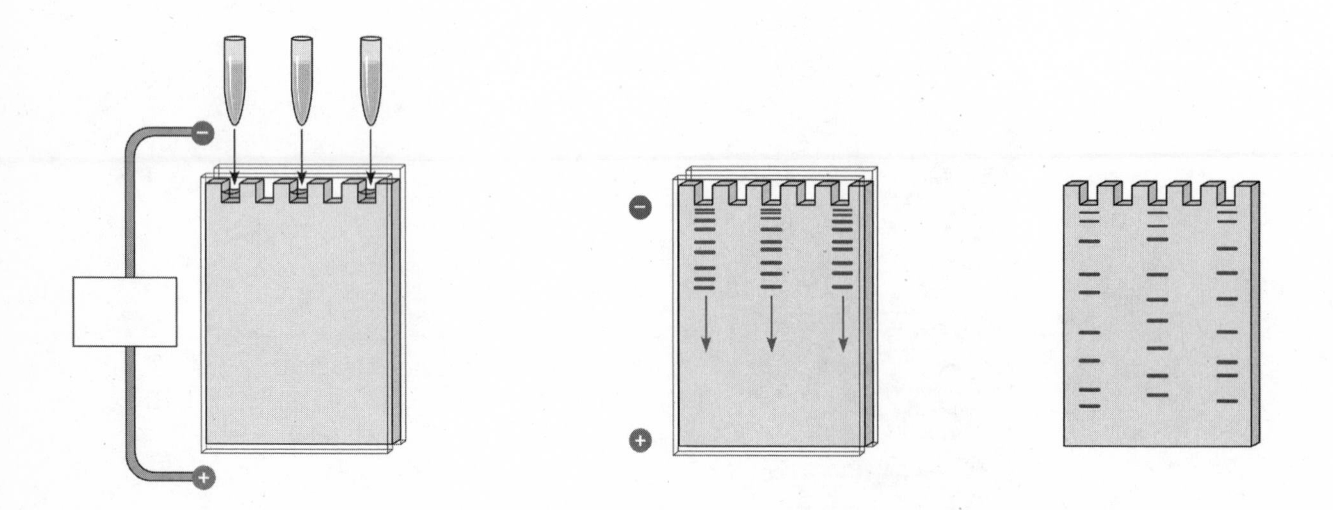

Figure 20.8 Gel electrophoresis of macromolecules, page 384

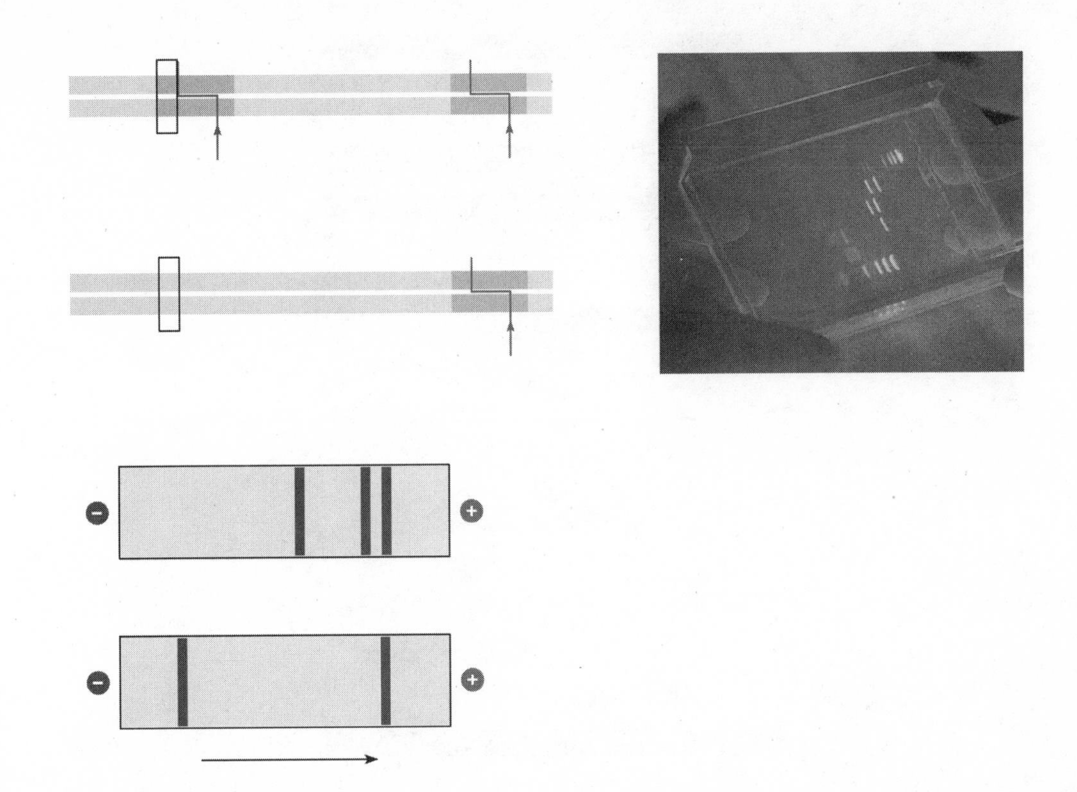

Figure 20.9 Using restriction fragment patterns to distinguish DNA from different alleles, page 384

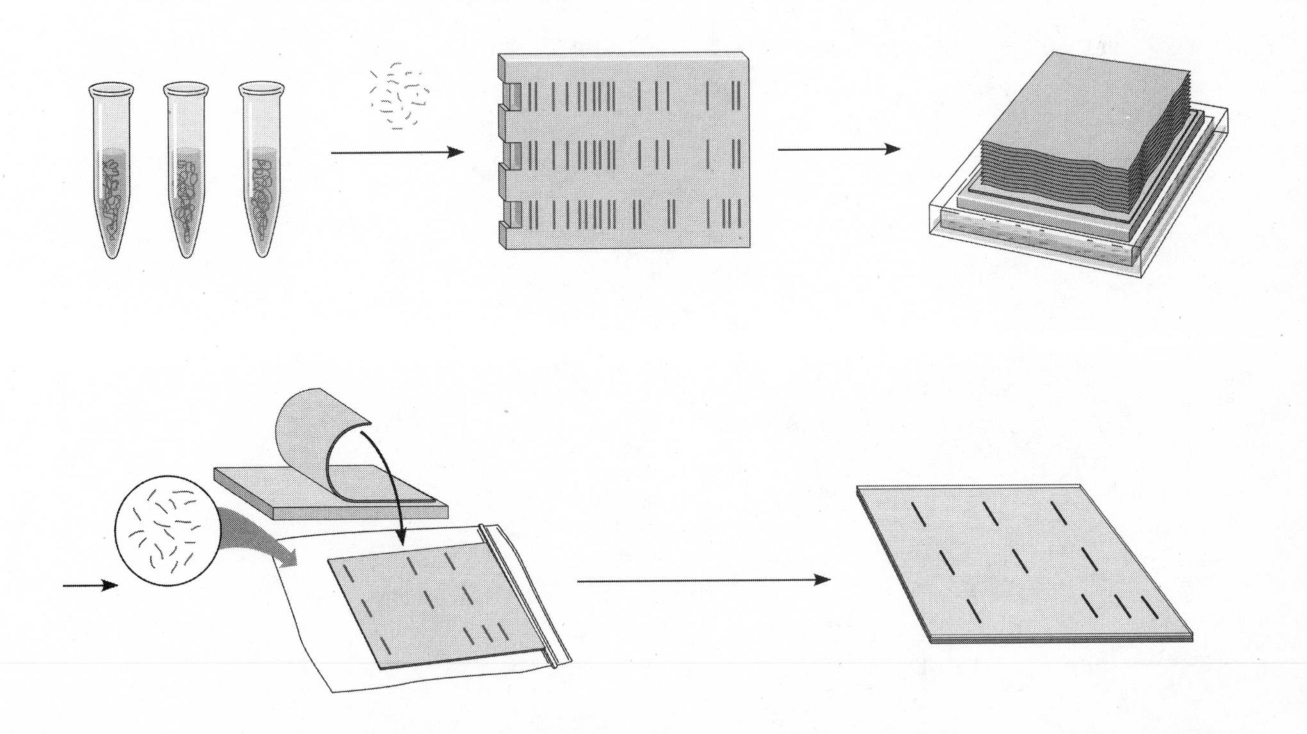

Figure 20.10 Restriction fragment analysis by Southern blotting, page 385

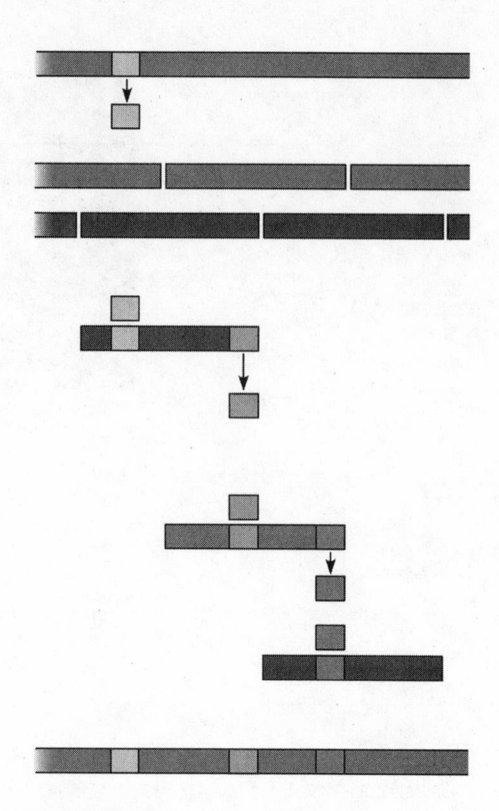

Figure 20.11 Chromosome walking, page 387

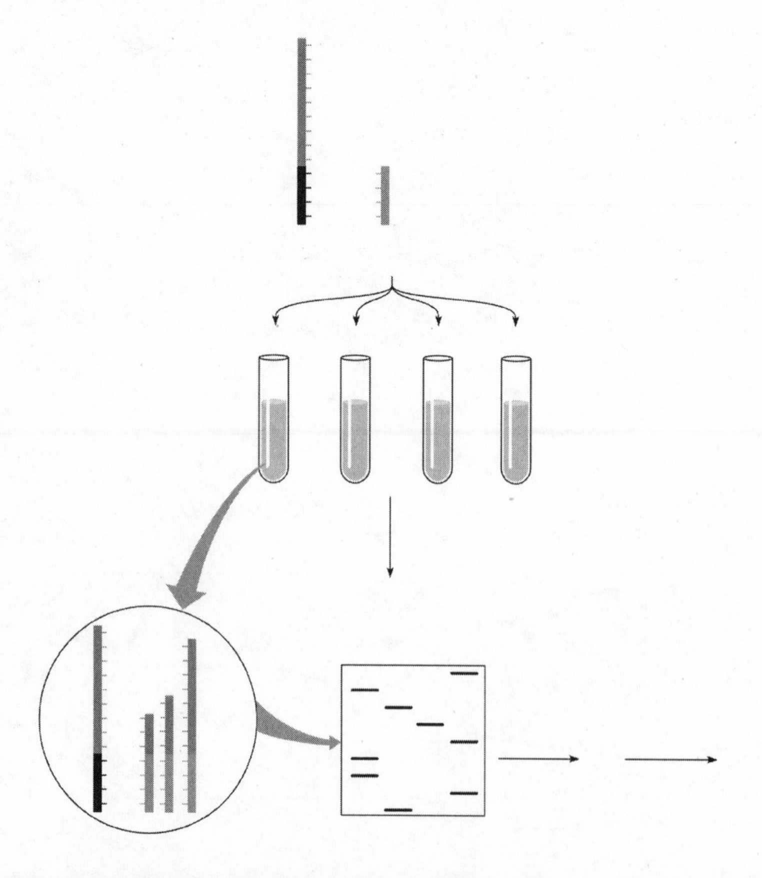

Figure 20.12 Sequencing of DNA by the Sanger method, page 388

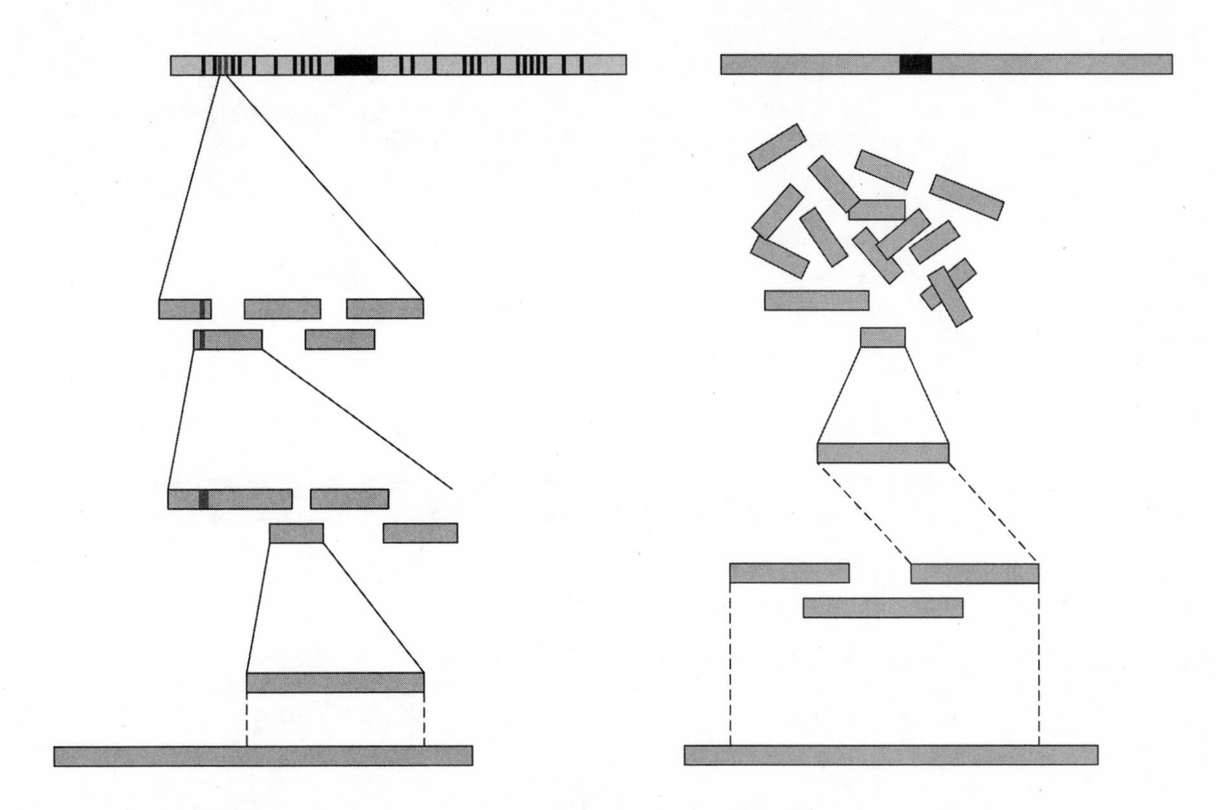

Figure 20.13 Alternative strategies for sequencing an entire genome, page 389

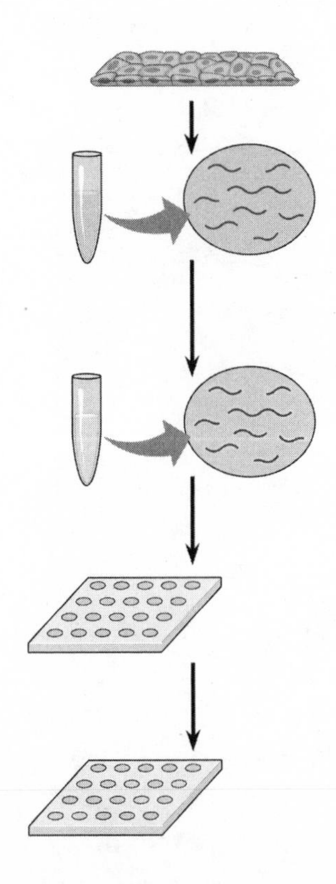

Figure 20.14a DNA microarray assay for gene expression, page 391

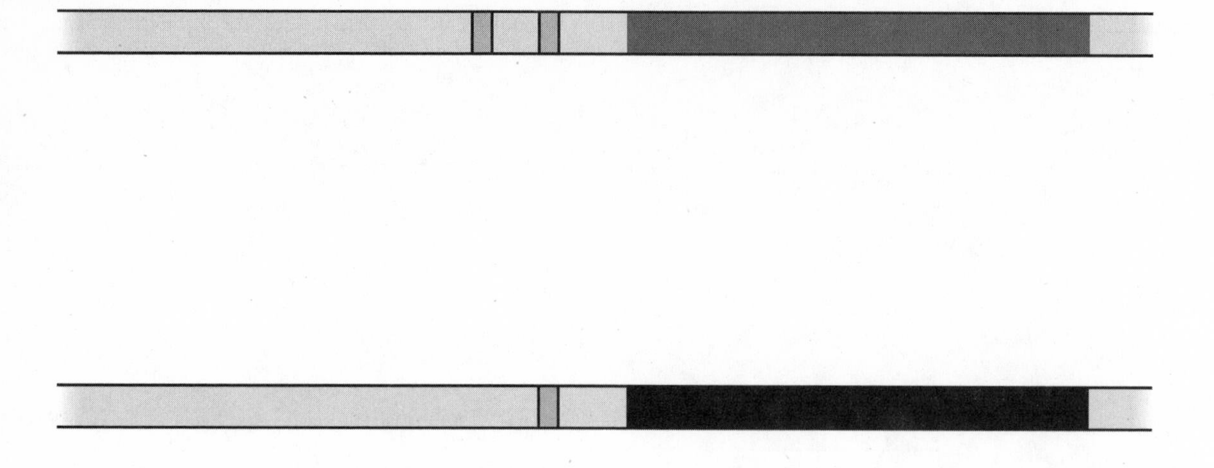

Figure 20.15 RFLP makers close to a gene, page 393

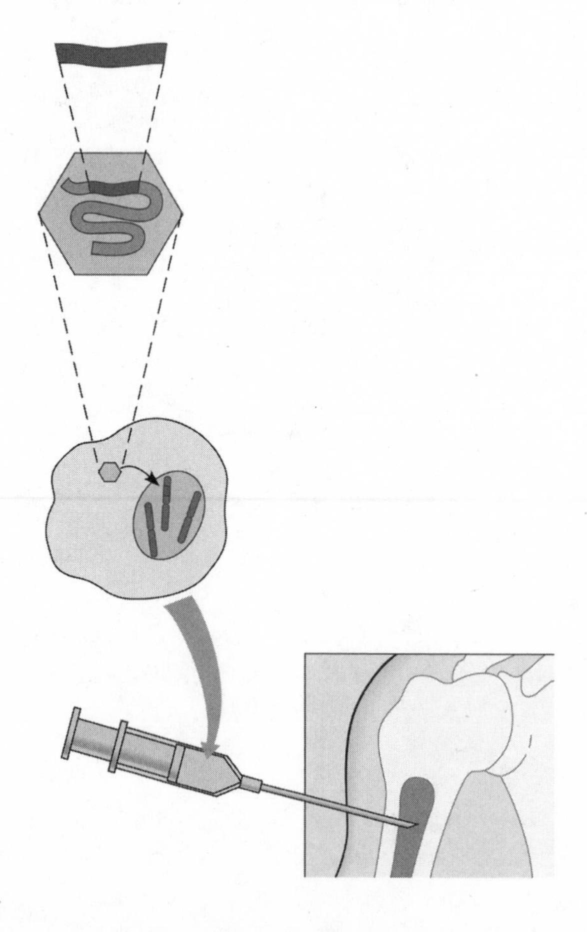

Figure 20.16 One type of gene therapy procedure, page 394

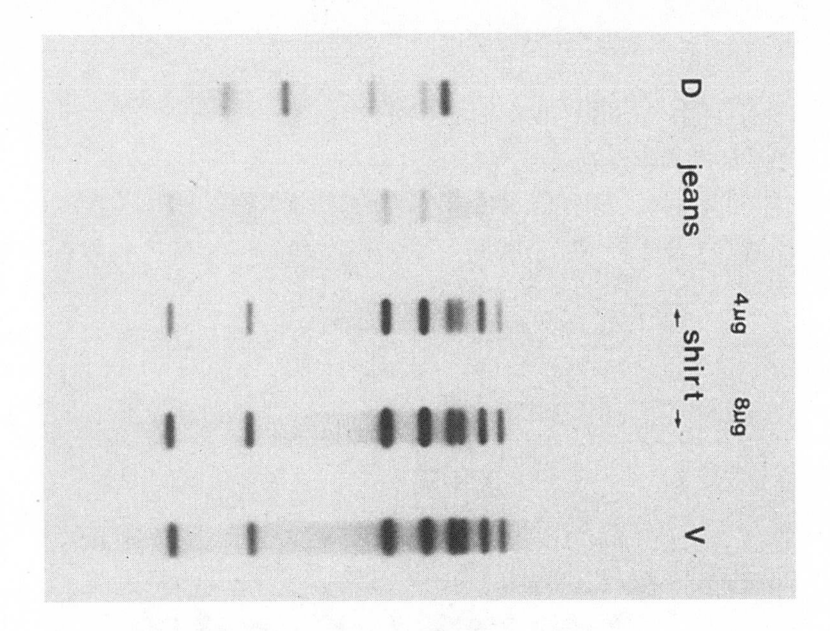

Figure 20.17 DNA fingerprints from a murder case, page 396

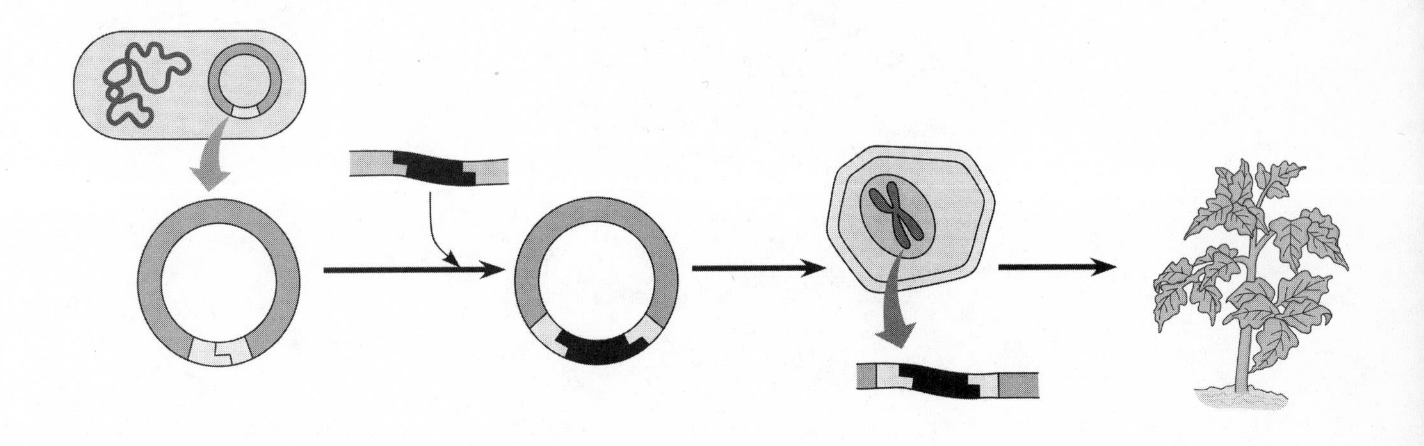

Figure 20.19 Using the Ti plasmid as a vector for genetic engineering in plants, page 398

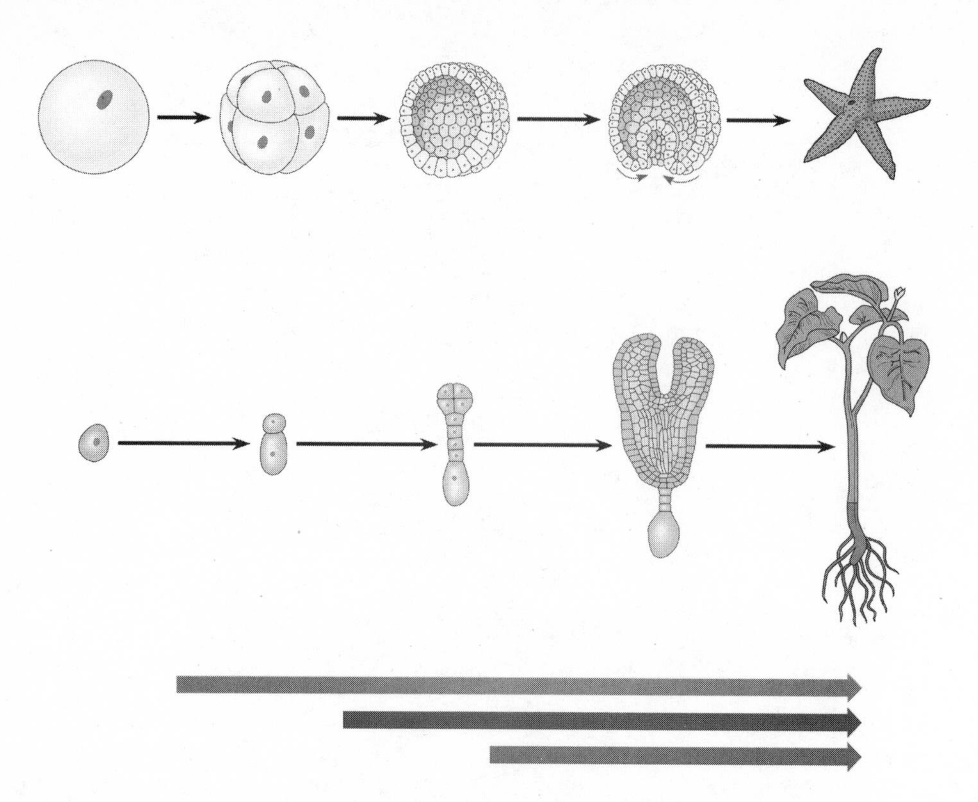

Figure 21.2 Some key stages of development in animals and plants, page 404

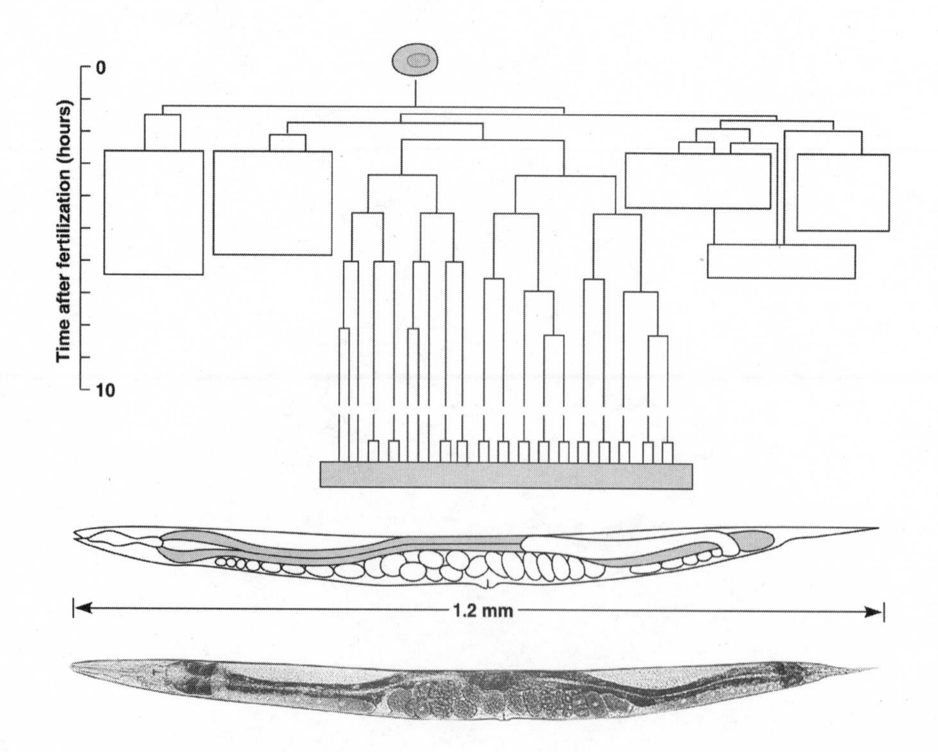

Figure 21.4 Cell lineage in *C. elegans*, page 406

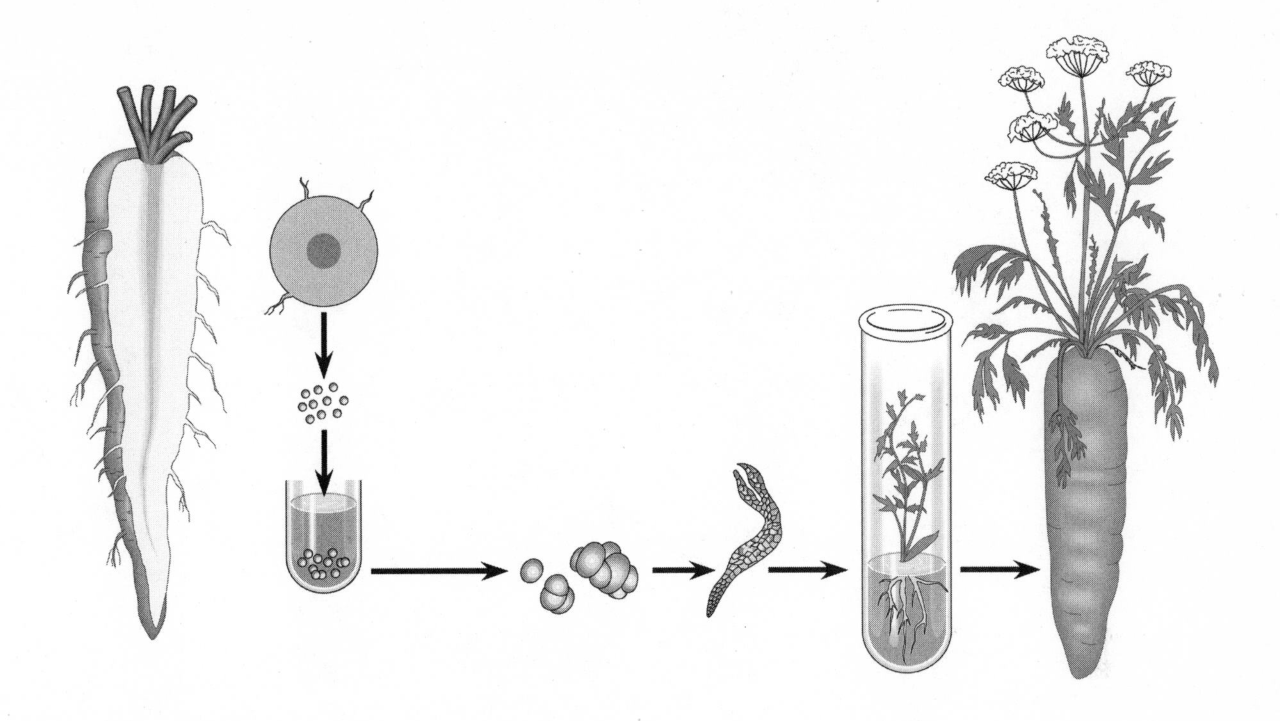

Figure 21.5 Test-tube cloning of carrots, page 407

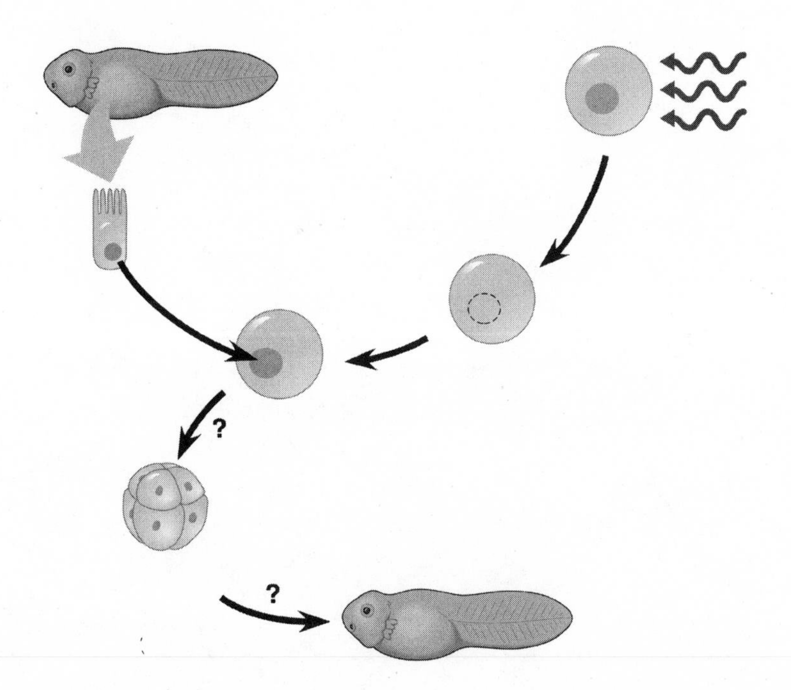

Figure 21.6 Nuclear transplantation, page 407

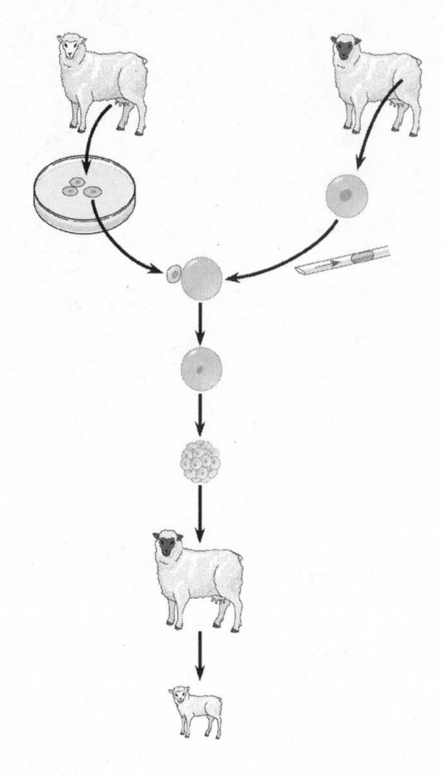

Figure 21.7 Cloning a mammal, page 408

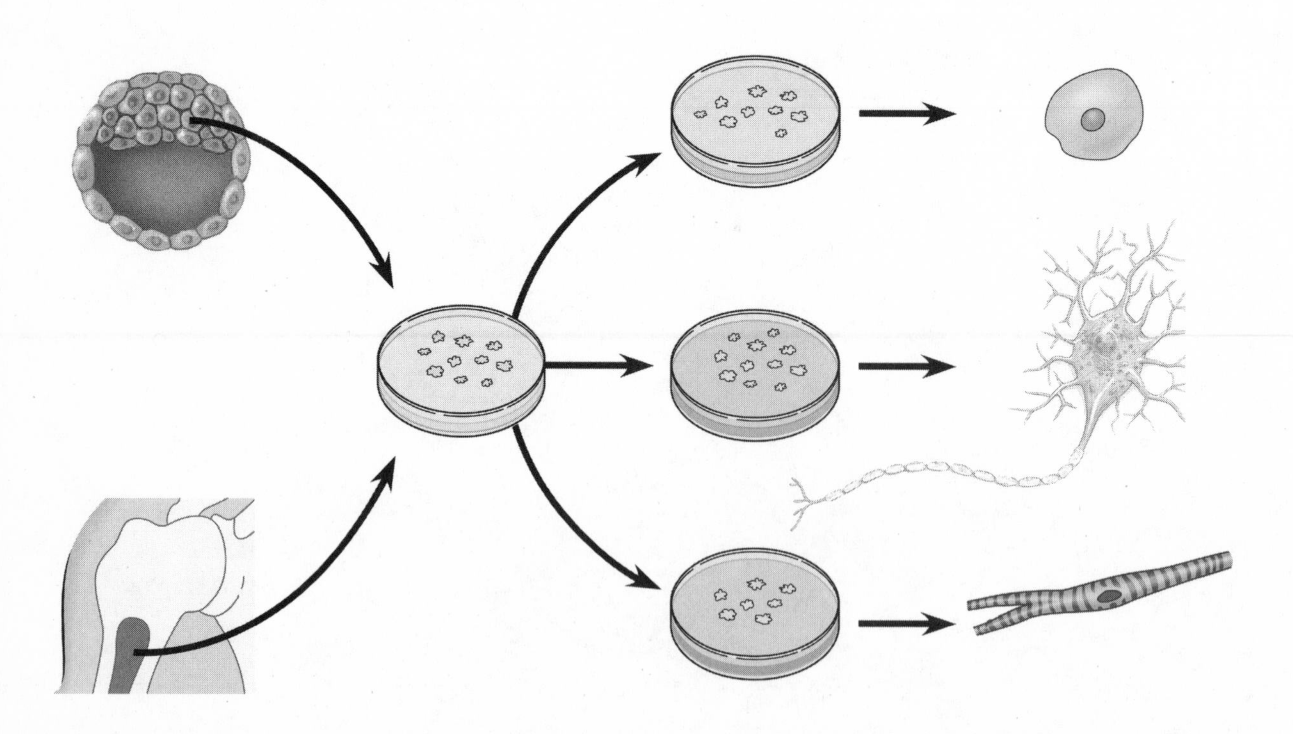

Figure 21.8 Working with stem cells, page 409

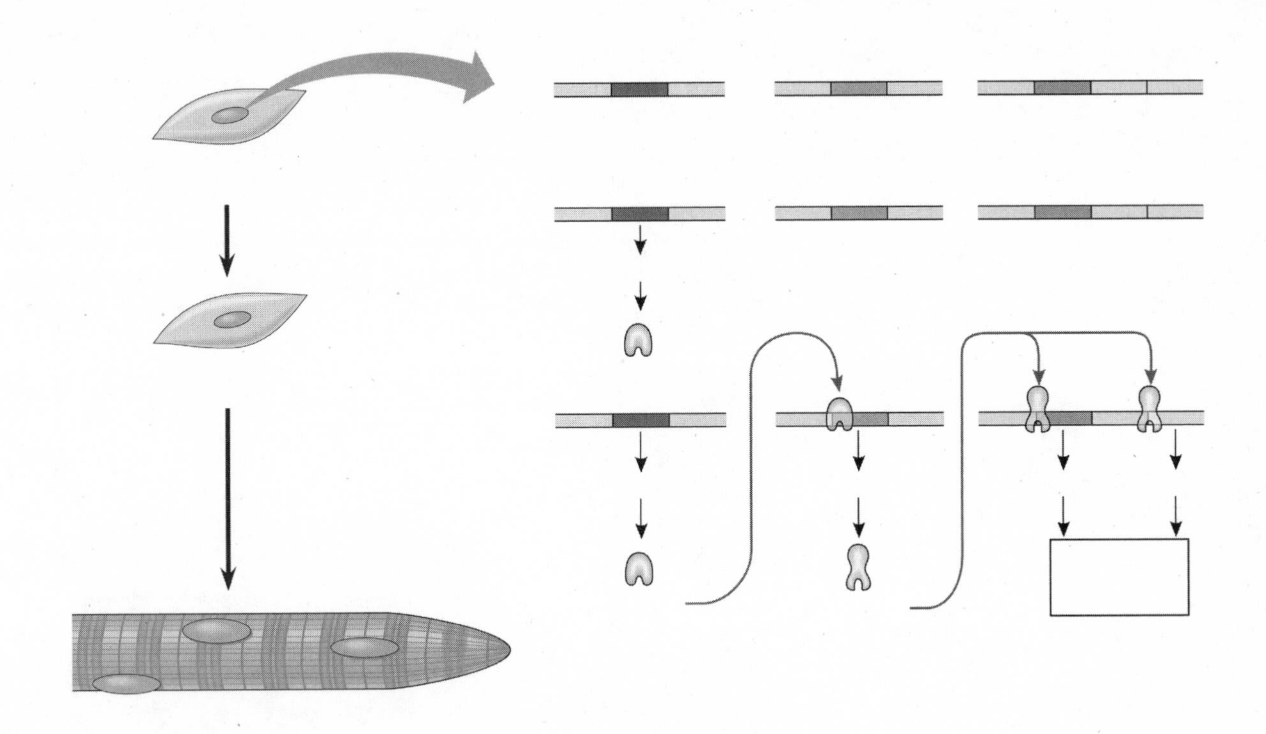

Figure 21.9 Determination and differentiation of muscle cells, page 411

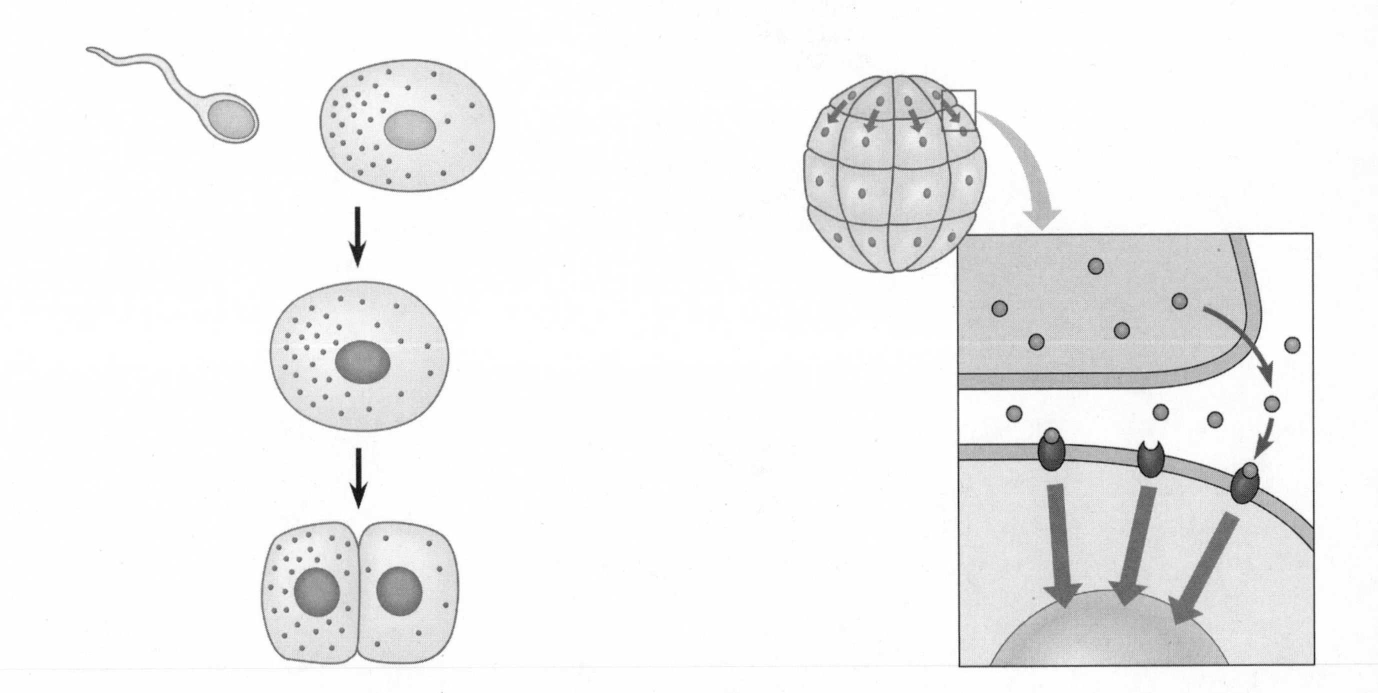

Figure 21.10 Sources of developmental information for the early embryo, page 412

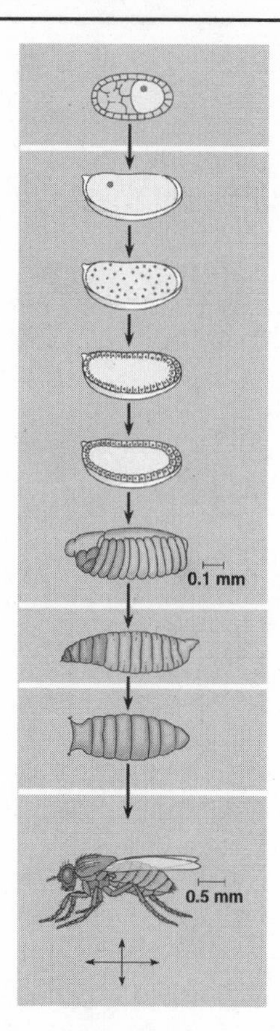

Figure 21.11 Key developmental events in the life cycle of *Drosophila*, page 413

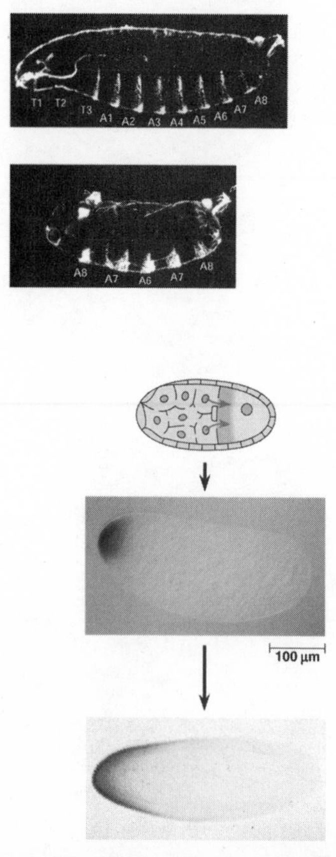

Figure 21.12 The effect of the *bicoid* gene, a material effect (egg-polarity) gene in *Drosophila*, page 415

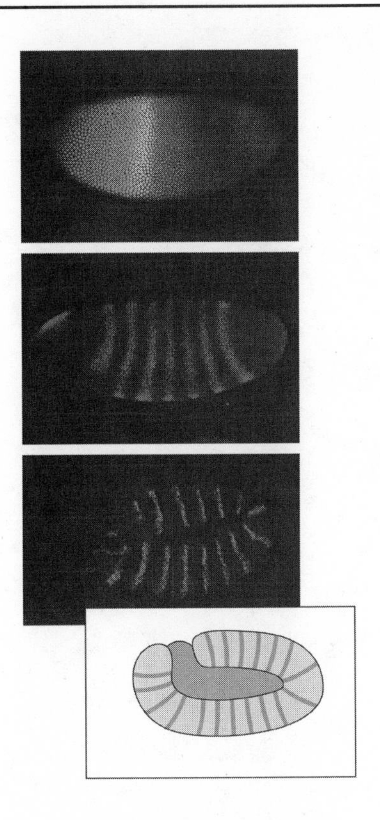

Figure 21.13 Segmentation genes in *Drosophila*, page 416

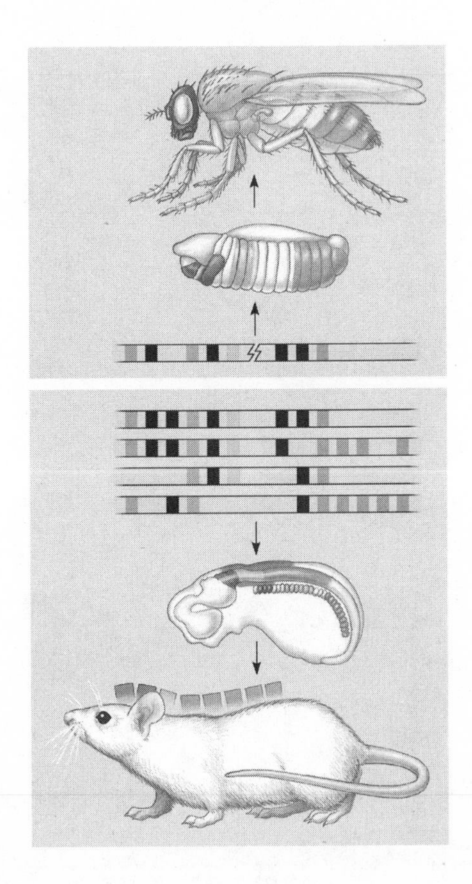

Figure 21.15 Homologous genes that affect pattern formation in a fruit fly and a mouse, page 418

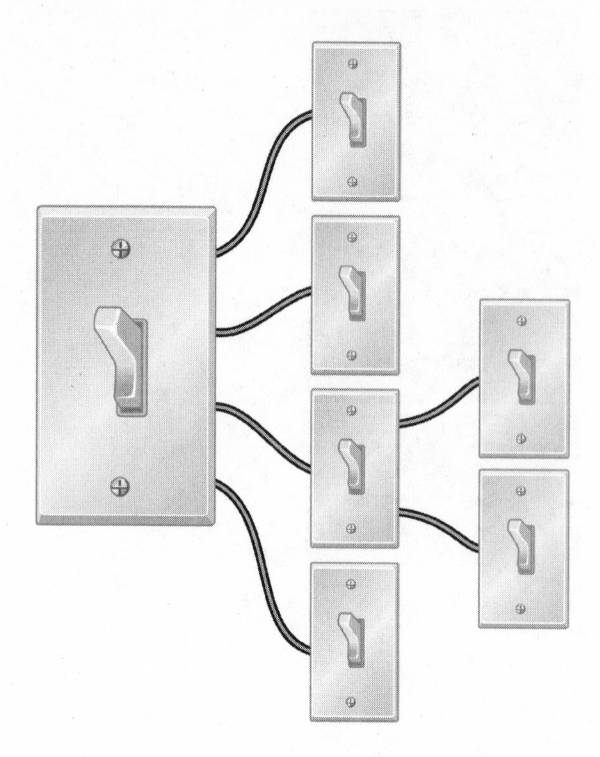

Figure 21.16 Homeobox-containing genes as switches, page 418

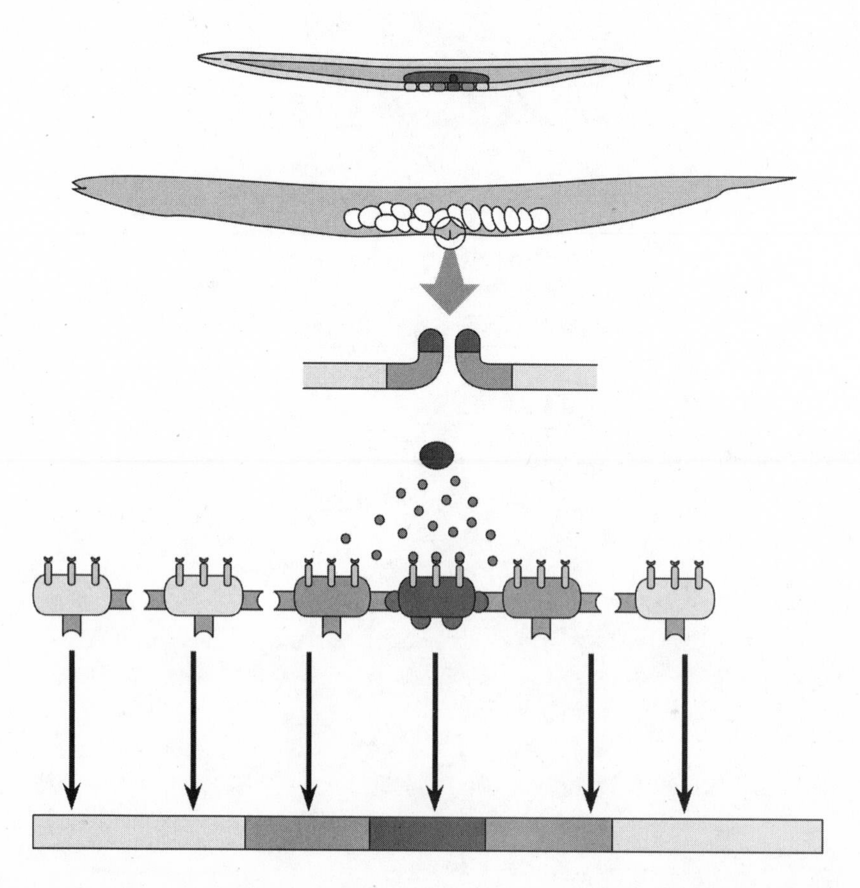

Figure 21.17 Cell signaling and induction in the development of the nematode vulva, page 419

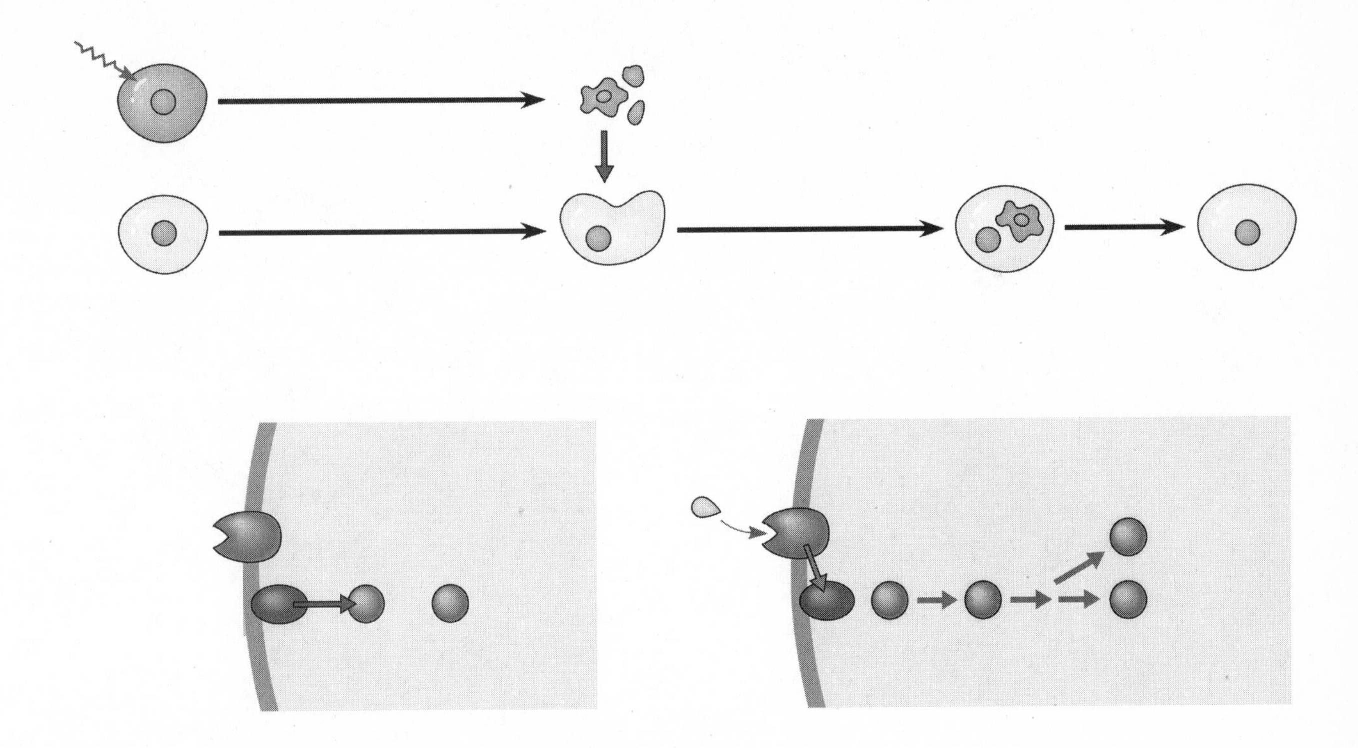

Figure 21.18 Apoptosis (programmed cell death), page 420

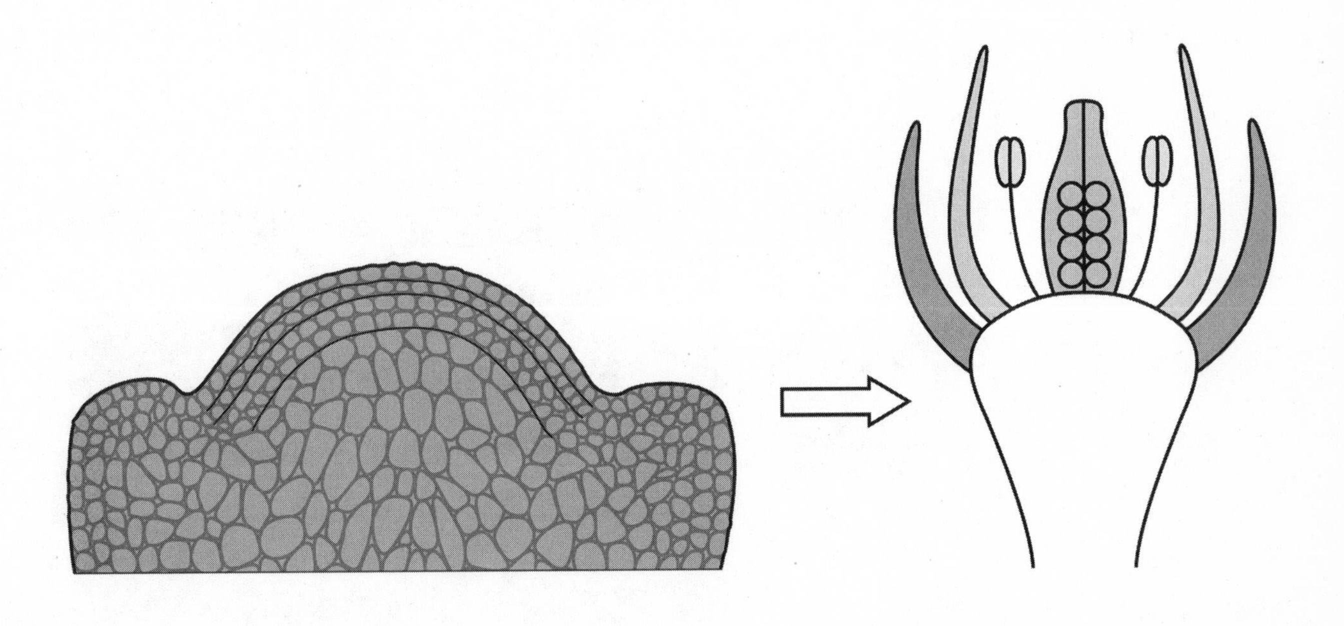

Figure 21.19 Induction in flower development, page 422

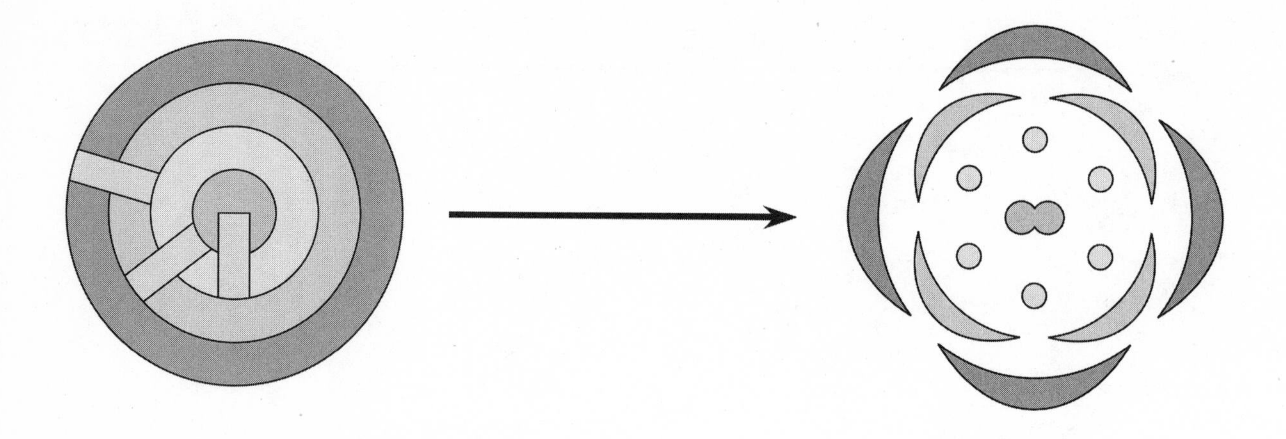

Figure 21.20a Organ identity genes and pattern formation in flower development: Normal flower development, page 423

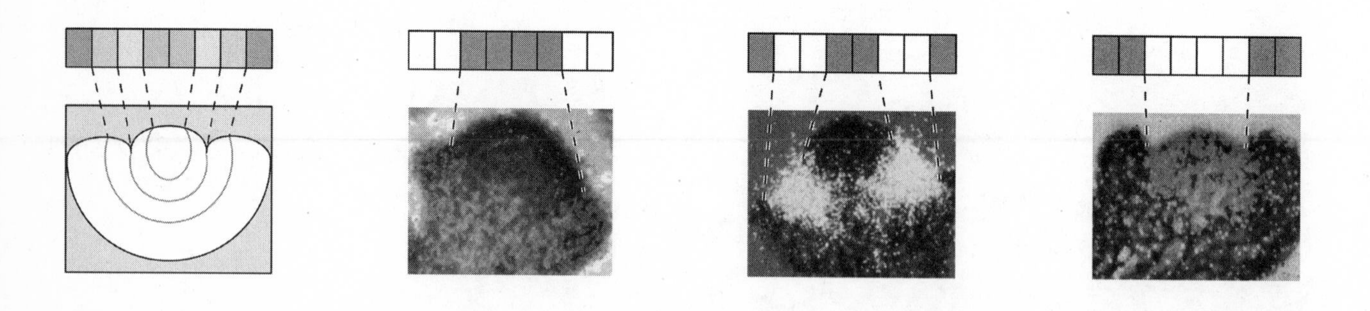

Figure 21.20b Organ identity genes and pattern formation in flower development: *In situ* hybridization, page 423

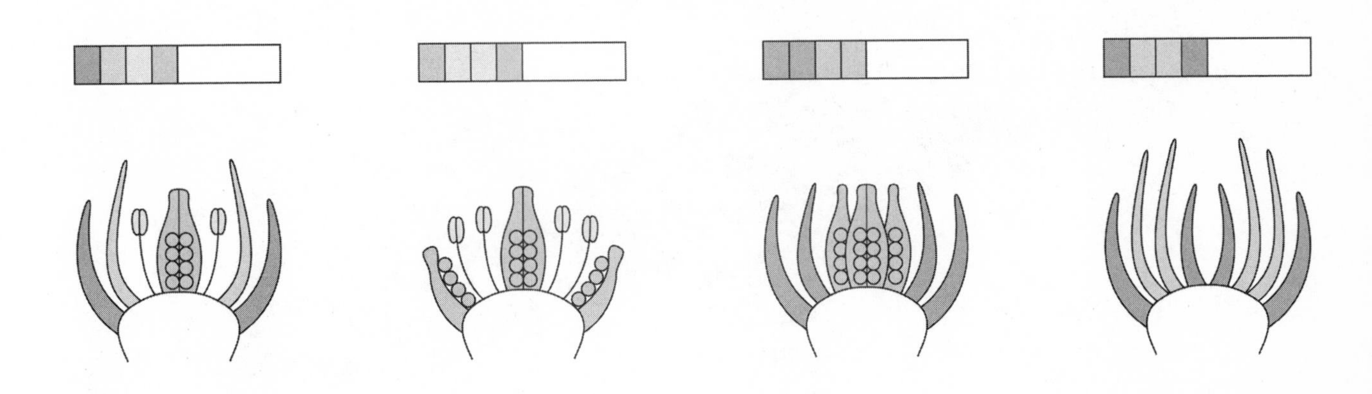

Figure 21.20c Organ identity genes and pattern formation in flower development: Organ identity mutants, page 423

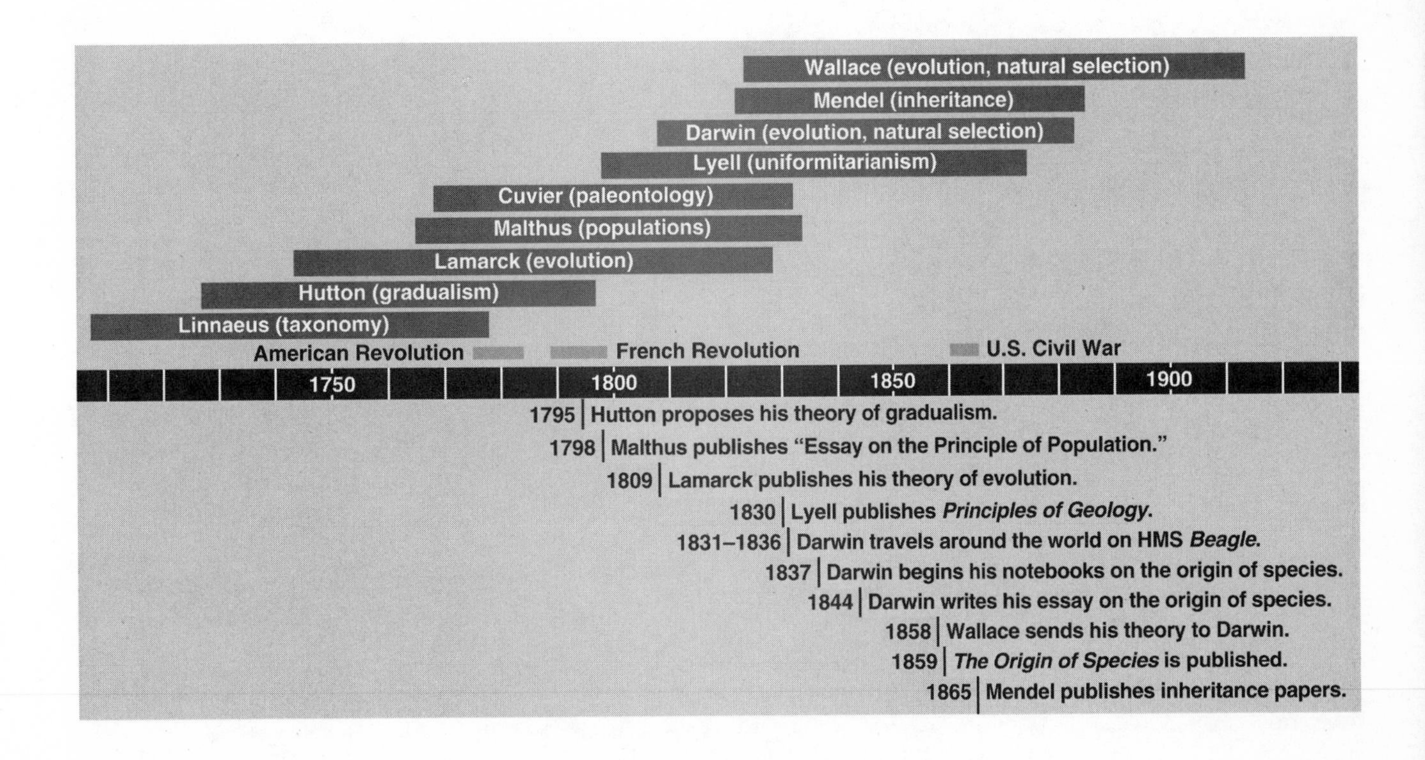

Figure 22.1 The historical context of Darwin's life and ideas, page 429

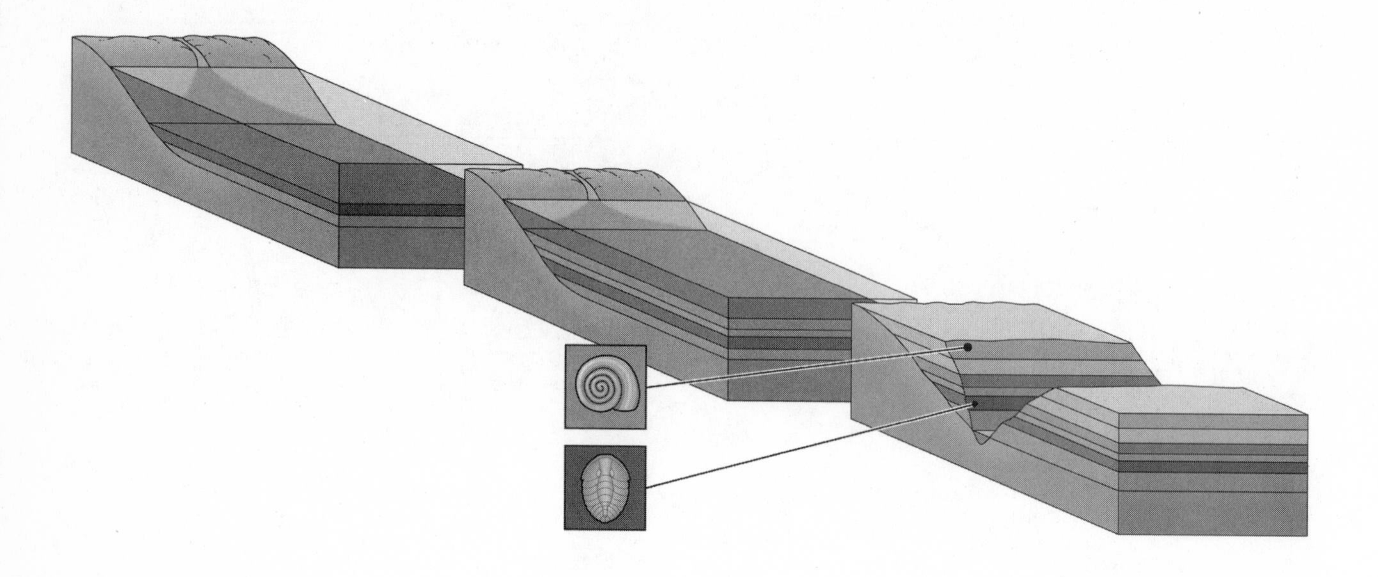

Figure 22.3 Formation of sedimentary rock and deposition of fossils from different time periods, page 430

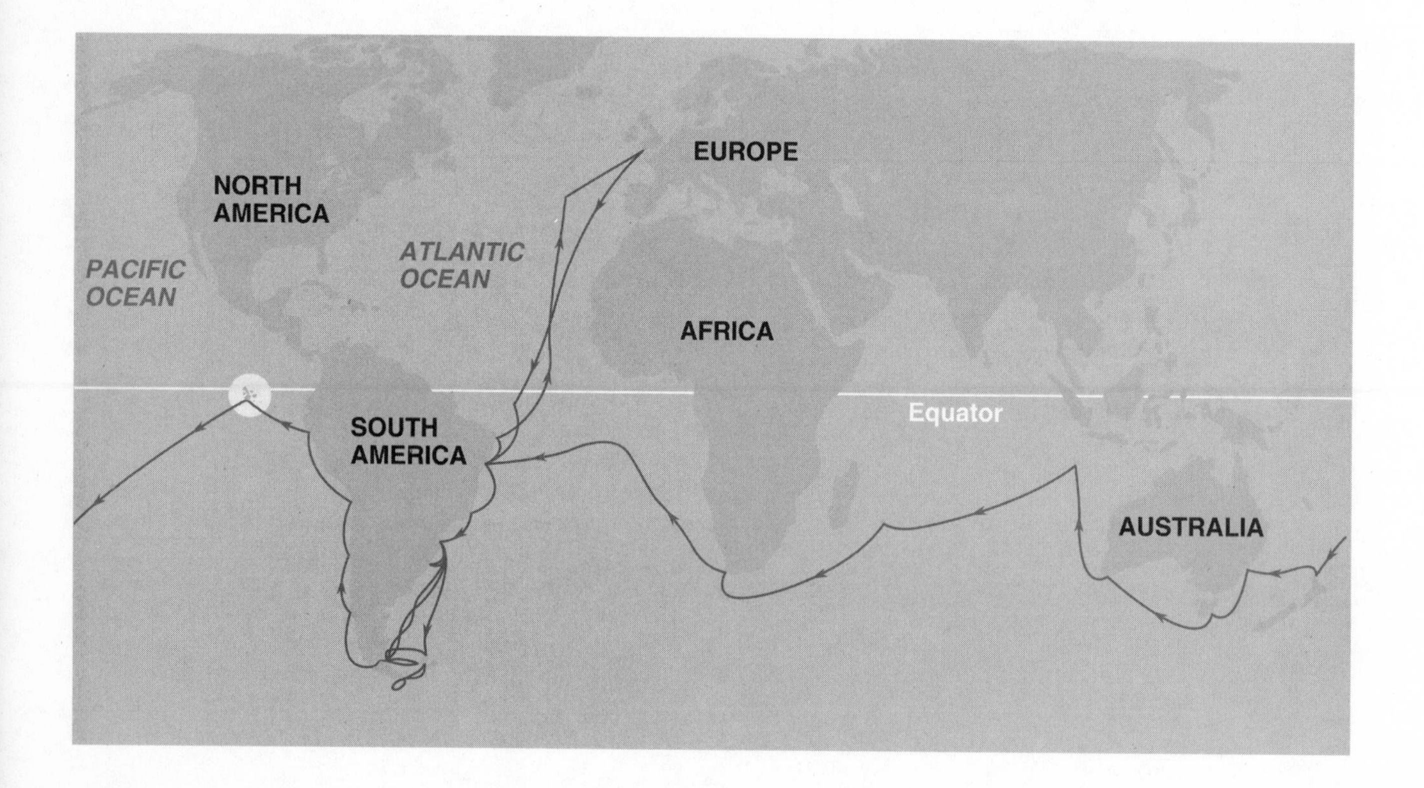

Figure 22.5 The Voyage of HMS *Beagle*, page 432

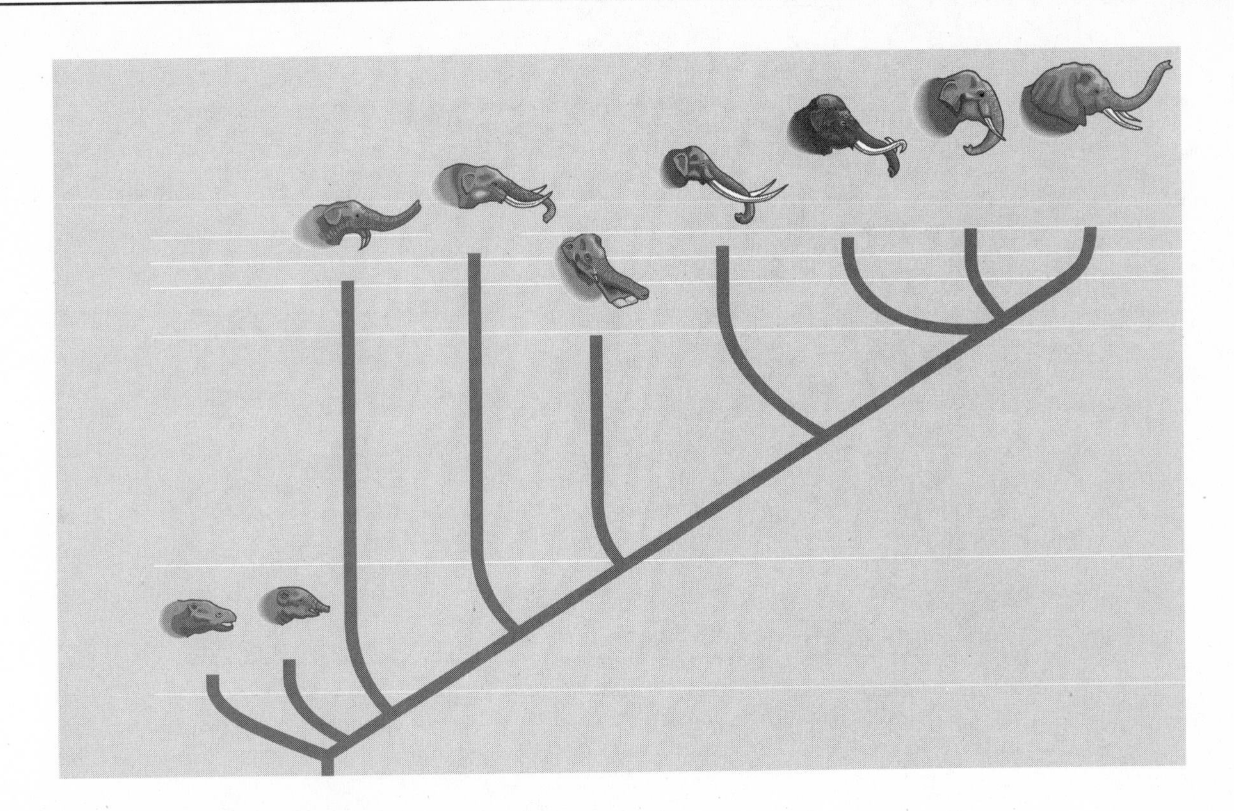

Figure 22.7 Descent with modification, page 434

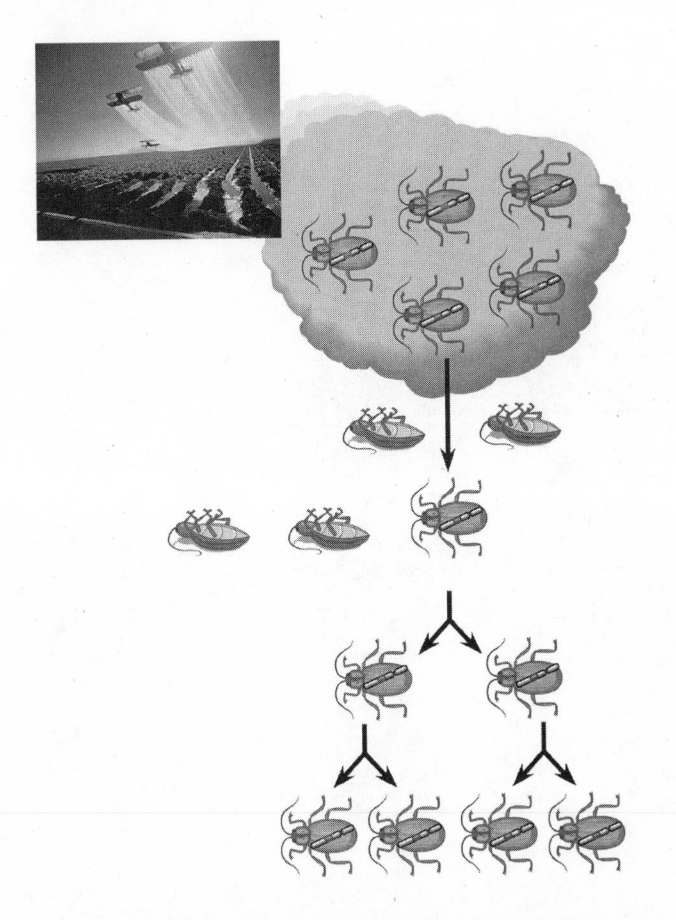

Figure 22.12 Evolution of insecticide resistance in insect populations, page 437

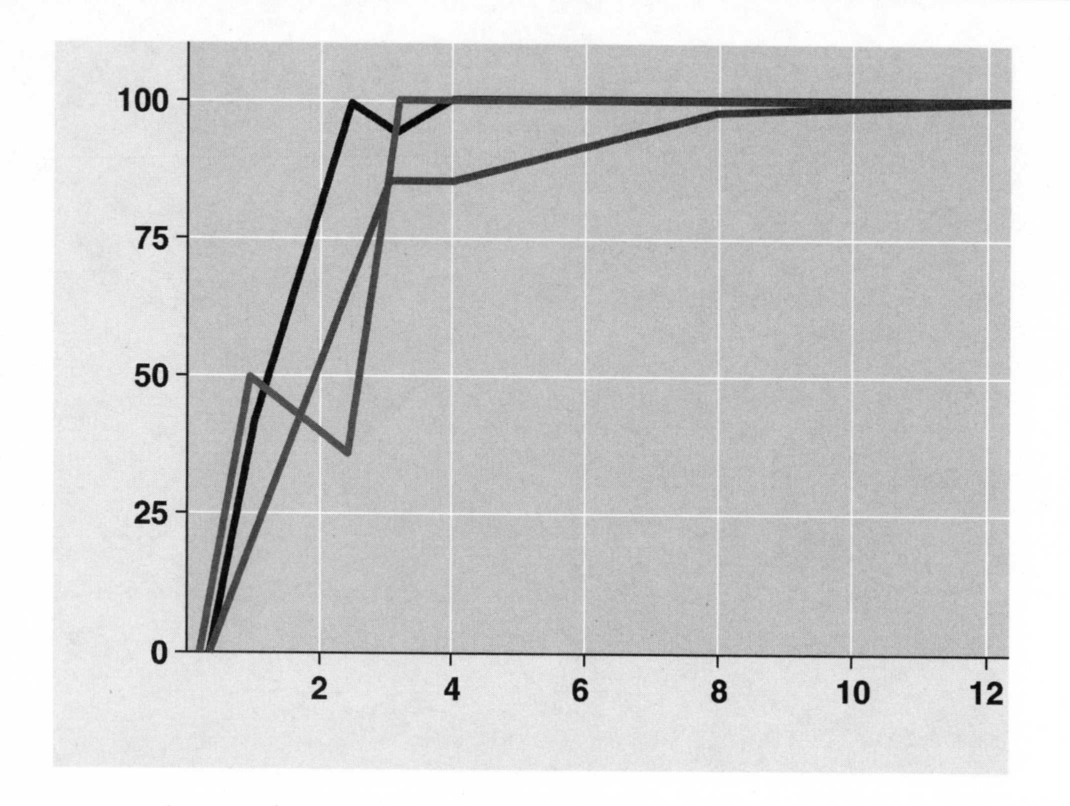

Figure 22.13 Evolution of drug resistance in HIV, page 438

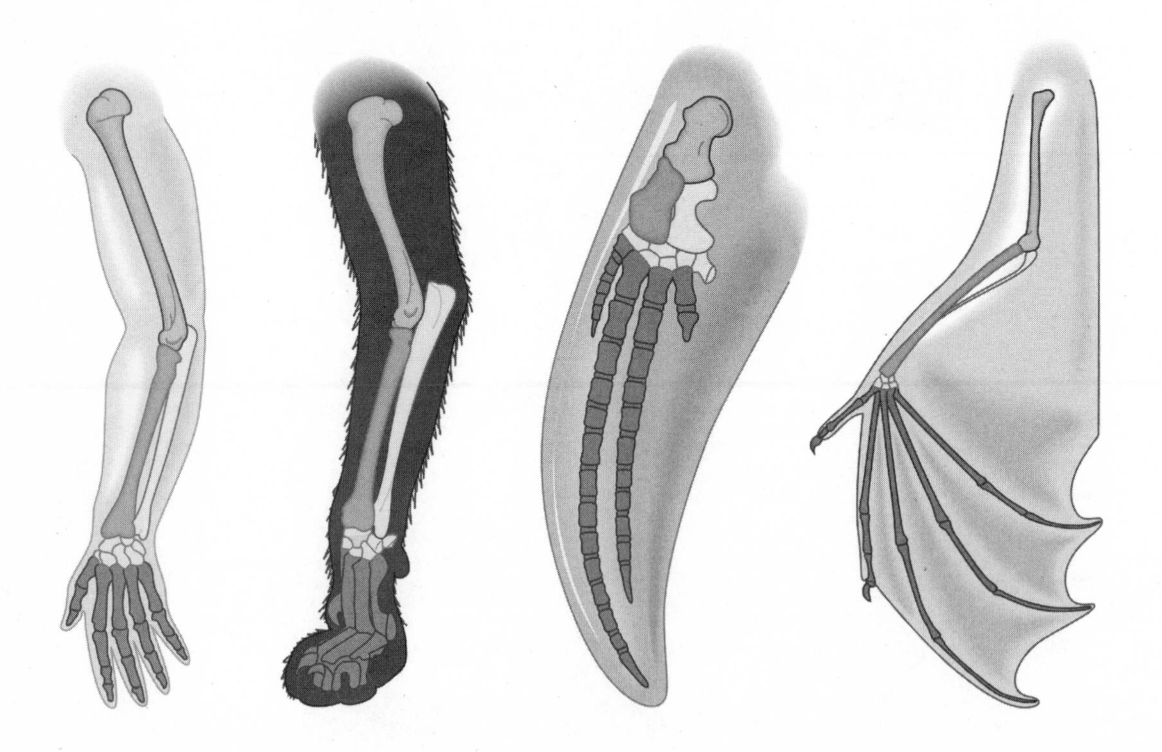

Figure 22.14 Homologous structures: anatomical signs of descent with modification, page 439

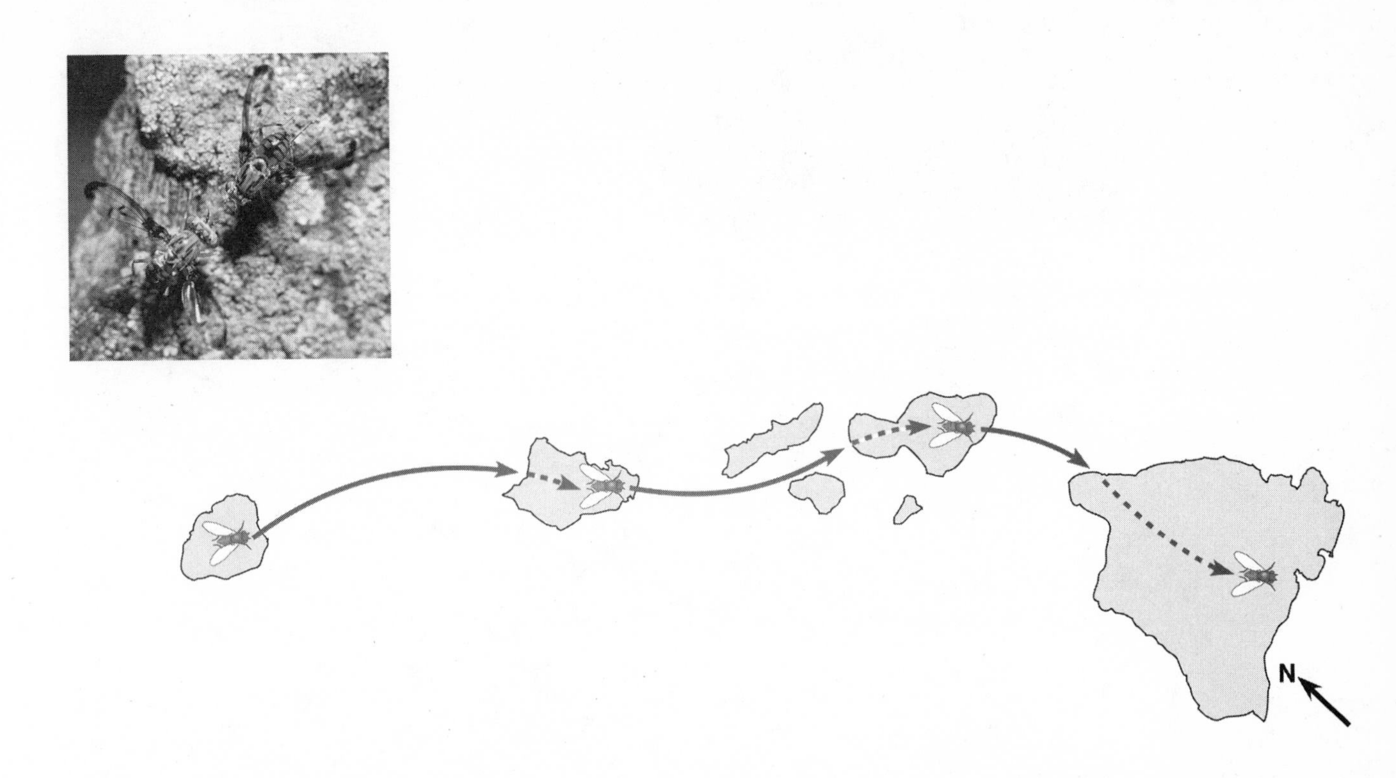

Figure 22.16 The evolution of fruit fly (*Drosophila*) species on the Hawaiian archipelago, page 441

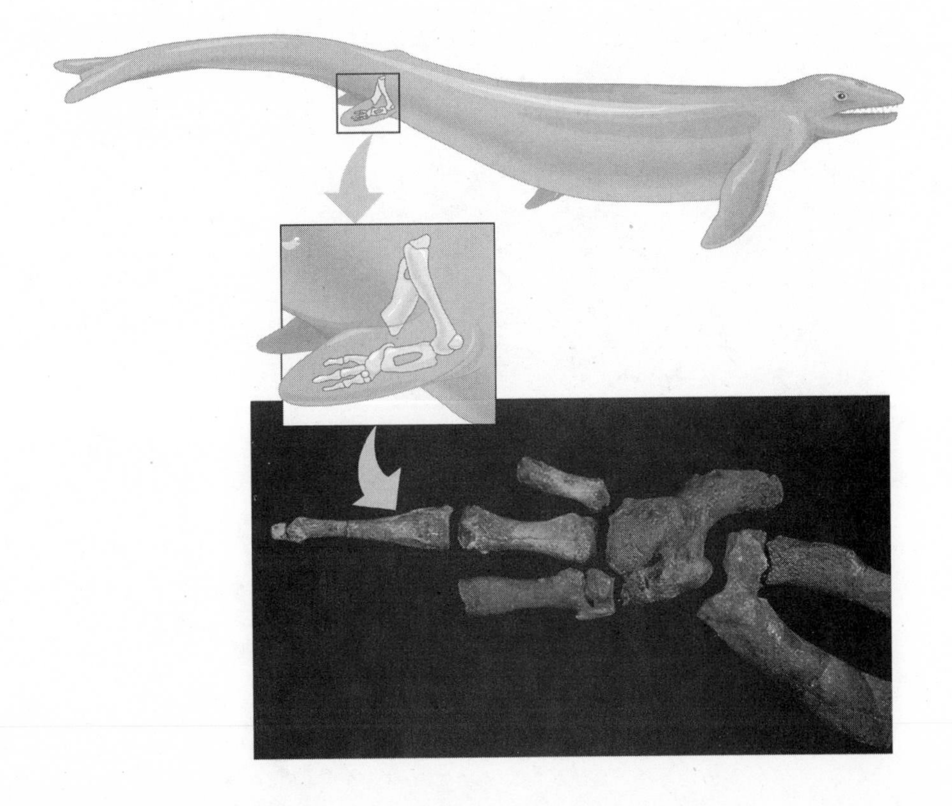

Figure 22.17 A transitional fossil linking past and present, page 442

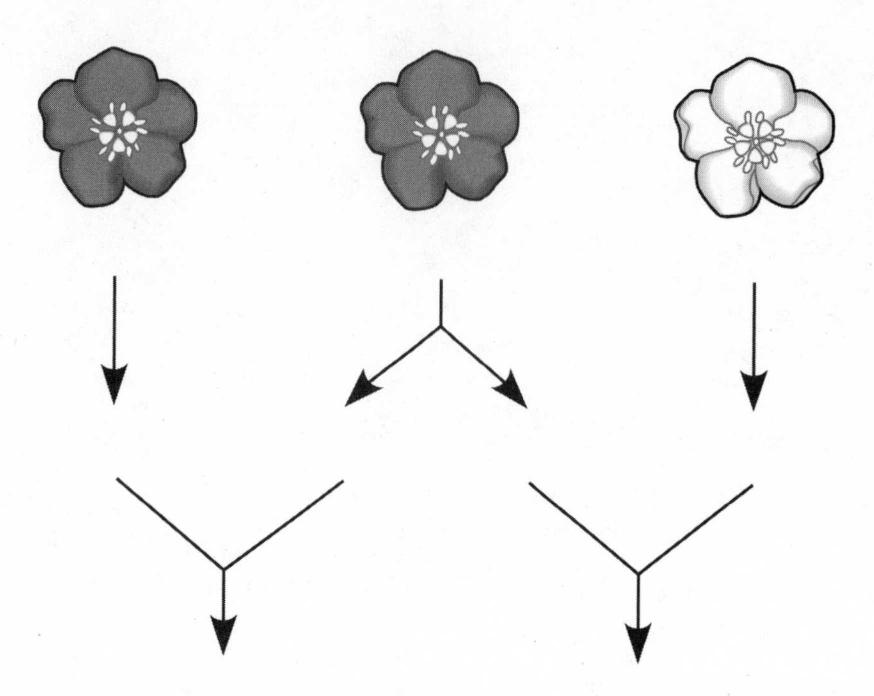

Figure 23.3a The Hardy-Weinberg theorem, page 448

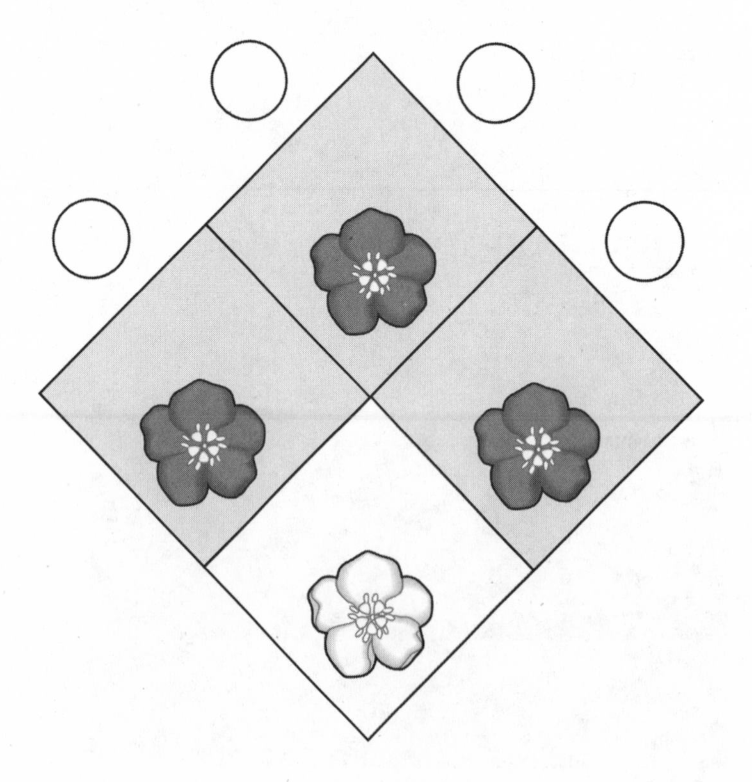

Figure 23.3b The Hardy-Weinberg theorem, page 448

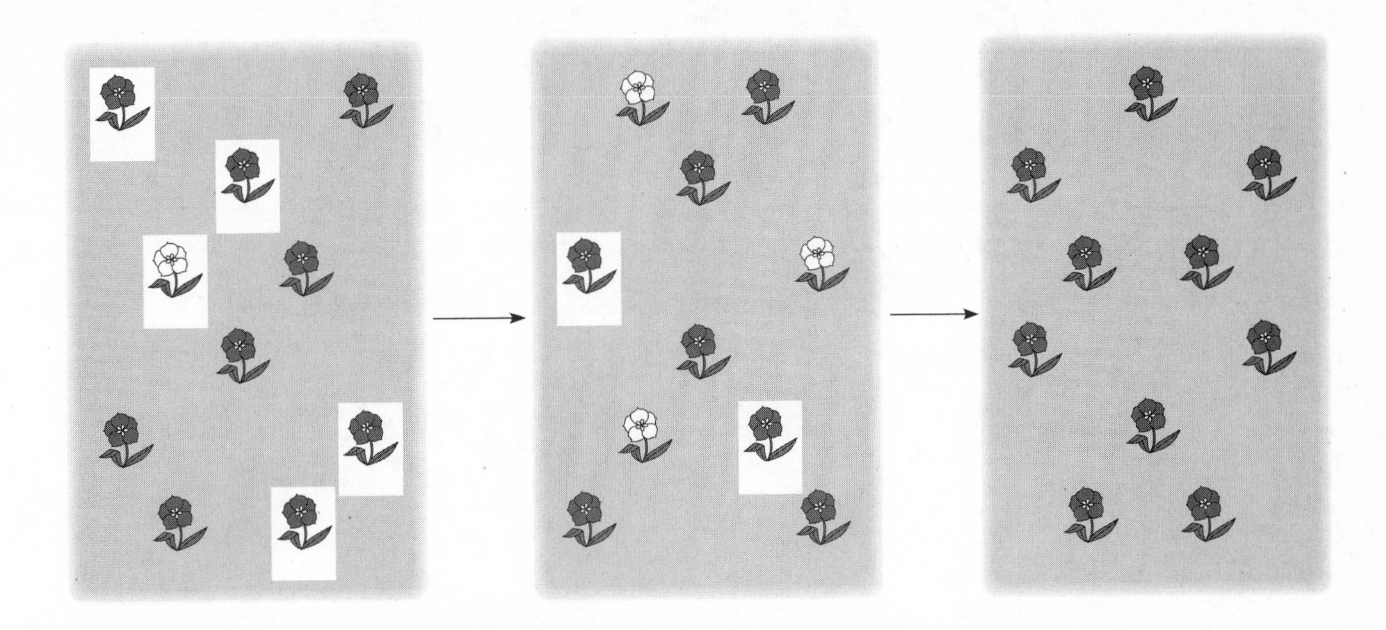

Figure 23.4 Genetic drift, page 451

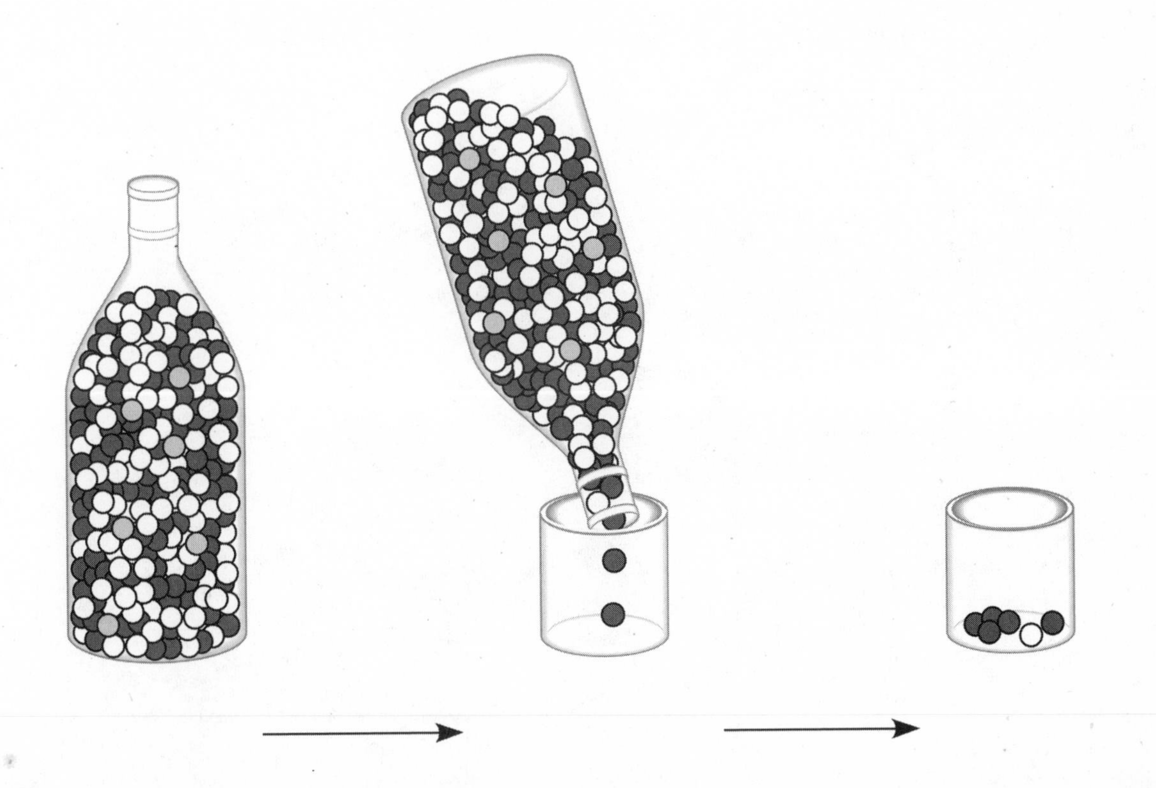

Figure 23.5 The bottleneck effect: an analogy, page 451

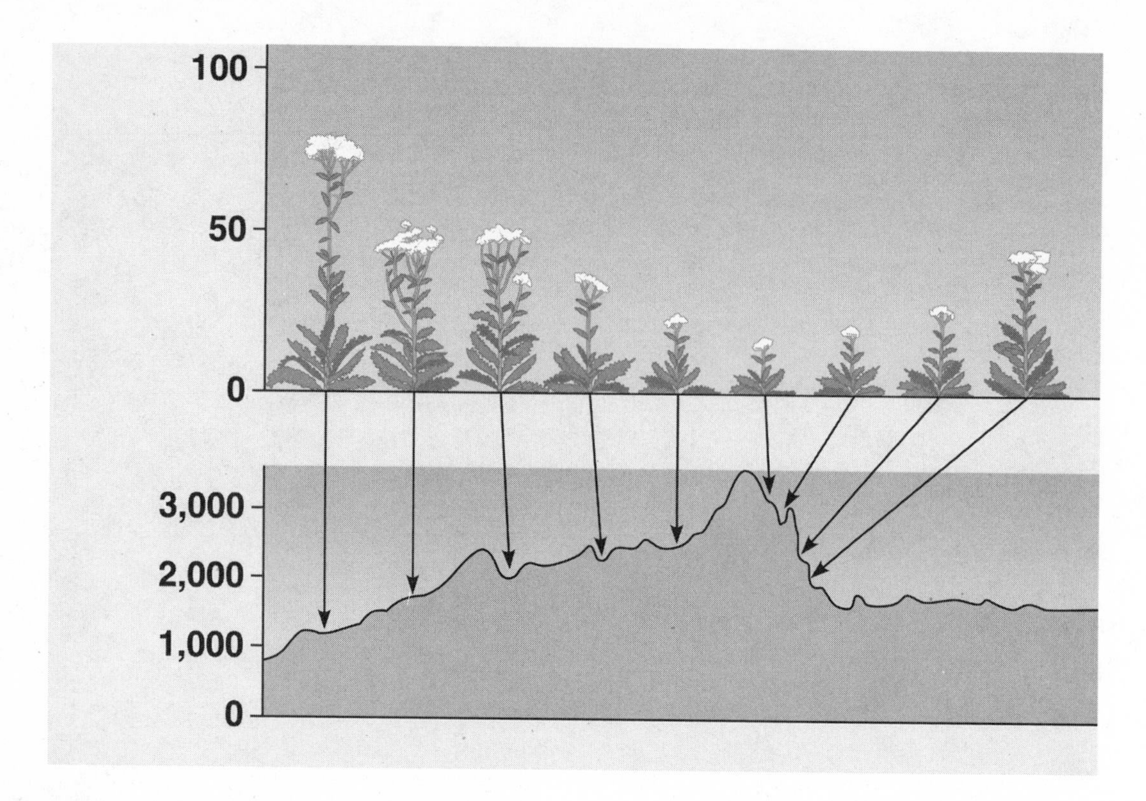

Figure 23.8 Clinal variation in a plant, page 454

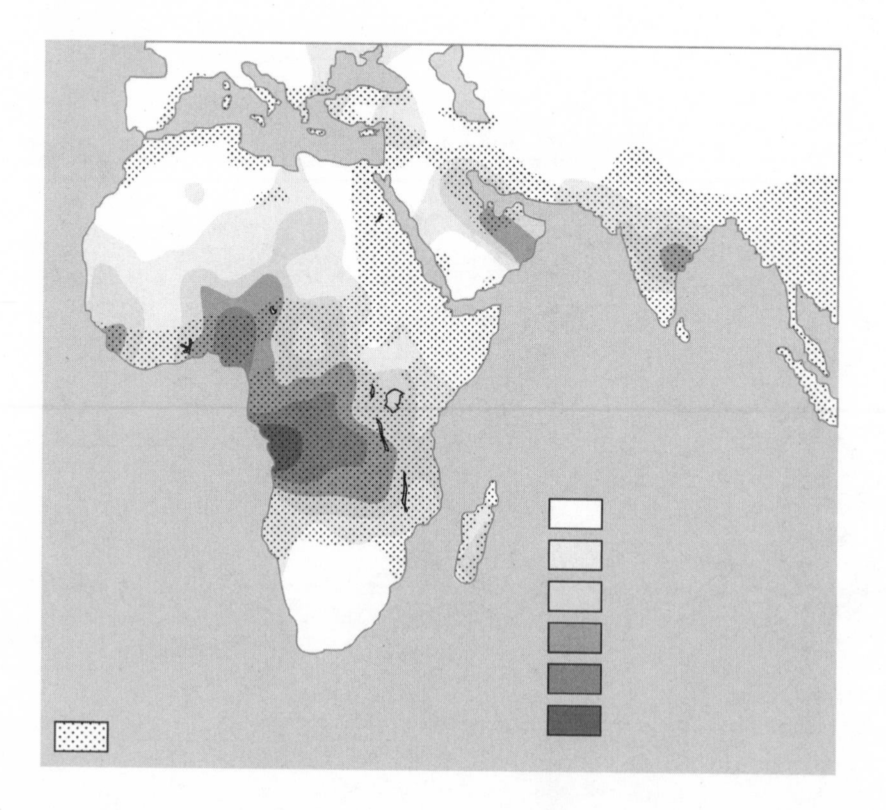

Figure 23.10 Mapping malaria and the sickle-cell allele, page 456

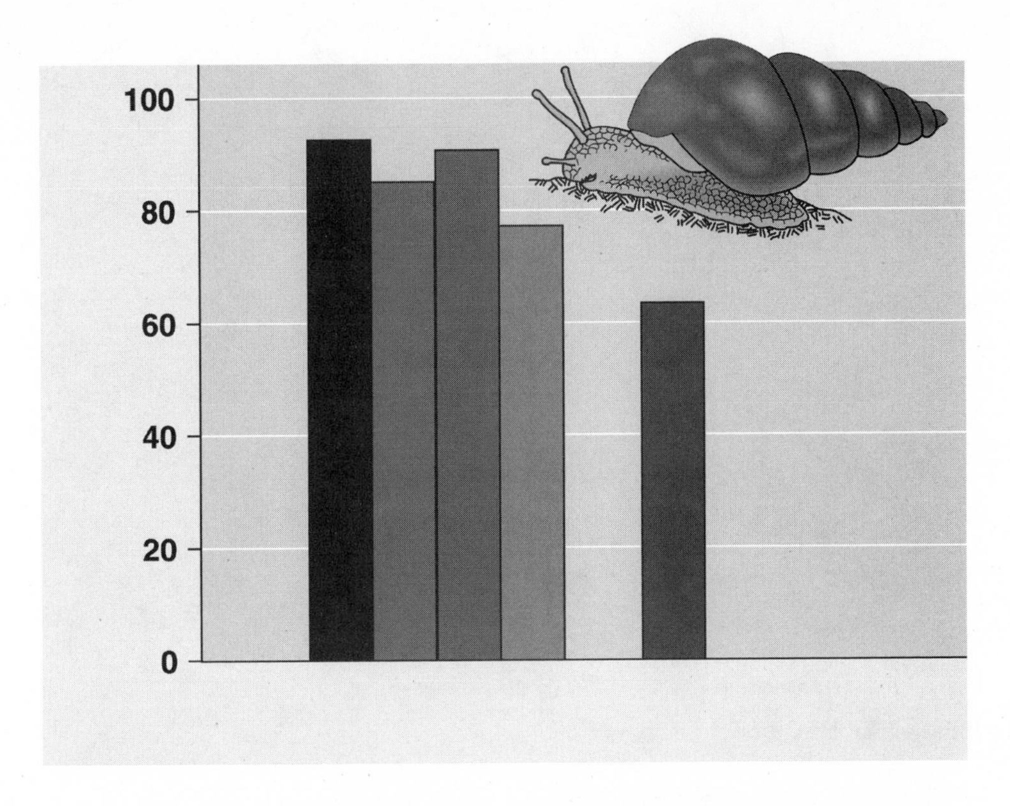

Figure 23.11 Frequency-dependent selection in a host-parasite relationship, page 457

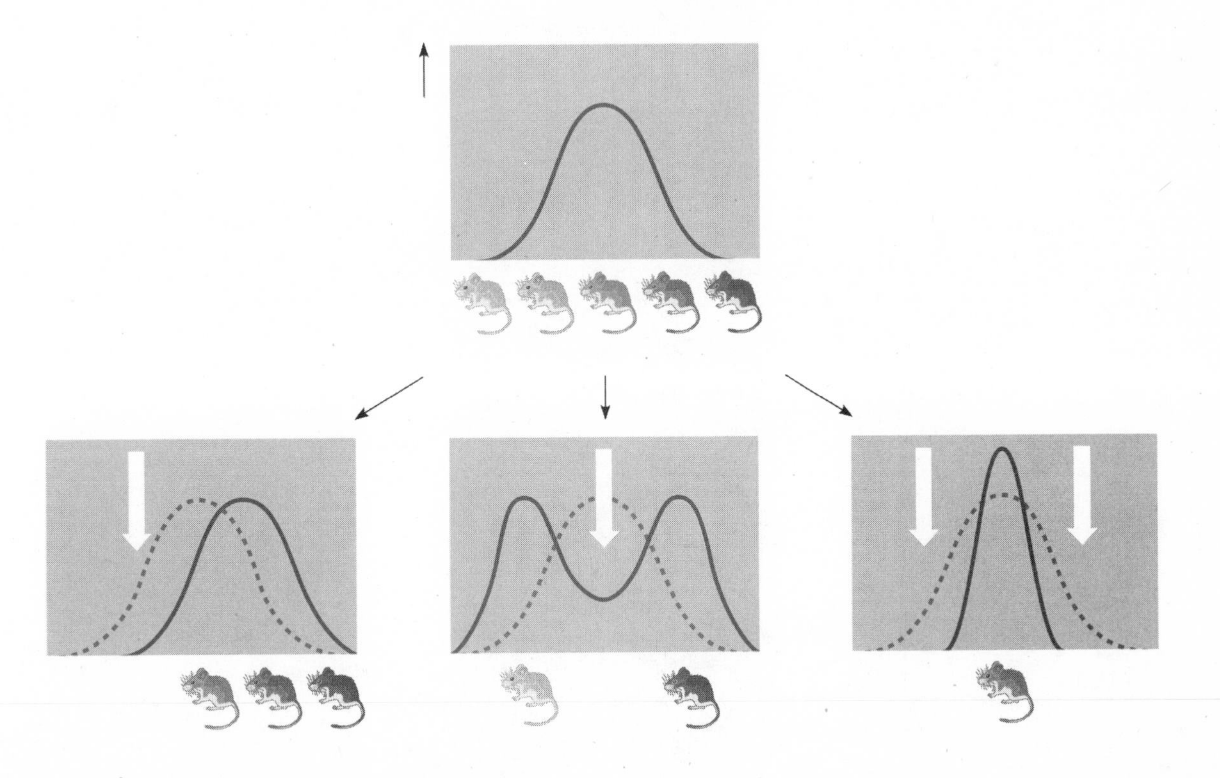

Figure 23.12 Modes of selection, page 458

Figure 24.1 Two patterns of speciation, page 464

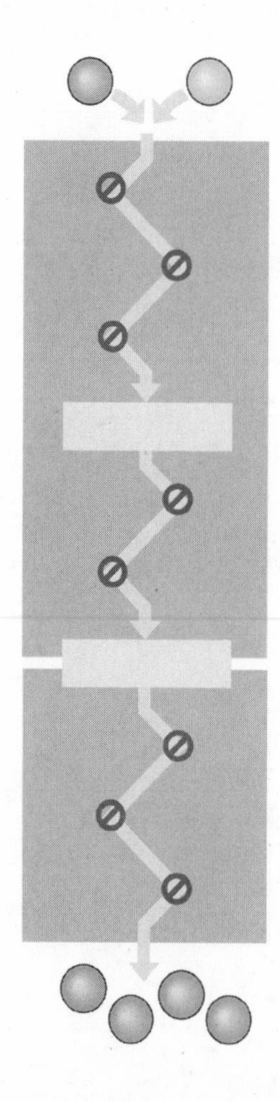

Figure 24.5 A summary of reproductive barriers between closely related species, page 467

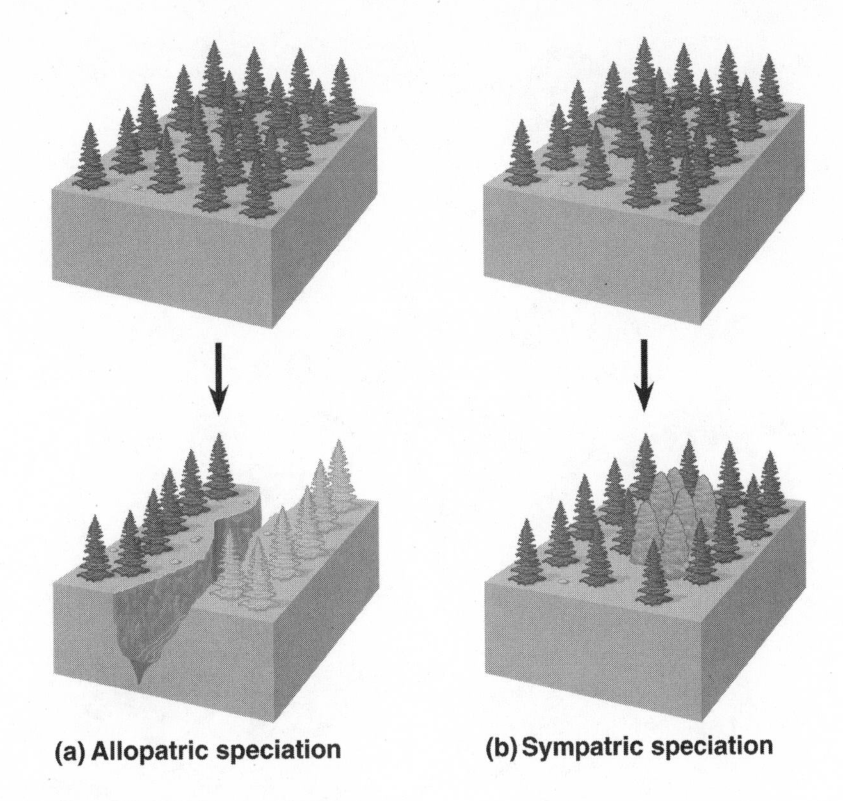

Figure 24.6 Two modes of speciation, page 468

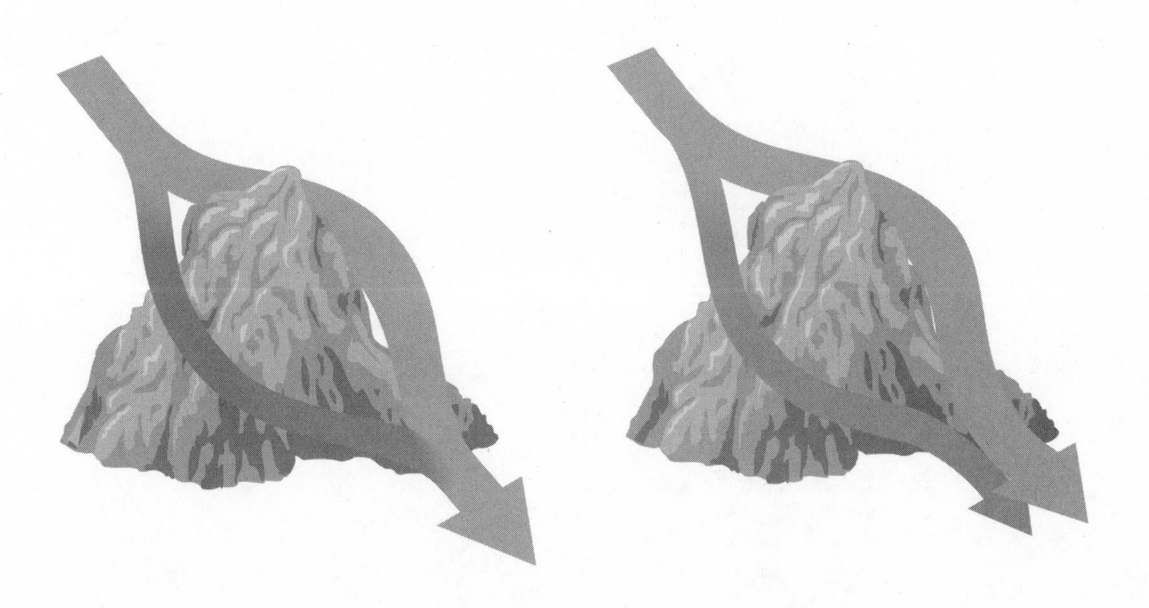

Figure 24.8 Has speciation occurred during geographic isolation?, page 469

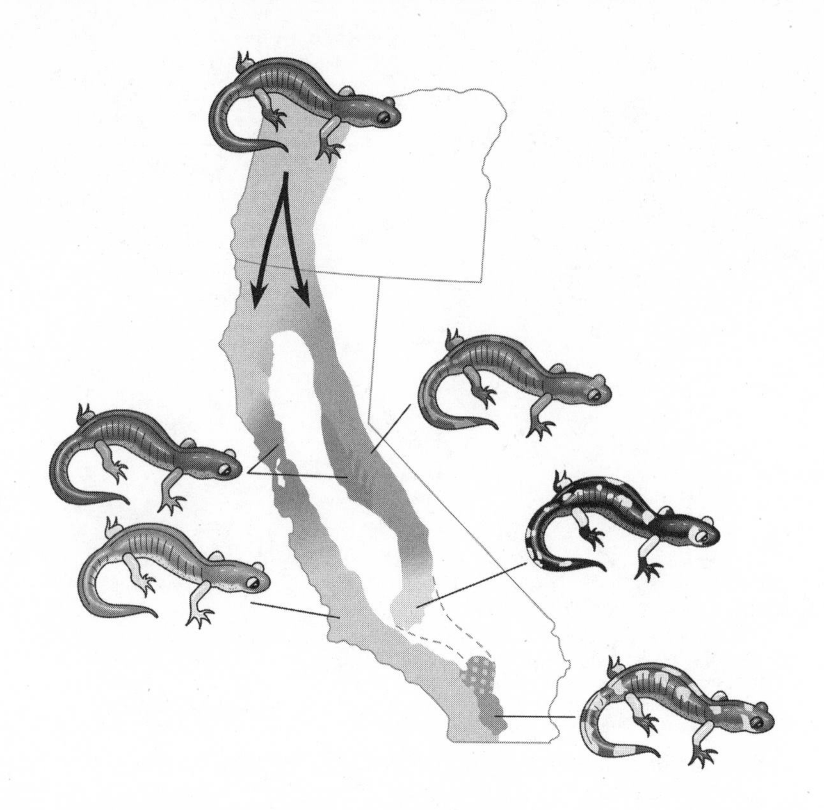

Figure 24.9 ***Ensatina eschscholtzii,*** **a ring species, page 470**

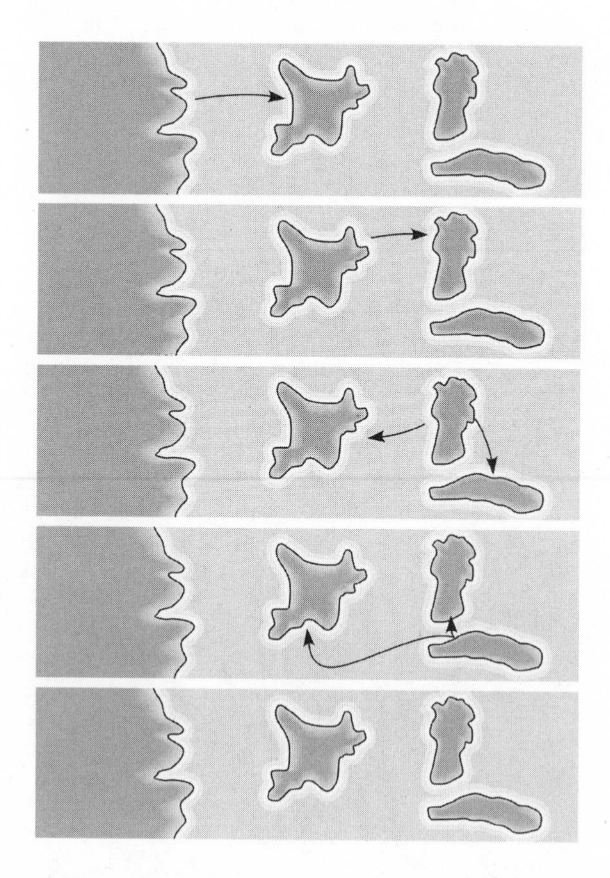

Figure 24.11 A model for adaptive radiation on island chains, page 471

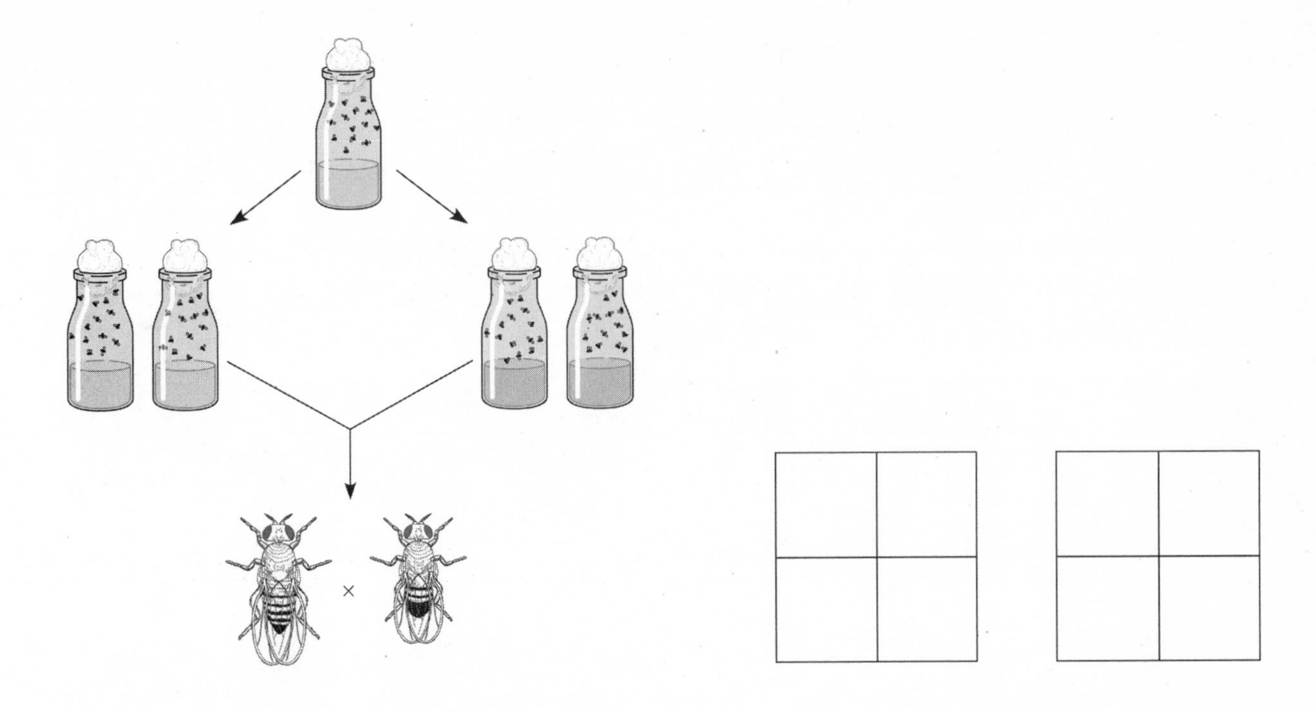

Figure 24.12 Evolution of reproductive isolation in lab populations of *Drosophila*, page 472

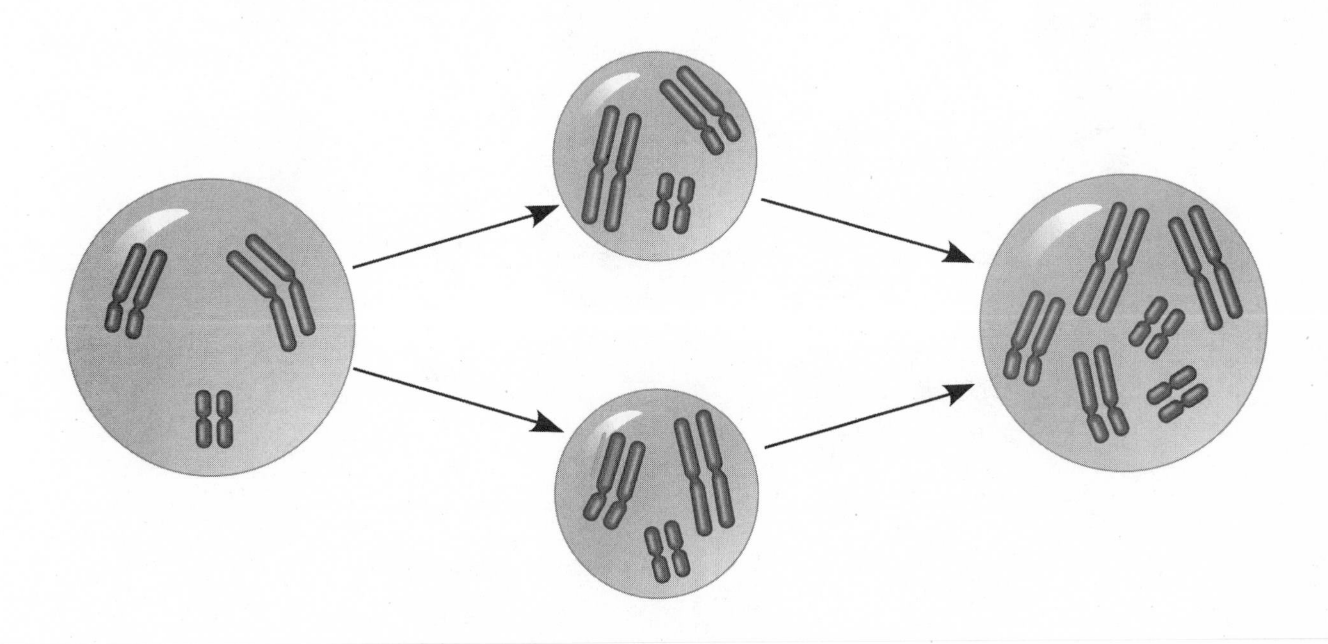

Figure 24.13 Sympatric speciation by autopolyploidy in plants, page 473

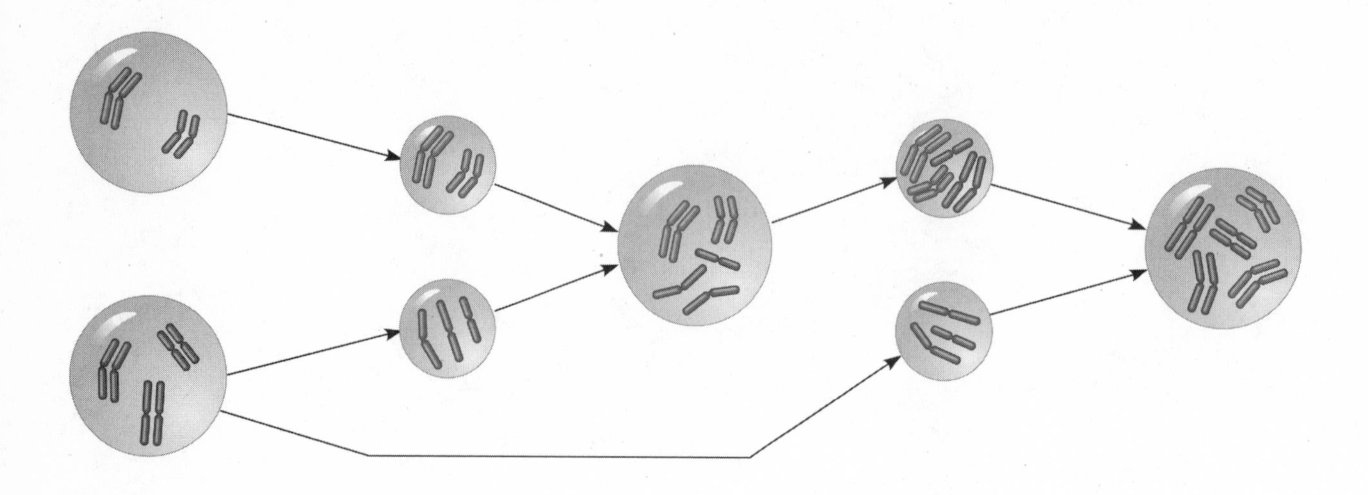

Figure 24.15 One mechanism for allopolyploid speciation in plants, page 474

Figure 24.17 Two models for the tempo of speciation, page 476

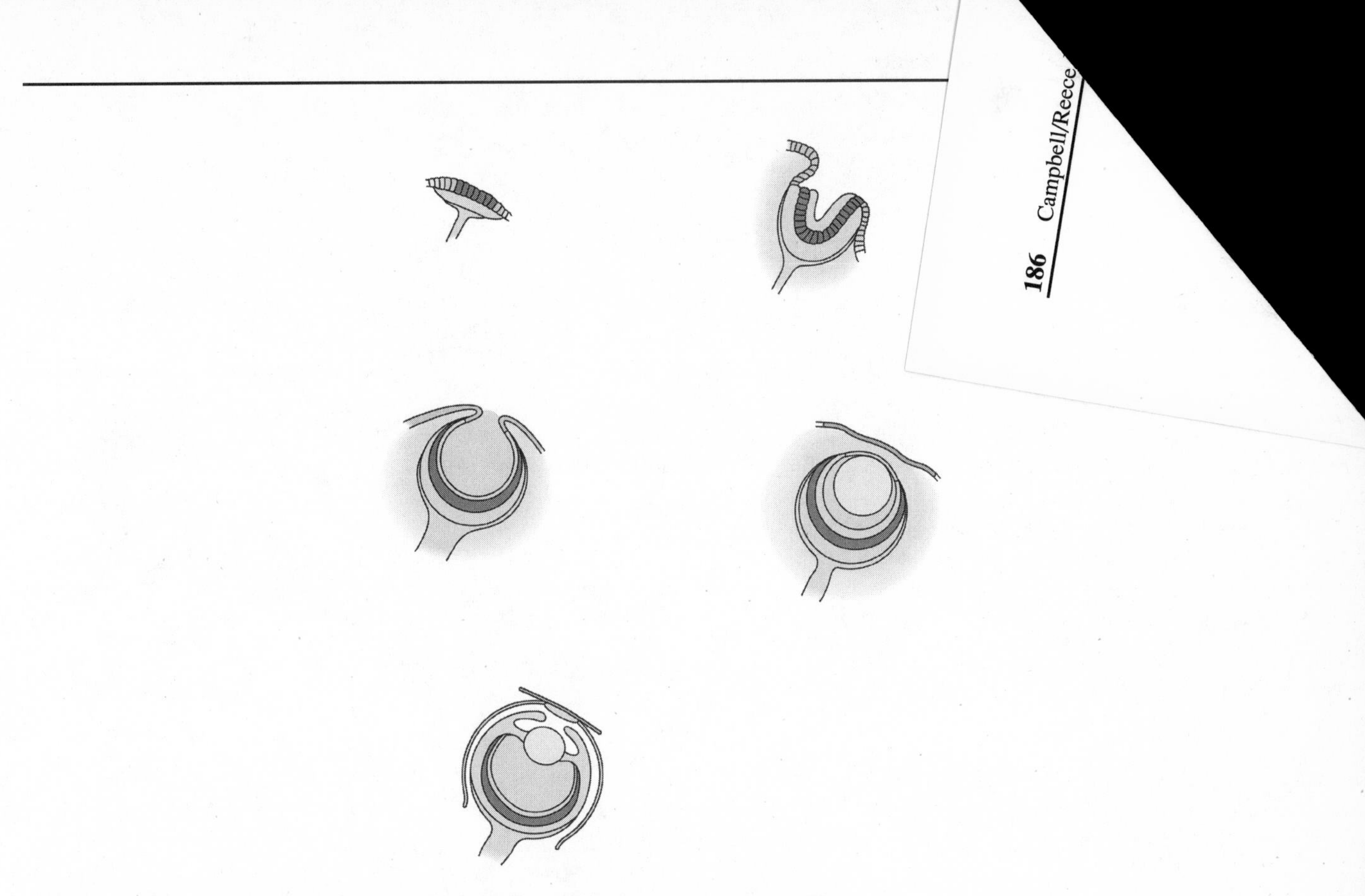

Figure 24.18 A range of eye complexity among mollusks, page 477

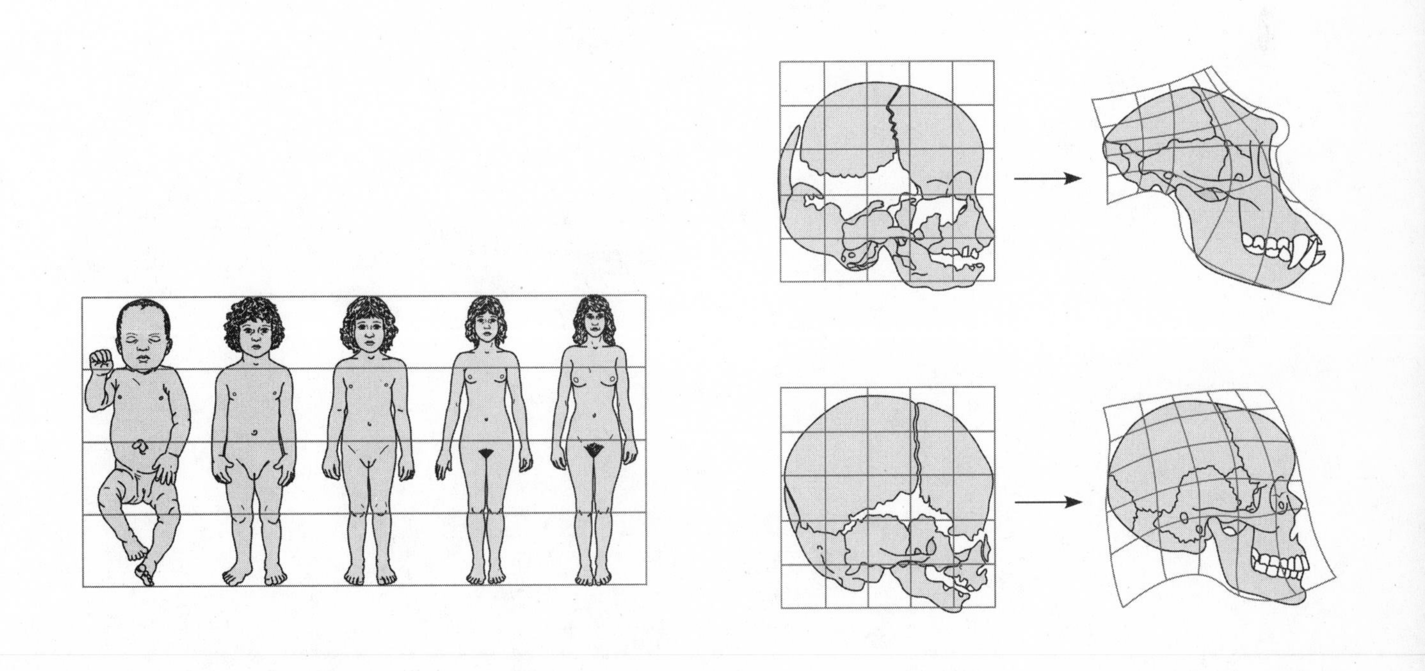

Figure 24.19 Allometric growth, page 478

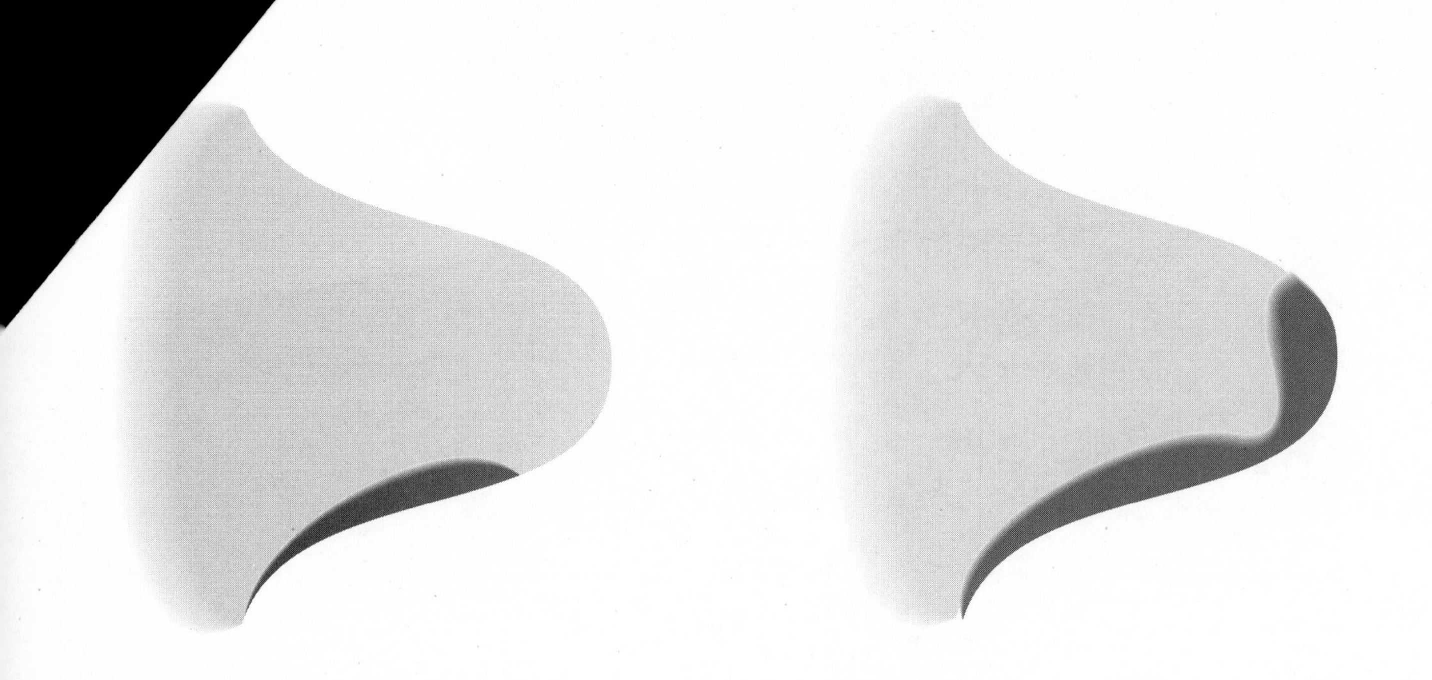

Figure 24.22 ***Hox* genes and the evolution of tetrapod limbs, page 479**

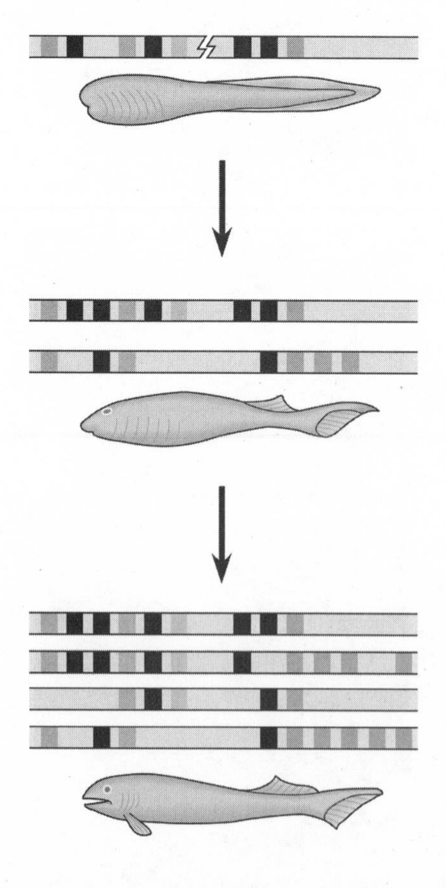

Figure 24.23 ***Hox* mutations and the origin of vertebrates, page 480**

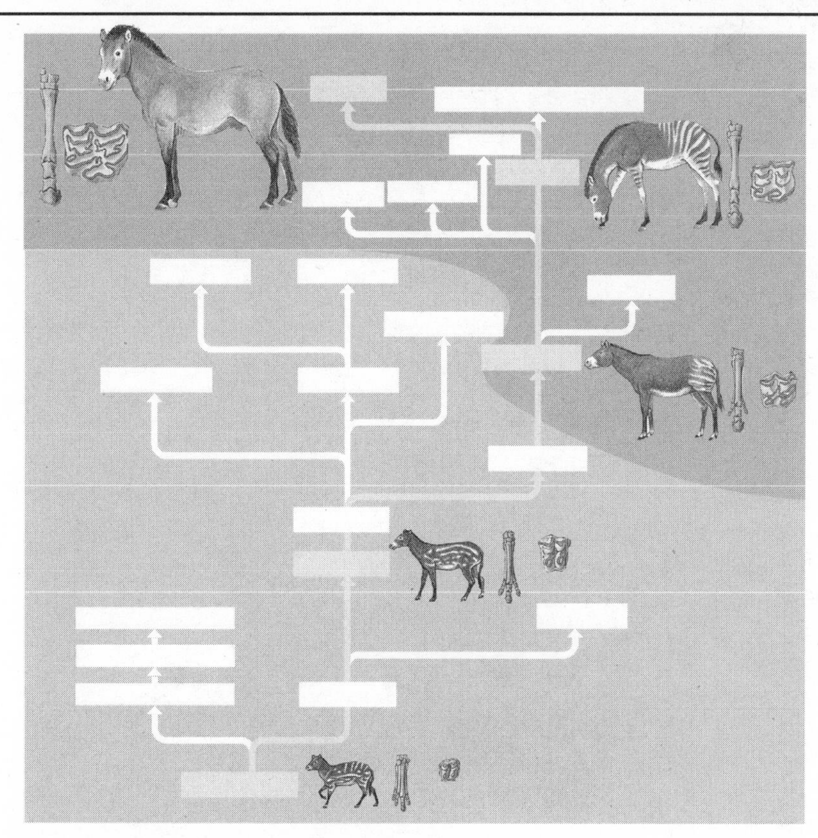

Figure 24.24 The branched evolution of horses, page 481

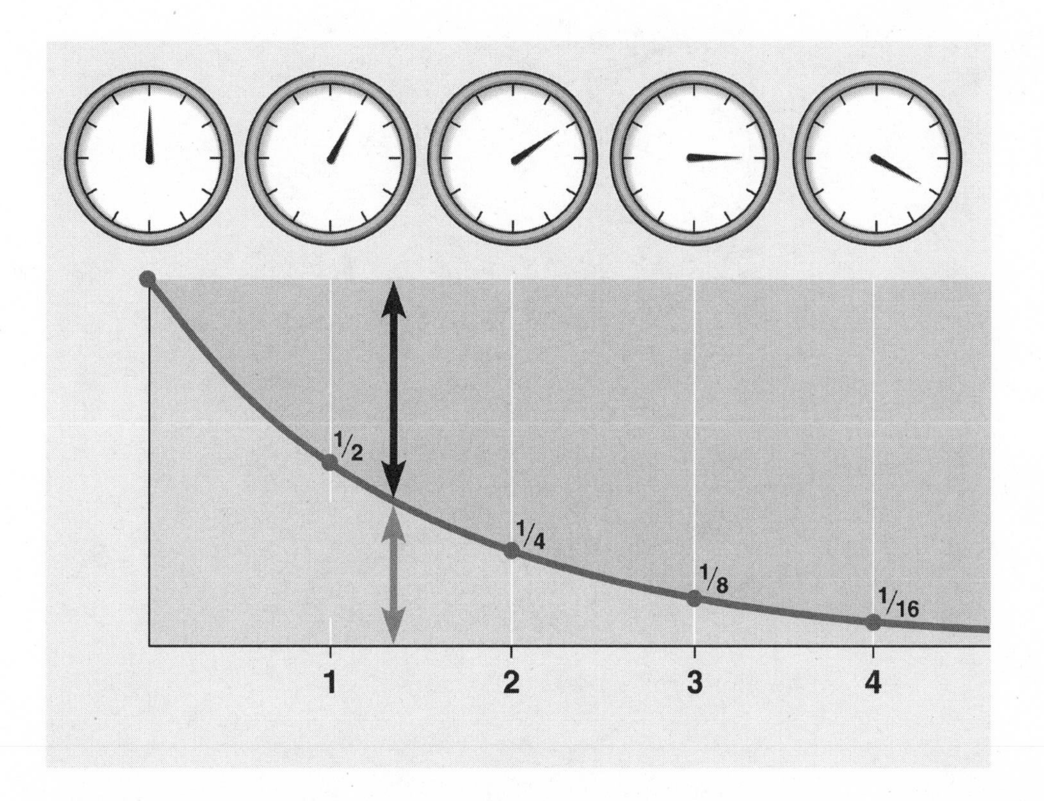

Figure 25.2 Radiometric dating, page 488

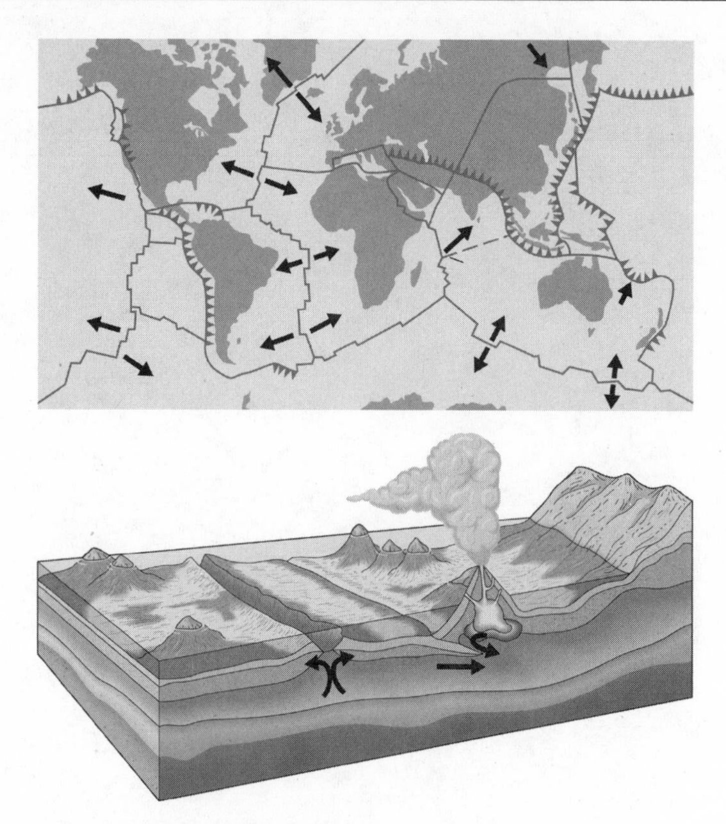

Figure 25.3 Earth's crustal plates and plate tectonics (geologic processes resulting from plate movements), page 489

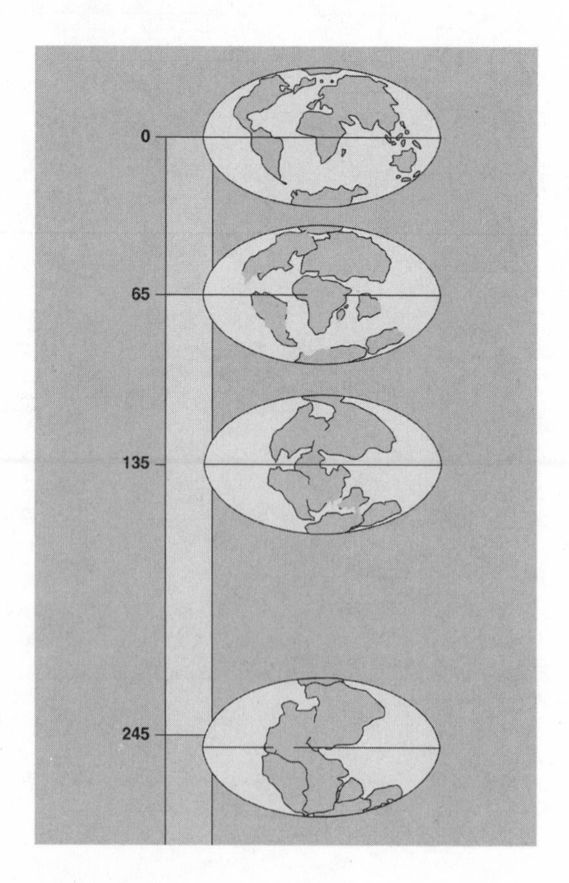

Figure 25.4 The history of continental drift, page 490

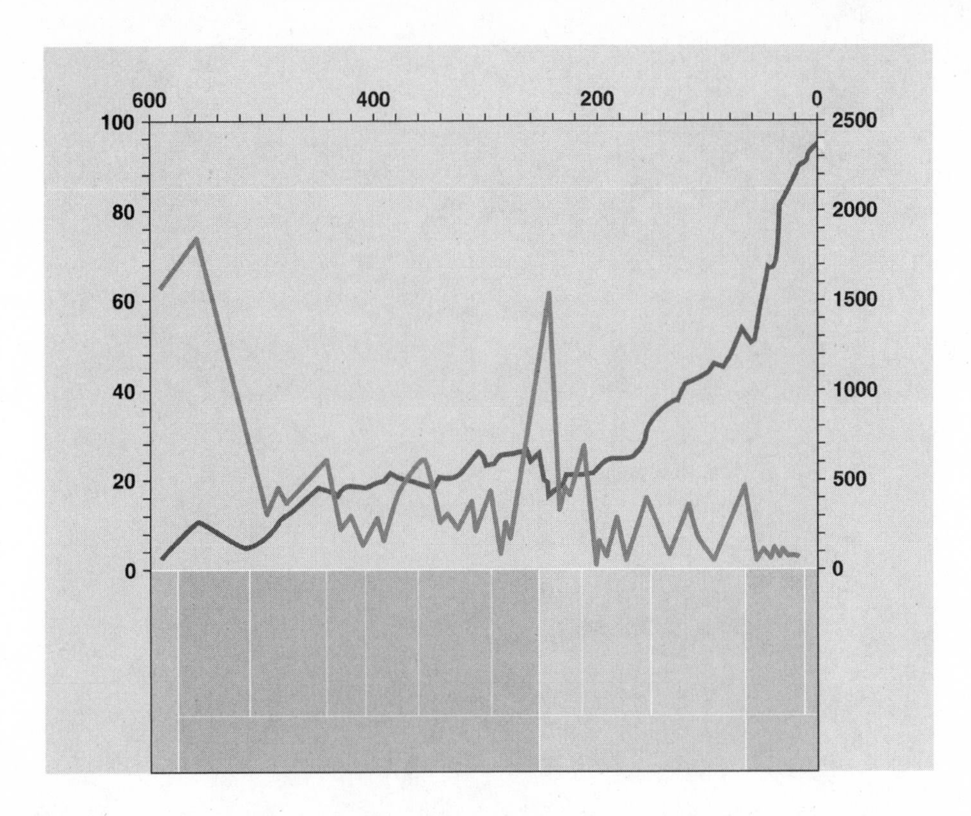

Figure 25.5 Diversity of life and periods of mass extinction, page 491

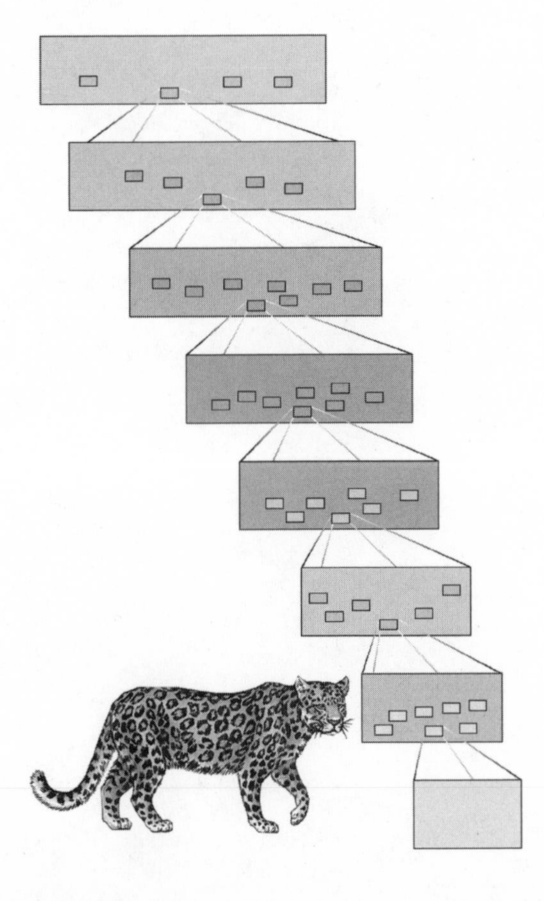

Figure 25.7 Hierarchical classification, page 493

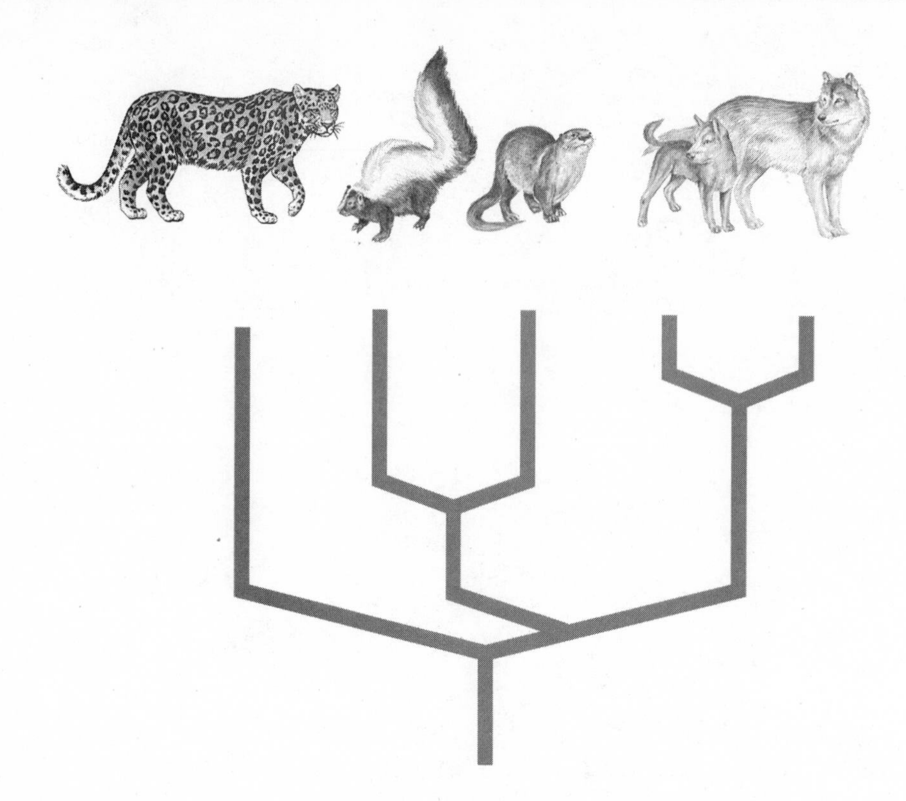

Figure 25.8 The connection between classification and phylogeny, page 494

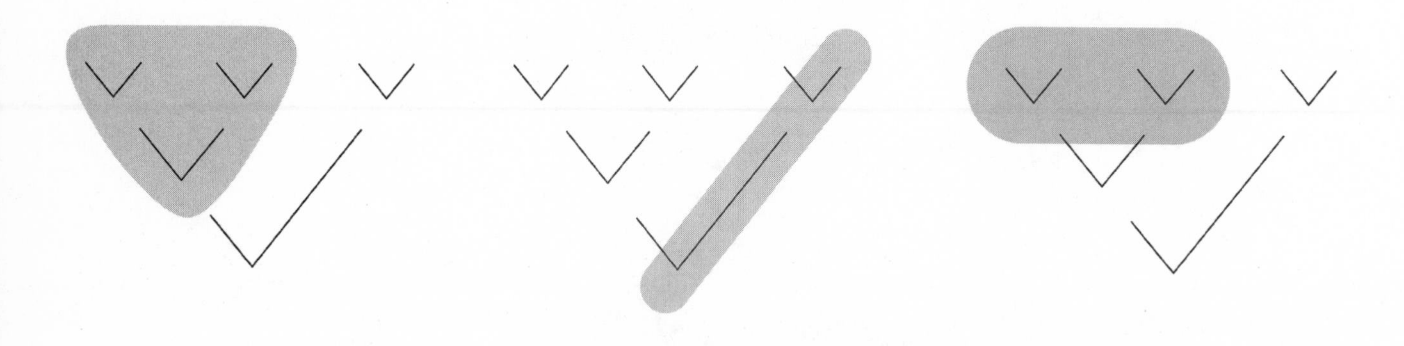

Figure 25.9 Monophyletic versus paraphyletic and polyphyletic groups, page 495

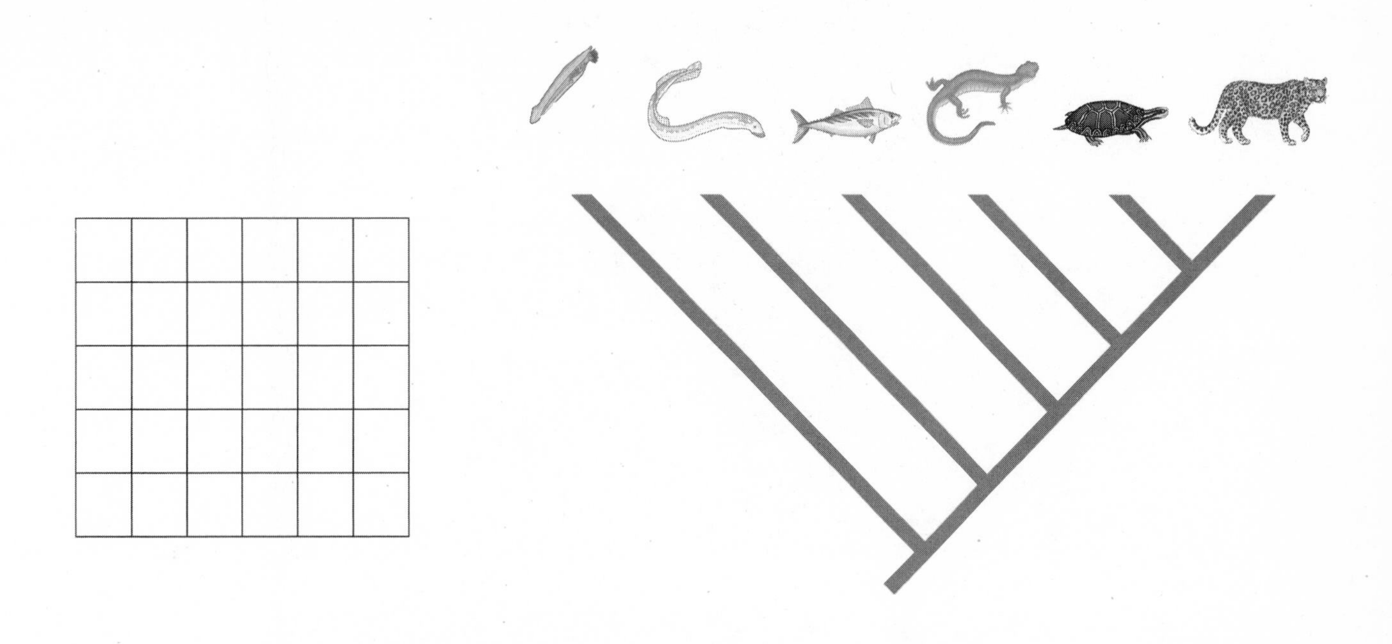

Figure 25.11 Constructing a cladogram, page 497

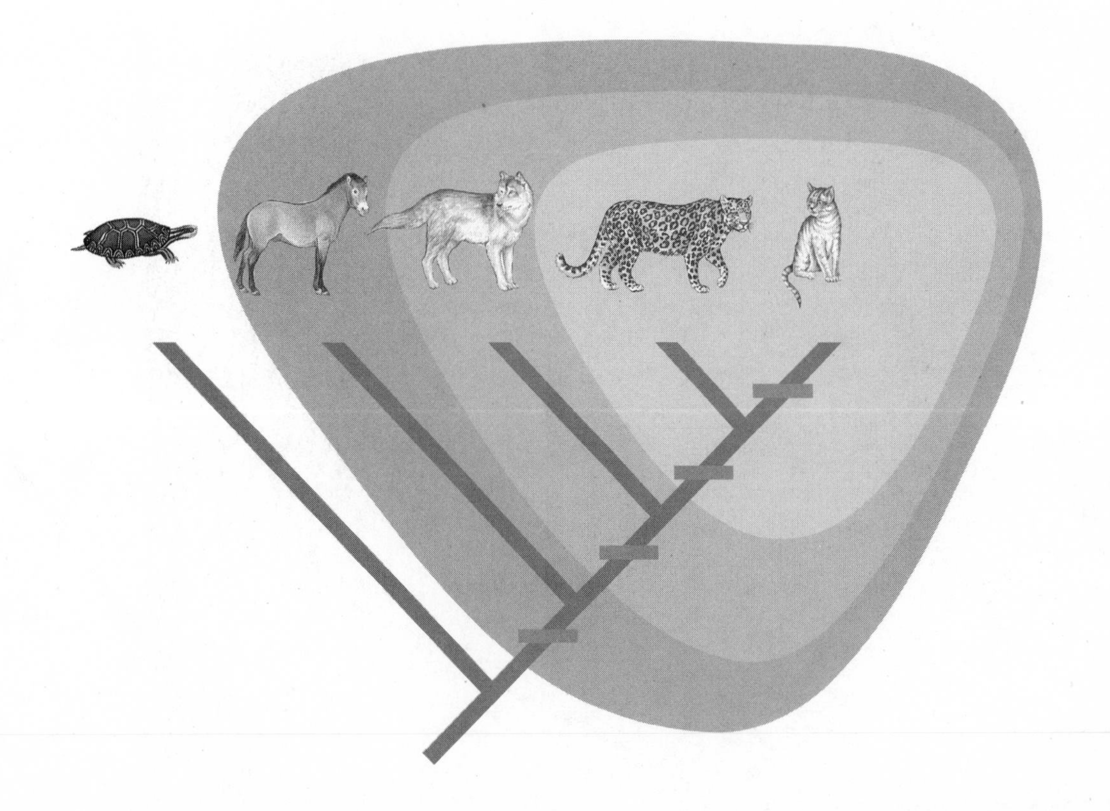

Figure 25.12 Cladistics and taxonomy, page 498

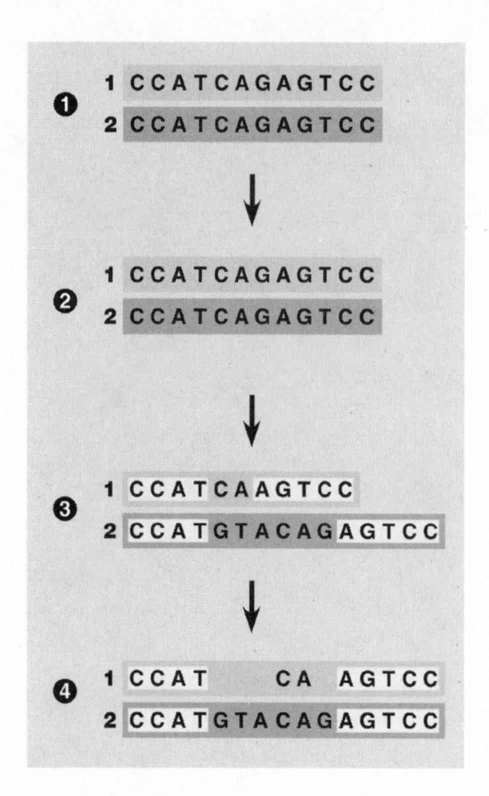

Figure 25.13 Aligning segments of DNA, page 499

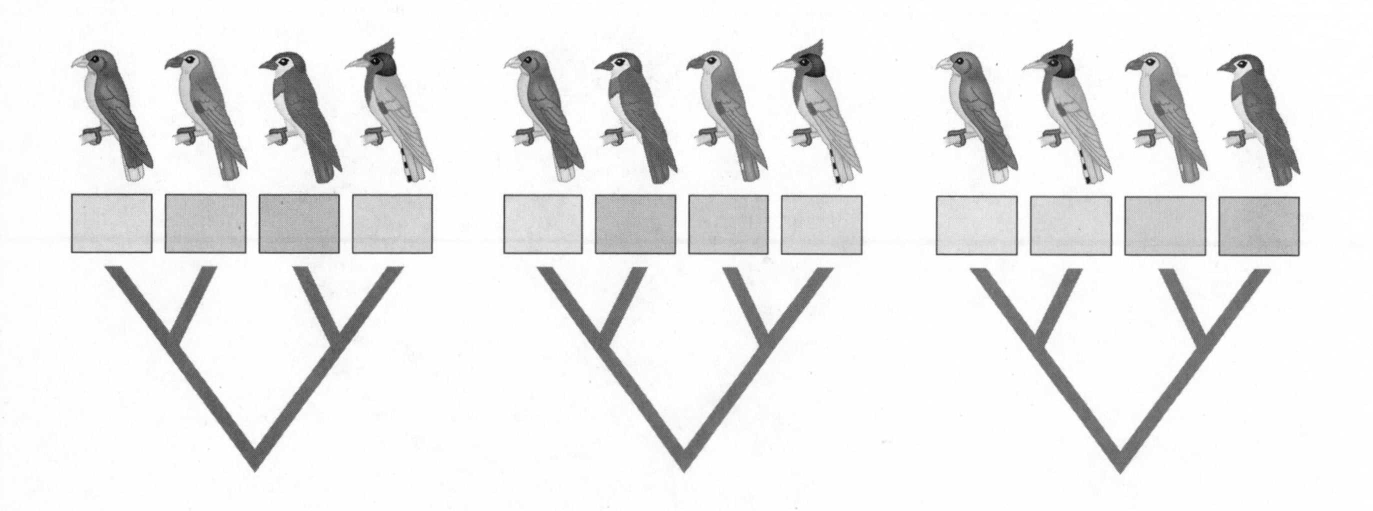

Figure 25.14 Simplified versions of a four-species problem in phylogenetics, page 500

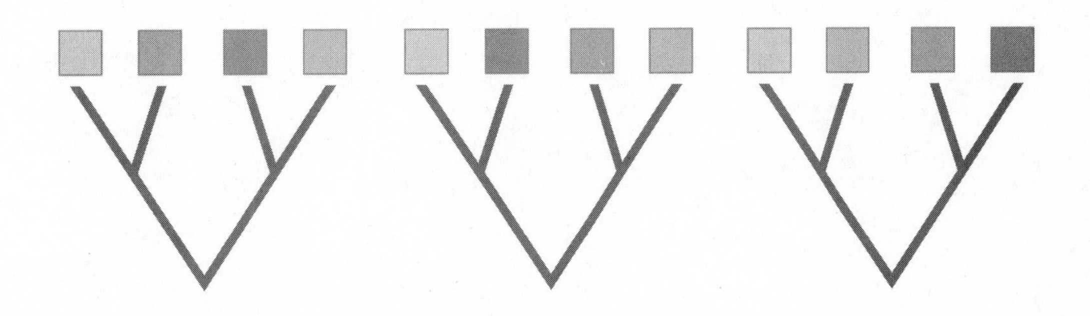

Figure 25.15a Parsimony and molecular systematics, page 500

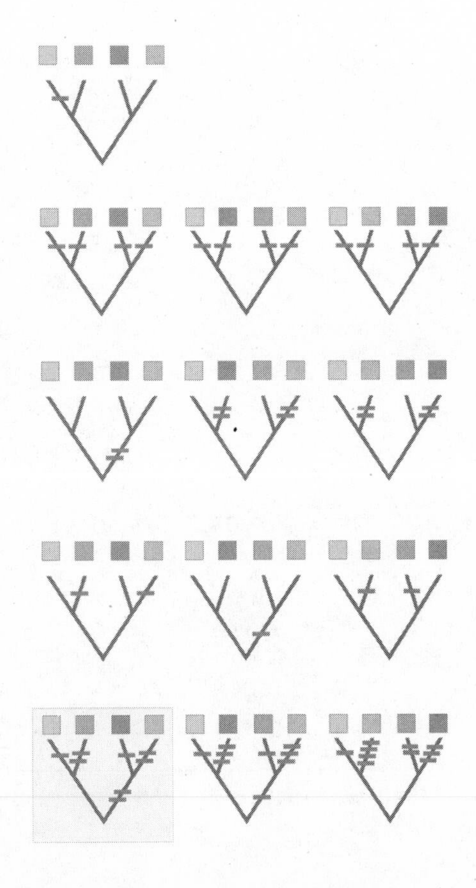

Figure 25.15b Parsimony and molecular systematics, page 501

Figure 25.16 Parsimony and the analogy-versus-homology pitfall, page 502

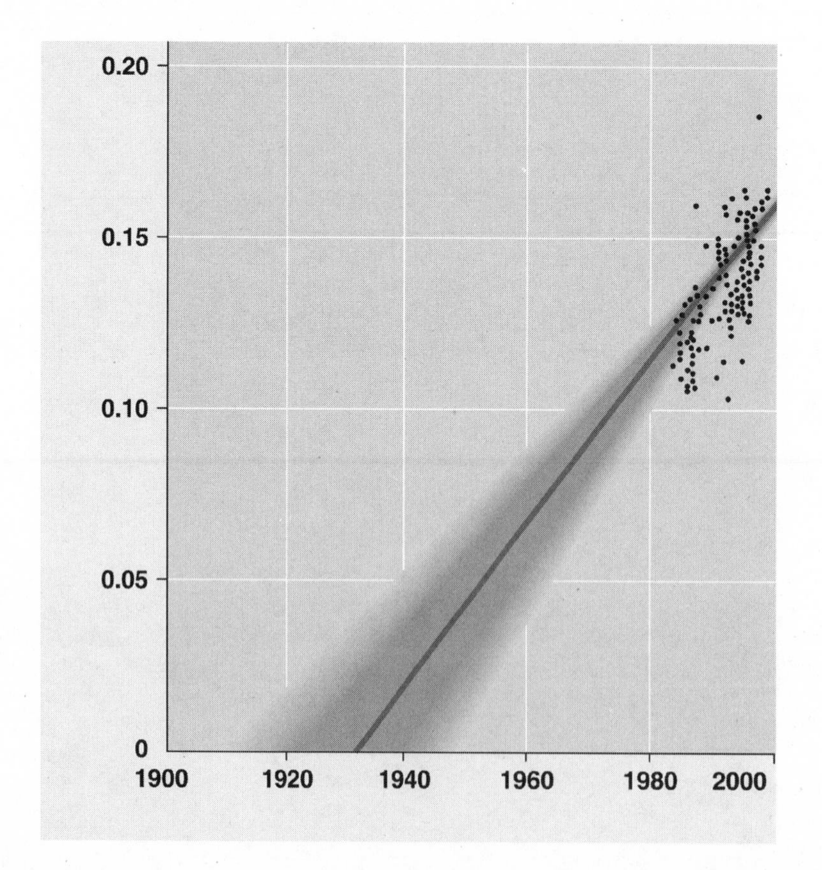

Figure 25.17 Dating the origin of HIV-1 M with a molecular clock, page 504

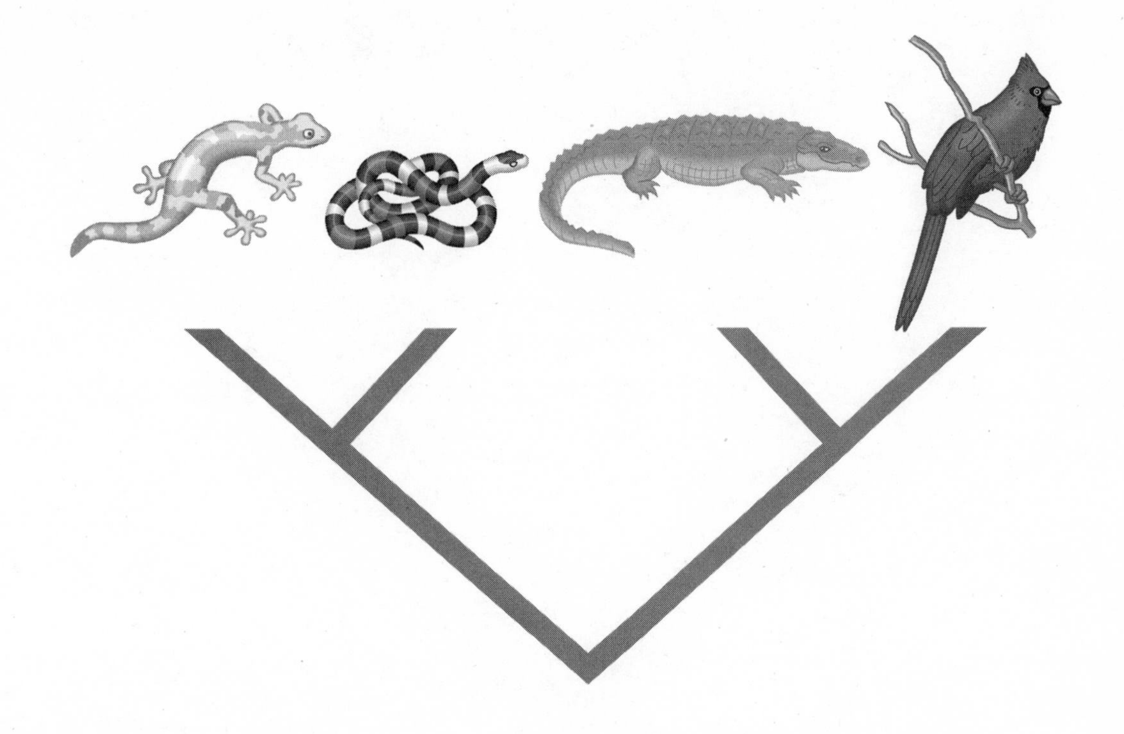

Figure 25.18 Modern systematics is shaking some phylogenetic trees, page 504

Figure 25.19 When did most major mammalian orders originate? page 505

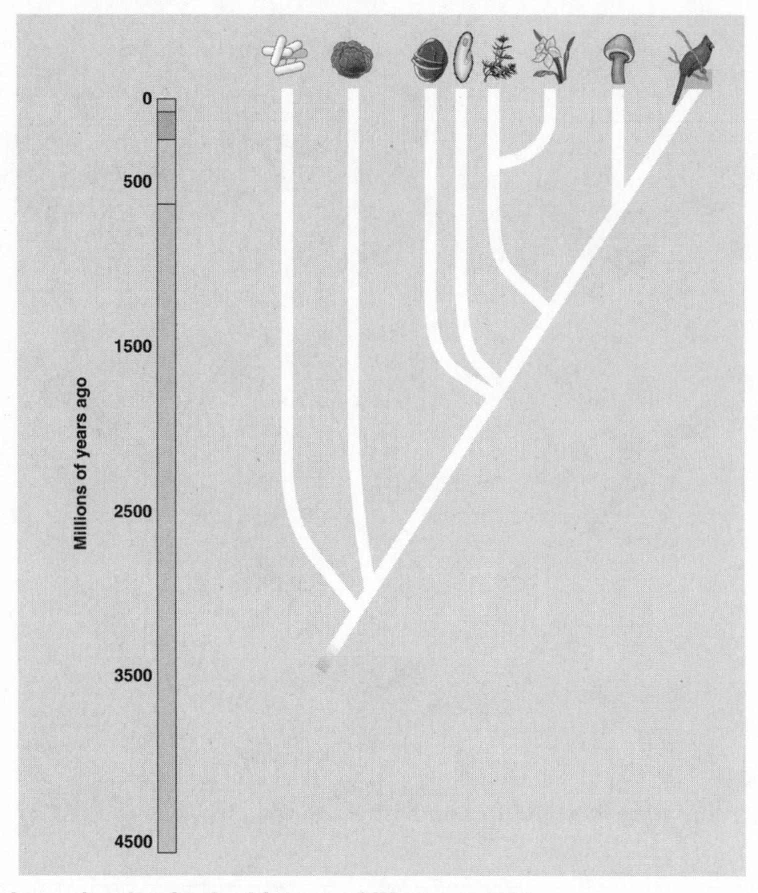

Figure 26.1 Some major episodes in the history of life, page 511

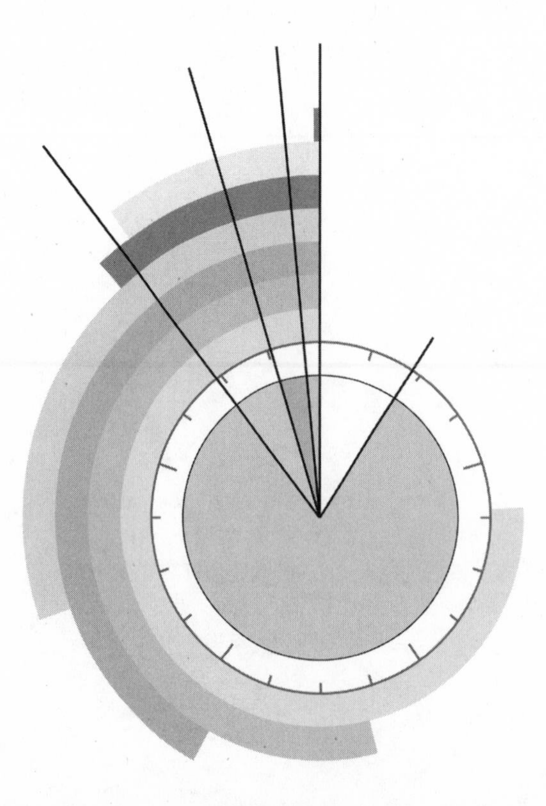

Figure 26.2 Clock analogy for some key events in evolutionary history, page 512

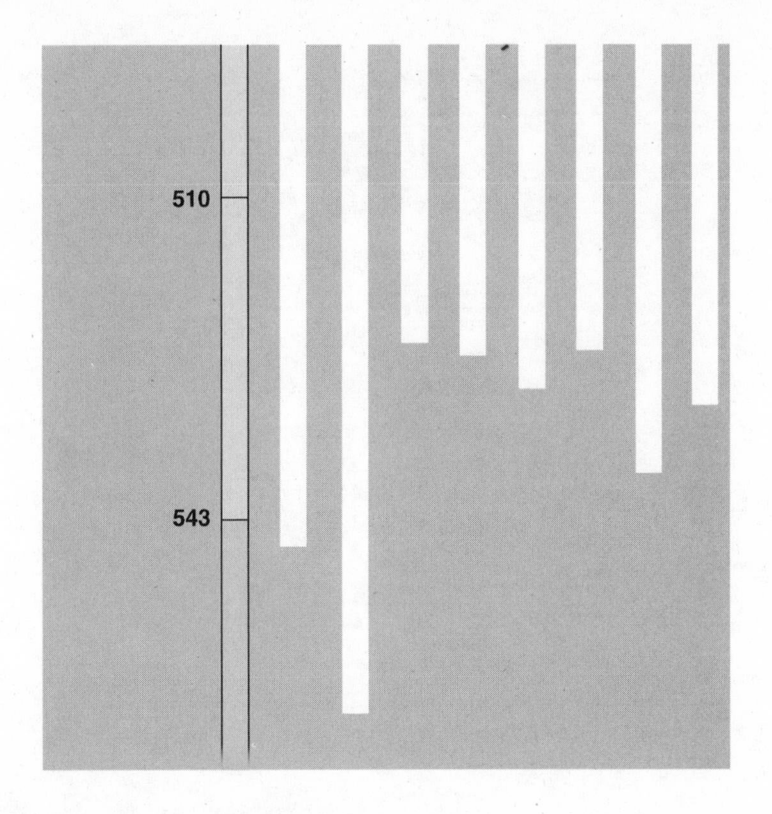

Figure 26.8 The Cambrian radiation of animals, page 515

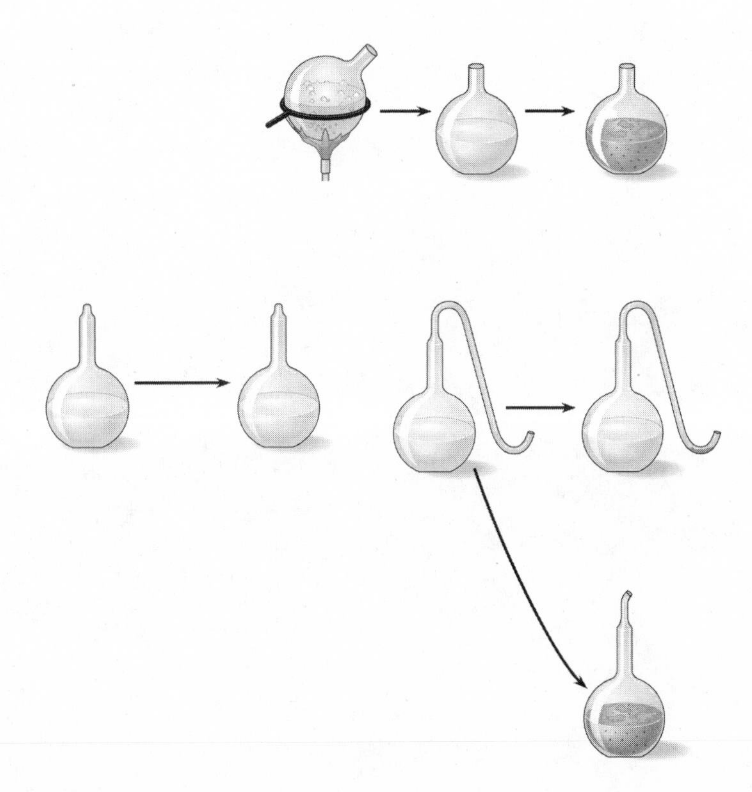

Figure 26.9 Pasteur and biogenesis of microorganisms, page 517

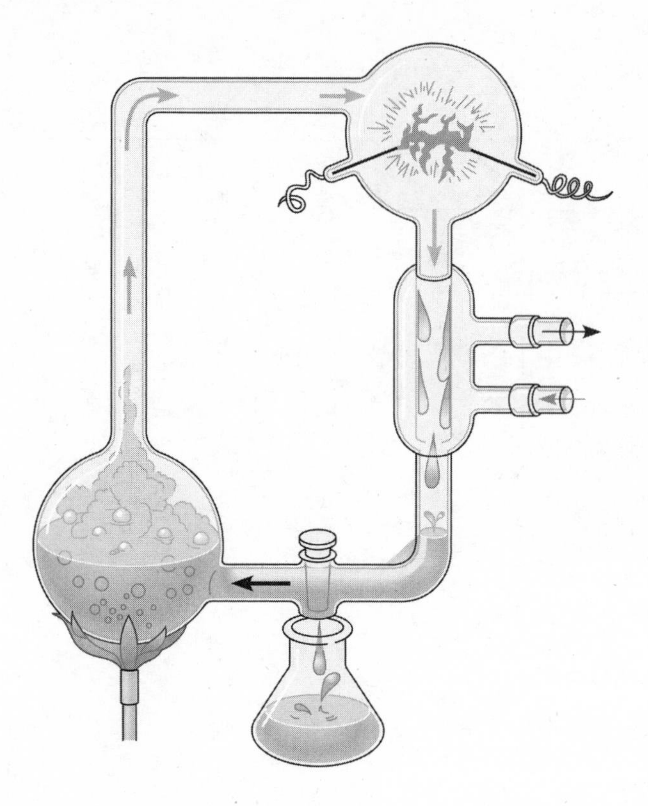

Figure 26.10 The Miller-Urey experiment, page 518

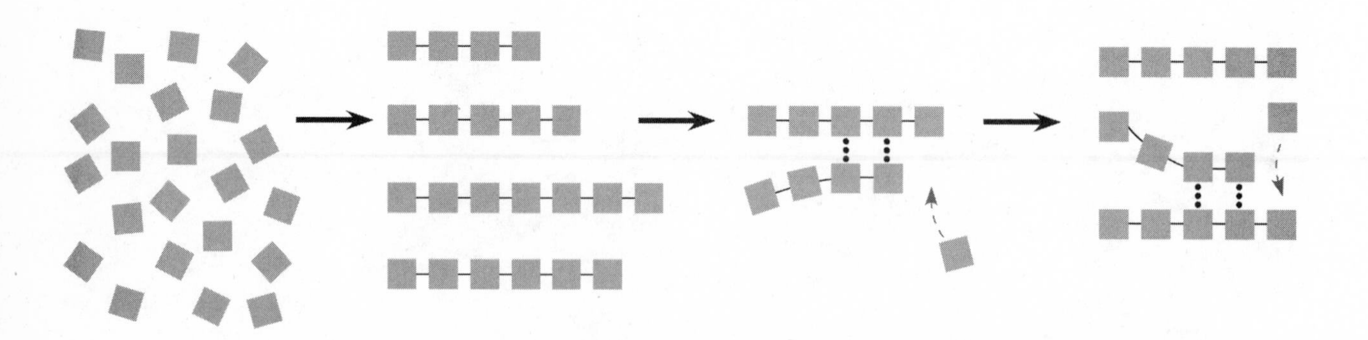

Figure 26.11 Abiotic replication of RNA, page 519

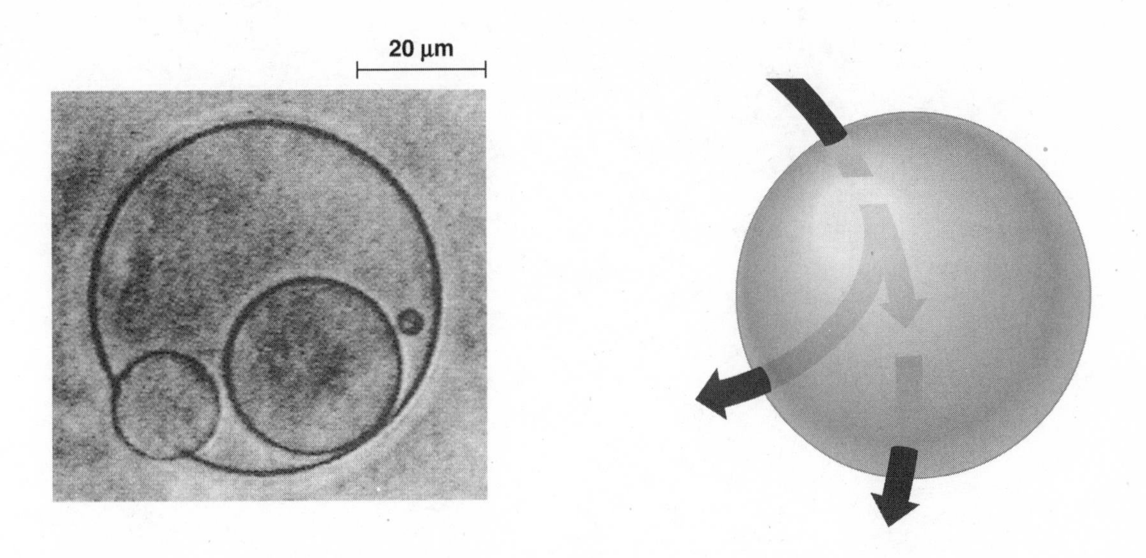

Figure 26.12 Laboratory versions of protobionts, page 520

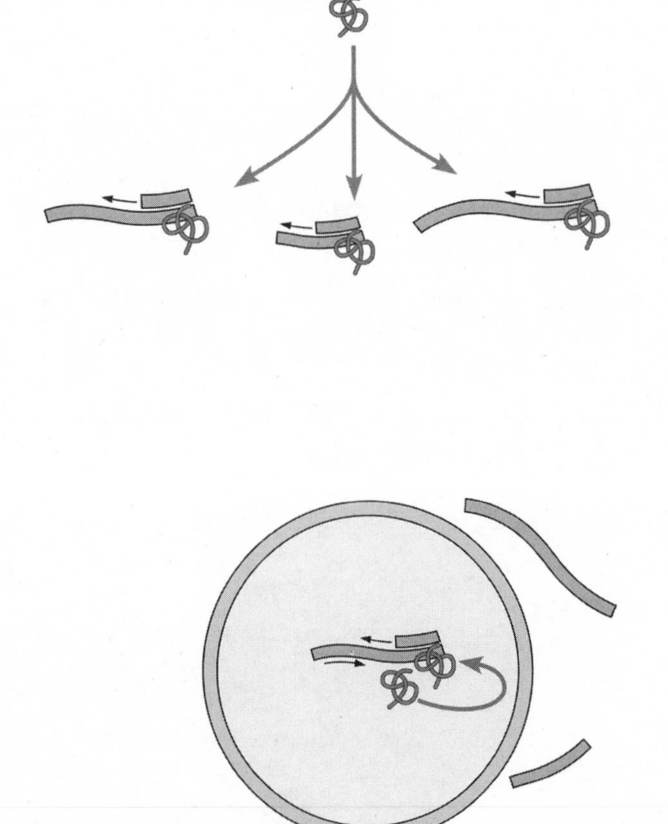

Figure 26.13 Hypotheses for the beginnings of molecular cooperation, page 521

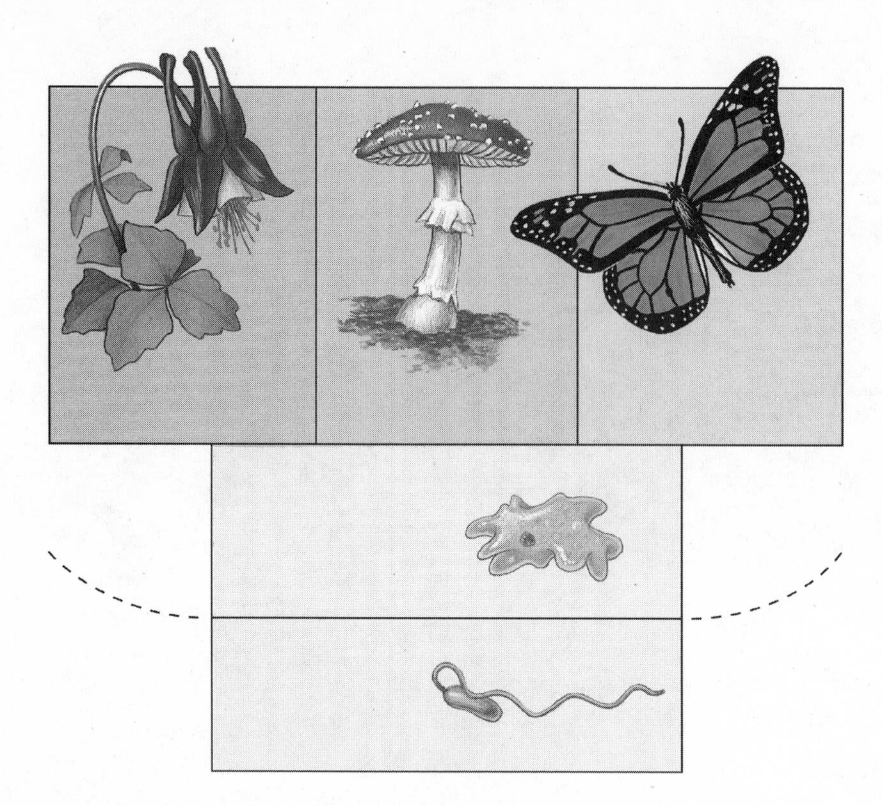

Figure 26.15 Whittaker's five-kingdom system, page 522

Figure 26.16 Our changing view of biological diversity, page 523

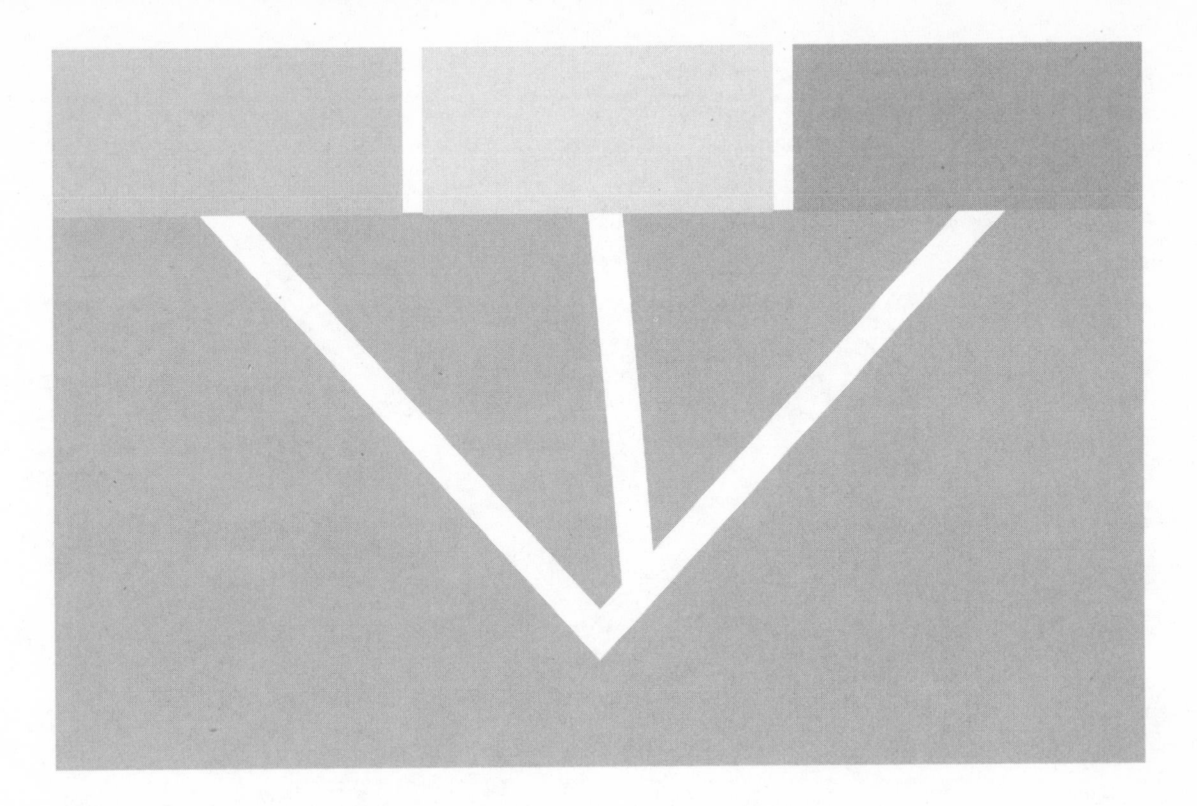

Figure 27.2 The three domains of life, page 527

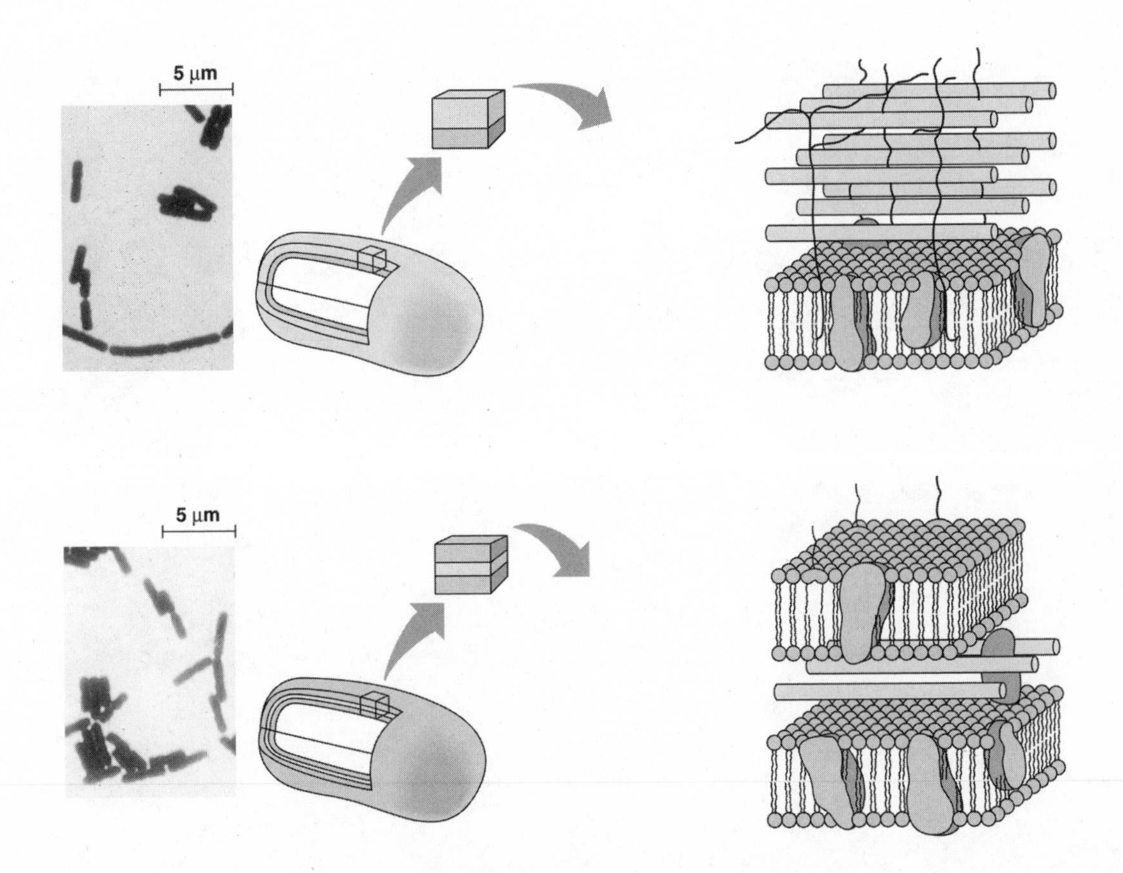

Figure 27.5 Gram-positive and gram-negative bacteria, page 529

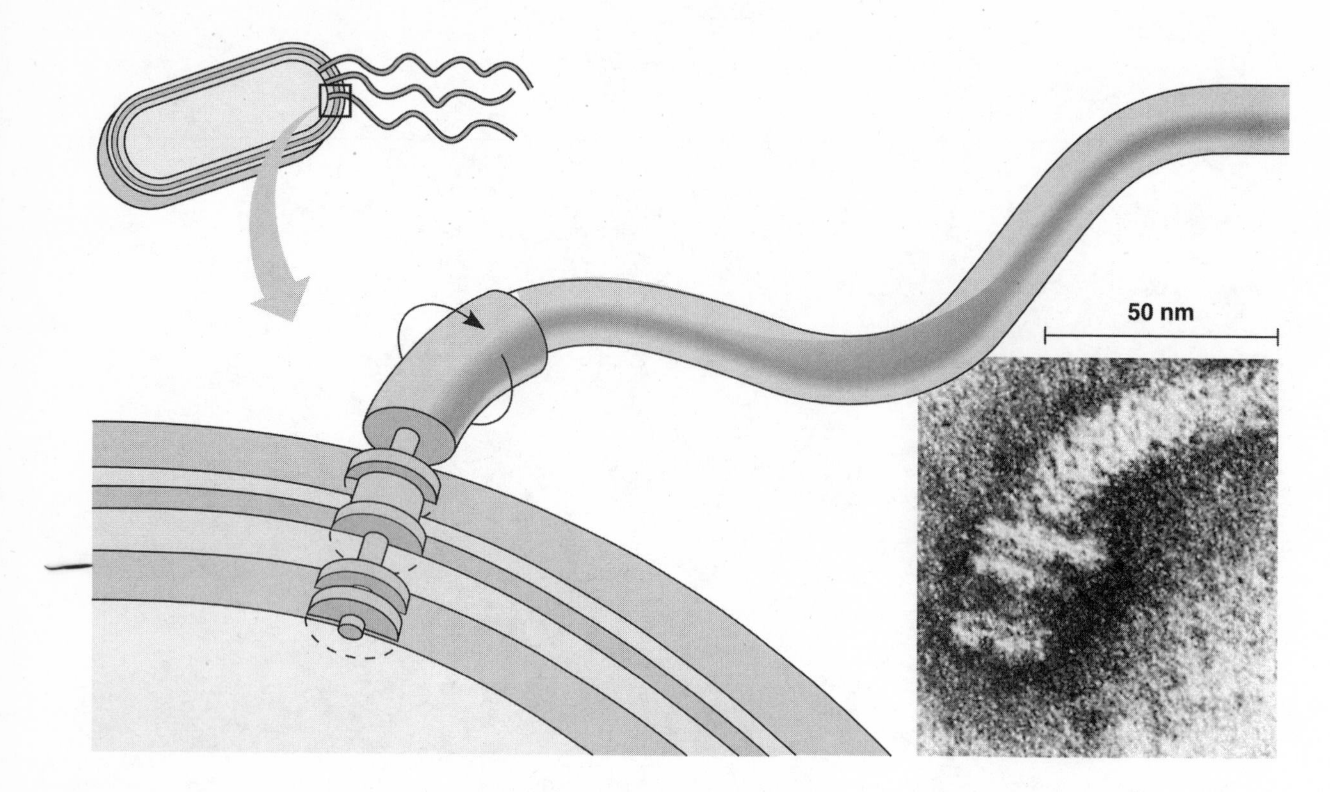

Figure 27.7 Form and function of prokaryotic flagella, page 530

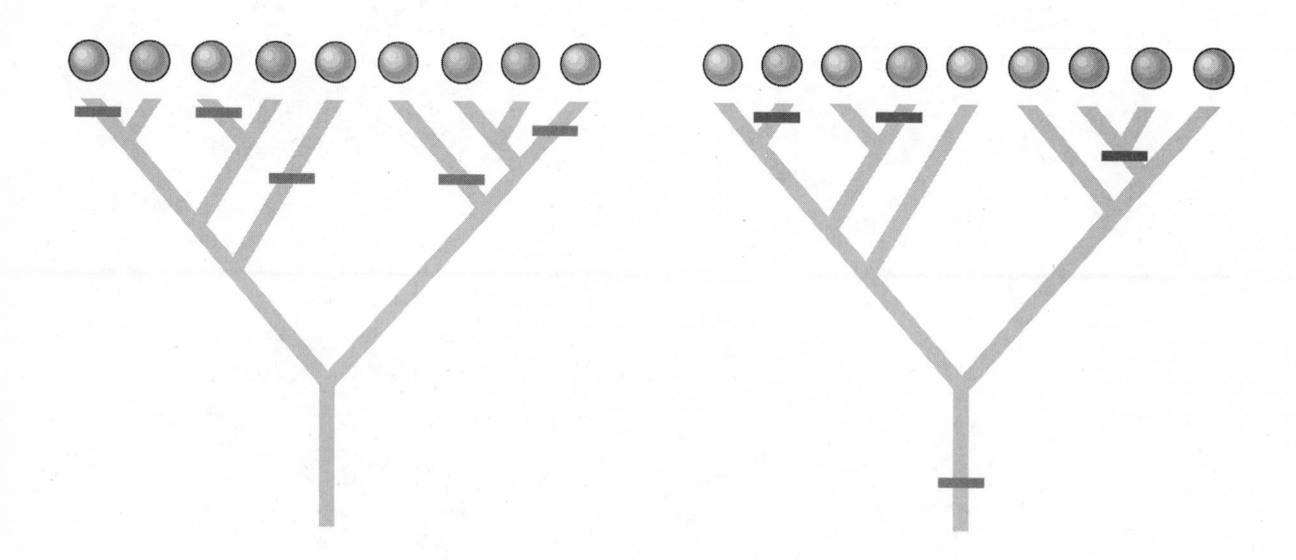

Figure 27.12 Contrasting hypotheses for the taxonomic distribution of photosynthesis among prokaryotes, page 534

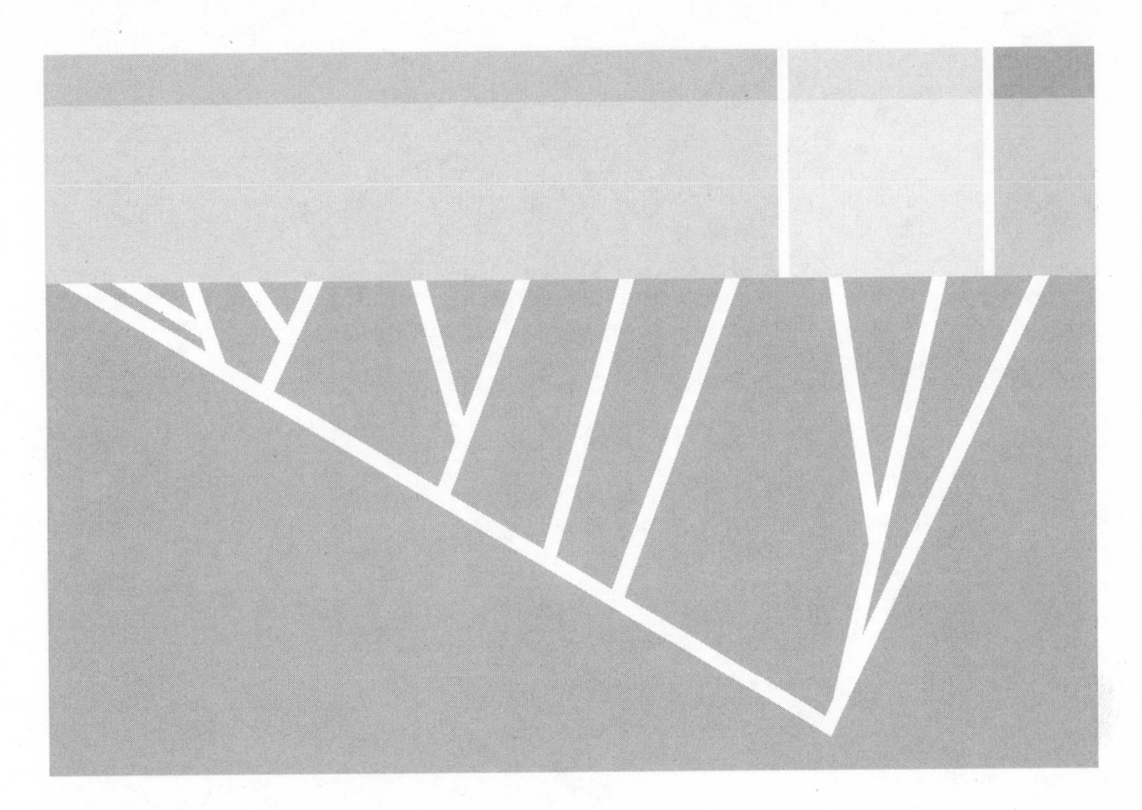

Figure 27.13 Some major groups of prokaryotes, page 536

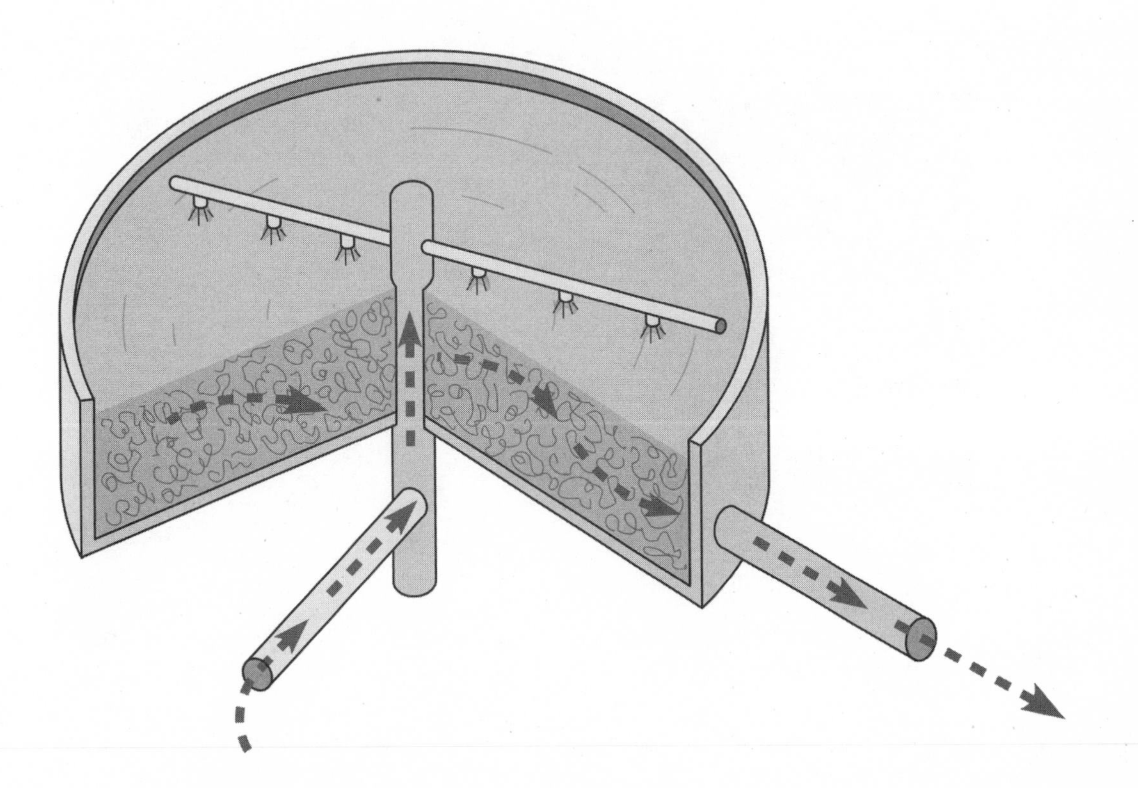

Figure 27.18 Putting prokaryotes to work in sewage treatment, page 542

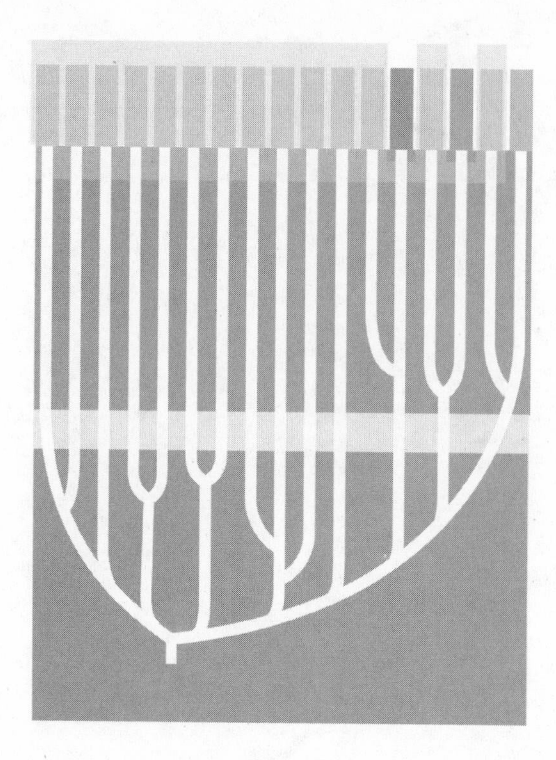

Figure 28.2 The kingdom Protista problem, page 547

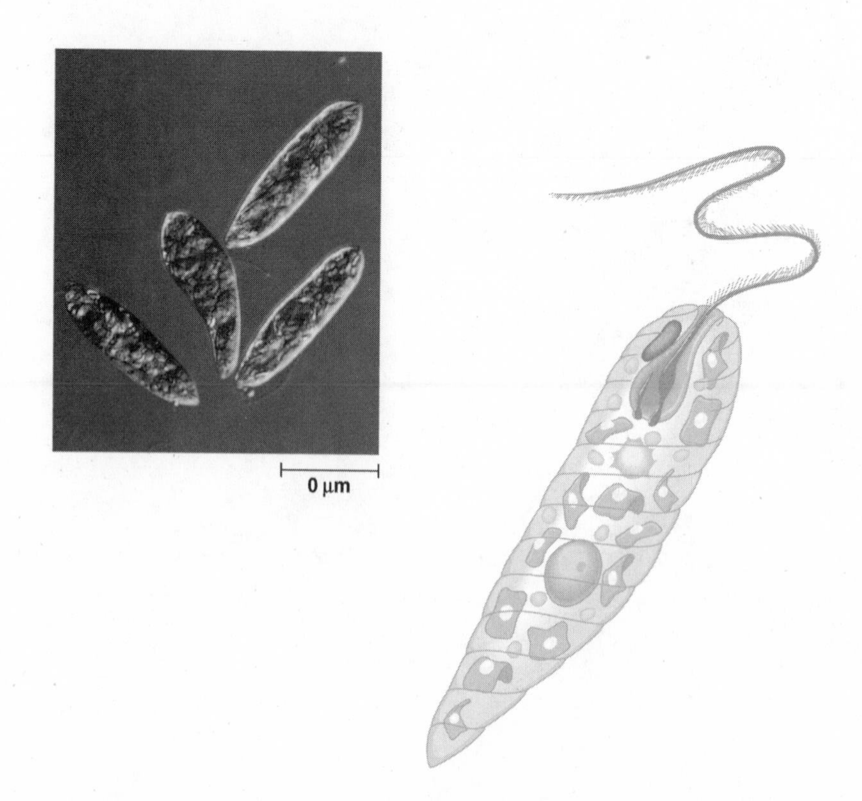

Figure 28.3 *Euglena*: an example of a single-celled protist, page 547

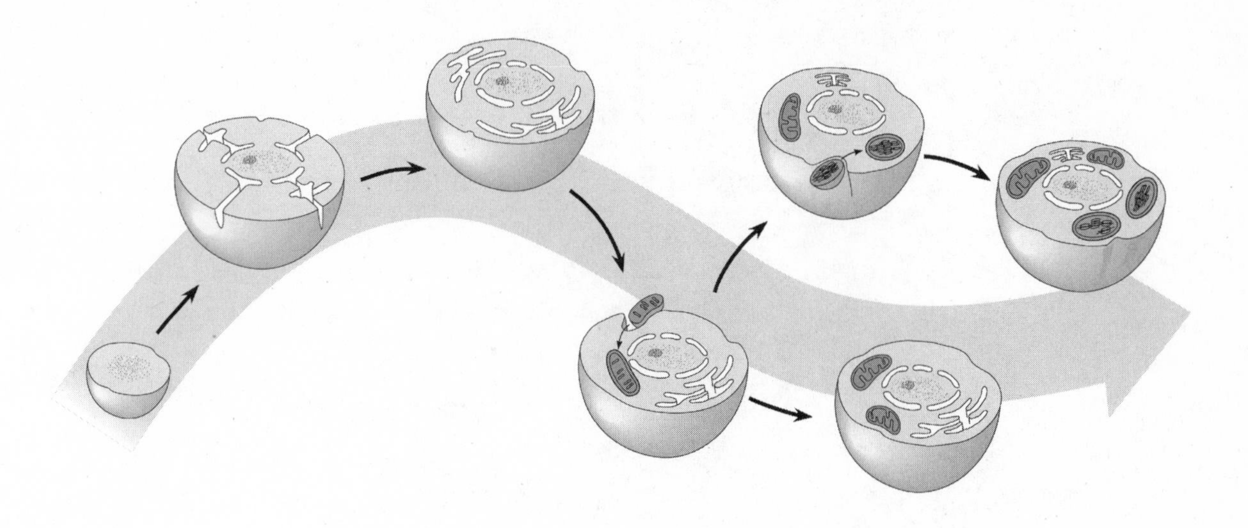

Figure 28.4 A model of the origin of eukaryotes, page 549

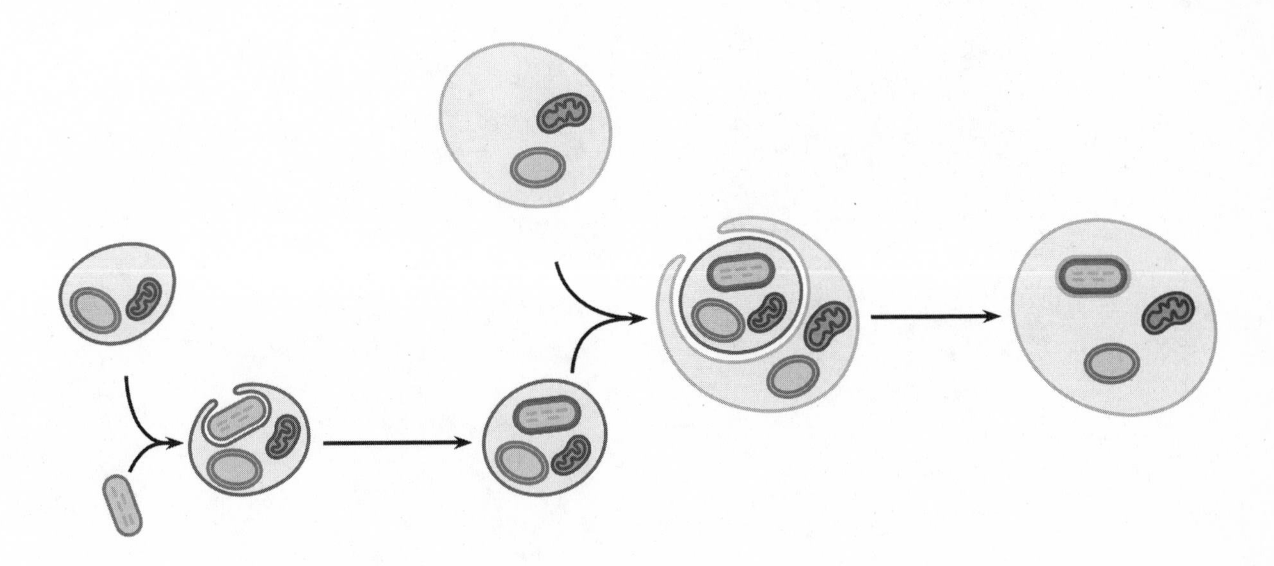

Figure 28.5 Secondary endosymbiosis and the origin of algal diversity, page 551

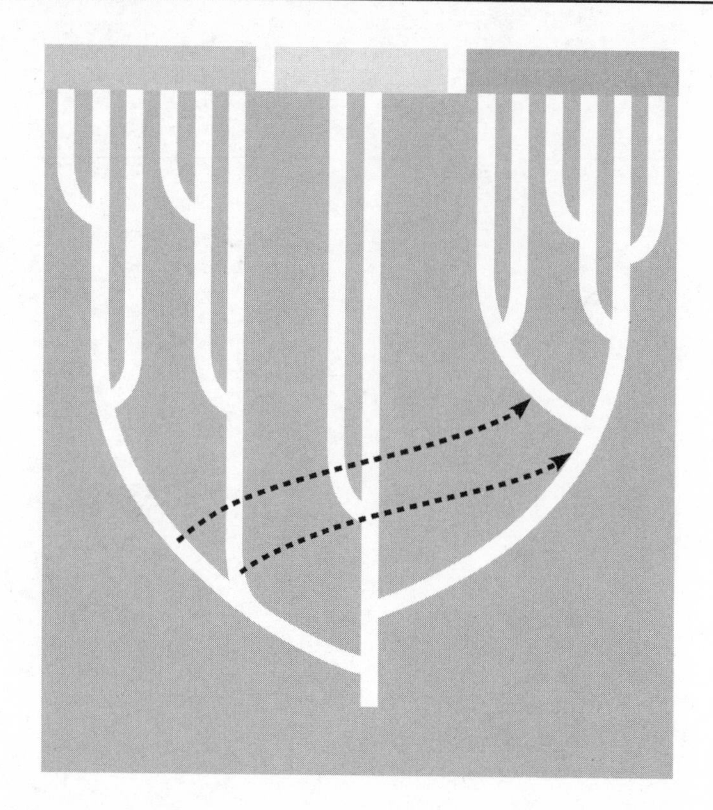

Figure 28.6 Traditional hypothesis for how the three domains of life are related, page 552

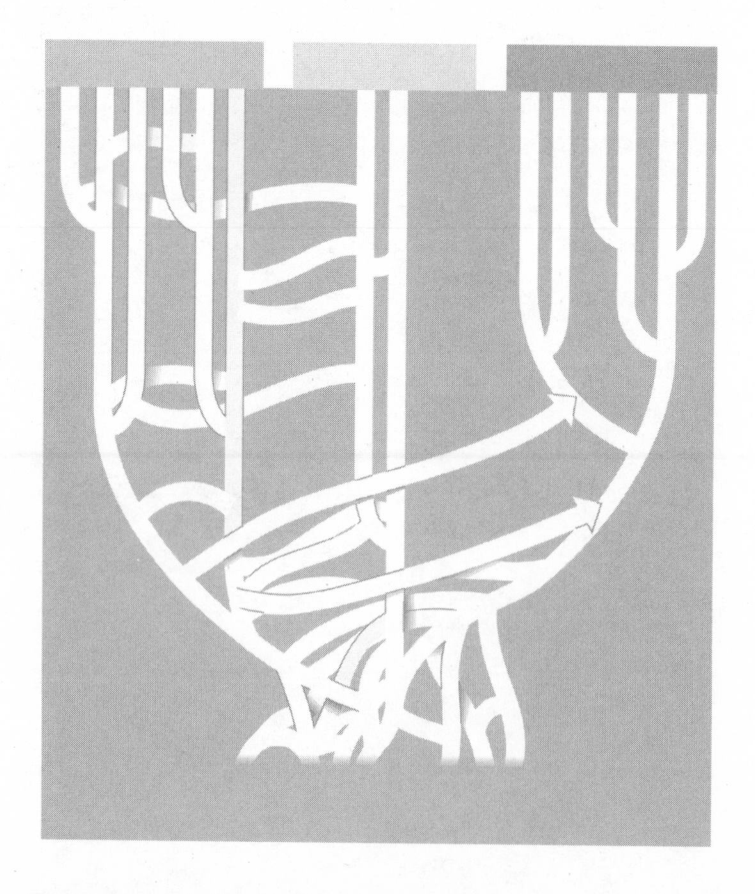

Figure 28.7 An alternative hypothesis for how the three domains of life are related, page 553

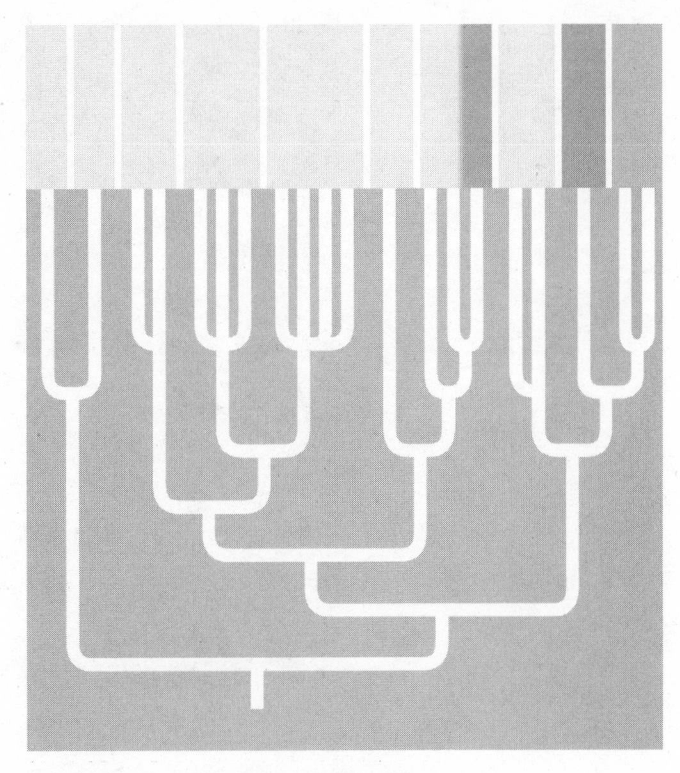

Figure 28.8 A tentative phylogeny of eukaryotes, page 554

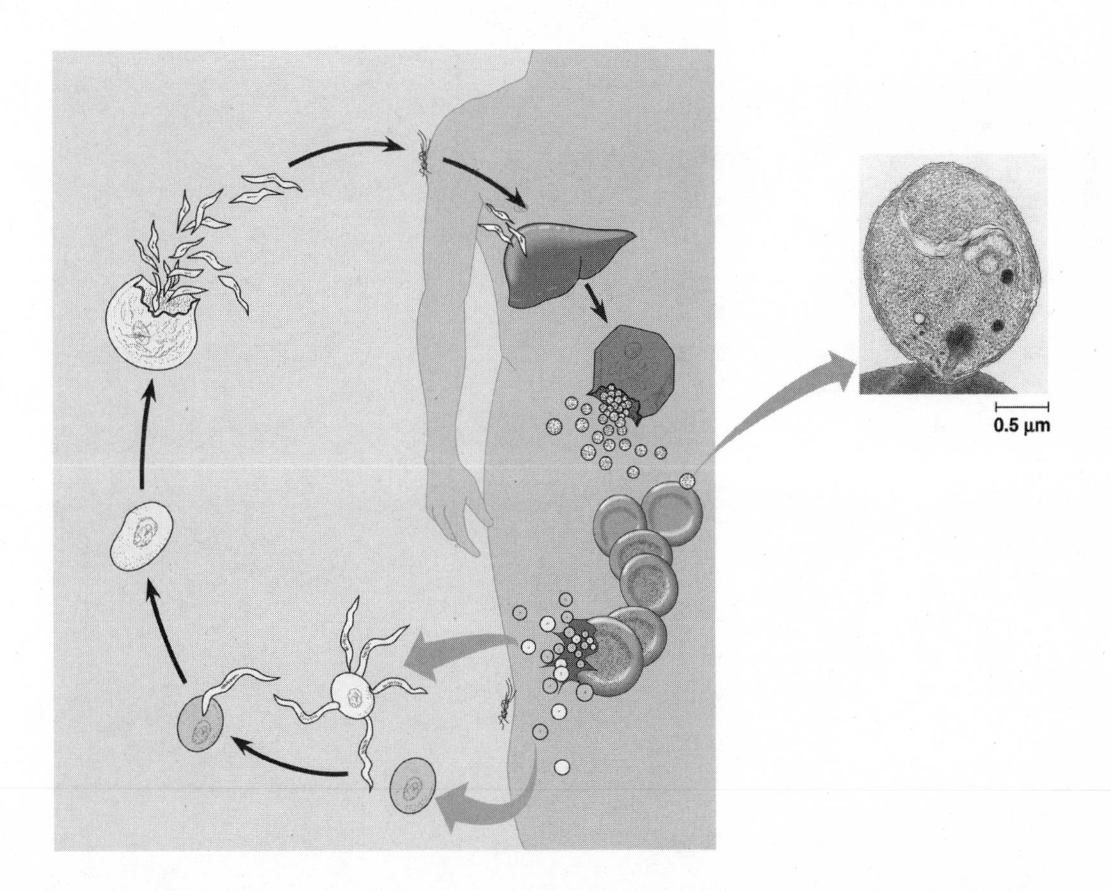

Figure 28.13 The two-host life history of *Plasmodium*, the apicomplexan that causes malaria, page 557

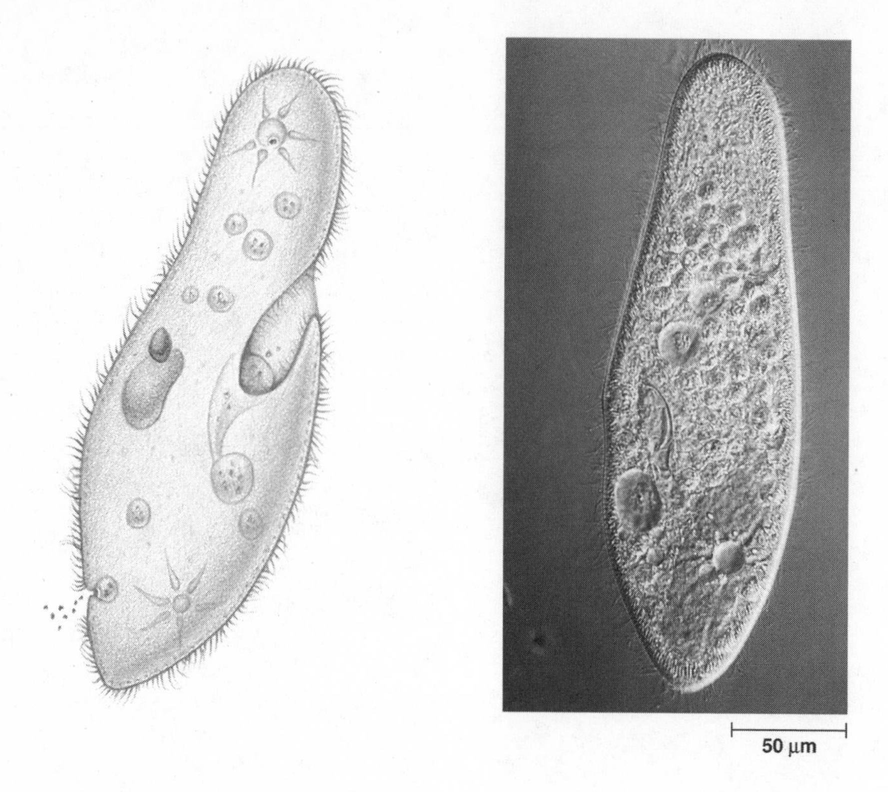

Figure 28.14c Ciliates: *Paramecium*, page 558

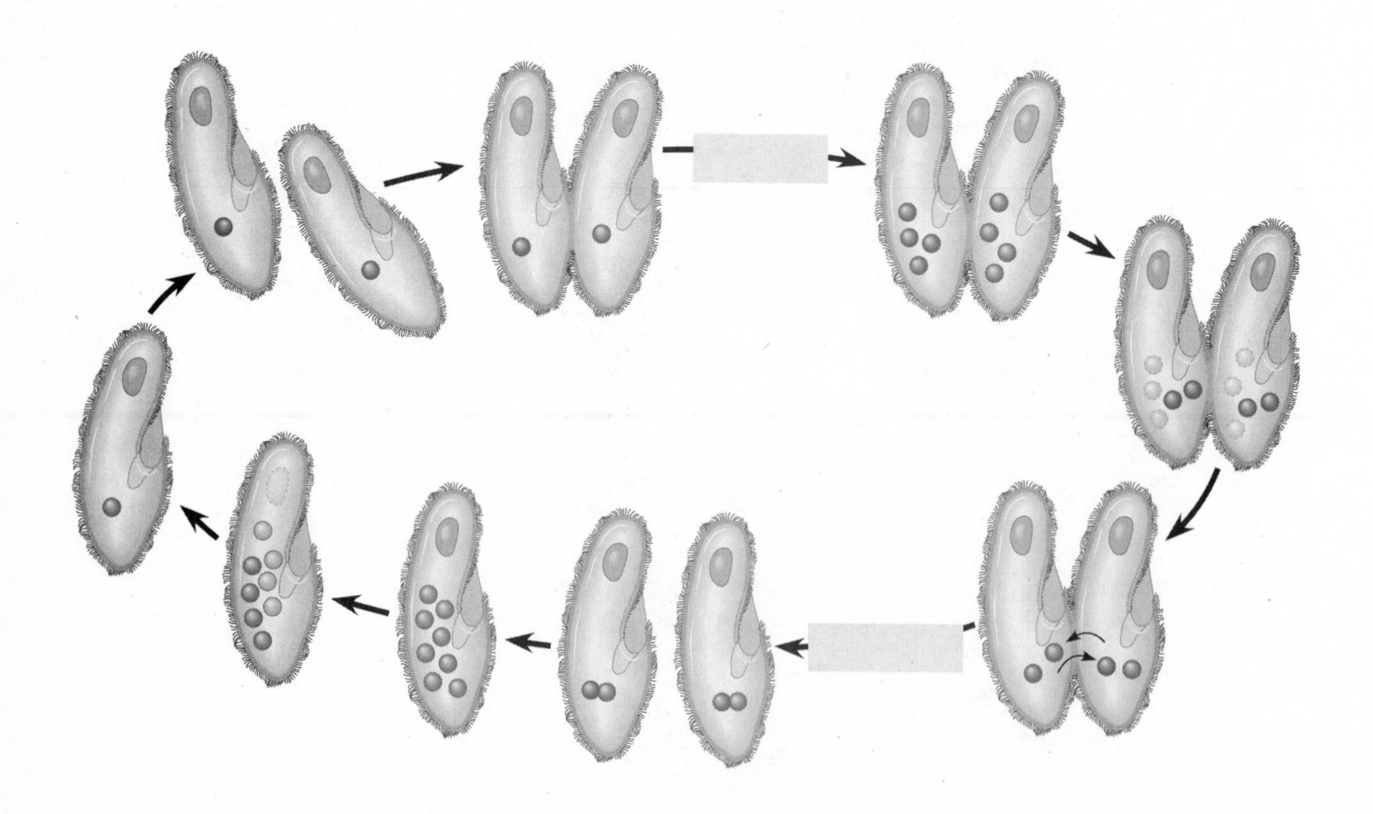

Figure 28.15 Conjugation and genetic recombination in *Paramecium caudatum*, page 559

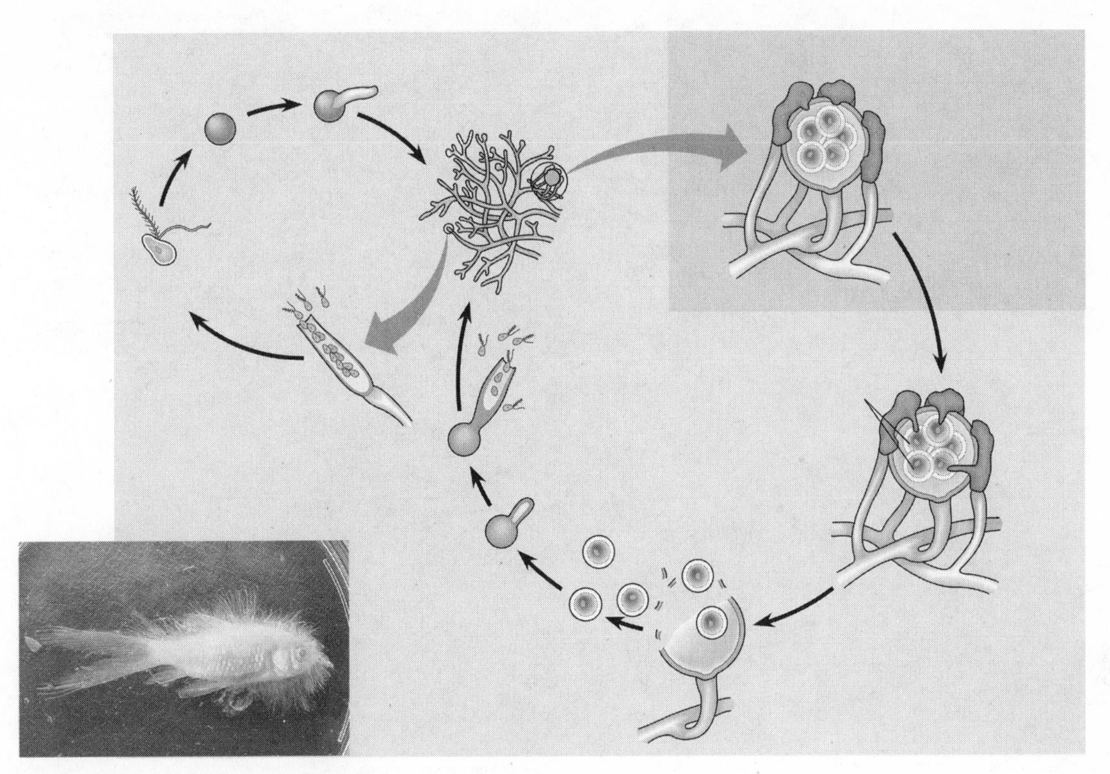

Figure 28.16 The life cycle of a water mold, page 561

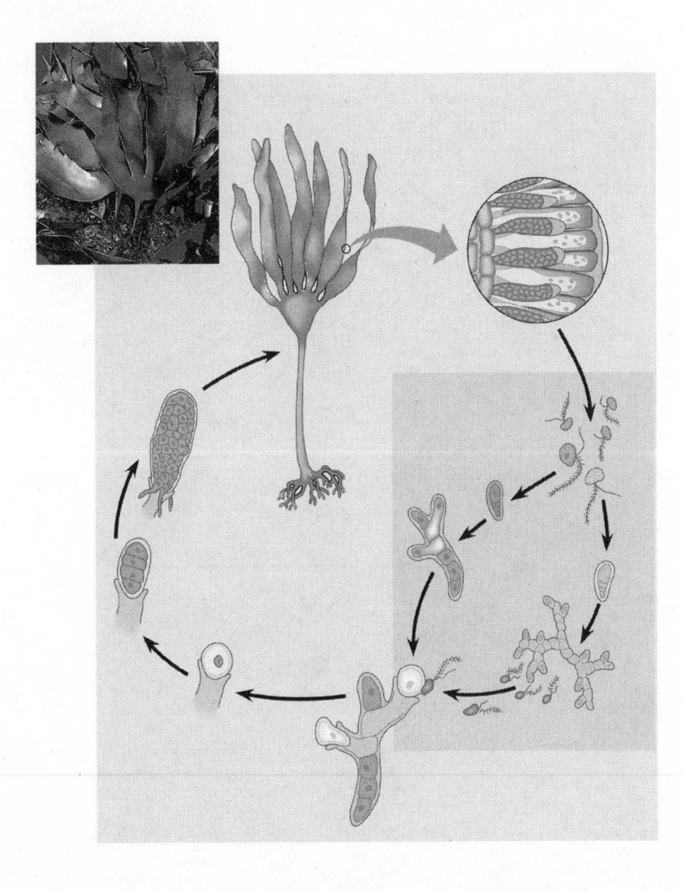

Figure 28.21 The life cycle of *Laminaria*: an example of alternation of generations, pate 564

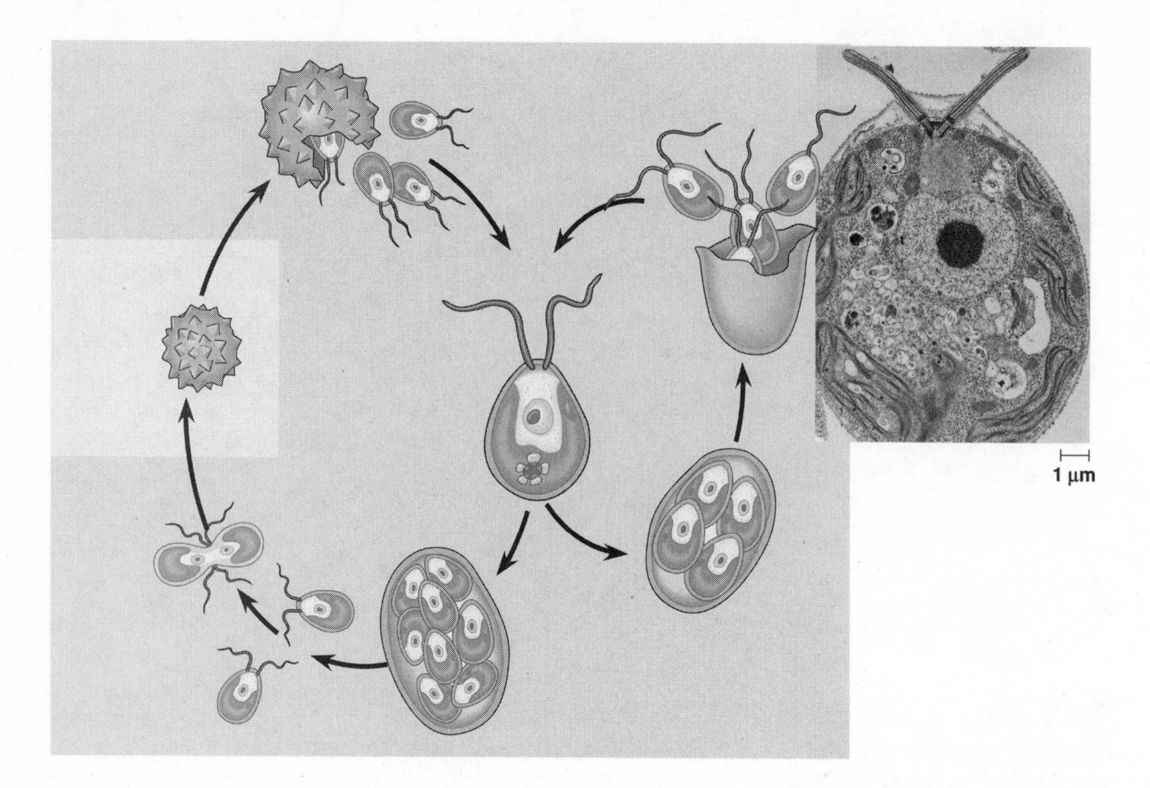

Figure 28.24 The life cycle of *Chlamydomonas*, page 567

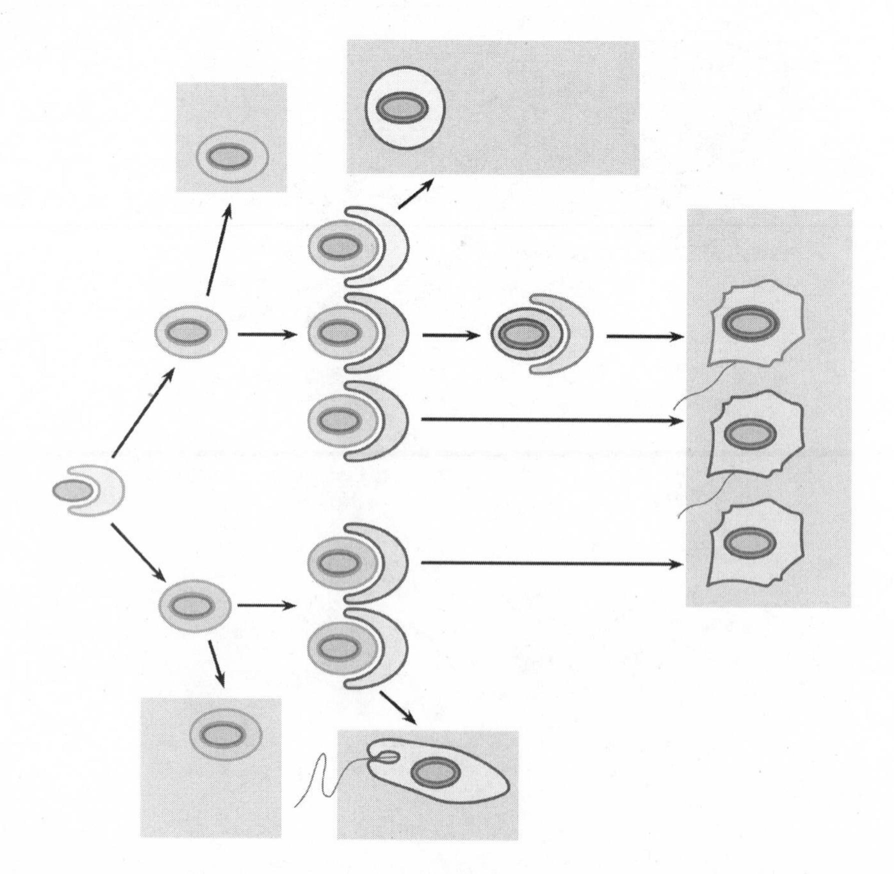

Figure 28.25 A simplified history of plastids in the photosynthetic eukaryotes, page 568

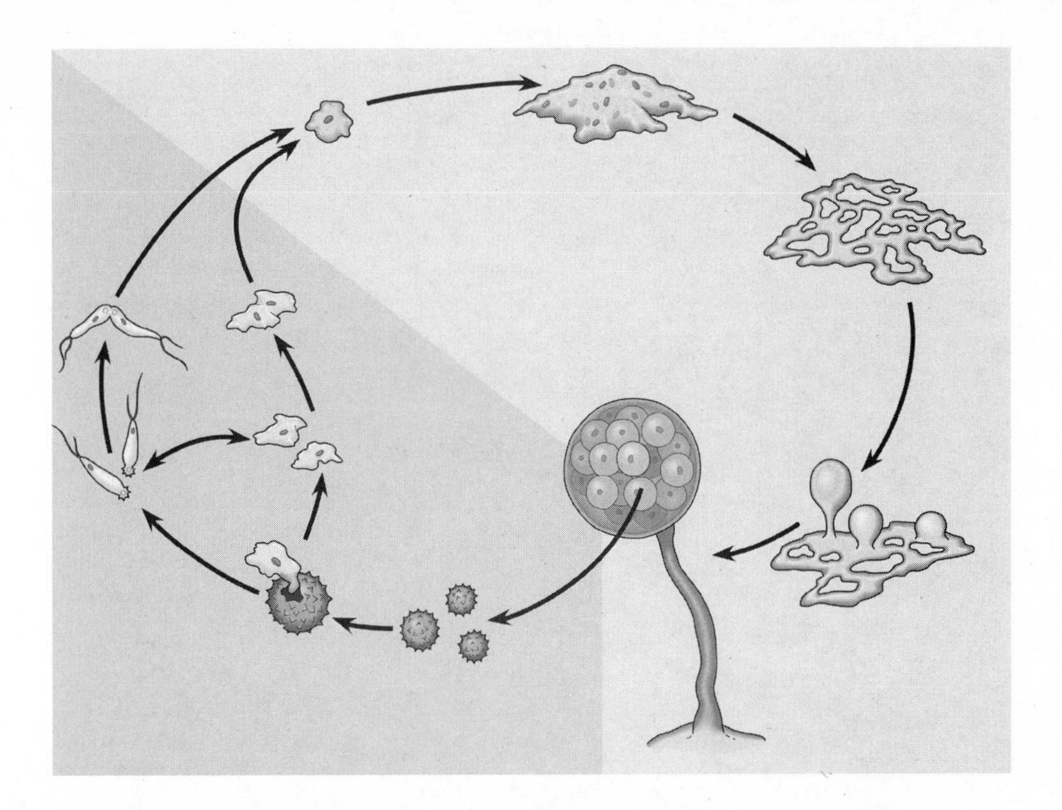

Figure 28.29 The life cycle of a plasmodial slime mold, such as *Physarum*, page 571

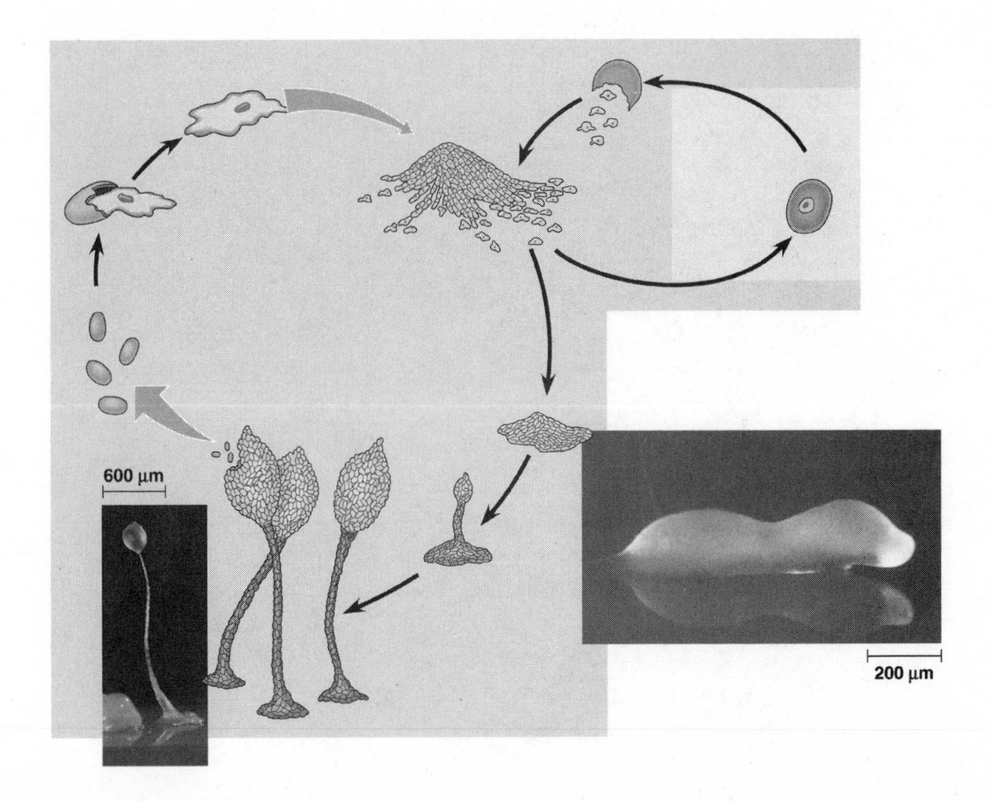

Figure 28.30 The life cycle of a cellular slime mold (*Dictyostelium*), page 572

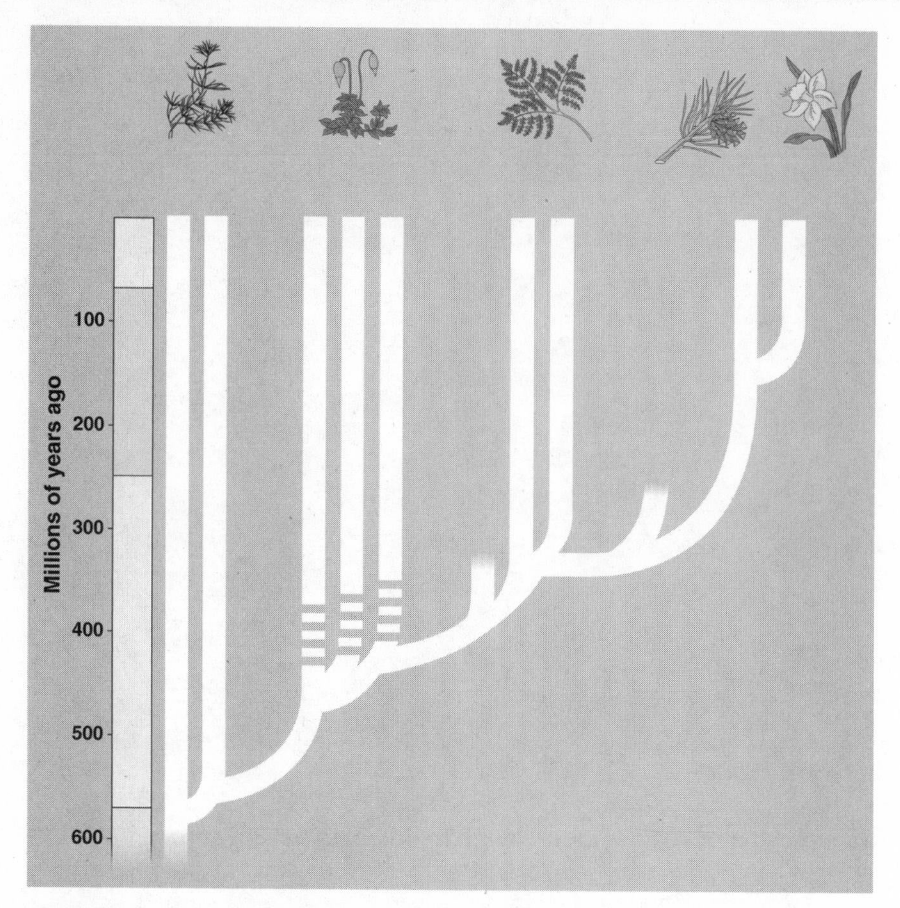

Figure 29.1 Some highlights of plant evolution, page 577

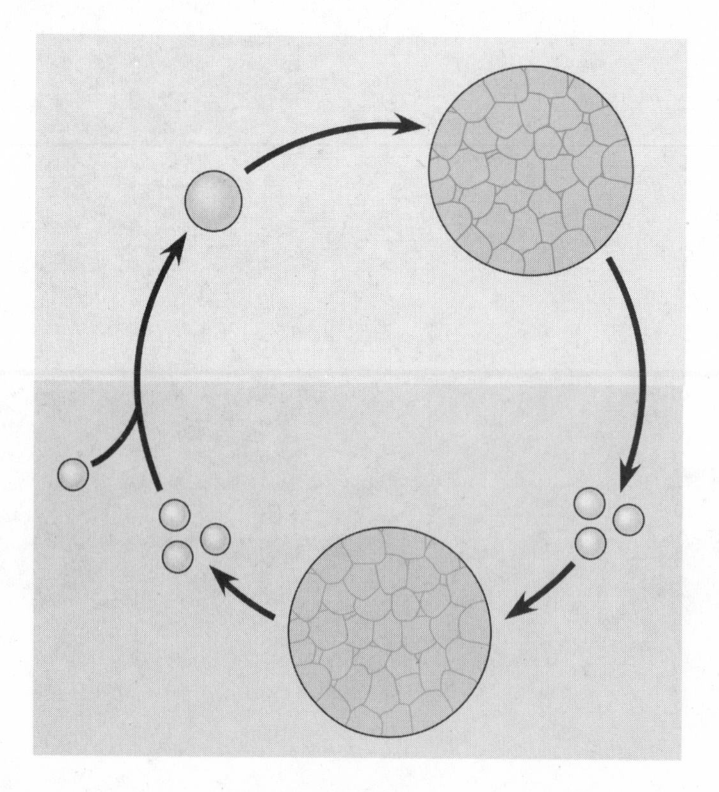

Figure 29.6 Alternation of generations: a generalized scheme, page 580

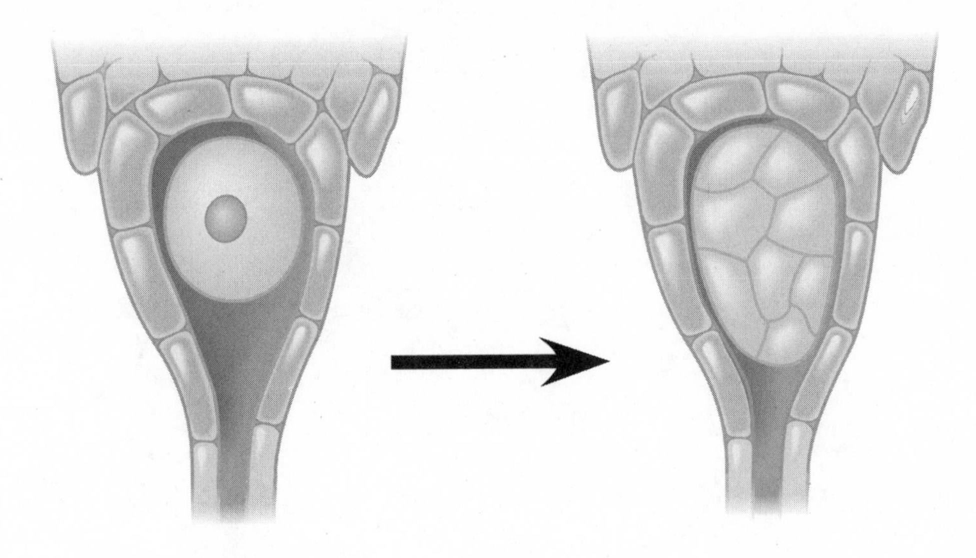

Figure 29.13 A hypothetical mechanism for the origin of alternation of generations in the ancestor of plants, page 583

Figure 29.14 Three clades competing for designation as the plant kingdom, page 584

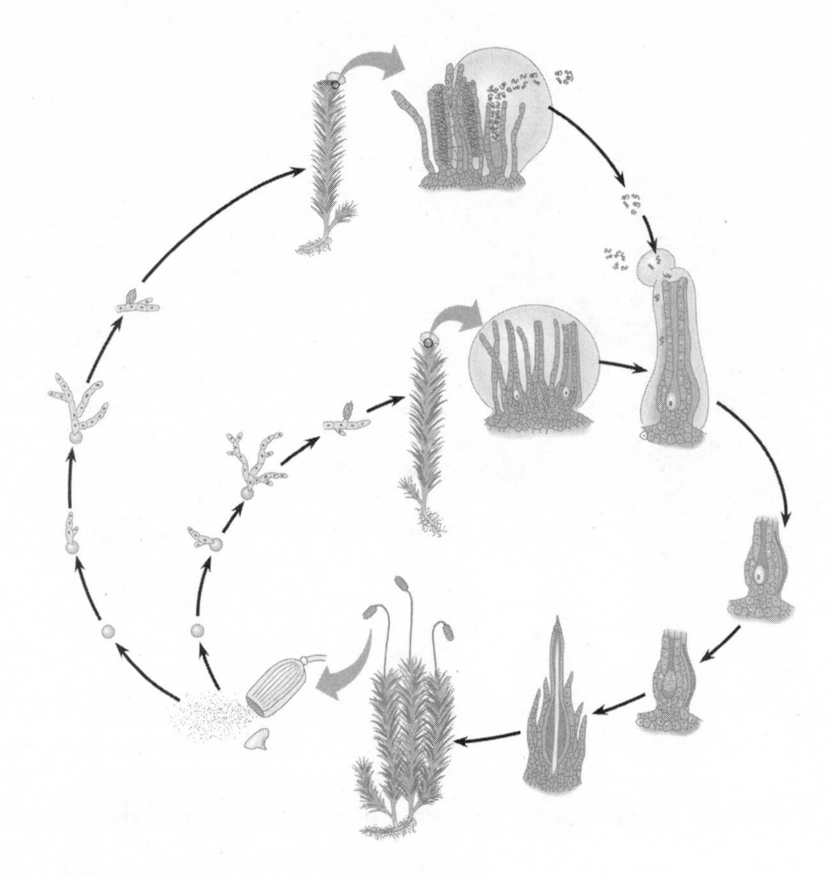

Figure 29.16 The life cycle of *Polytrichum*, a moss, page 586

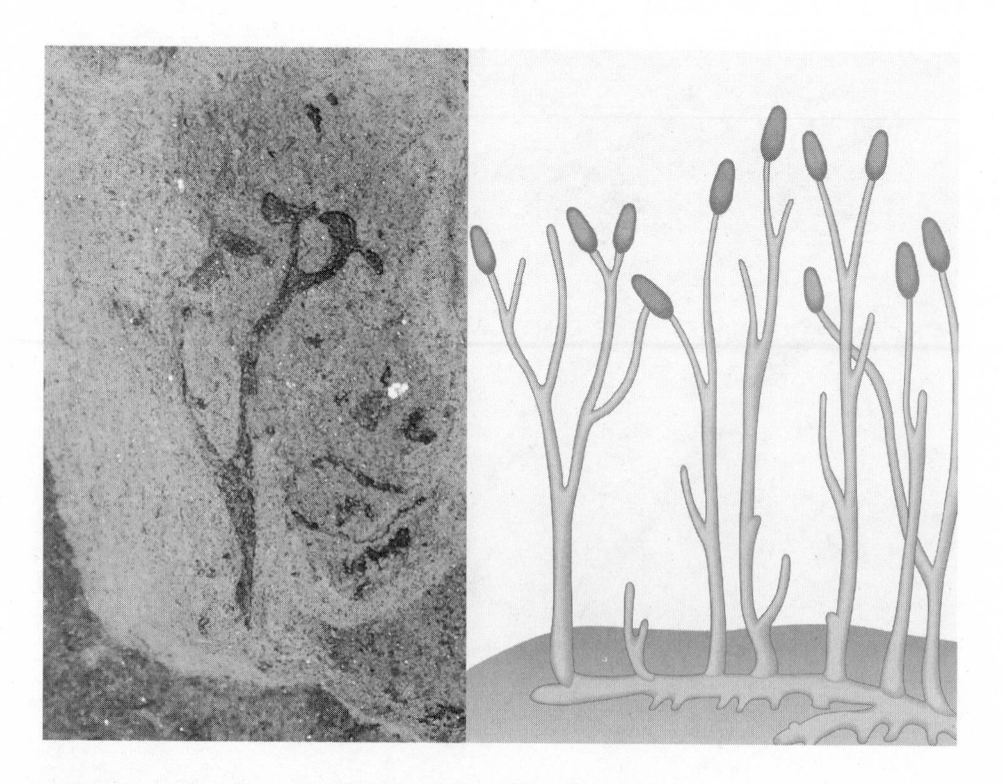

Figure 29.20 *Cooksonia*, a vascular plant of the Silurian, page 589

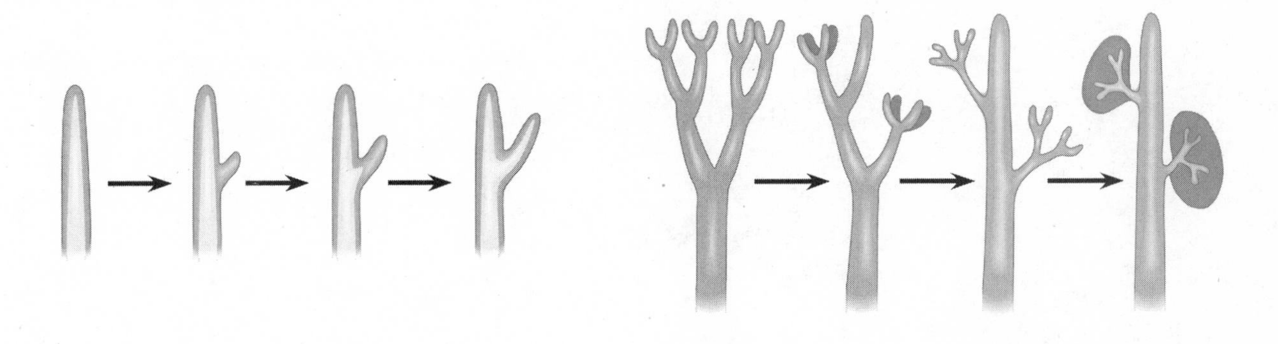

Figure 29.22 Hypotheses for the evolution of leaves, page 591

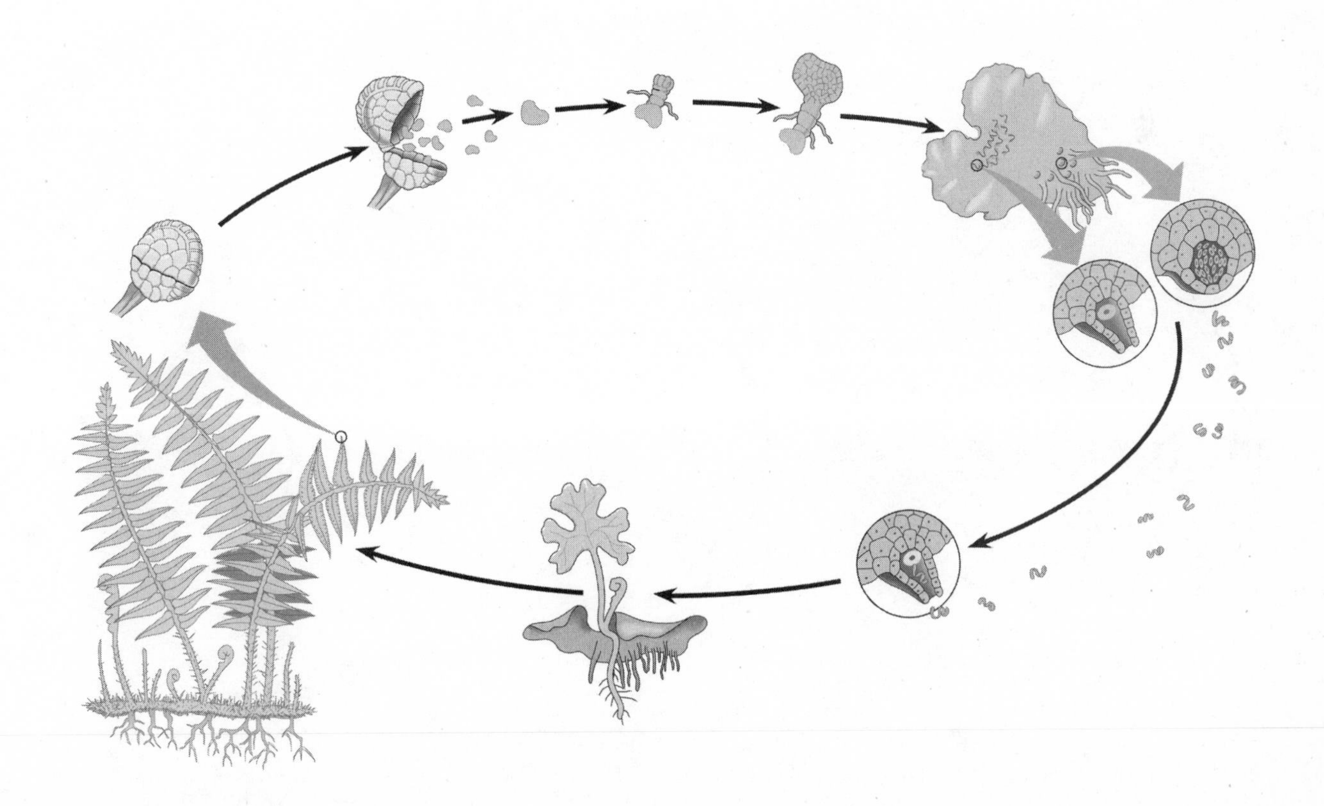

Figure 29.23 The life cycle of a fern, page 592

Figure 30.1 Three variations on gametophyte/sporophyte relationships, page 598

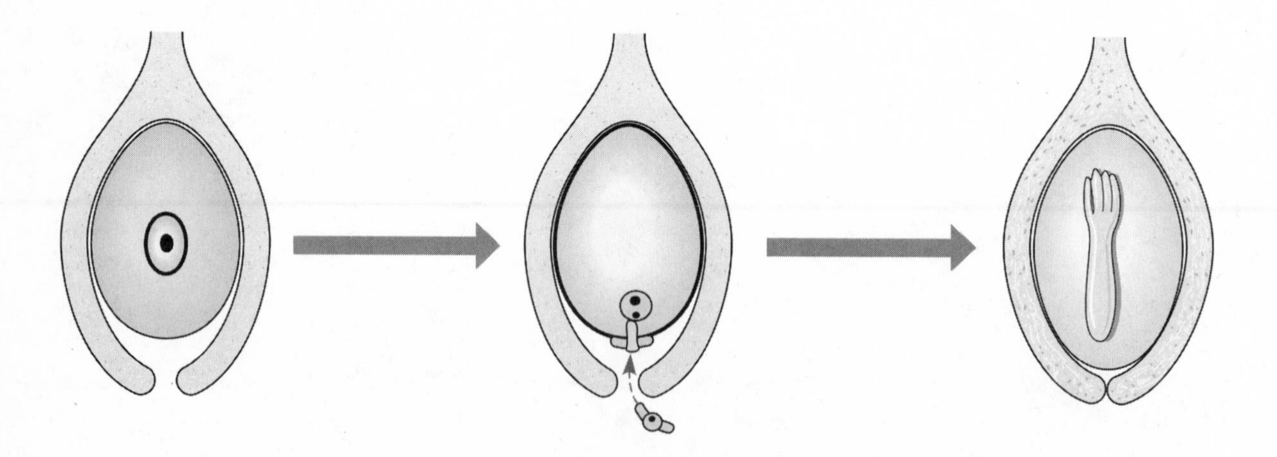

Figure 30.2 From ovule to seed, page 599

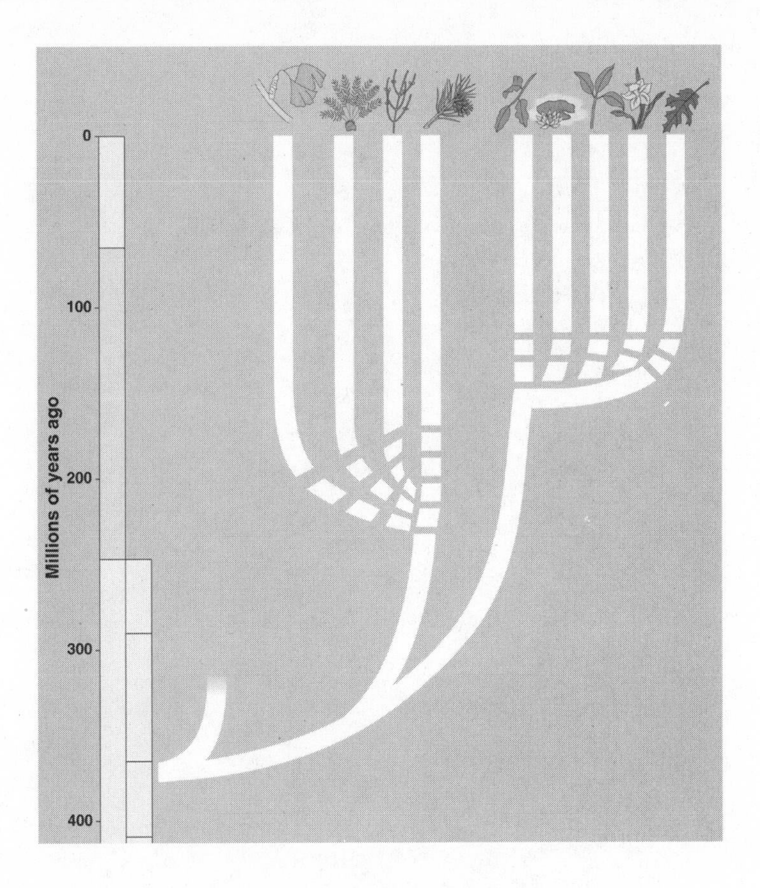

Figure 30.4 Hypothetical phylogeny of the seed plants, page 601

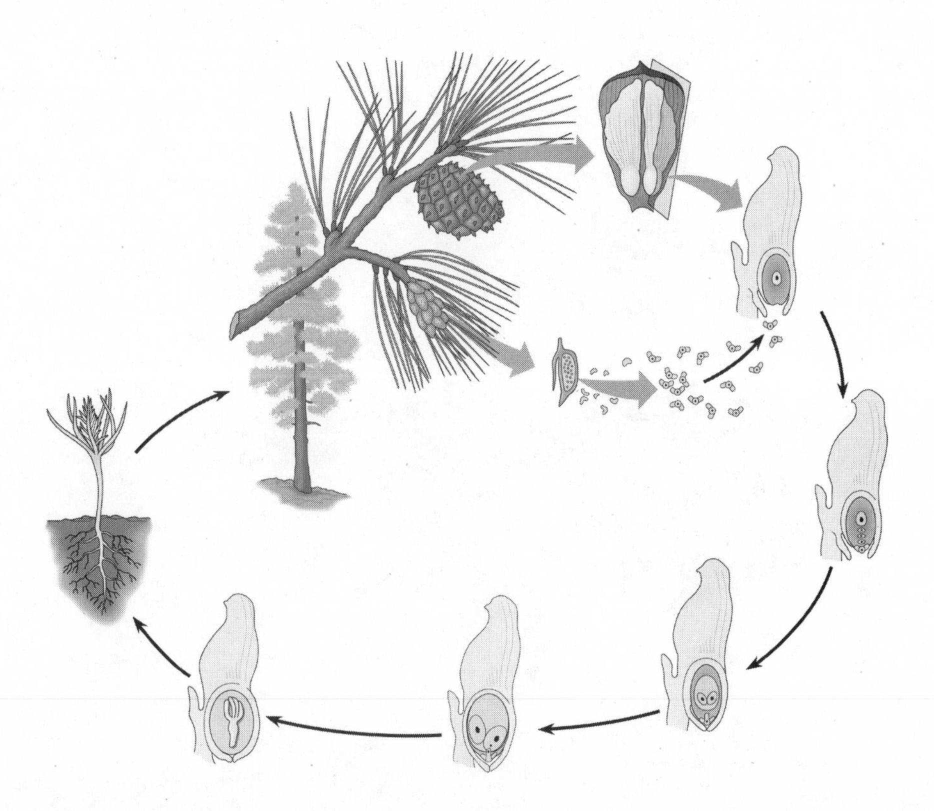

Figure 30.9 The life cycle of a pine, page 605

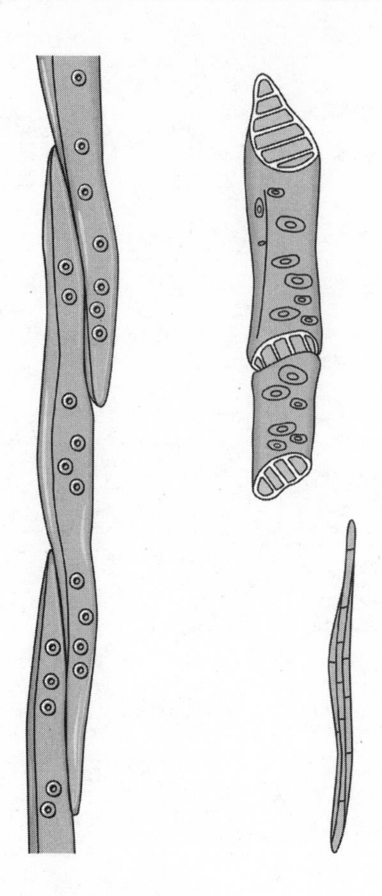

Figure 30.12 Xylem cells in angiosperms, page 607

Figure 30.13 The structure of a flower, page 608

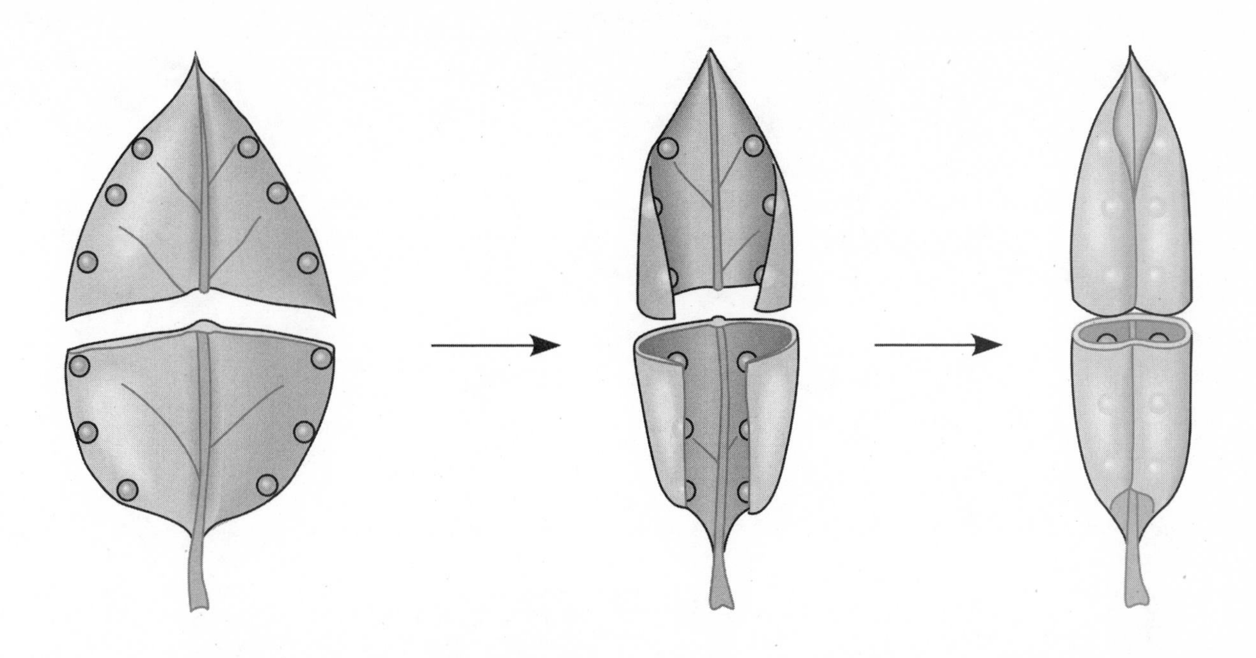

Figure 30.14 Hypothesis for the origin of the carpel from a reproductive leaf (sporophyll), page 609

Figure 30.15 Relationship between a pea flower and a fruit (pea pod), page 609

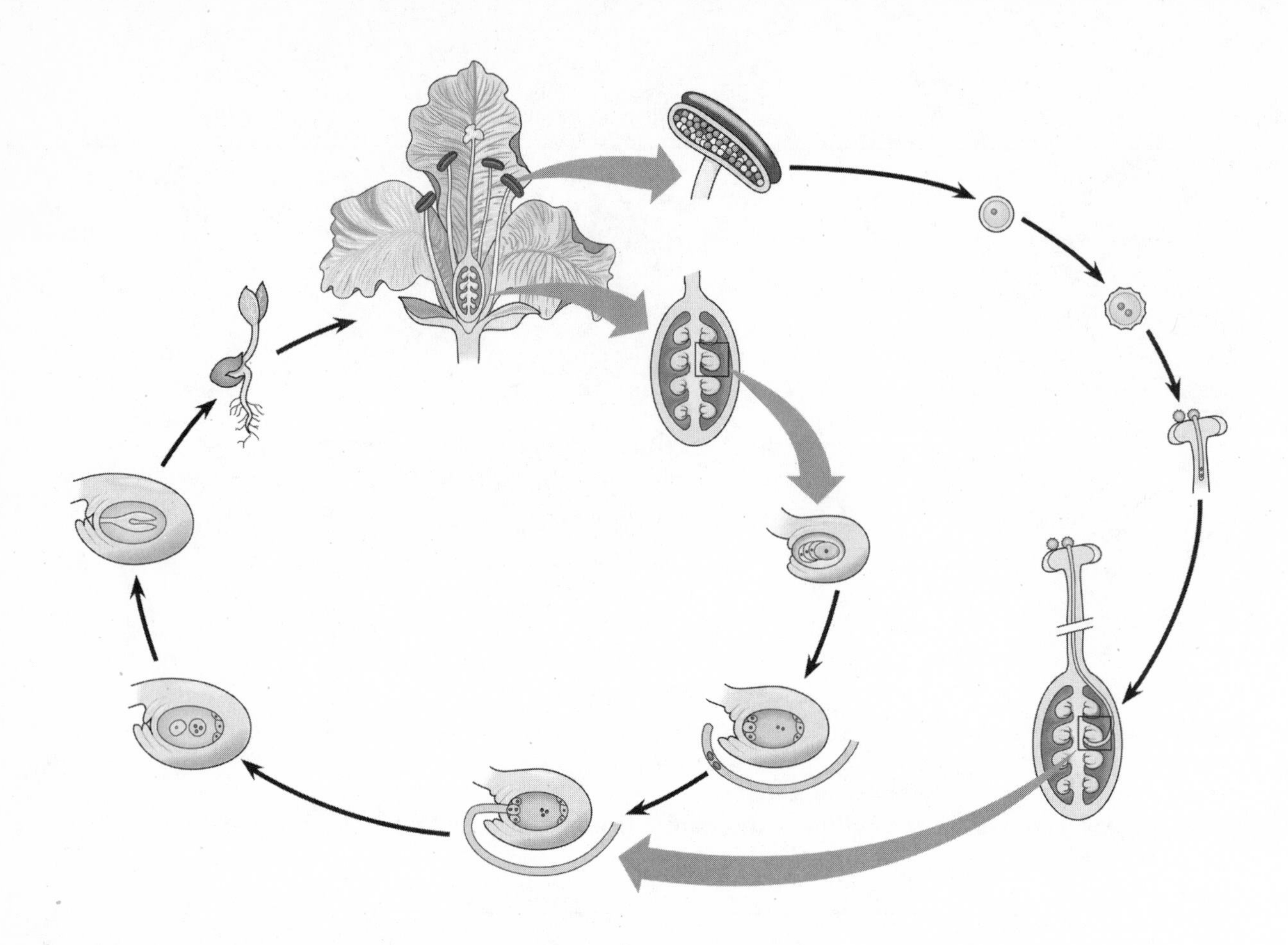

Figure 30.17 The life cycle of an angiosperm, page 611

Figure 30.Q7-10 Cladogram, page 615

Figure 31.1 Fungal mycelia, page 617

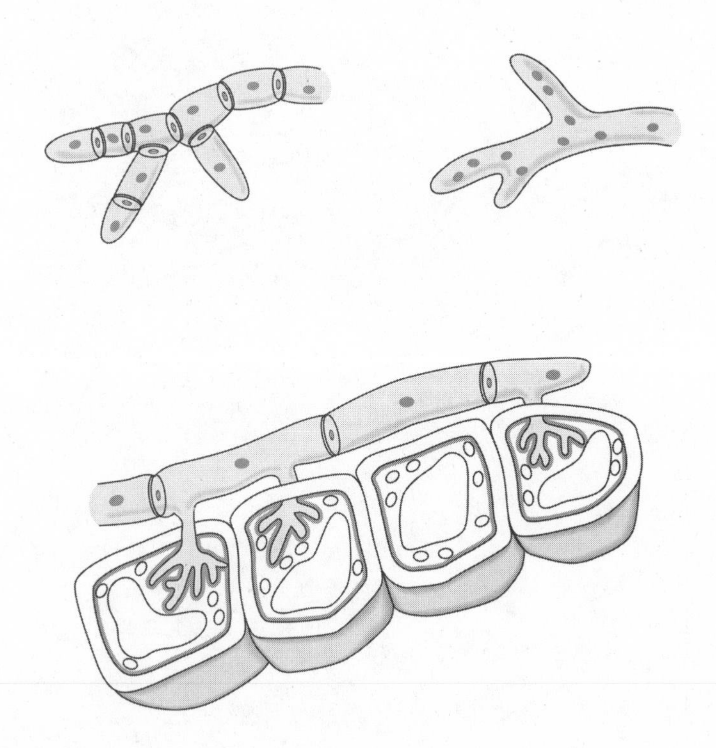

Figure 31.2 Examples of fungal hyphae, page 618

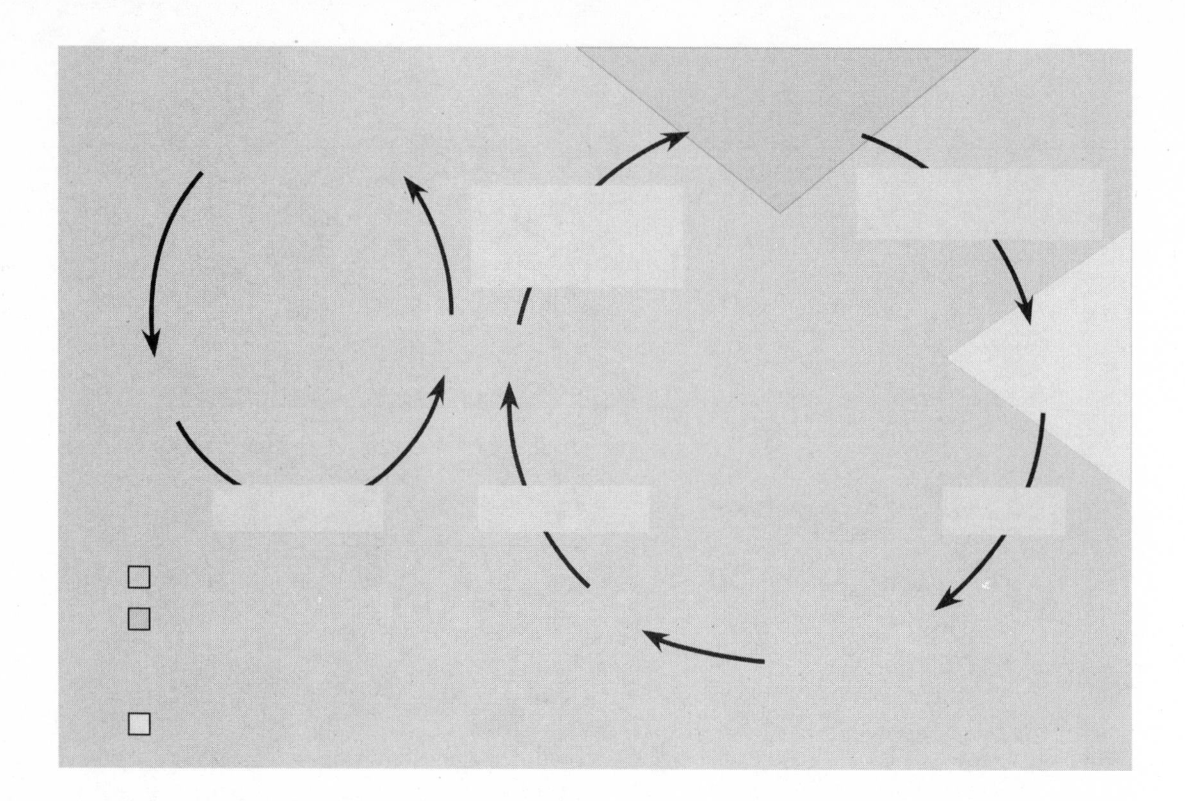

Figure 31.3 Generalized life cycle of fungi, page 619

Figure 31.4 Phylogeny of fungi, page 619

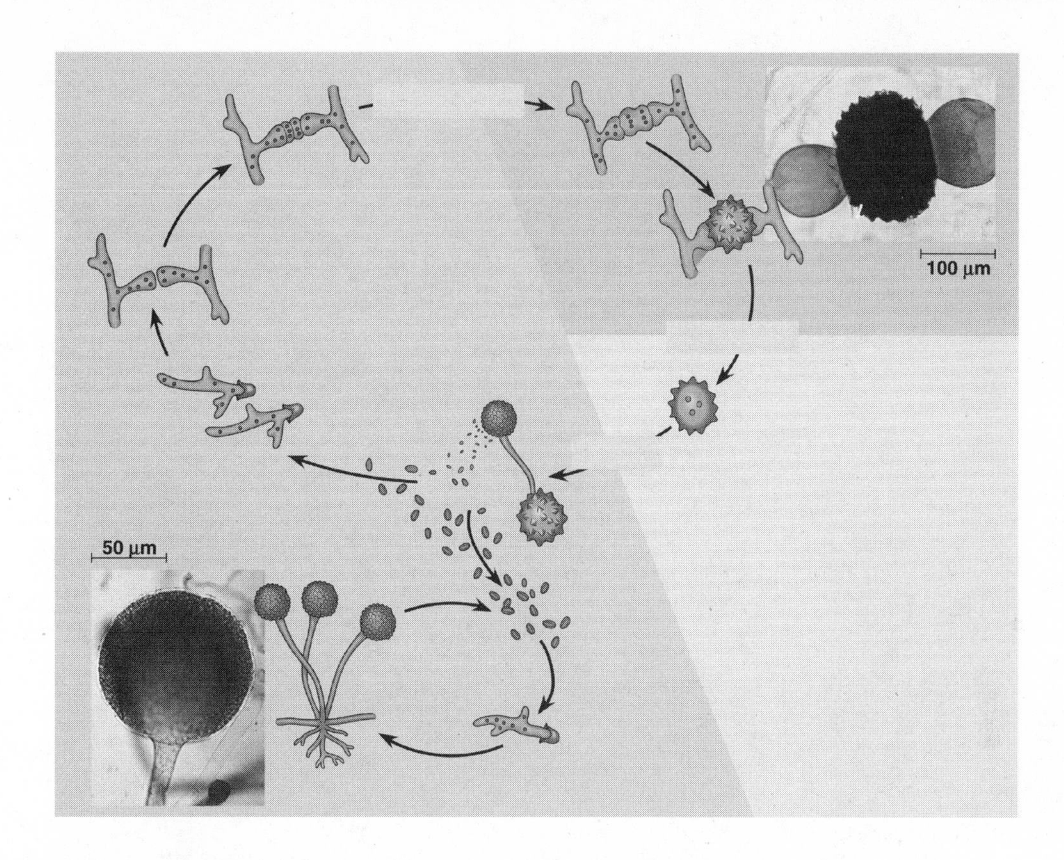

Figure 31.7 The life cycle of the zygomycete *Rhizopus* (black bread mold), page 621

Figure 31.10 The life cycle of an ascomycete, page 623

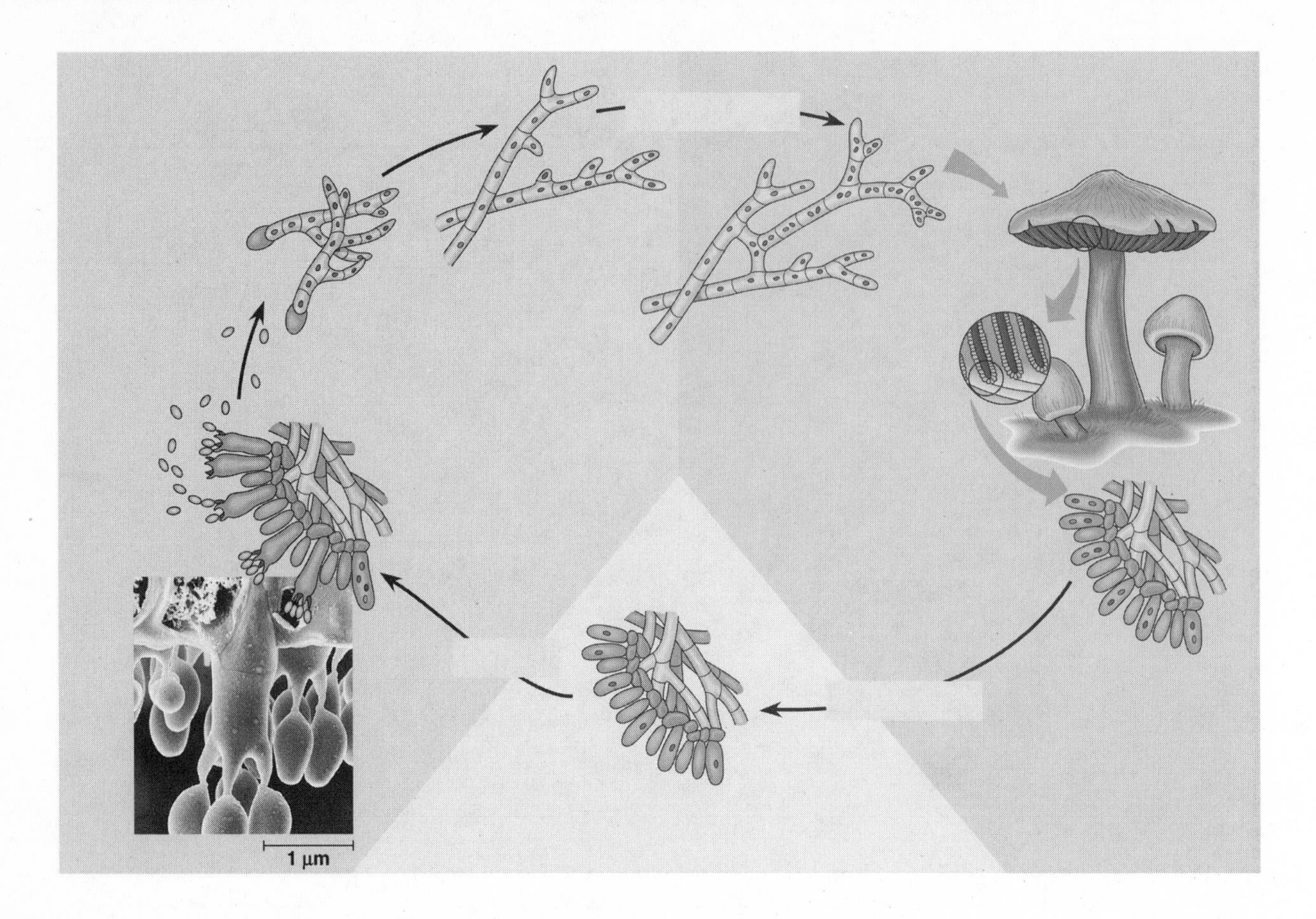

Figure 31.12 The life cycle of a mushroom-forming basidiomycete, page 625

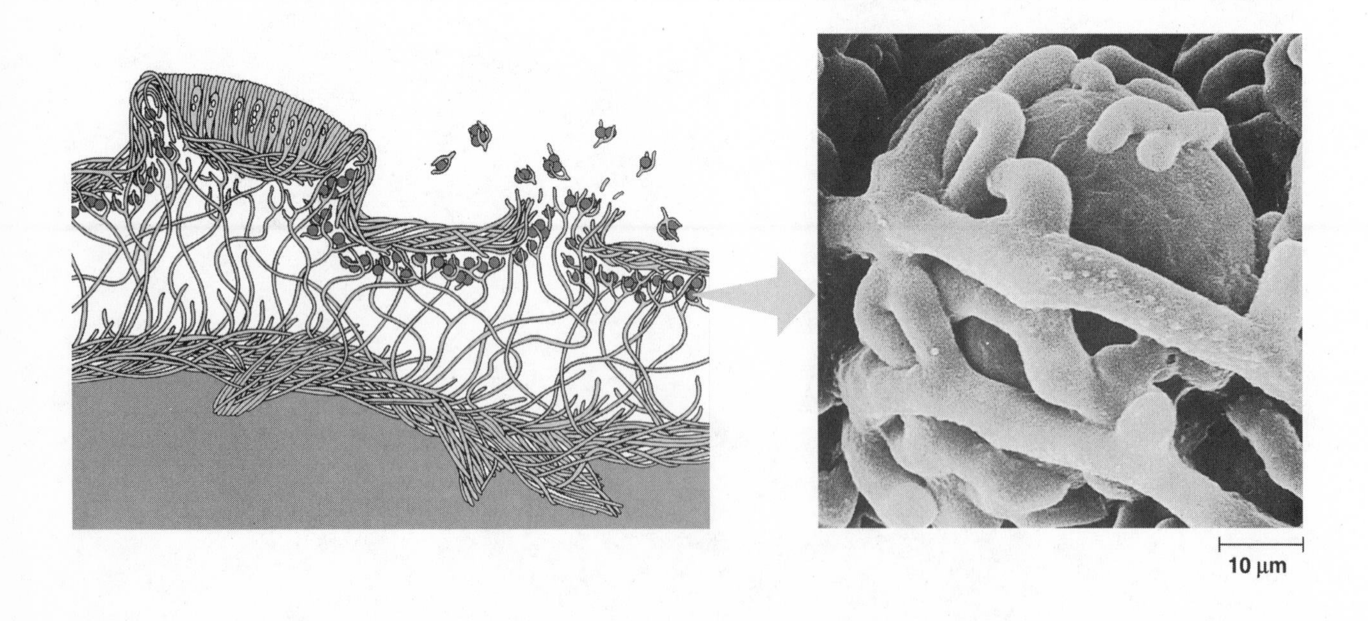

Figure 31.17 Anatomy of a lichen, page 627

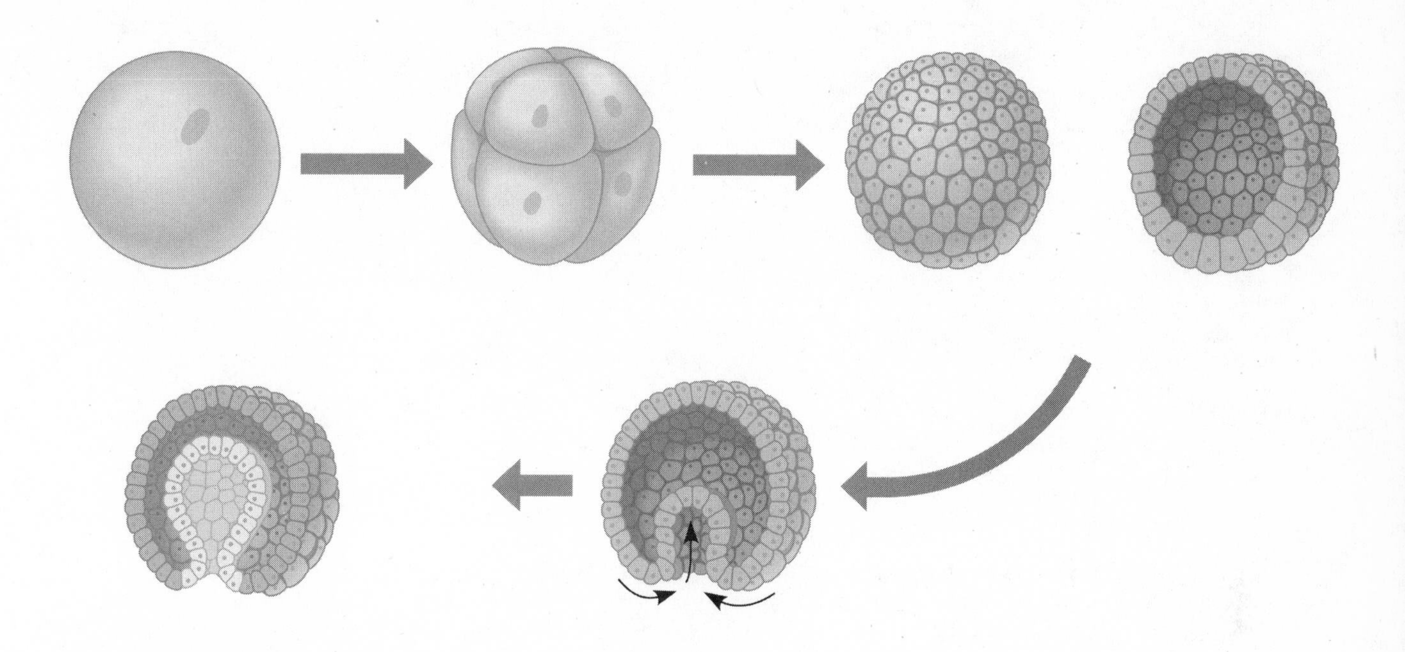

Figure 32.1 Early embryonic development, page 634

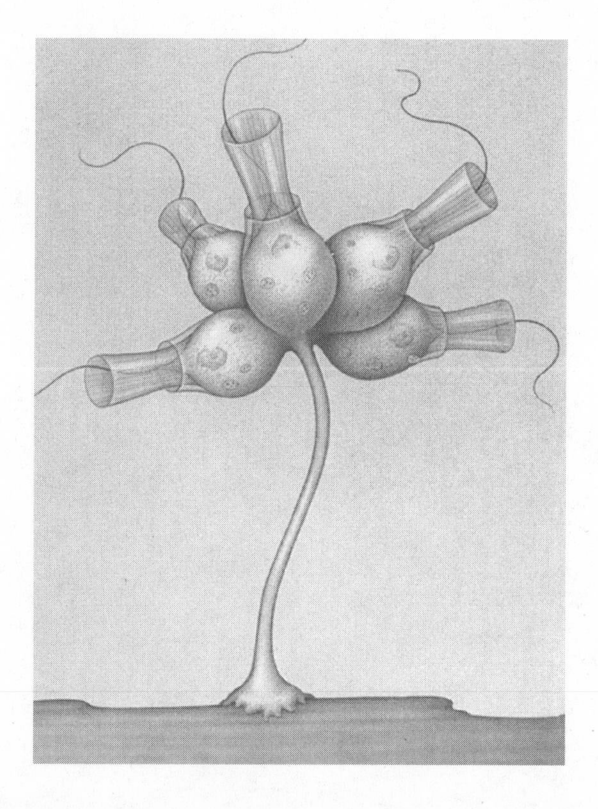

Figure 32.2 A choanoflagellate colony, page 635

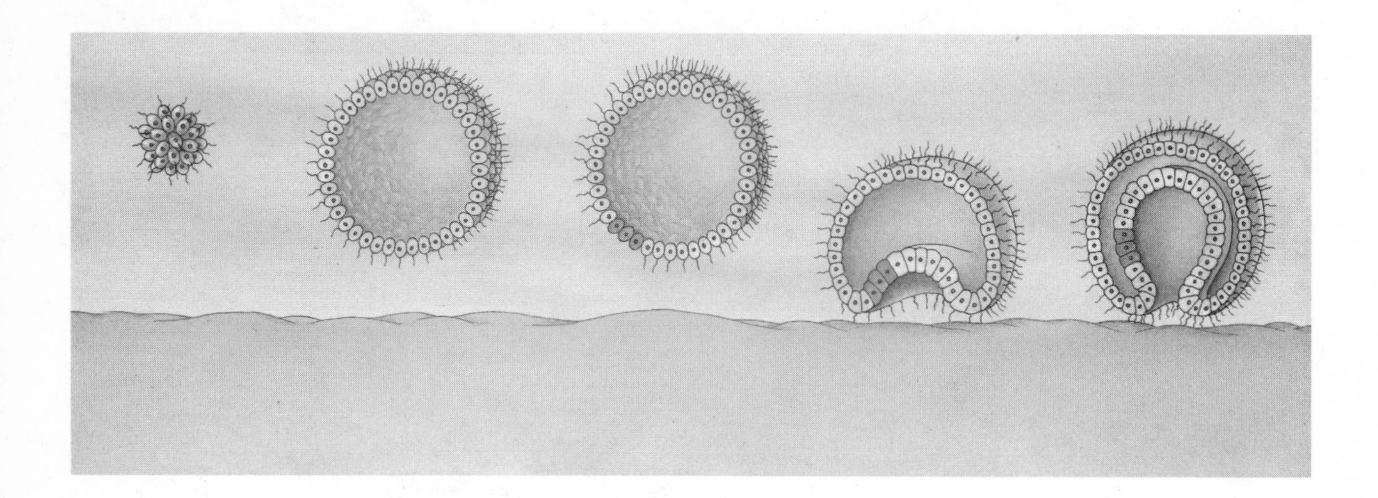

Figure 32.3 One hypothesis for the origin of animals from a flagellated protist, page 635

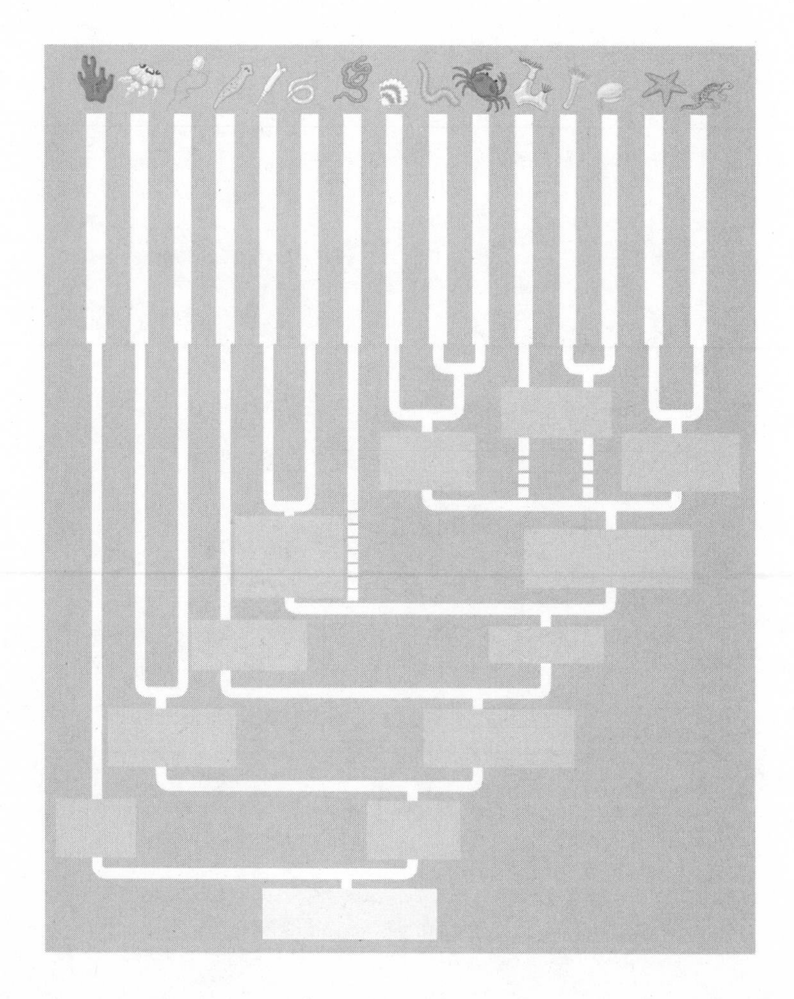

Figure 32.4 A traditional view of animal diversity based on body-plan grades, page 636

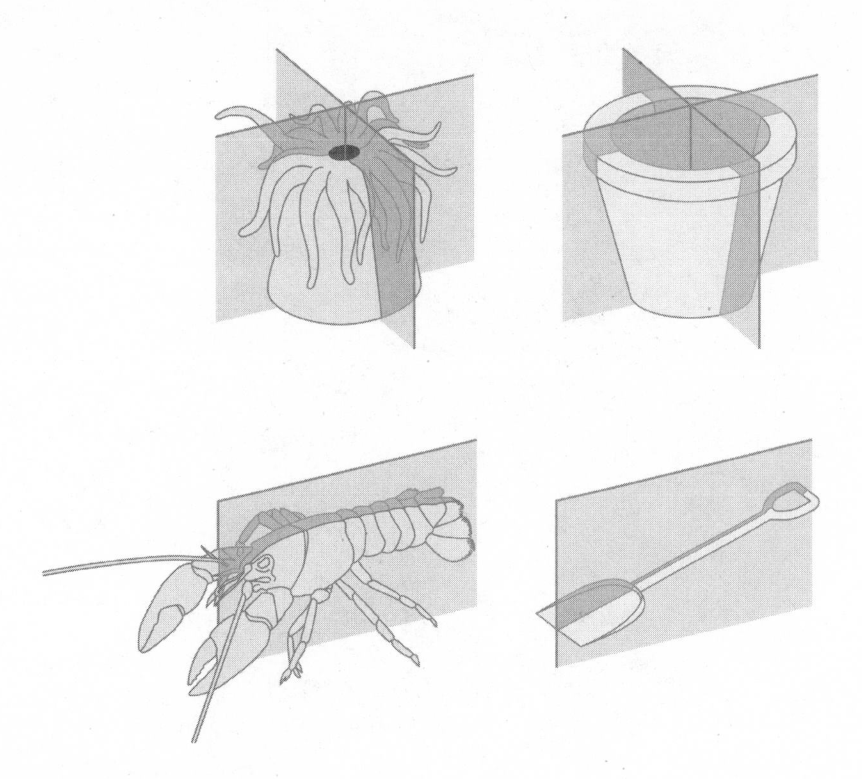

Figure 32.5 Body symmetry, page 637

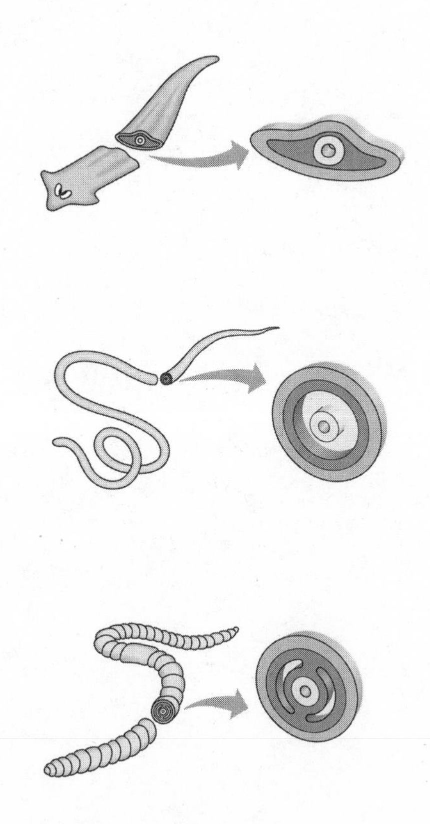

Figure 32.6 Body plans of the bilateria, page 638

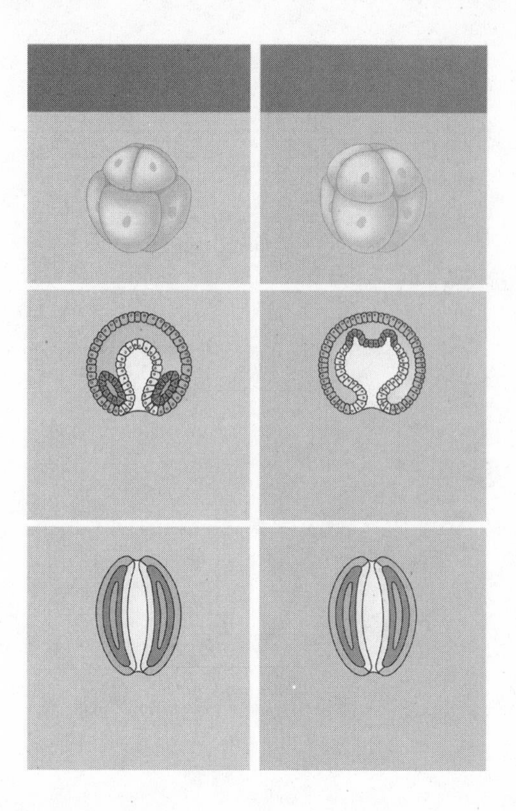

Figure 32.7 A comparison of early development in protostomes and deuterostomes, page 639

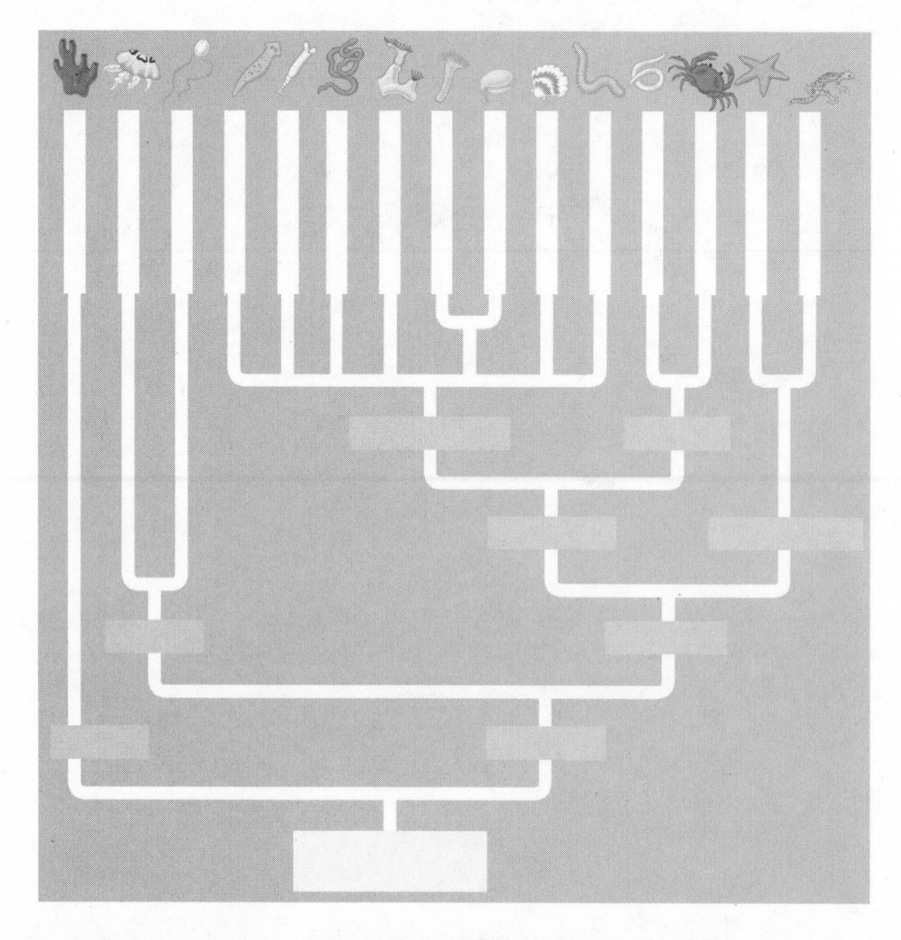

Figure 32.8 Animal phylogeny based on seqencing of SSU-rRNA, page 640

Figure 32.9 A trochophore larva, page 641

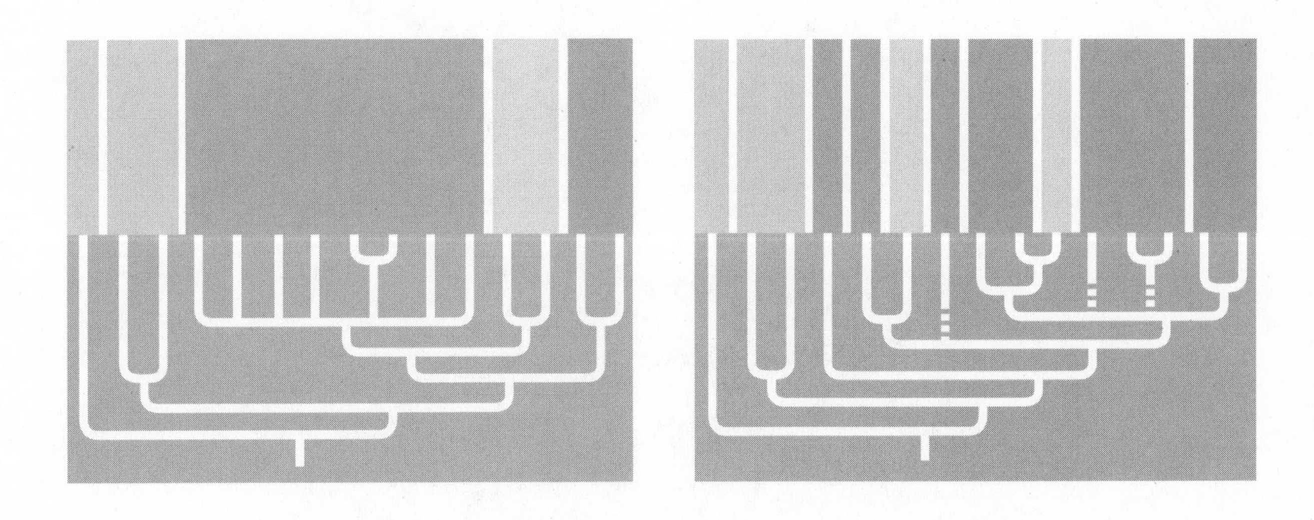

Figure 32.12 Comparing the molecular-based and grade-based trees of animal phylogeny, page 642

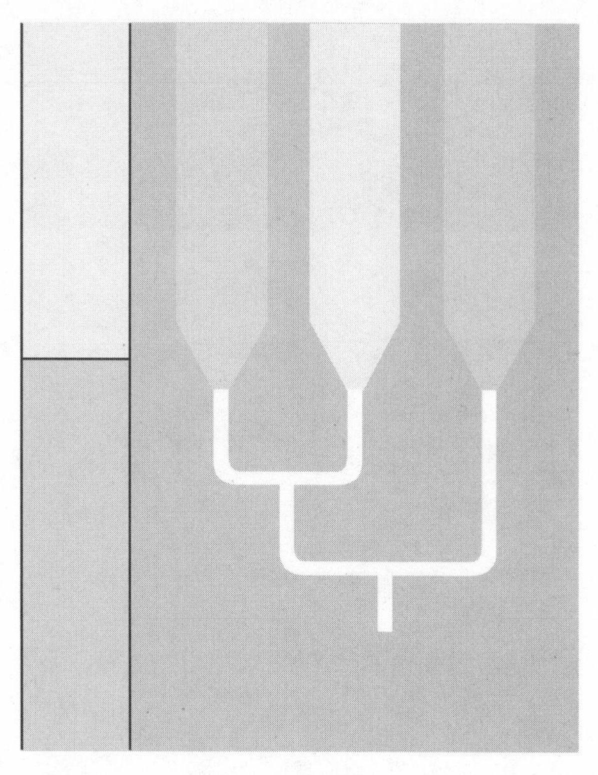

Figure 32.14 One Cambrian explosion, or three? page 644

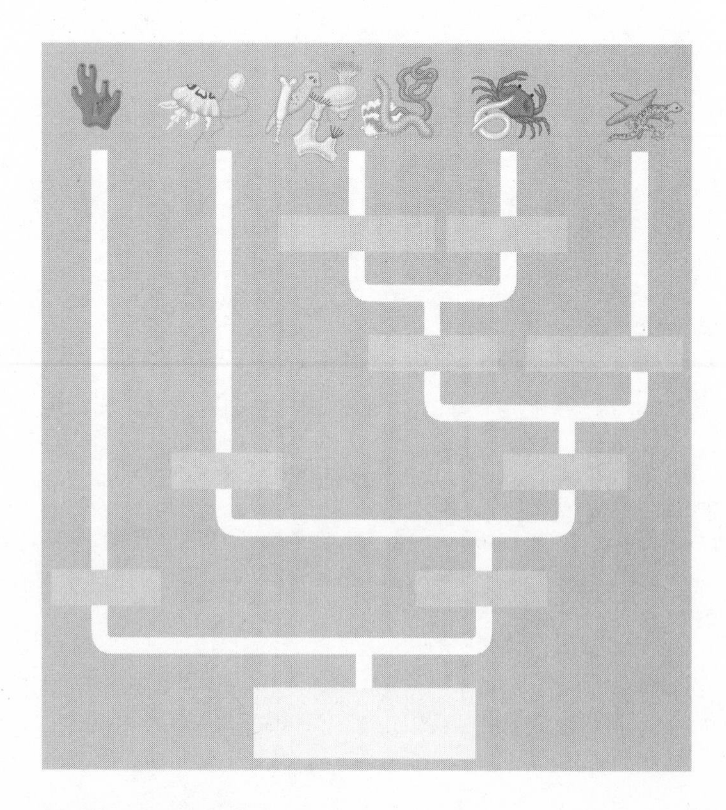

Figure 33.1 Review of animal phylogeny, page 647

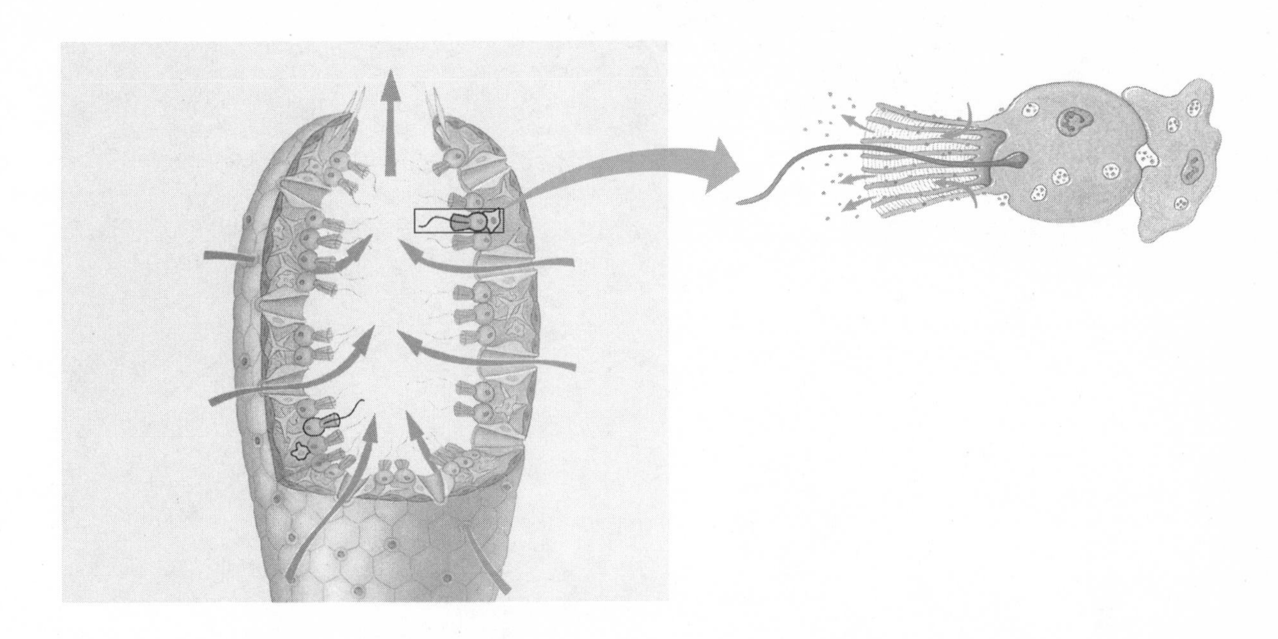

Figure 33.3 Anatomy of a sponge, page 648

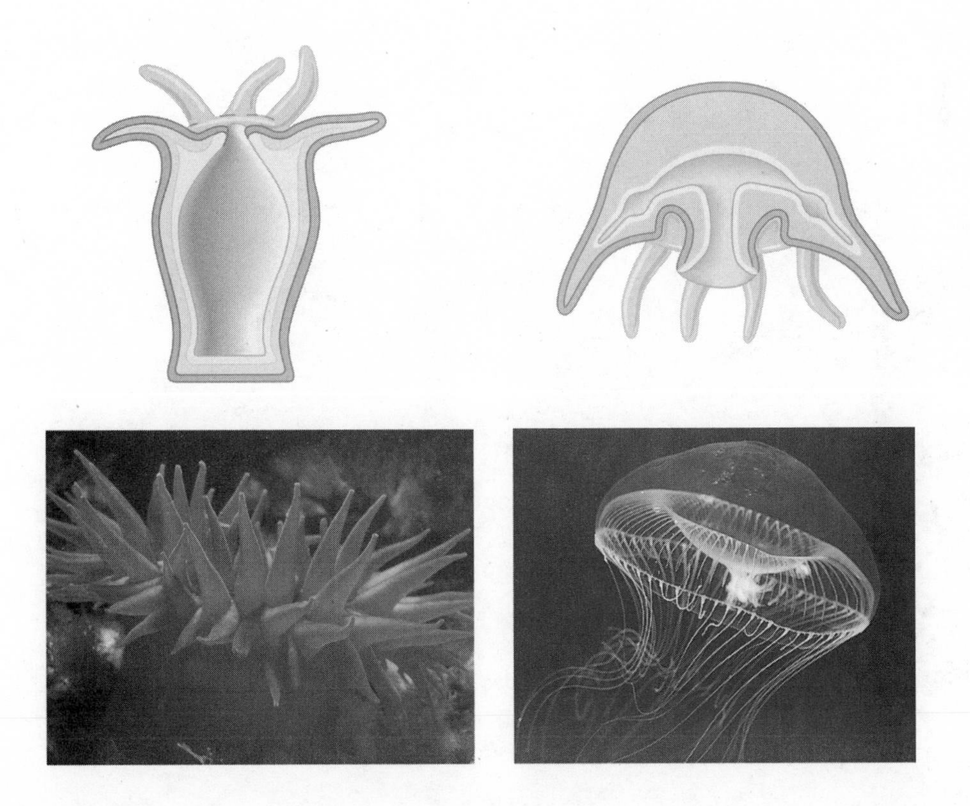

Figure 33.4 Polyp and medusa forms of cnidarians, page 649

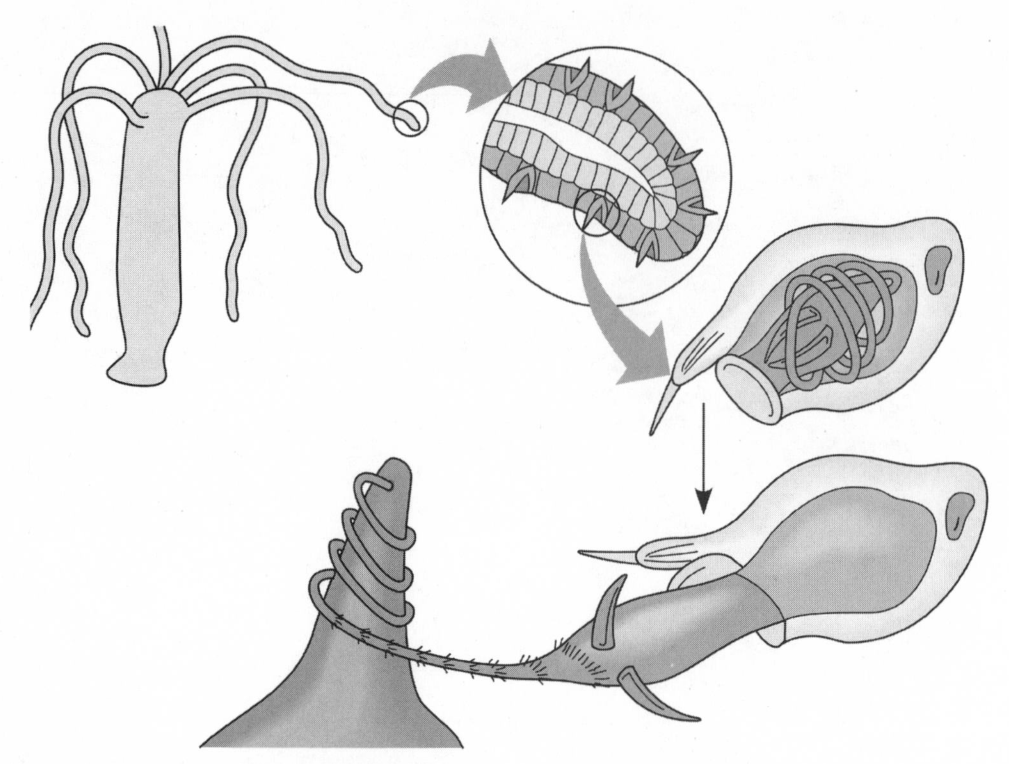

Figure 33.5 A cnidocyte of a hydra, page 649

Figure 33.7 The life cycle of the hydrozoan *Obelia*, page 651

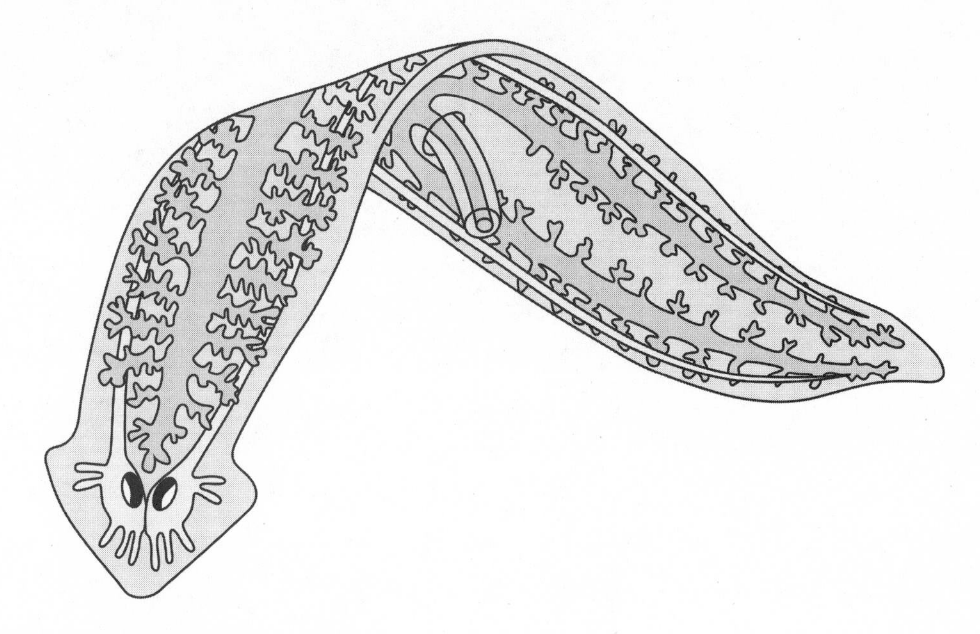

Figure 33.10 Anatomy of a planarian, page 653

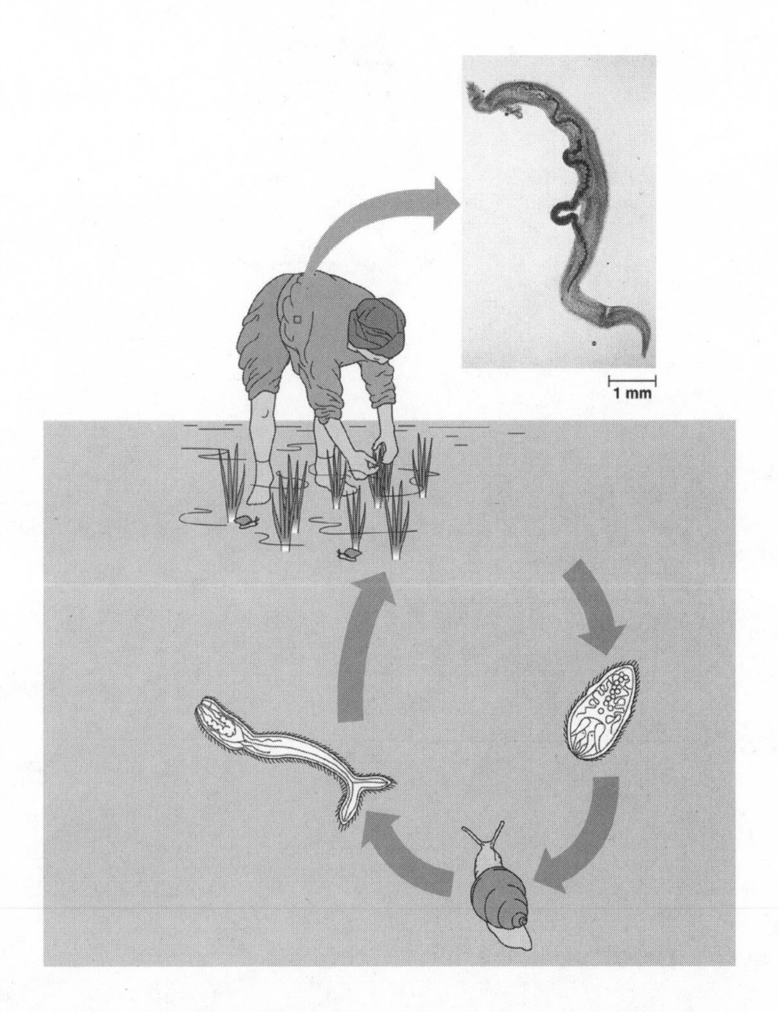

Figure 33.11 The life history of a blood fluke (*Schistosoma mansoni*), page 653

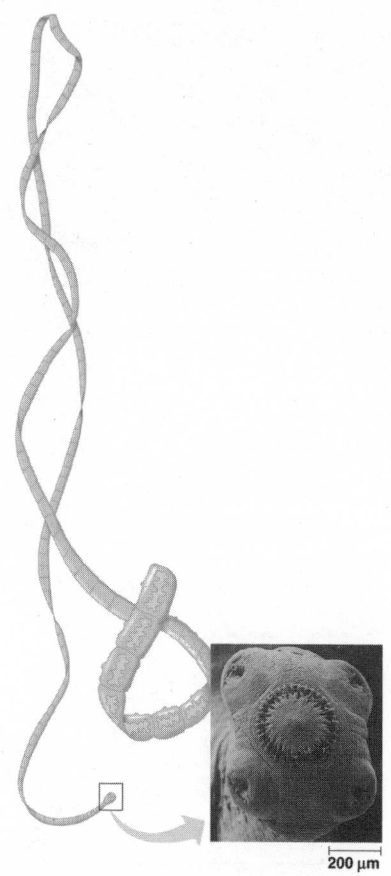

Figure 33.12 Anatomy of a tapeworm, page 654

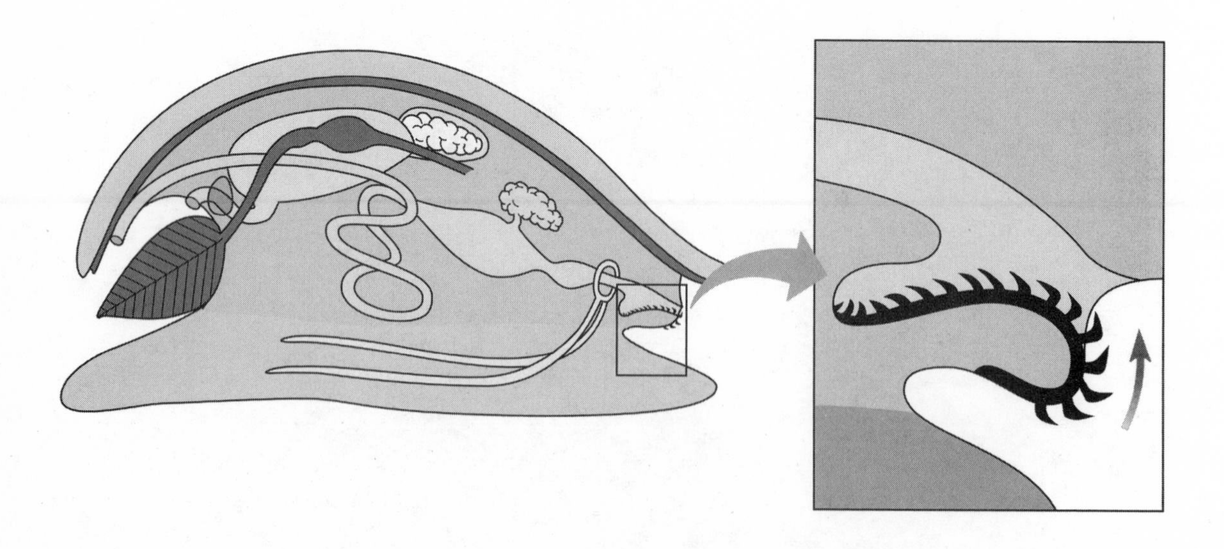

Figure 33.16 The basic body plan of mollusks, page 656

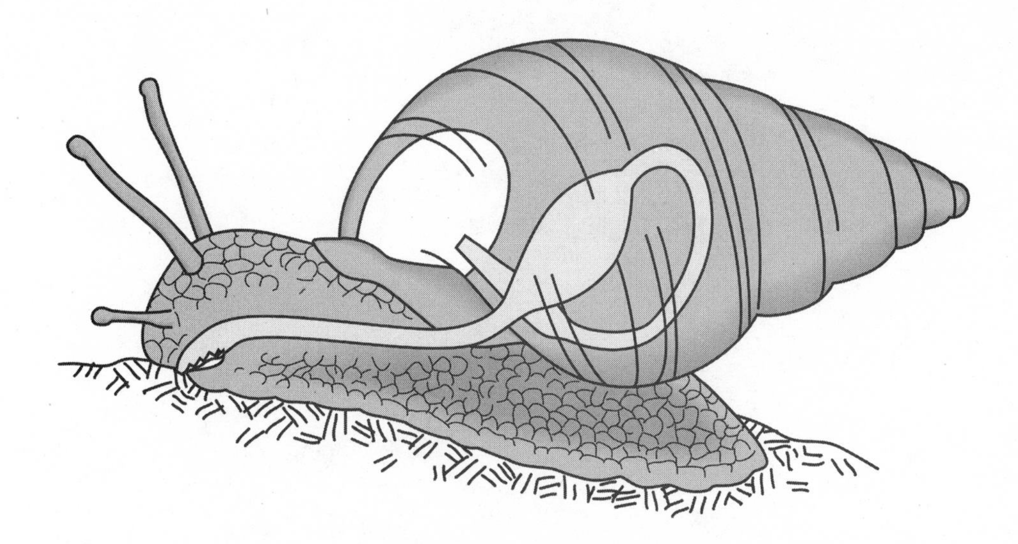

Figure 33.18 The results of torsion in a gastropod, page 657

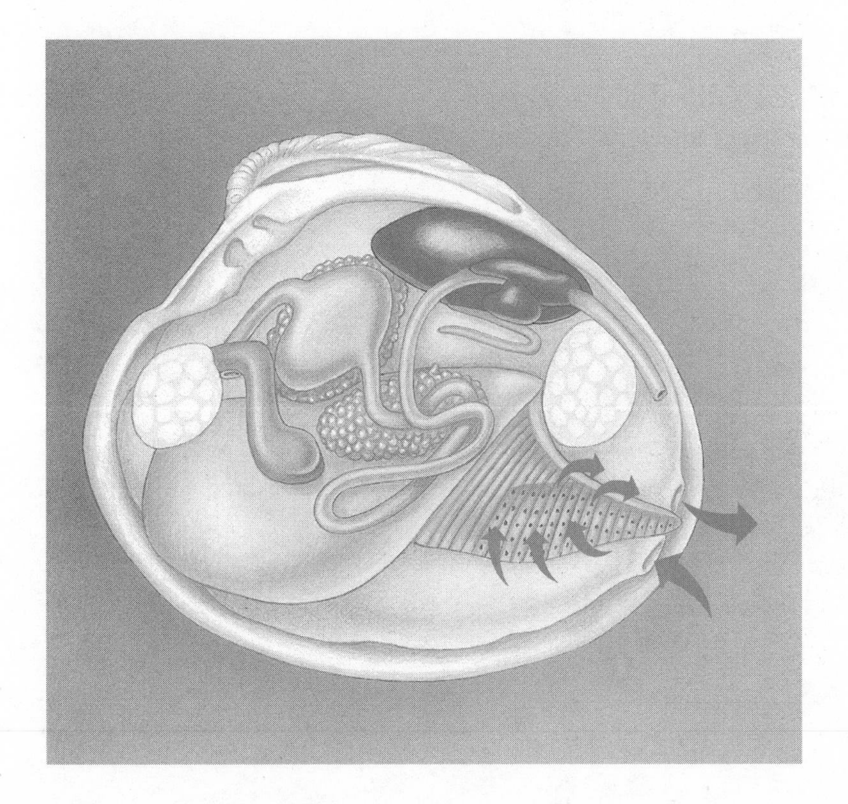

Figure 33.21 Anatomy of a clam, page 658

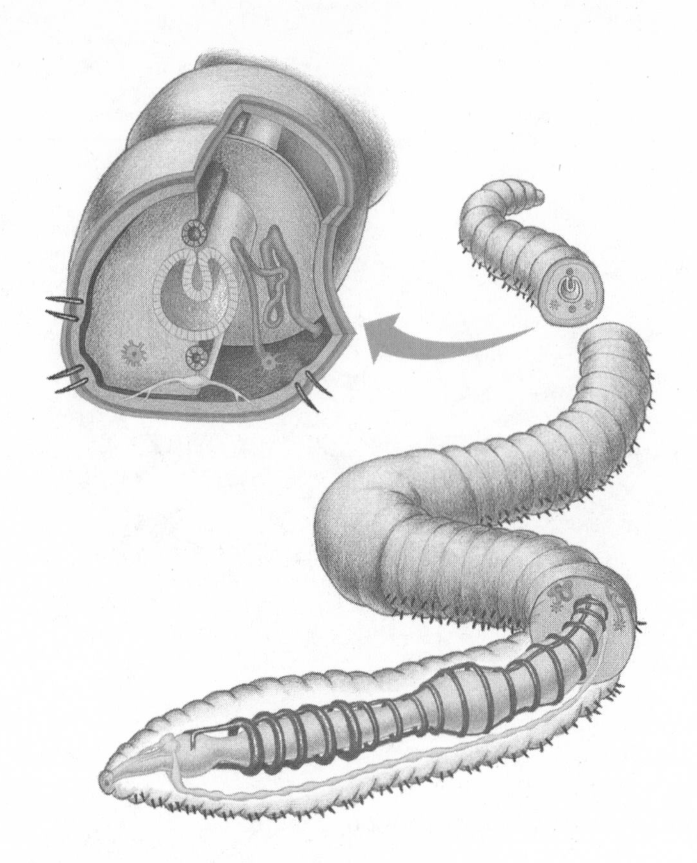

Figure 33.23 Anatomy of an earthworm, page 659

Figure 33.26 External anatomy of an arthropod, page 663

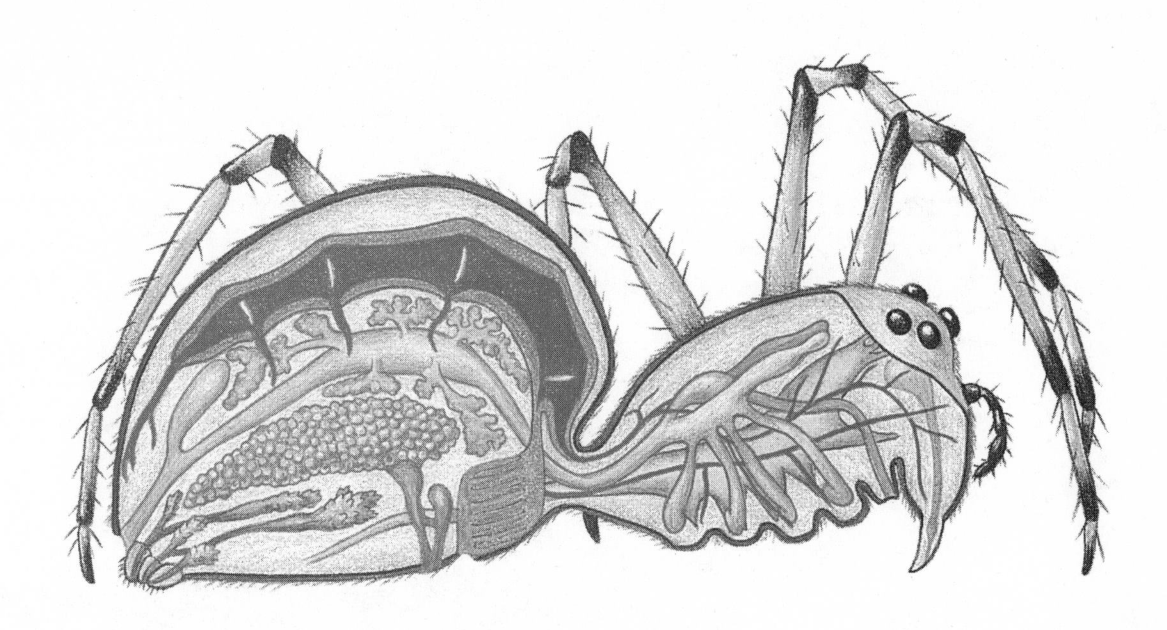

Figure 33.30b Spiders (Class Arachnida), page 665

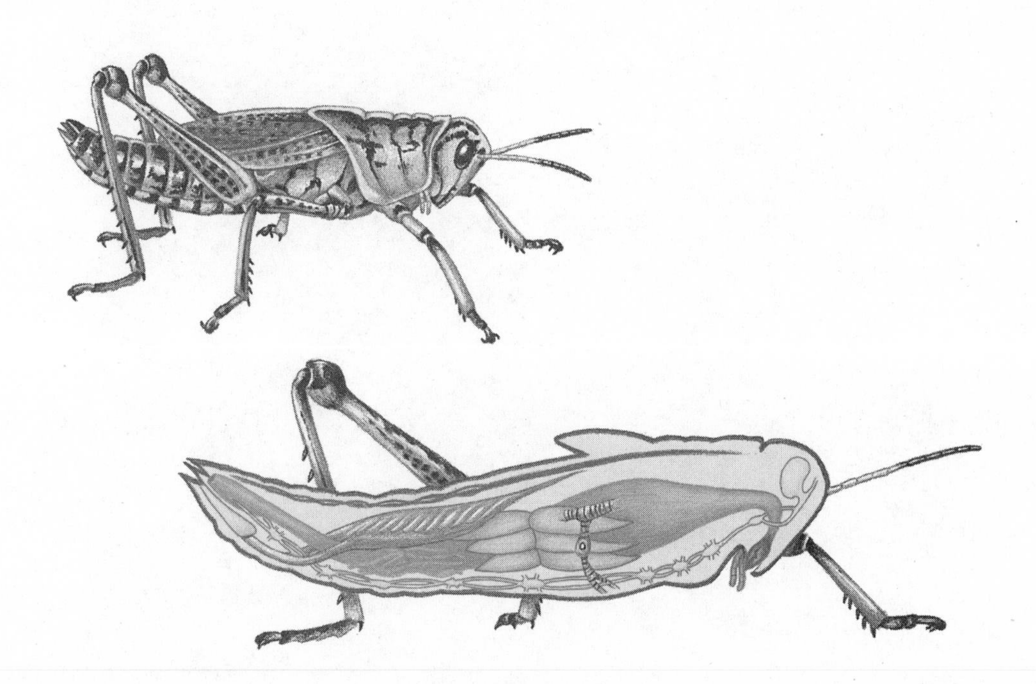

Figure 33.33 Anatomy of a grasshopper, an insect, page 667

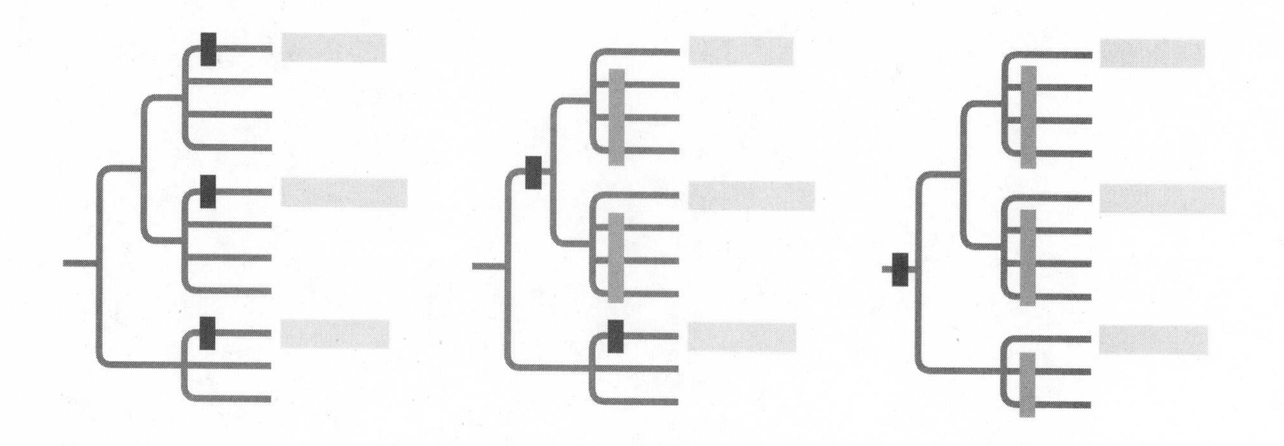

Figure 33.36 Three hypotheses for the origin of segmentation, page 672

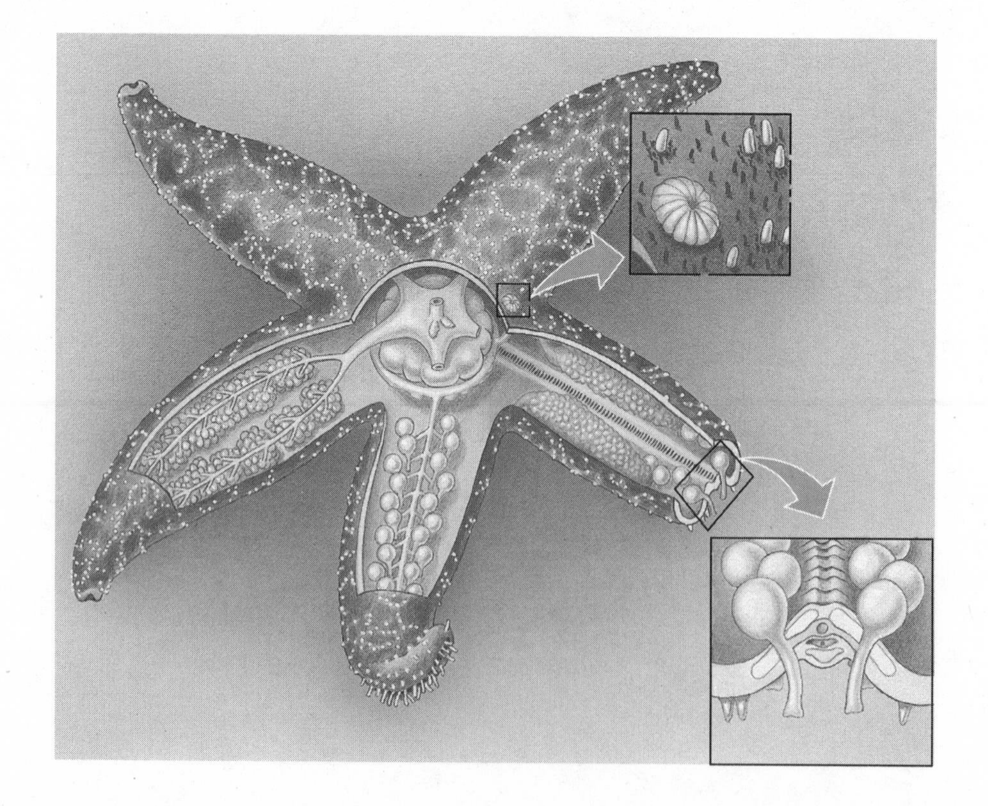

Figure 33.38 Anatomy of a sea star, page 674

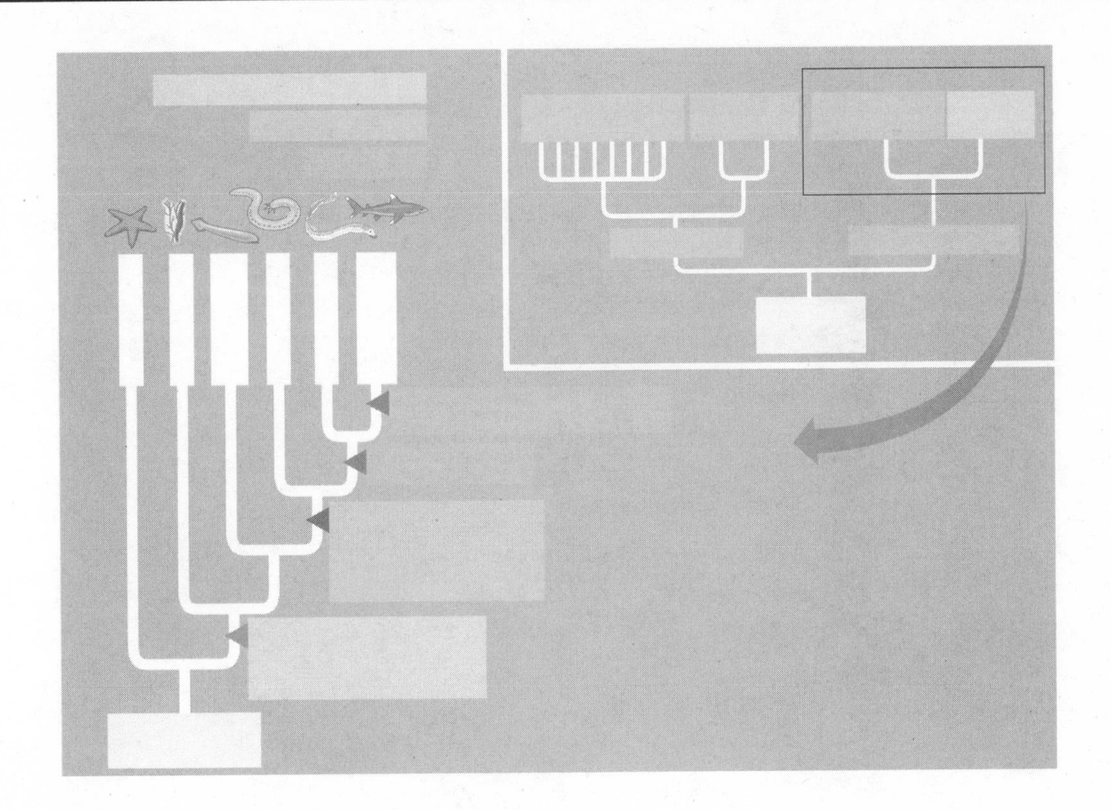

Figure 34.1 Clades of extant chordates, page 679

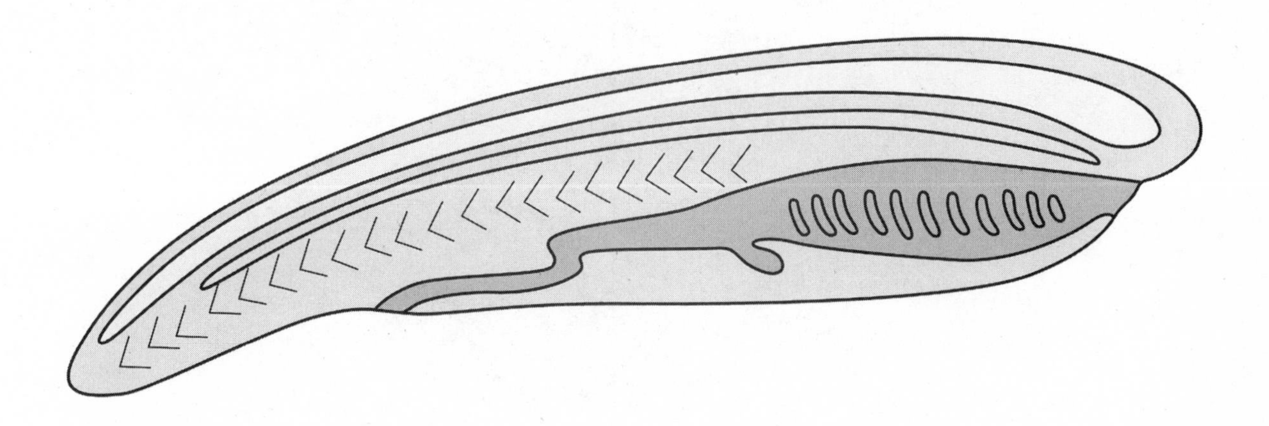

Figure 34.2 Chordate characteristics, page 680

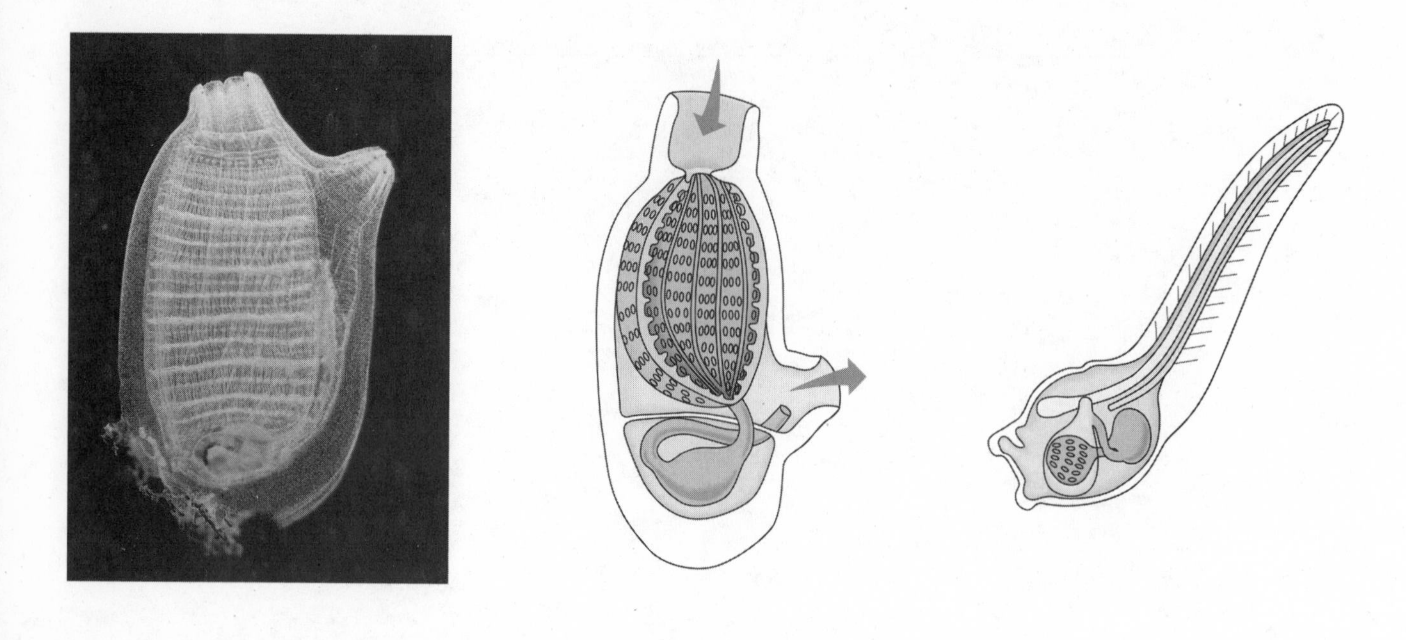

Figure 34.3 Subphylum Urochordata: a tunicate, page 681

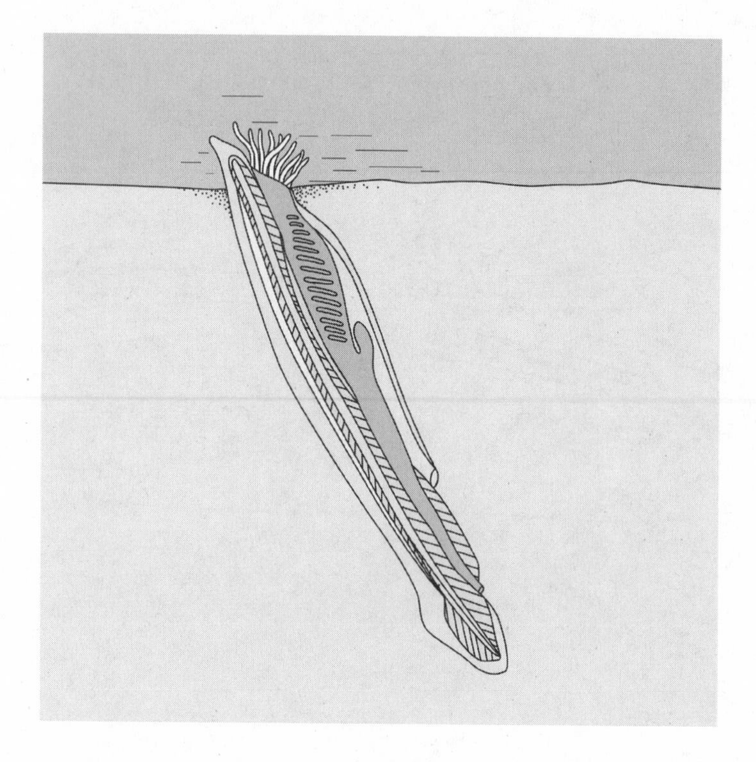

Figure 34.4a Subphylum Cephalochordata: the lancelet *Branchiostoma*, page 681

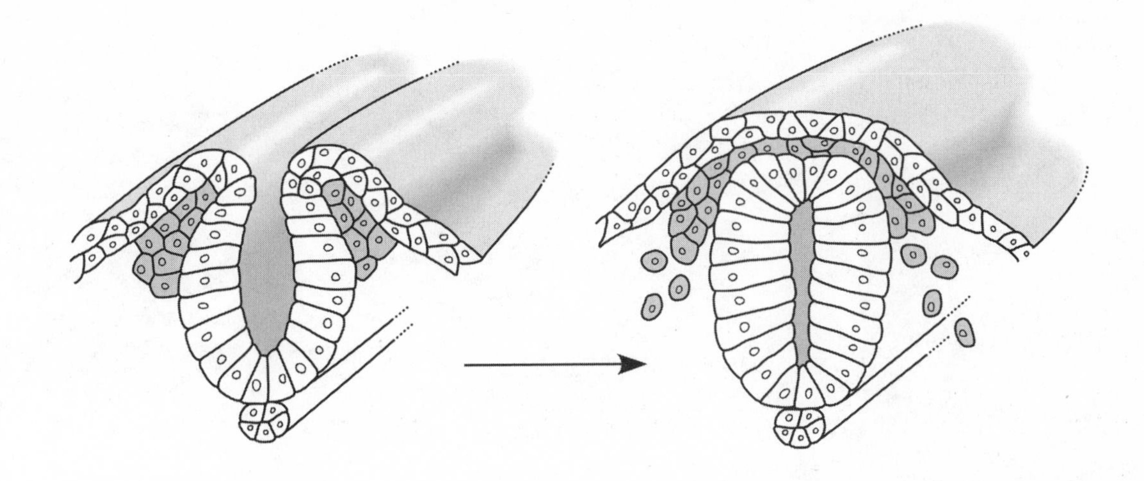

Figure 34.6 The neural crest, embryonic source of many unique vertebrate characters, page 683

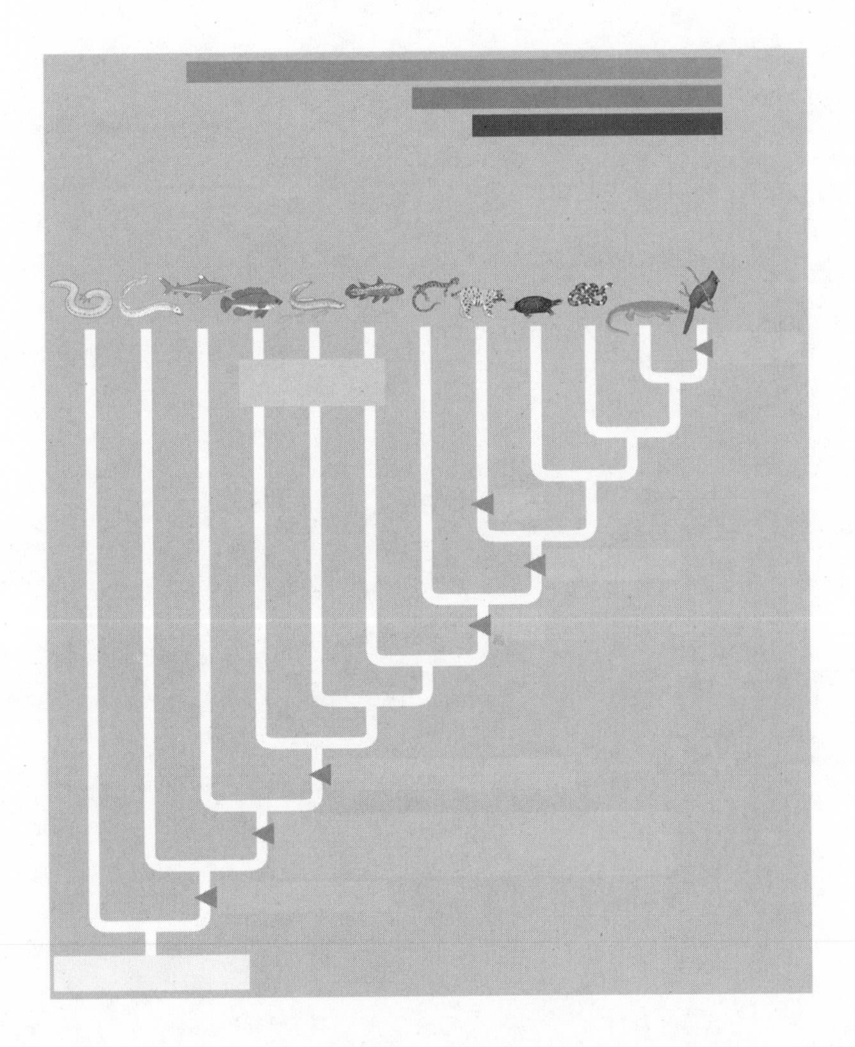

Figure 34.7 Phylogeny of the major groups of extant vertebrates, page 684

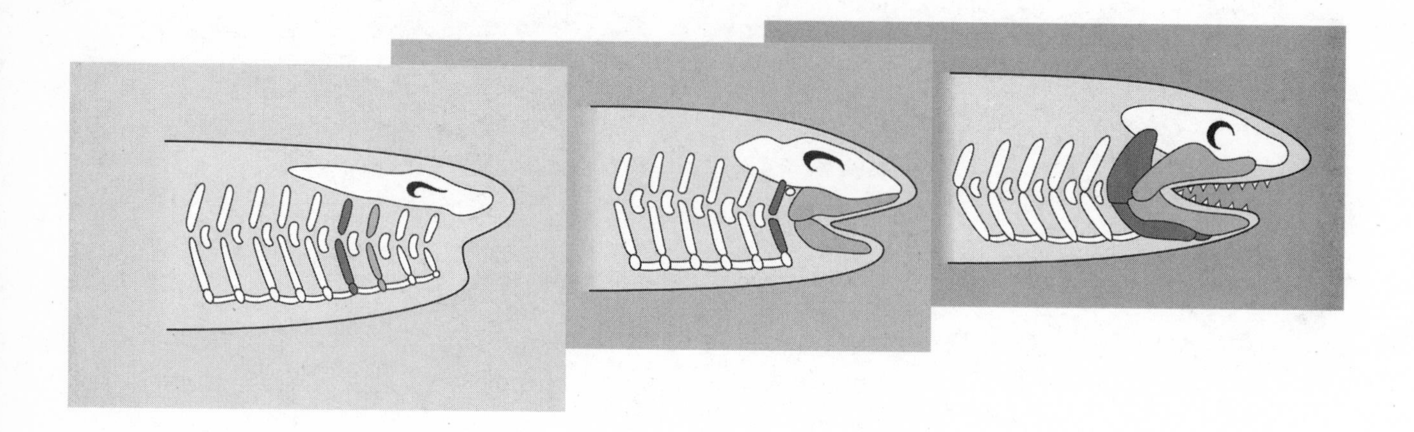

Figure 34.10 Hypothesis for the evolution of vertebrate jaws, page 687

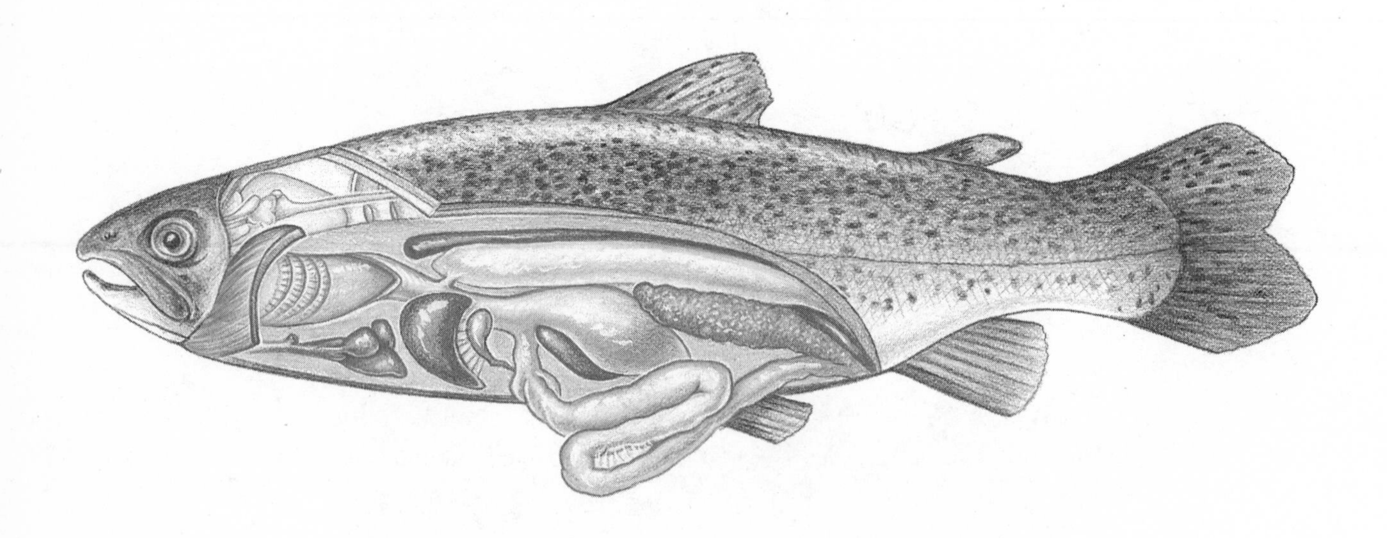

Figure 34.13 Anatomy of a trout, a representative ray-finned fish, page 689

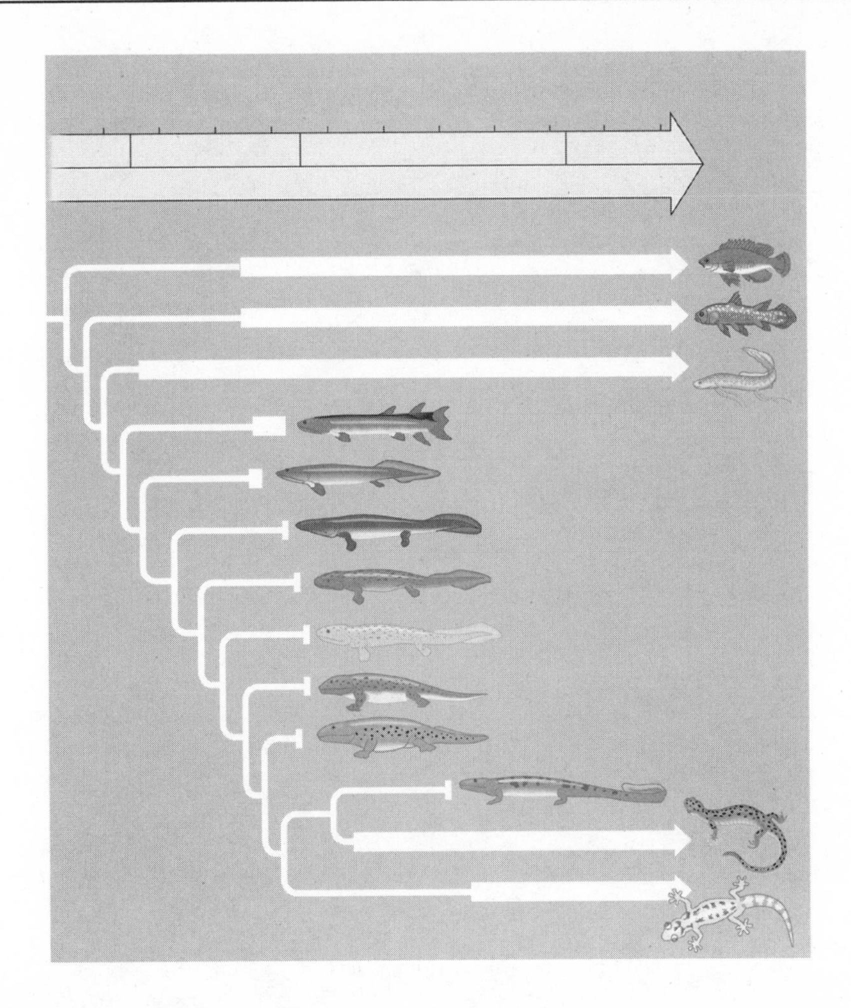

Figure 34.15 The origin of tetrapods, page 690

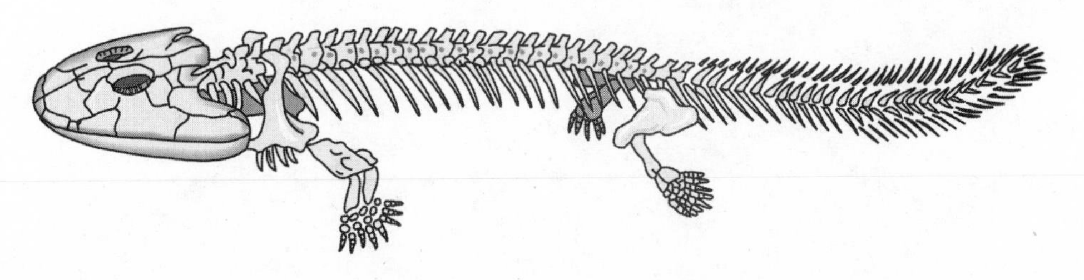

Figure 34.16 Skeleton of *Acanthostega*, a Devonian tetrapod fish, page 691

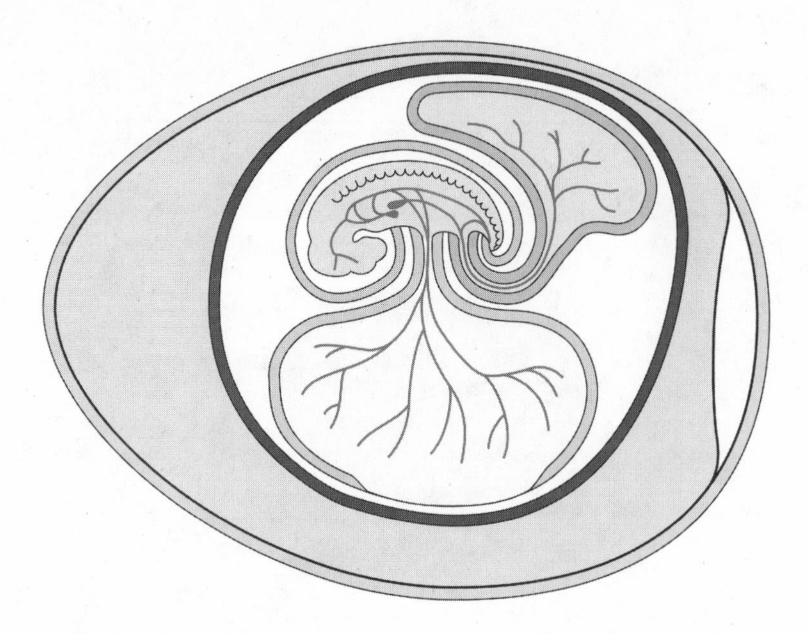

Figure 34.19 The amniotic egg, page 693

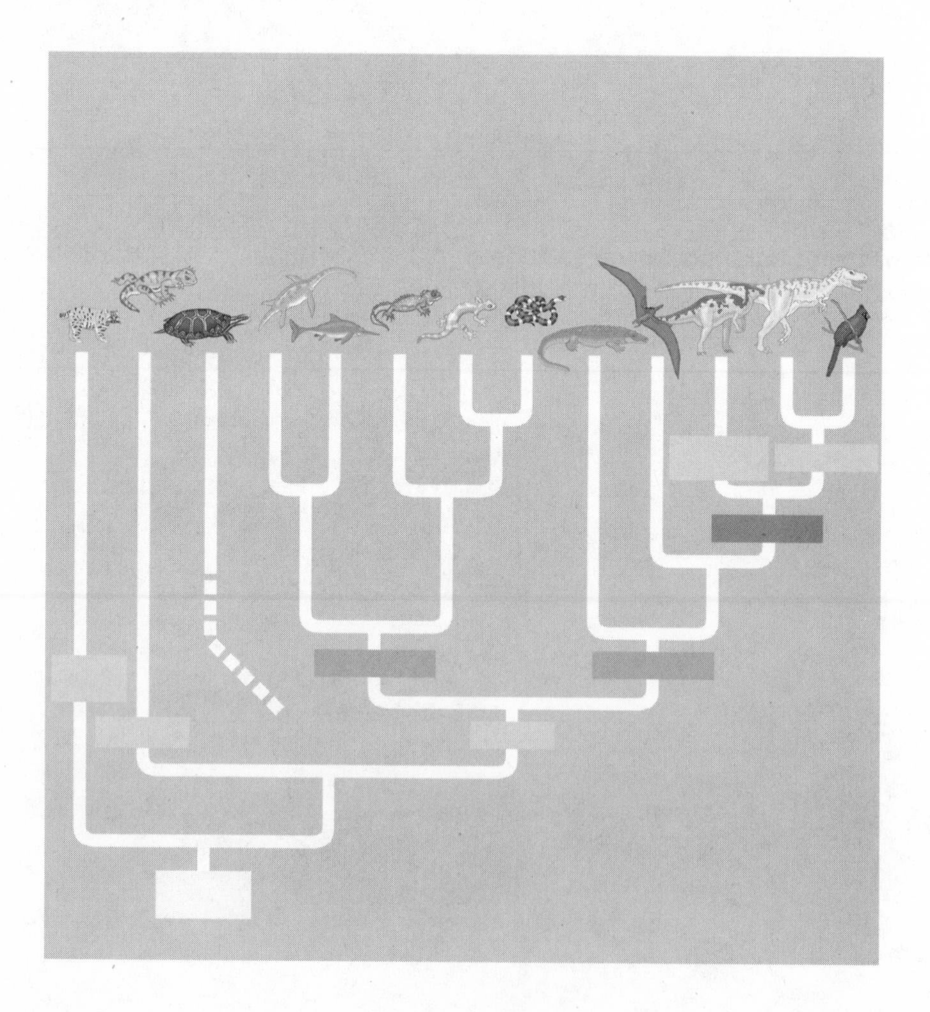

Figure 34.20 A hypothetical phylogeny of amniotes, page 694

Figure 34.21 Taxonomic classes of amniotes, page 695

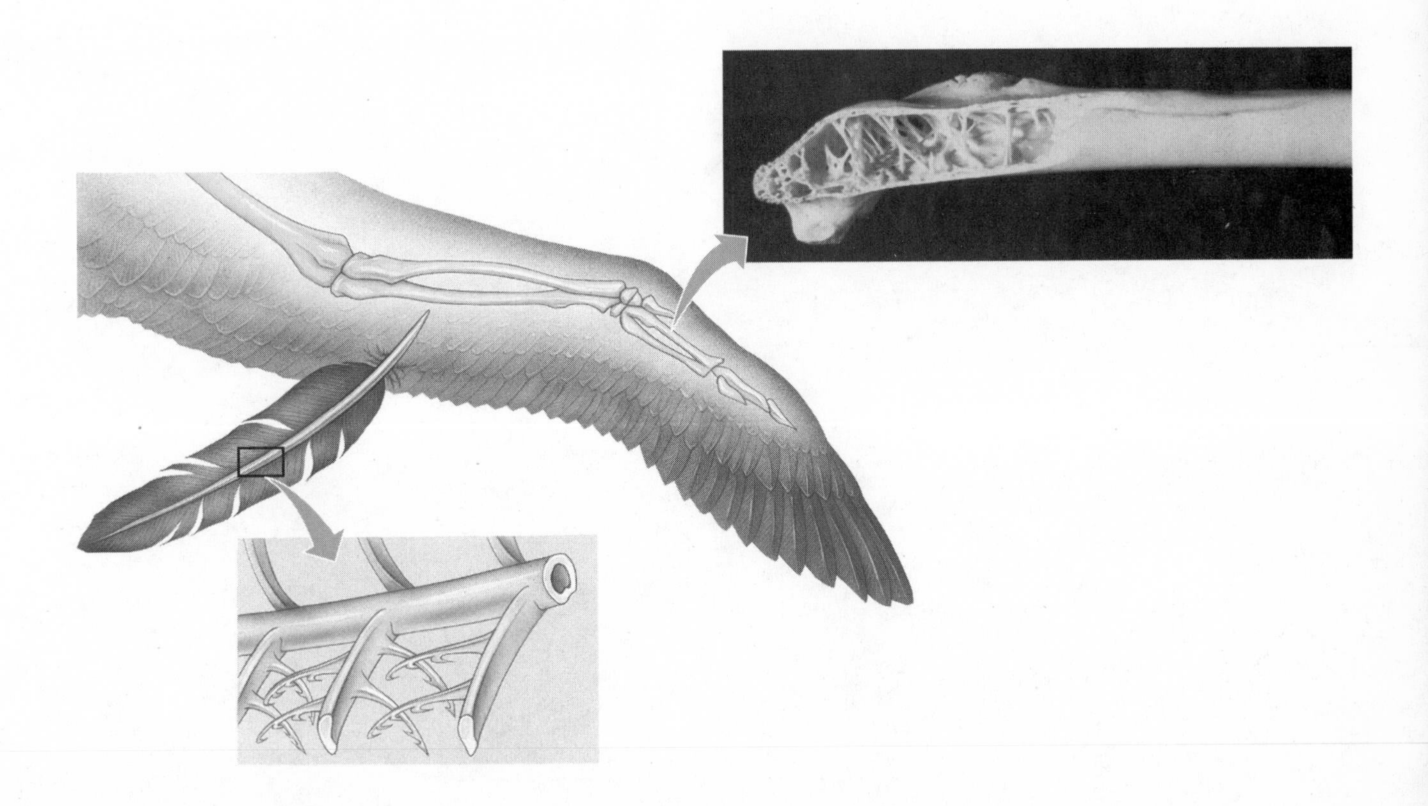

Figure 34.25 Form fits function: the avian wing and feather, page 698

Figure 34.27 ***Archaeopteryx*, a Jurassic bird-reptile, page 699**

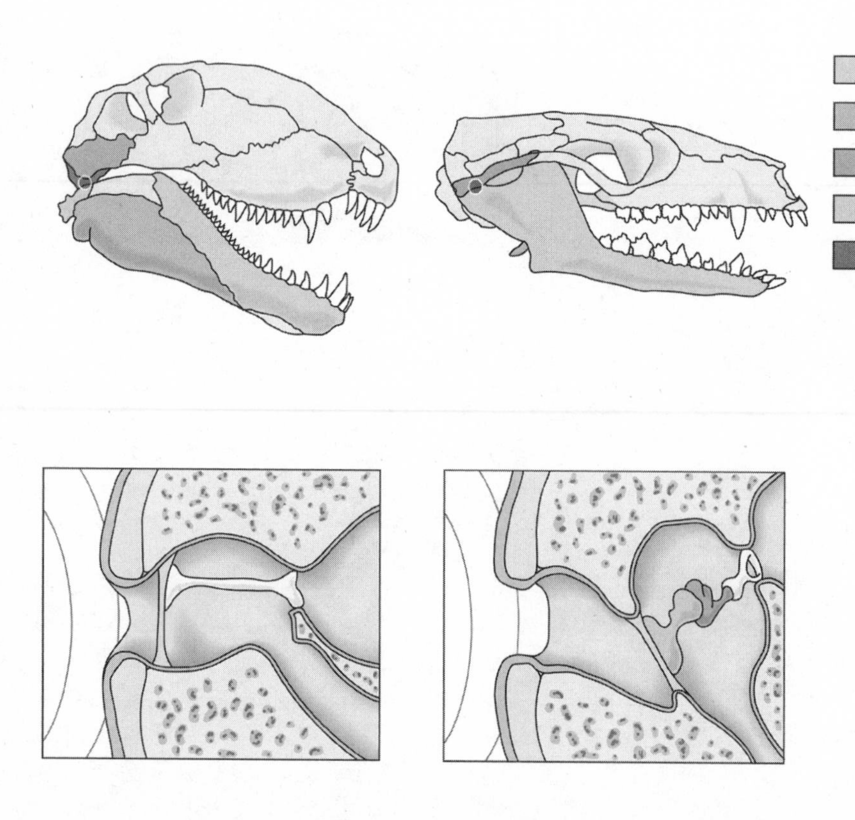

Figure 34.30 The evolution of the mammalian jaw and ear bones, page 702

Figure 34.32 Evolutionary convergence of marsupial and eutherian (placental) mammals, page 704

Figure 34.33 Hypothetical cladogram of mammals, page 706

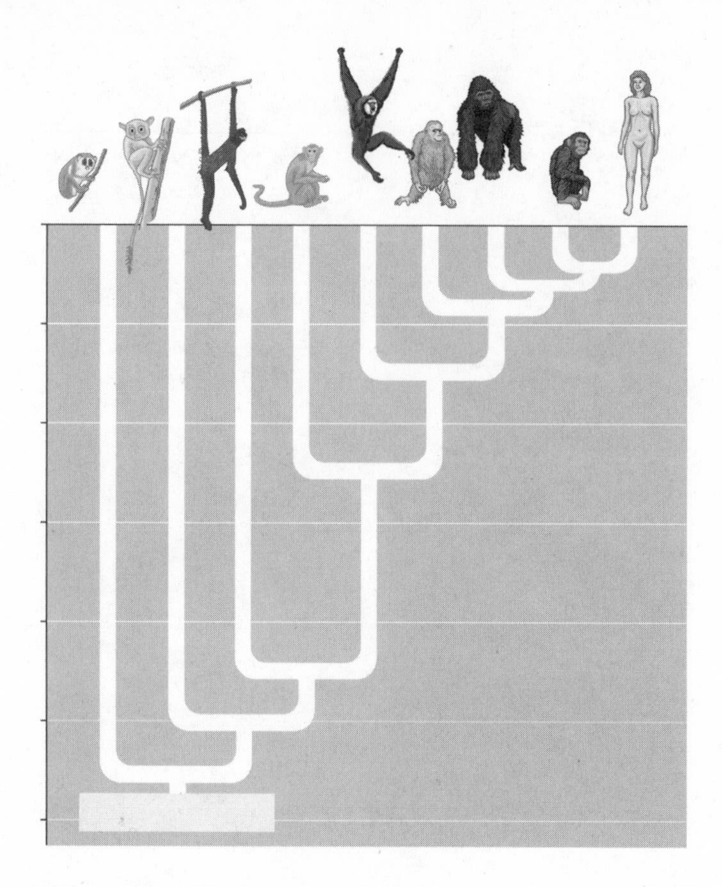

Figure 34.35 A phylogenetic tree of primates, page 708

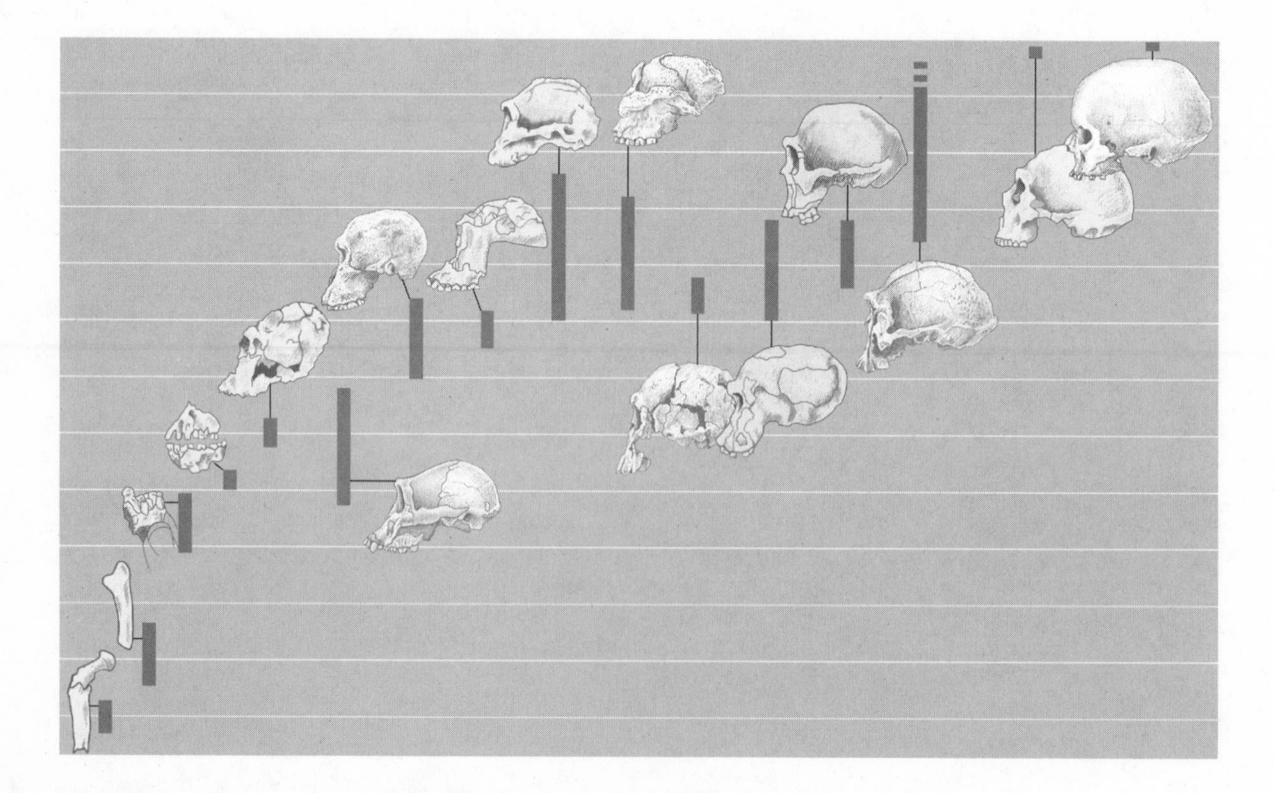

Figure 34.38 A timeline for some hominid species, page 710

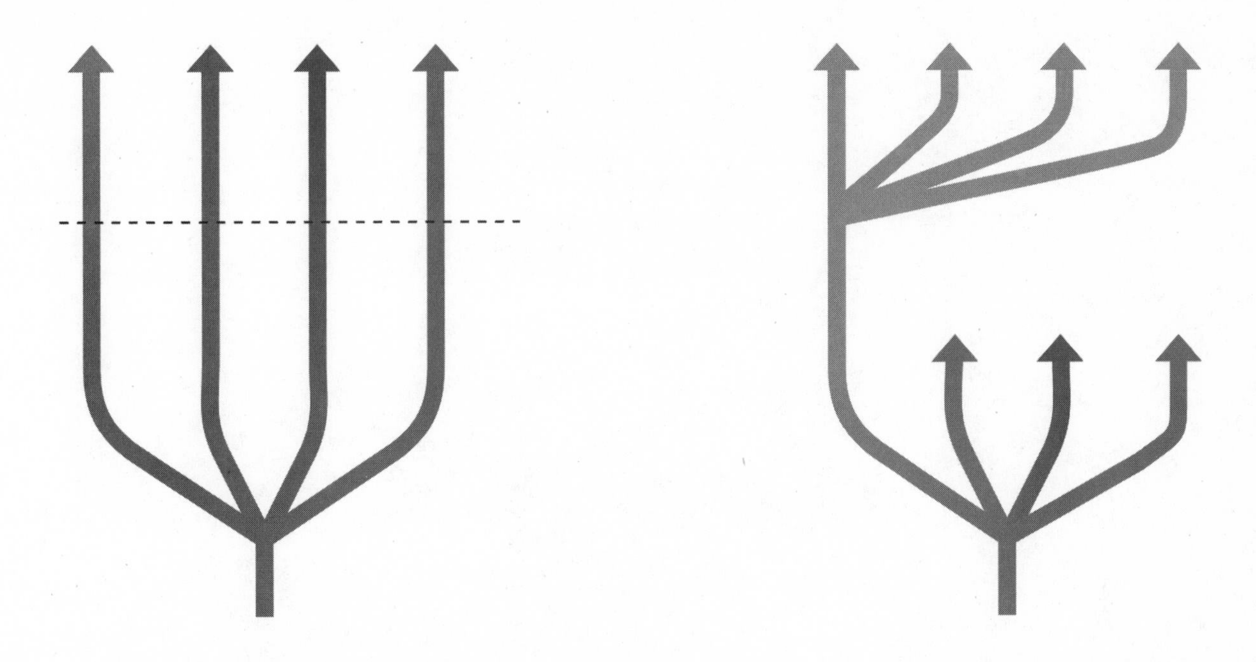

Figure 34.41 Two hypotheses for the origin of anatomically modern humans, page 714

Figure 35.1 A comparison of monocots and dicots, page 721

Figure 35.2 Morphology of a flowering plant: an overview, page 722

Figure 35.5 Simple versus compound leaves, page 724

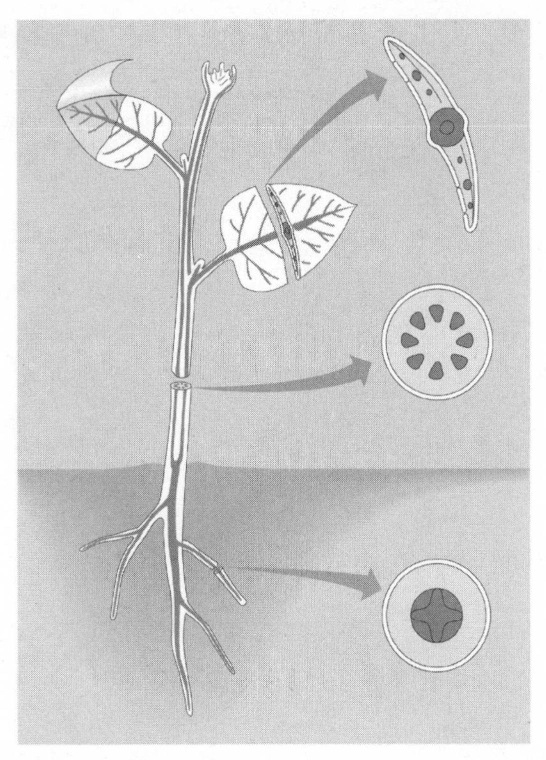

Figure 35.7 The three tissue systems, page 725

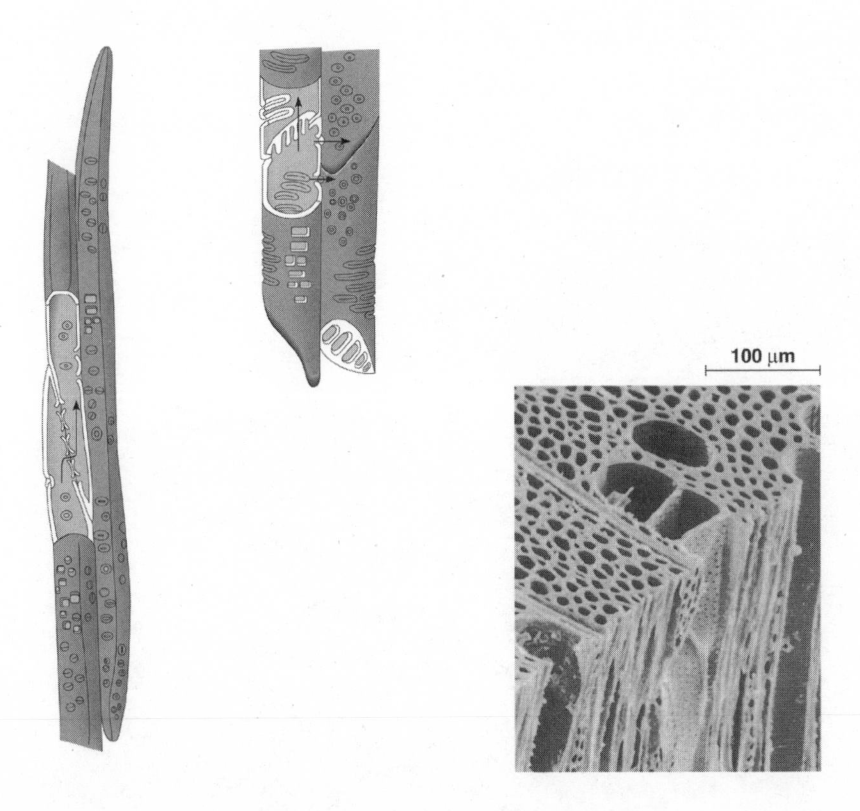

Figure 35.8 Water-conducting cells of xylem, page 725

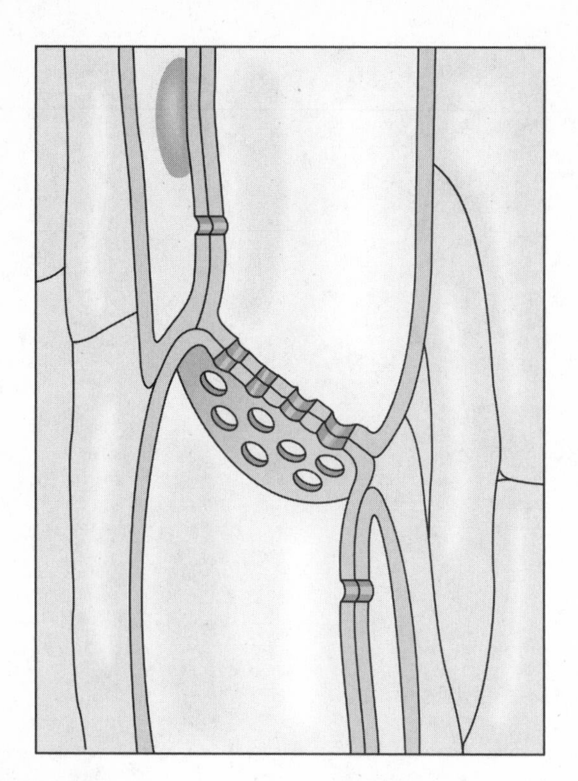

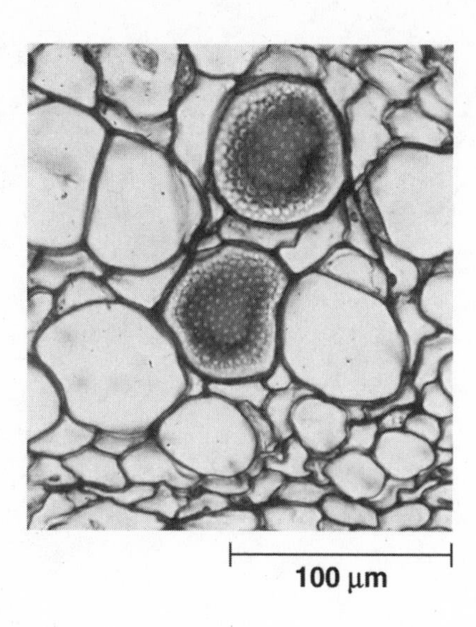

Figure 35.9 Food-conducting cells of the phloem, page 726

Figure 35.12 Locations of major meristems: an overview of plant growth, page 729

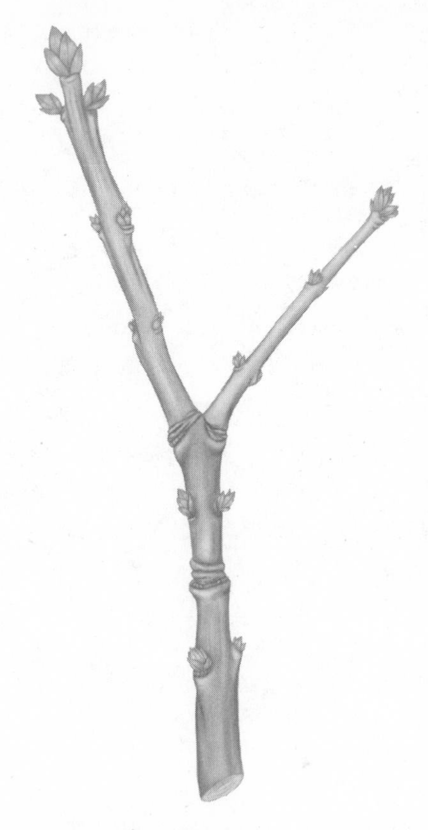

Figure 35.13 Morphology of a winter twig, page 730

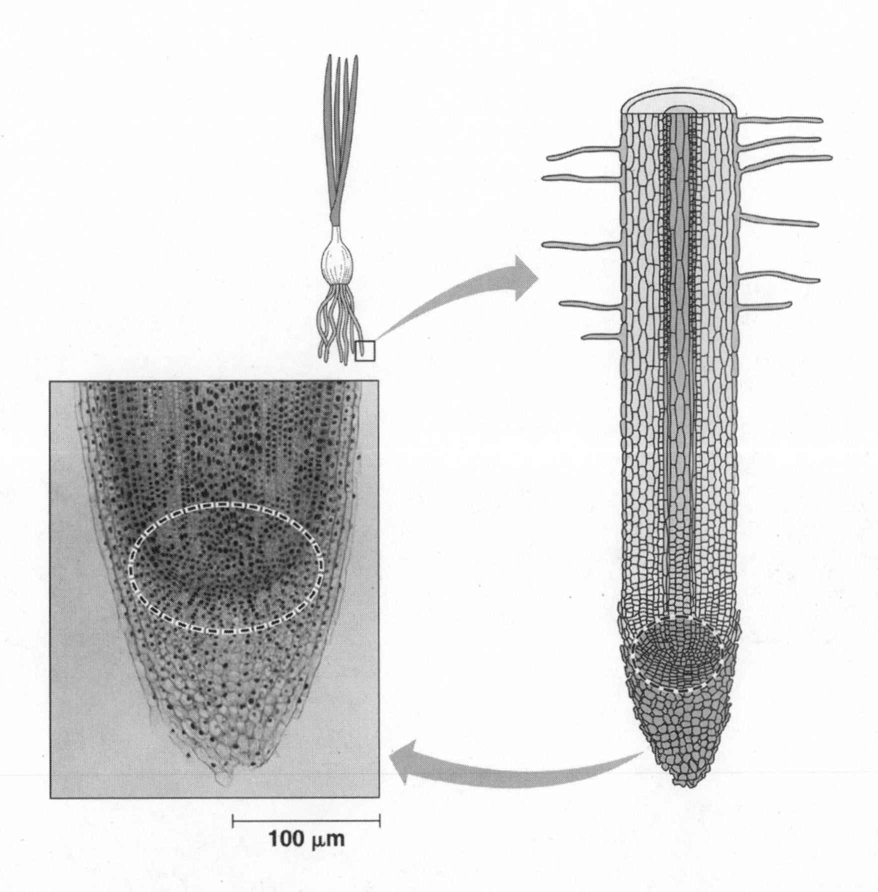

Figure 35.14 Primary growth of a root, page 730

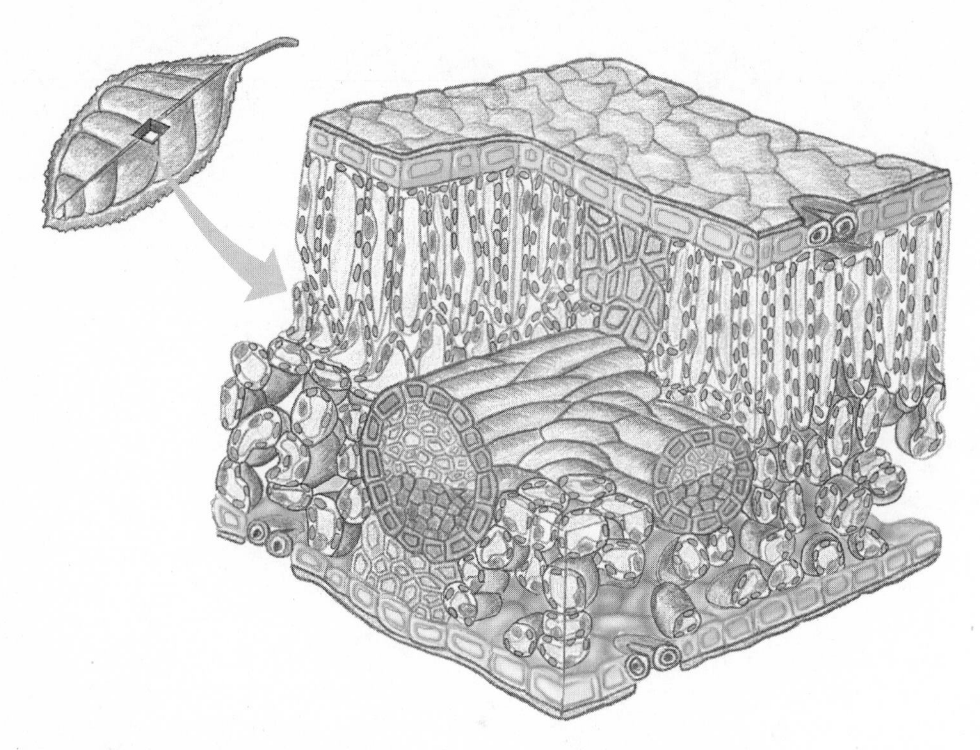

Figure 35.19 Leaf anatomy, page 734

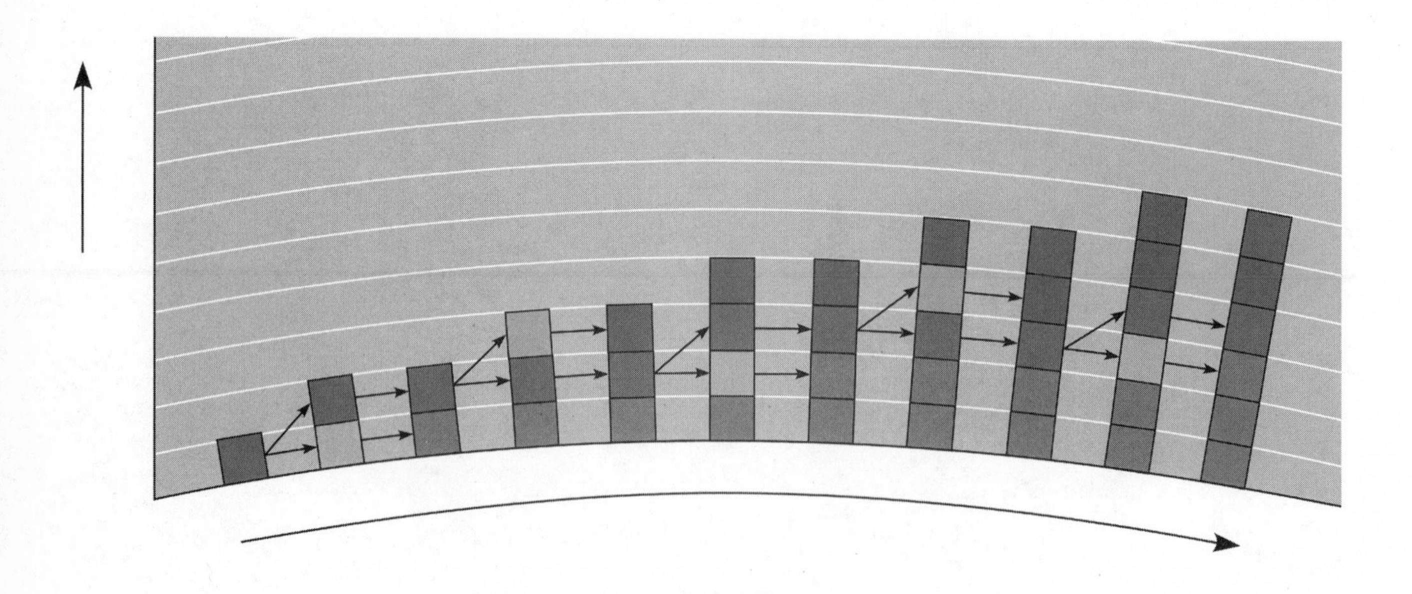

Figure 35.20 Production of secondary xylem and phloem by the vascular cambium, page 735

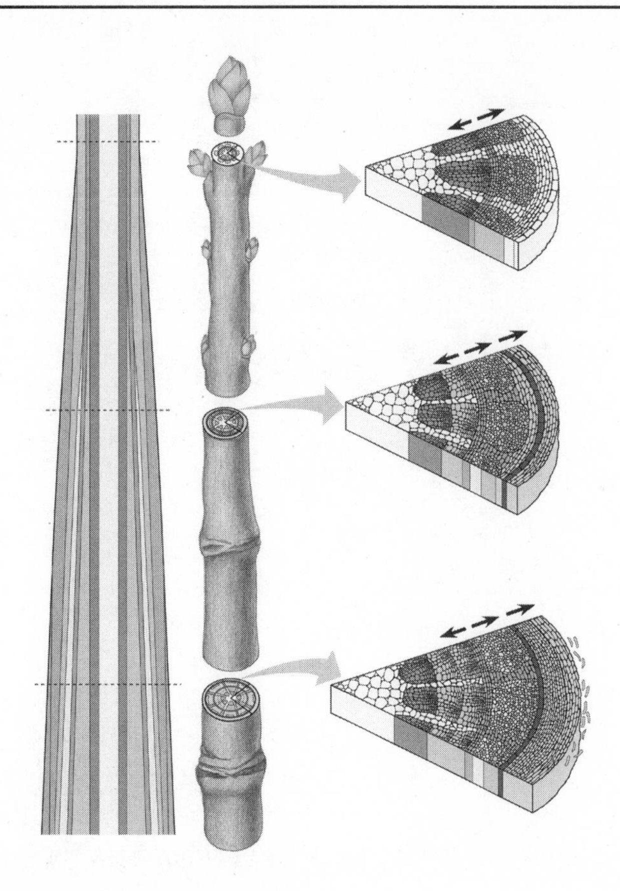

Figure 35.21 Secondary growth of a stem, page 736

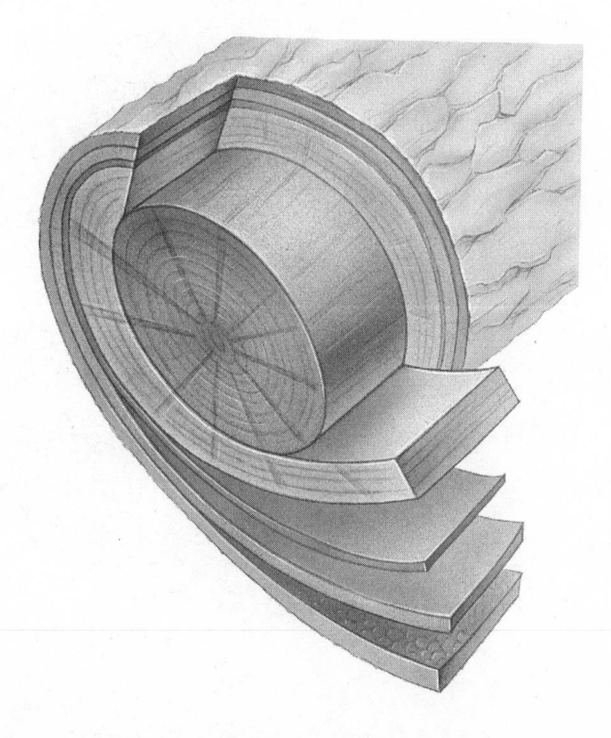

Figure 35.23 Anatomy of a tree trunk, page 737

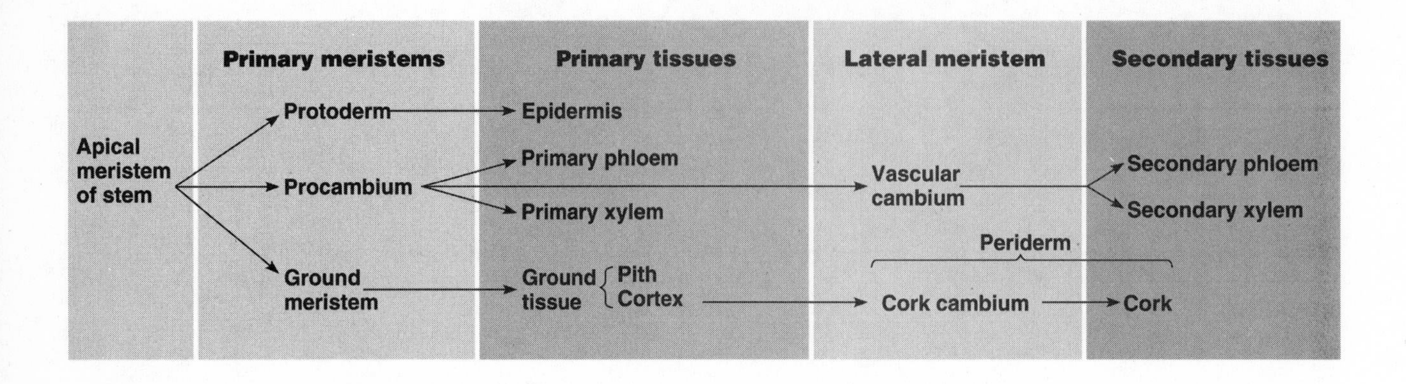

Figure 35.24 A summary of primary and secondary growth in a woody stem, page 737

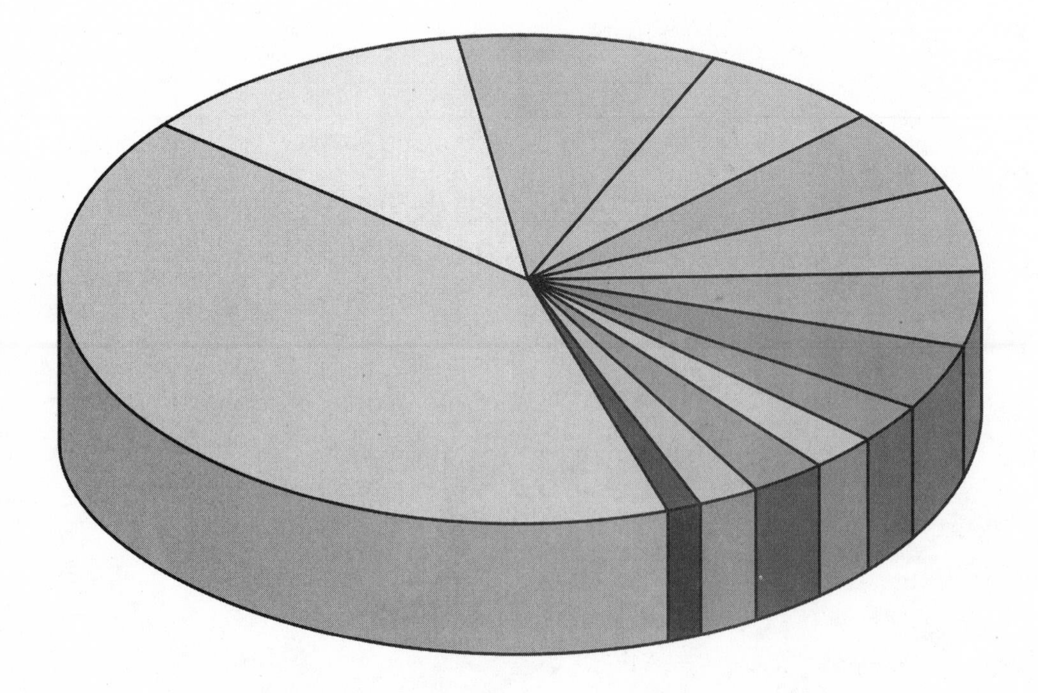

Figure 35.25 *Arabidopsis thaliana*, page 738

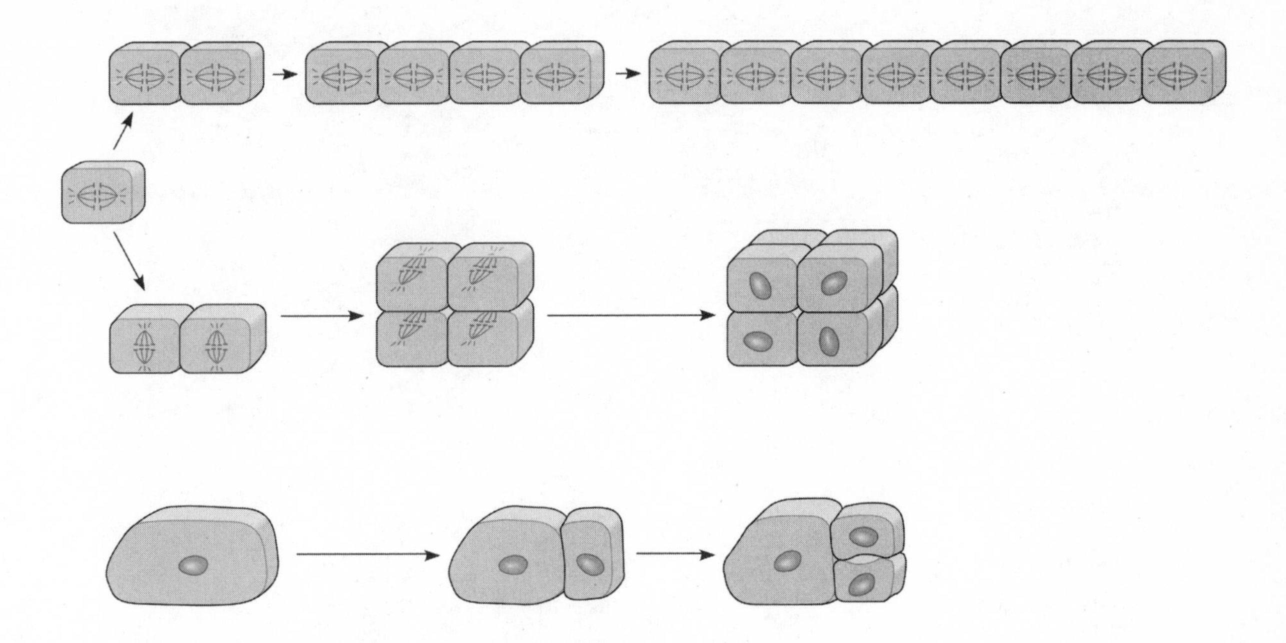

Figure 35.26 The plane and symmetry of cell division influence development of form, page 739

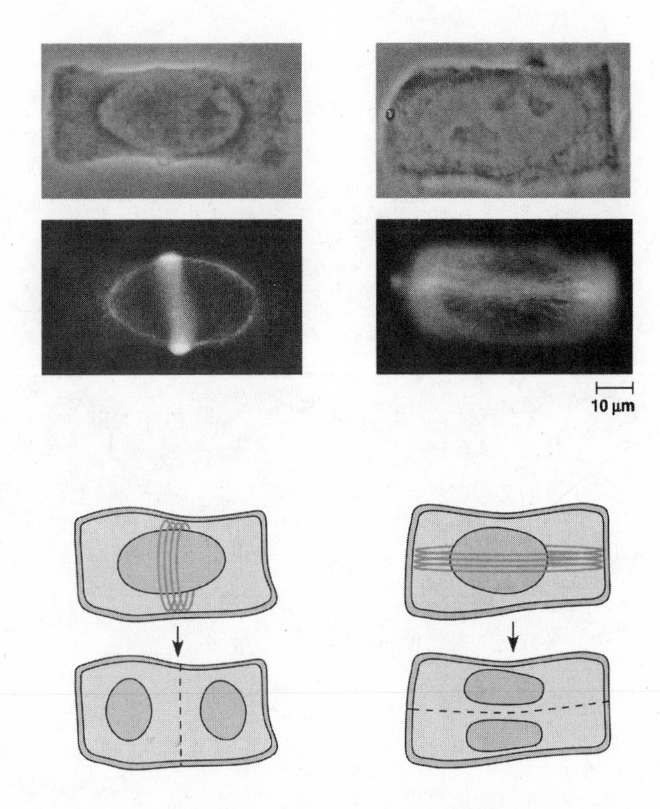

Figure 35.27 The preprophase band and the plane of cell division, page 740

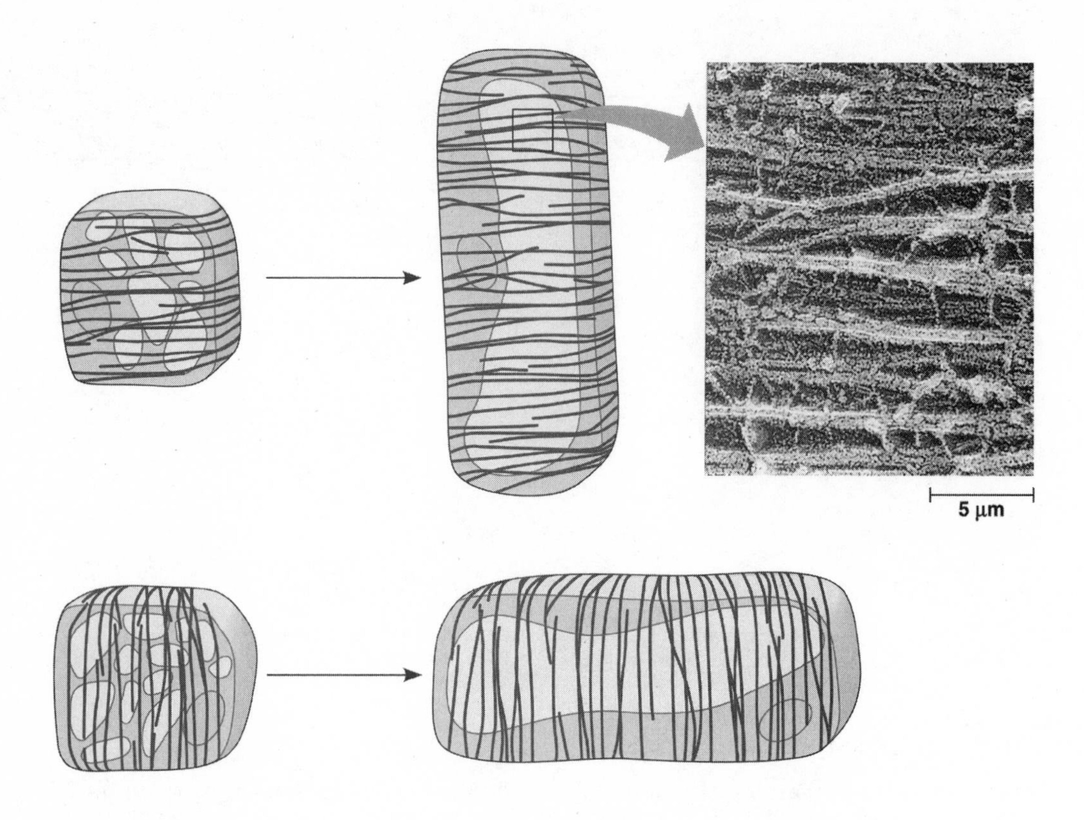

Figure 35.28 The orientation of plant cell expansion, page 741

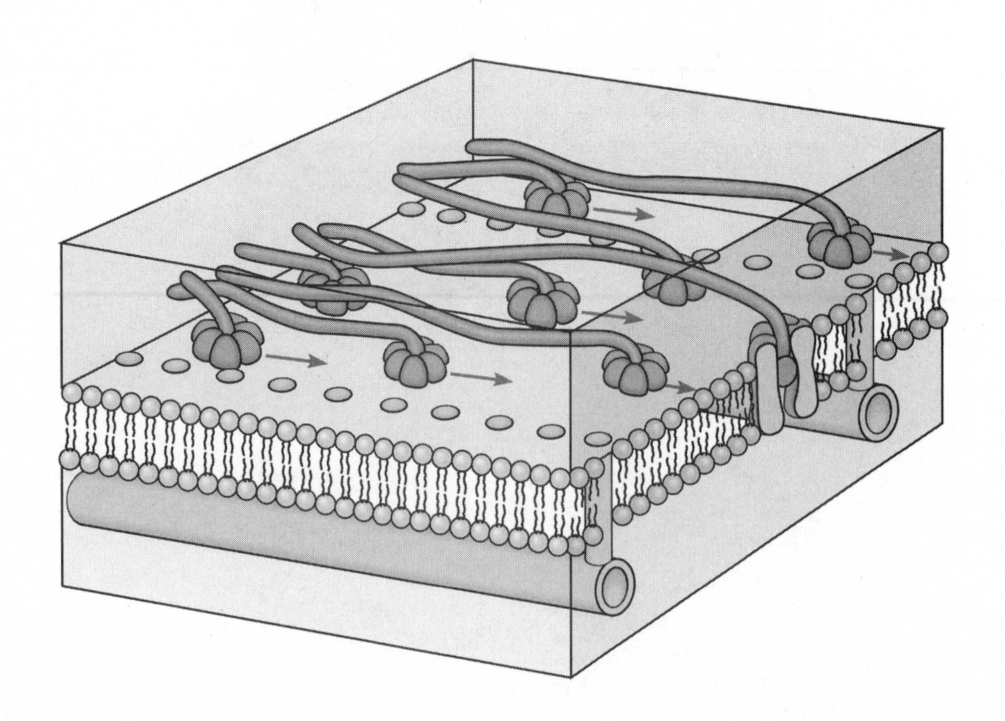

Figure 35.29 A hypothetical mechanism for how microtubules orient cellulose microfibrils, page 741

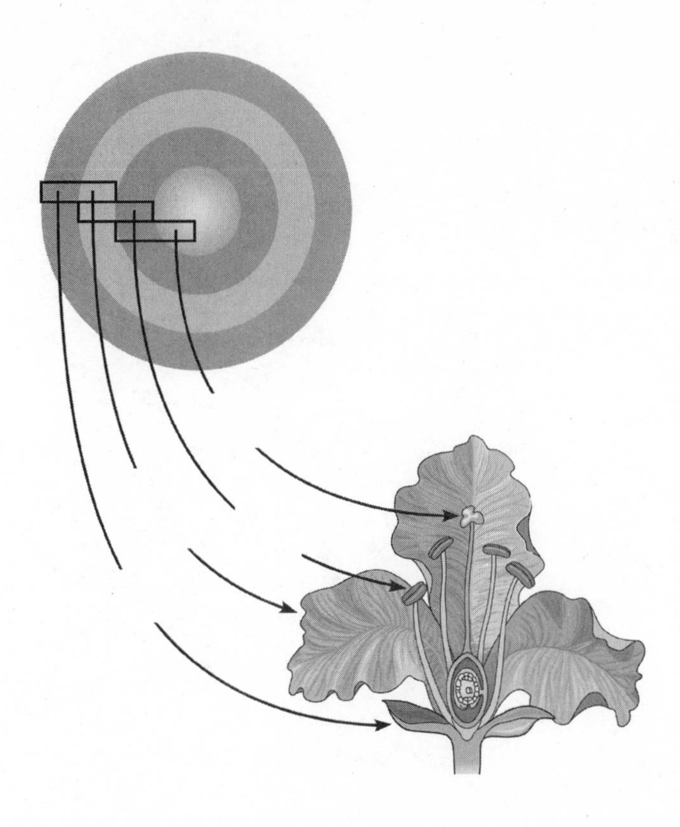

Figure 35.36 The ABC hypothesis for the functioning of organ identity genes in flower development, page 745

Figure 36.1 An overview of transport in whole plants, page 749

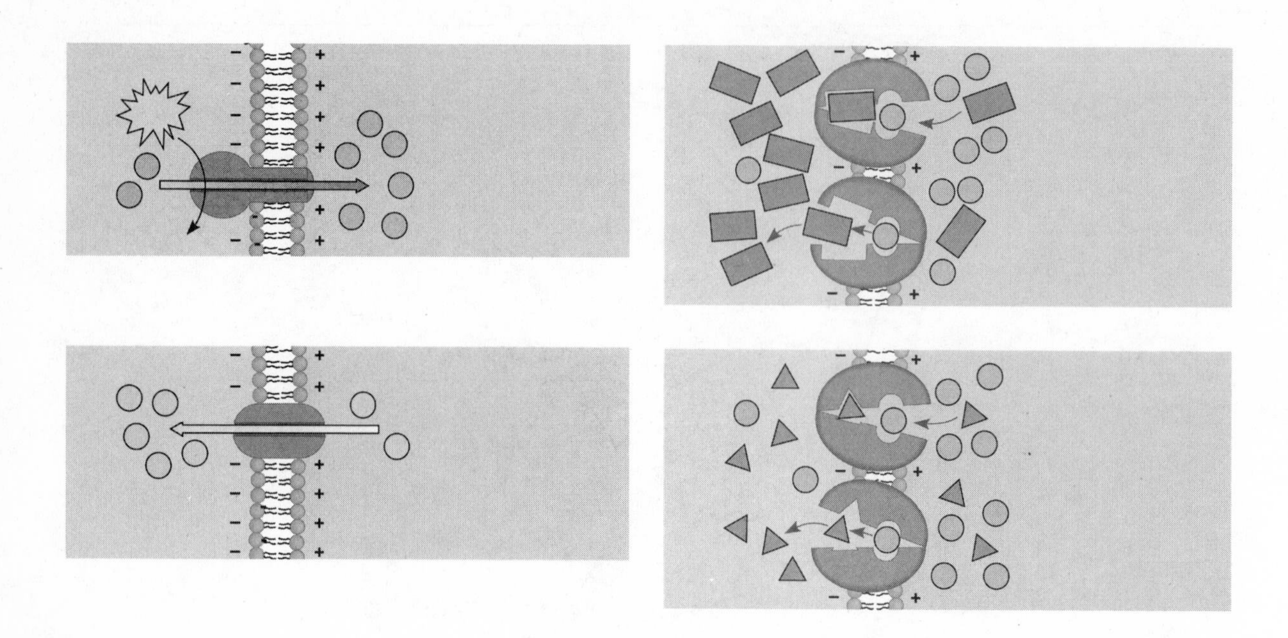

Figure 36.2 A chemiosmotic model of solute transport in plant cells, page 750

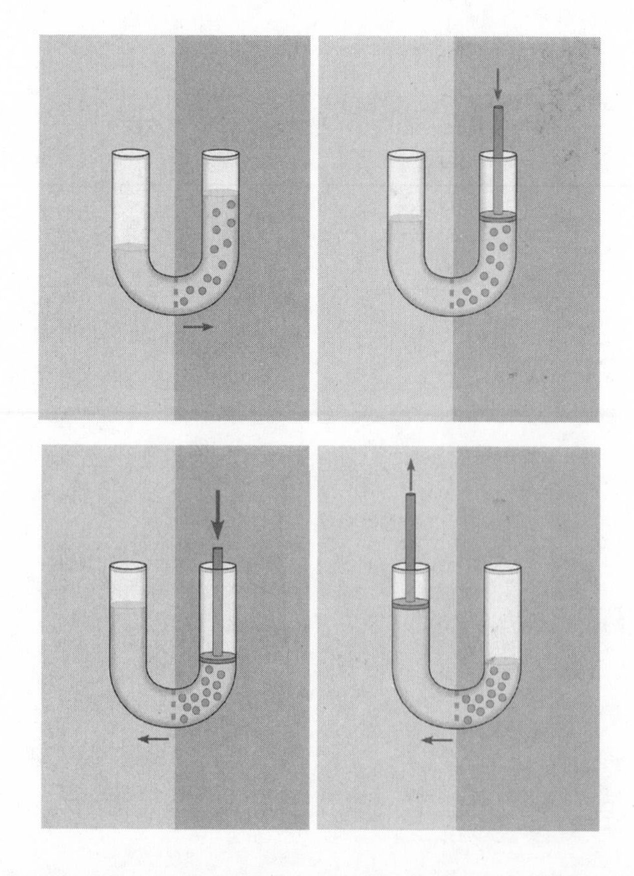

Figure 36.3 Water potential and water movement: a mechanical model, page 751

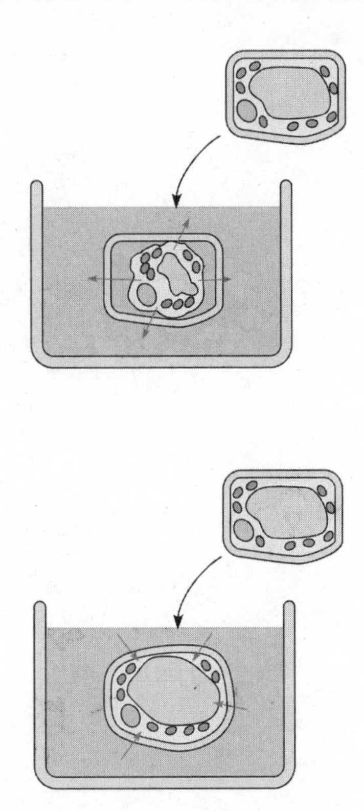

Figure 36.4 Water relations of plant cells, page 752

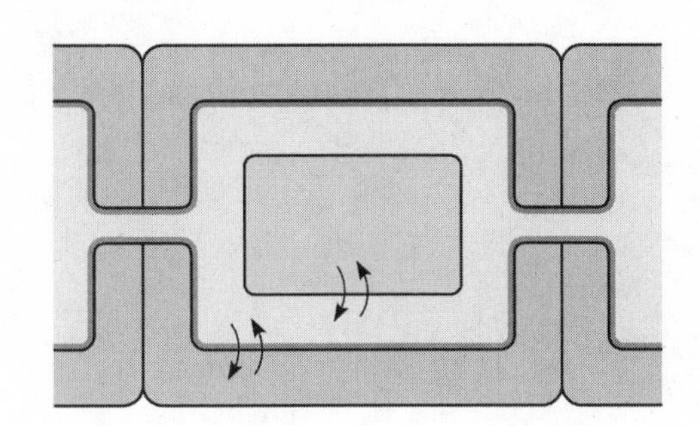

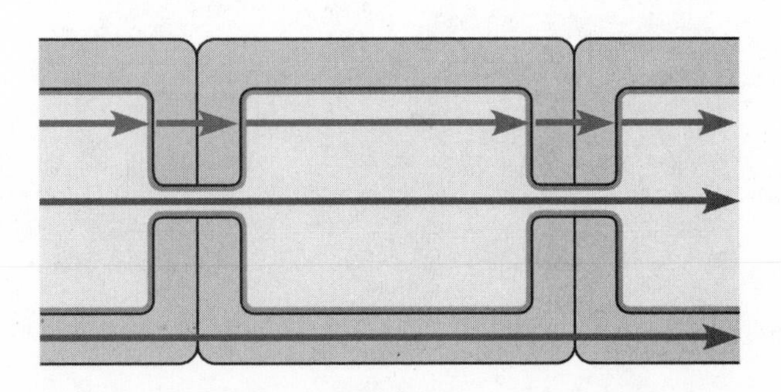

Figure 36.6 Compartments of plant cells and tissues and routes for lateral transport, page 753

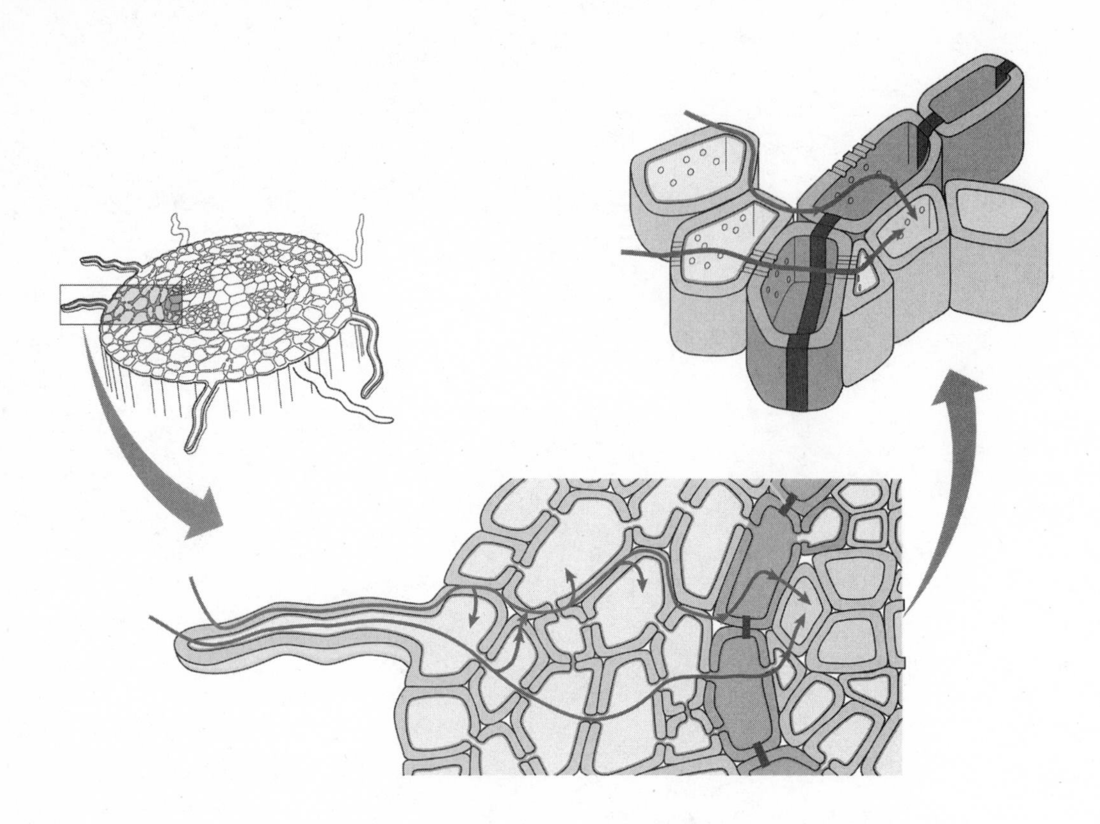

Figure 36.7 Lateral transport of minerals and water in roots, page 755

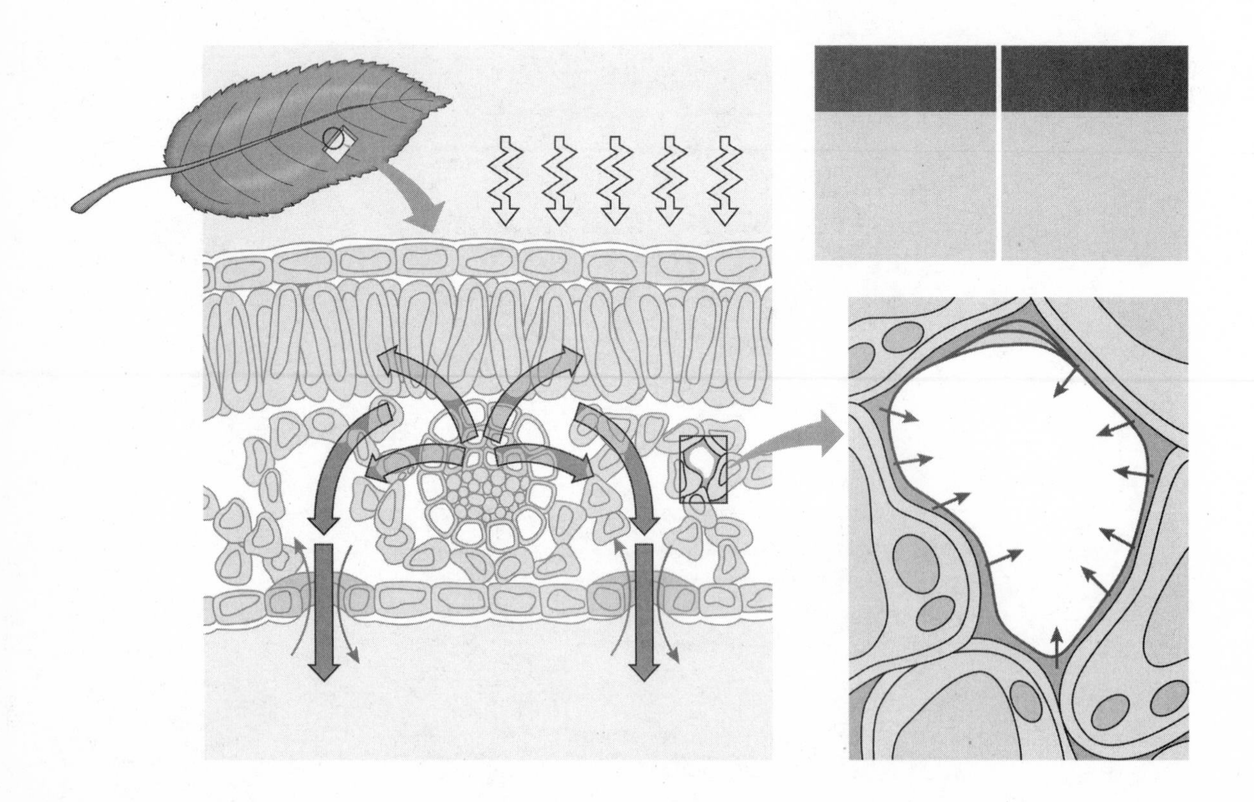

Figure 36.10 The generation of transpirational pull in a leaf, page 757

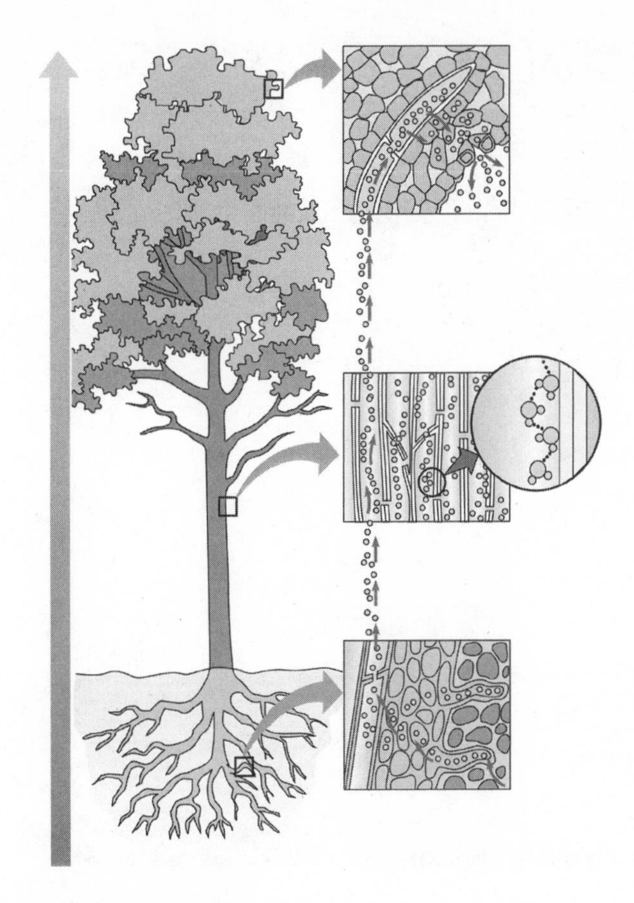

Figure 36.11 Ascent of water in a tree, page 758

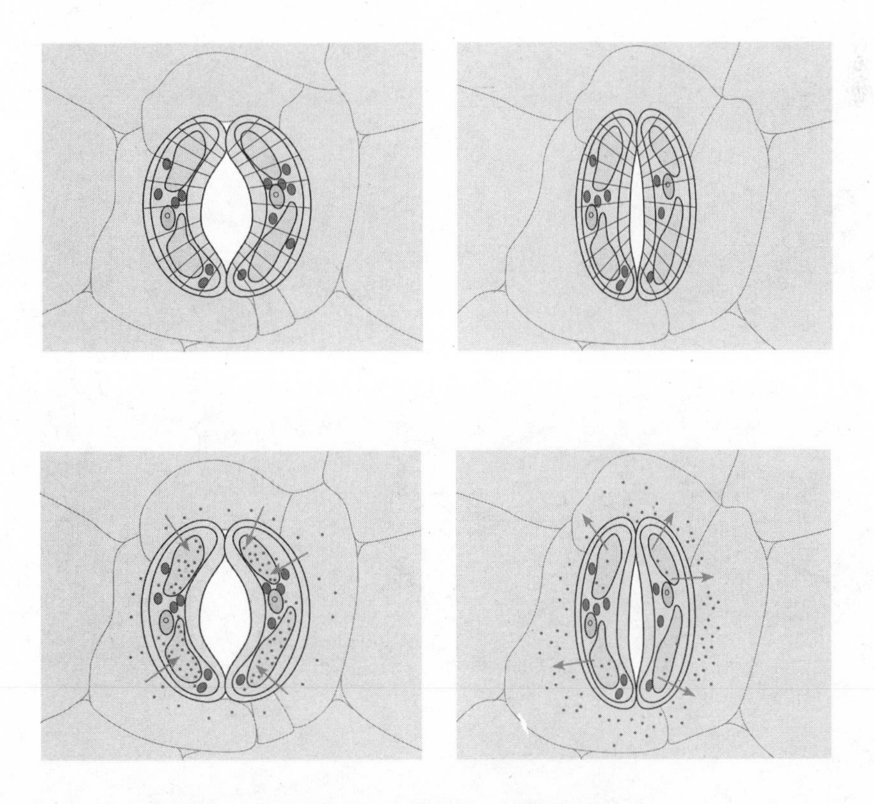

Figure 36.13 The control of stomatal opening and closing, page 760

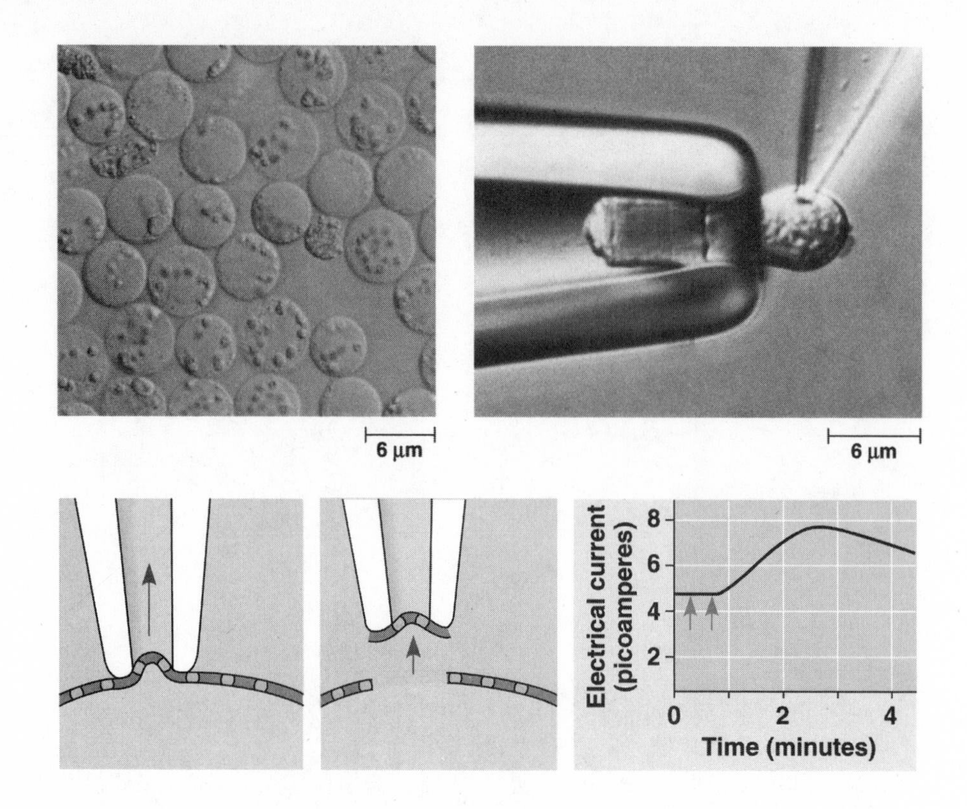

Figure 36.14 A patch-clamp study of guard cell membranes, page 761

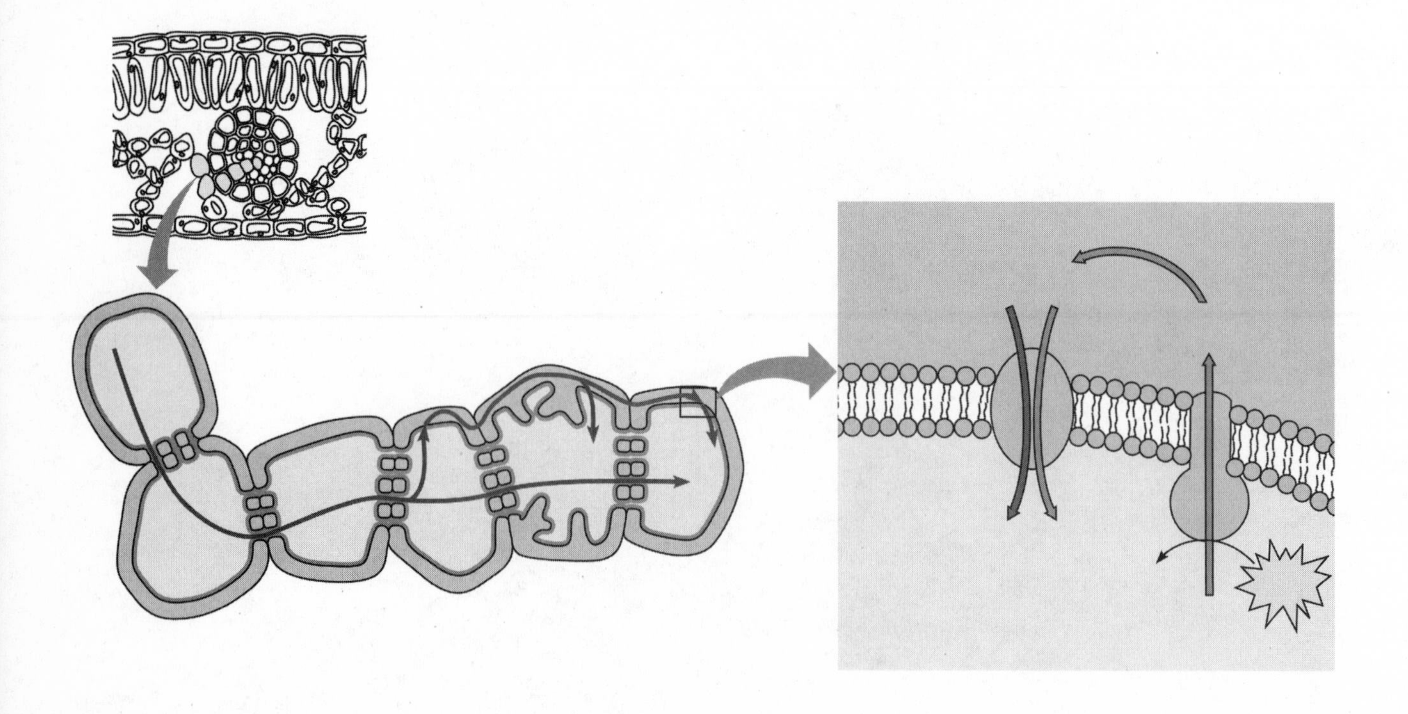

Figure 36.16 Loading of sucrose into phloem, page 763

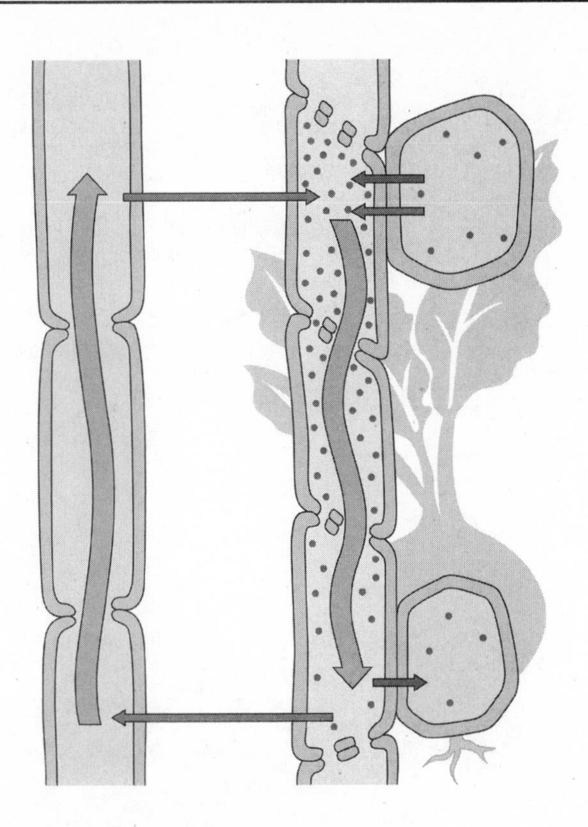

Figure 36.17 Pressure flow in a sieve tube, page 764

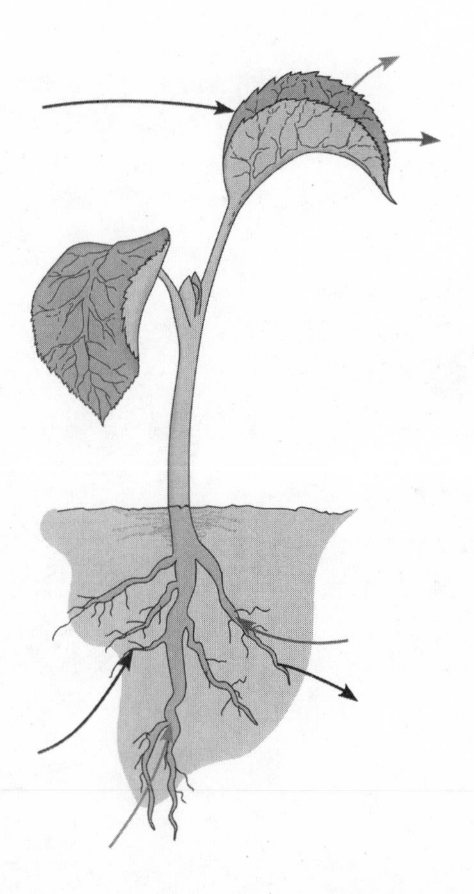

Figure 37.1 The uptake of nutrients by a plant: an overview, page 768

Figure 37.2 Using hydroponic culture to identify essential nutrients, page 768

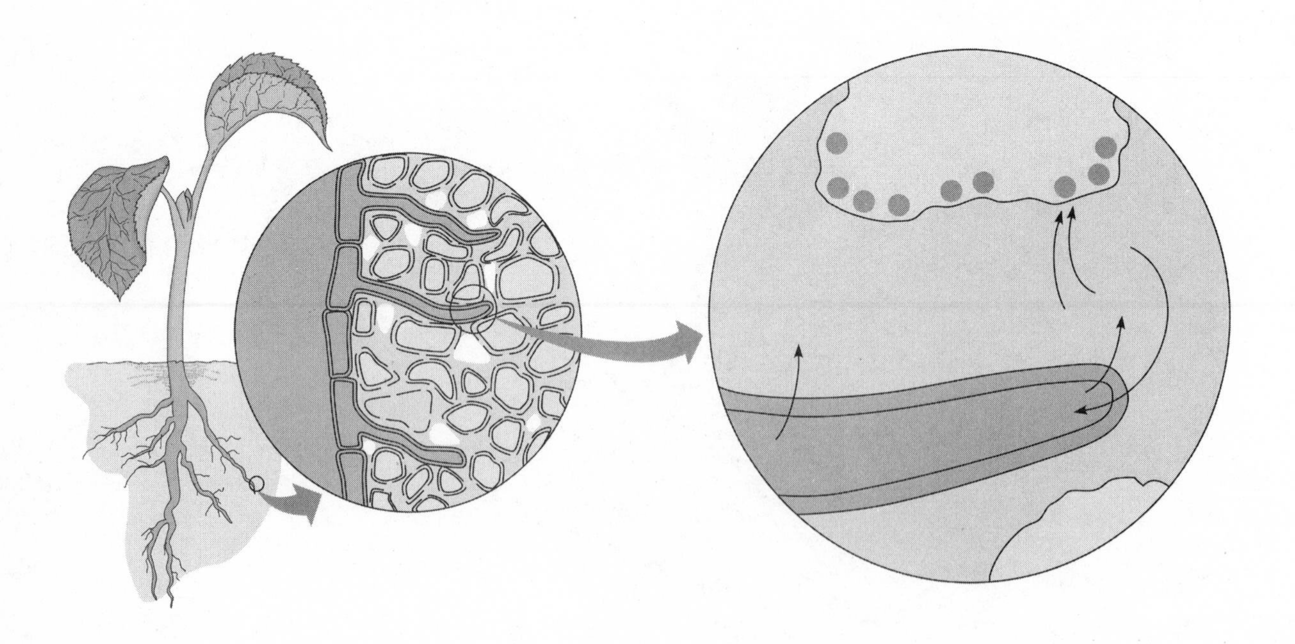

Figure 37.6 The availability of soil water and minerals, page 772

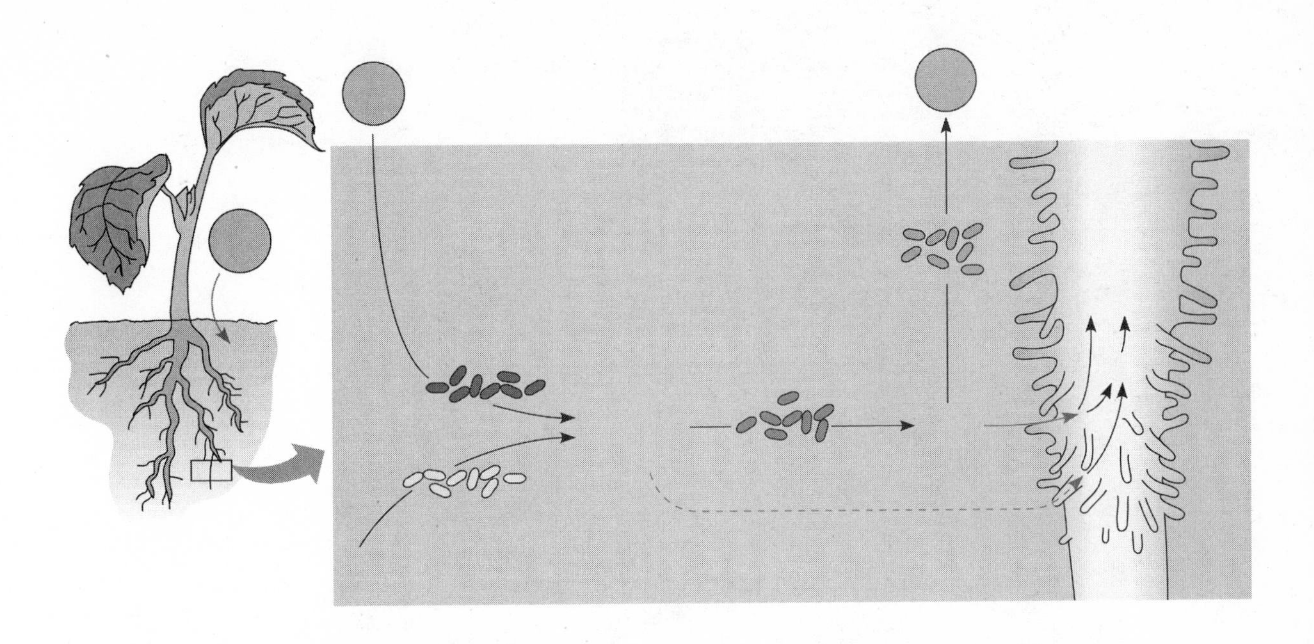

Figure 37.9 The role of soil bacteria in the nitrogen nutrition of plants, page 775

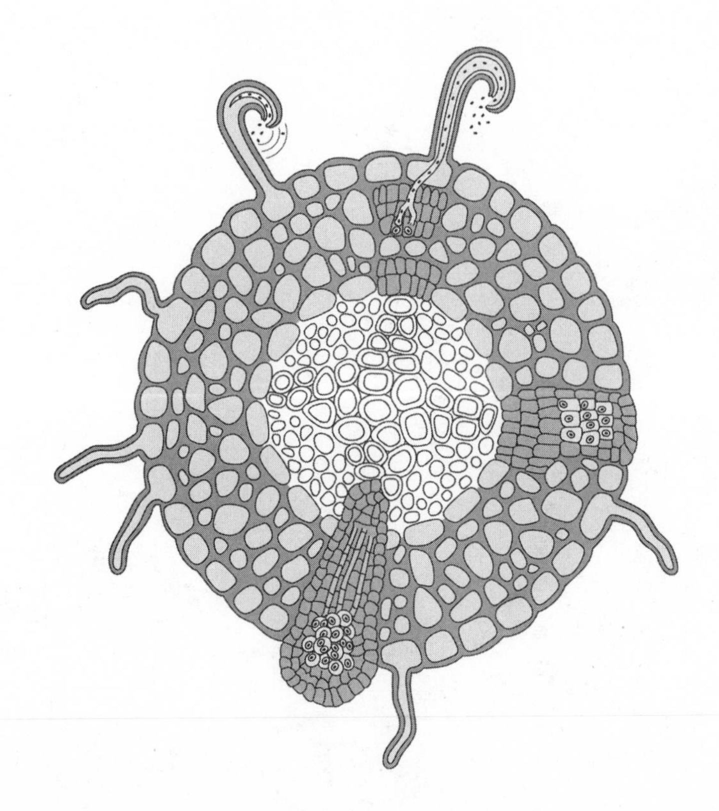

Figure 37.11 Development of a soybean root nodule, page 776

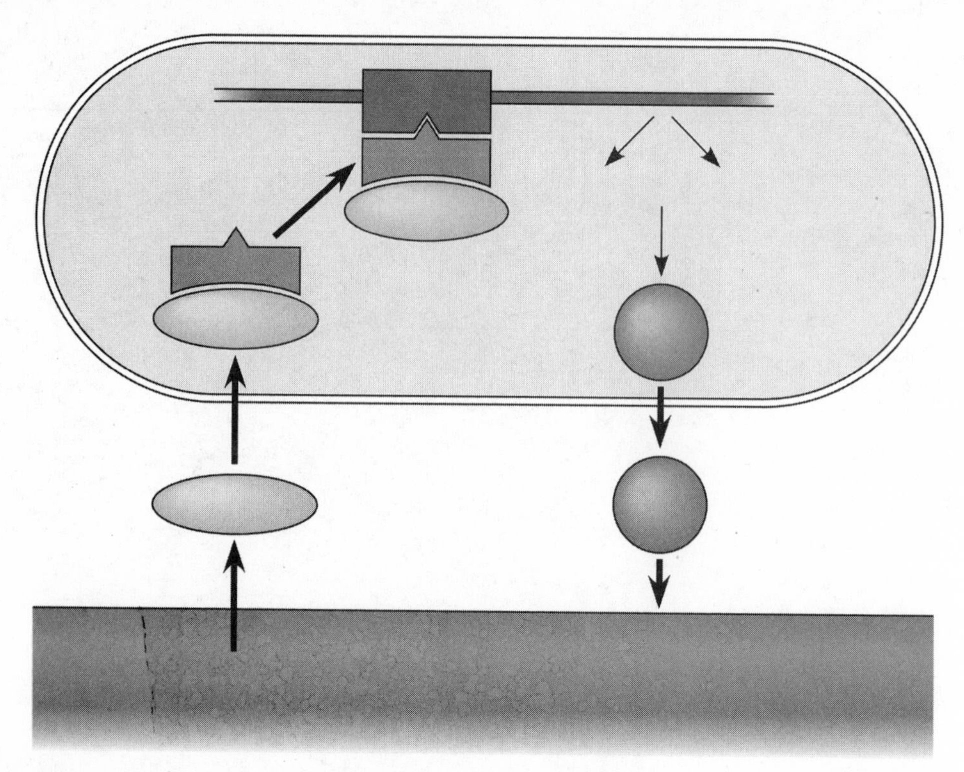

Figure 37.13 Molecular biology of root nodule formation, page 777

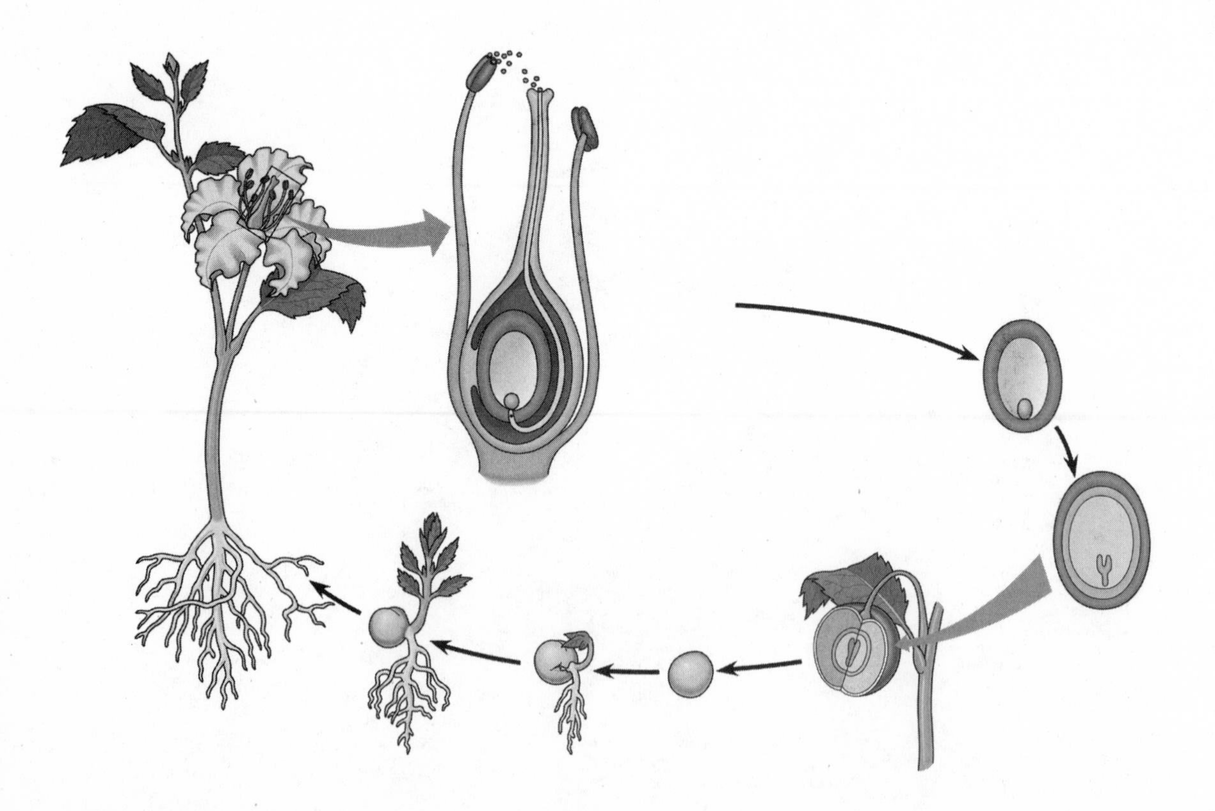

Figure 38.1 Simplified overview of angiosperm life cycle, page 784

Figure 38 2 Review of an idealized flower, page 785

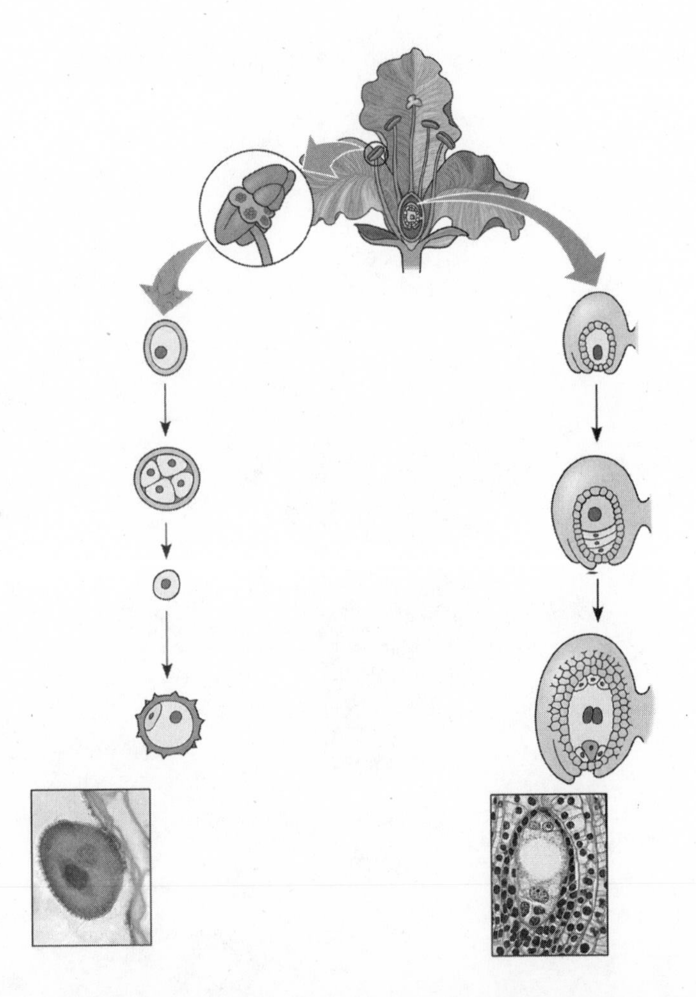

Figure 38.4 The development of angiosperm gametophytes (pollen and embryo sacs), page 787

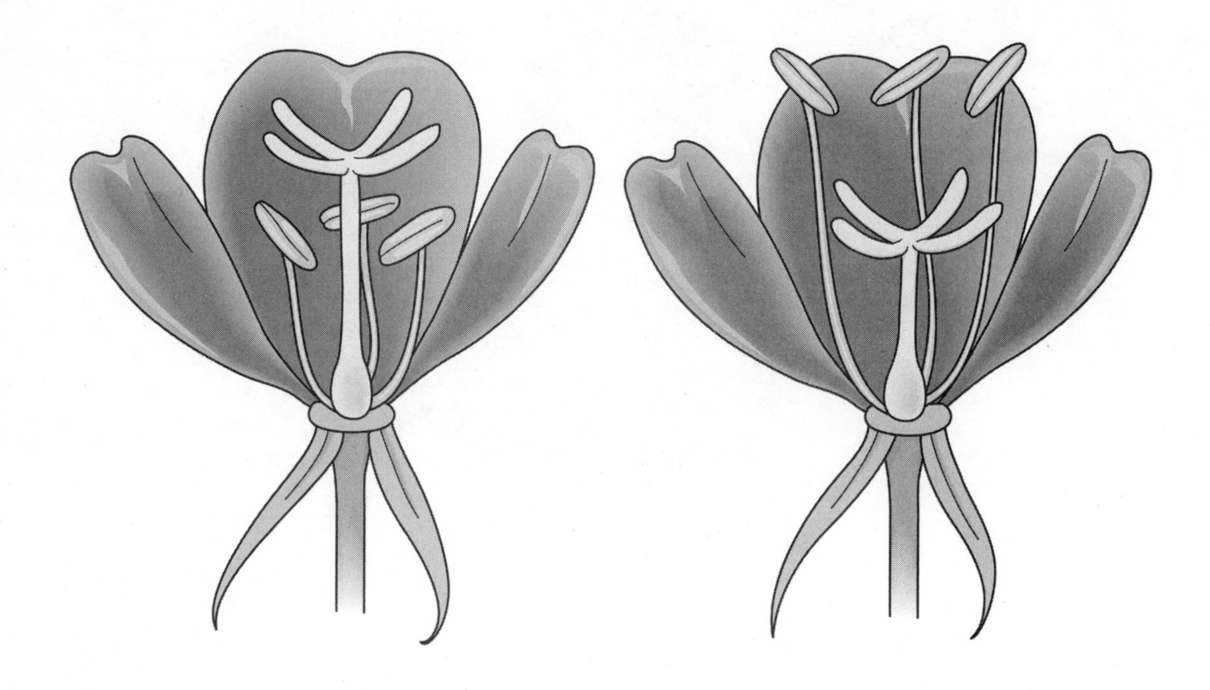

Figure 38.6 "Pin" and "thrum" flower types reduce self-fertilization, page 788

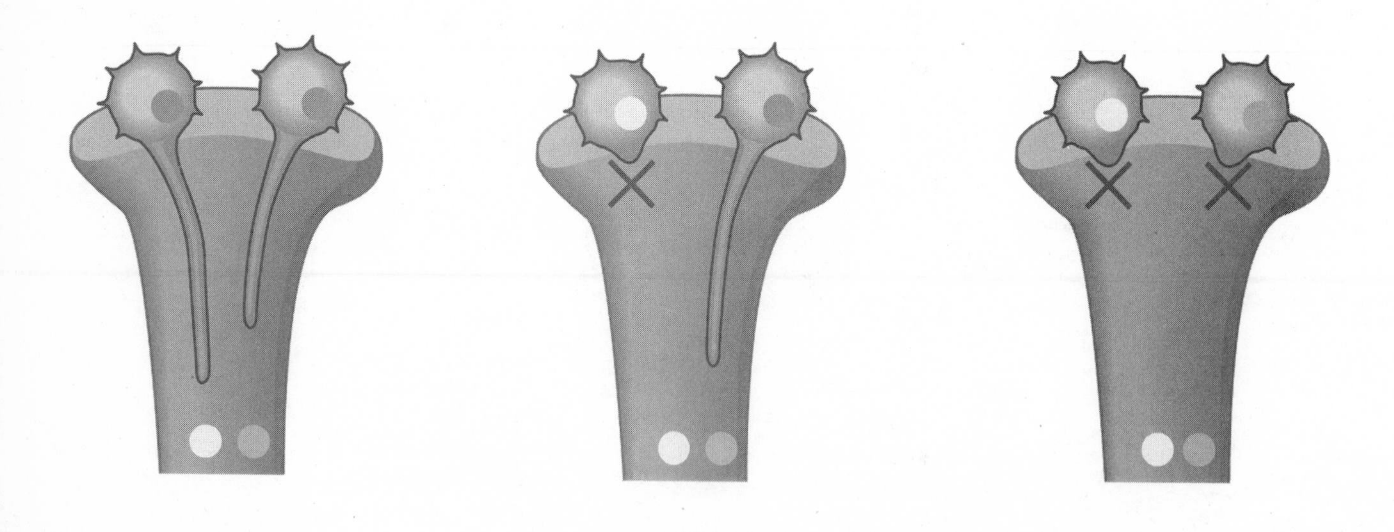

Figure 38.7 Genetic basis of self-incompatibility, page 788

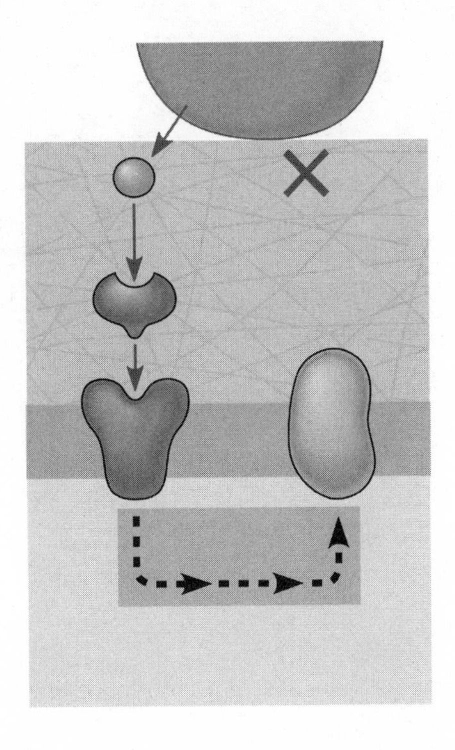

Figure 38.8 A possible mechanism of sporophytic self-incompatibility, page 789

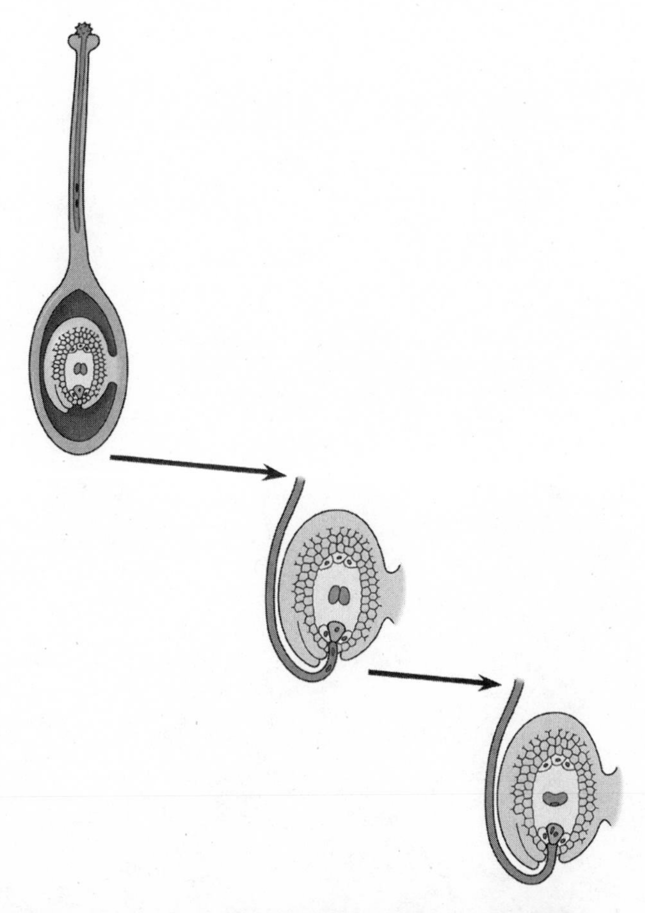

Figure 38.9 Growth of the pollen tube and double fertilization, page 790

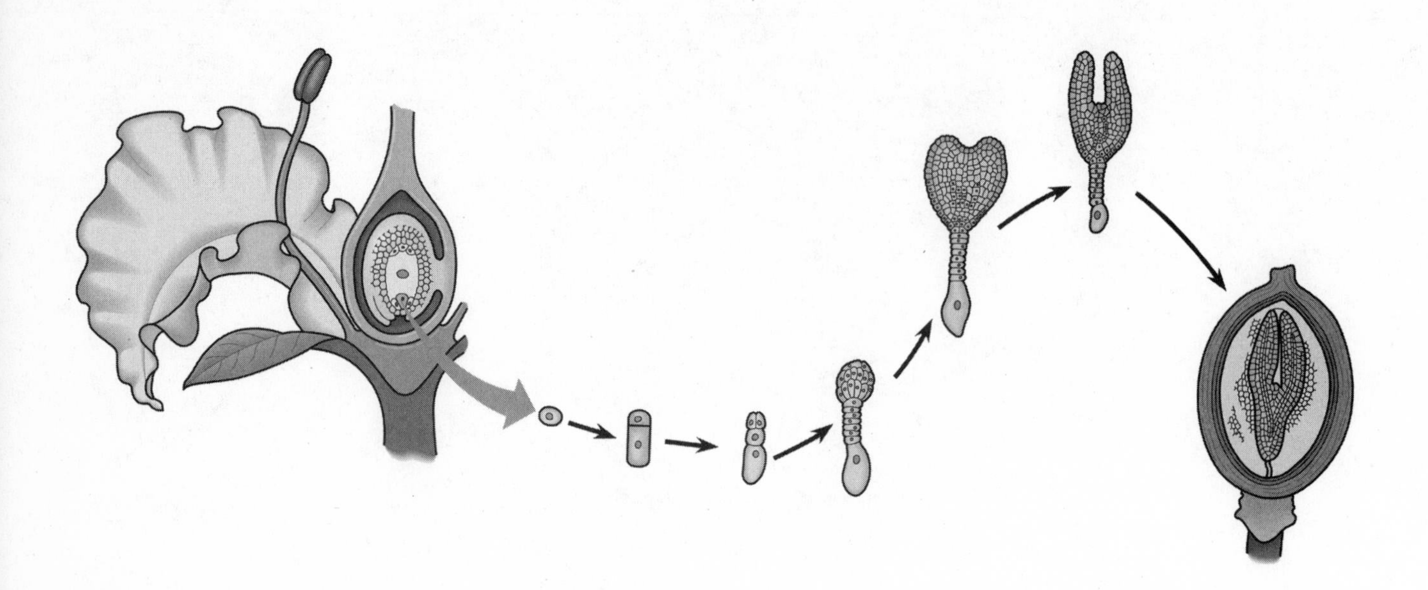

Figure 38.10 The development of a dicot plant embryo, page 791

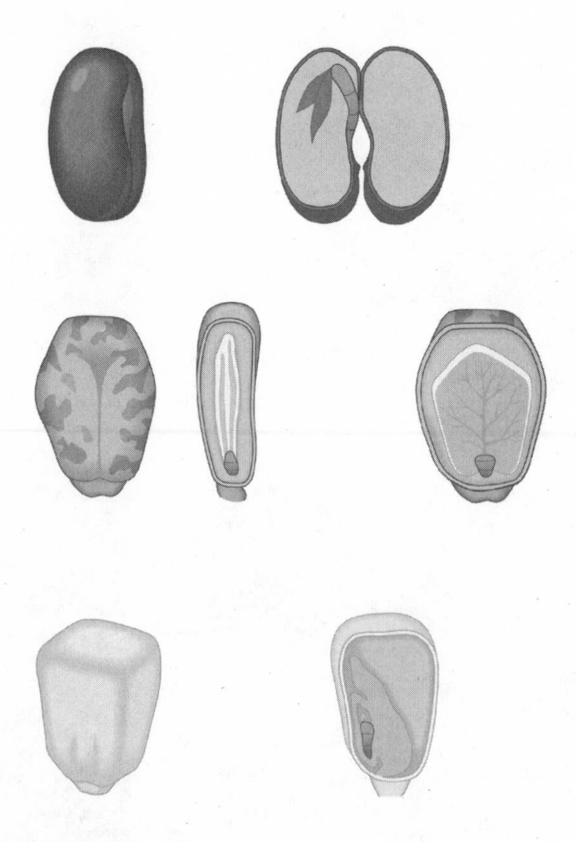

Figure 38.11 Seed structure, page 792

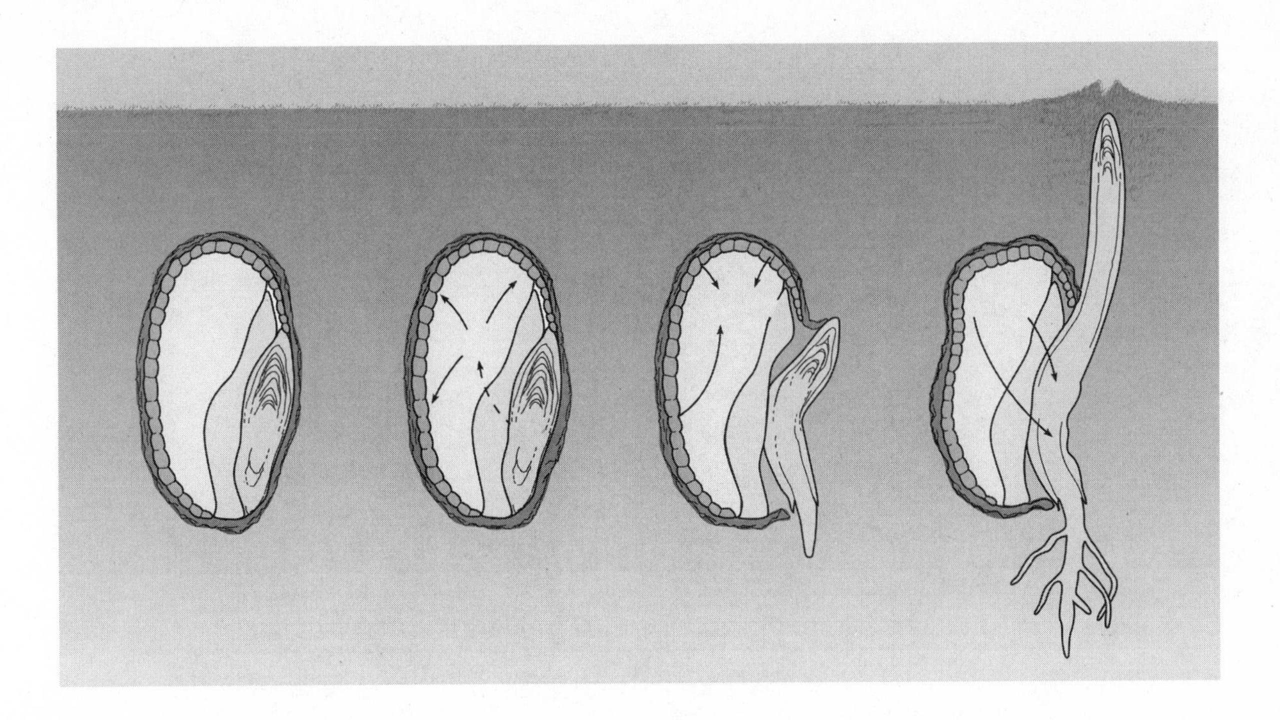

Figure 38.13 Mobilization of nutrients during the germination of a barley seed, page 793

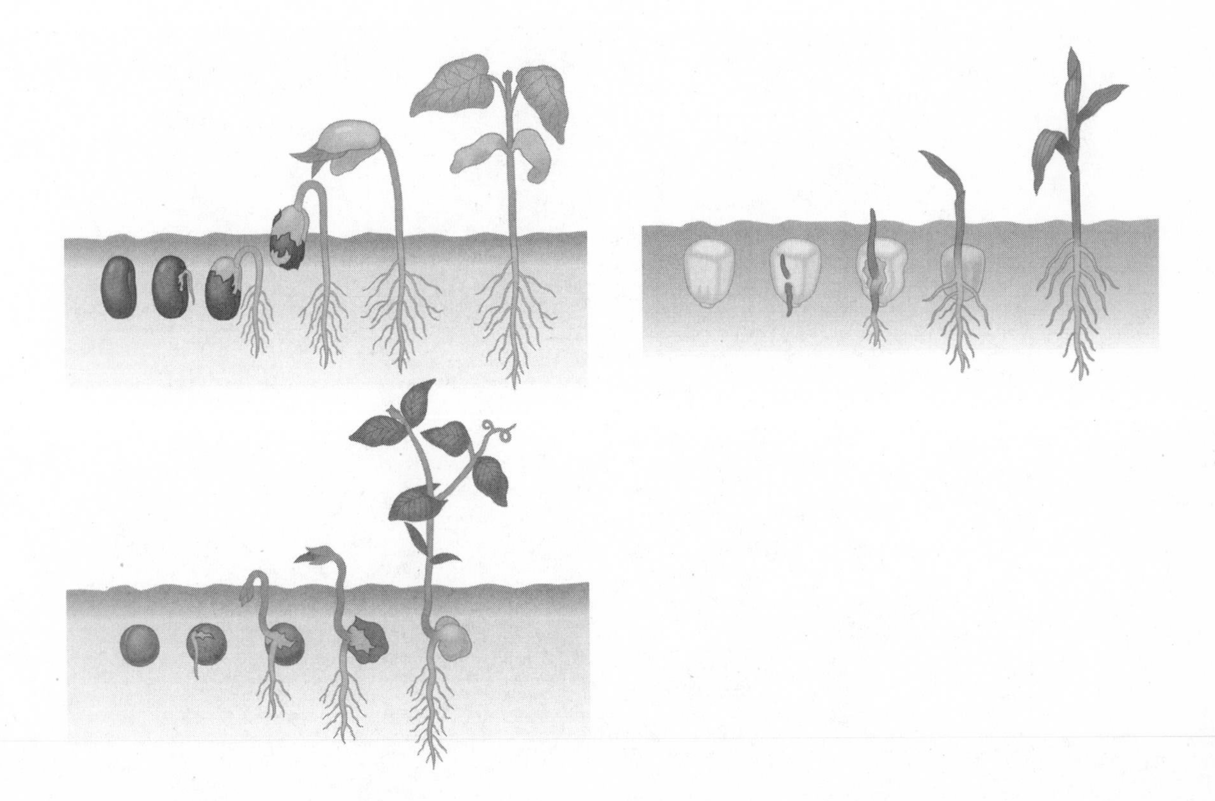

Figure 38.14 Seed germination, page 794

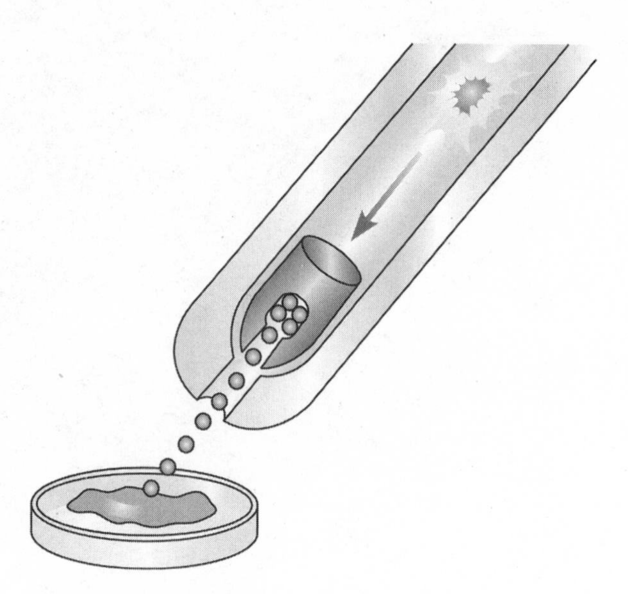

Figure 38.17 A DNA gun, page 796

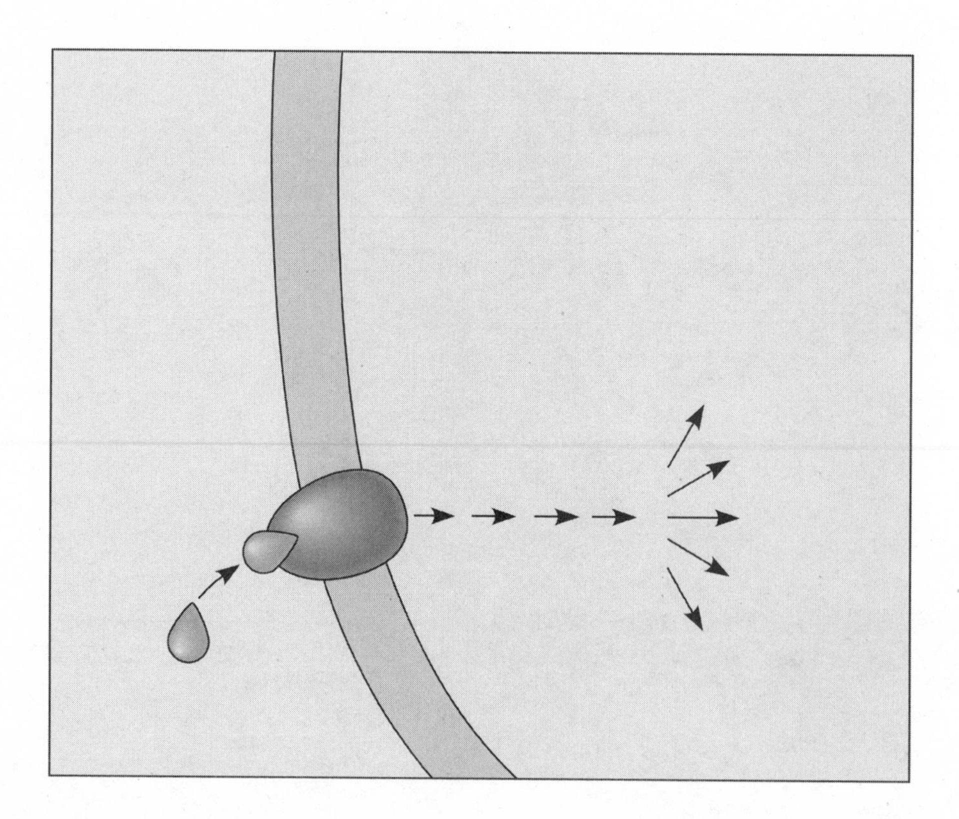

Figure 39.2 Review of a general model for signal-transduction pathways, page 803

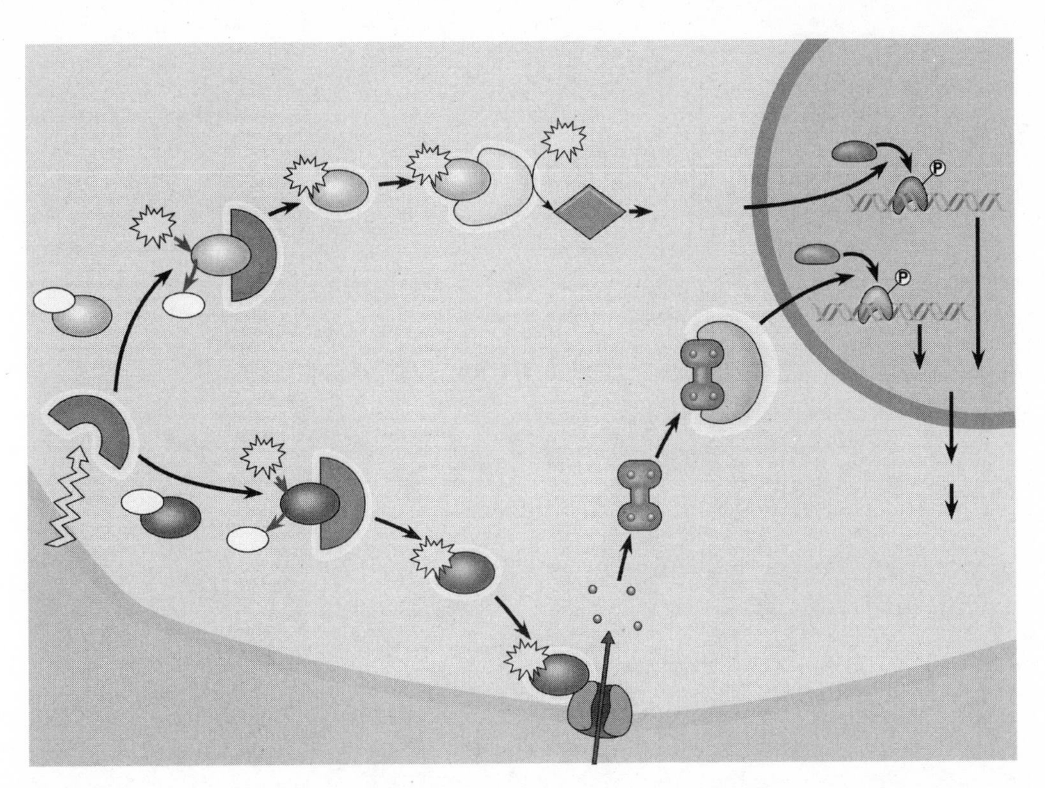

Figure 39.3 An example of signal transduction in plants: the role of phytochrome in the greening response, page 805

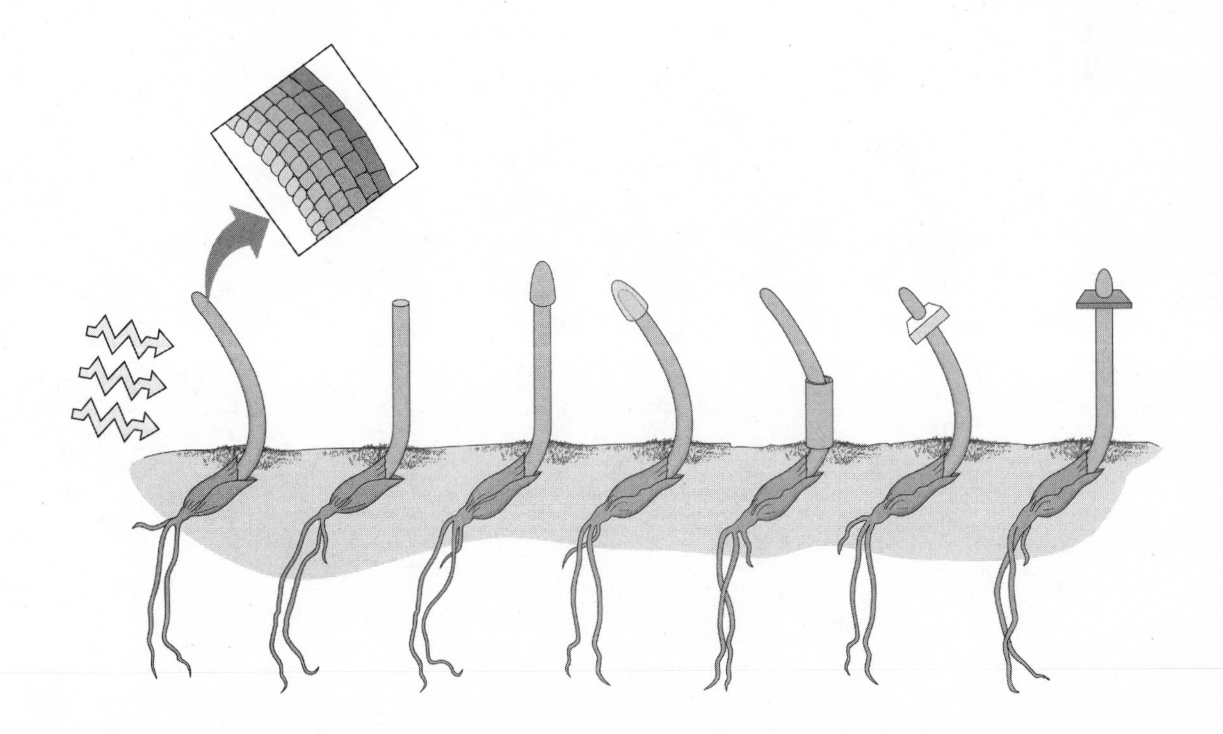

Figure 39.4 Early experiments of phototropism, page 807

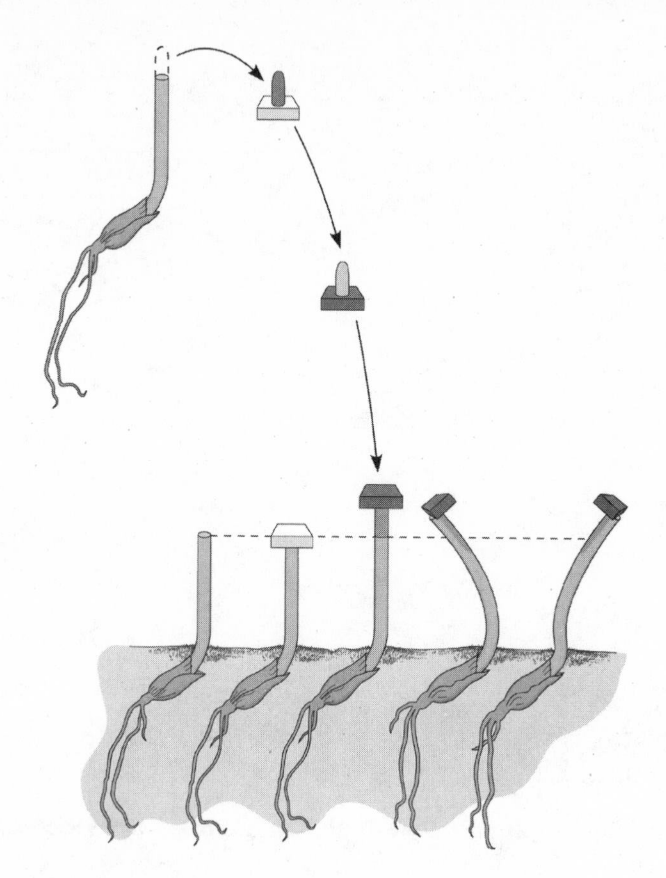

Figure 39.5 The Went experiments, page 807

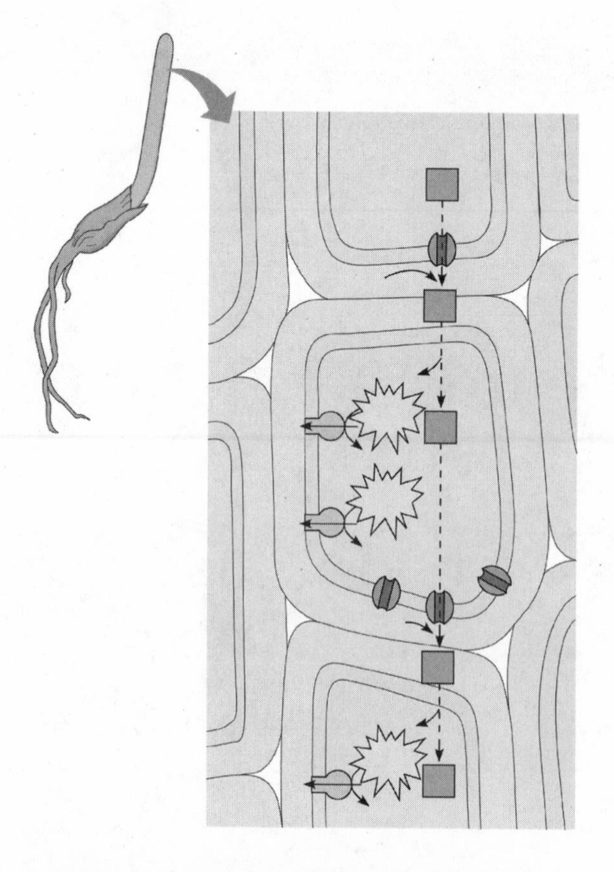

Figure 39.6 Polar auxin transport: a chemiosmotic model, page 809

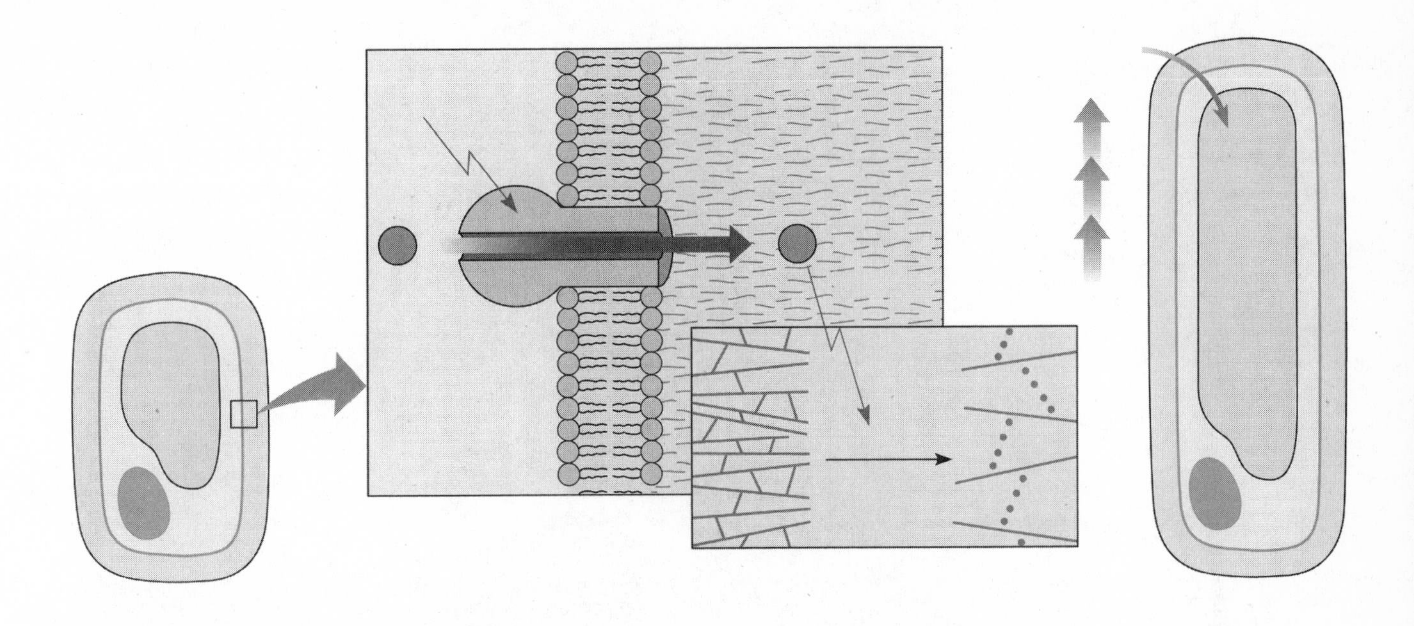

Figure 39.7 Cell elongation in response to auxin: the acid growth hypothesis, page 810

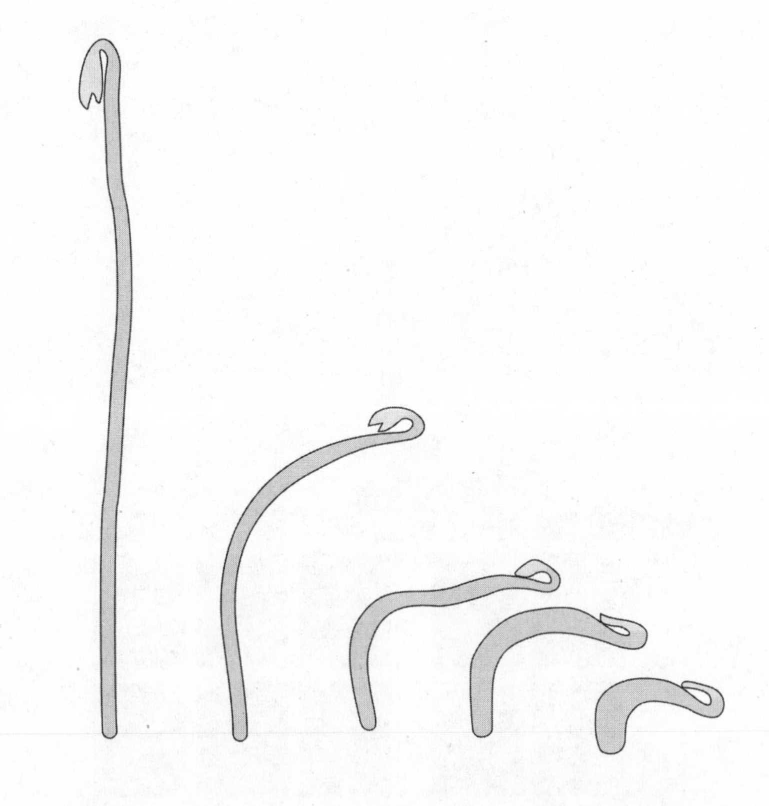

Figure 39.13 Ethylene induces the triple response in pea seedlings, page 814

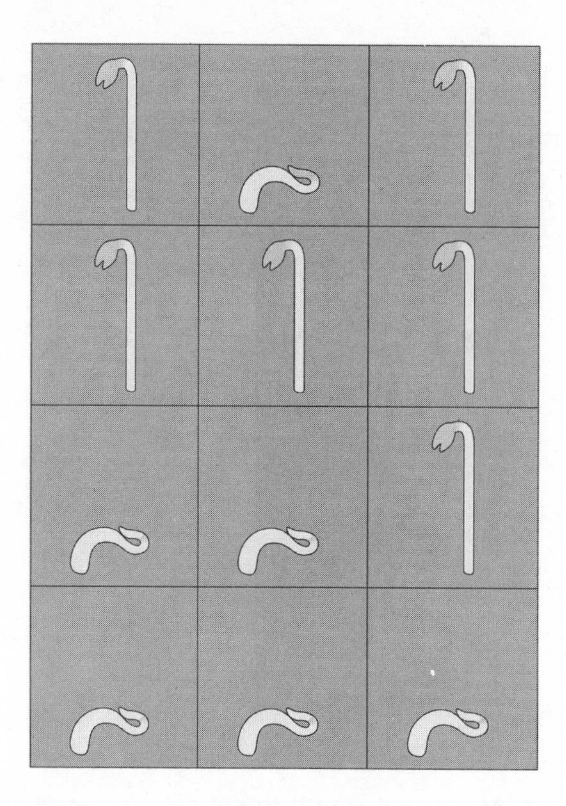

Figure 39.15 Ethylene signal-transduction mutants can be distinguished by their different responses to experimental treatments, page 815

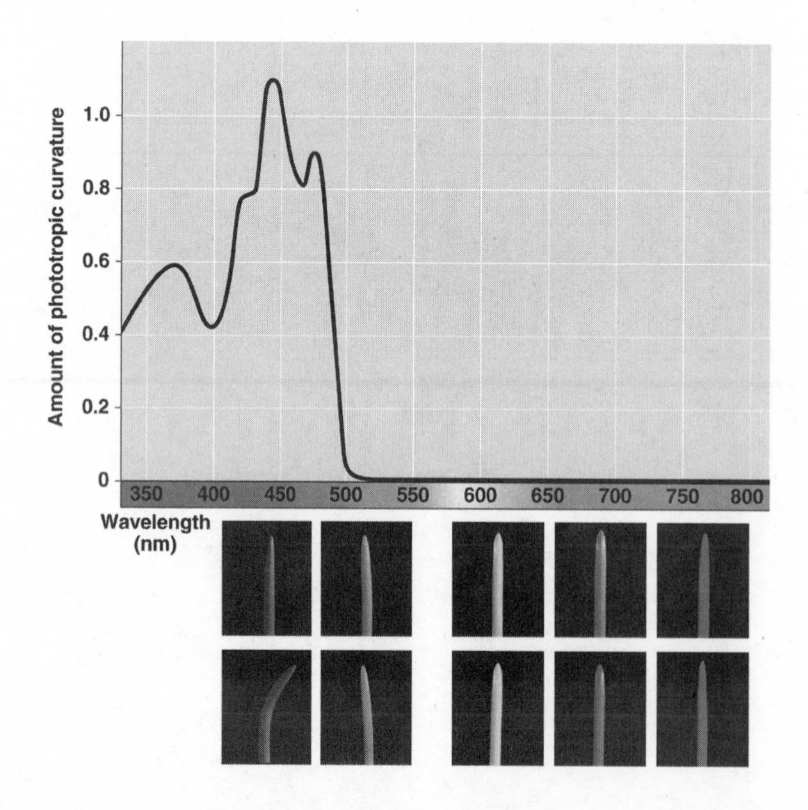

Figure 39.17 Action spectrum for blue-light-stimulated phototropism, page 817

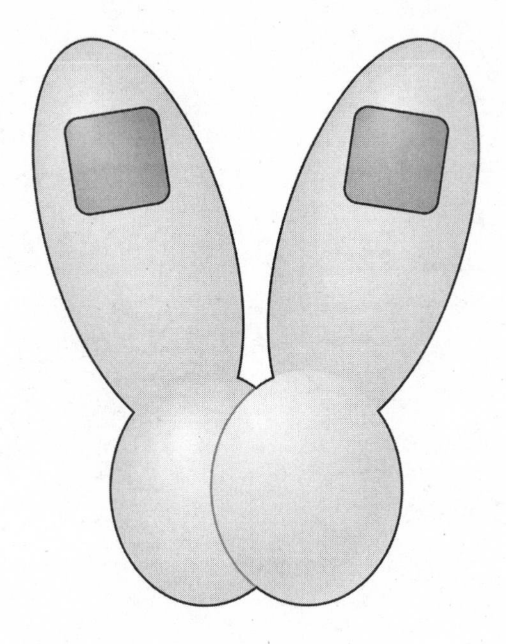

Figure 39.19 Structure of a phytochrome, page 819

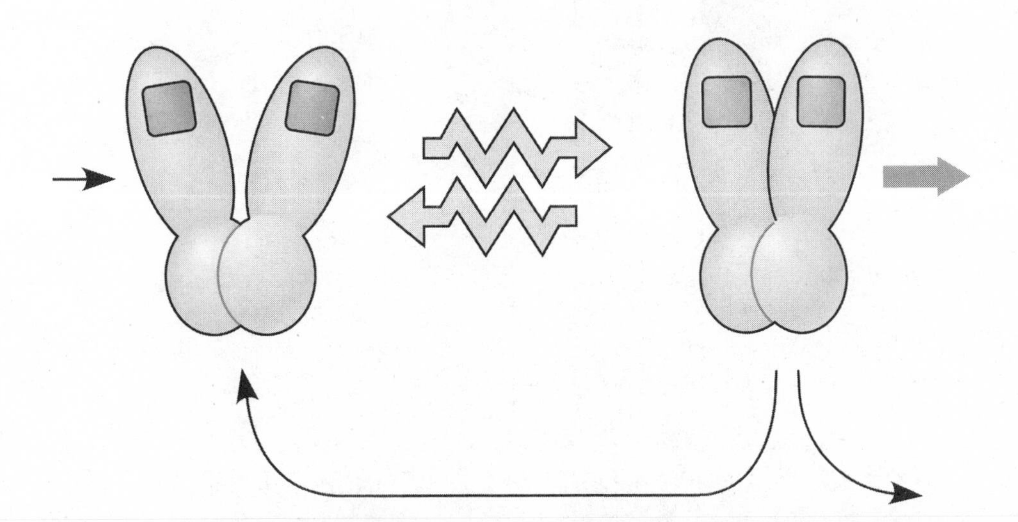

Figure 39.20 Phytochrome: a molecular switching mechanism, page 819

Figure 39.22 Photoperiodic control of flowering, page 822

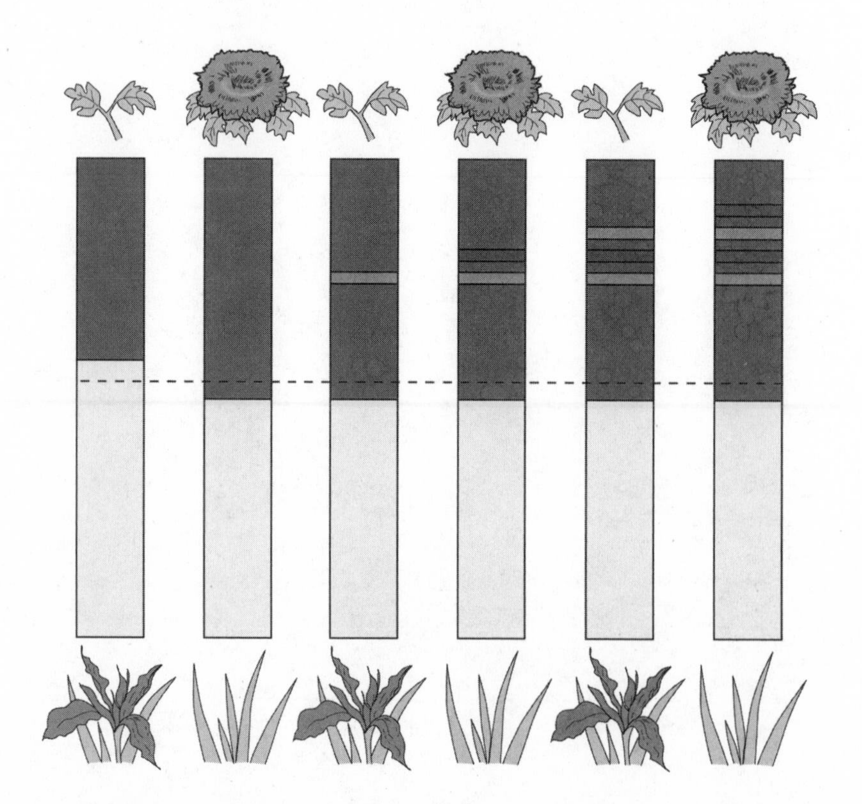

Figure 39.23 Reversible effects of red and far-red light on photoperiodic response, page 822

Figure 39.24 Experimental evidence for a flowering hormone(s), page 823

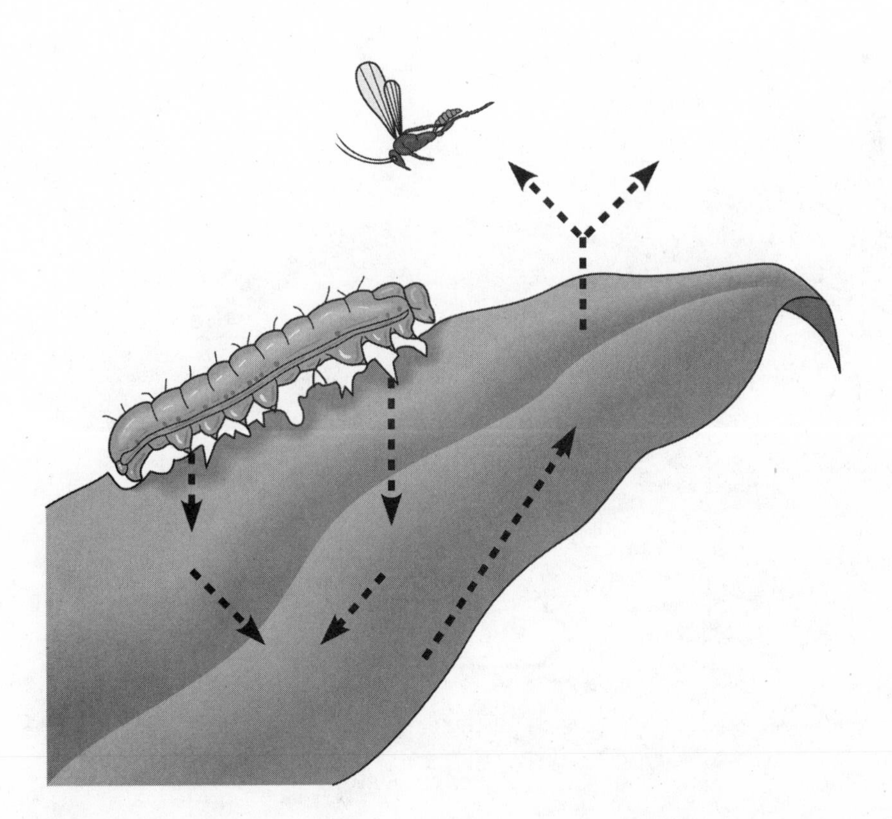

Figure 39.29 A corn leaf recruits a parasitoid wasp as a defensive response to an herbivore, an army-worm caterpillar, page 827

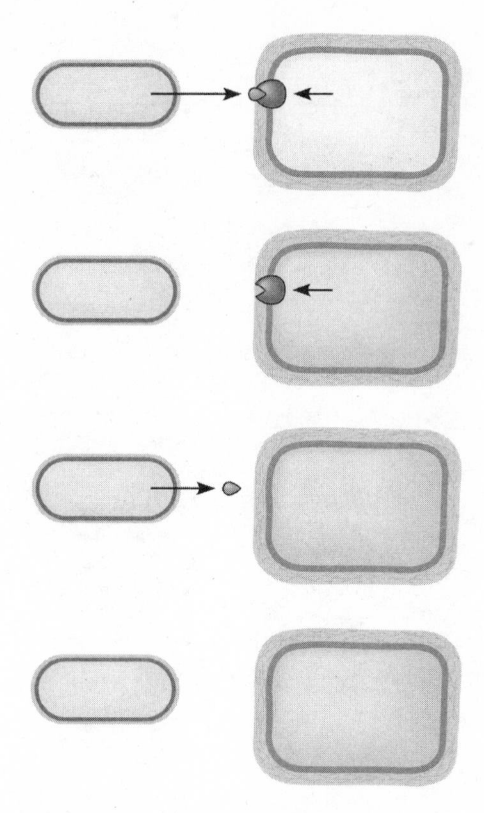

Figure 39.30 Gene-for-gene resistance of plants to pathogens, page 828

Figure 39.31 Defense responses against an avirulent pathogen, page 829

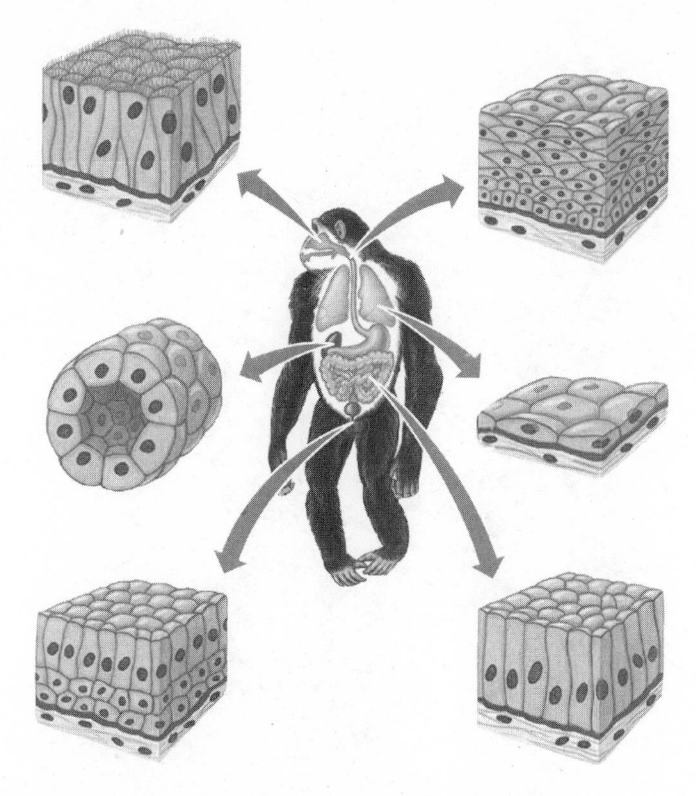

Figure 40.1 The structure and function of epithelial tissues, page 836

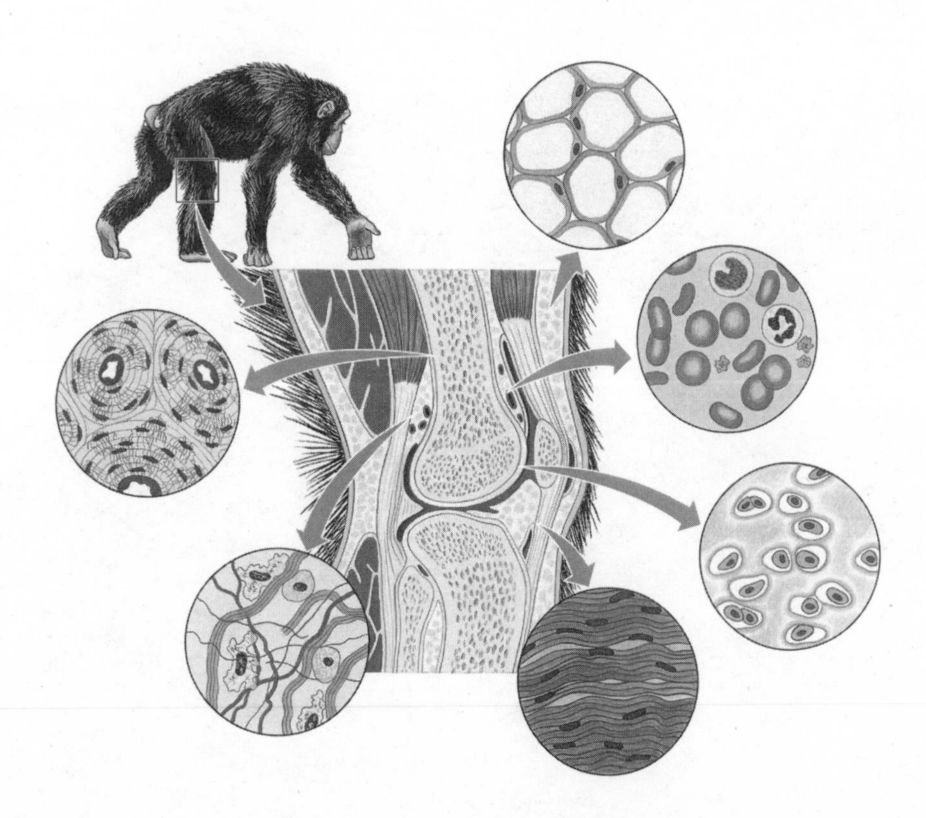

Figure 40.2 Some representative types of connective tissue, page 837

Figure 40.4 Three kinds of vertebrate muscle, page 838

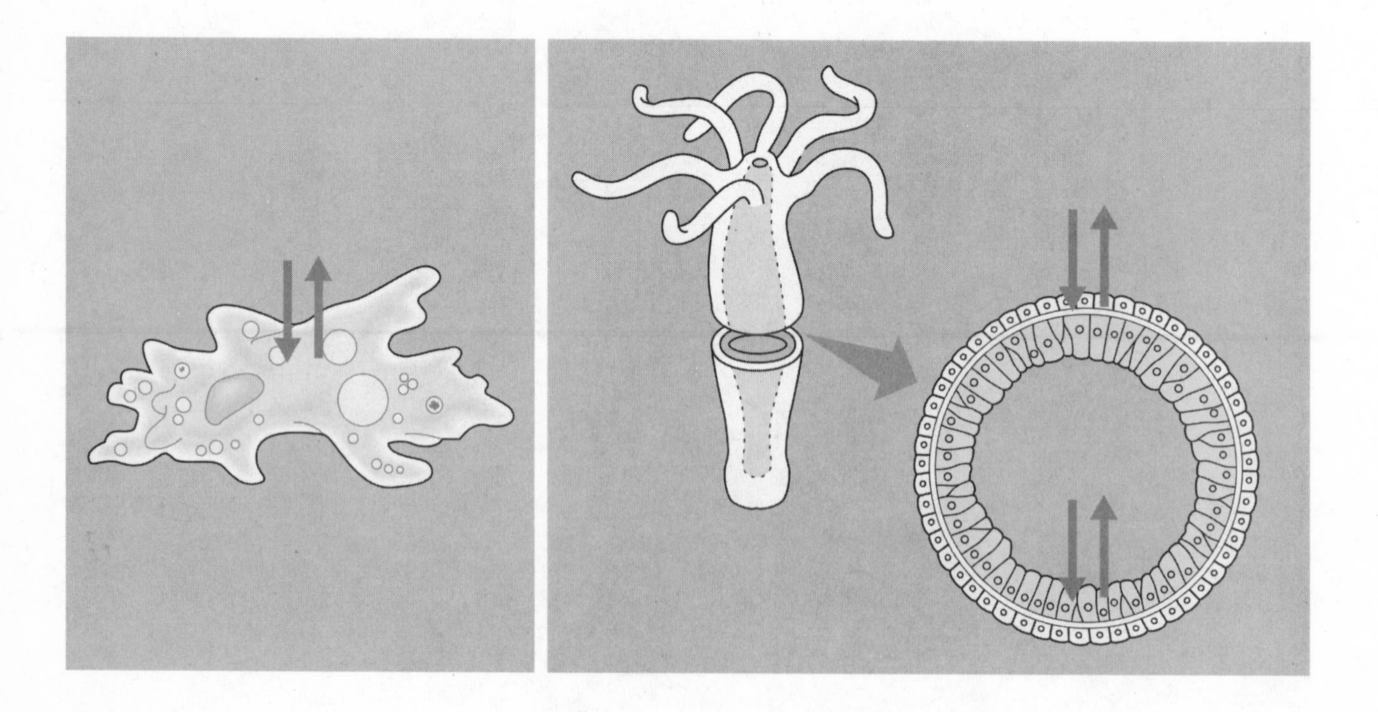

Figure 40.7 Contact with the environment, page 841

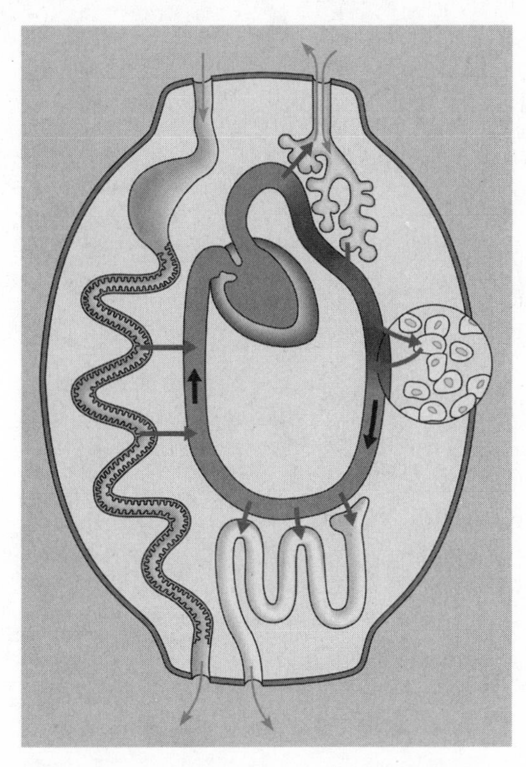

Figure 40.8 Internal exchange surfaces of complex animals, page 842

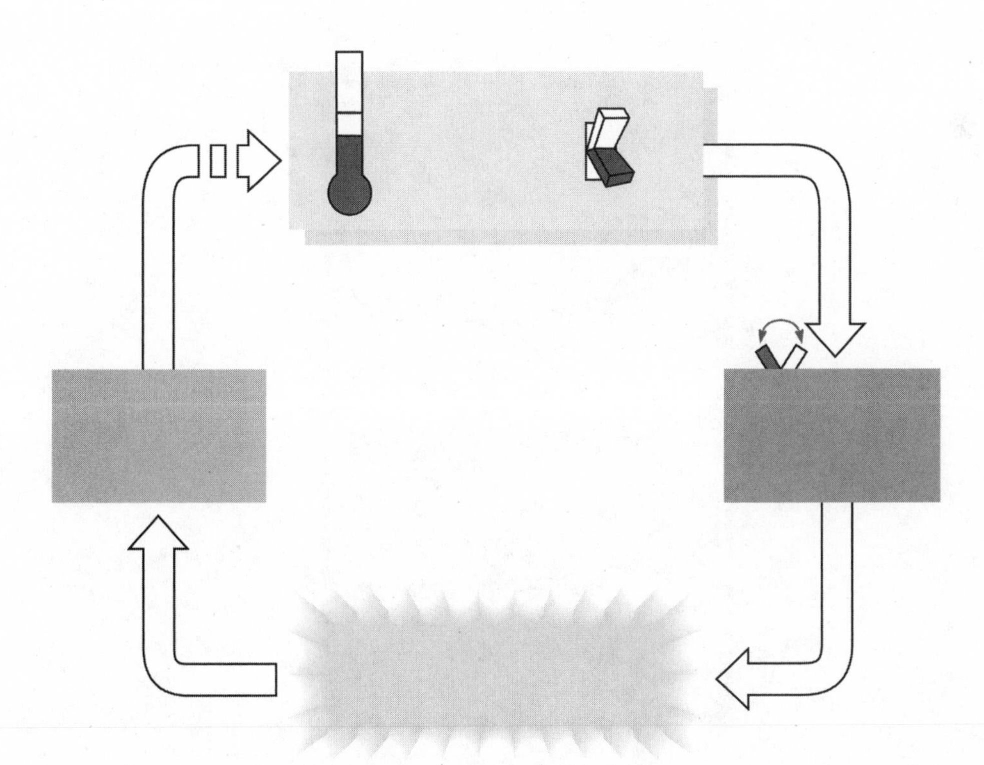

Figure 40.9a An example of negative feedback: Control of room temperature, page 843

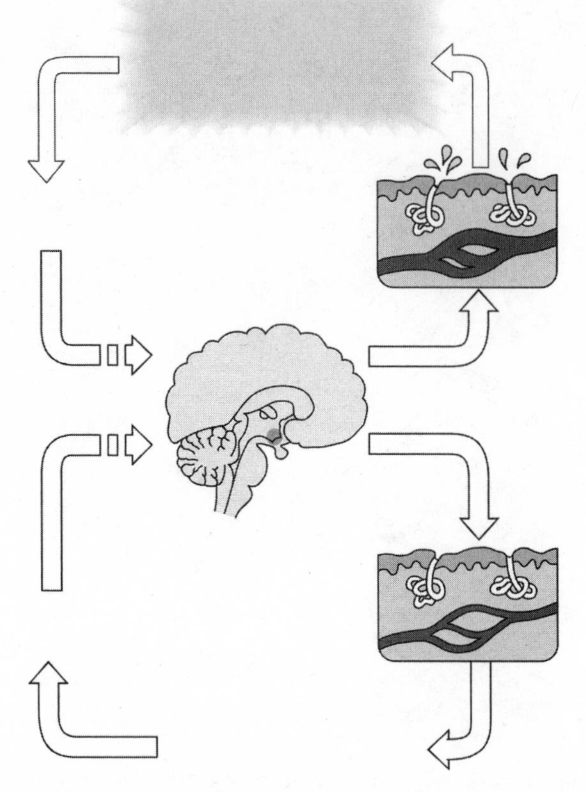

Figure 40.9b An example of negative feedback: Control of body temperature, page 843

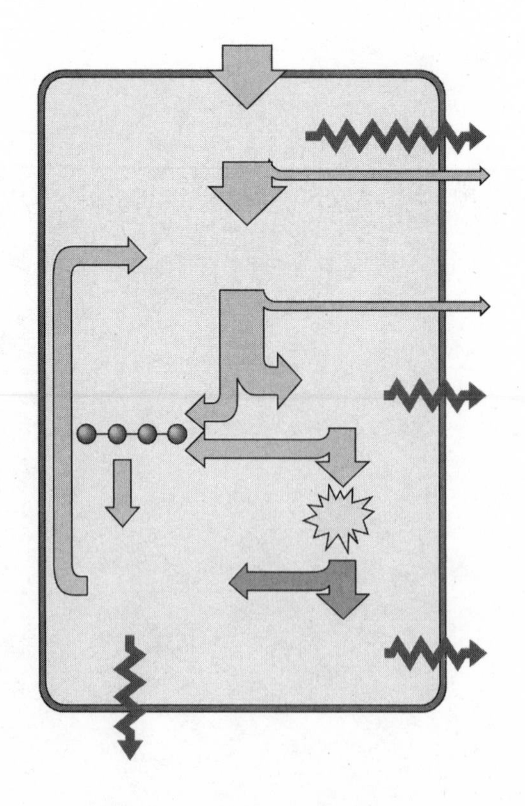

Figure 40.10 Bioenergetics of an animal: an overview, page 844

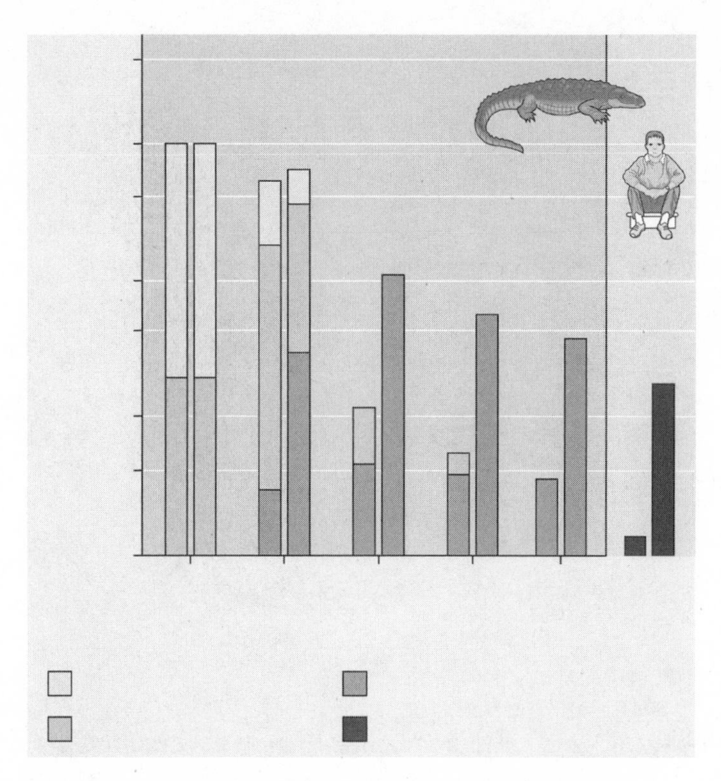

Figure 40.12 Maximum metabolic rates over different time spans, page 846

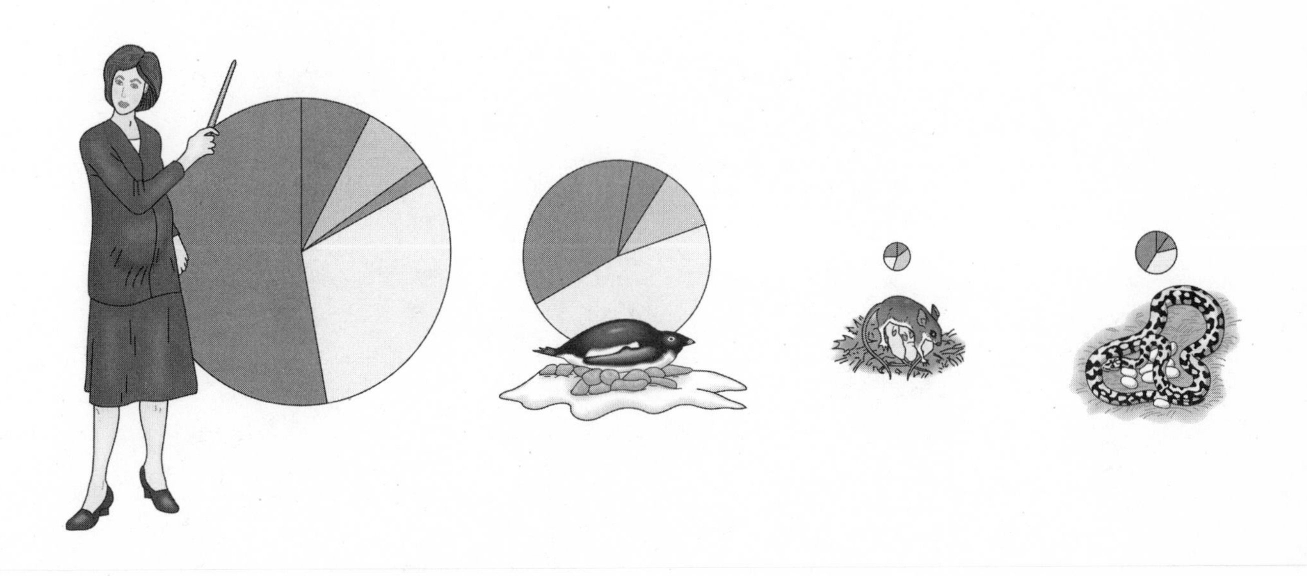

Figure 40.13a Annual energy budgets for four animals: Total annual energy expenditures, page 847

Figure 40.13b Annual energy budgets for four animals: Energy expenditure per unit mass, page 847

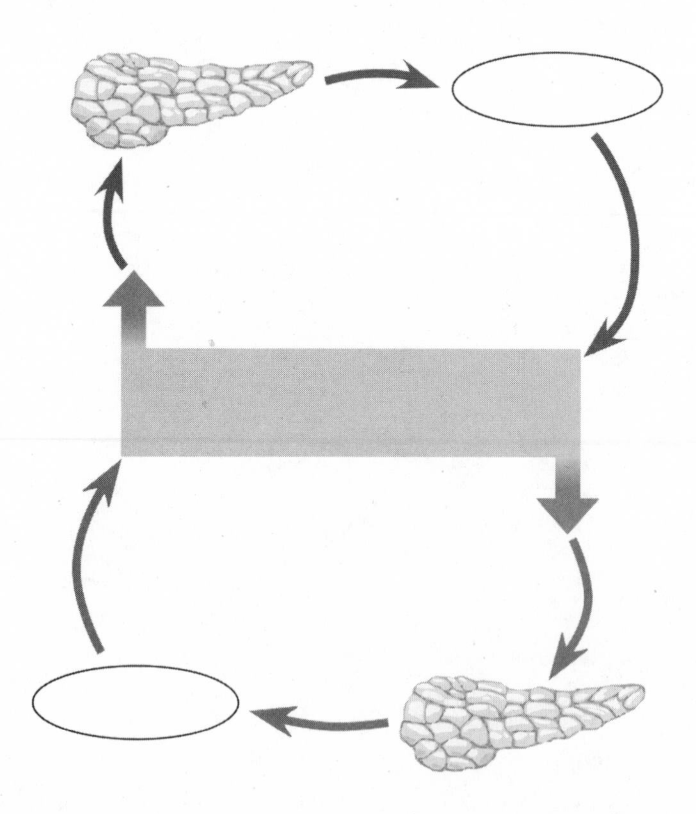

Figure 41.1 Homeostatic regulation of cellular fuel, page 851

Figure 41.4 Essential amino acids from a vegetarian diet, page 853

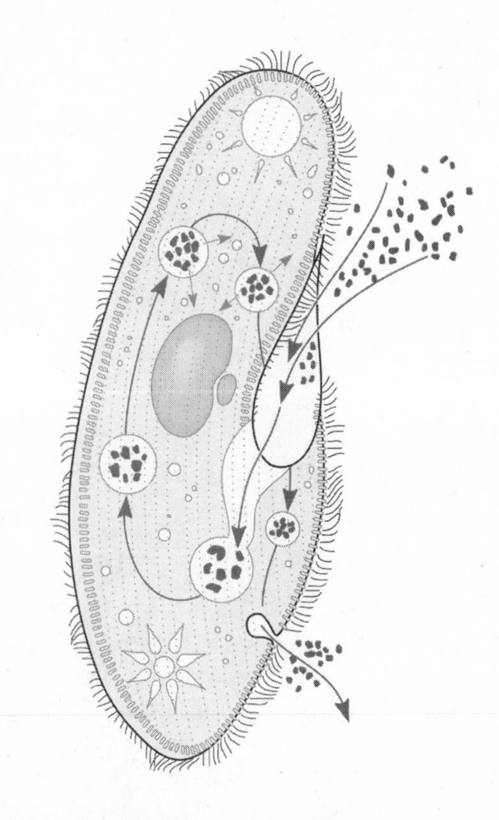

Figure 41.10 Intracellular digestion in *Paramecium*, page 858

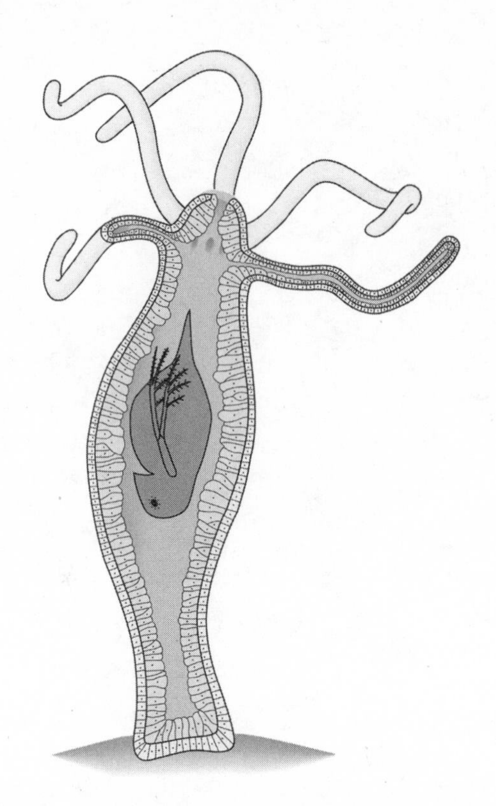

Figure 41.11 Extracellular digestion in a gastrovascular cavity, page 859

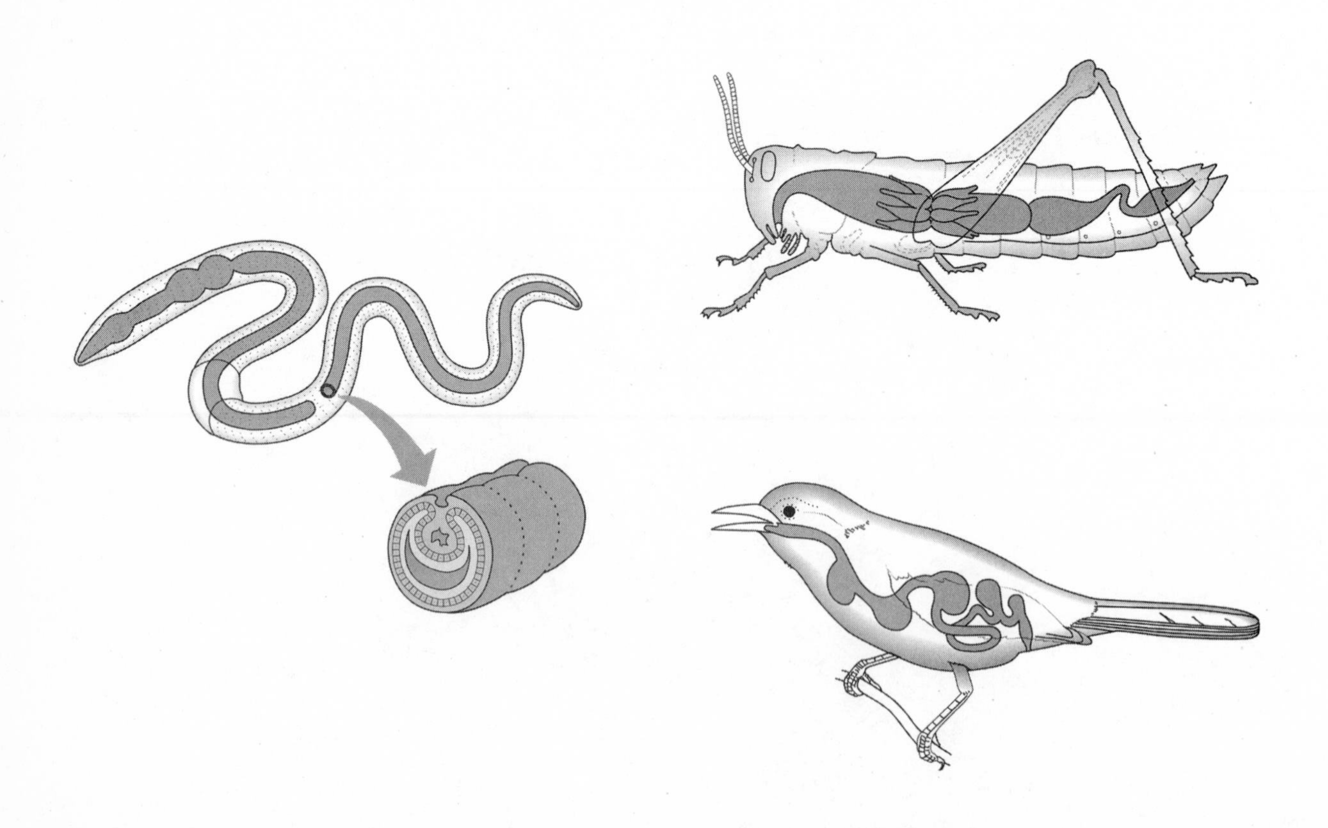

Figure 41.12 Alimentary canals, page 859

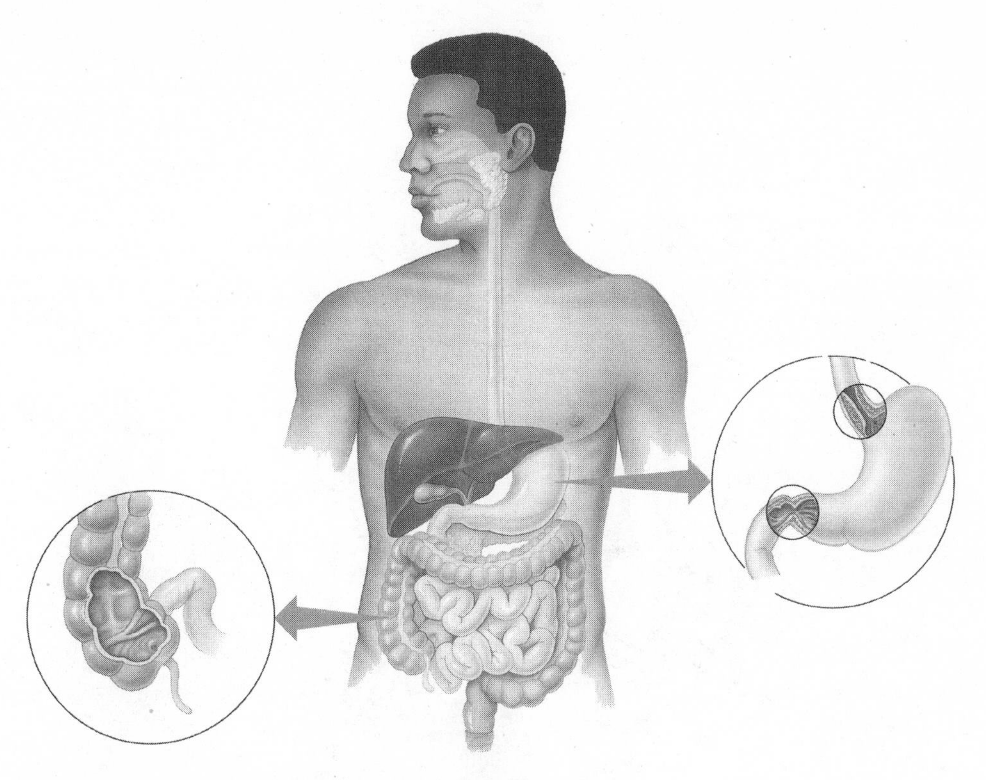

Figure 41.13 The human digestive system, page 860

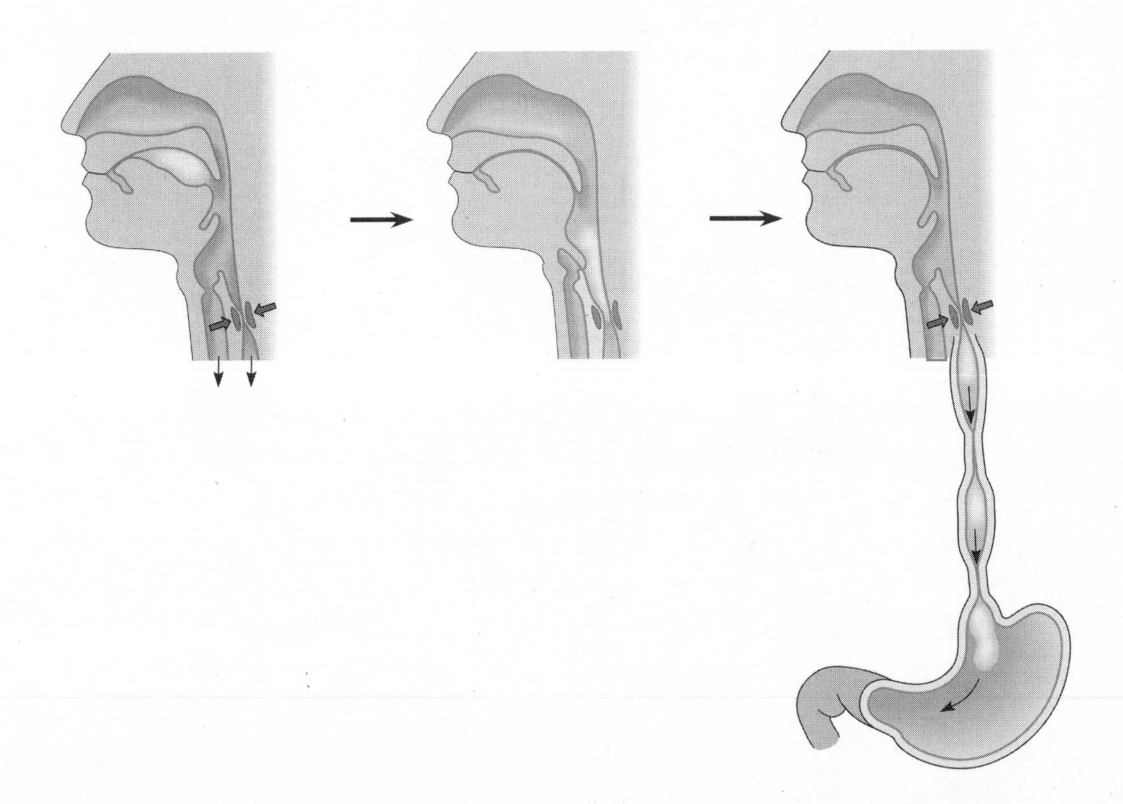

Figure 41.14 From mouth to stomach: the swallowing reflex and esophageal peristalsis, page 861

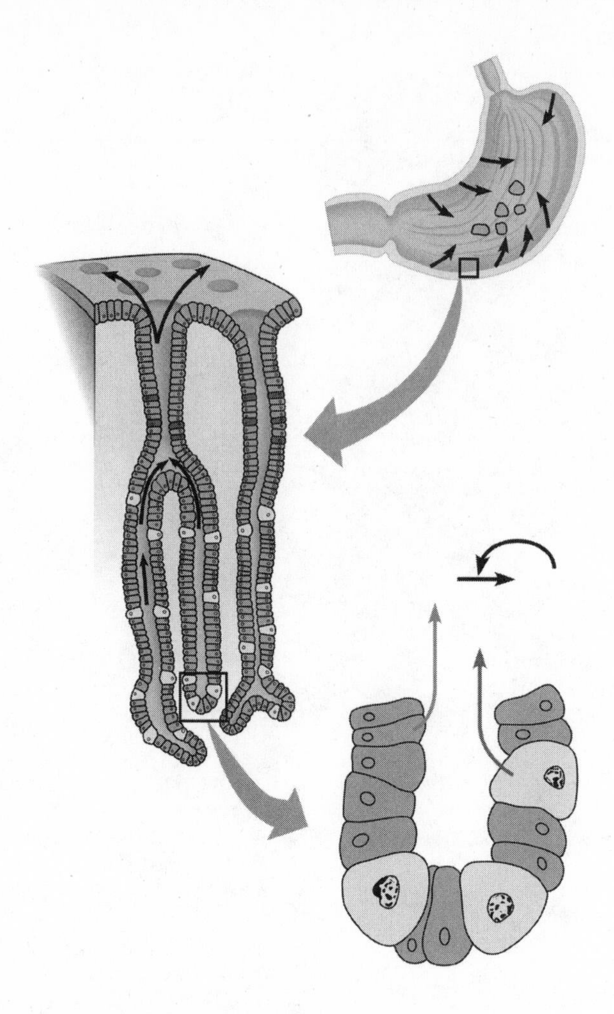

Figure 41.15 Secretion of gastric juice, page 862

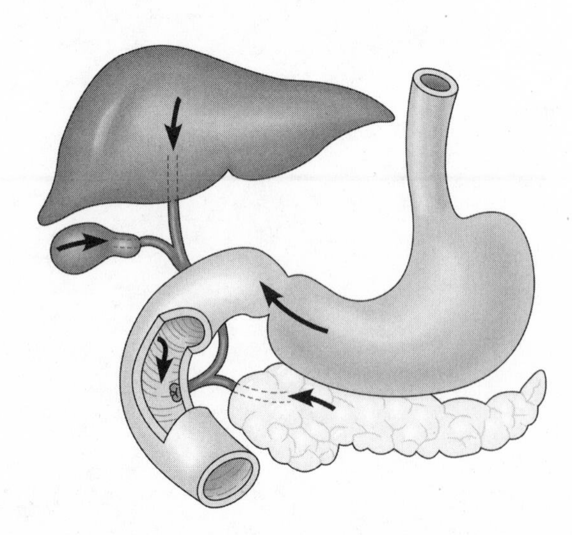

Figure 41.16 The duodenum, page 863

	(a) Carbohydrate digestion	(b) Protein digestion	(c) Nucleic acid digestion	(d) Fat digestion
Oral cavity, pharynx, esophagus	Polysaccharides (starch, glycogen) ↓ Salivary amylase Smaller polysaccharides, maltose			
Stomach		Proteins ↓ Pepsin Small polypeptides		
Lumen of small intestine	Polysaccharides ↓ Pancreatic amylases Maltose and other disaccharides	Polypeptides ↓ Trypsin, Chymotrypsin Smaller polypeptides ↓ Aminopeptidase, Carboxypeptidase Amino acids	DNA, RNA ↓ Nucleases Nucleotides	Fat globules ↓ Bile salts Fat droplets (emulsified) ↓ Lipase Glycerol, fatty acids, glycerides
Epithelium of small intestine (brush border)	↓ Disaccharidases Monosaccharides	Small peptides ↓ Dipeptidases Amino acids	↓ Nucleotidases Nucleosides ↓ Nucleosidases Nitrogenous bases, sugars, phosphates	

Figure 41.17 Enzymatic digestion in the human digestive system, page 864

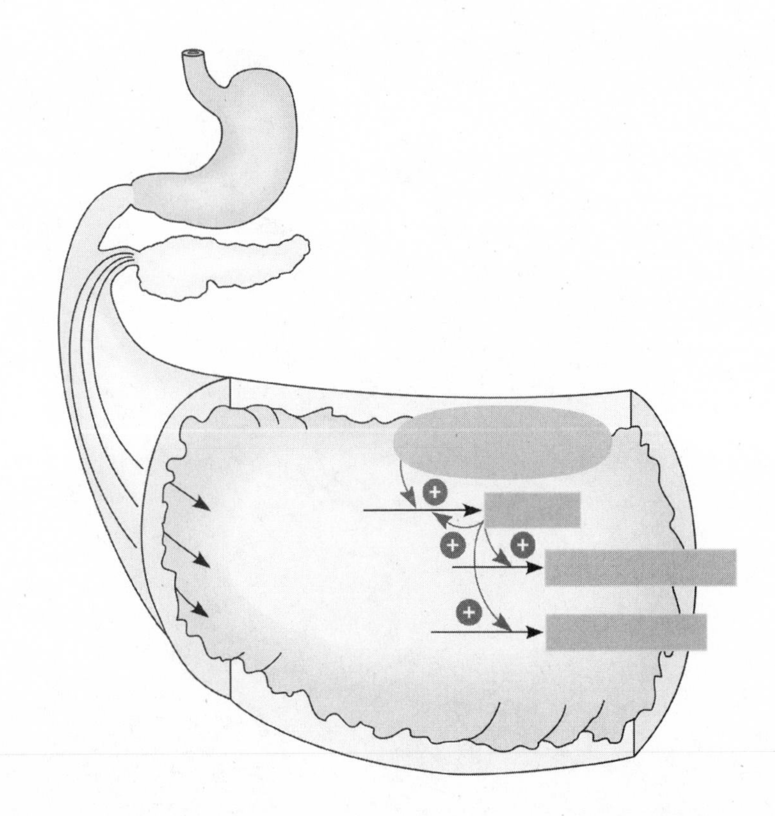

Figure 41.18 Activation of protein-digesting enzymes in the small intestine, page 864

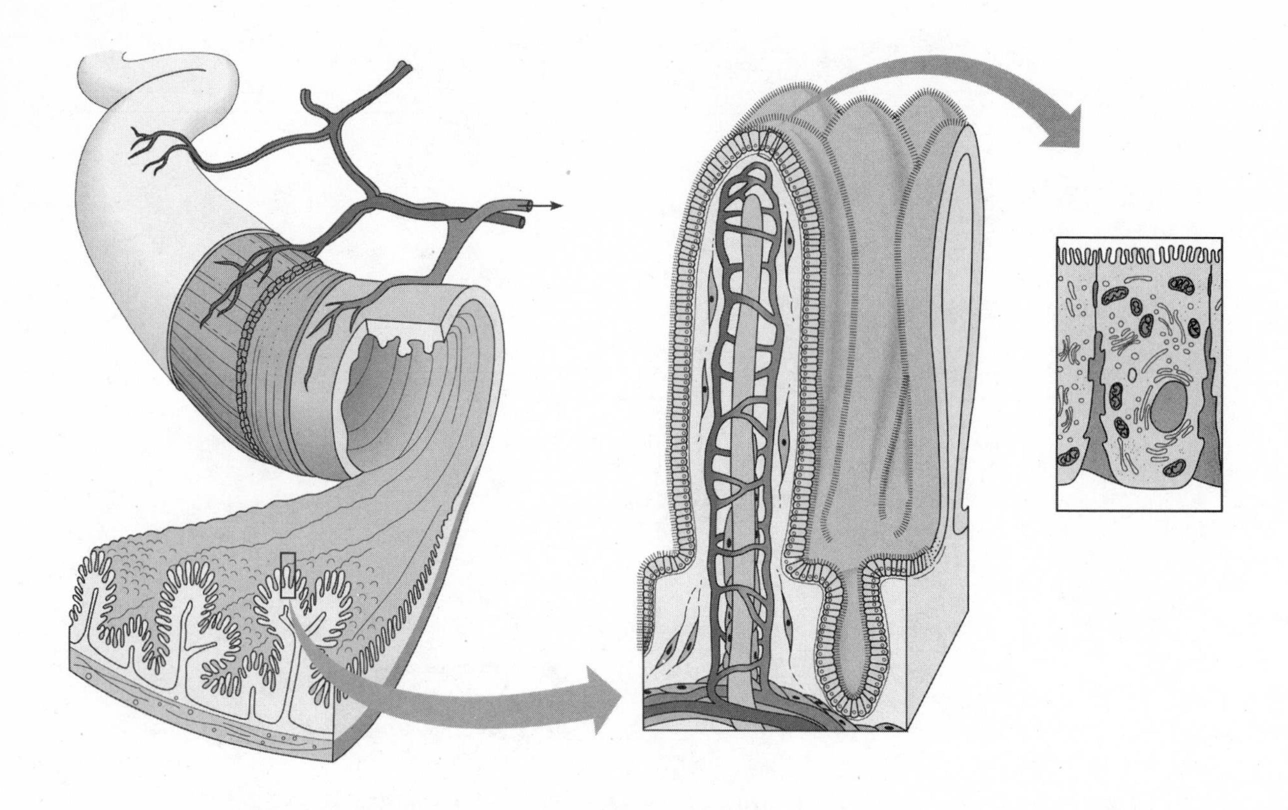

Figure 41.19 The structure of the small intestine, page 865

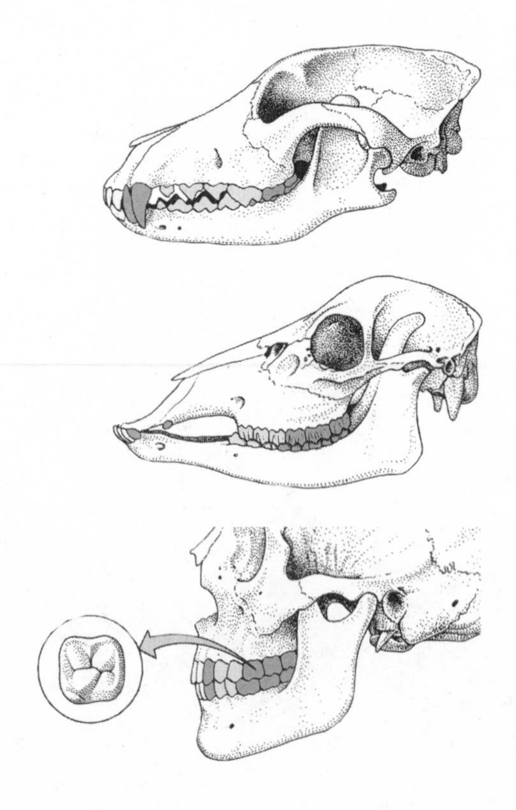

Figure 41.20 Dentition and diet, page 867

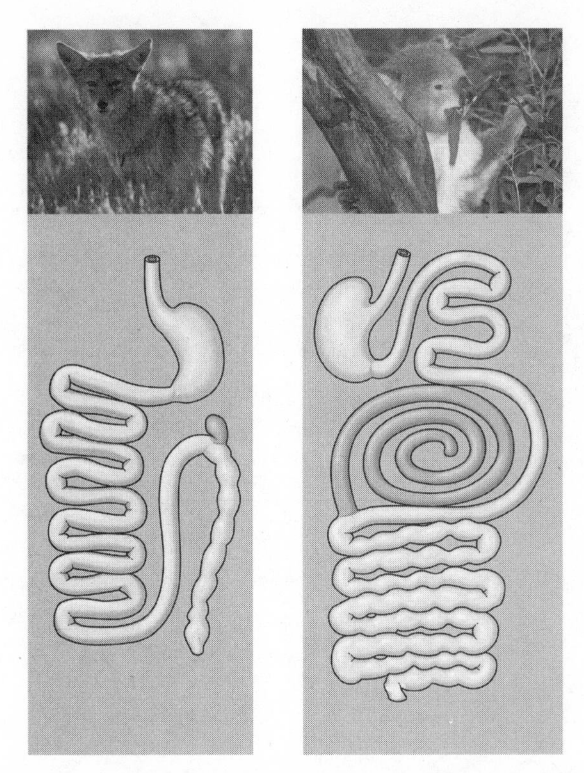

Figure 41.21 The digestive tracts of a carnivore (coyote) and a herbivore (koala) compared, page 867

Figure 41.22 Ruminant digestion, page 868

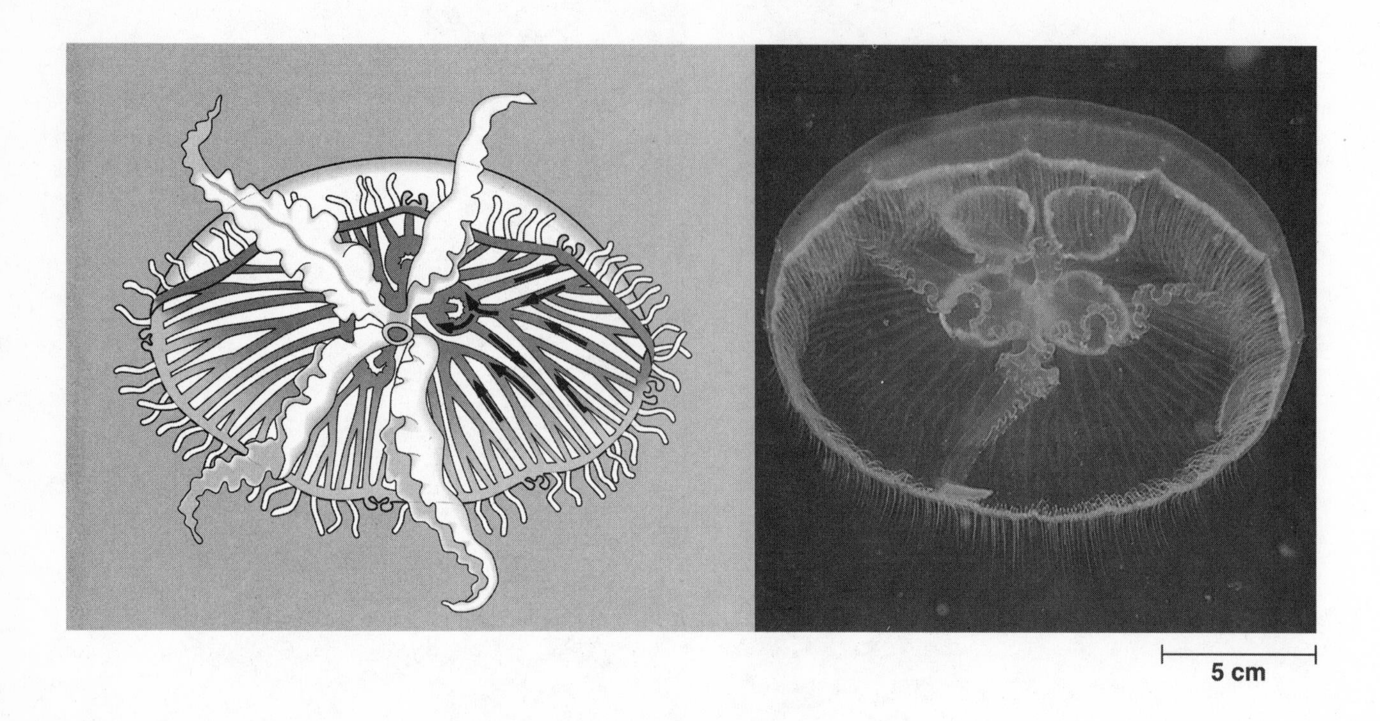

Figure 42.1 Internal transport in the cnidarian *Aurelia*, page 872

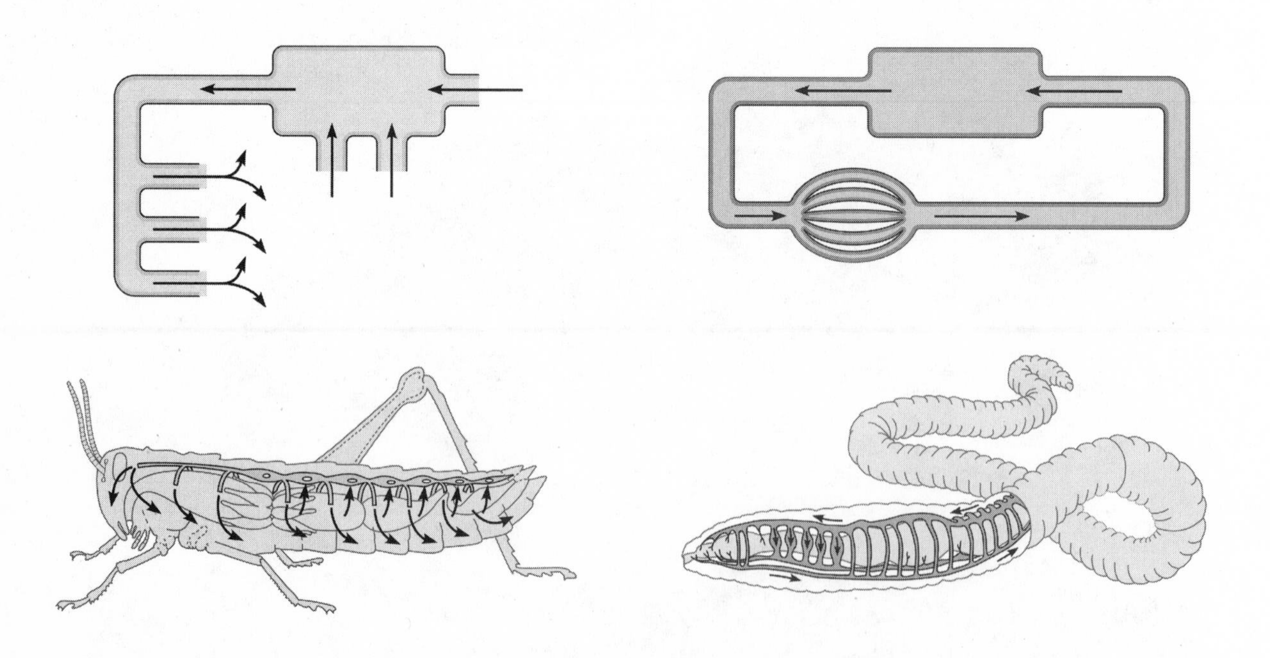

Figure 42.2 Open and closed circulatory systems, page 873

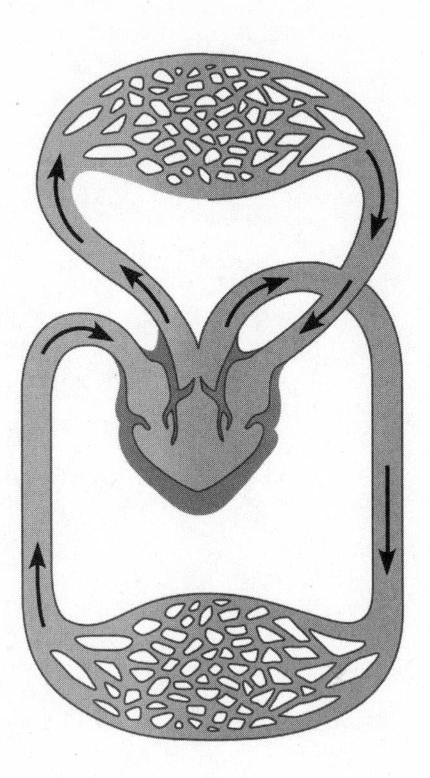

Figure 42.3 Generalized circulatory schemes of vertebrates, page 874

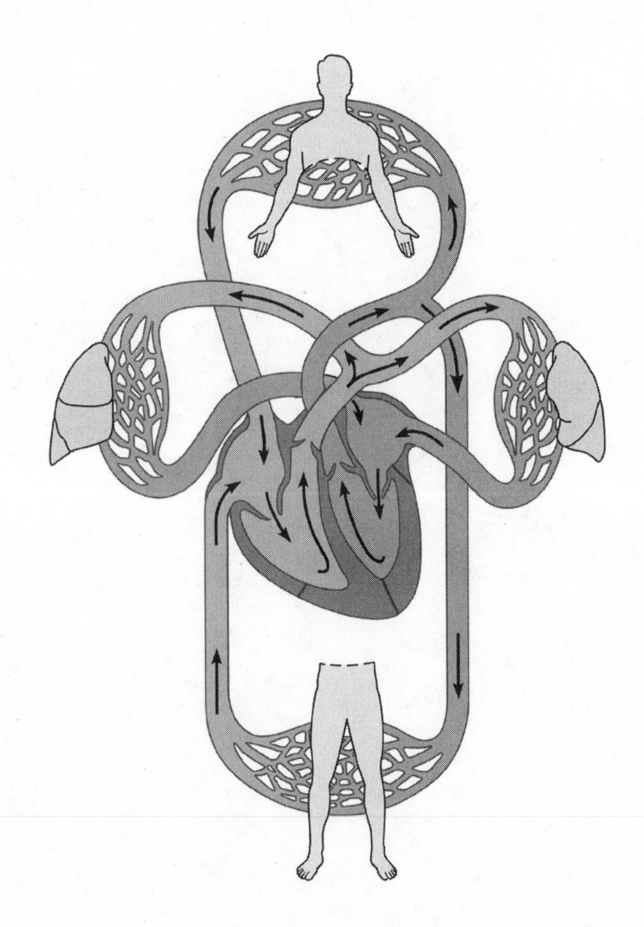

Figure 42.4 The mammalian cardiovascular system: an overview, page 875

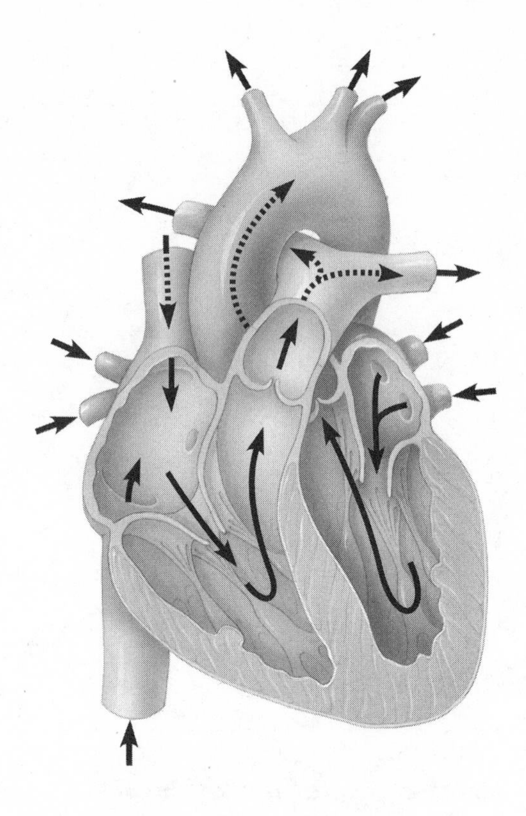

Figure 42.5 The mammalian heart: a closer look, page 876

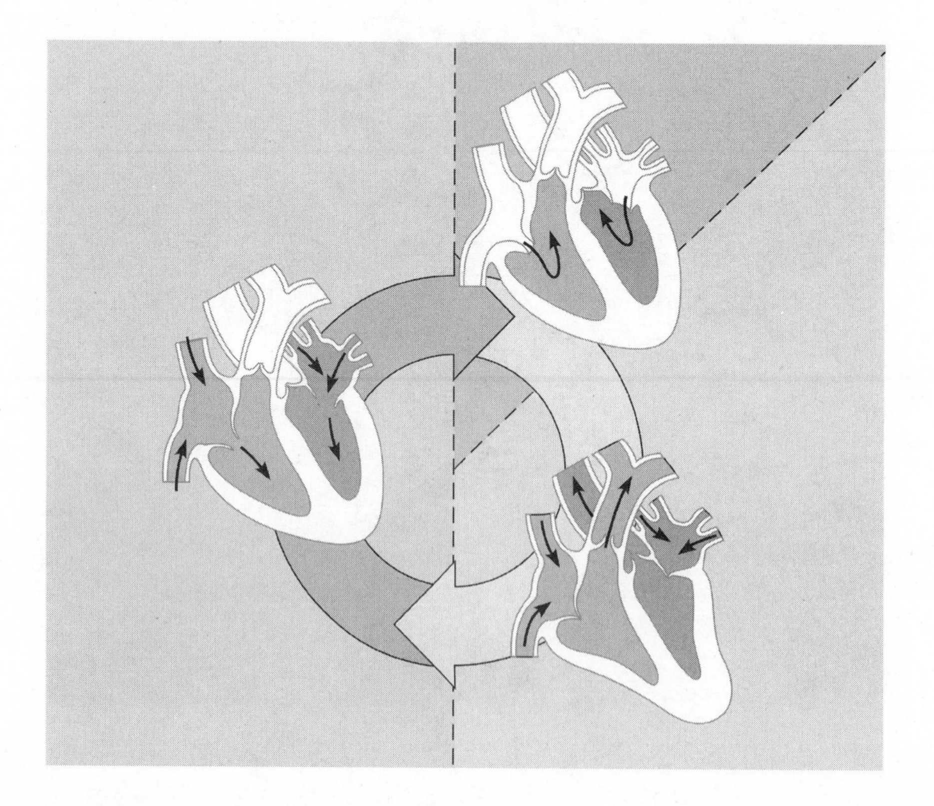

Figure 42.6 The cardiac cycle, page 876

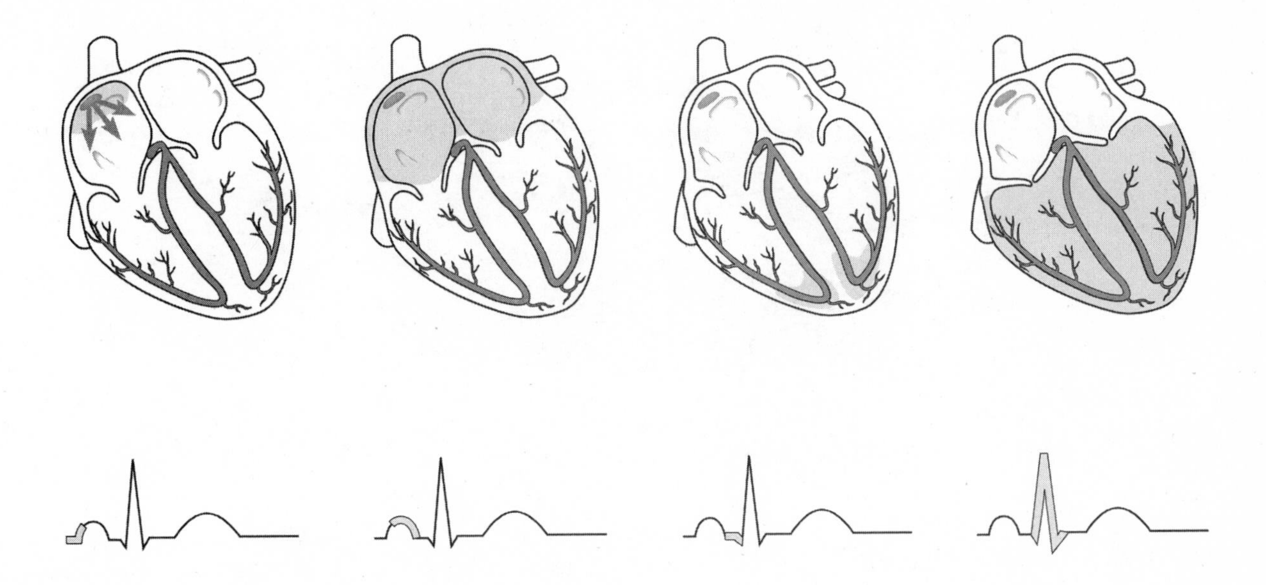

Figure 42.7 The control of heart rhythm, page 877

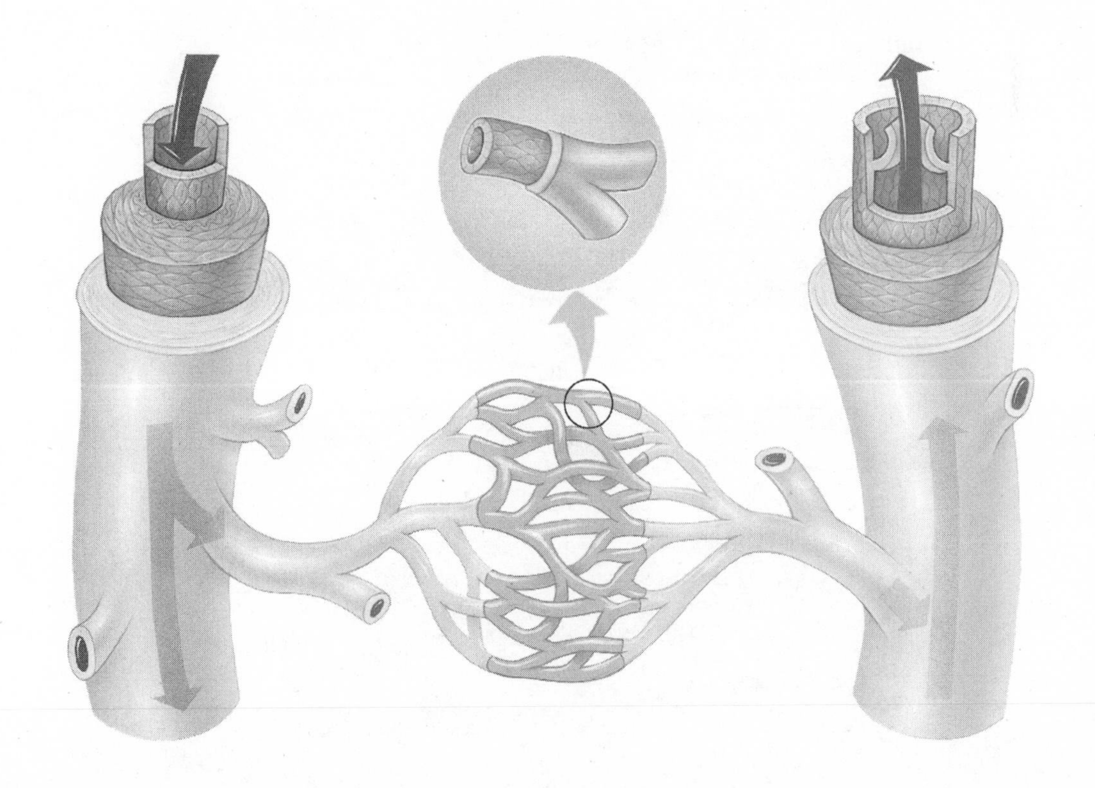

Figure 42.8 The structure of blood vessels, page 878

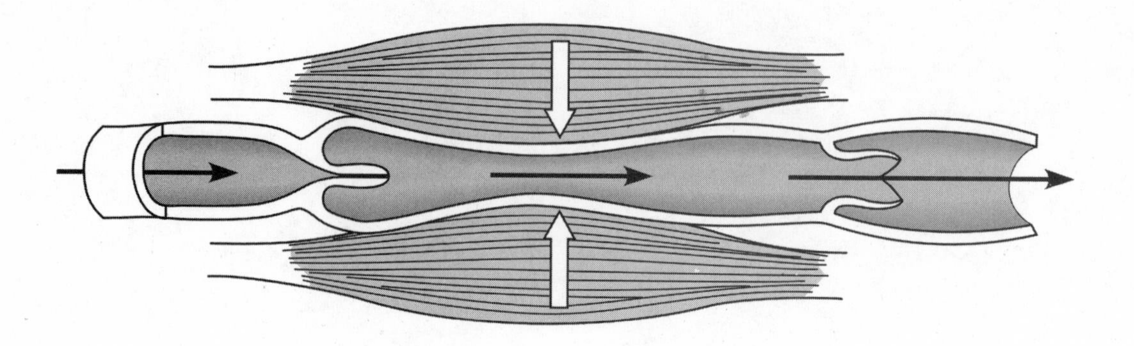

Figure 42.9 Blood flow in veins, page 878

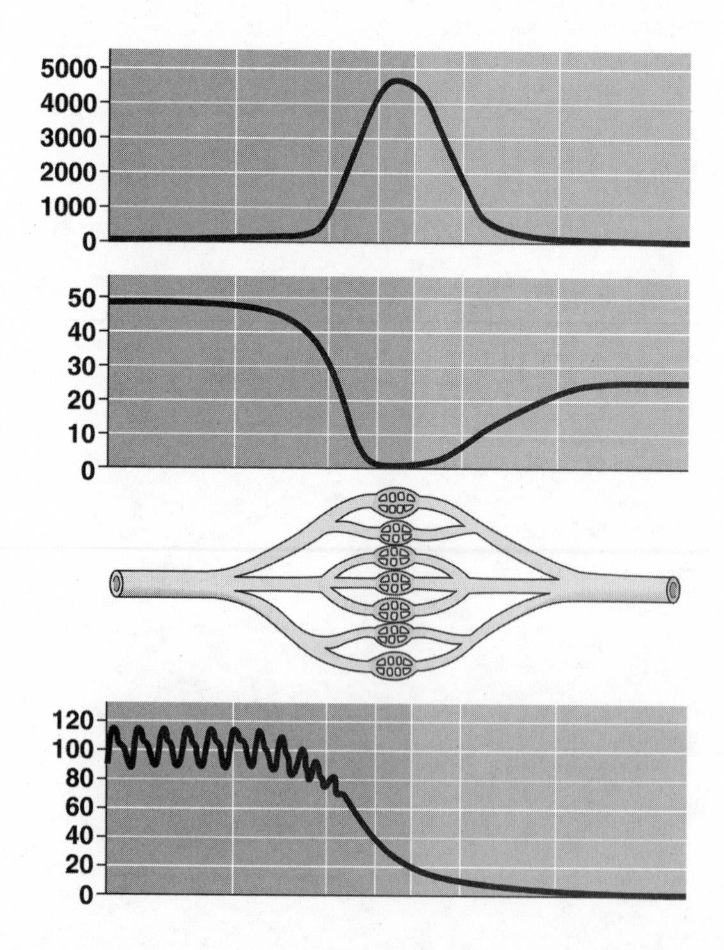

Figure 42.10 The interrelationship of blood flow velocity, cross-sectional area of blood vessels, and blood pressure, page 879

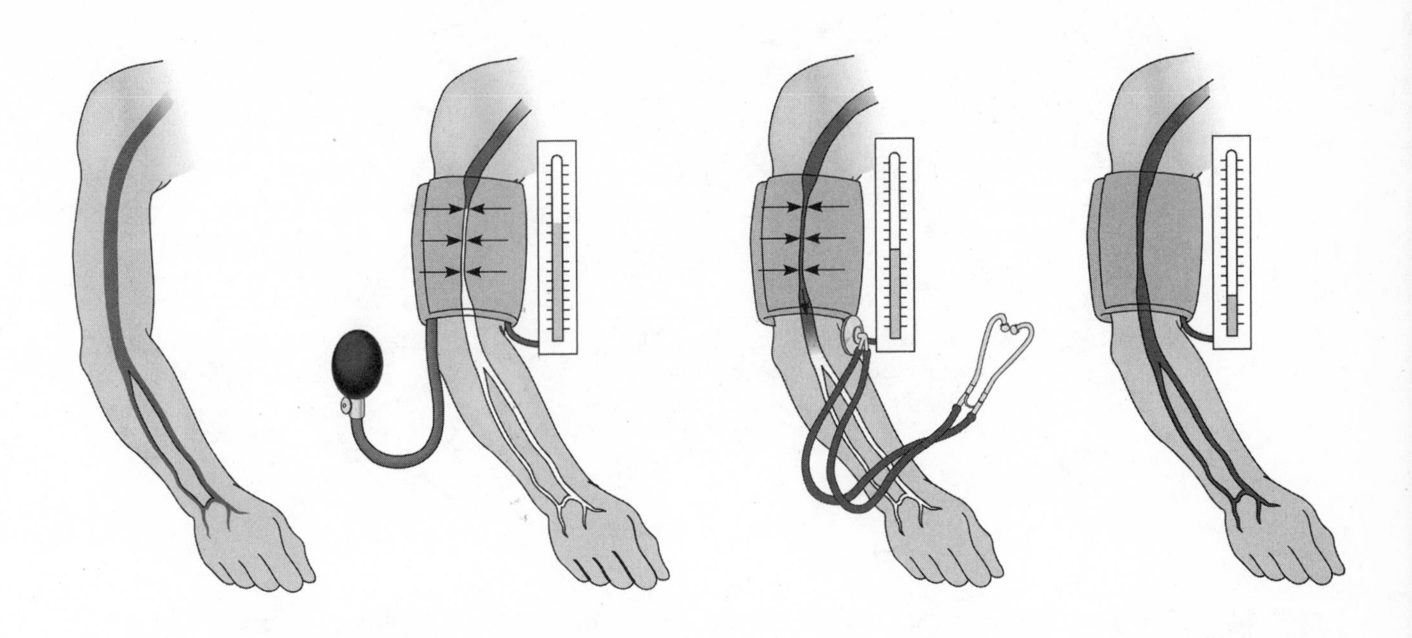

Figure 42.11 Measurement of blood pressure, page 880

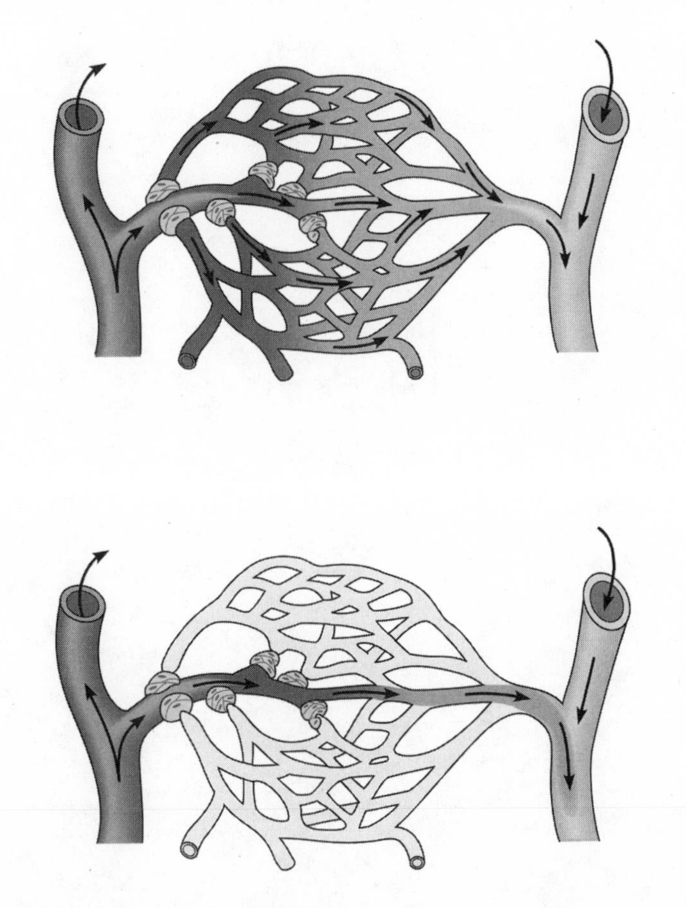

Figure 42.12 Blood flow in capillary beds, page 881

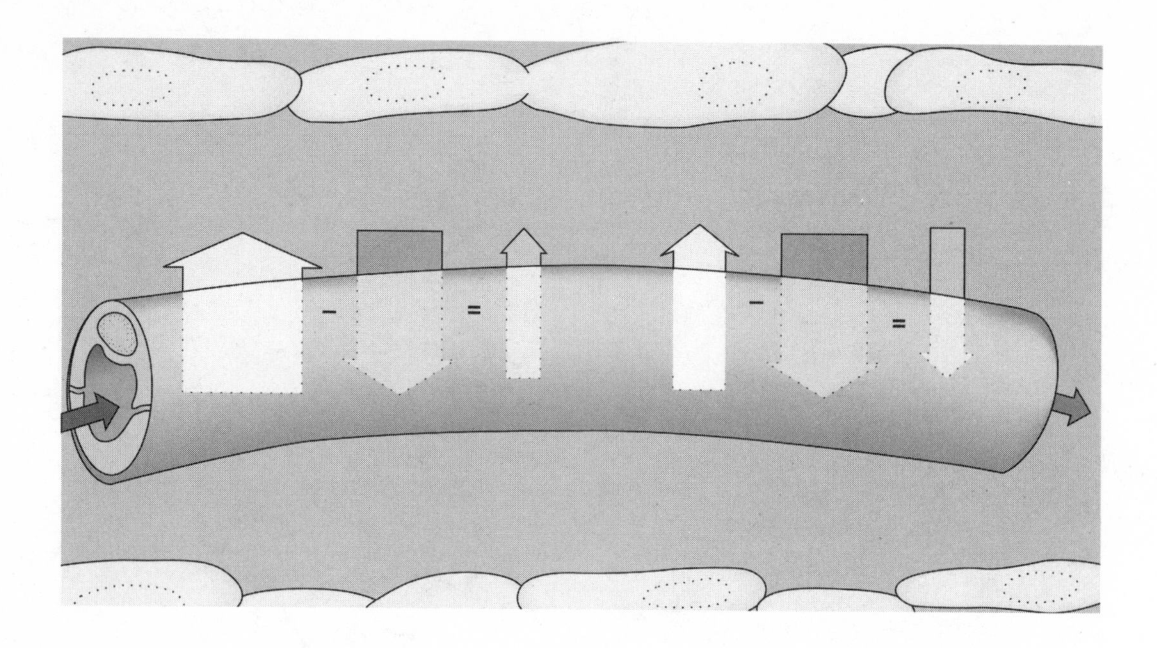

Figure 42.13 The movement of fluid between capillaries and the interstitial fluid, page 881

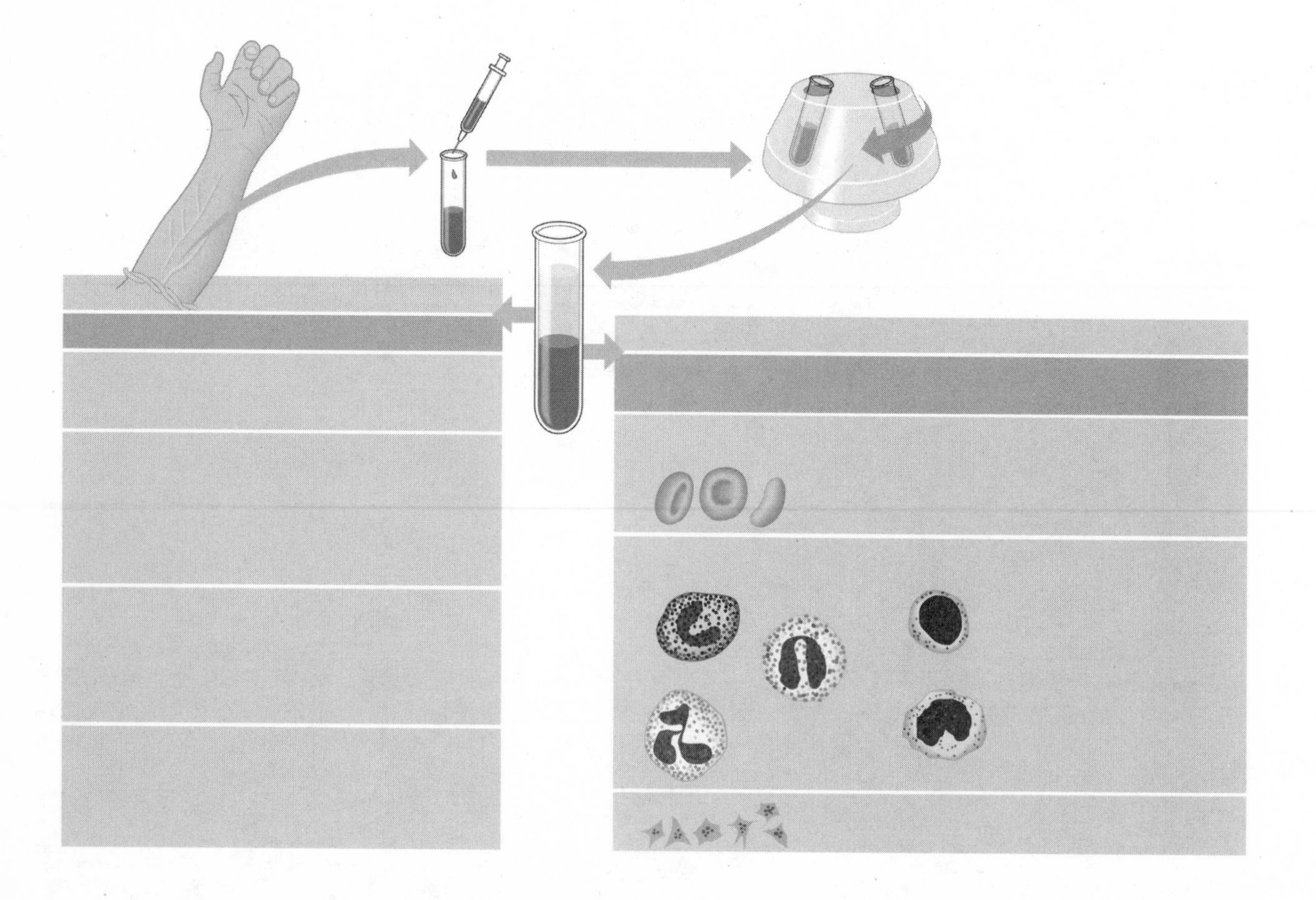

Figure 42.14 The composition of mammalian blood, page 882

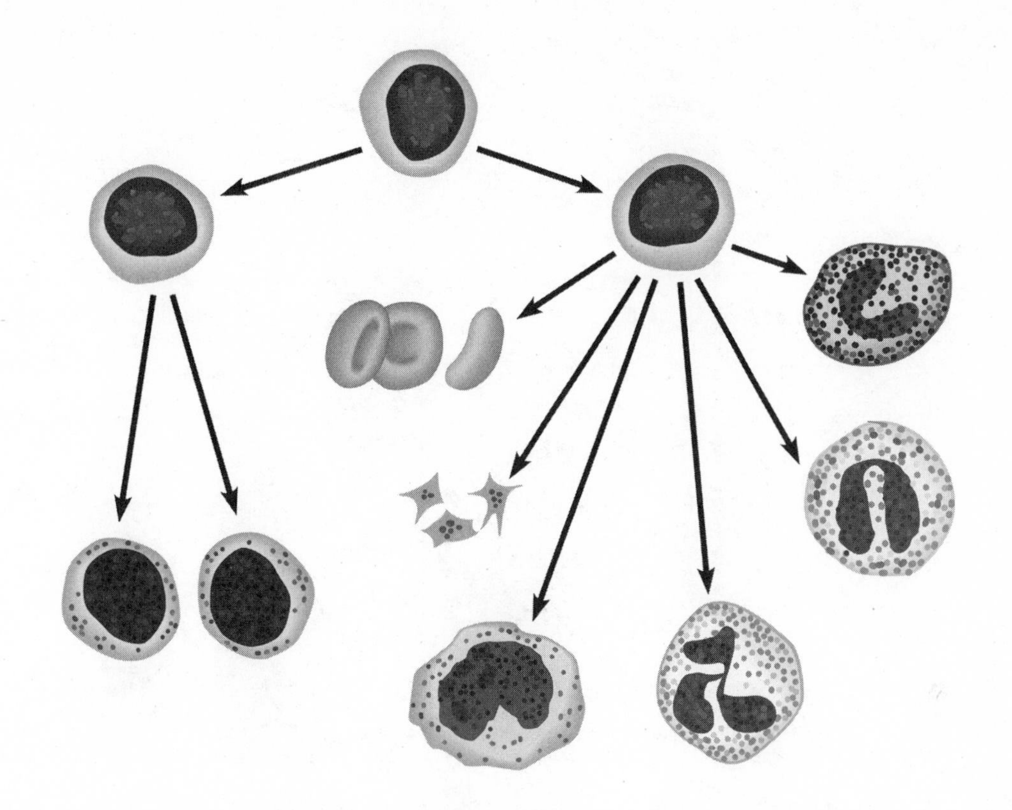

Figure 42.15 Differentiation of blood cells, page 884

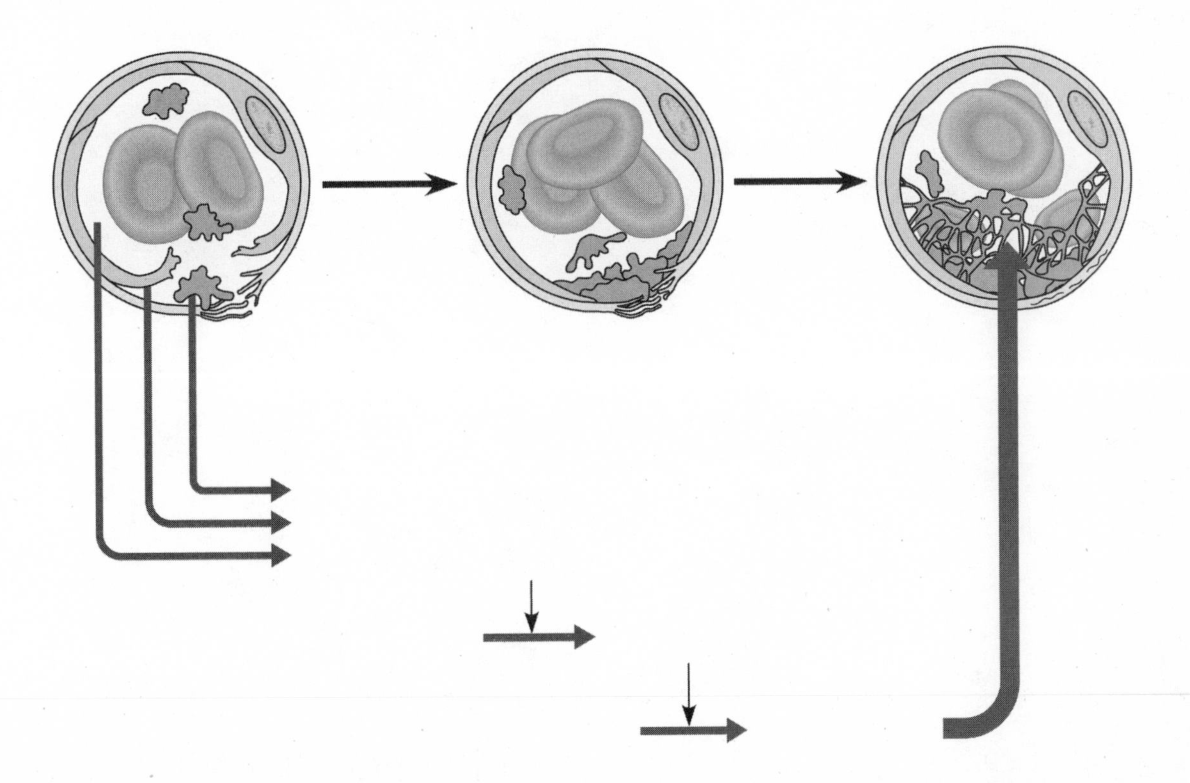

Figure 42.16 Blood clotting, page 885

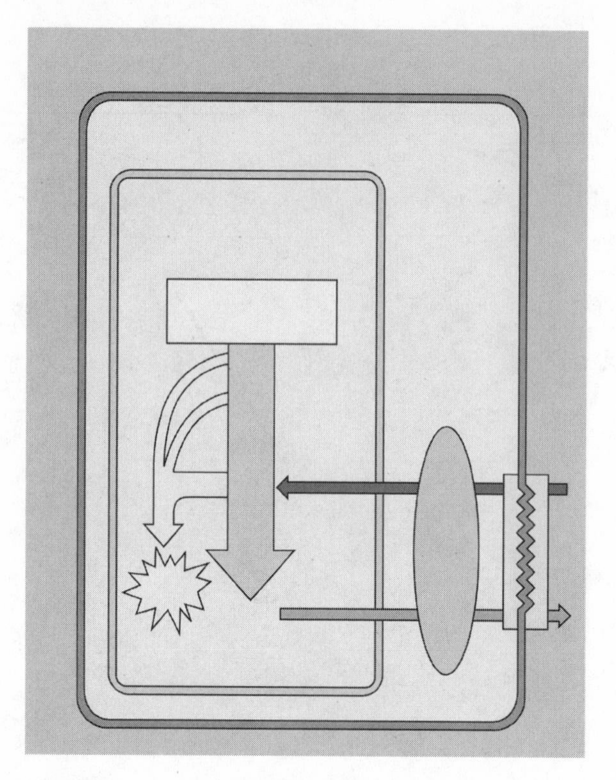

Figure 42.18 The role of gas exchange in bioenergetics, page 886

Figure 42.19 Diversity in the structure of gills, external body surfaces functioning in gas exchange, page 887

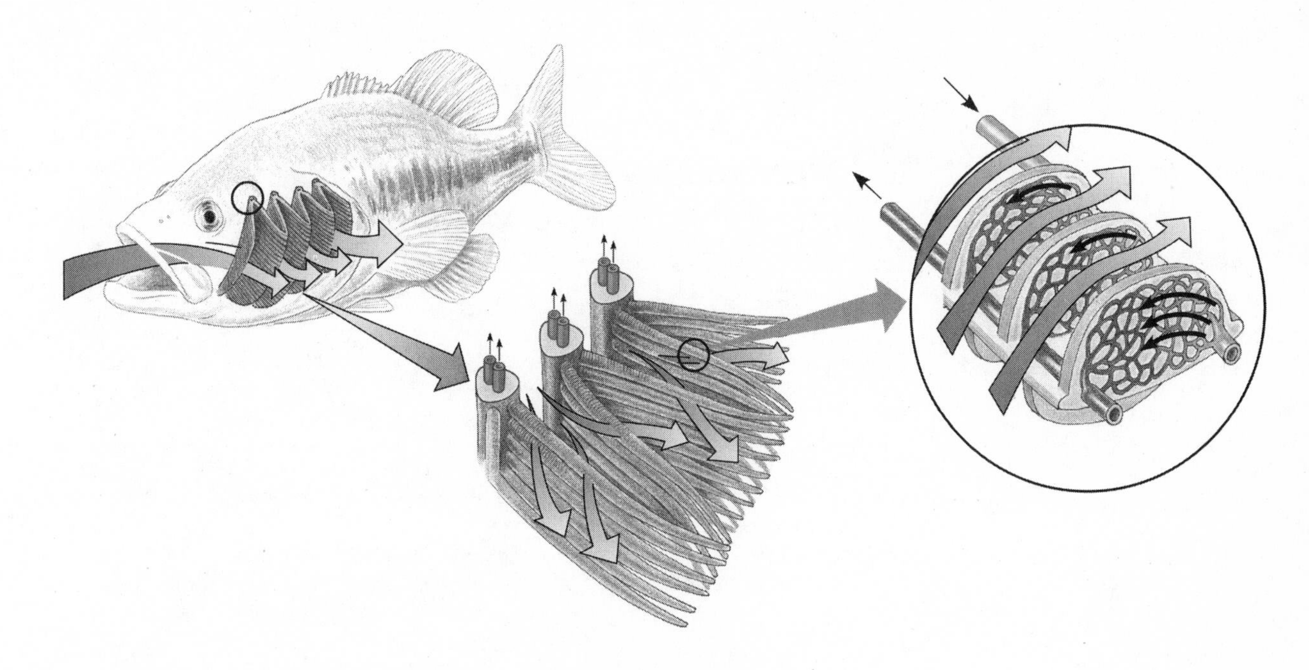

Figure 42.20 The structure and function of fish gills, page 888

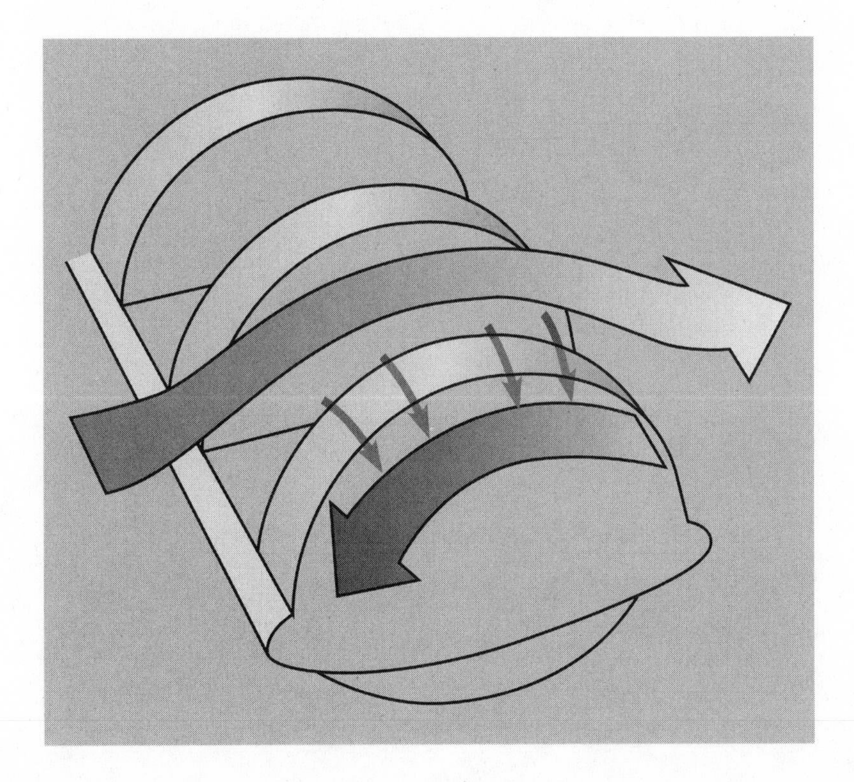

Figure 42.21 Countercurrent exchange, page 888

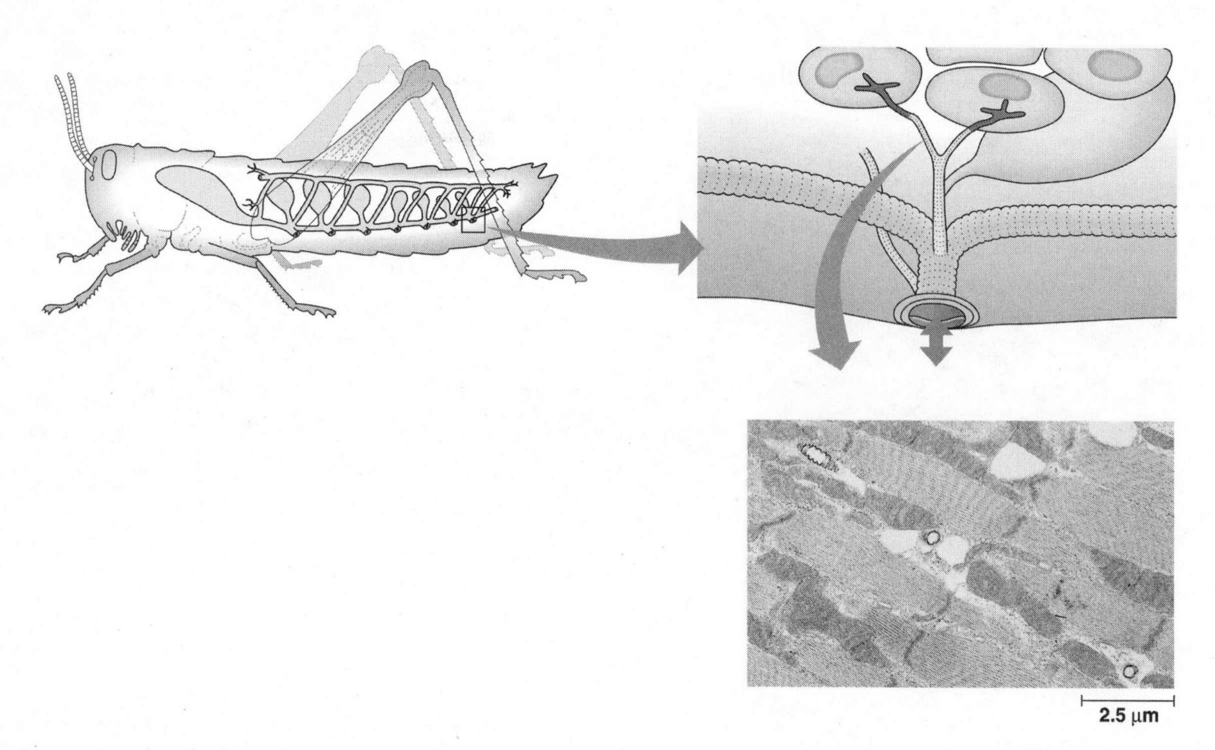

Figure 42.22 Tracheal systems, page 889

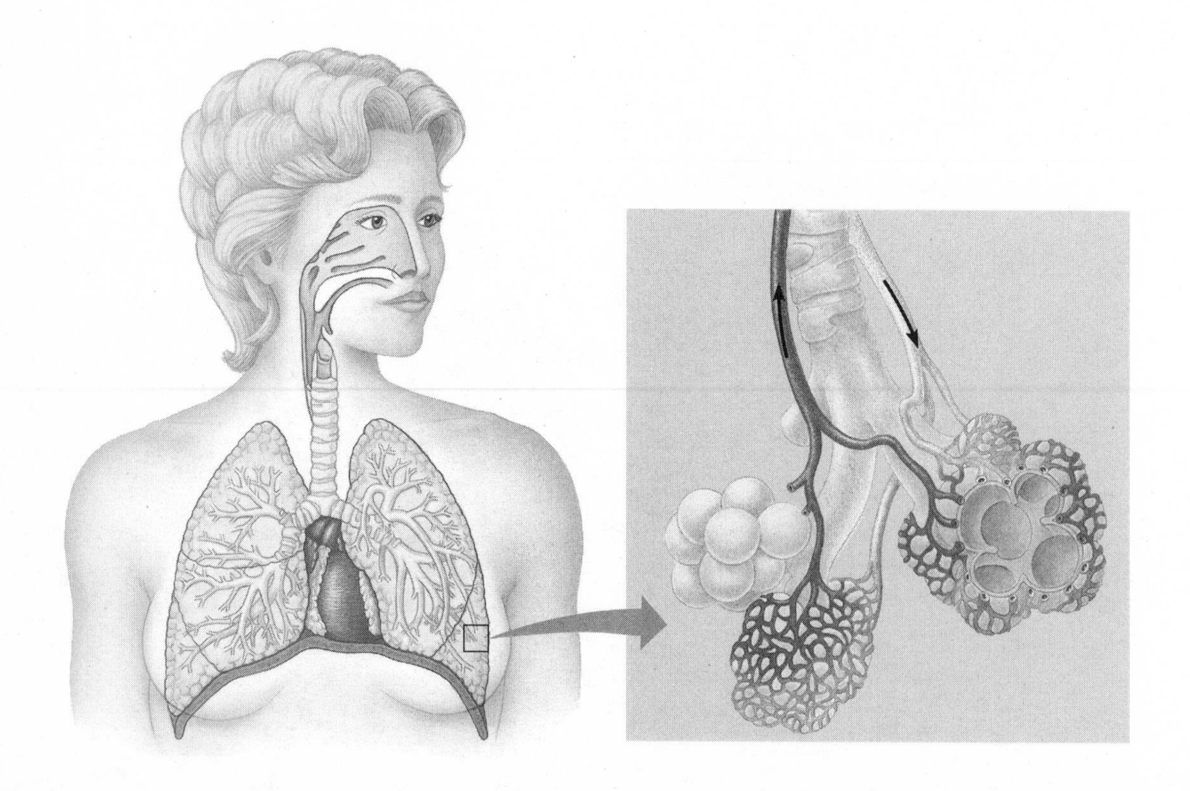

Figure 42.23 The mammalian respiratory system, page 890

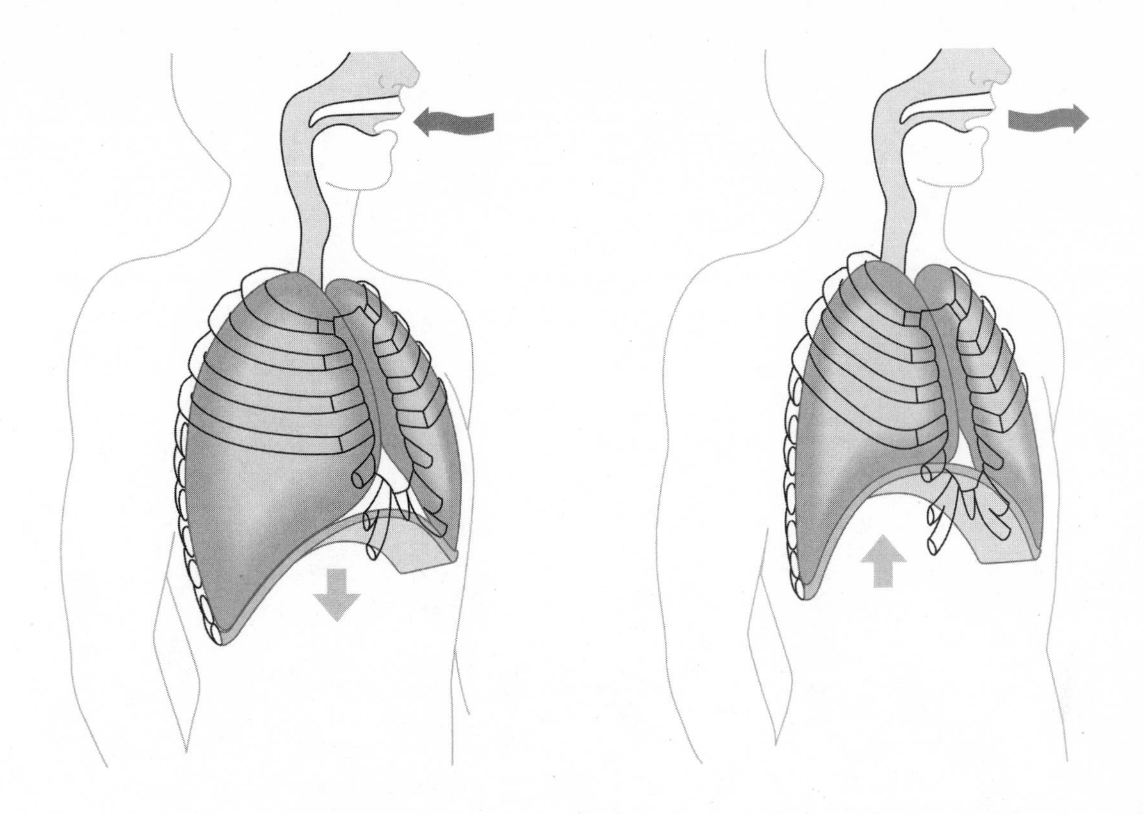

Figure 42.24 Negative pressure breathing, page 891

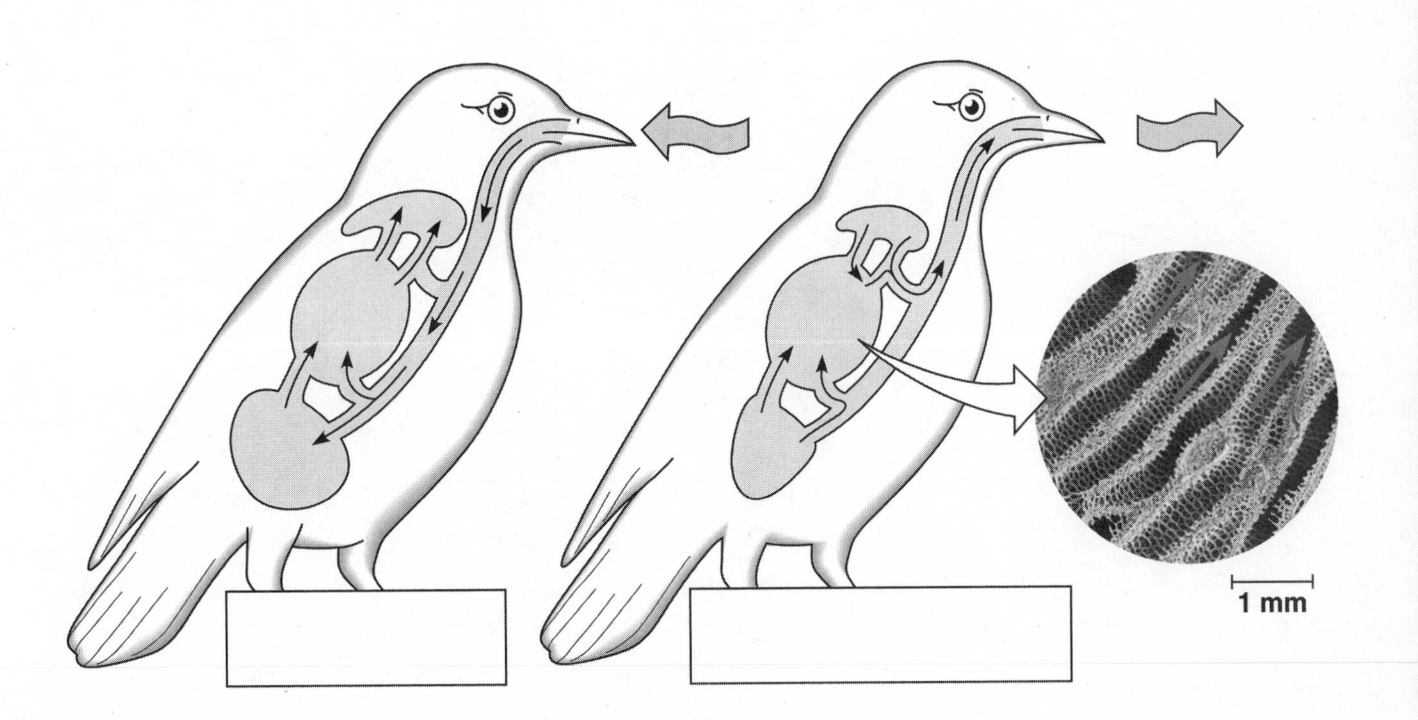

Figure 42.25 The avian respiratory system, page 892

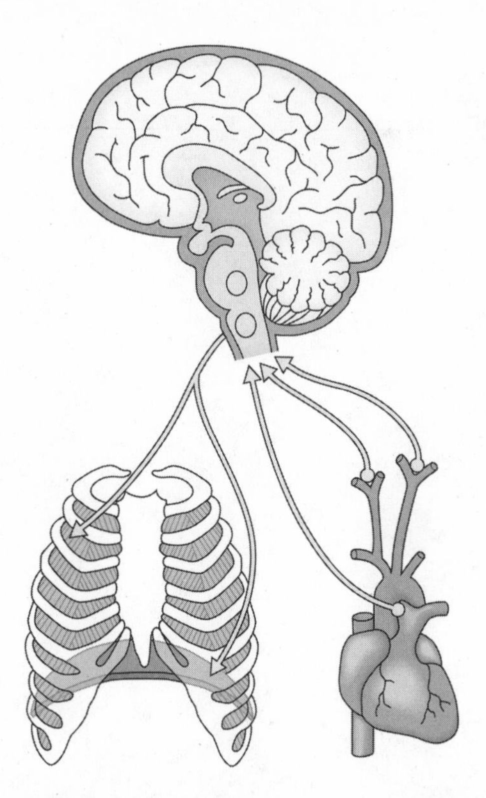

Figure 42.26 Automatic control of breathing, page 893

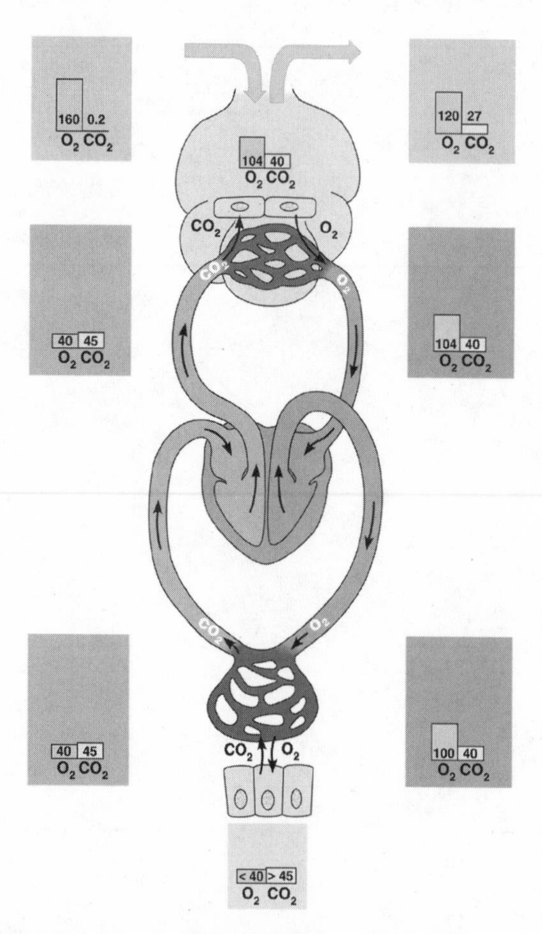

Figure 42.27 Loading and unloading of respiratory gases, page 894

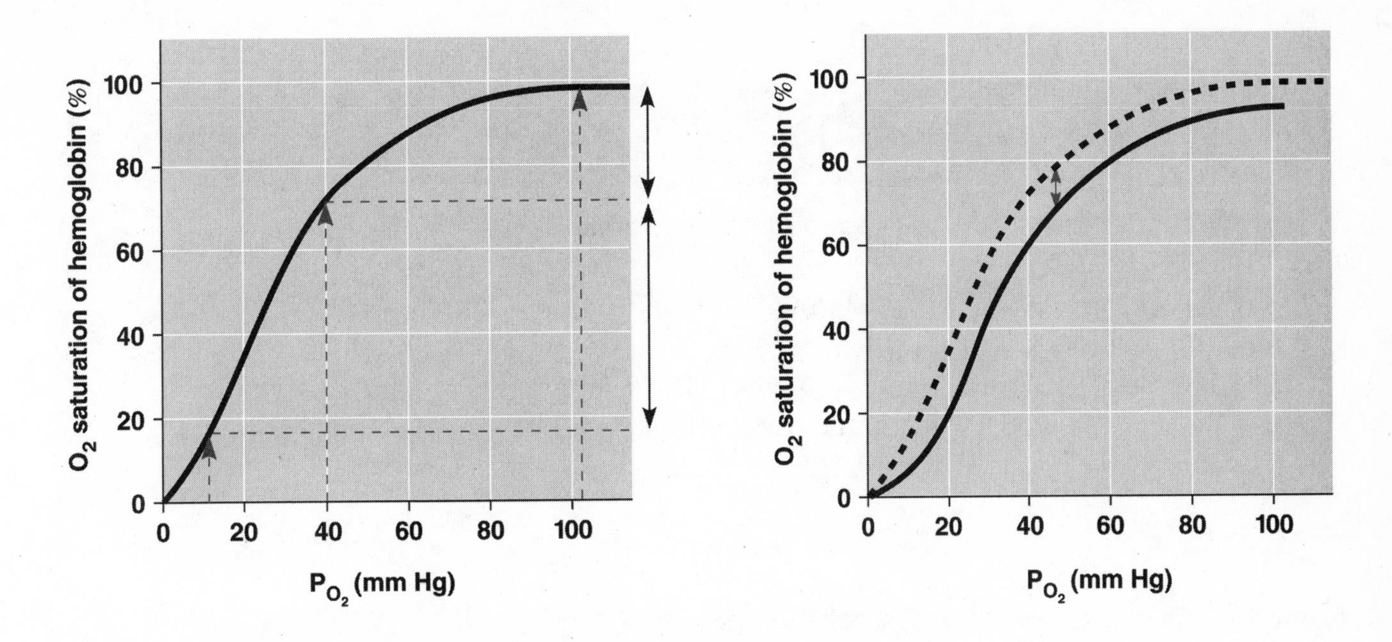

Figure 42.28 Oxygen dissociation curves for hemoglobin, page 895

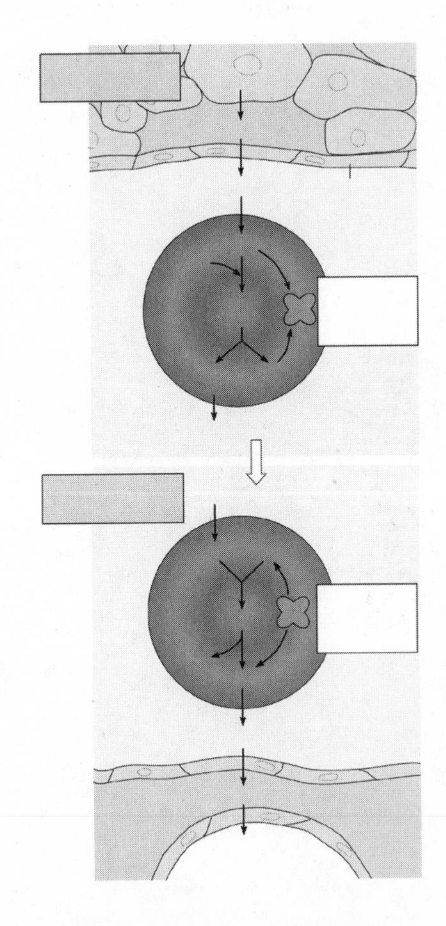

Figure 42.29 Carbon dioxide transport in the blood, page 896

Nonspecific defense mechanisms		Specific defense mechanisms (immune system)
First line of defense	**Second line of defense**	**Third line of defense**
• Skin • Mucous membranes • Secretions of skin and mucous membranes	• Phagocytic white blood cells • Antimicrobial proteins • The inflammatory response	• Lymphocytes • Antibodies

Figure 43.1 An overview of the body's defenses, page 901

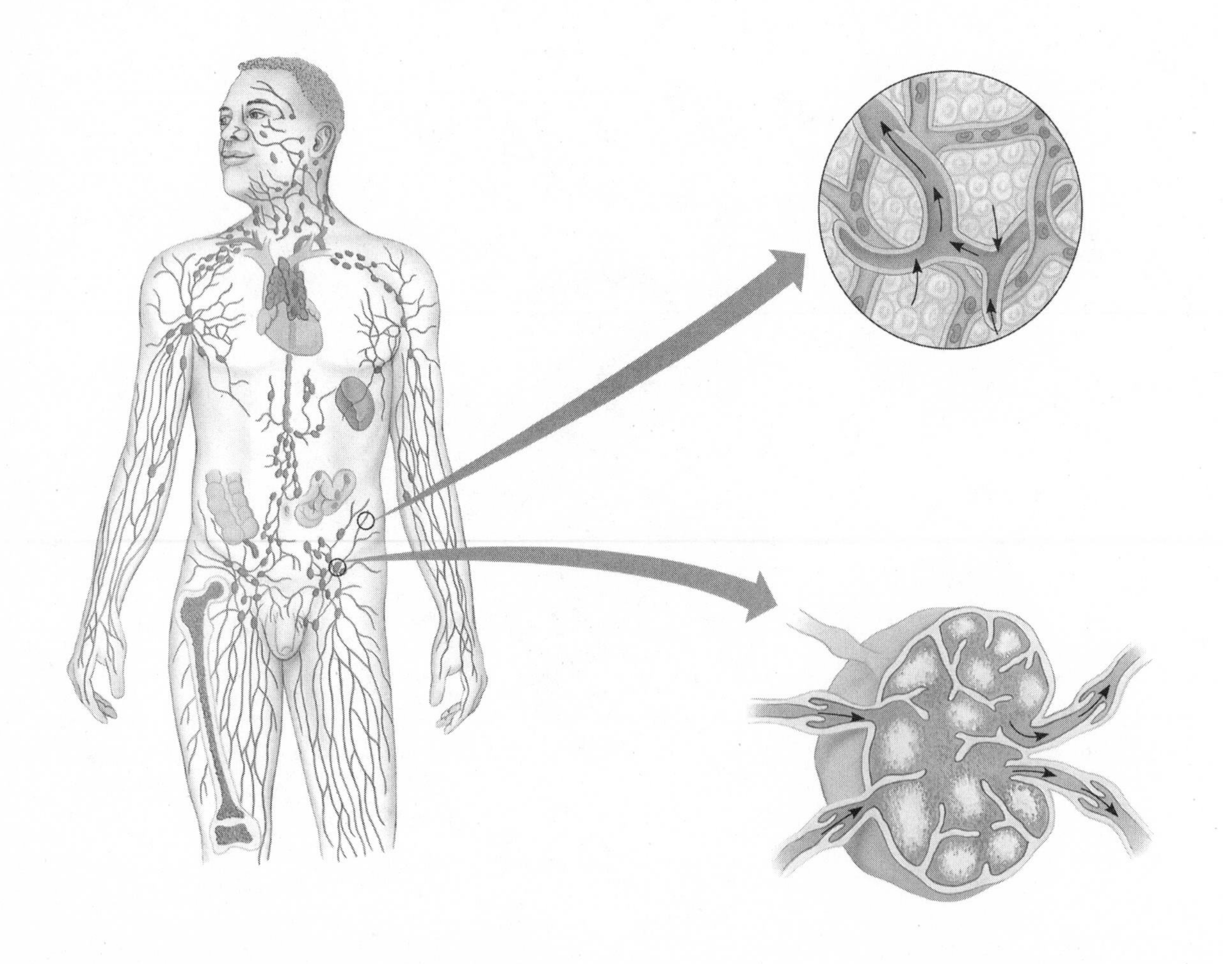

Figure 43.4 The human lymphatic system, page 902

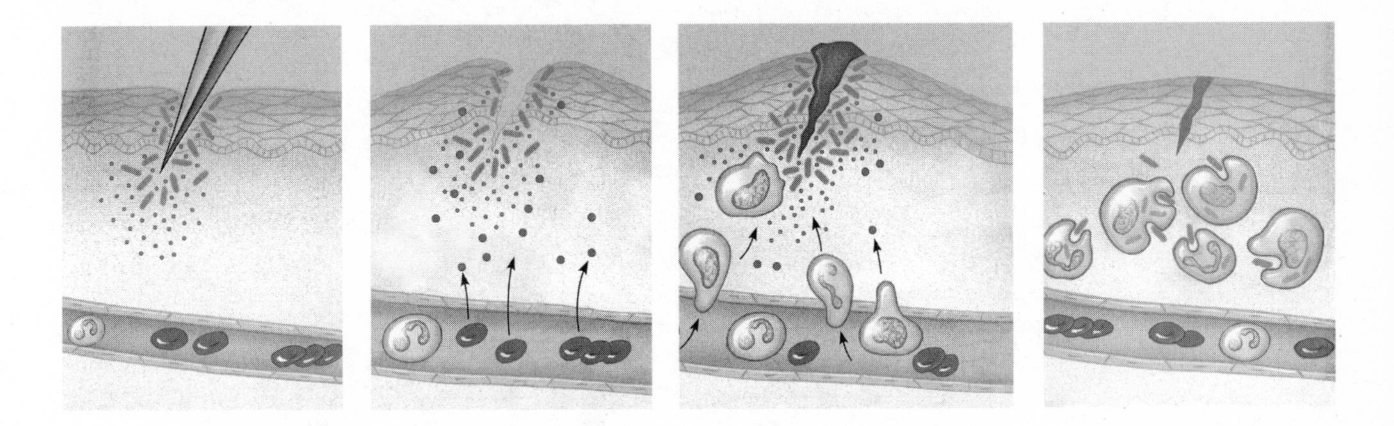

Figure 43.5 A simplified view of the inflammatory response, page 903

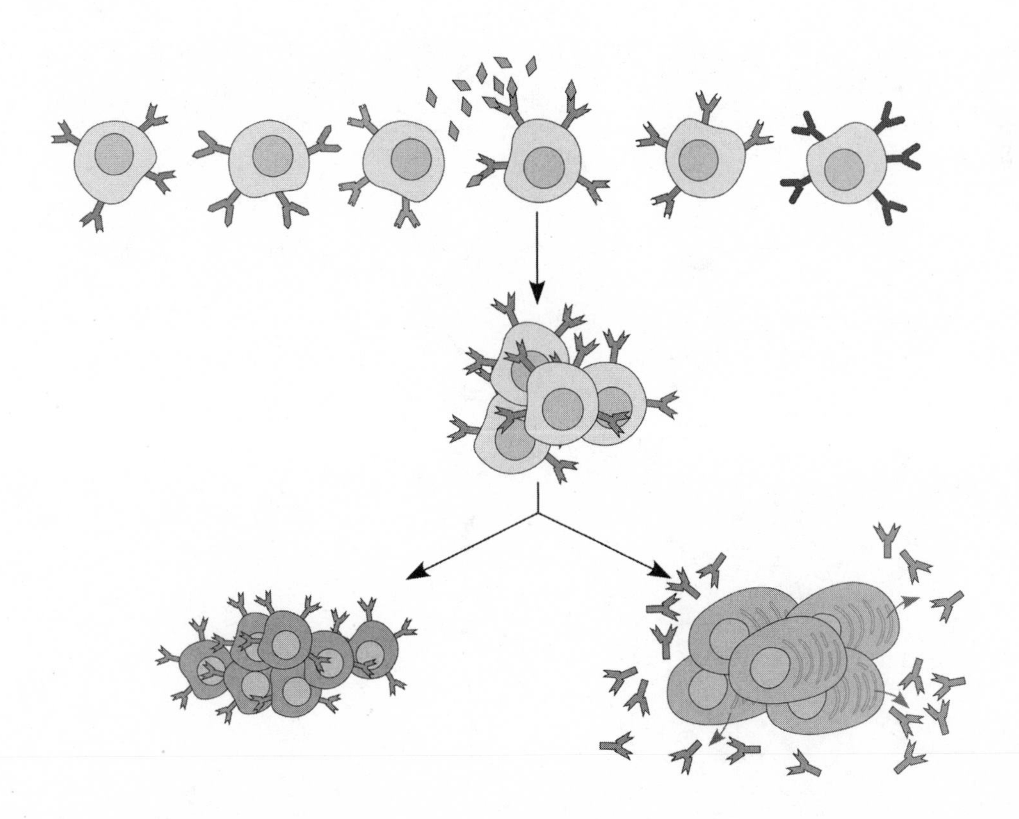

Figure 43.6 Clonal selection, page 905

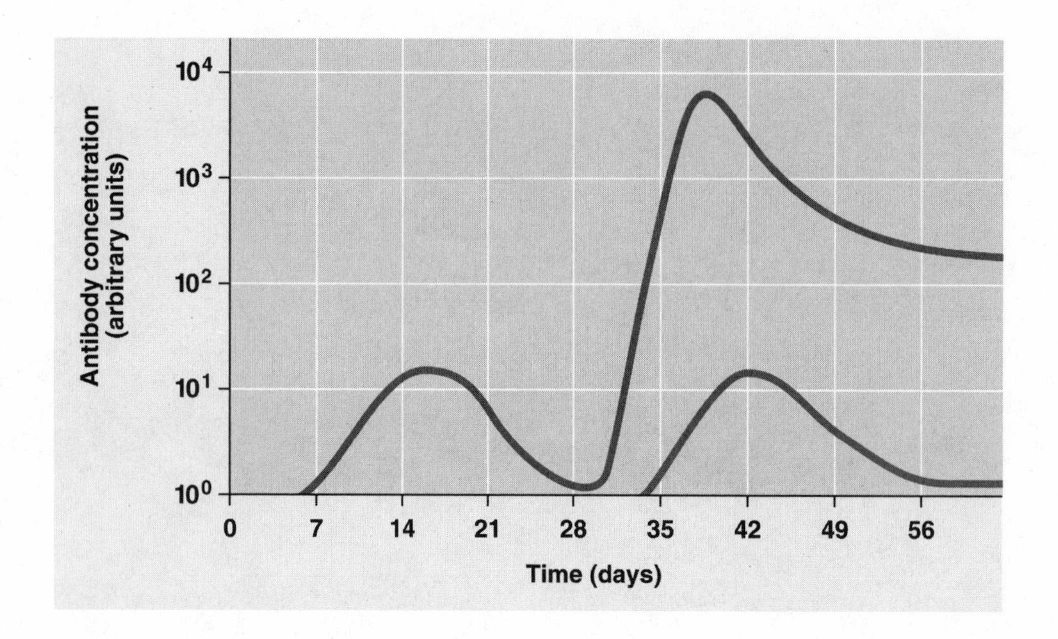

Figure 43.7 Immunological memory, page 906

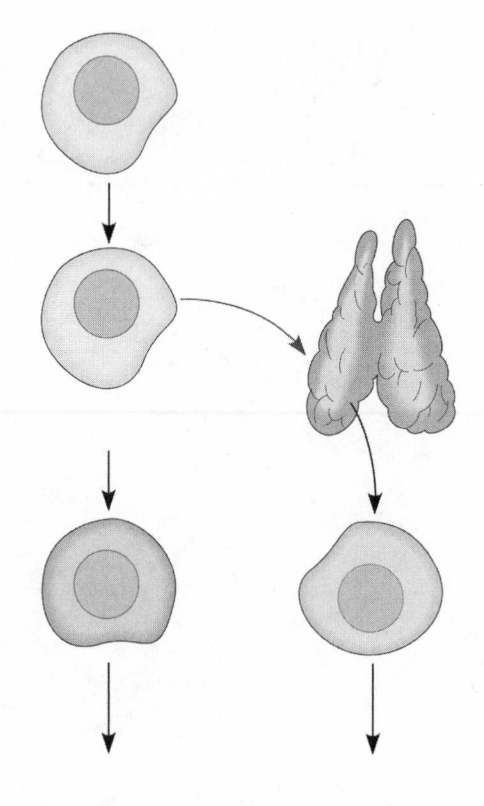

Figure 43.8 The development of lymphocytes, page 906

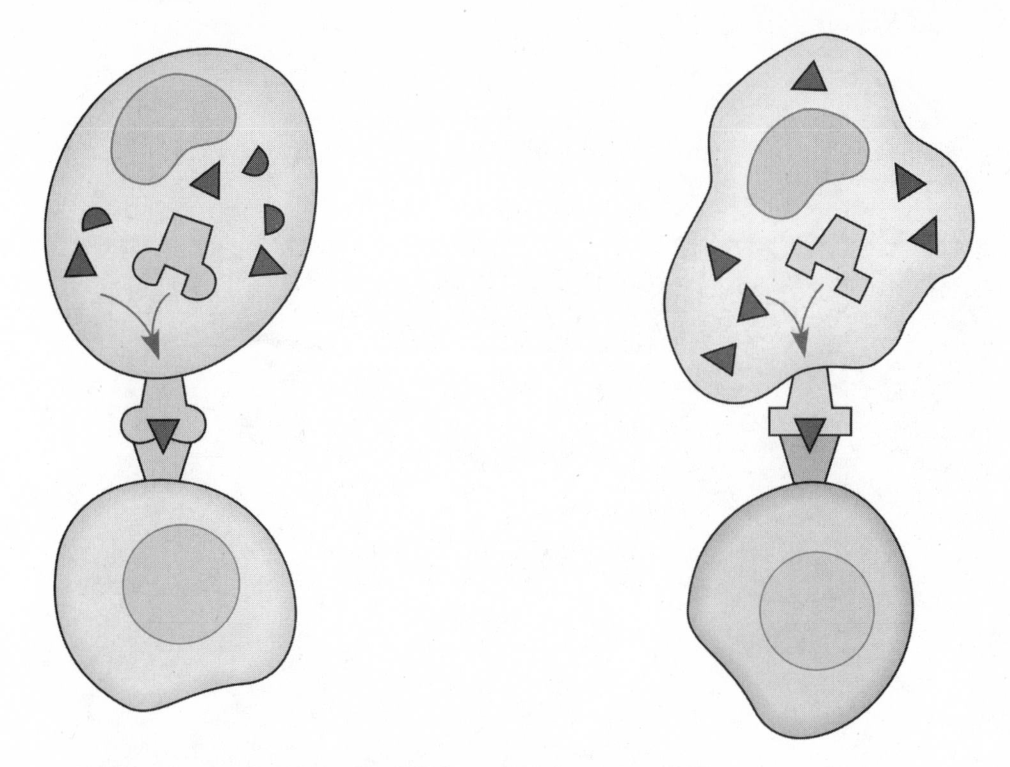

Figure 43.9 The interaction of T cells with MHC molecules, page 907

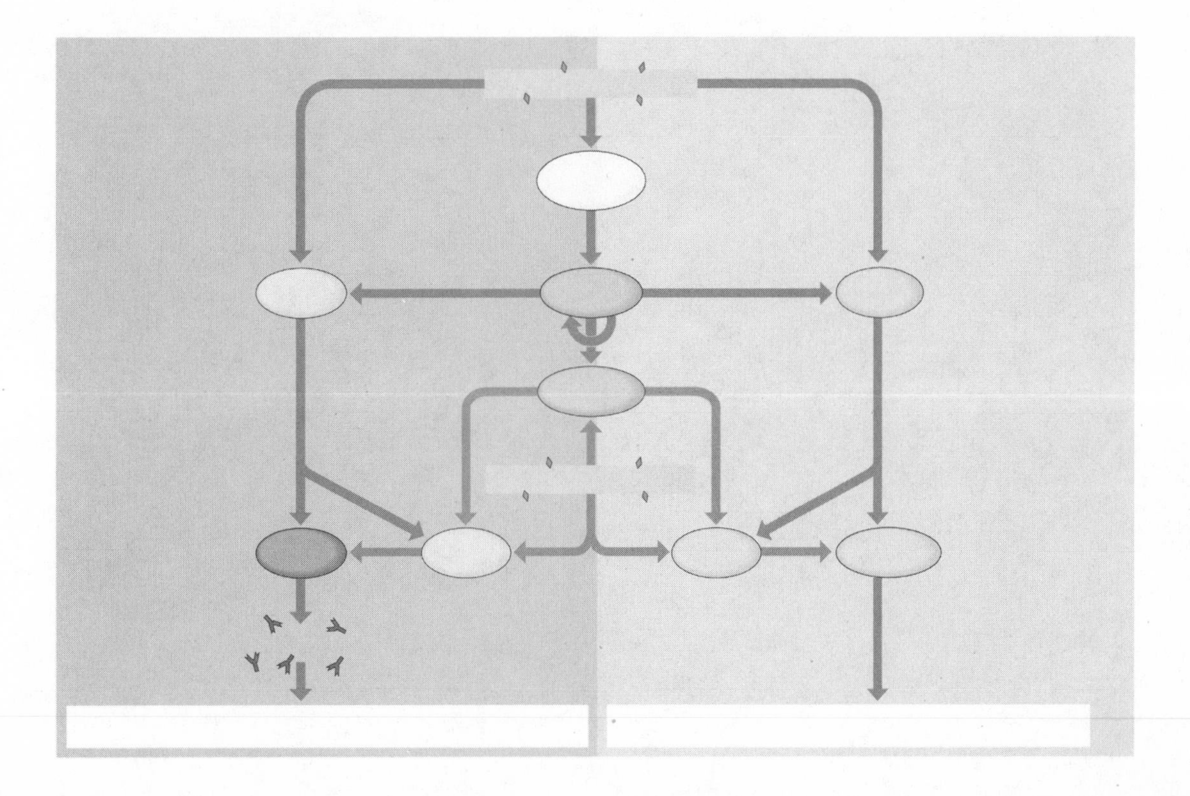

Figure 43.10 An overview of the immune responses, page 909

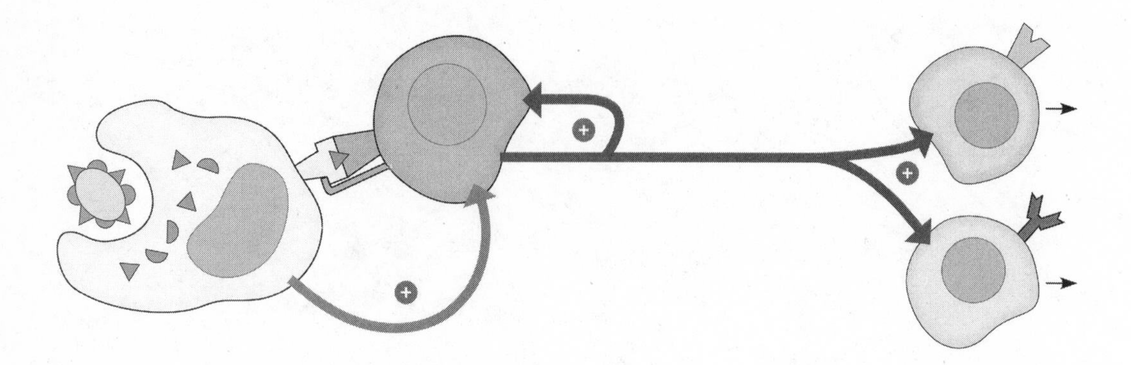

Figure 43.11 The central role of helper T cells: a closer look, page 910

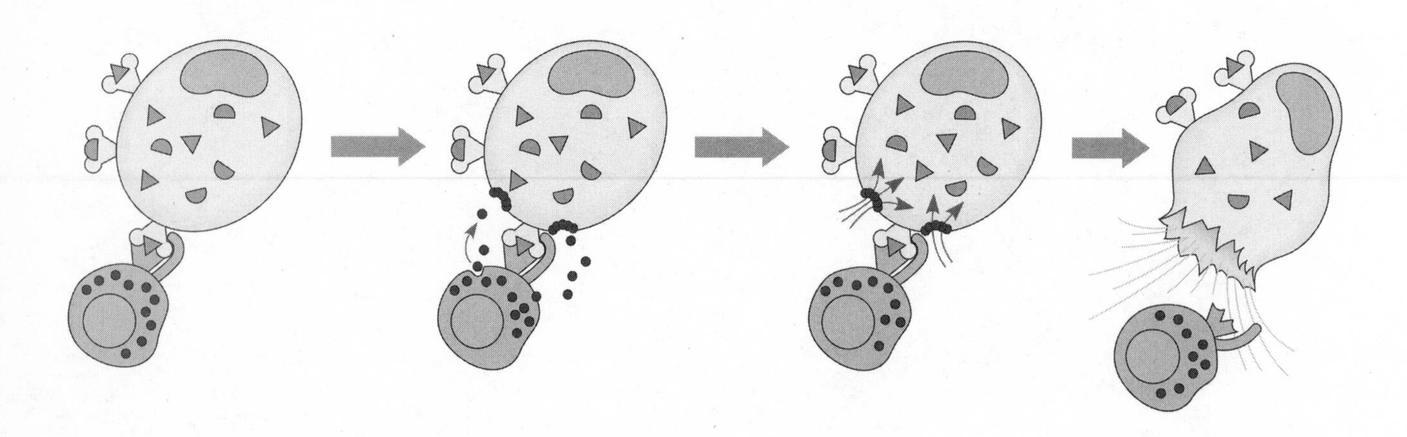

Figure 43.12a The functioning of cytotoxic T cells, page 910

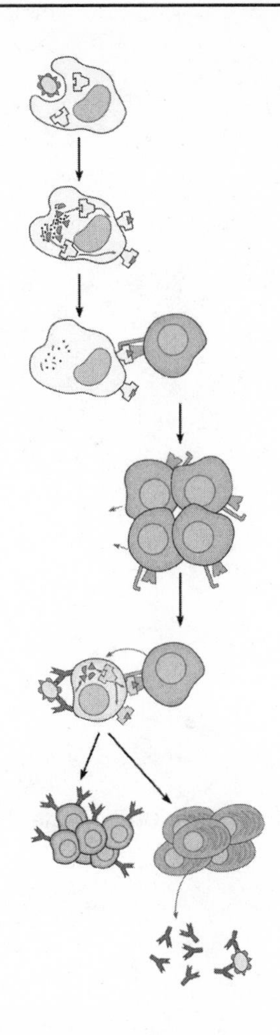

Figure 43.13 Humoral response to a T-dependent antigen, page 911

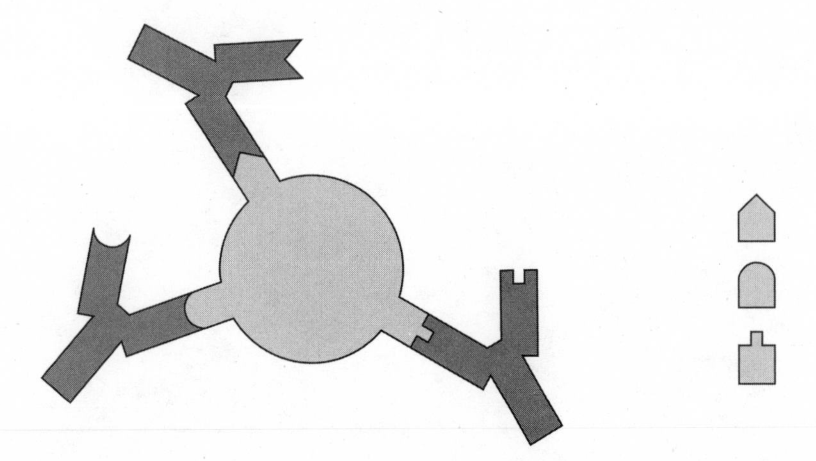

Figure 43.14 Epitopes (antigenic determinants), page 912

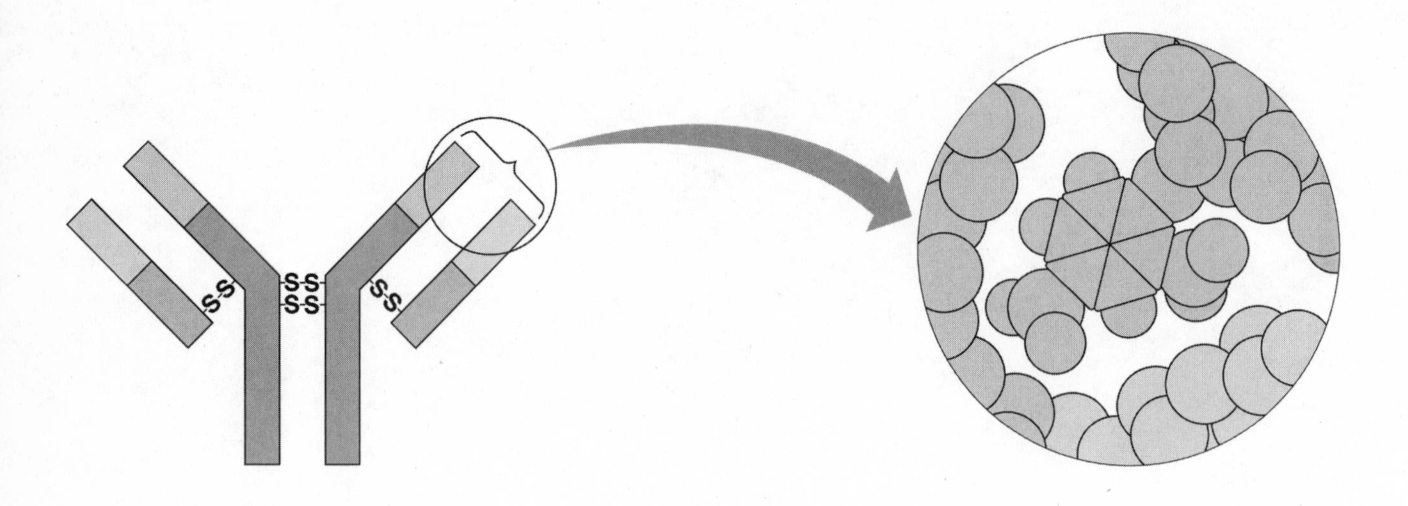

Figure 43.15 The structure of a typical antibody molecule, page 913

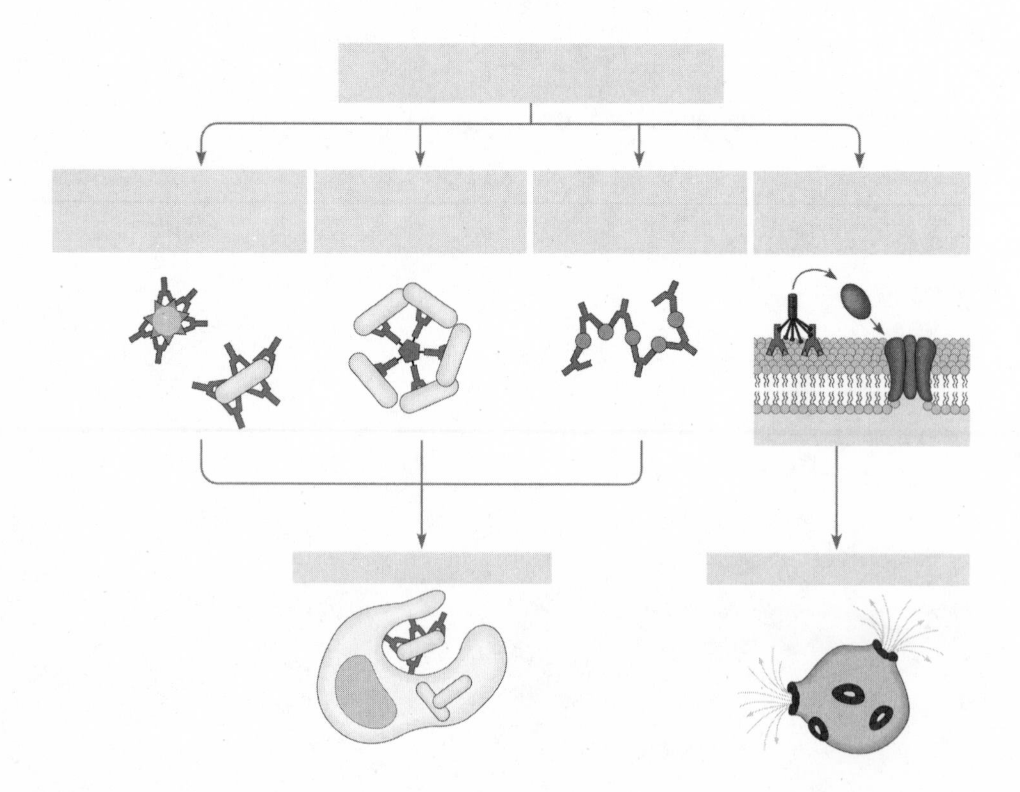

Figure 43.16 Effector mechanisms of humoral immunity, page 914

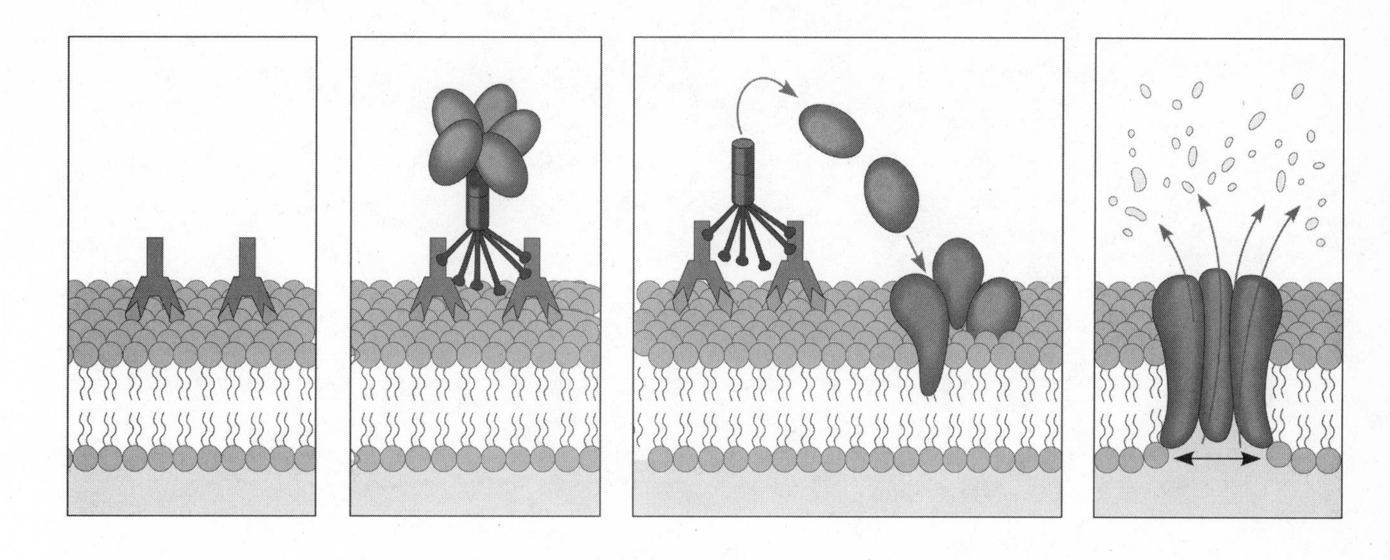

Figure 43.17 The classical complement pathway, resulting in lysis of a target cell, page 915

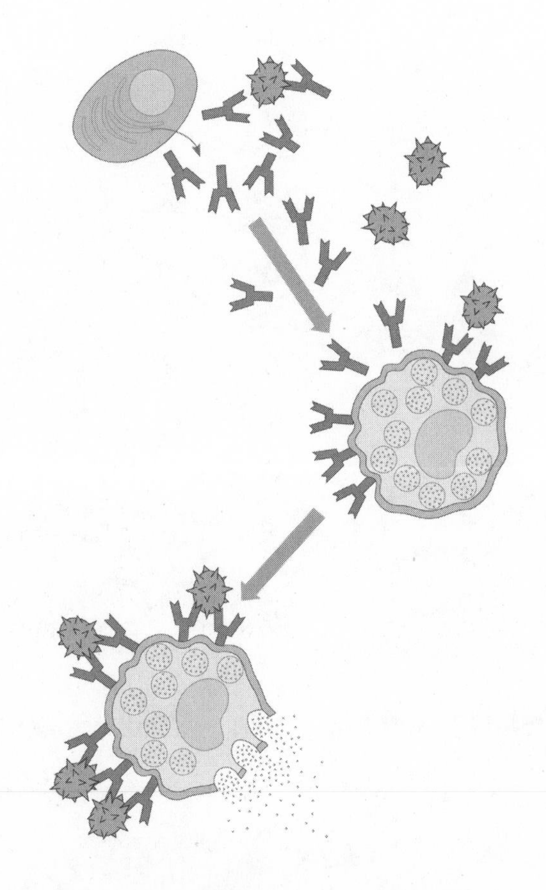

Figure 43.18 Mast cells, IgE, and the allergic response, page 918

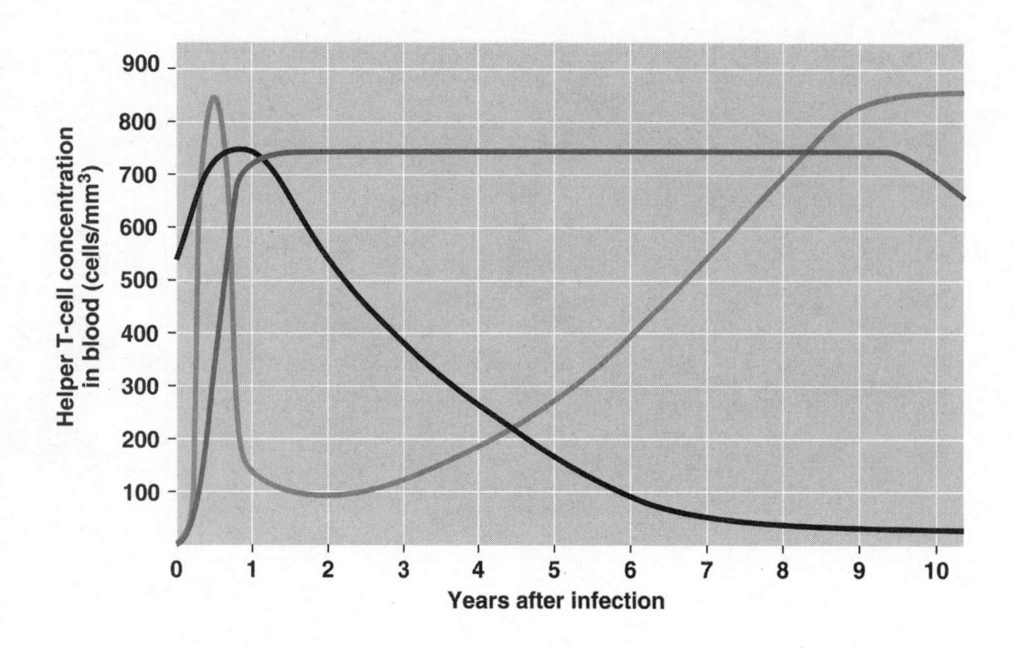

Figure 43.20 The stages of HIV infection, page 920

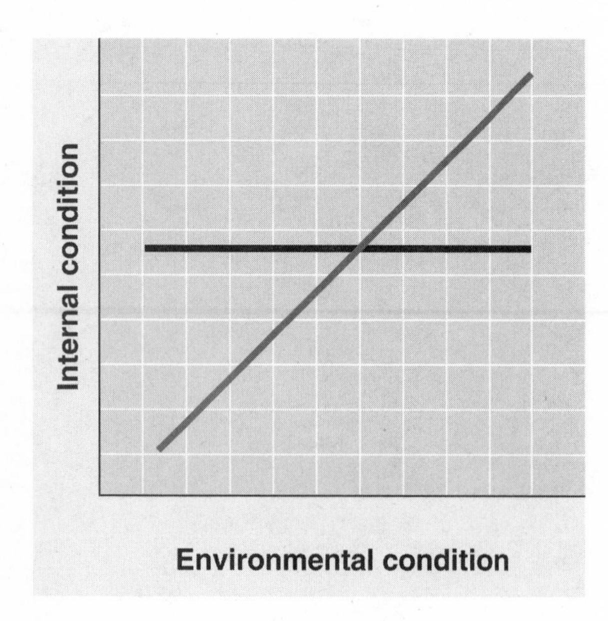

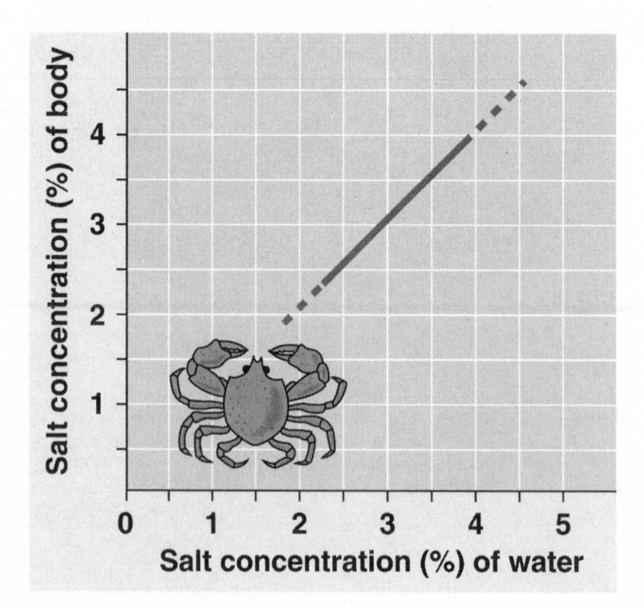

Figure 44.1 Regulators and conformers, page 926

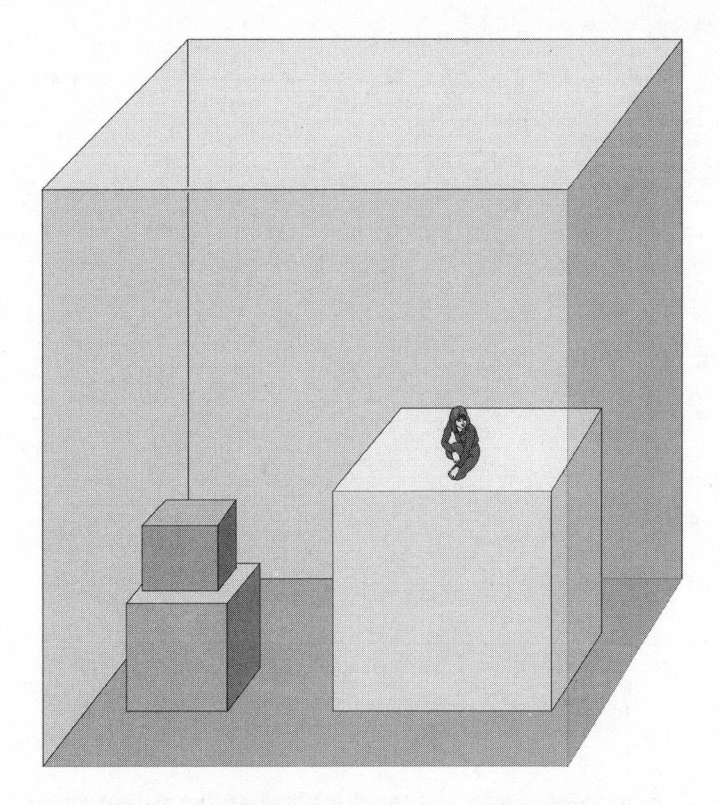

Figure 44.2 A partial energy and material bookkeeping for ten years in the life of a young woman, page 927

Figure 44.3 Heat exchange between an organism and its environment, page 927

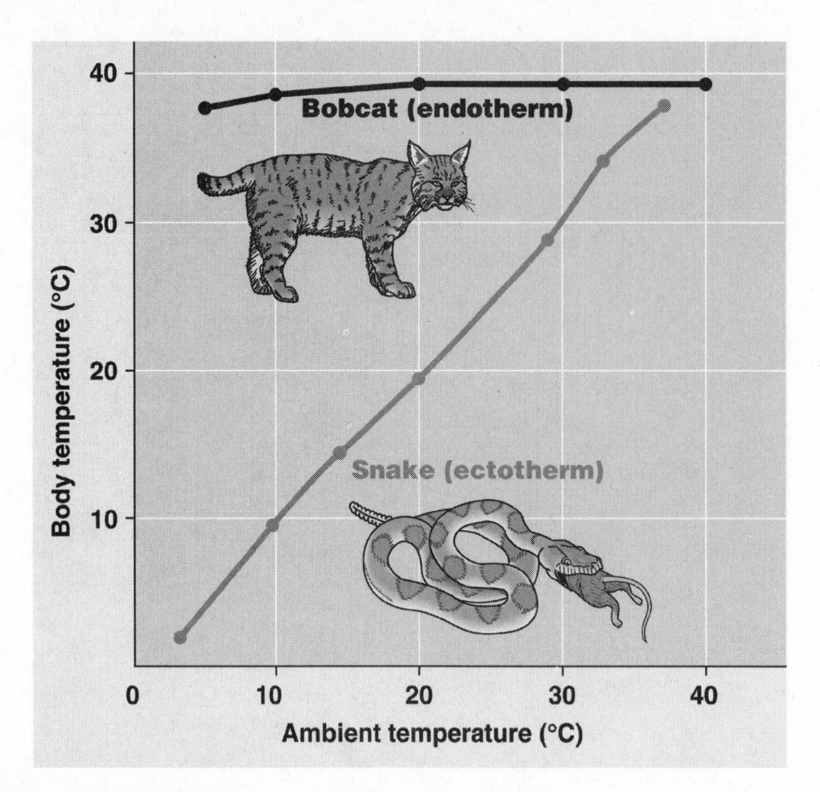

Figure 44.4 The relationship between body temperature and ambient (environmental) temperature in an ectotherm and an endotherm, page 928

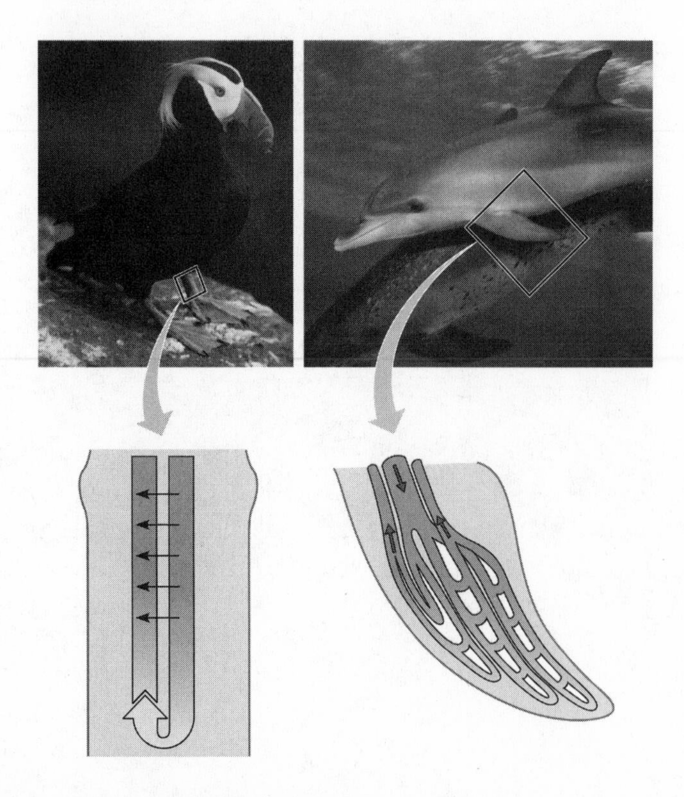

Figure 44.5 Countercurrent heat exchangers, page 929

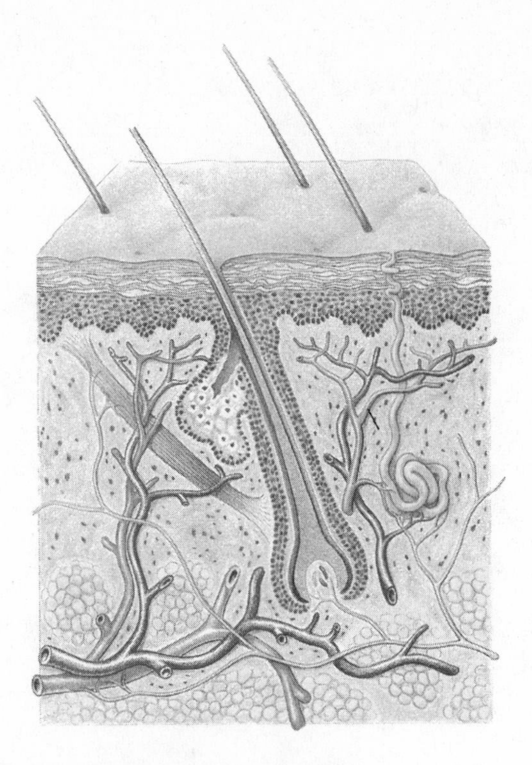

Figure 44.6 Skin as an organ of thermoregulation, page 931

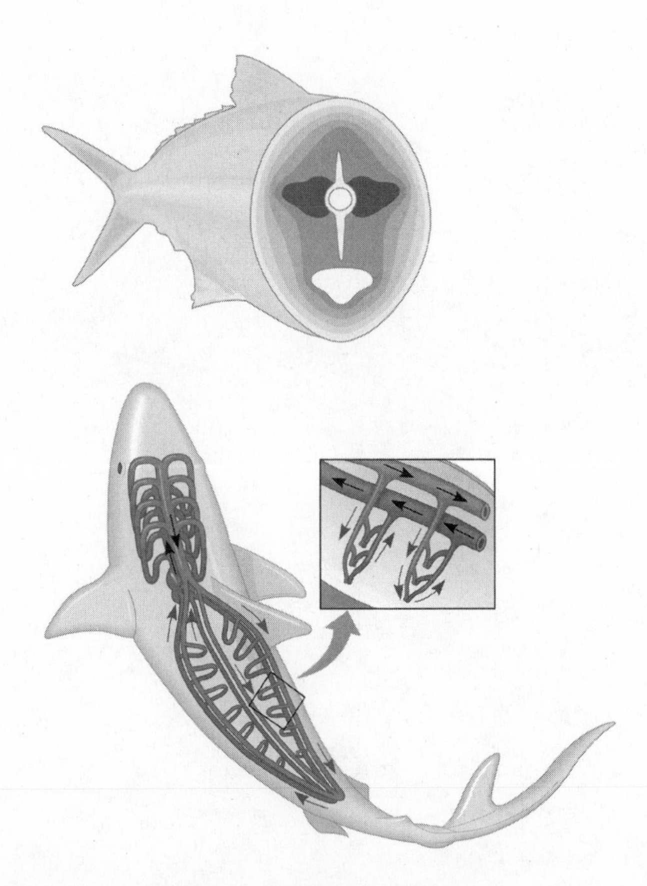

Figure 44.8 Thermoregulation in large, active fishes, page 932

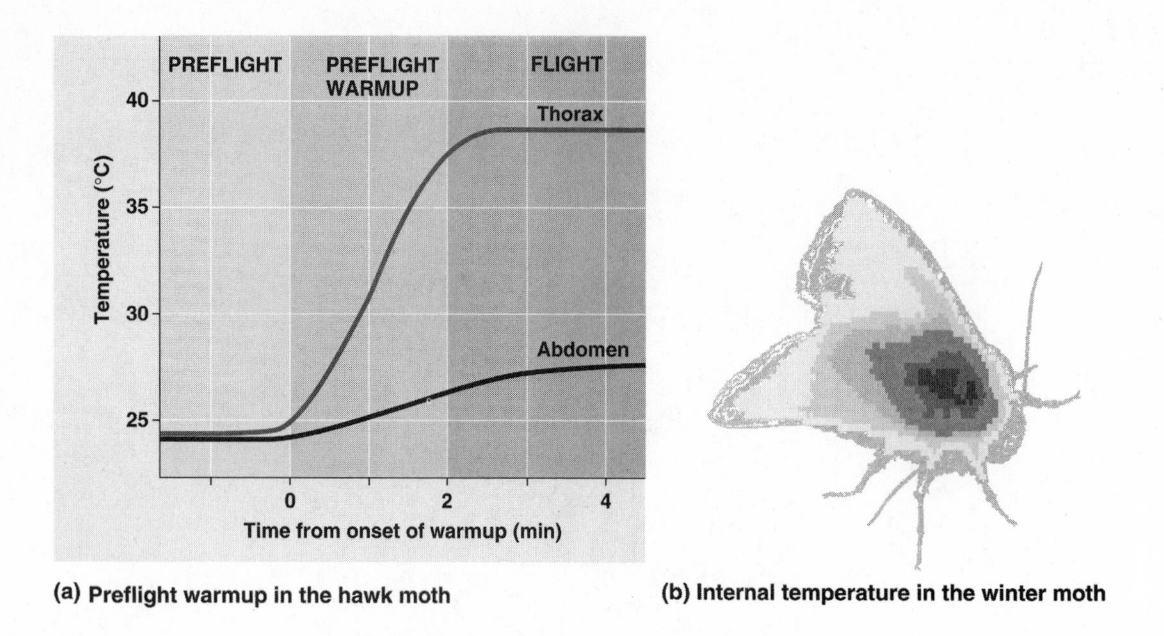

(a) Preflight warmup in the hawk moth

(b) Internal temperature in the winter moth

Figure 44.9 Thermoregulation in moths, page 933

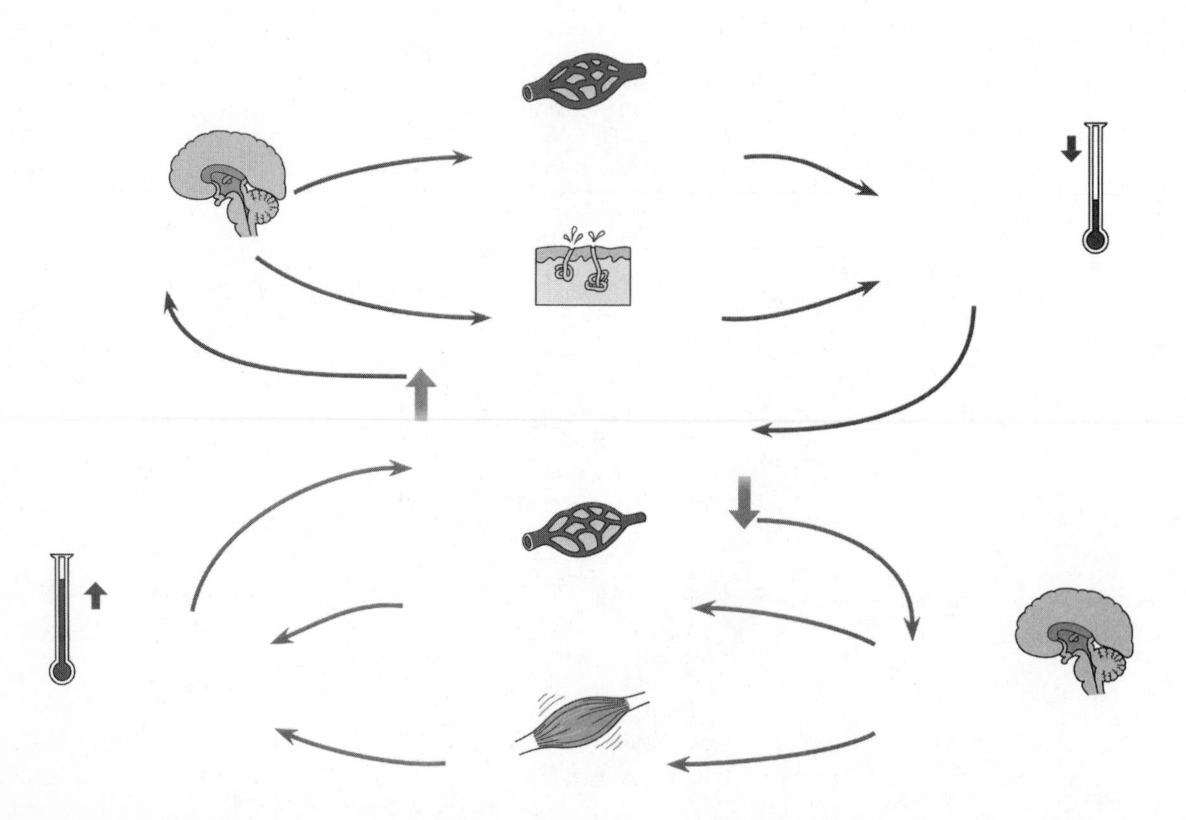

Figure 44.10 The thermostat function of the hypothalamus and feedback mechanisms in human thermoregulation, page 934

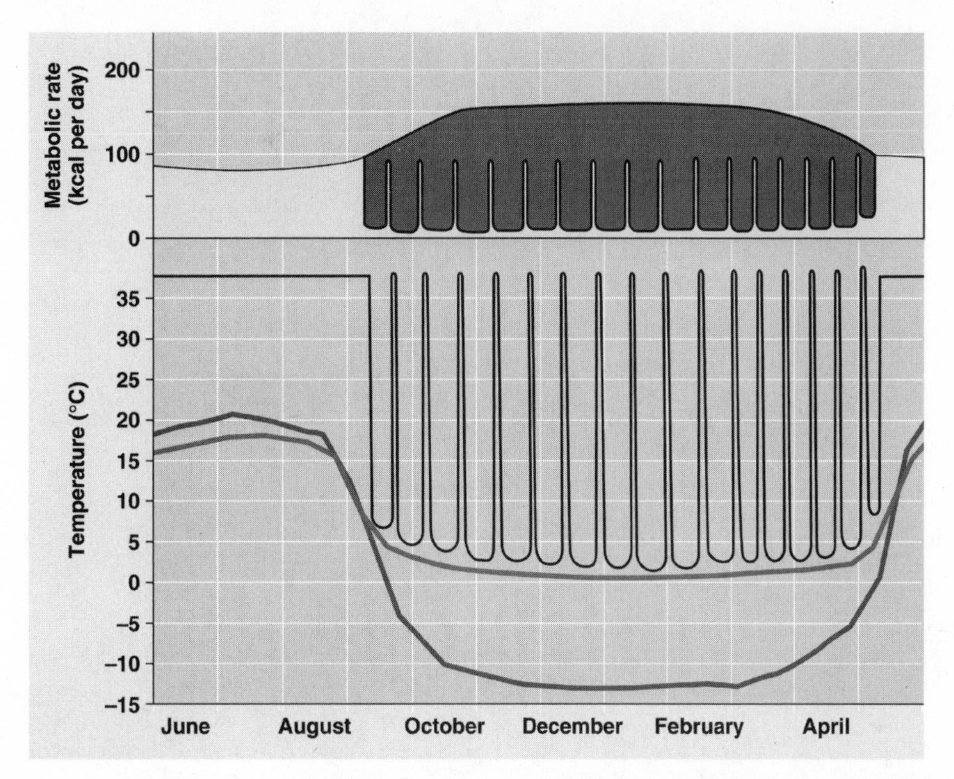

Figure 44.11 Body temperature and metabolism during hibernation of Belding's ground squirrel, page 935

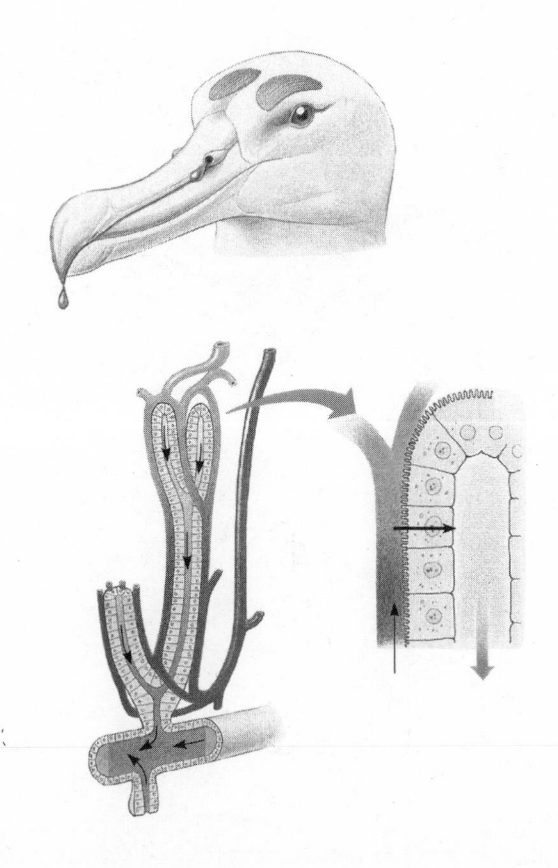

Figure 44.12 Salt-excreting glands in birds, page 937

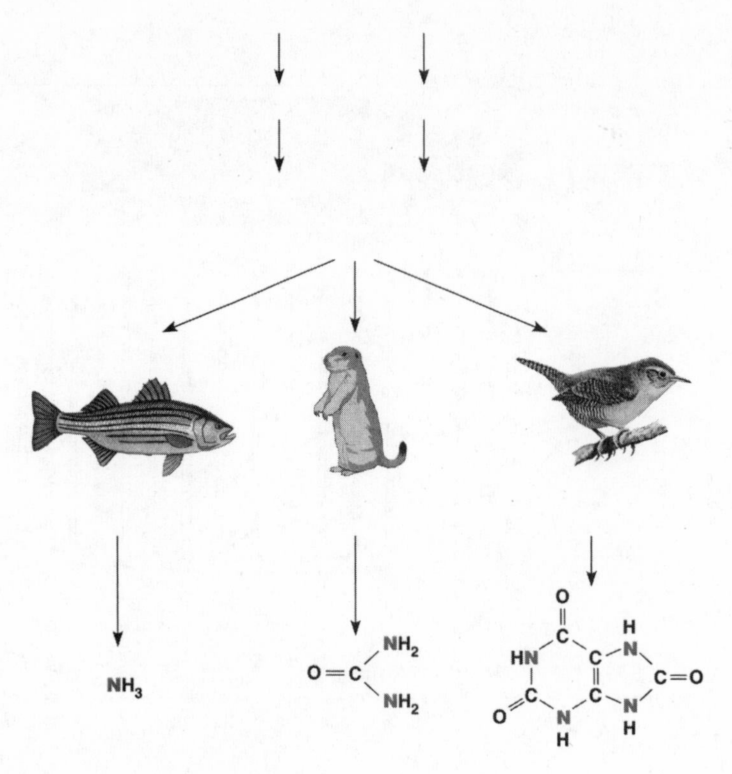

Figure 44.13 Nitrogenous wastes, page 938

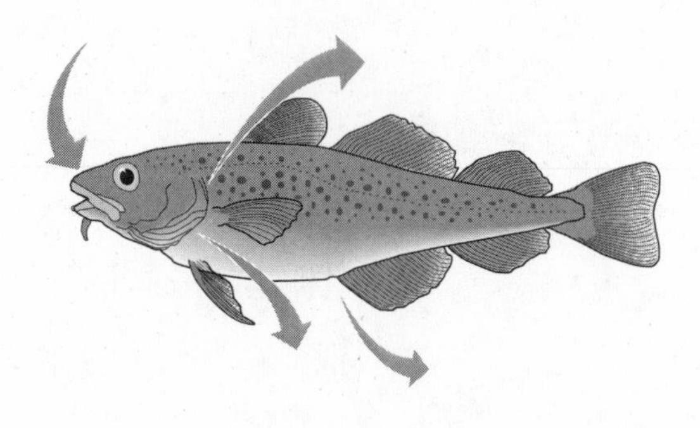

Figure 44.14 Osmoregulation in marine and freshwater bony fishes: a comparison, page 940

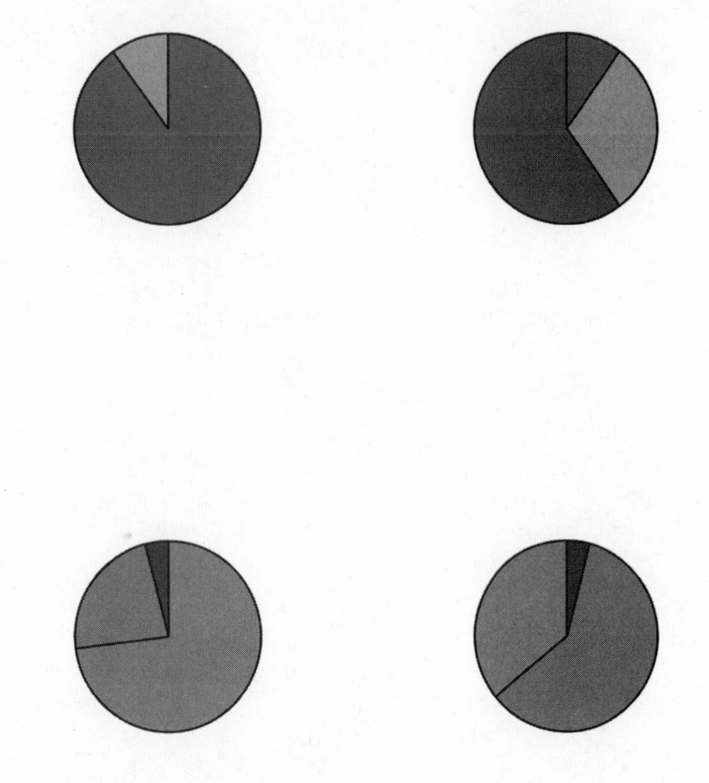

Figure 44.16 Water balance in two terrestrial mammals, page 941

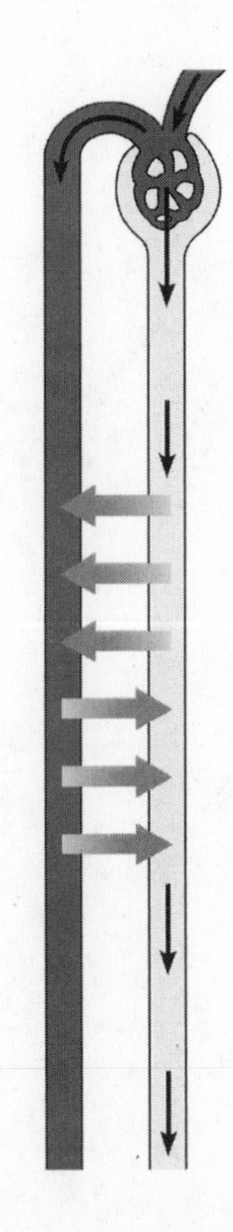

Figure 44.17 Key functions of excretory systems: an overview, page 942

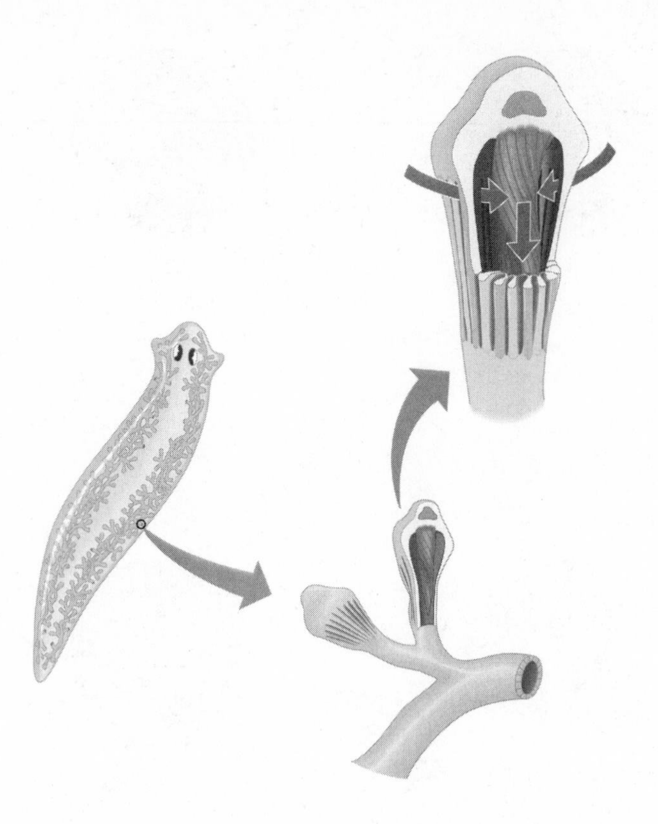

Figure 44.18 Protonephridia: the flame-bulb system of a planarian, page 942

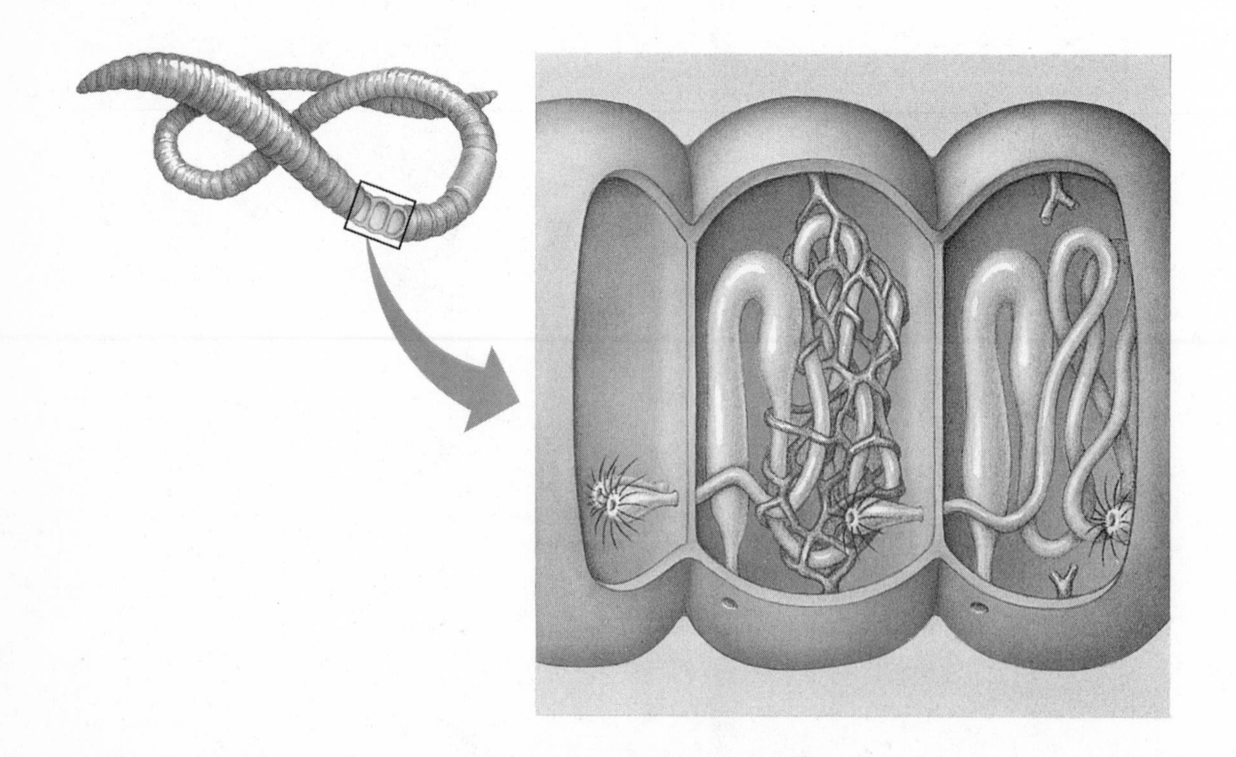

Figure 44.19 Metanephridia of an earthworm, page 943

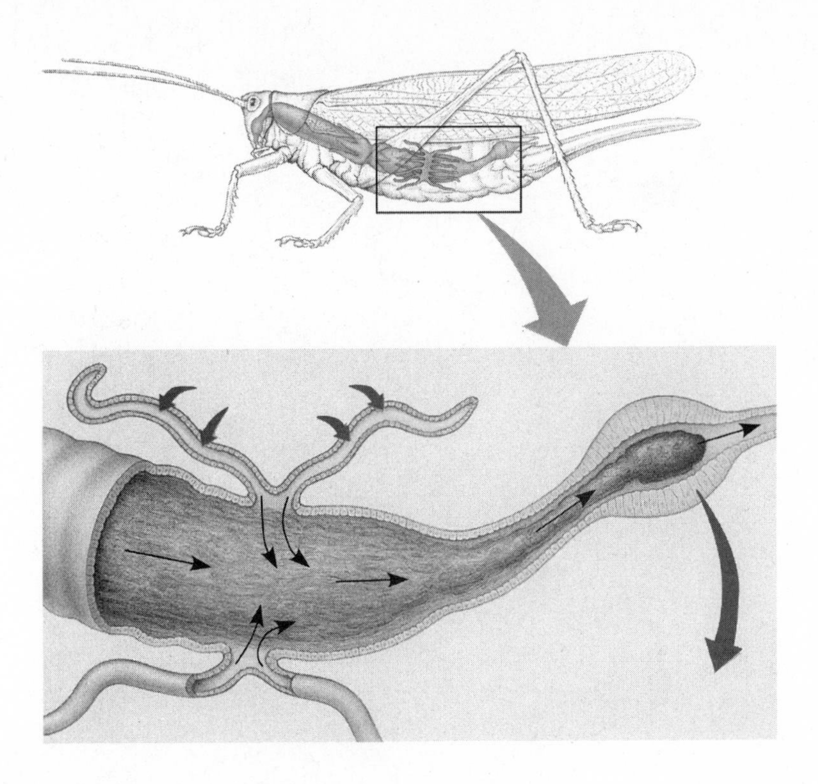

Figure 44.20 Malpighian tubules of insects, page 943

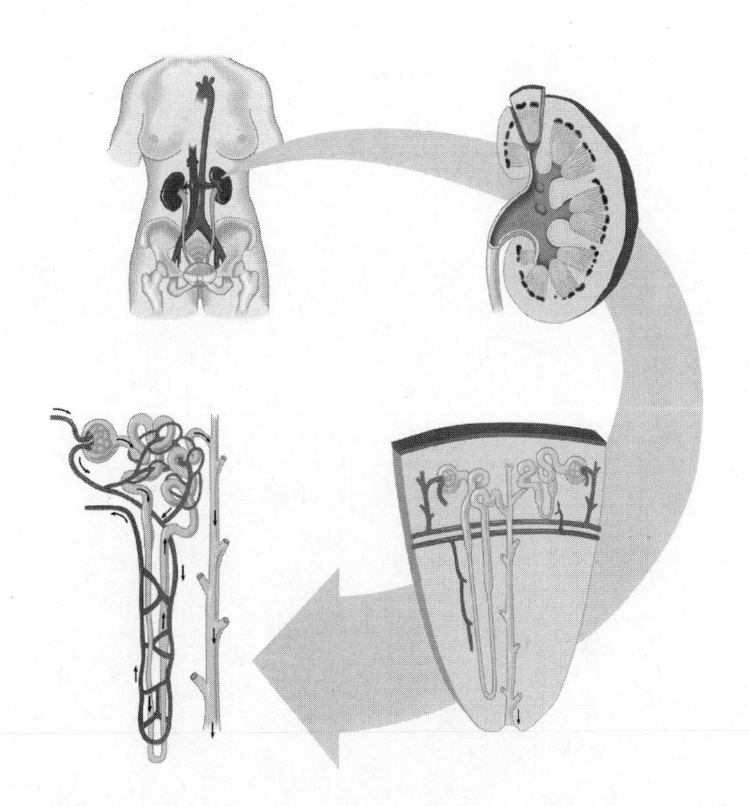

Figure 44.21 The human excretory system at four size scales, page 944

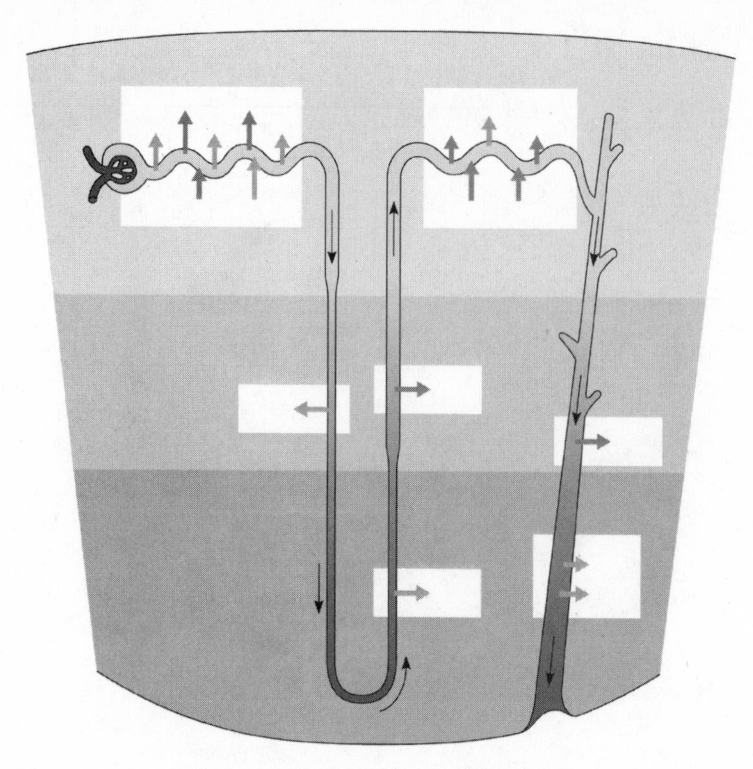

Figure 44.22 The nephron and collecting duct: regional functions of the transport epithelium, page 946

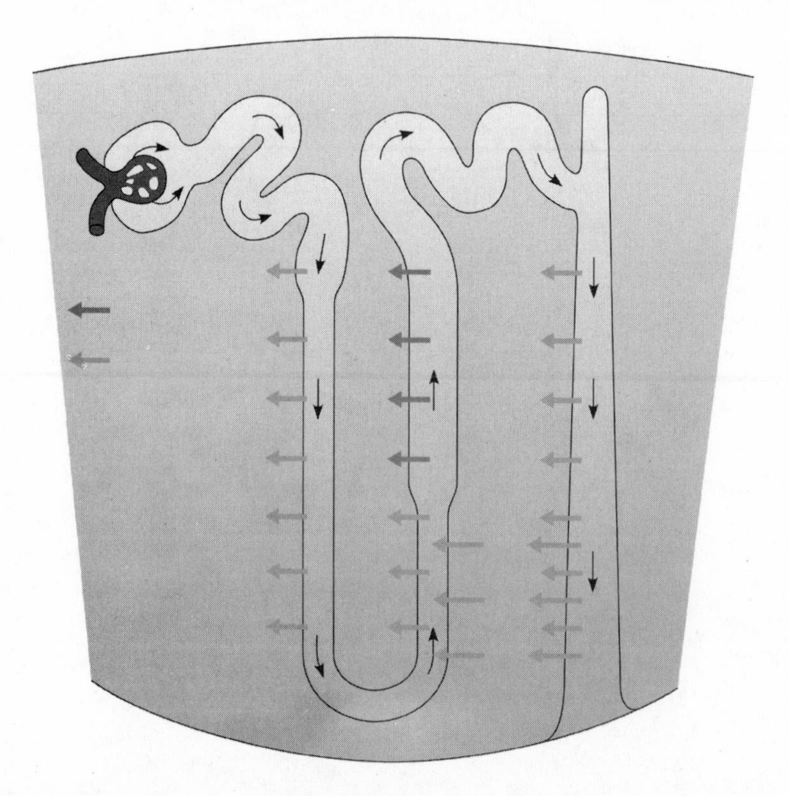

Figure 44.23 How the human kidney concentrates urine: the two-solute model, page 948

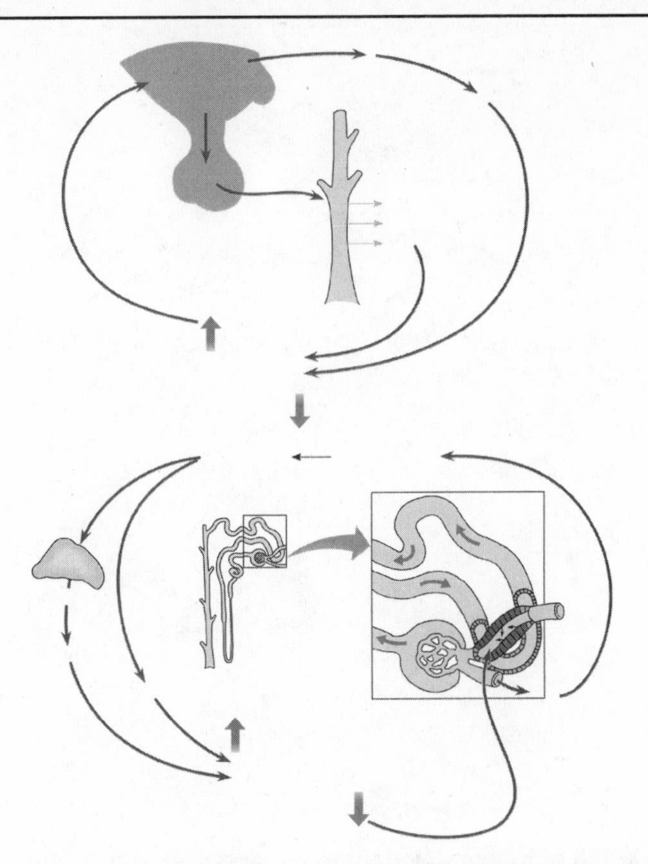

Figure 44.24 Hormonal control of the kidney by negative feedback circuits, page 950

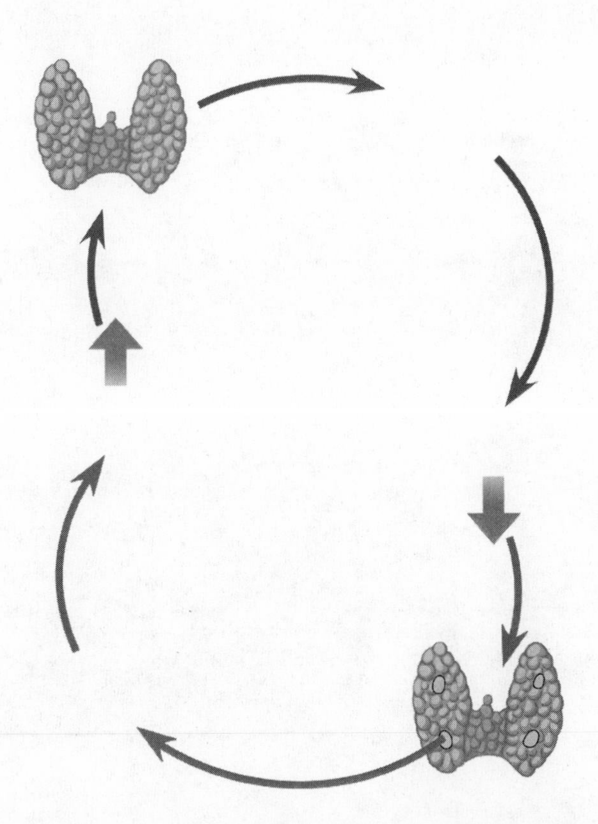

Figure 45.1 An example of how feedback regulation maintains homeostasis, page 956

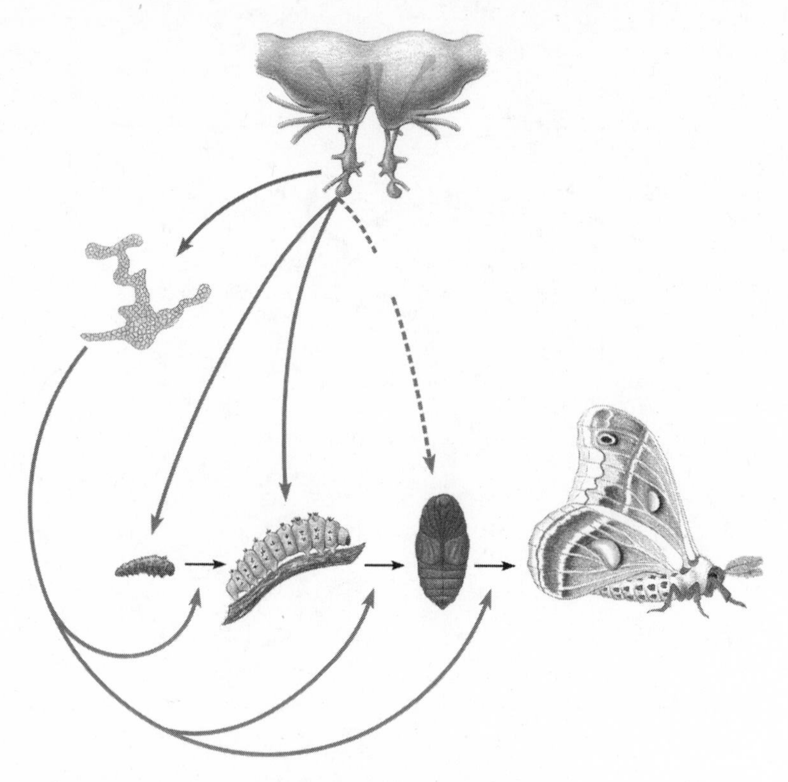

Figure 45.2 Hormonal regulation of insect development, page 957

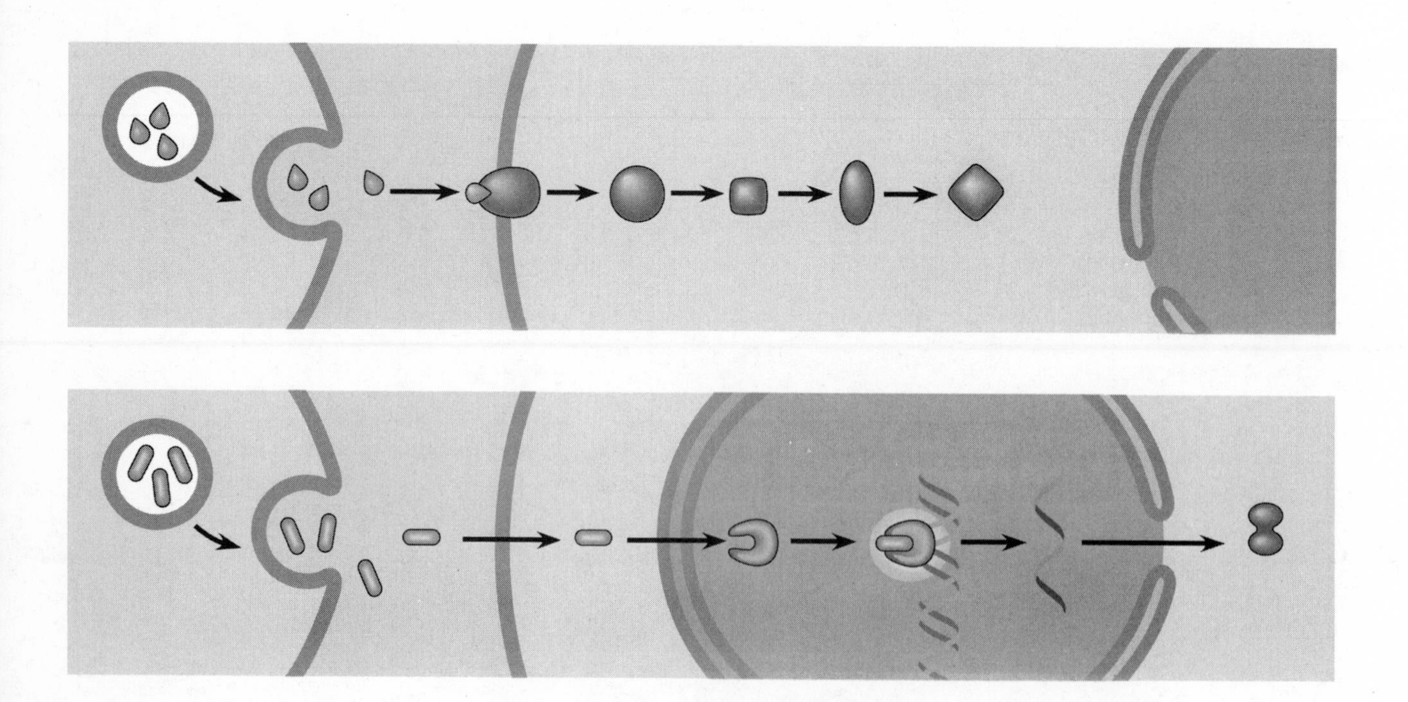

Figure 45.3 Mechanisms of chemical signaling: a review, page 959

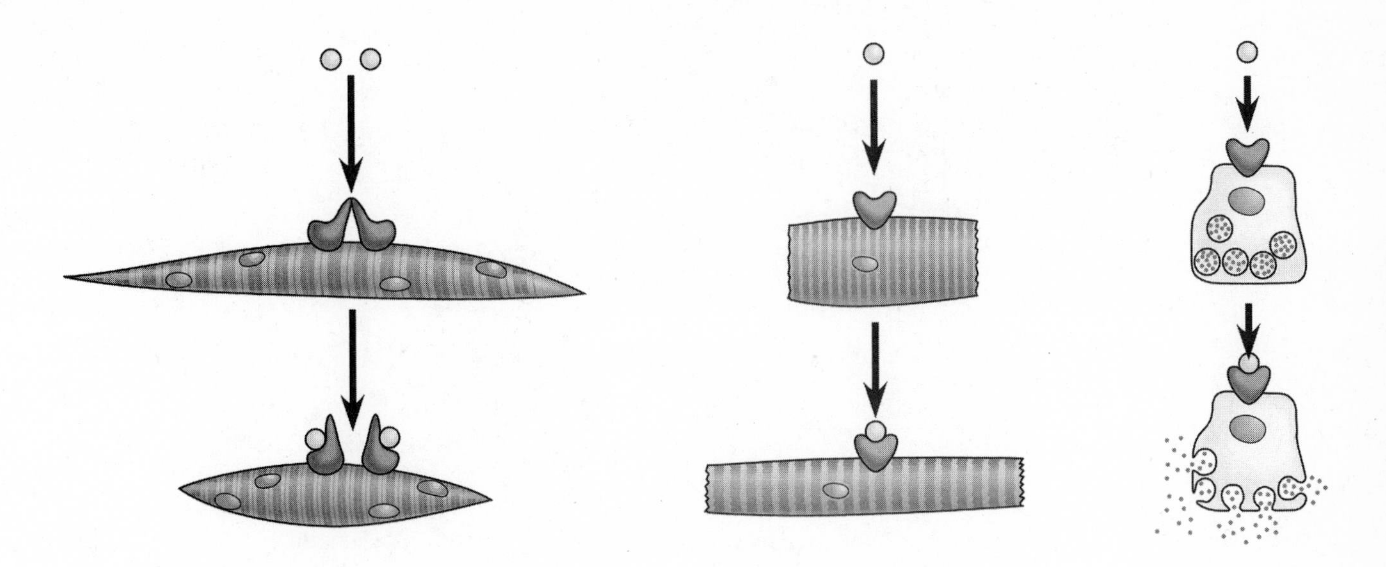

Figure 45.4 One chemical signal, different effects, page 959

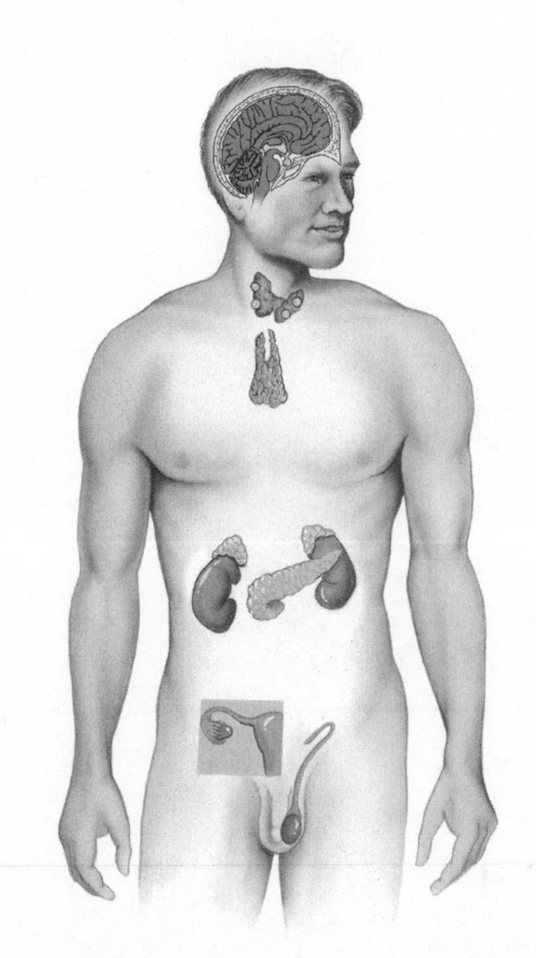

Figure 45.5 Human endocrine glands surveyed in this chapter, page 960

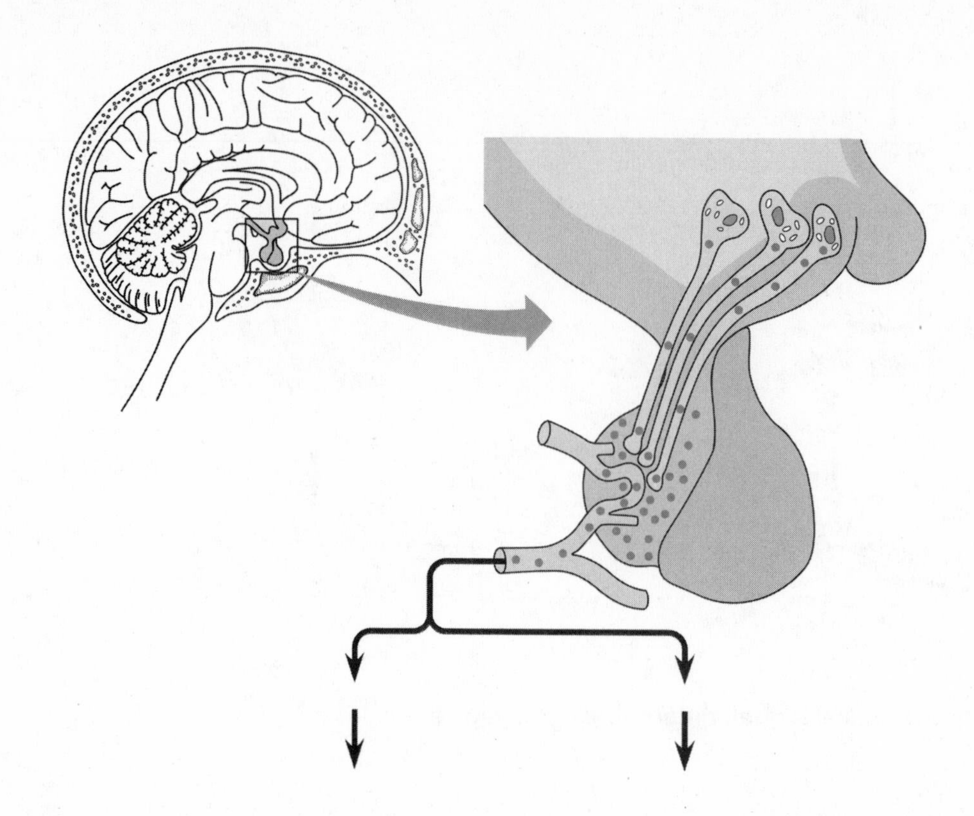

Figure 45.6a Hormones of the hypothalamus and pituitary glands, page 963

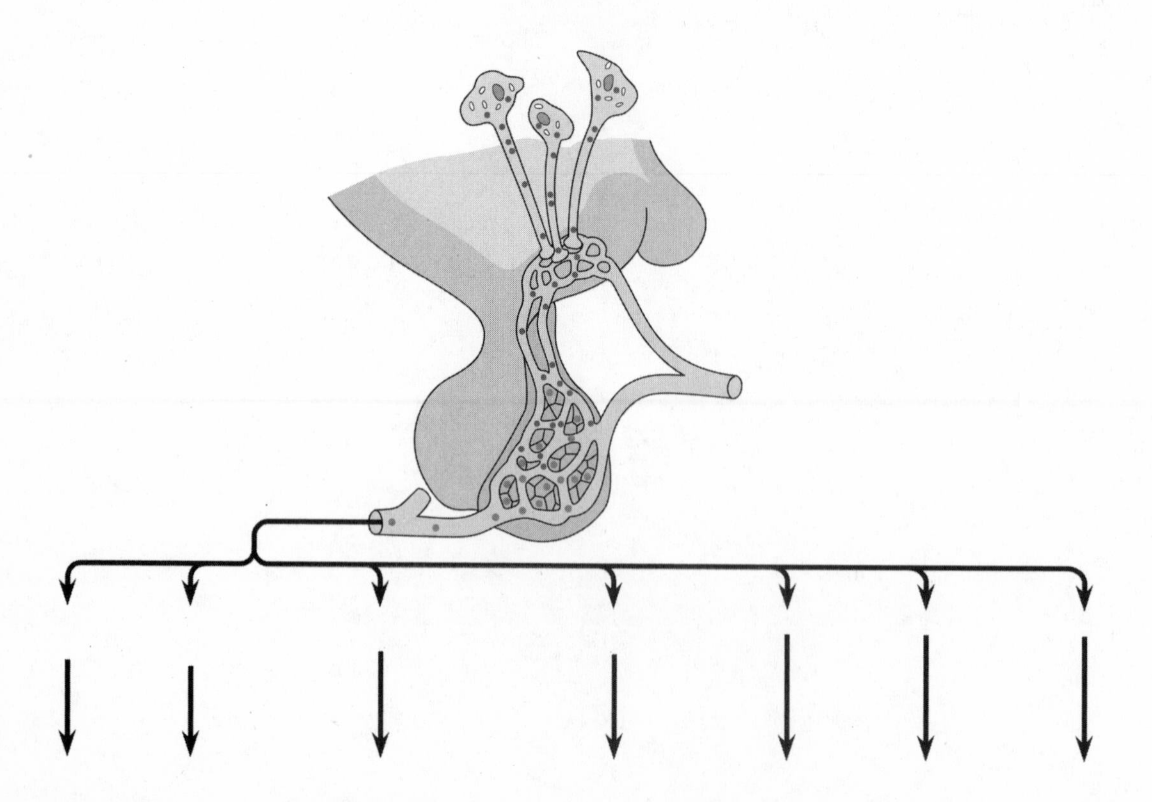

Figure 45.6b Hormones of the hypothalamus and pituitary glands, page 963

I I

HO — O — CH_2 — CH — C — OH

NH_2 O

I I

I I

HO — O — CH_2 — CH — C — OH

NH_2 O

I

Figure 45.7 Two thyroid hormones, page 965

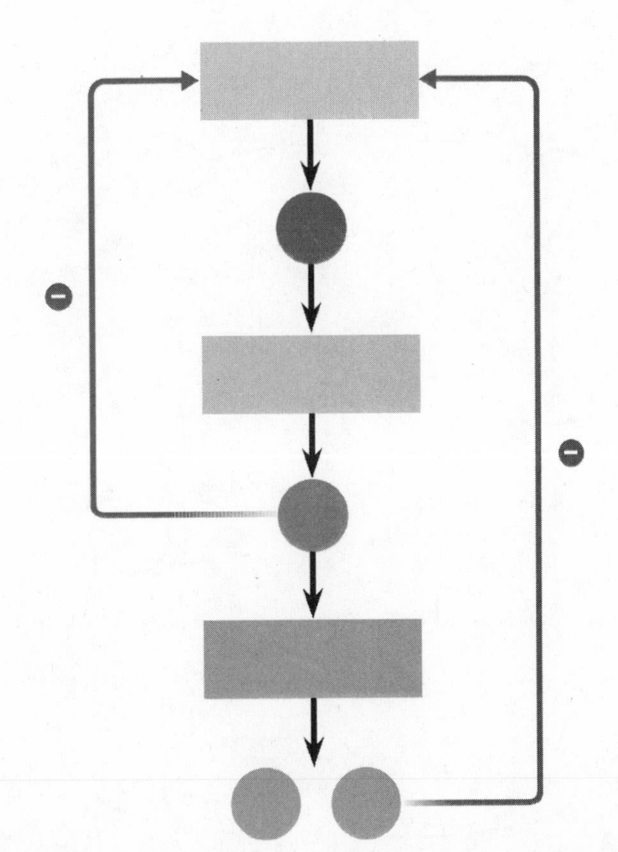

Figure 45.8 Feedback control loops regulating the secretion of thyroid hormones T_3 and T_4, page 965

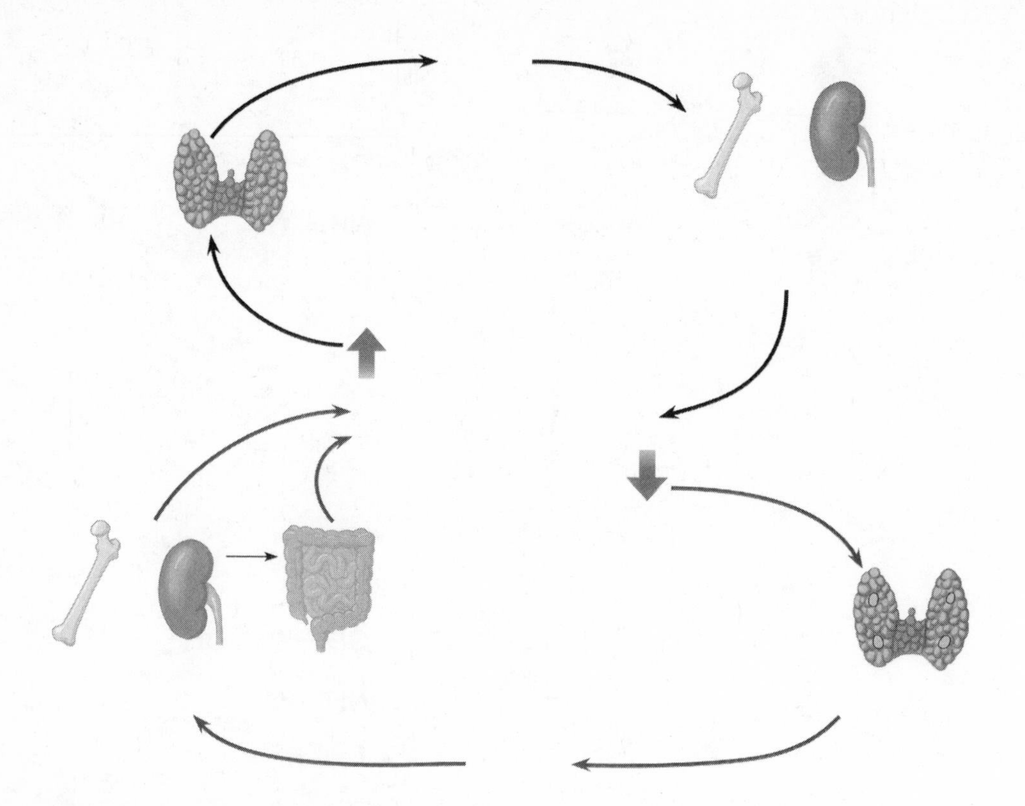

Figure 45.9 Hormonal control of calcium homeostasis in mammals, page 967

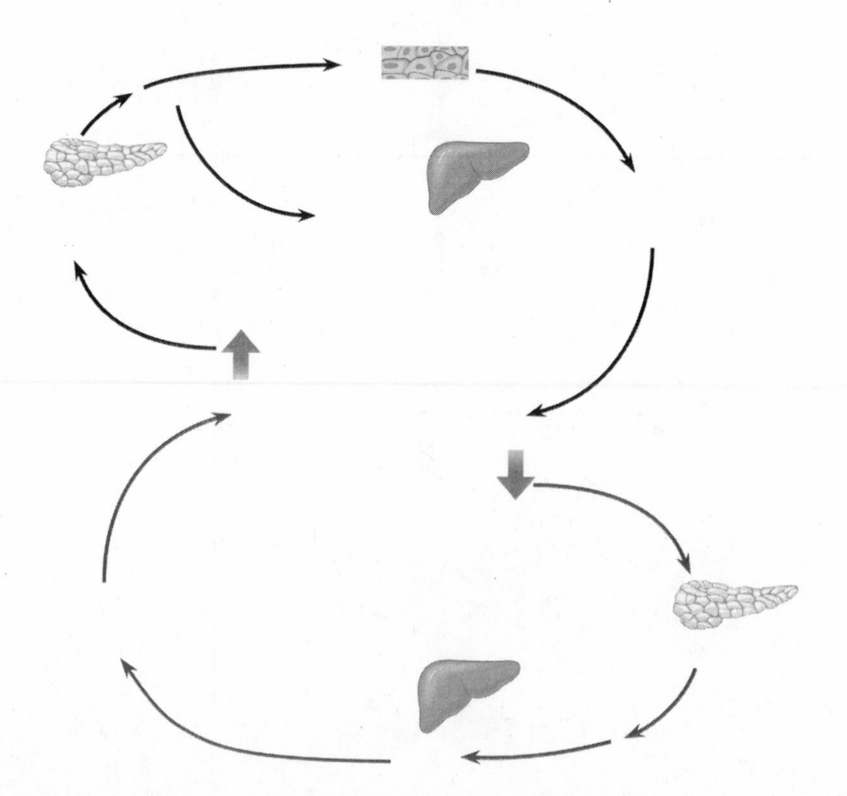

Figure 45.10 Glucose homeostasis maintained by insulin and glucagon, page 968

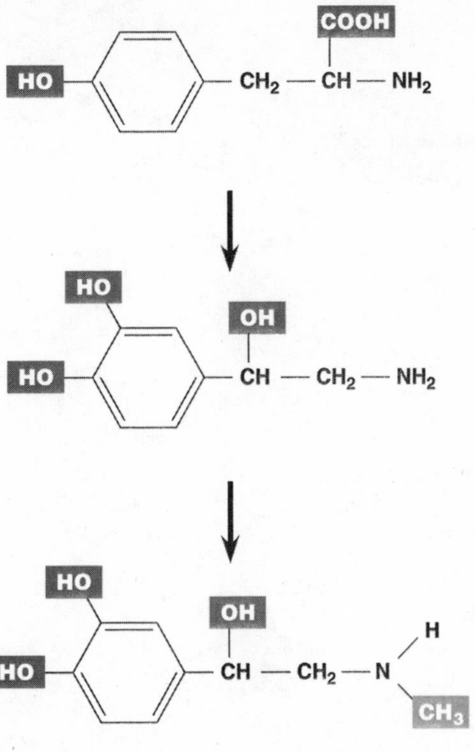

COOH
HO — CH2 — CH — NH2

HO
OH
HO — CH — CH2 — NH2

HO
OH
H
HO — CH — CH2 — N
CH3

Figure 45.12 The synthesis of catecholamine hormones, page 969

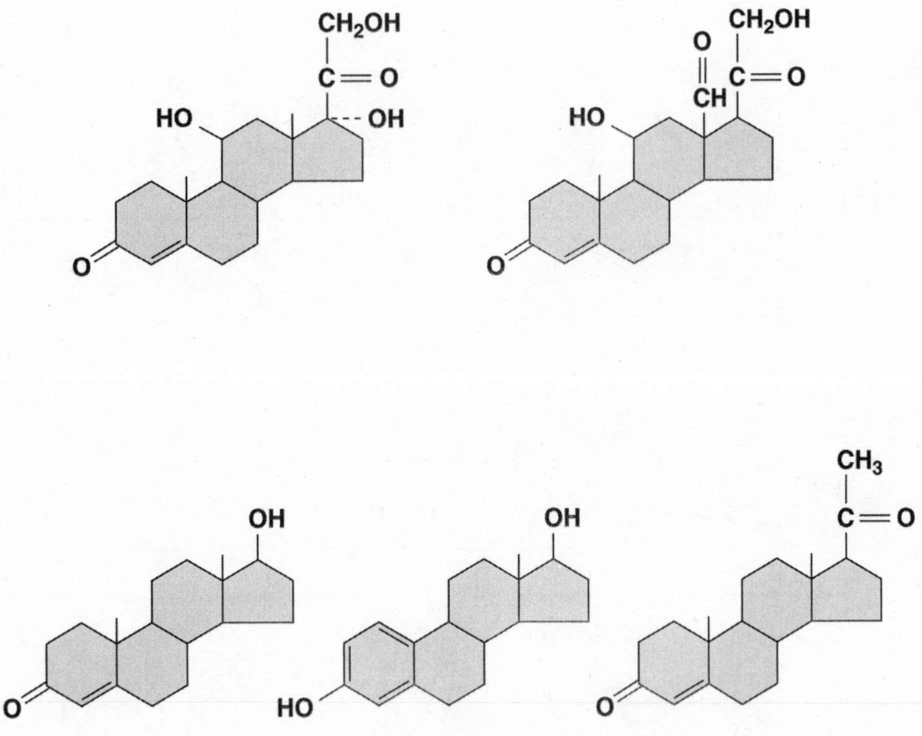

CH2OH
C = O
HO
OH
O

CH2OH
O
C = O
CH
HO
O

OH
O

OH
HO

CH3
C = O
O

Figure 45.13 Steroid hormones from the adrenal cortex and gonads, page 970

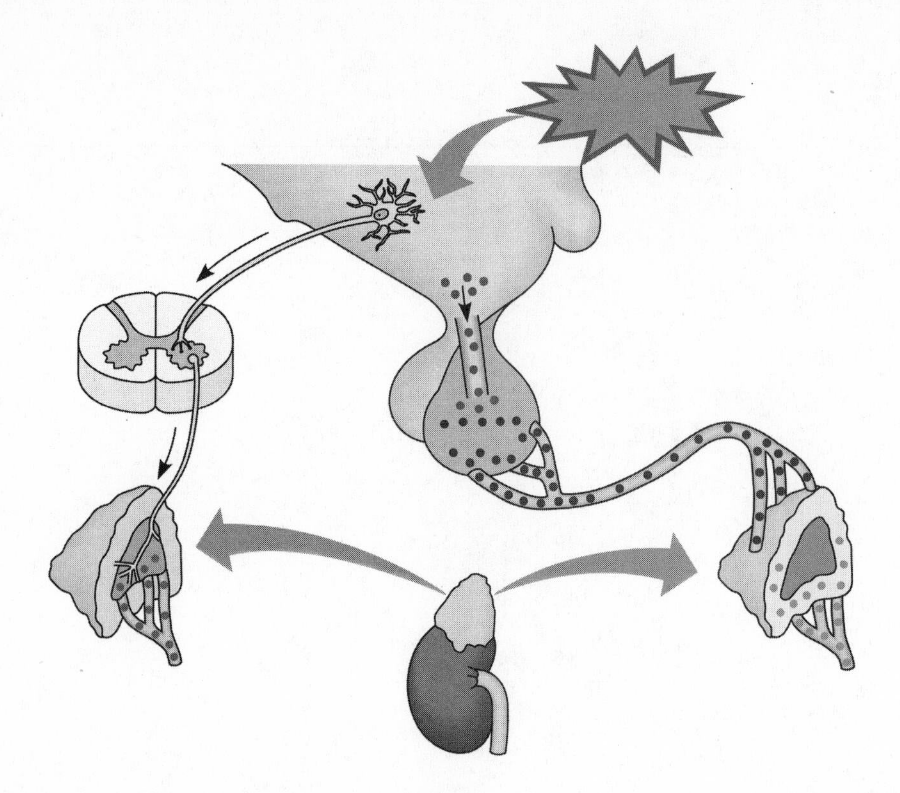

Figure 45.14 Stress and the adrenal gland, page 971

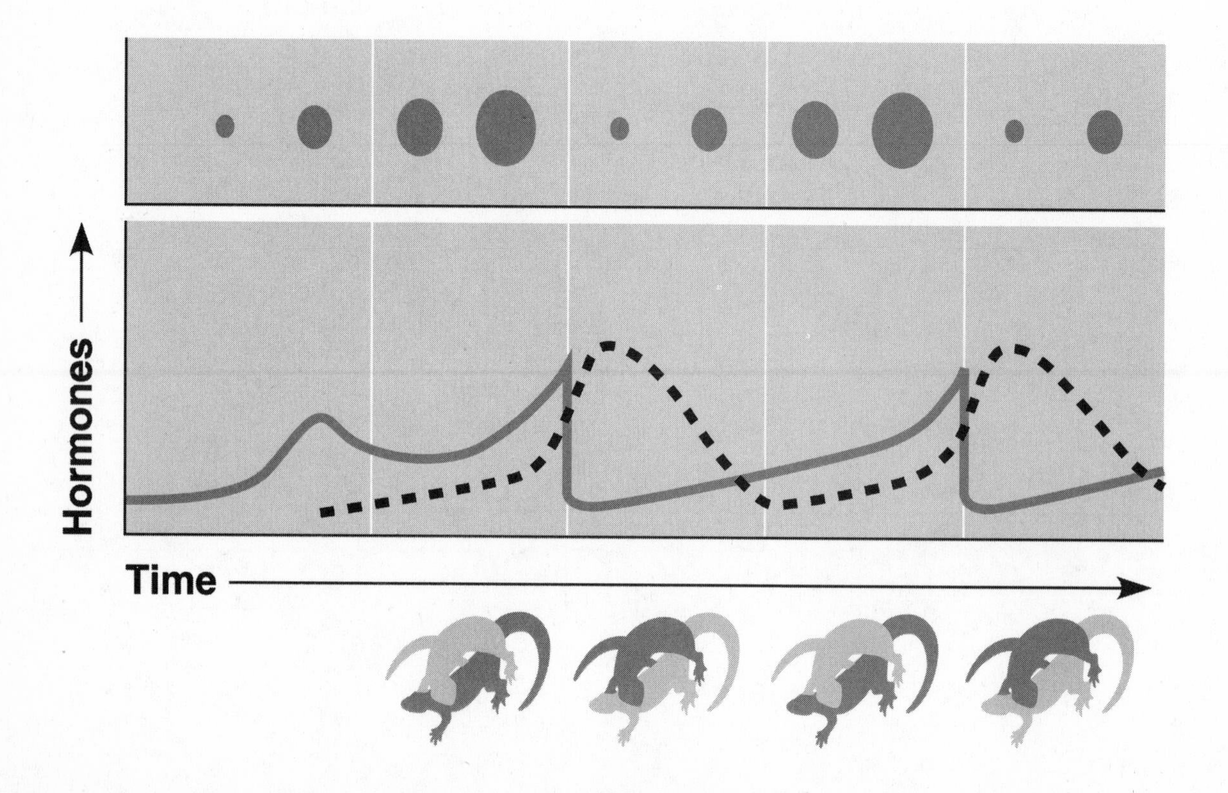

Figure 46.2b Sexual behavior in parthenogenetic lizards, page 977

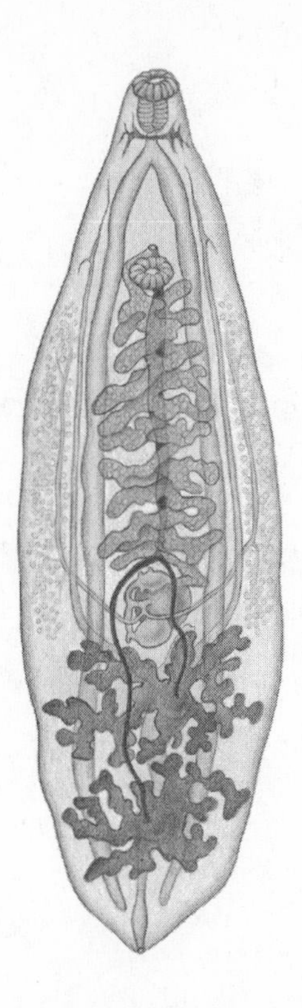

Figure 46 6 Reproductive anatomy of a parasitic flatworm, page 979

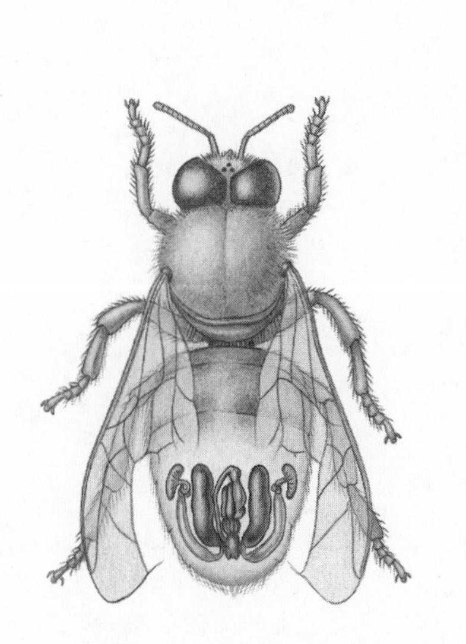

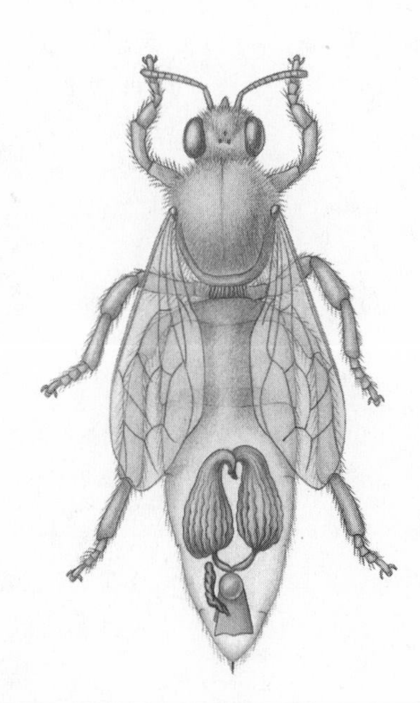

Figure 46.7 Insect reproductive anatomy, page 980

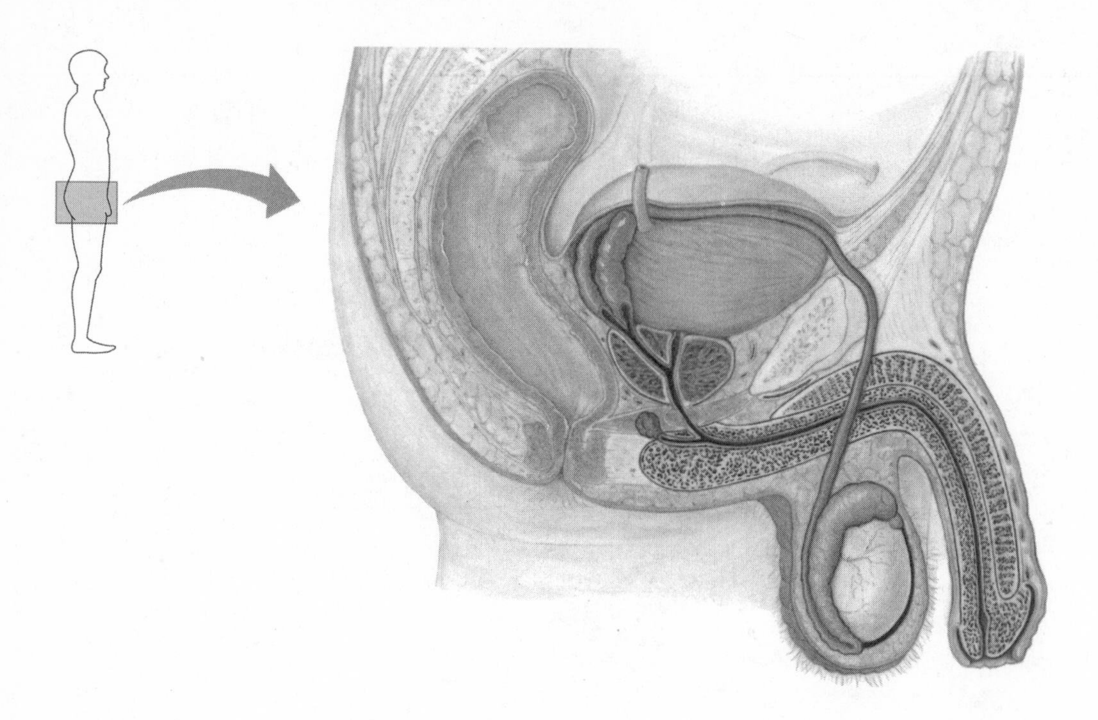

Figure 46.8 Reproductive anatomy of the human male, page 981

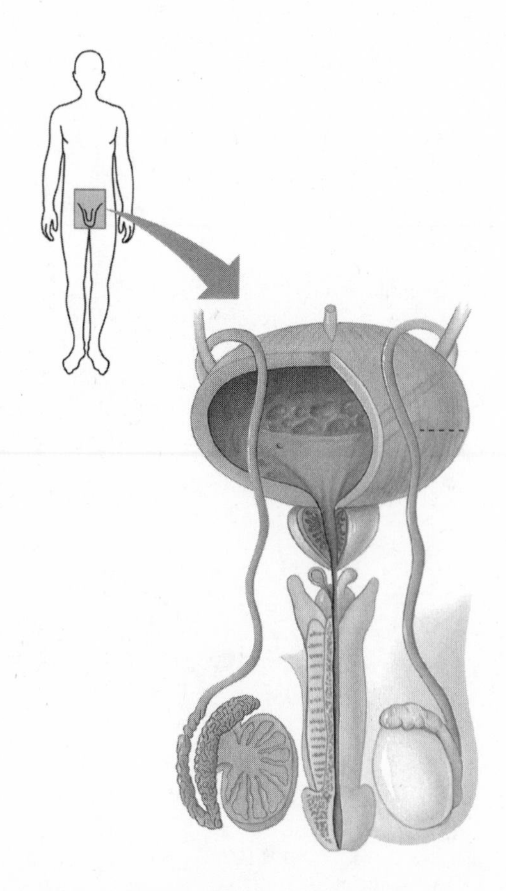

Figure 46.8 Reproductive anatomy of the human male (continued), page 981

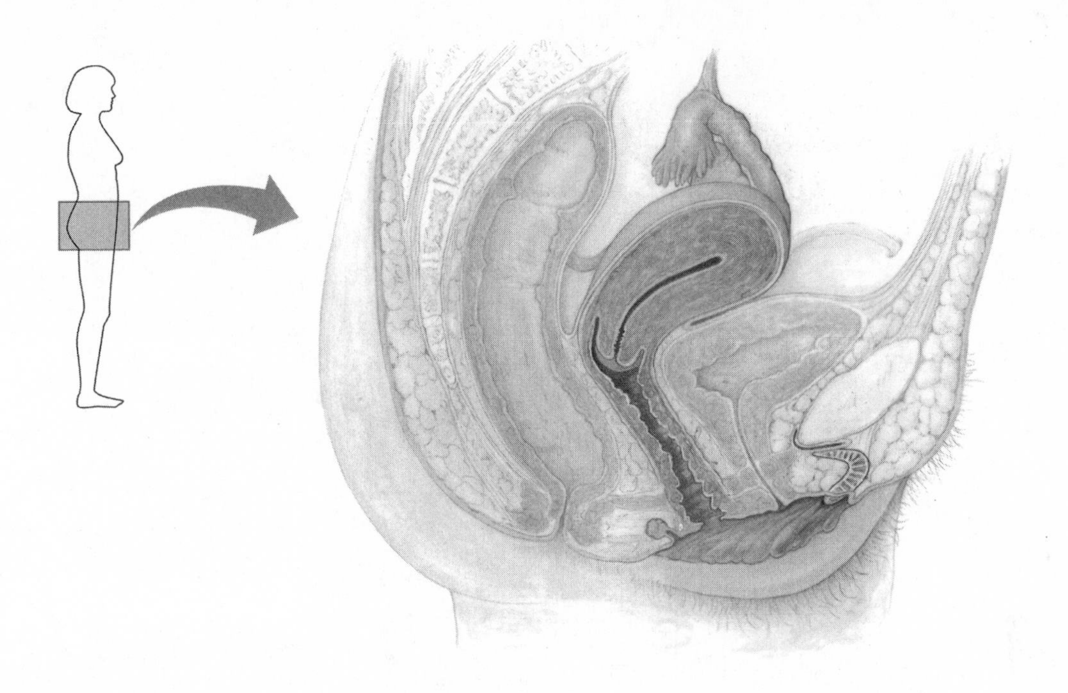

Figure 46.9 Reproductive anatomy of the human female, page 983

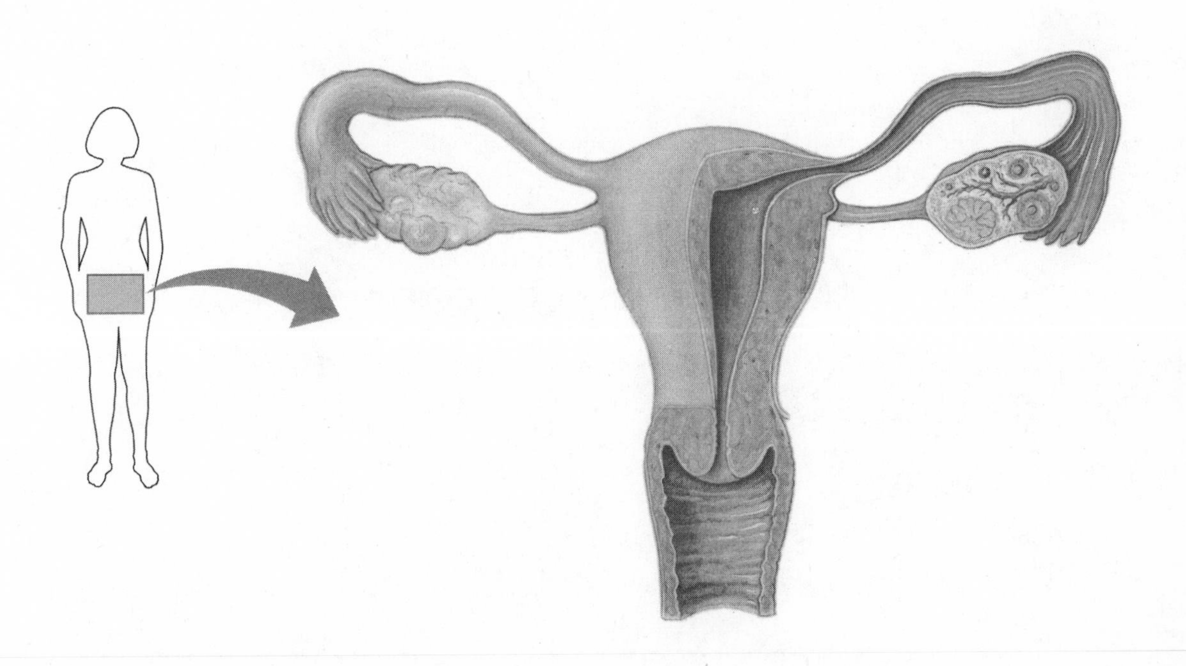

Figure 46.9 Reproductive anatomy of the human female (continued), page 983

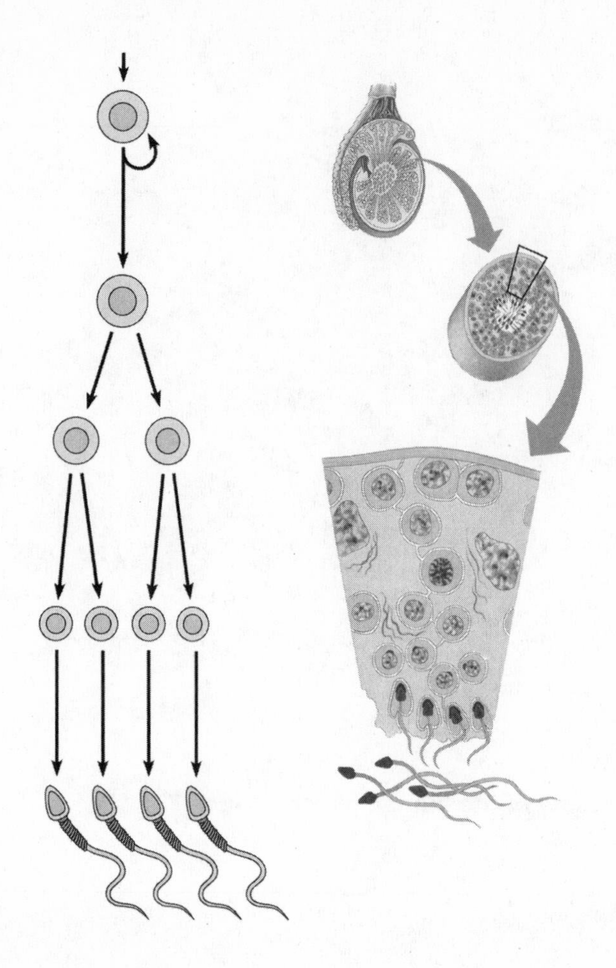

Figure 46.11 Spermatogenesis, page 985

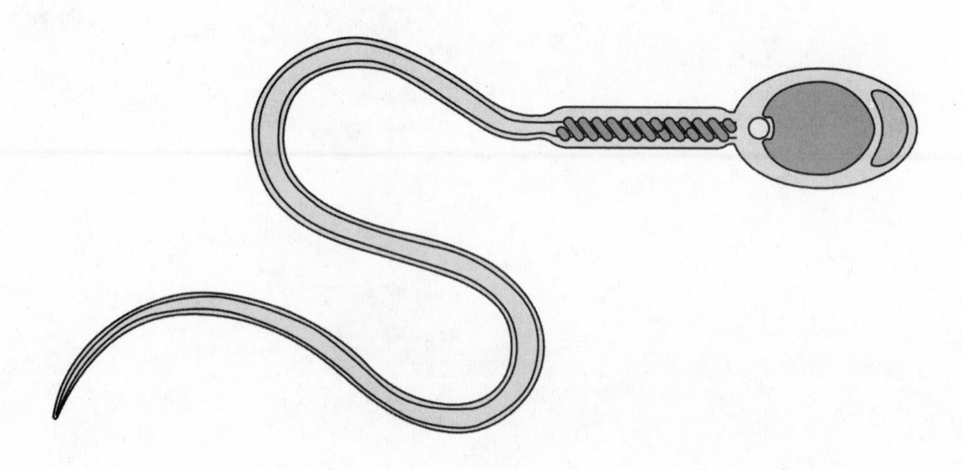

Figure 46.12 Structure of a human sperm cell, page 985

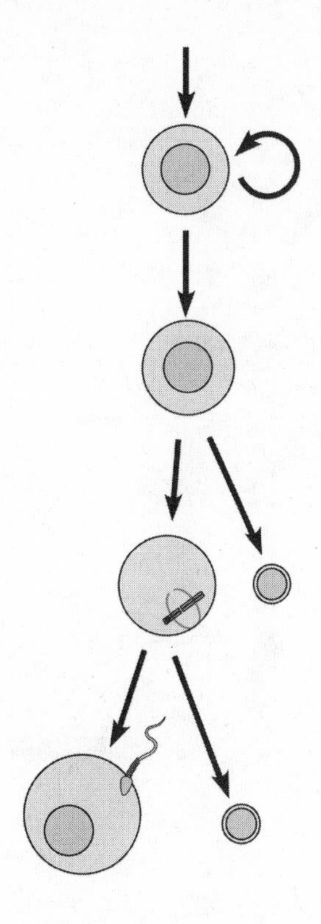

Figure 46.13a Oogenesis, page 986

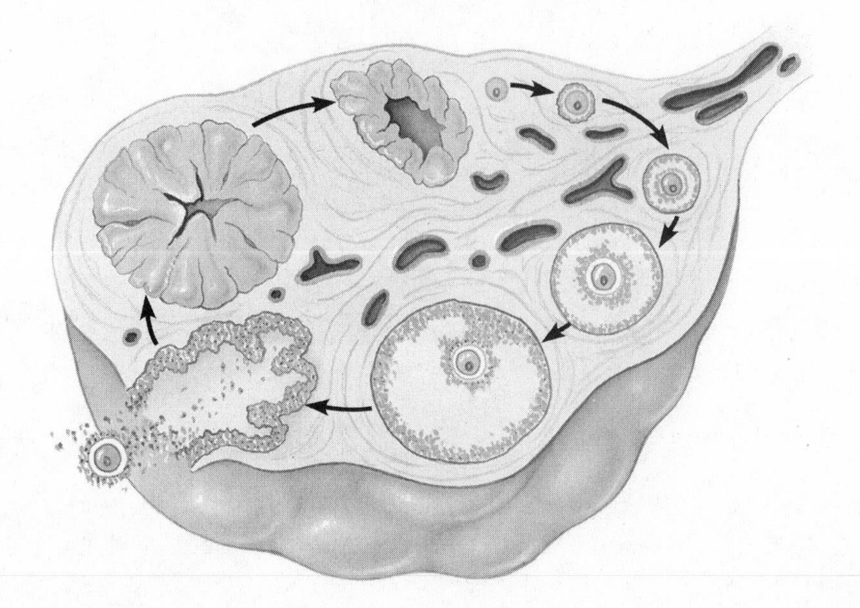

Figure 46.13b Oogenesis, page 986

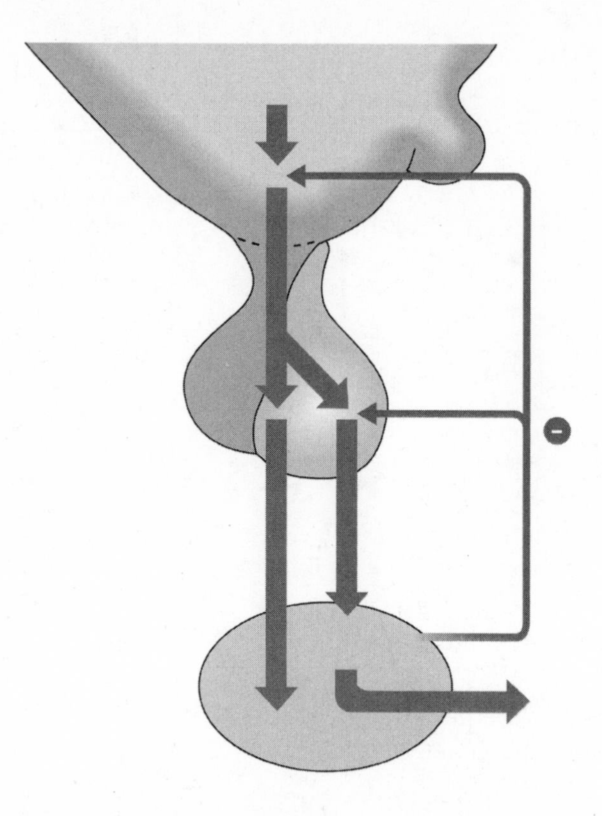

Figure 46.14 Hormonal control of the testes, page 987

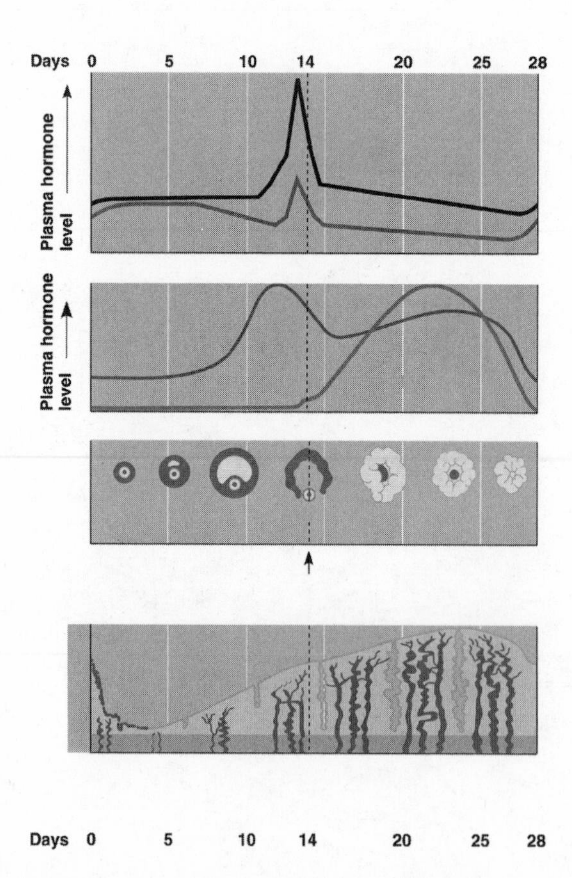

Figure 46.15 The reproductive cycle of the human female, page 988

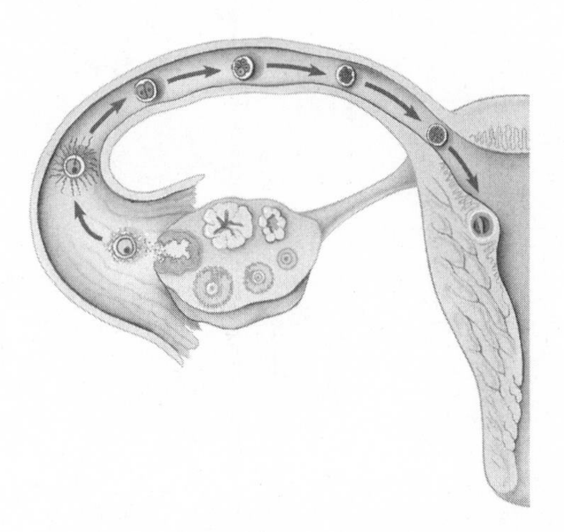

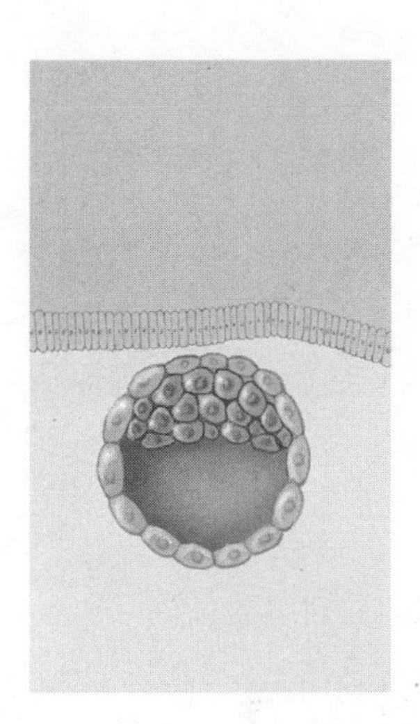

Figure 46.16 Formation of the zygote and early postfertilization events, page 990

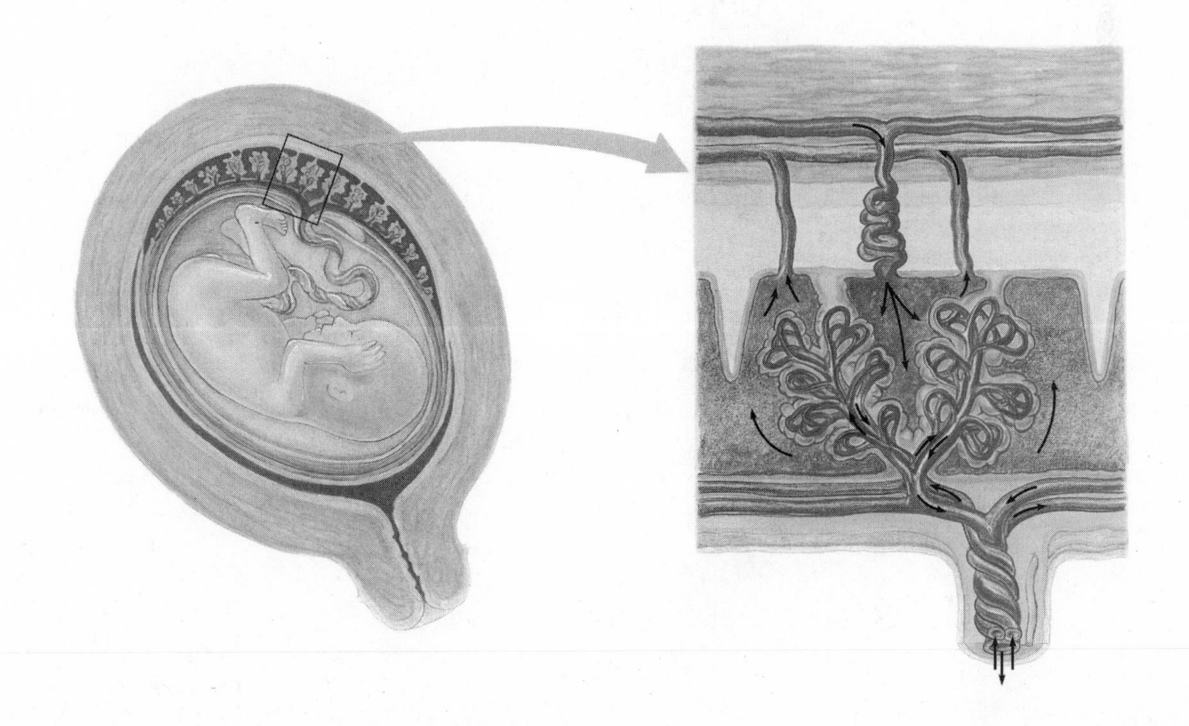

Figure 46.17 Placental circulation, page 991

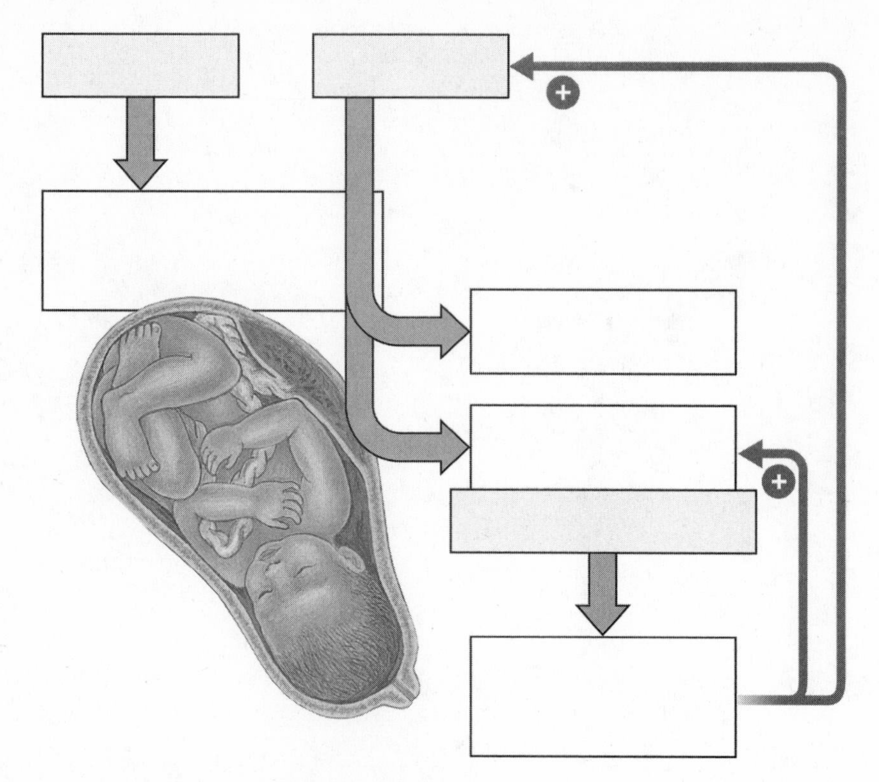

Figure 46.19 Hormonal induction of labor, page 992

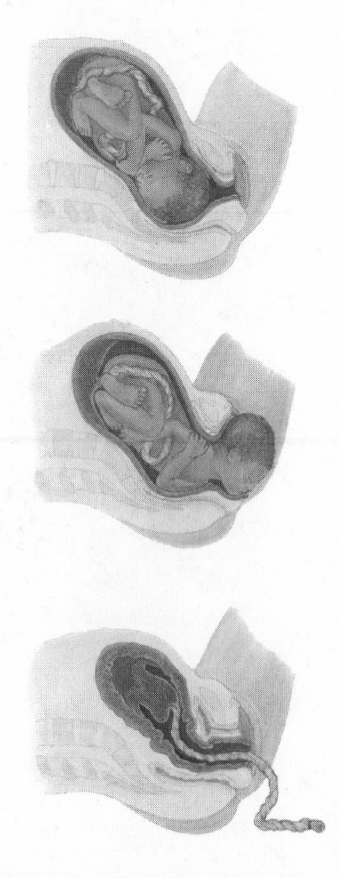

Figure 46.20 The three stages of labor, page 992

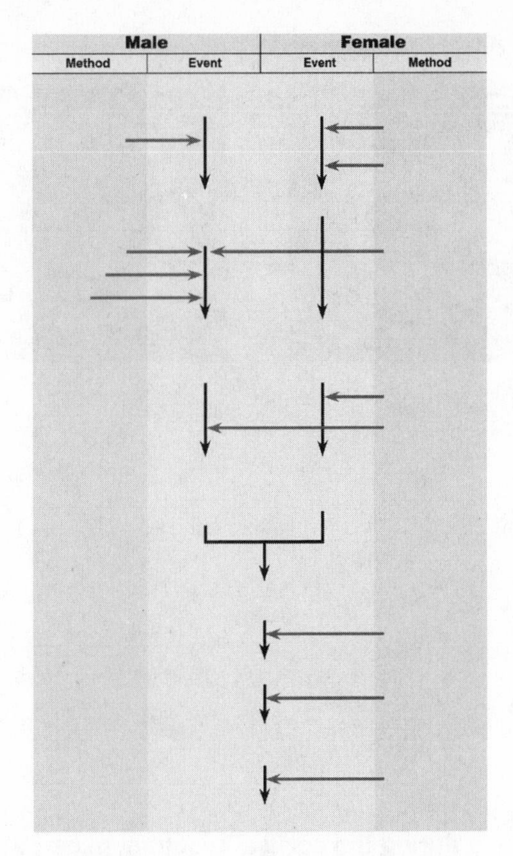

Figure 46.21 Mechanisms of some contraceptive methods, page 994

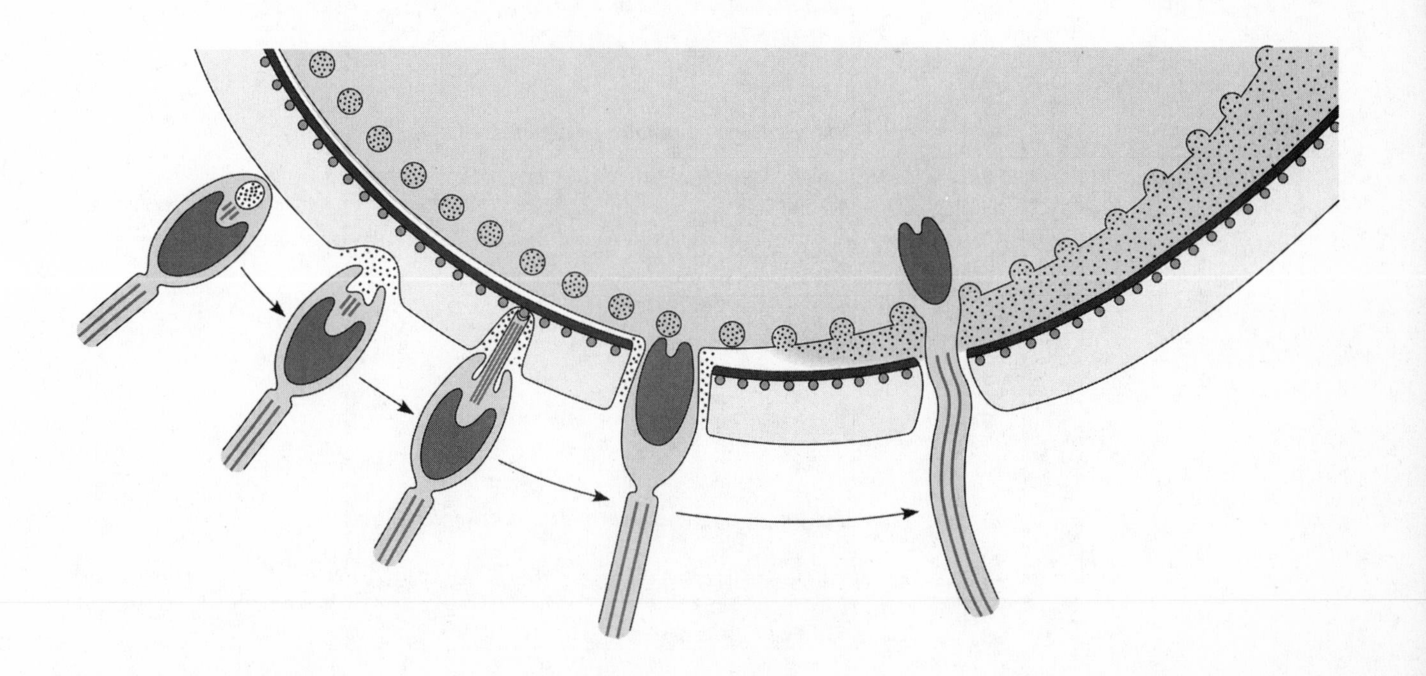

Figure 47.2 The acrosomal and cortical reactions during sea urchin fertilization, page 1000

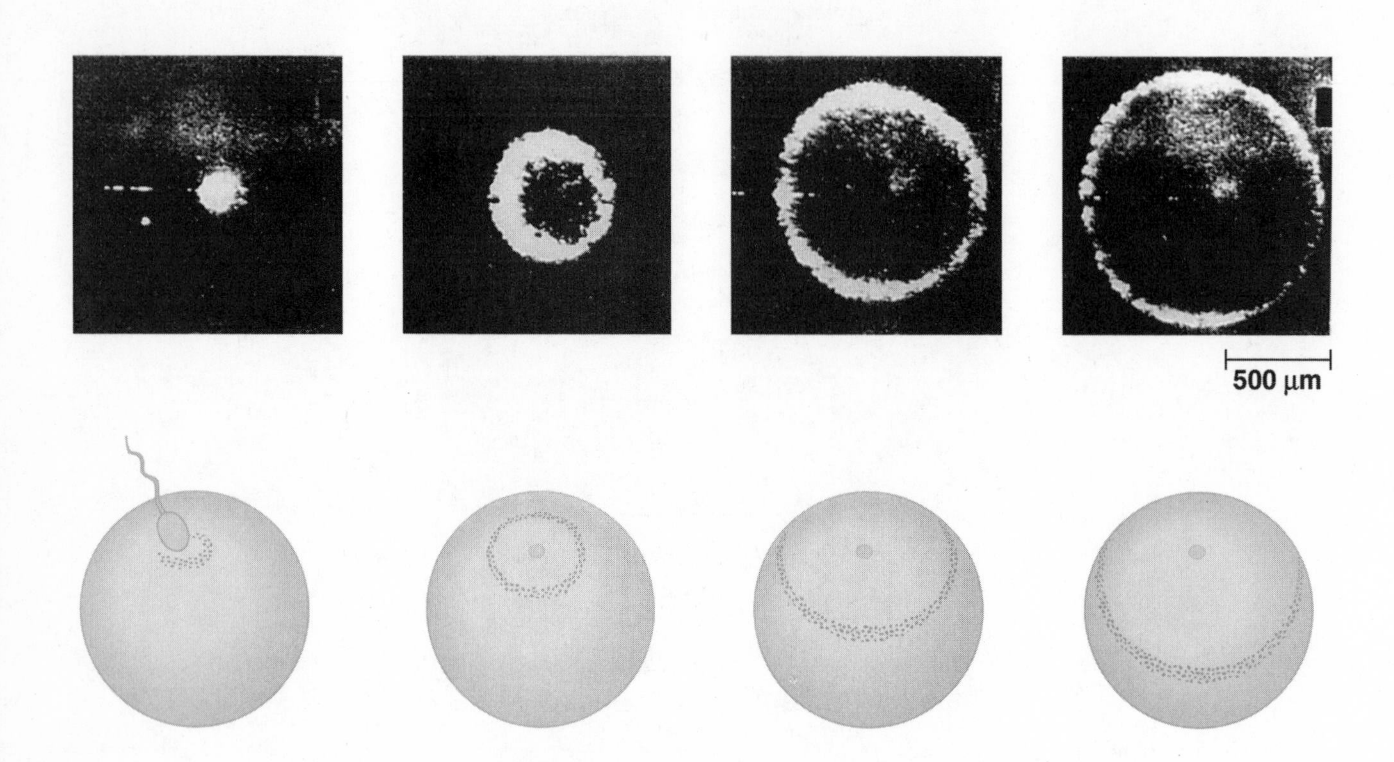

Figure 47.3 A view of CA^{2+} release during the cortical reaction, page 1001

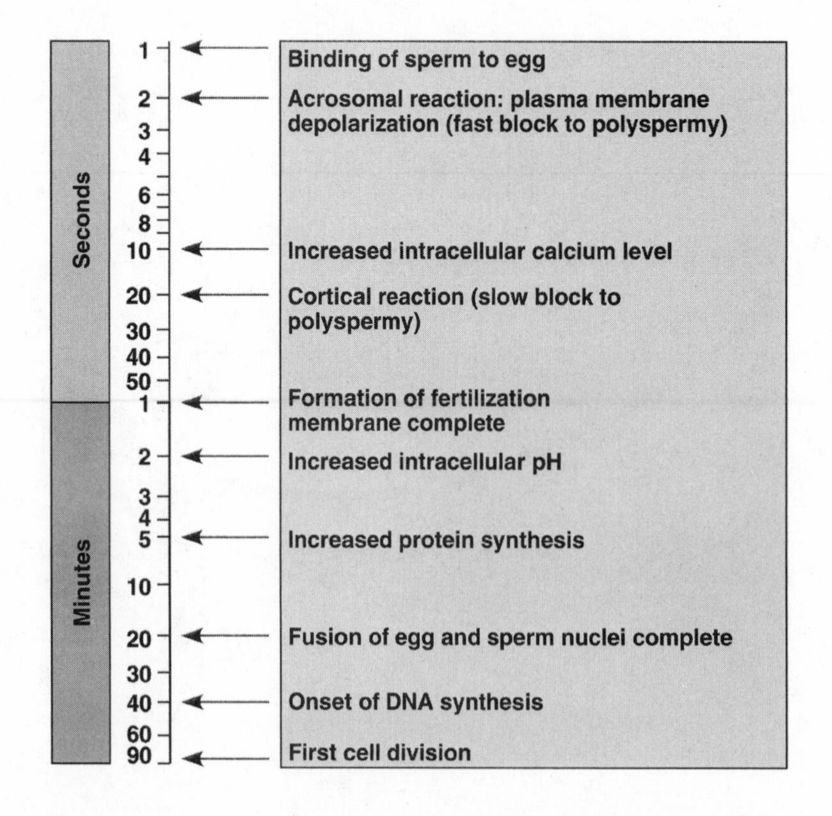

Figure 47.4 Timeline for the fertilization of sea urchin eggs, page 1001

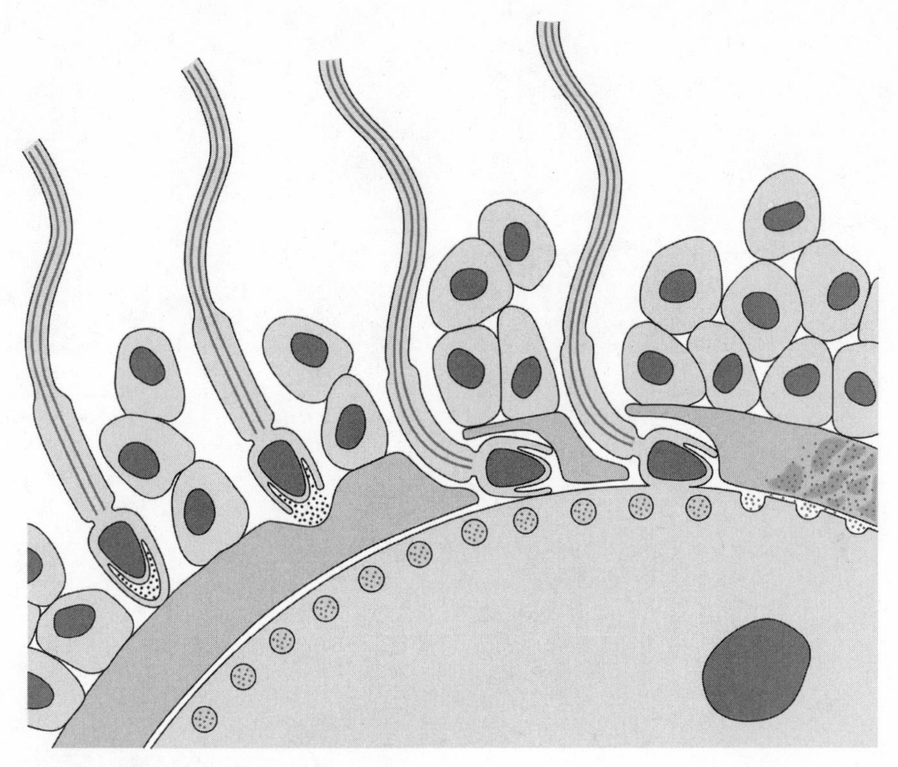

Figure 47.5 Fertilization in mammals, page 1002

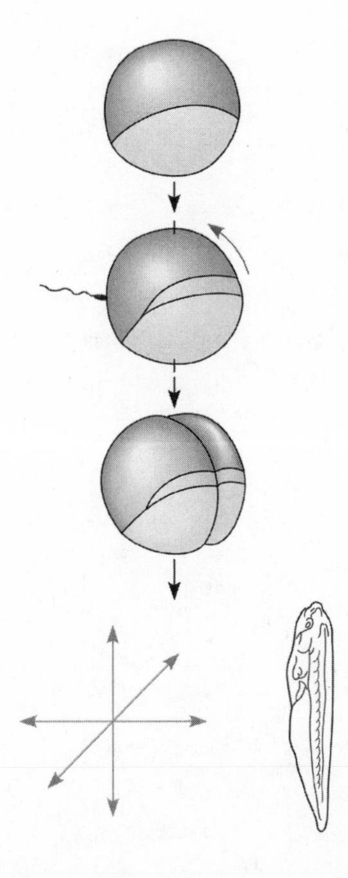

Figure 47.7 The establishment of the body axes and the first cleavage plane in an amphibian, page 1003

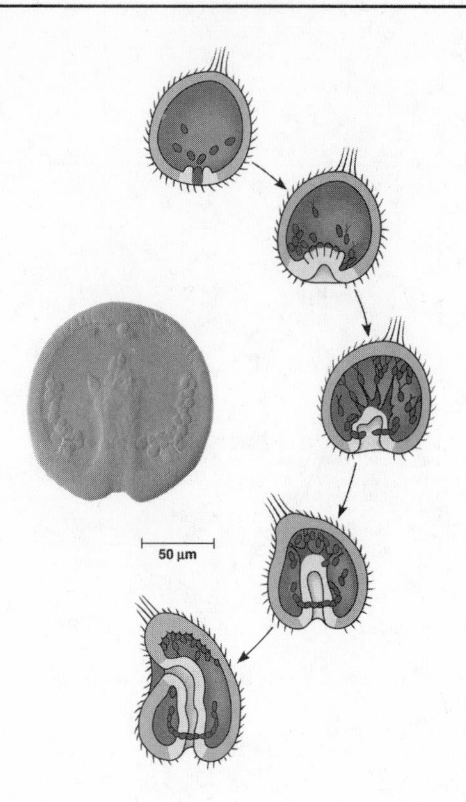

Figure 47.9 Sea urchin gastrulation, page 1005

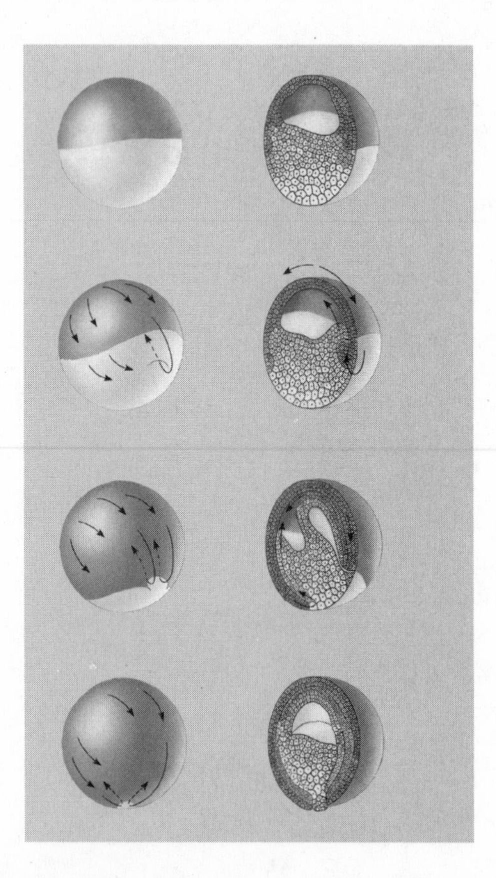

Figure 47.10 Gastrulation in a frog embryo, page 1006

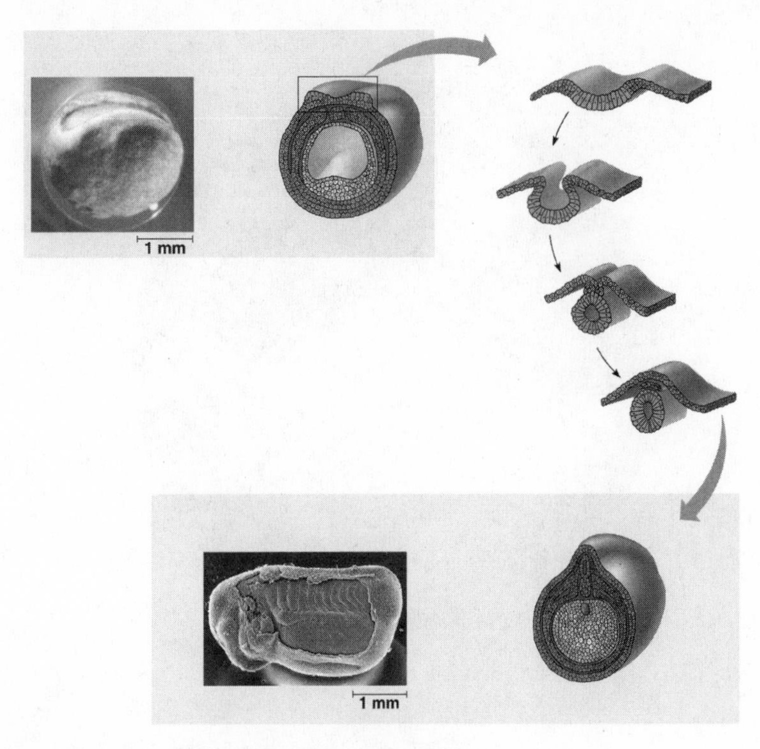

Figure 47.11 Organogenesis in a frog embryo, page 1008

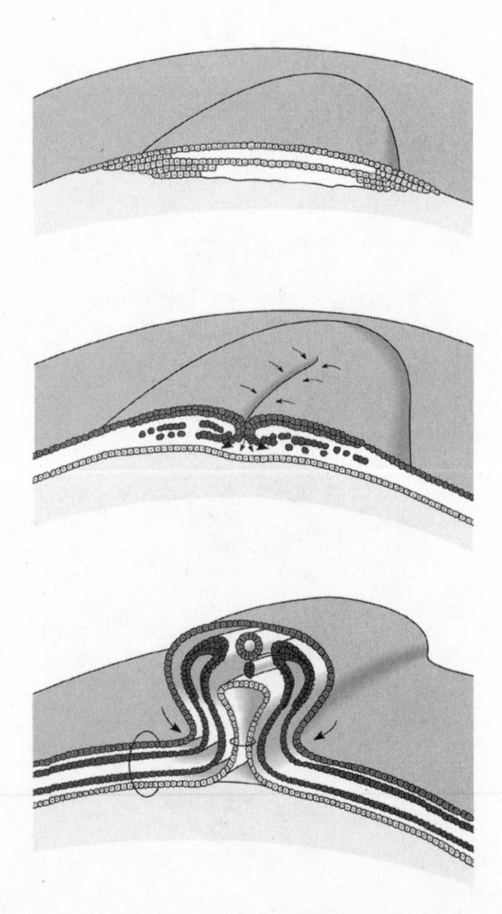

Figure 47.12 Cleavage, gastrulation, and early organogenesis in a chick embryo, page 1009

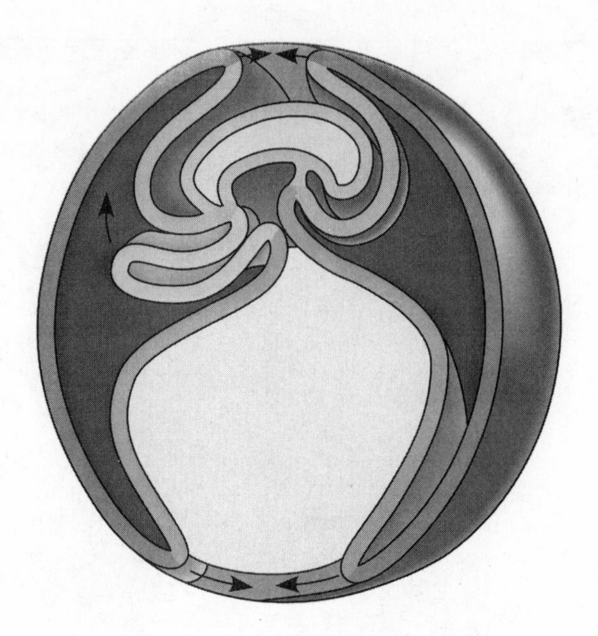

Figure 47.14 The development of extraembryonic membranes in a chick, page 1010

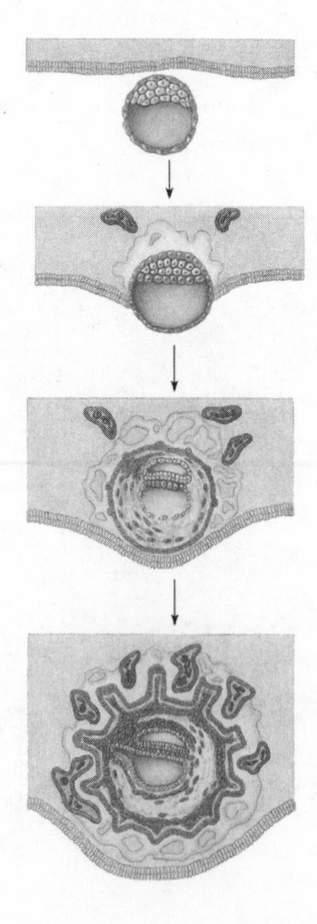

Figure 47.15 Early development of a human embryo and its extraembryonic membranes, page 1011

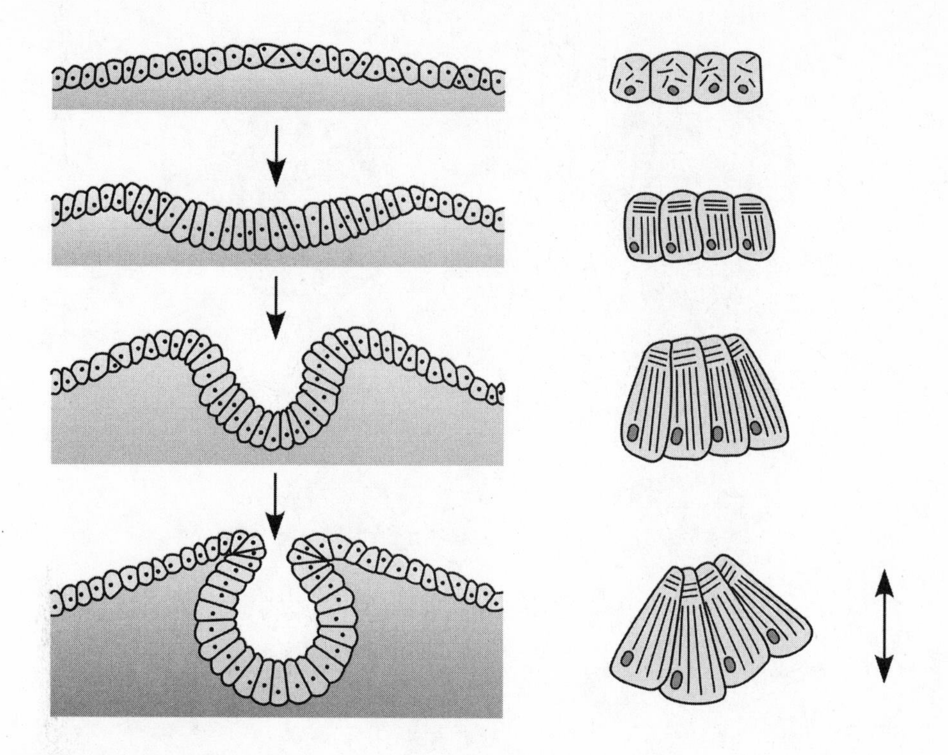

Figure 47.16 Change in cellular shape during morphogenesis, page 1012

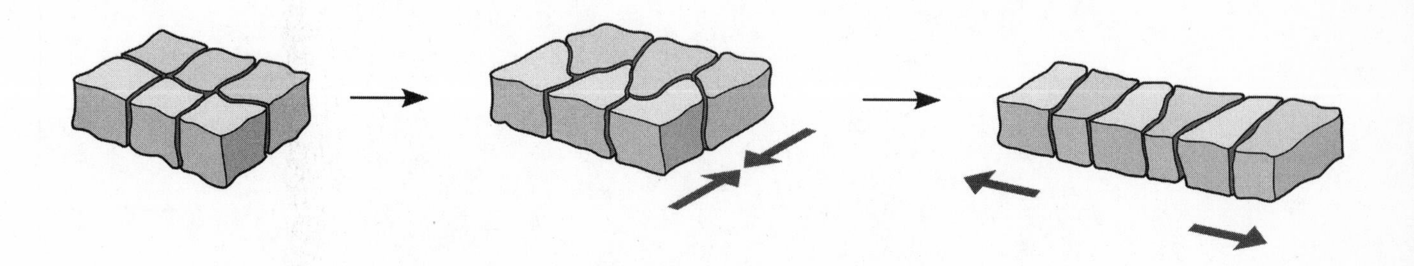

Figure 47.17 Convergent extension of a sheet of cells, page 1012

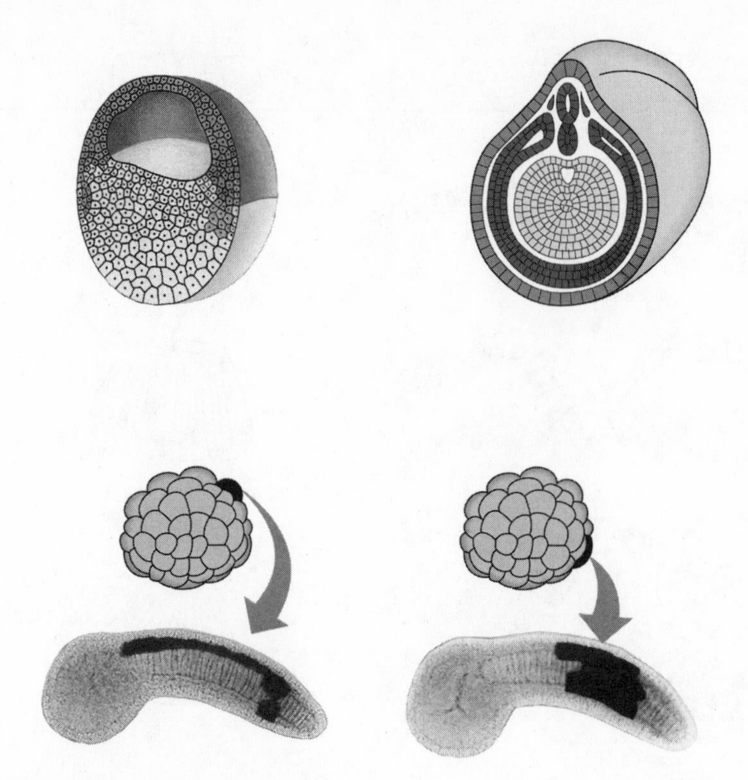

Figure 47.20 Fate maps for two chordates, page 1015

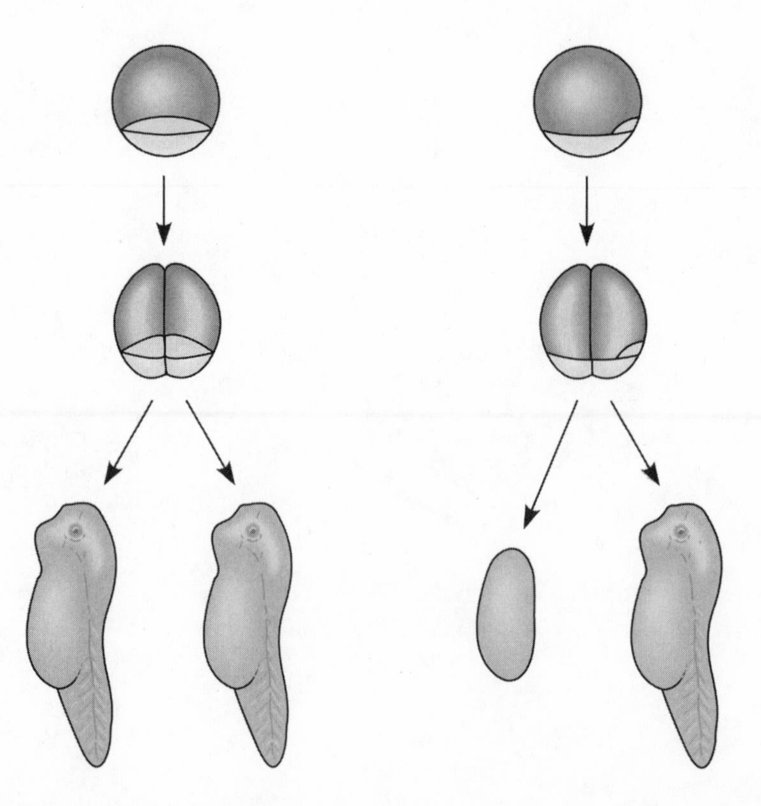

Figure 47.21 Experimental demonstration of the importance of cytoplasmic determinants in amphibians, page 1016

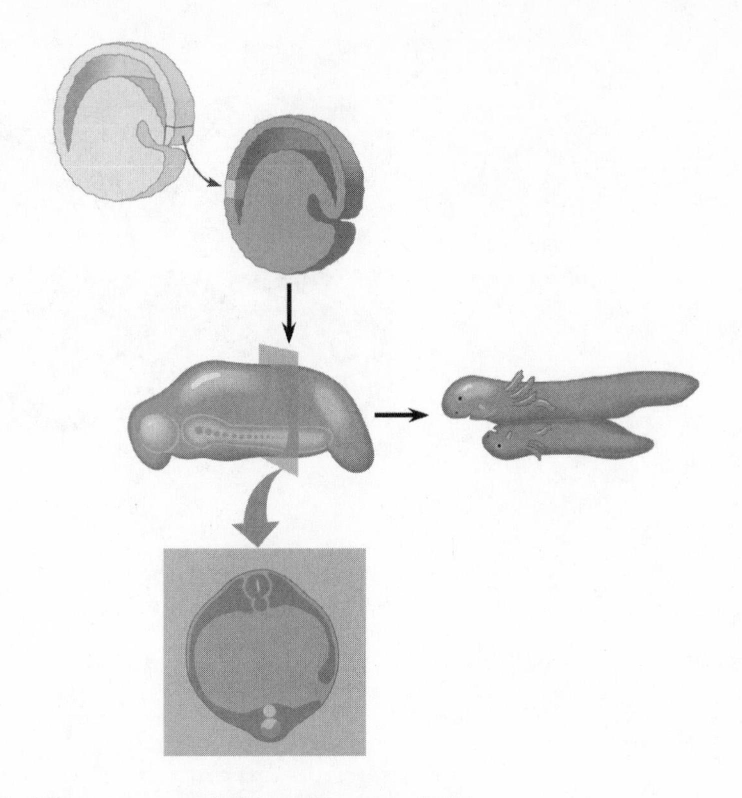

Figure 47.22 The "organizer" of Spemann and Mangold, page 1017

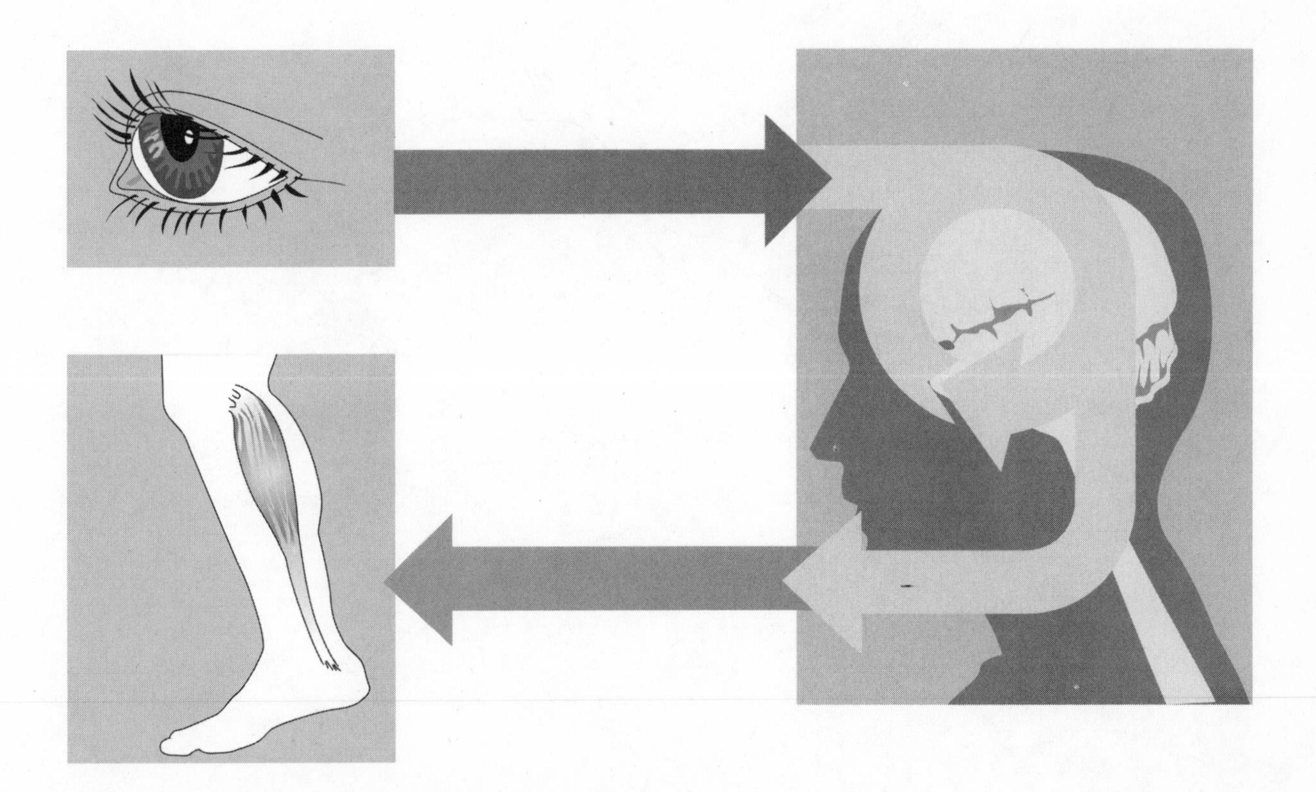

Figure 48.1 Overview of a vertebrate nervous system, page 1023

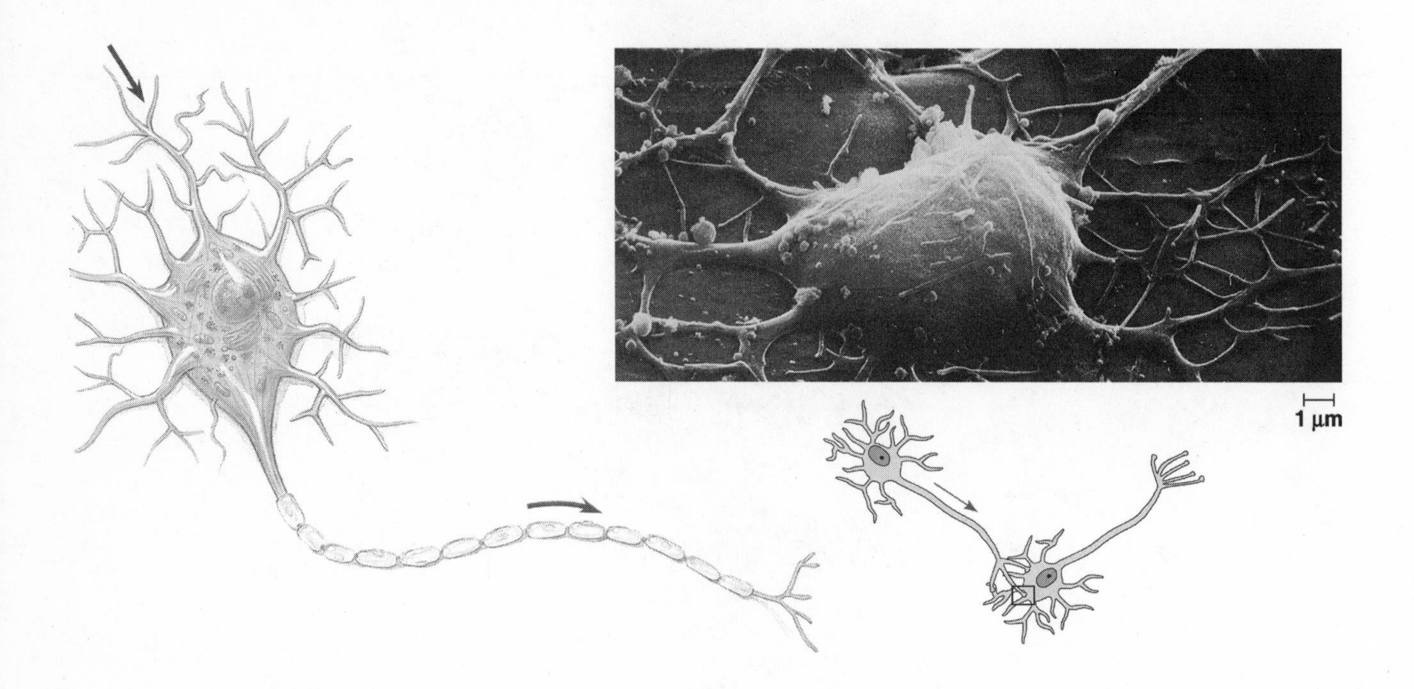

Figure 48.2 Structure of a vertebrate neuron, page 1023

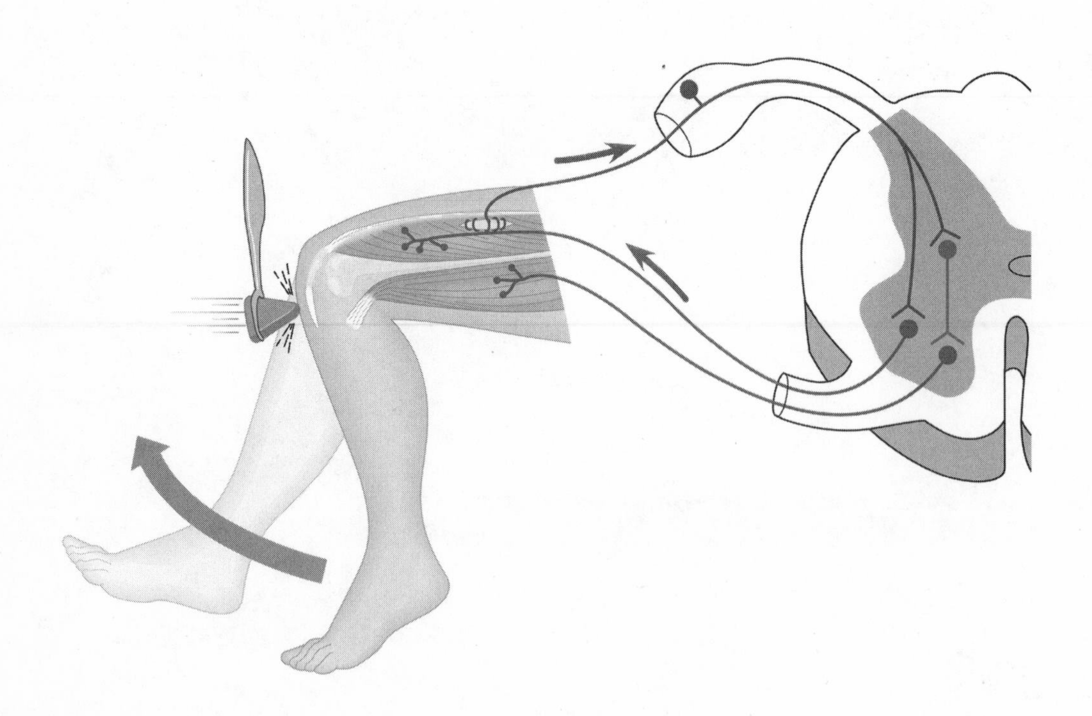

Figure 48.3 The knee-jerk reflex, page 1024

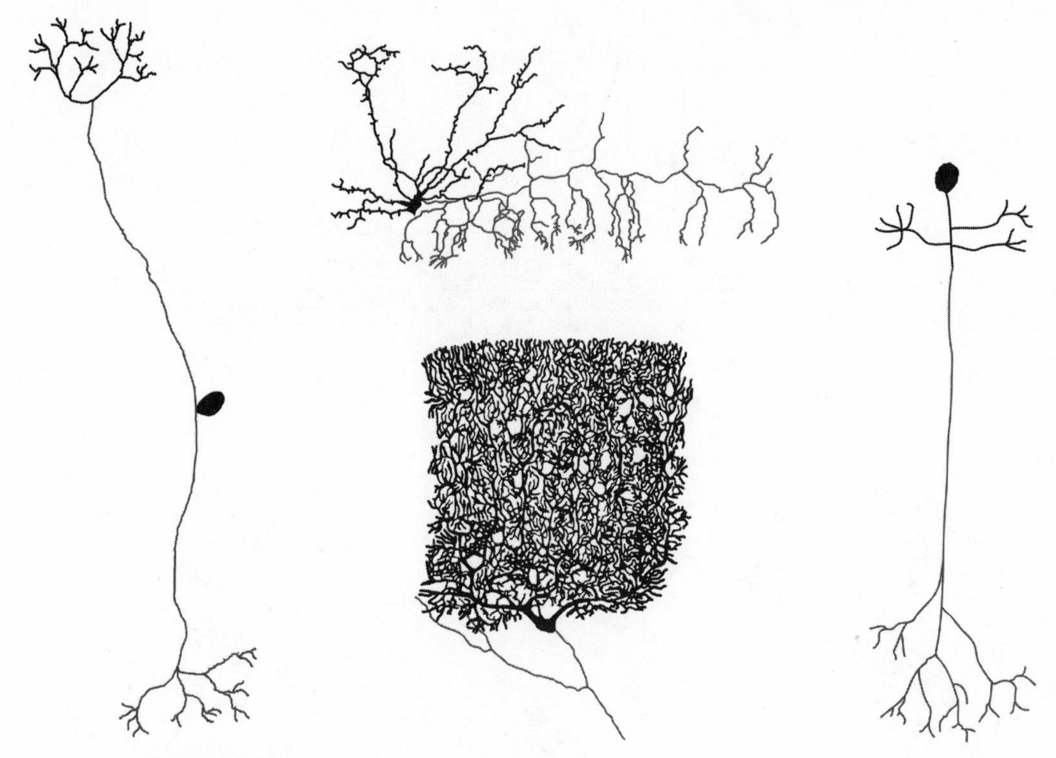

Figure 48.4 Structural diversity of neurons, page 1025

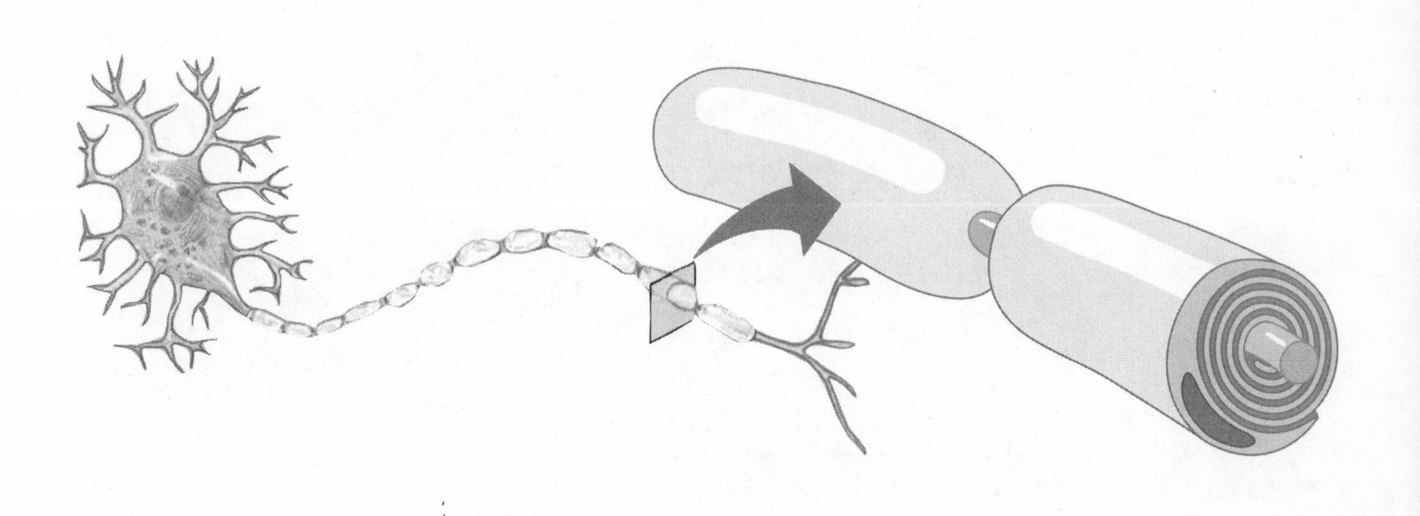

Figure 48.5 Schwann cells, page 1026

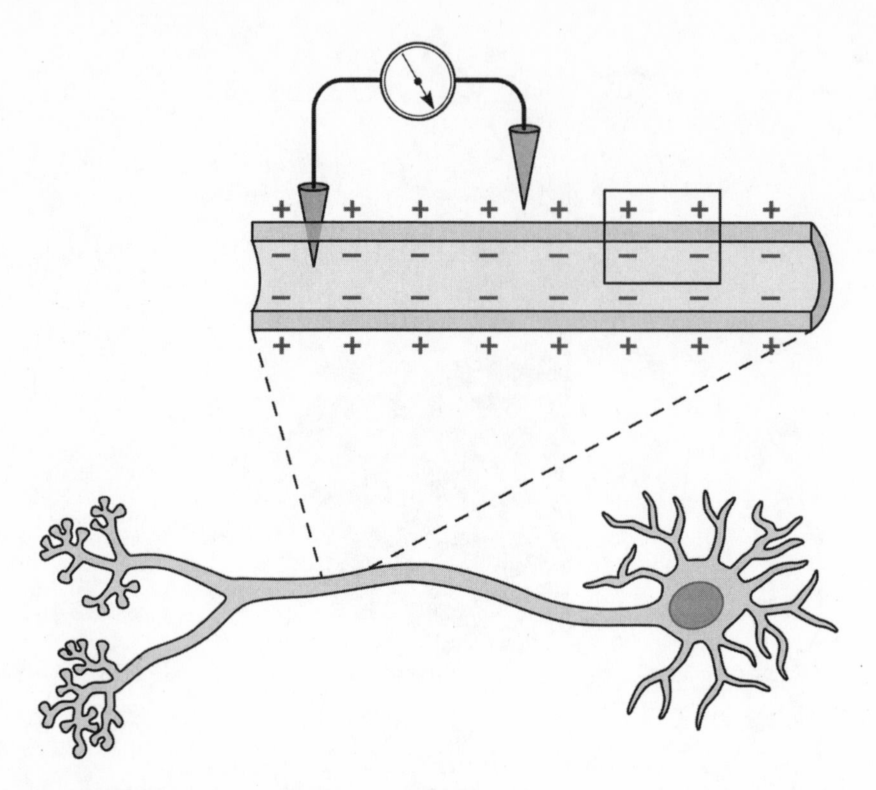

Figure 48.6a Measuring membrane potentials, page 1027

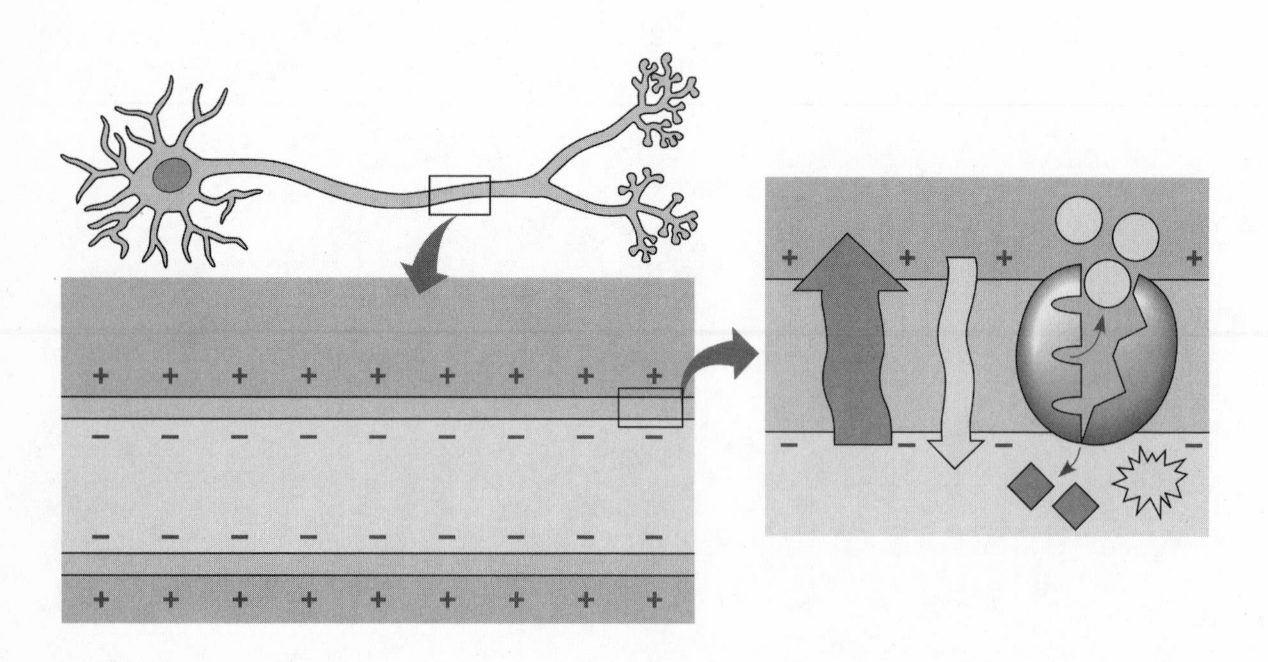

Figure 48.7 The basis of the membrane potential, page 1027

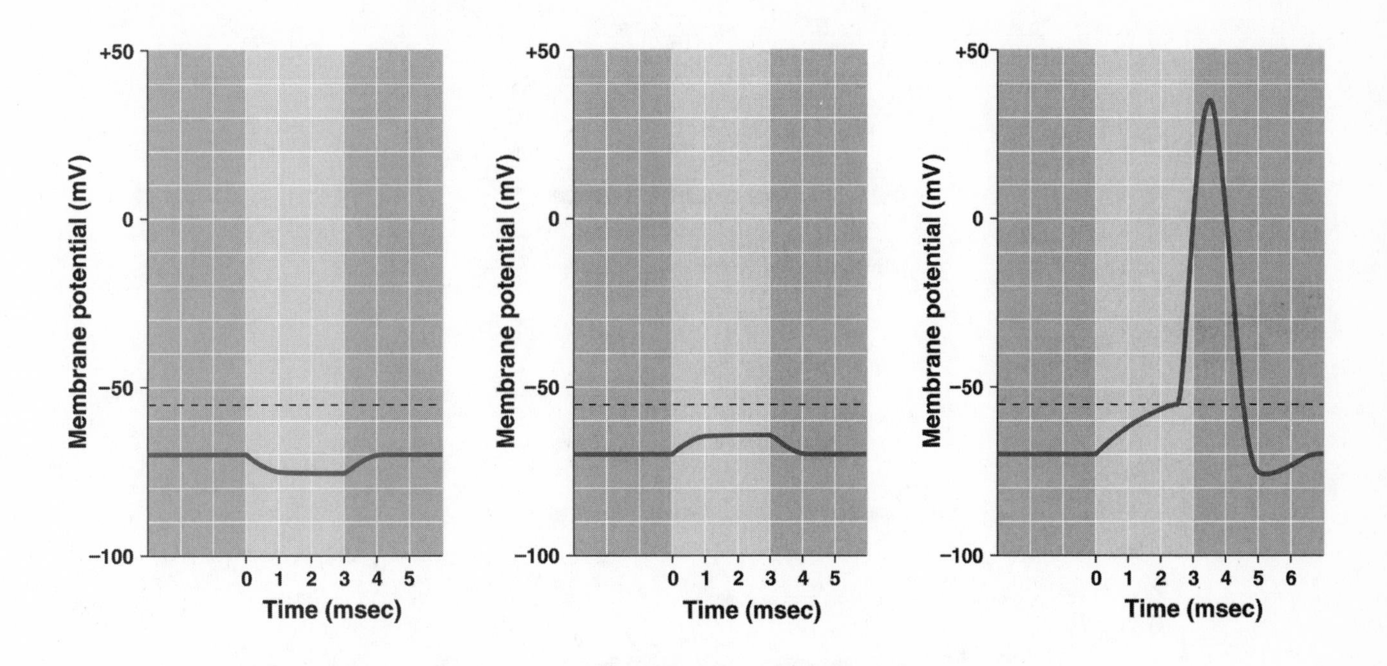

Figure 48.8 Graded potentials and the action potential in a neuron, page 1029

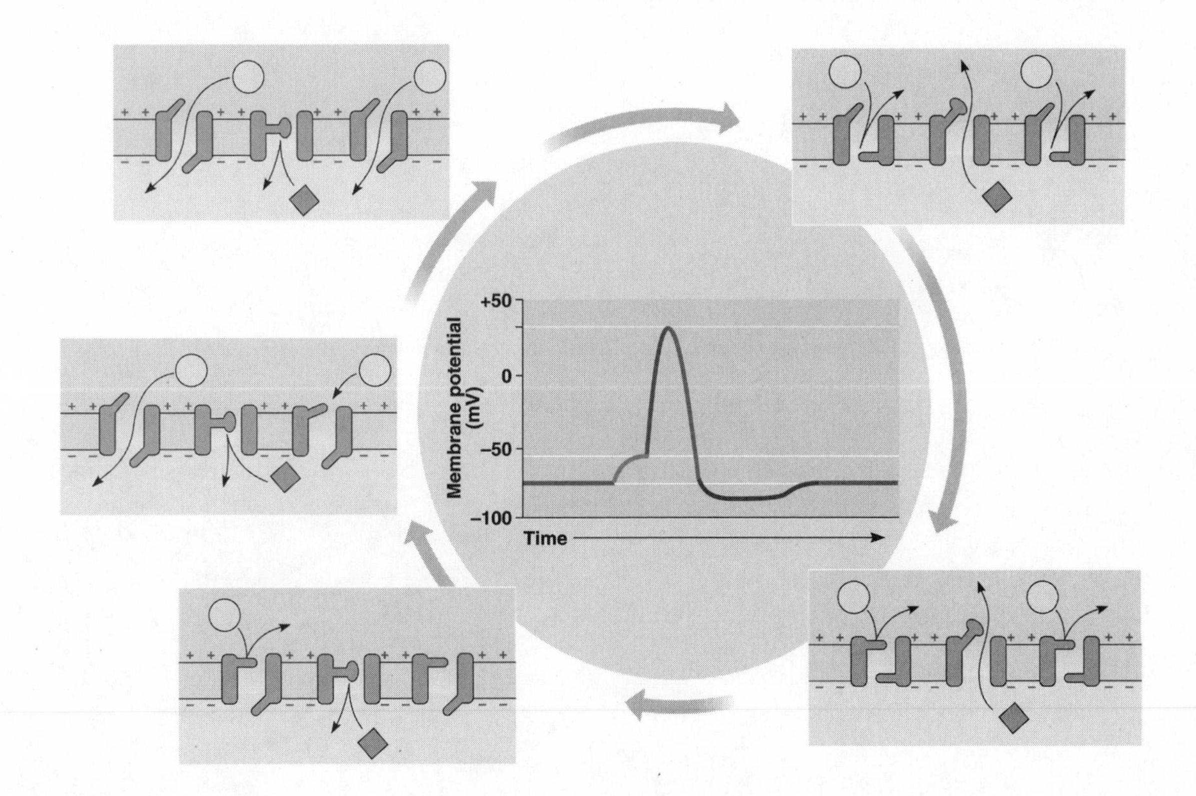

Figure 48.9 The role of voltage-gated ion channels in the action potential, page 1030

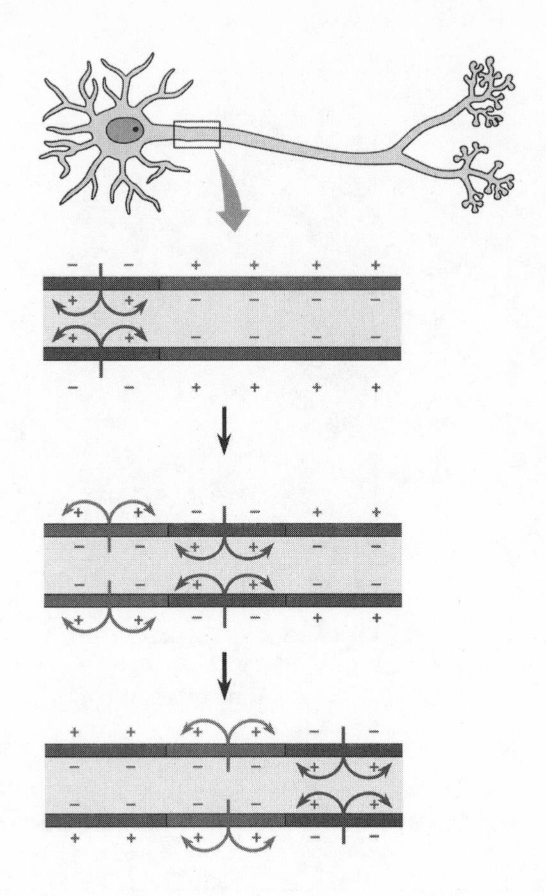

Figure 48.10 Propagation of the action potential, page 1032

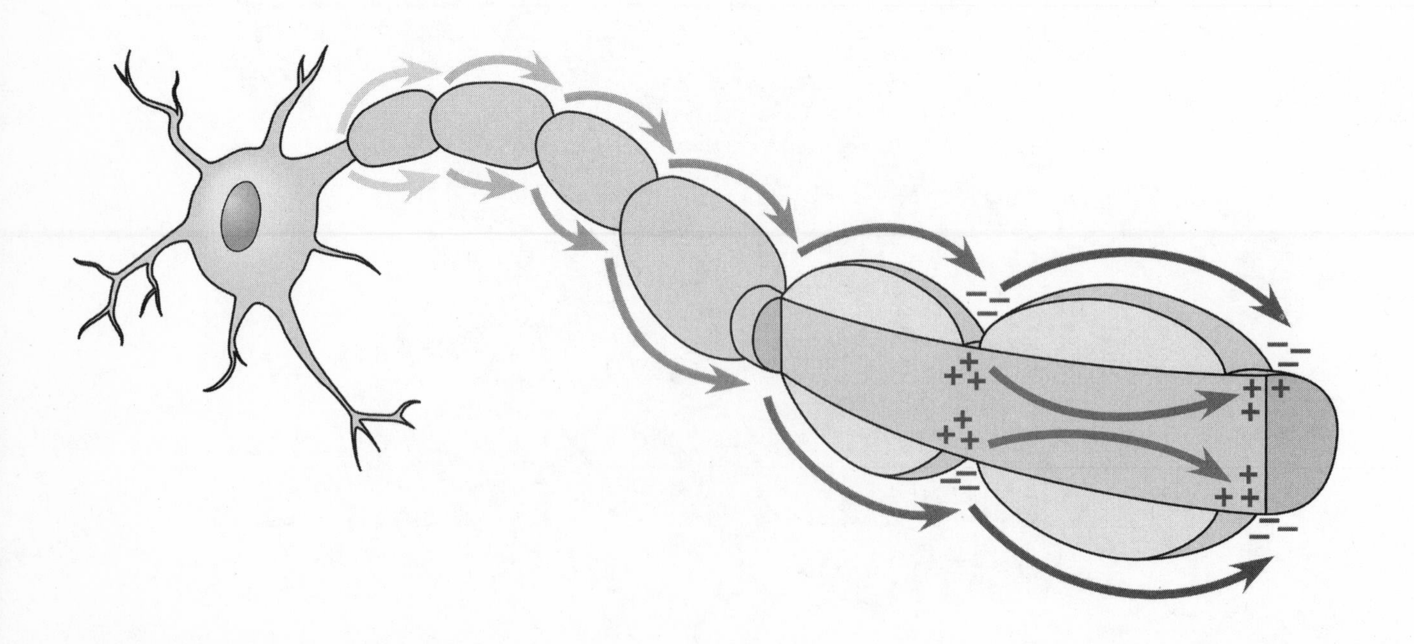

Figure 48.11 Saltatory conduction, page 1032

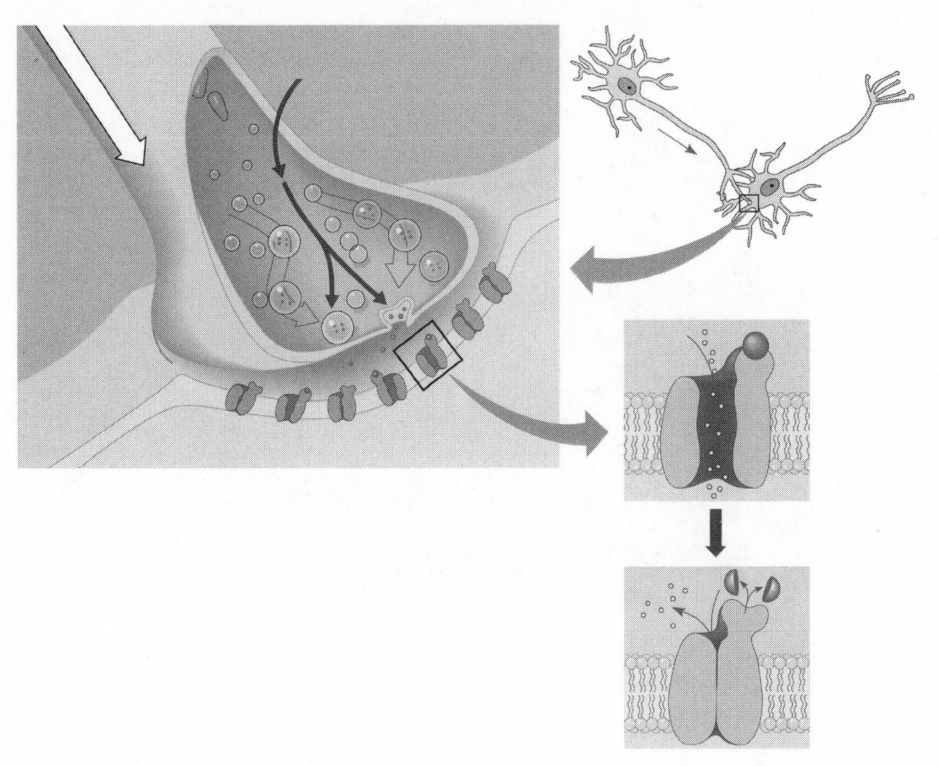

Figure 48.12 A chemical synapse, page 1033

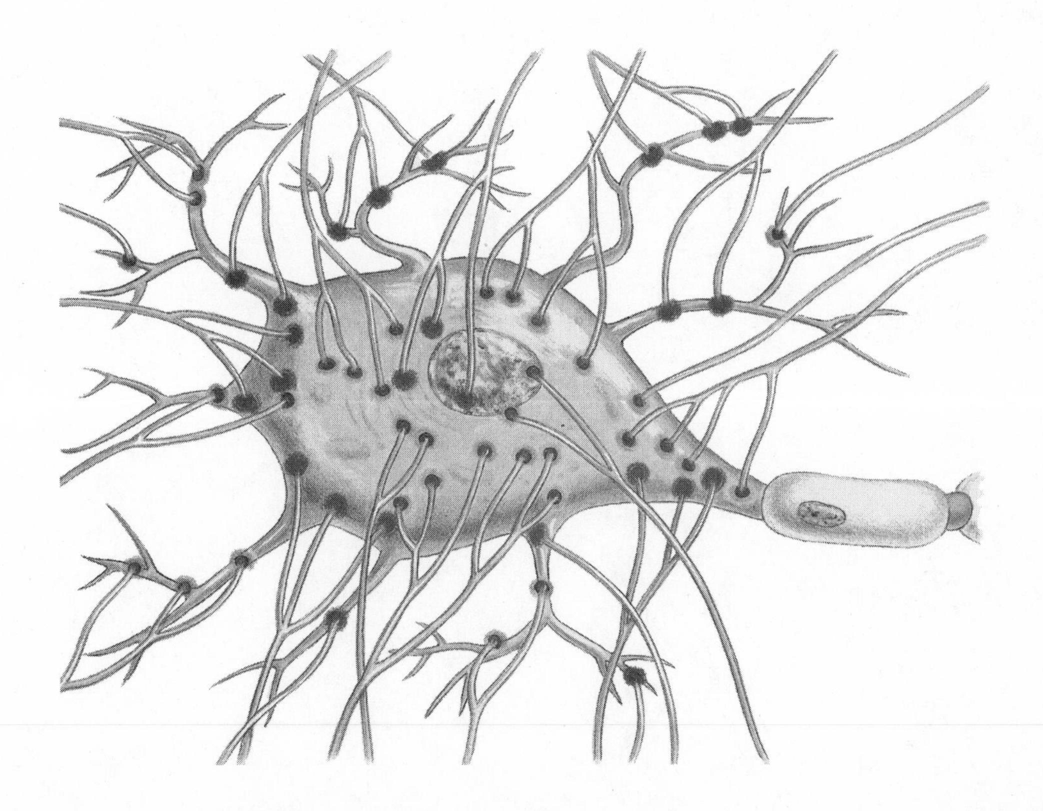

Figure 48.13a Integration of multiple synaptic inputs, page 1035

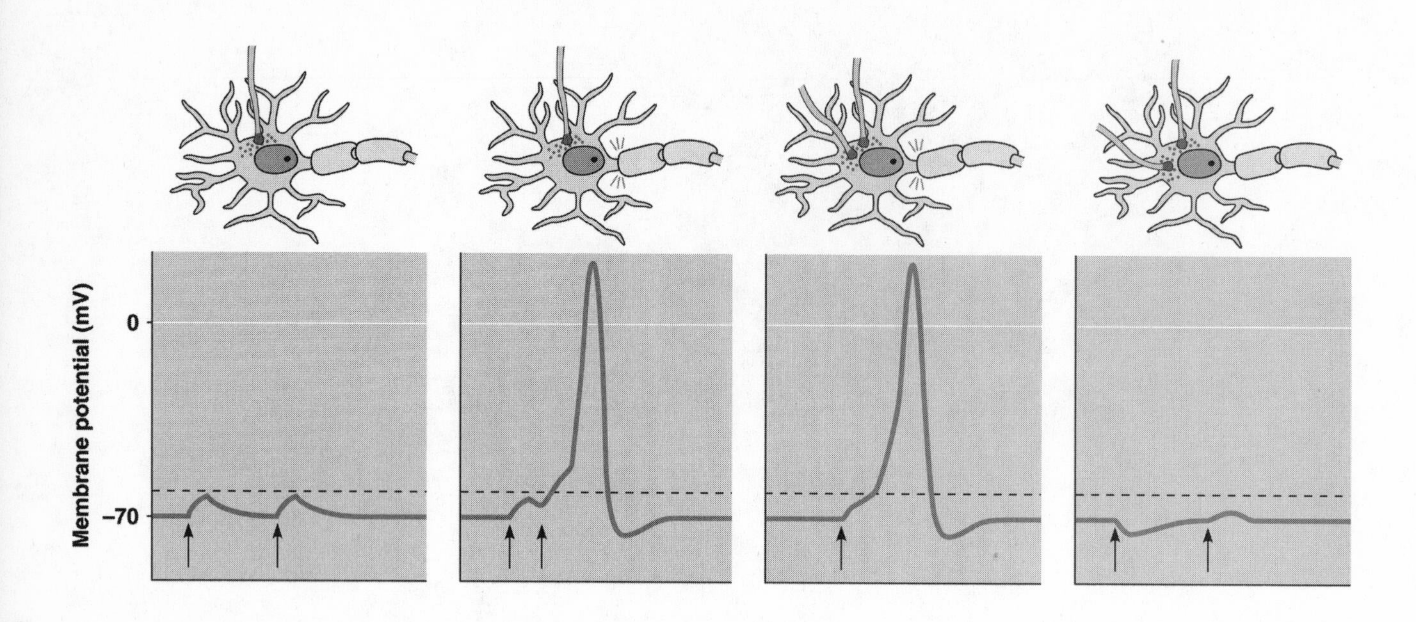

Figure 48.14 Summation of postsynaptic potentials, page 1036

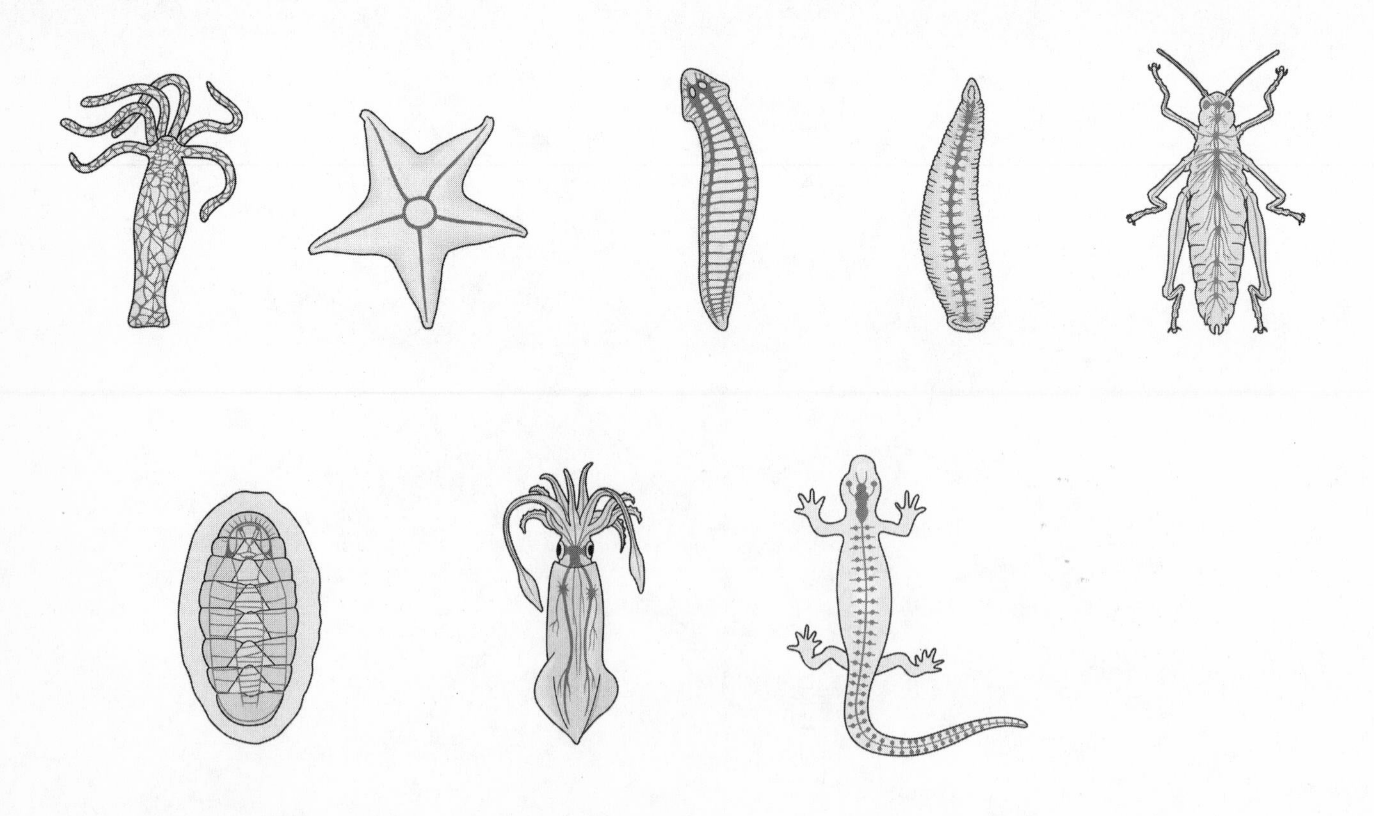

Figure 48.15 Diversity in nervous systems, page 1039

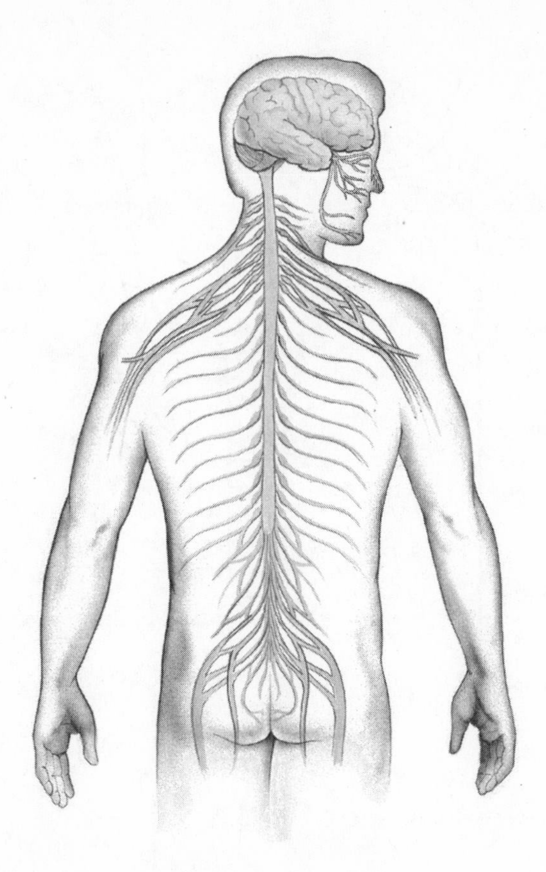

Figure 48.16 The nervous system of a vertebrate, page 1040

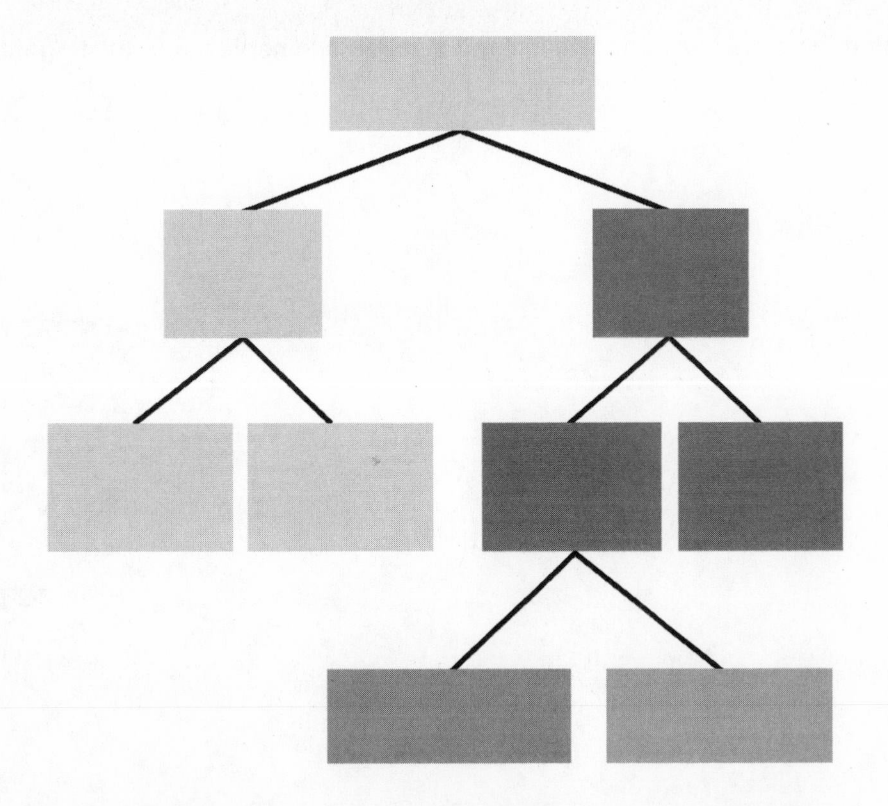

Figure 48.17 Functional hierarchy of the peripheral nervous system, page 1041

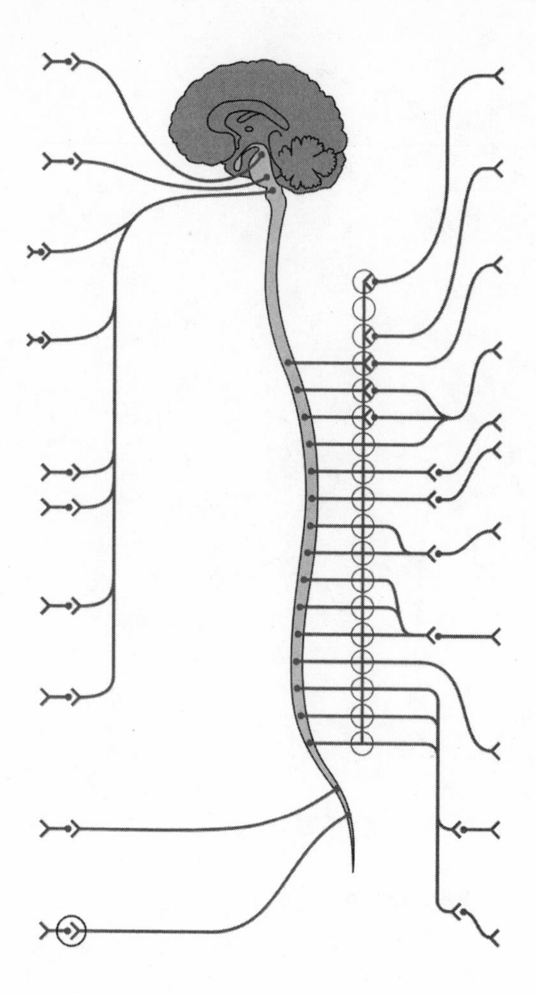

Figure 48.18 The main roles of the parasympathetic and sympathetic nerves in regulating internal body functions, page 1041

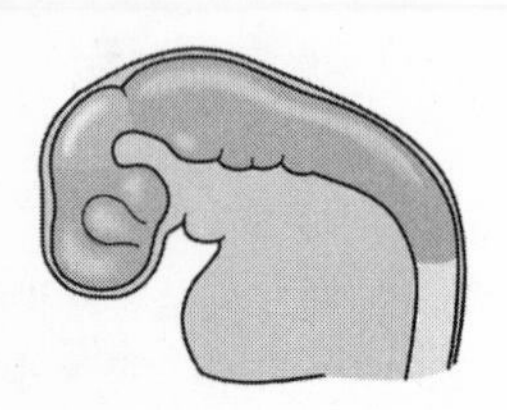

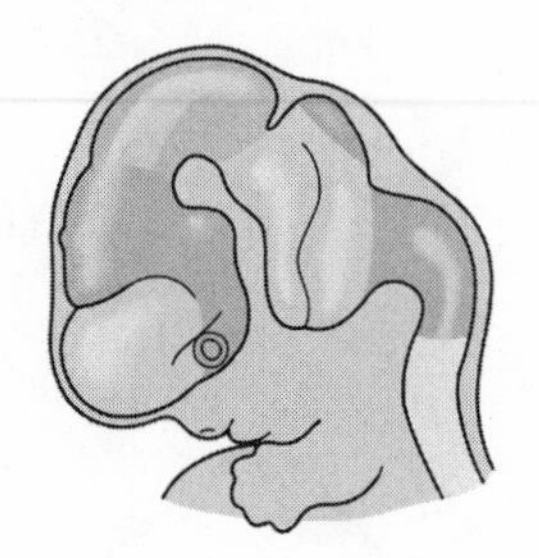

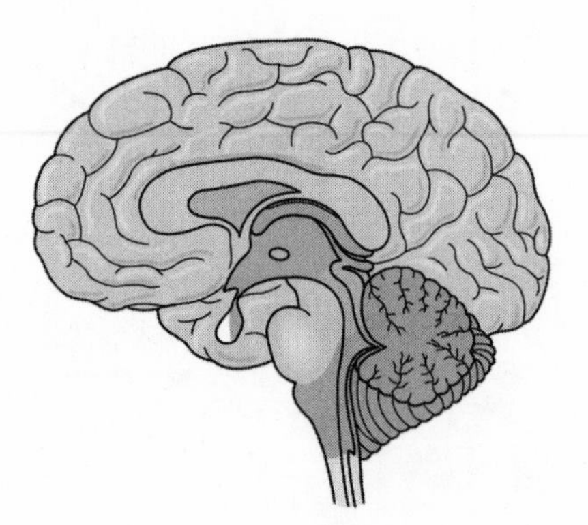

Figure 48.19 Embryonic development of the brain, page 1042

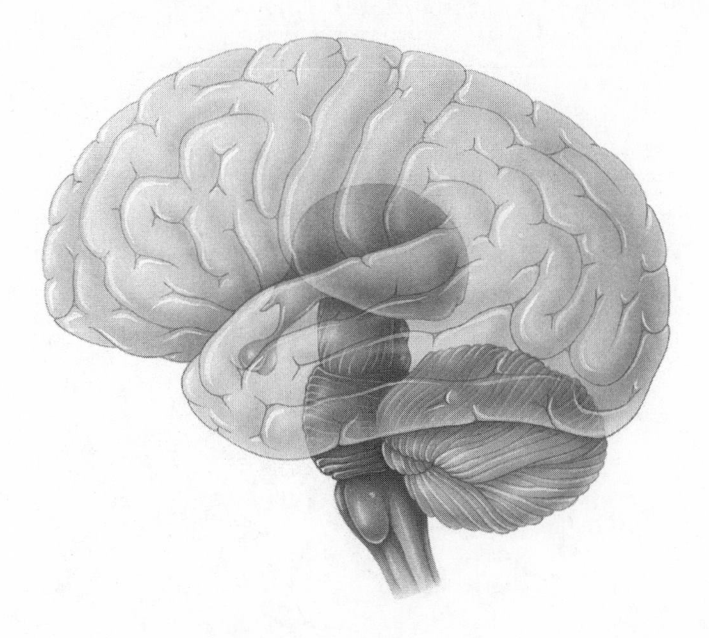

Figure 48.20 The main parts of the human brain, page 1043

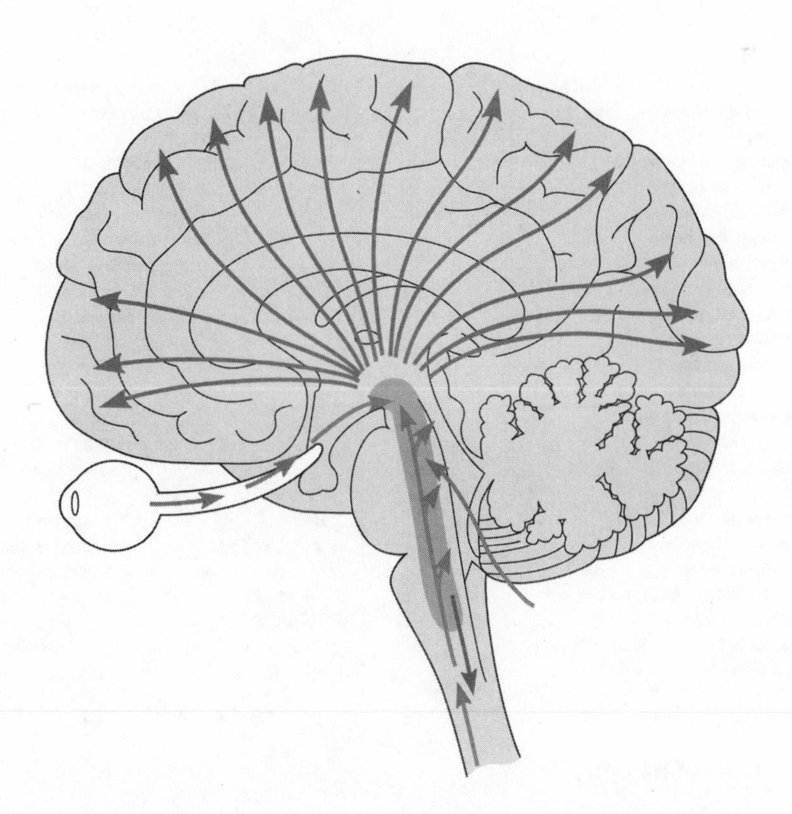

Figure 48.21 The reticular formation, page 1044

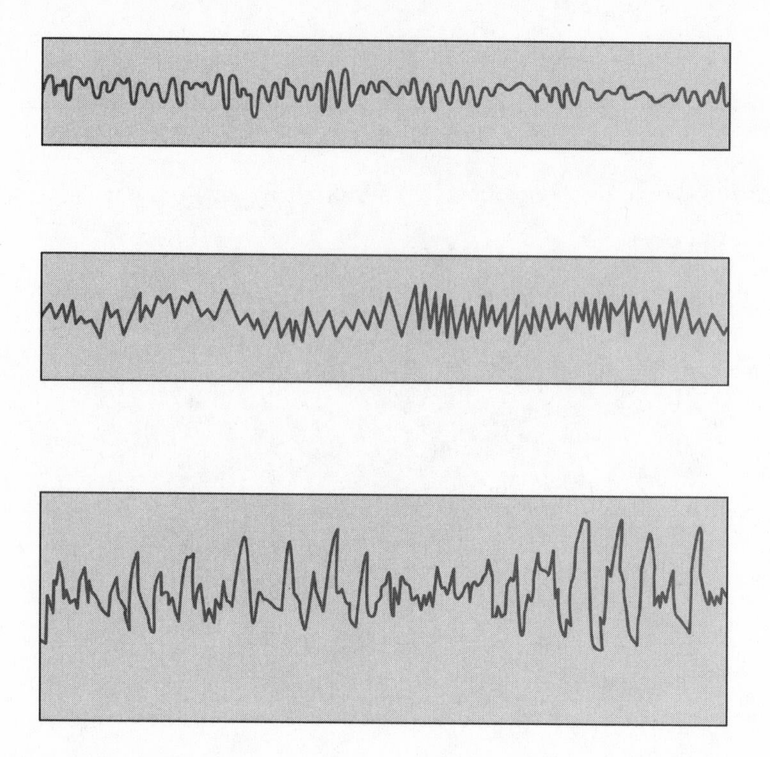

Figure 48.22b-d Brain waves recorded by an electroencephalogram (EEG), page 1044

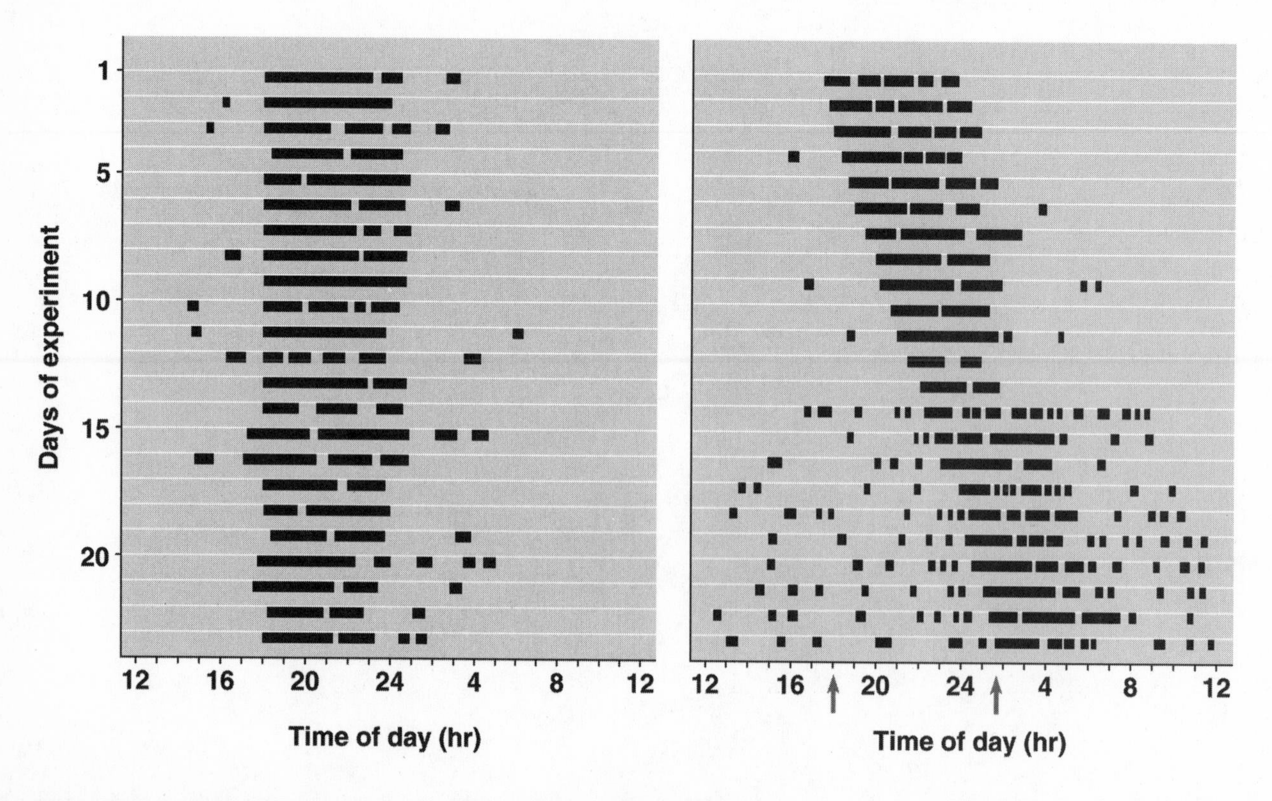

Figure 48.23 Activity rhythms in a nocturnal mammal, page 1046

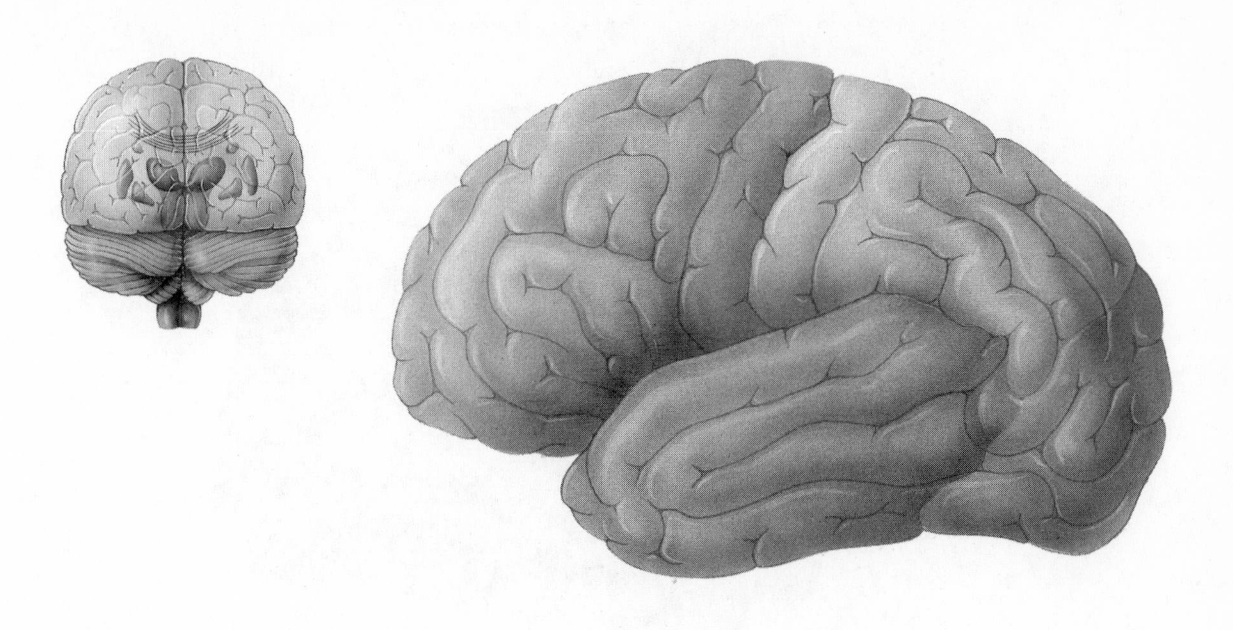

Figure 48.24 Structure and functional areas of the cerebrum, page 1047

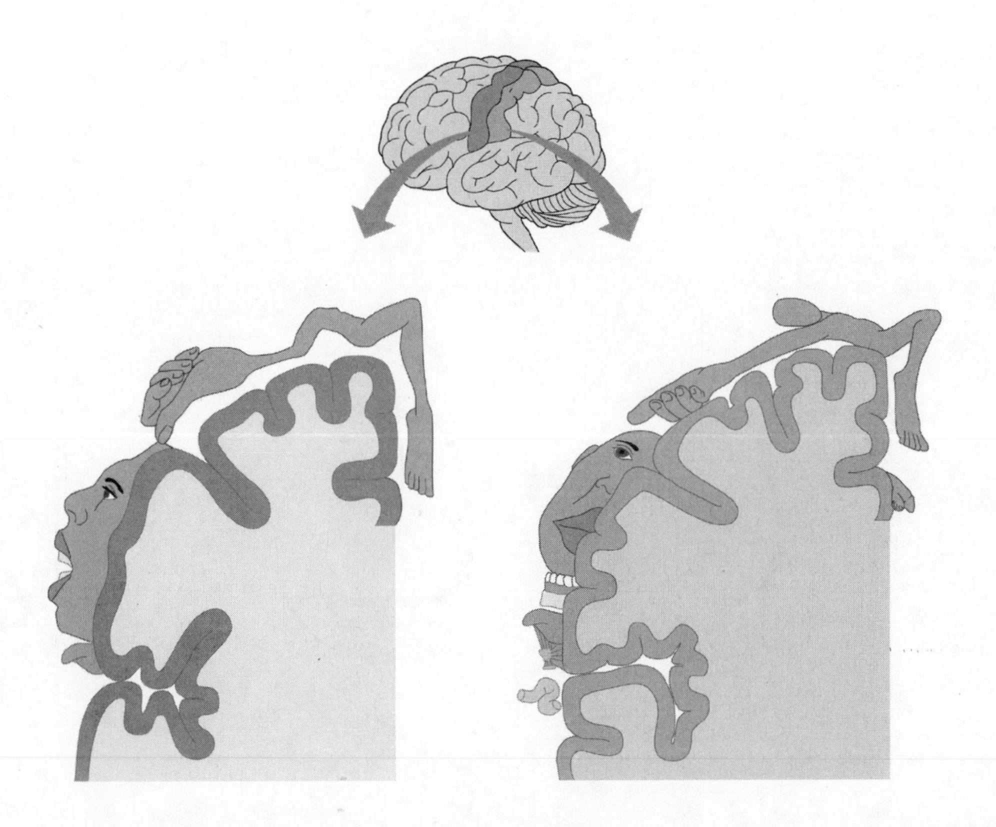

Figure 48.25 Primary motor and somatosensory areas of the human cerebral cortex, page 1048

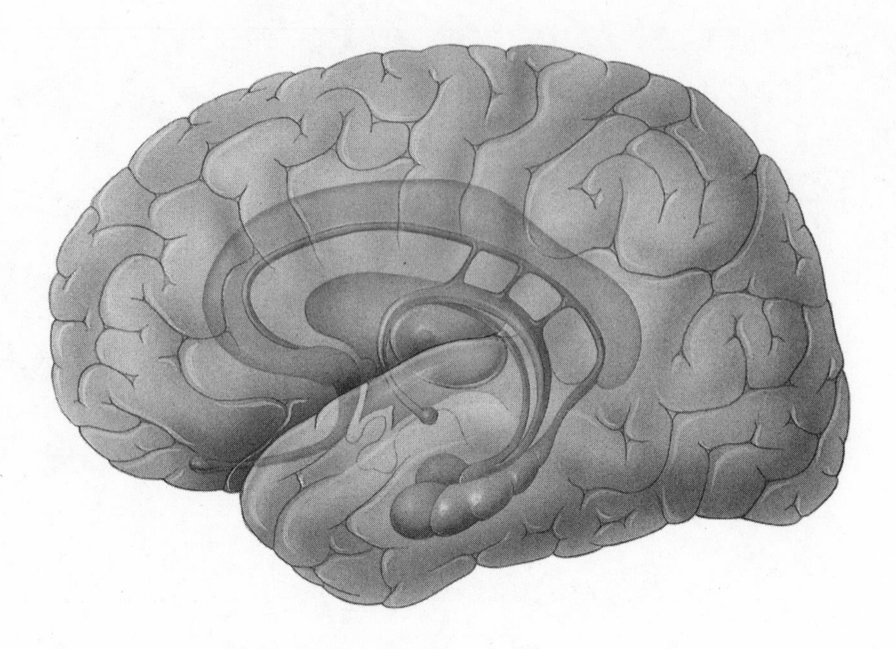

Figure 48.27 The limbic system, page 1050

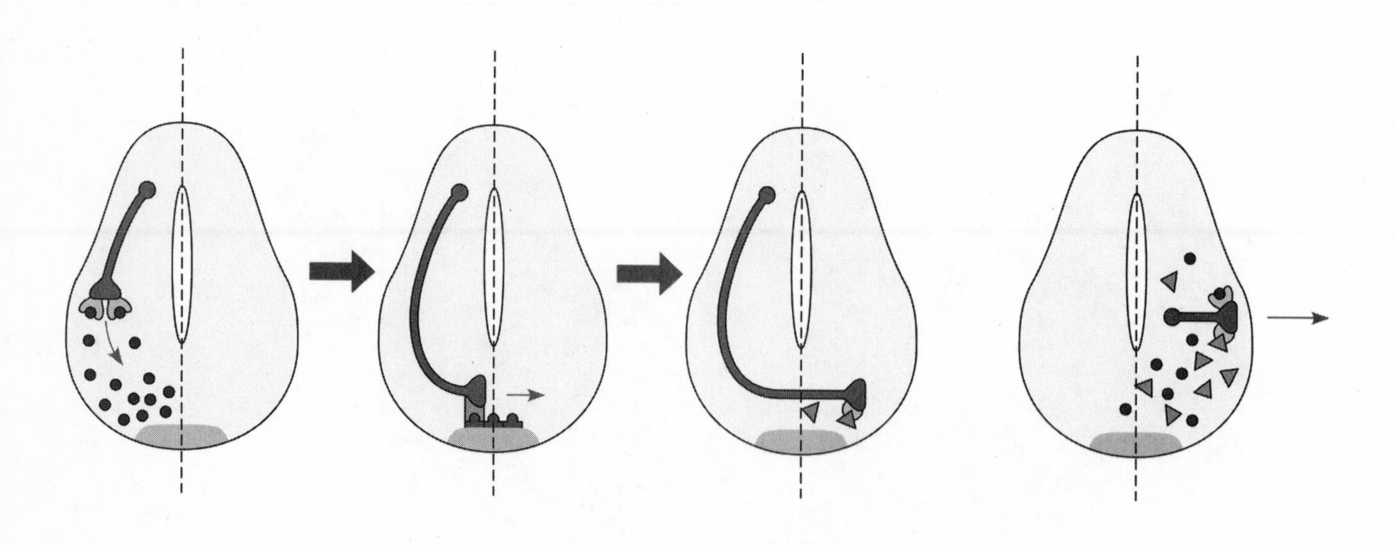

Figure 48.28 How do developing axons know which way to go? Page 1052

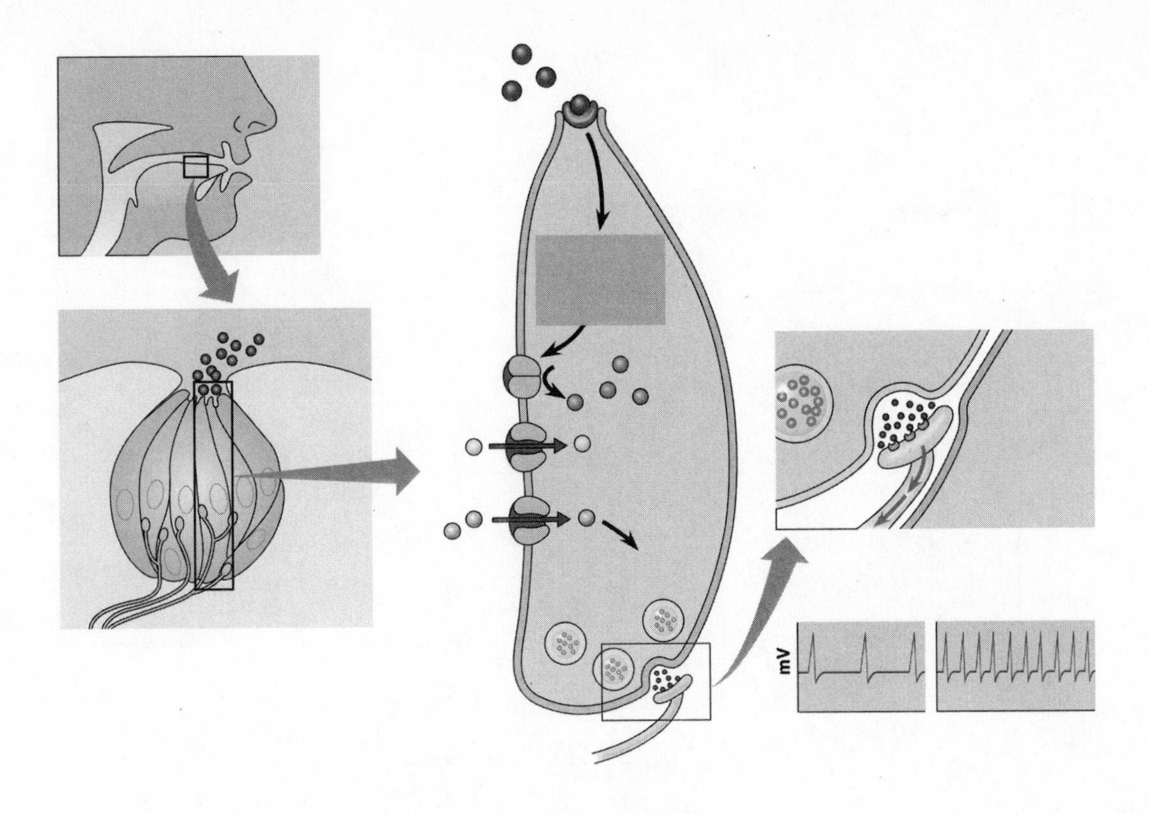

Figure 49.2 Sensory transduction by a taste receptor, page 1060

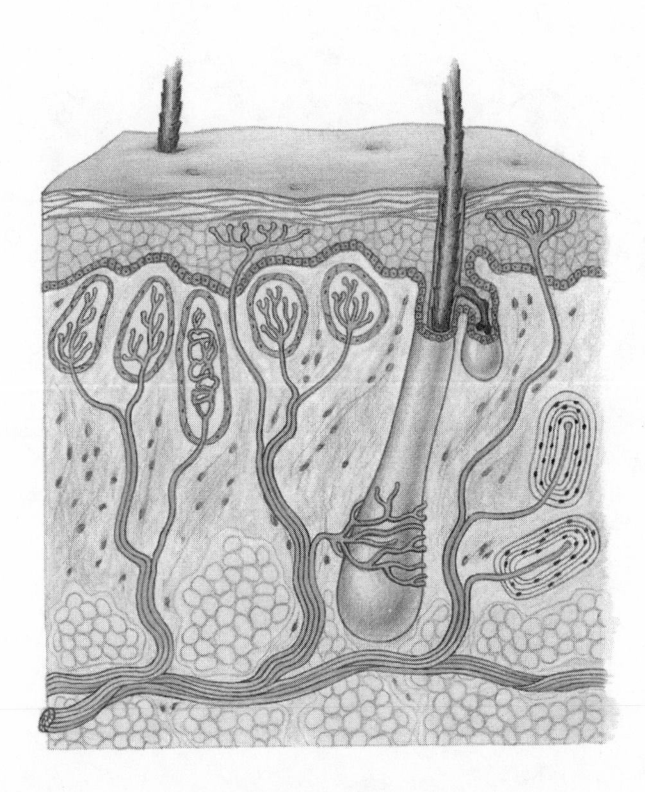

Figure 49.3 Sensory receptors in human skin, page 1061

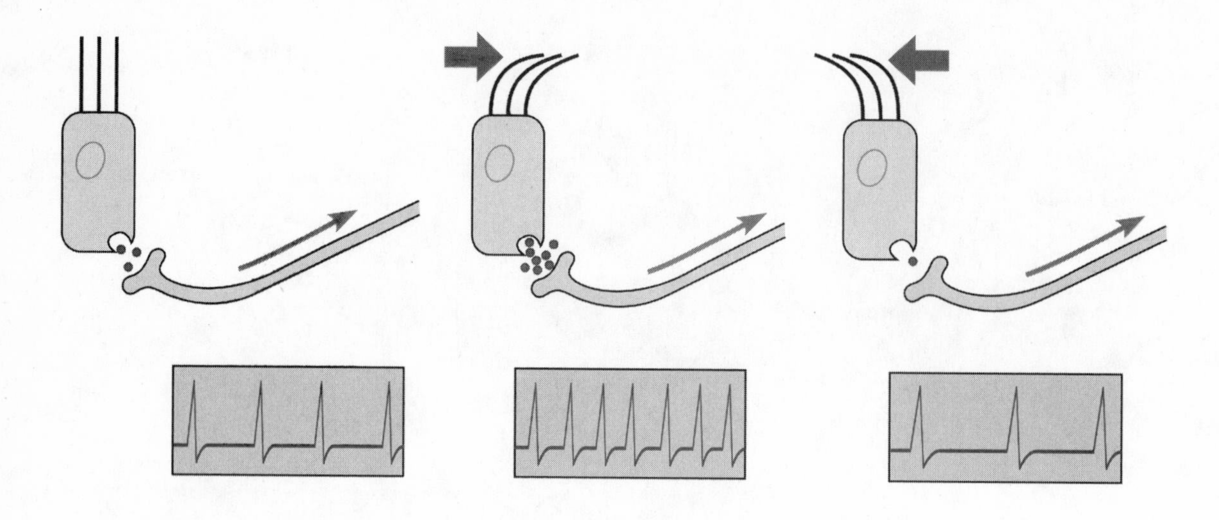

Figure 49.4 Mechanoreception by a hair cell, page 1061

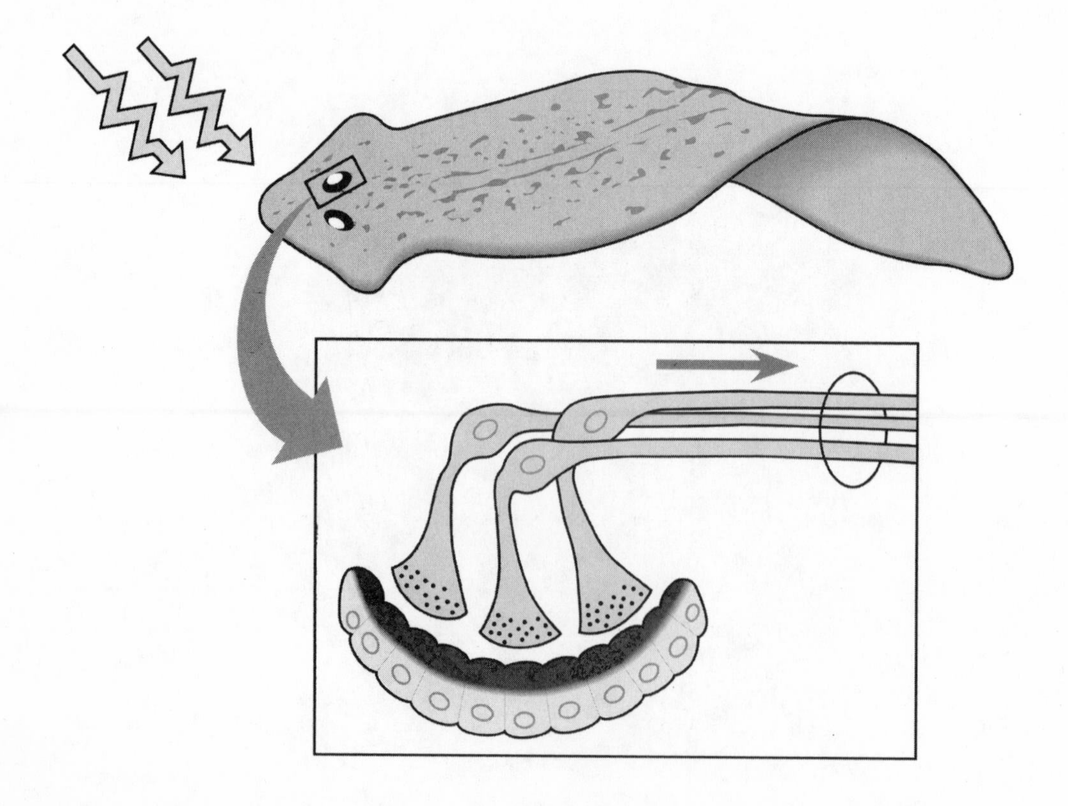

Figure 49.7 Eye cups and orientation behavior of a planarian, page 1063

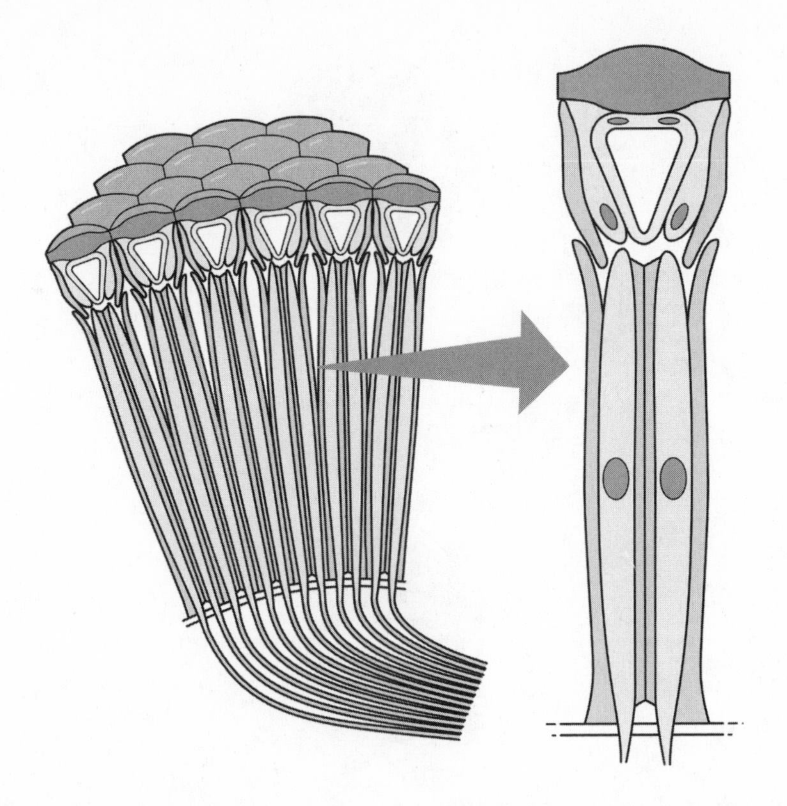

Figure 49.8b Compound eyes, page 1063

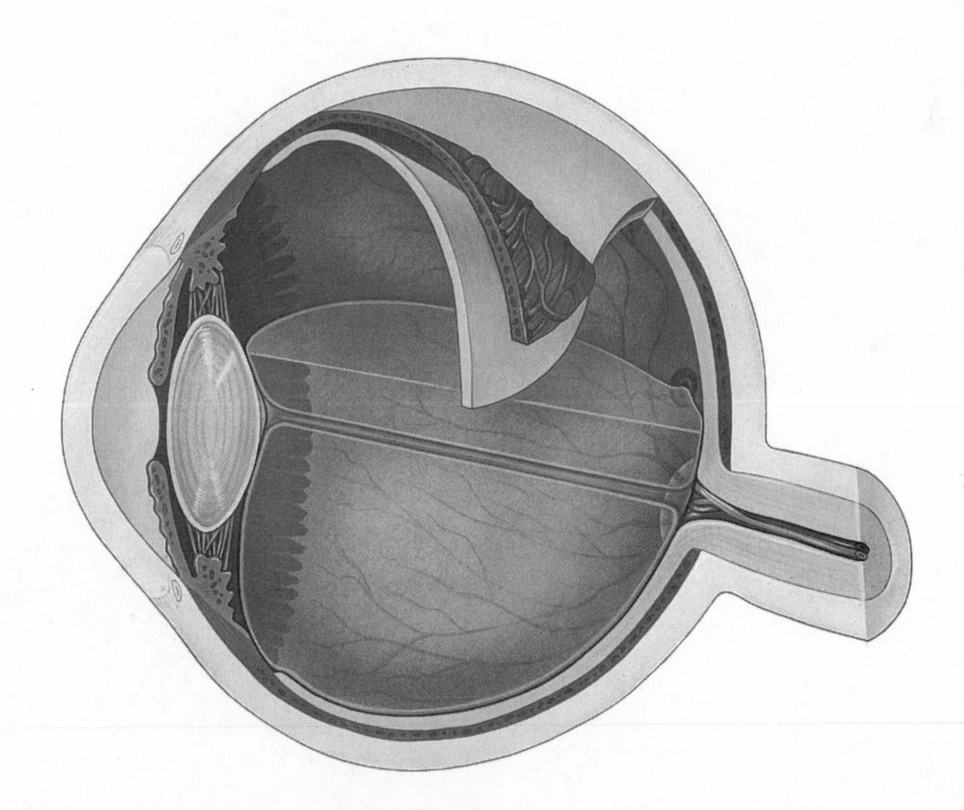

Figure 49.9 Structure of the vertebrate eye, page 1064

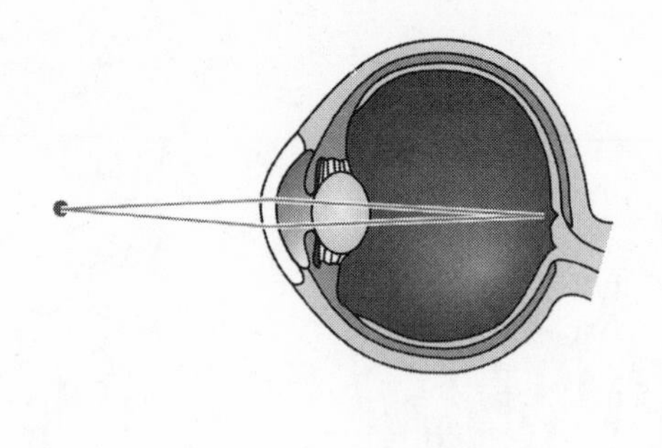

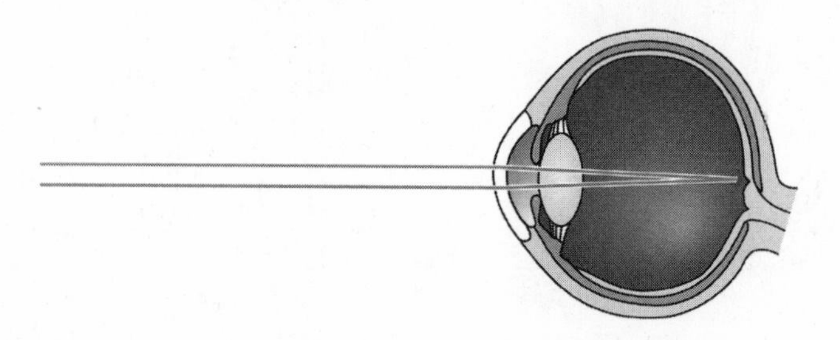

Figure 49.10 Focusing in the mammalian eye, page 1065

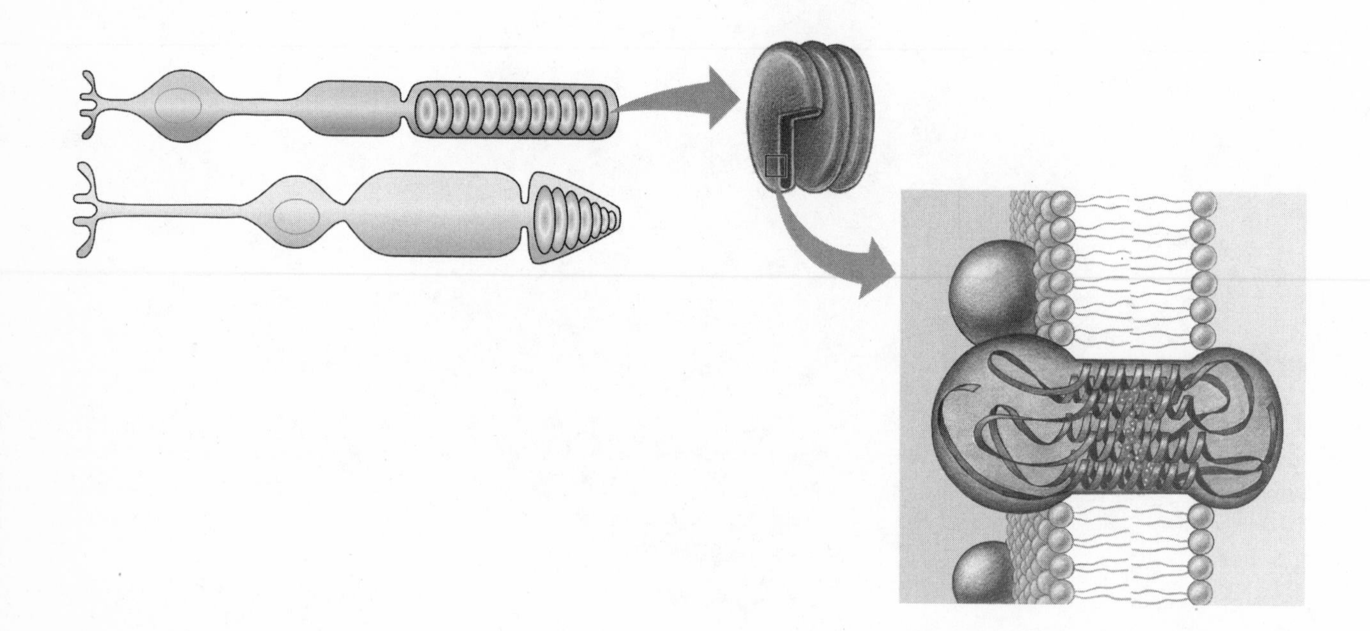

Figure 49.11 Photoreceptors in the vertebrate retina, page 1066

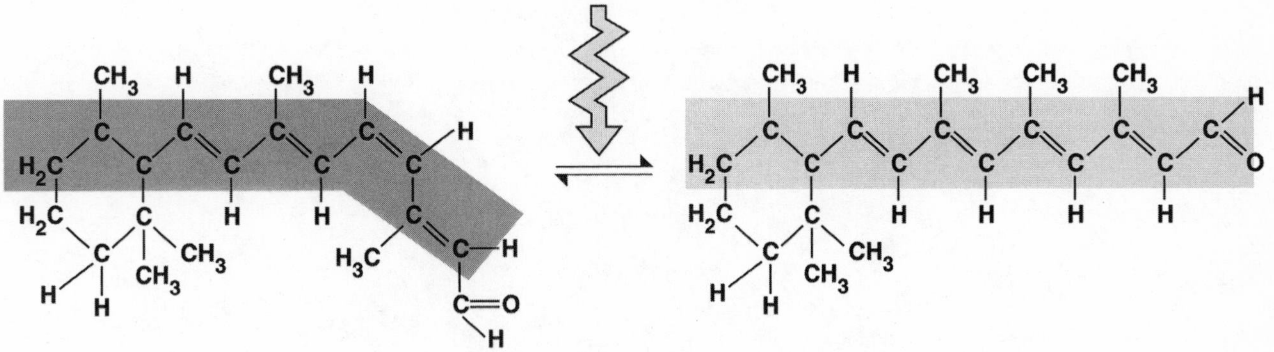

Figure 49.12 Effect of light on retinal, page 1066

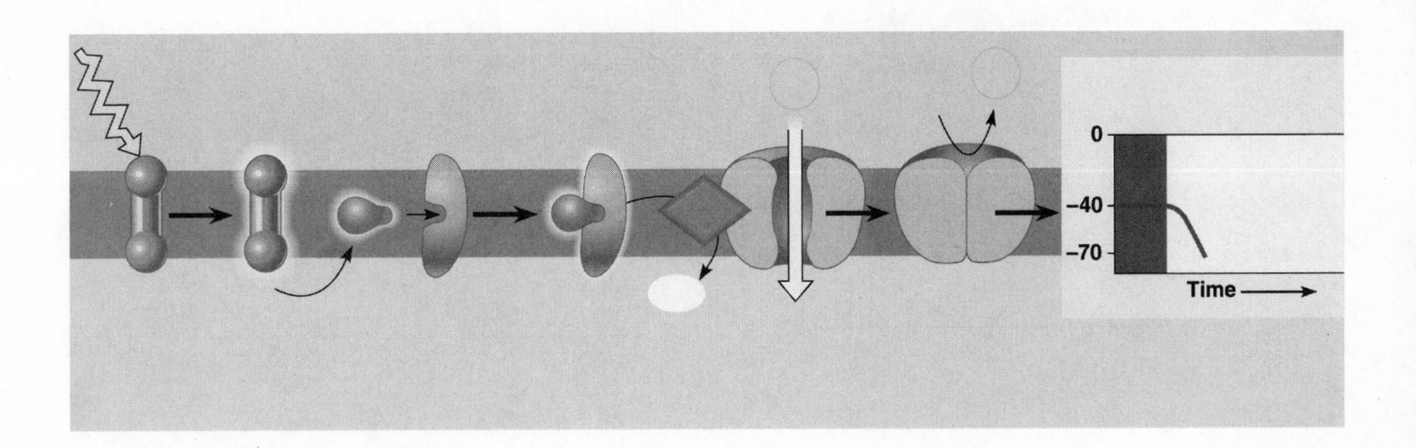

Figure 49.13 From light reception to receptor potential: A rod cell's signal-transduction pathway, page 1067

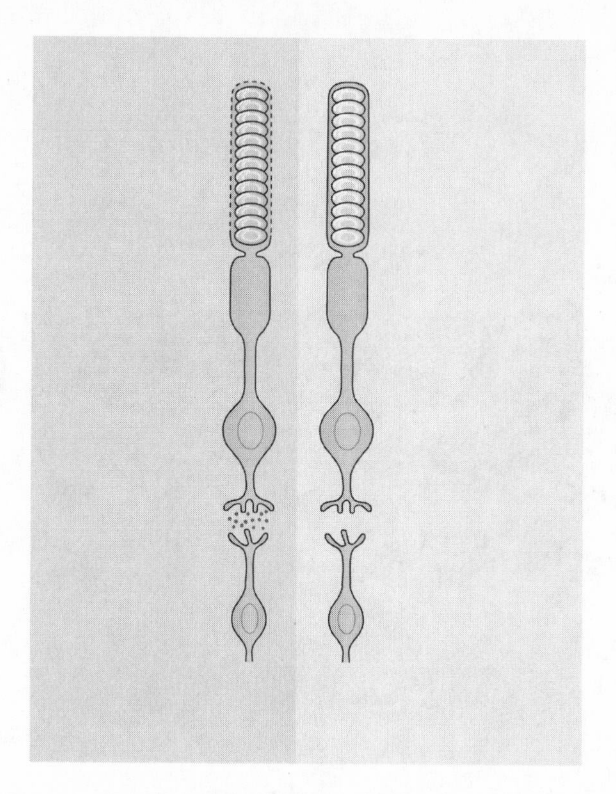

Figure 49.14 The effect of light on synapses between rod cells and bipolar cells, page 1067

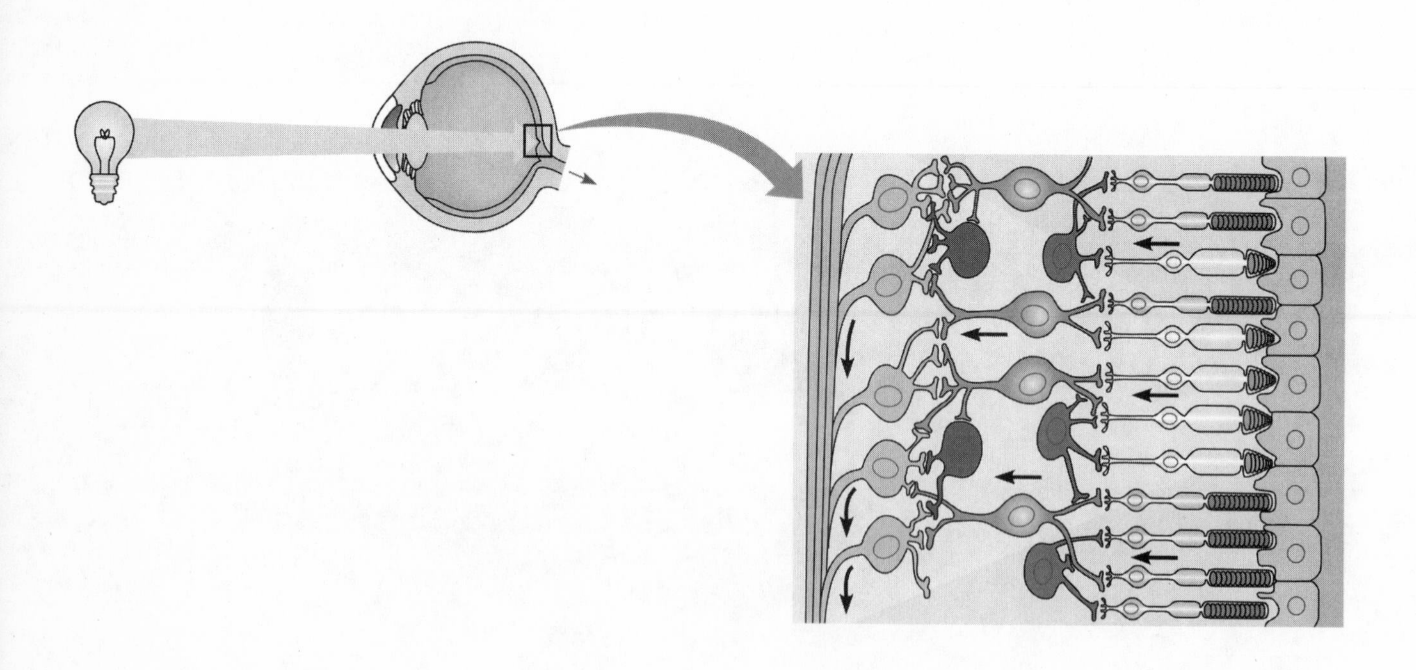

Figure 49.15 The vertebrate retina, page 1068

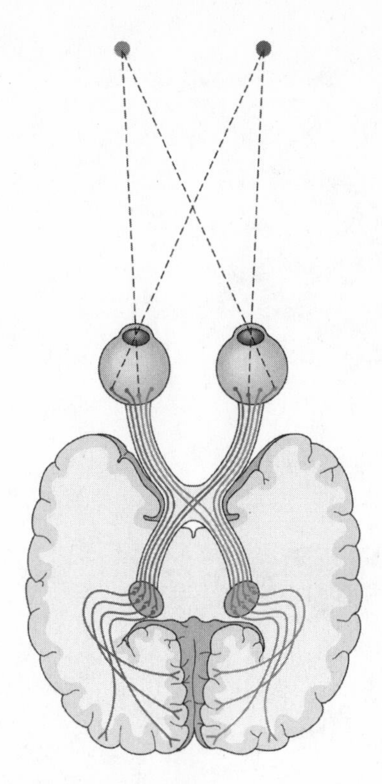

Figure 49.16 Neural pathways for vision, page 1068

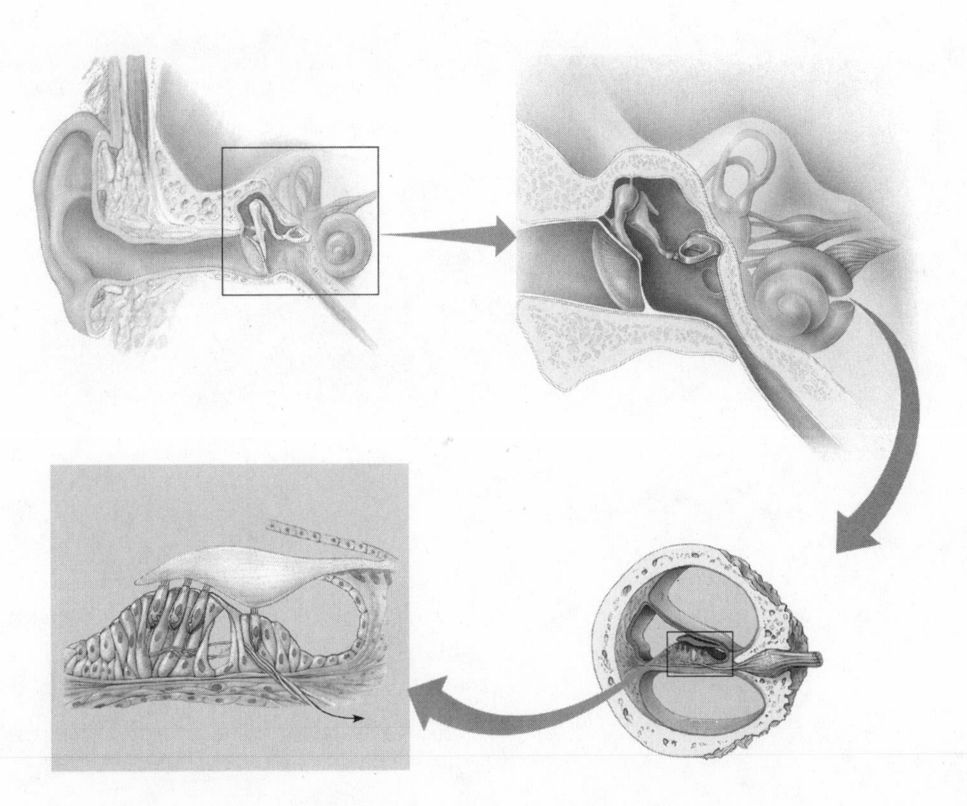

Figure 49.17 Structure and function of the human ear, page 1070

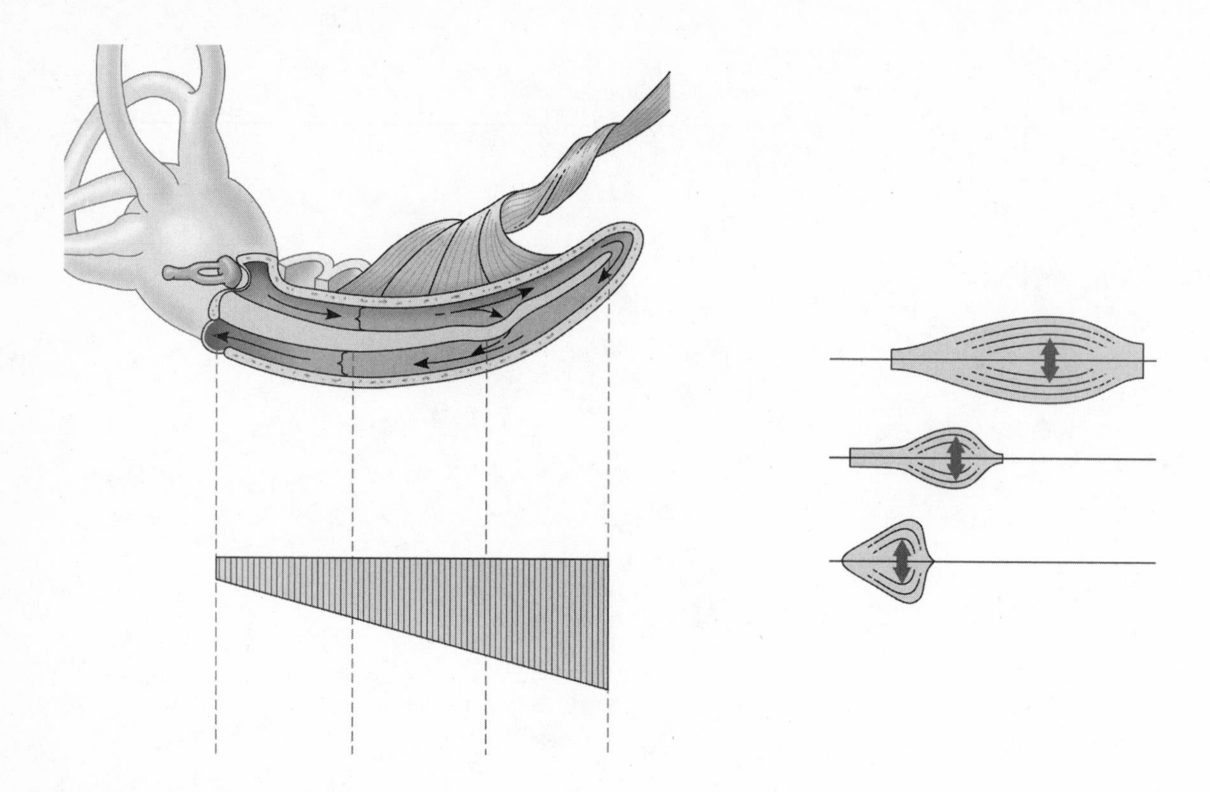

Figure 49.18 How the cochlea distinguishes pitch, page 1071

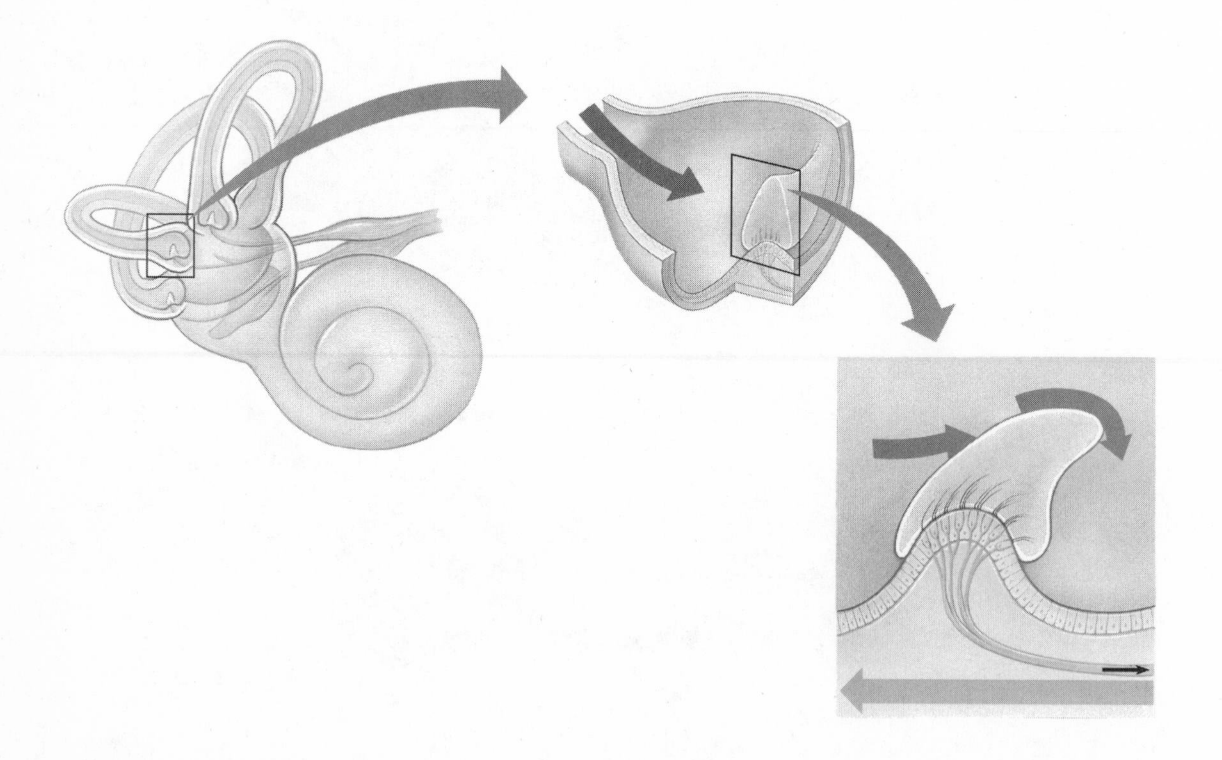

Figure 49.19 Organs of balance in the inner ear, page 1071

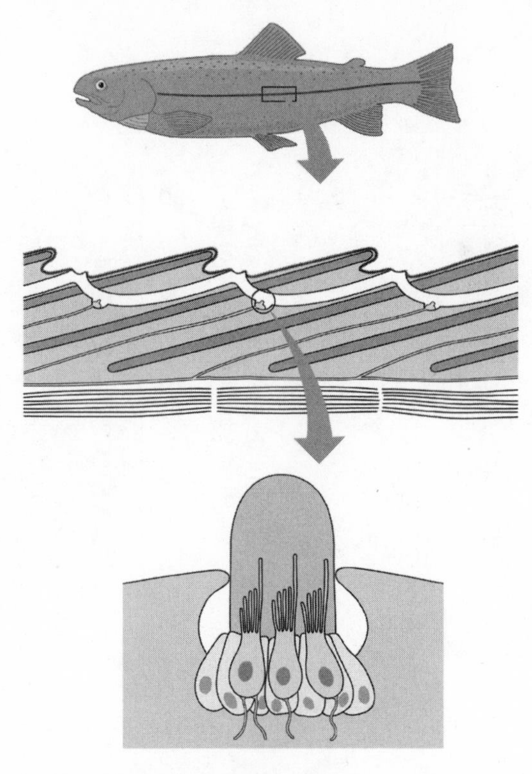

Figure 49.20 The lateral line system in a fish, page 1072

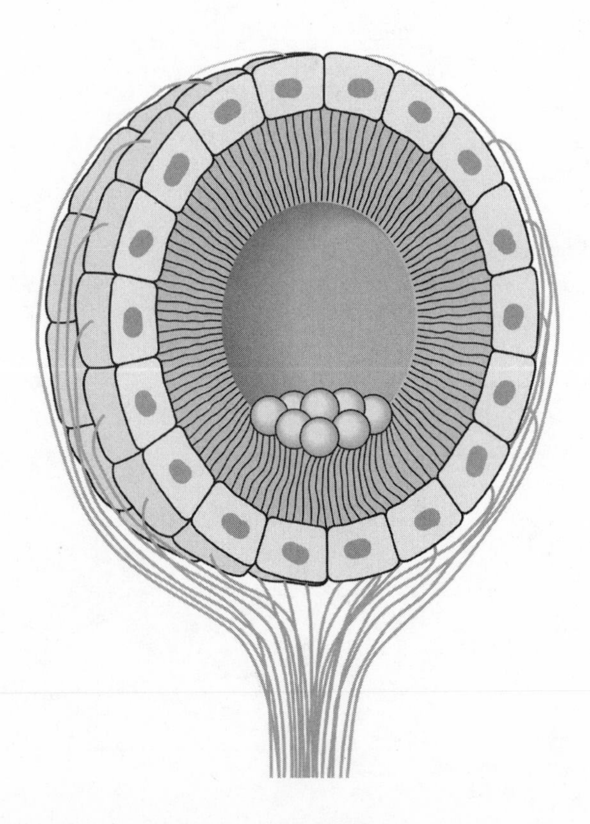

Figure 49.21 The statocyst of an invertebrate, page 1073

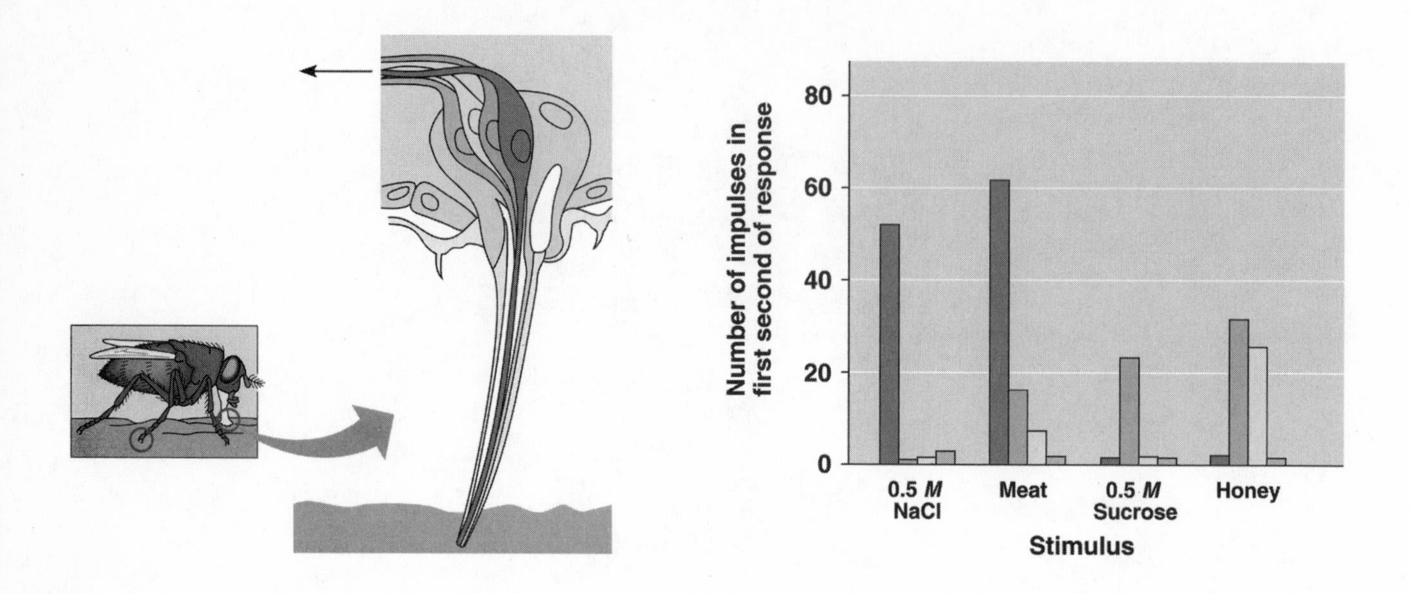

Figure 49.23 The mechanism of taste in a blowfly, page 1074

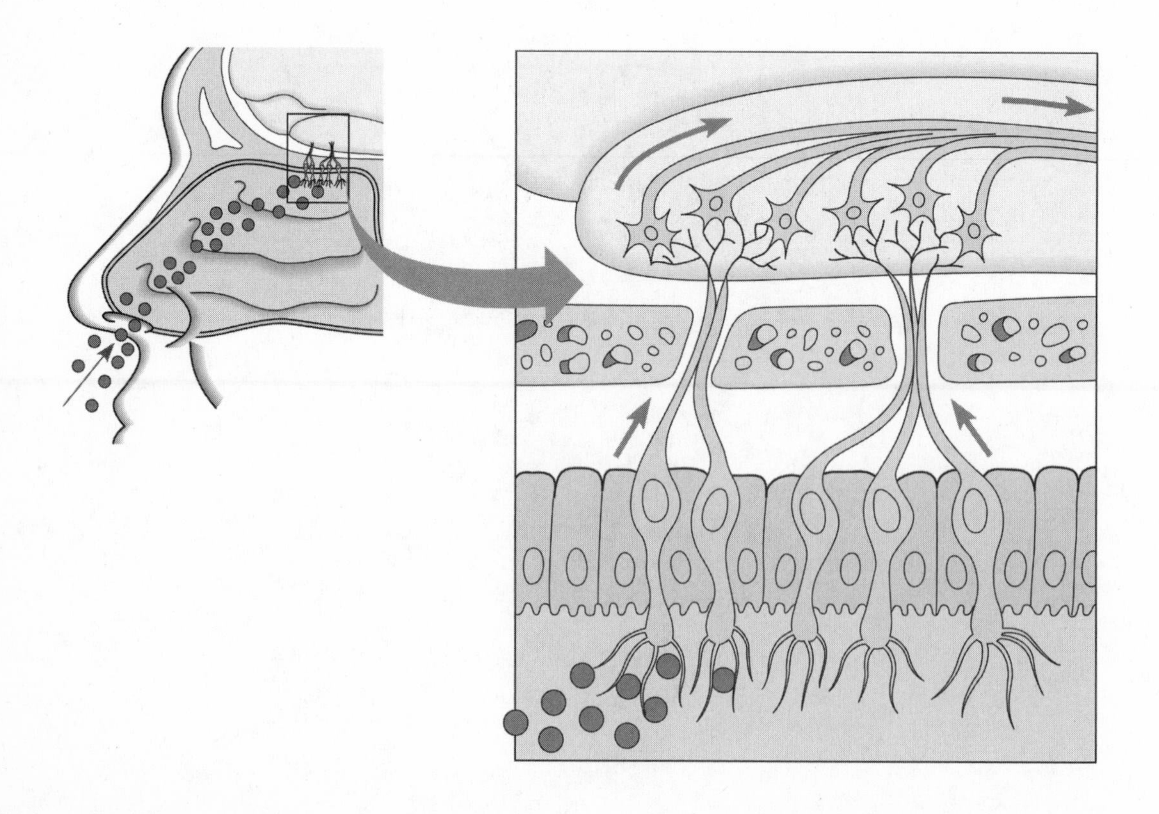

Figure 49.24 Olfaction in humans, page 1075

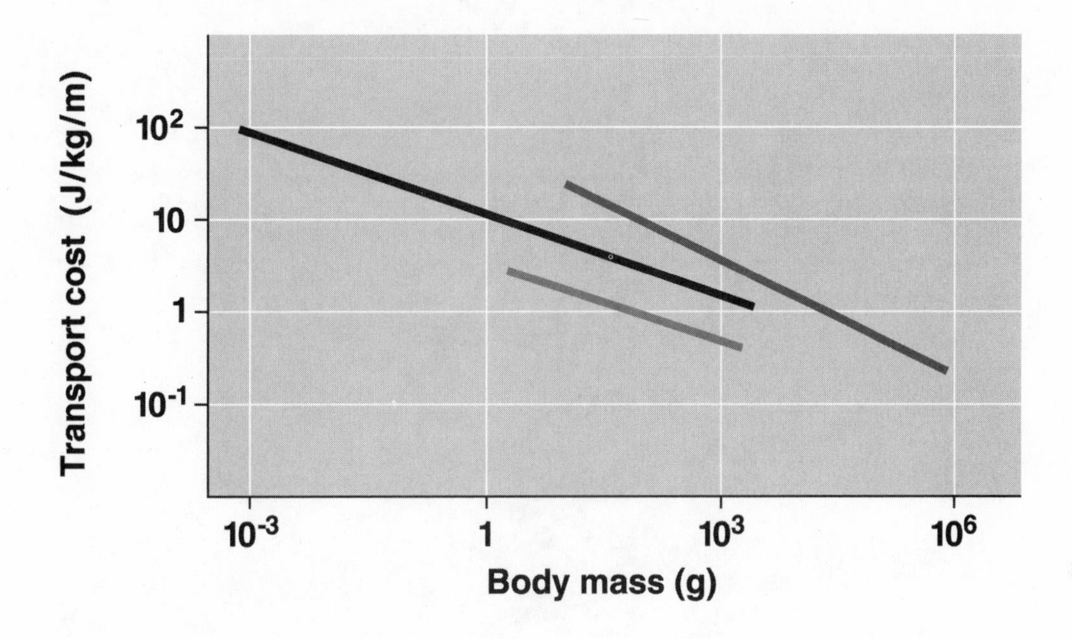

Figure 49.25 The cost of transport, page 1076

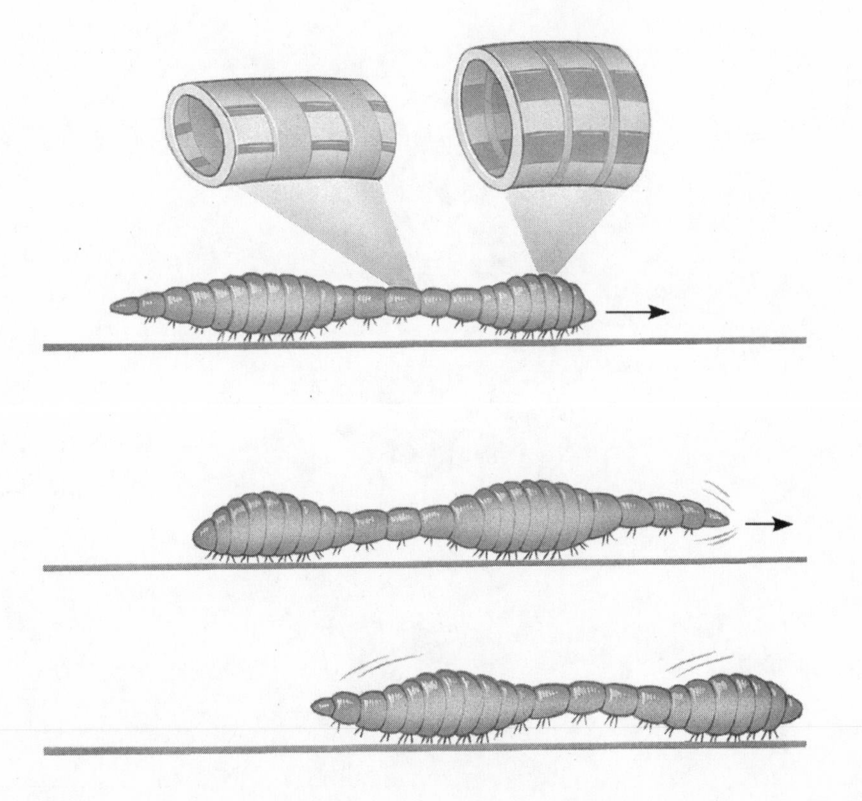

Figure 49.27 Peristaltic locomotion in an earthworm, page 1078

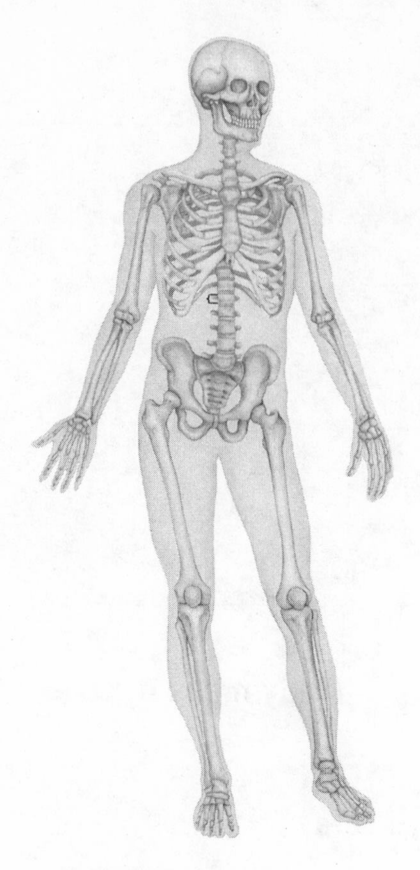

Figure 49.28a The human skeleton, page 1079

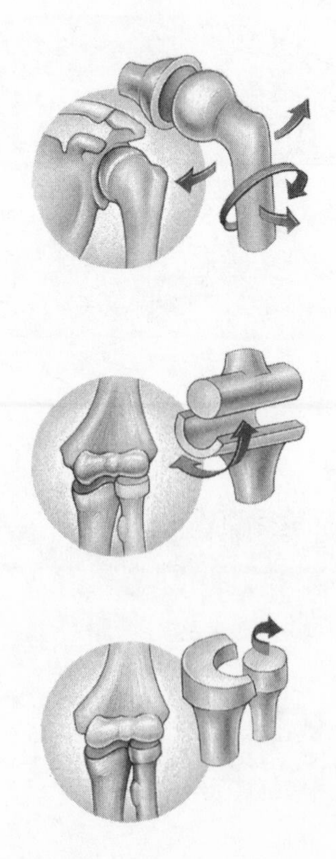

Figure 49.28b The human skeleton, page 1079

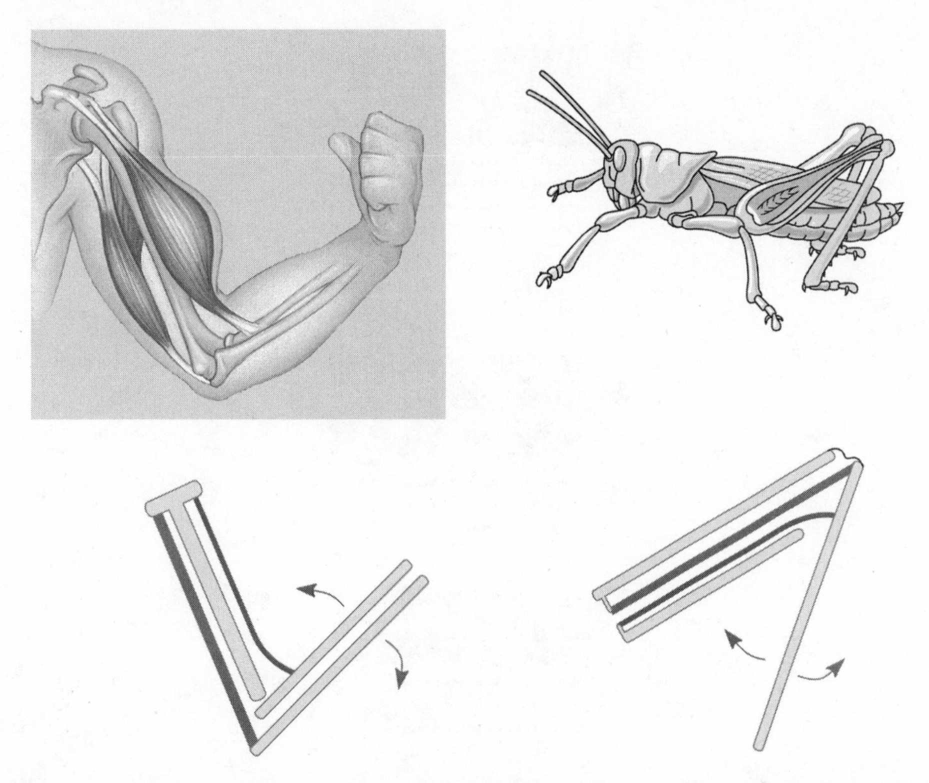

Figure 49.30 The cooperation of muscles and skeletons in movement, page 1080

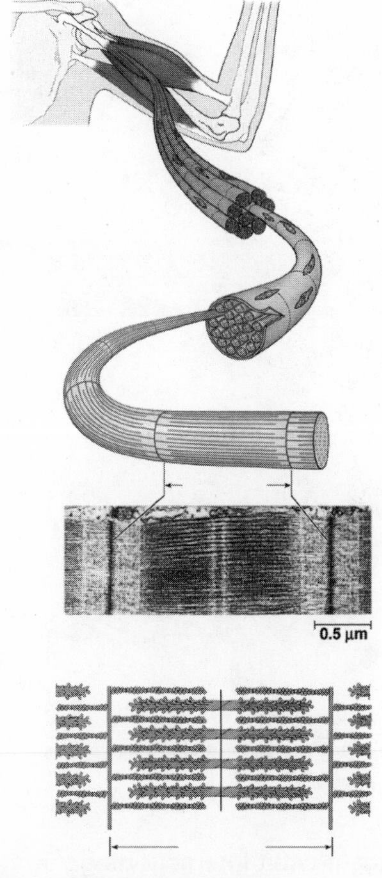

Figure 49.31 The structure of skeletal muscle, page 1081

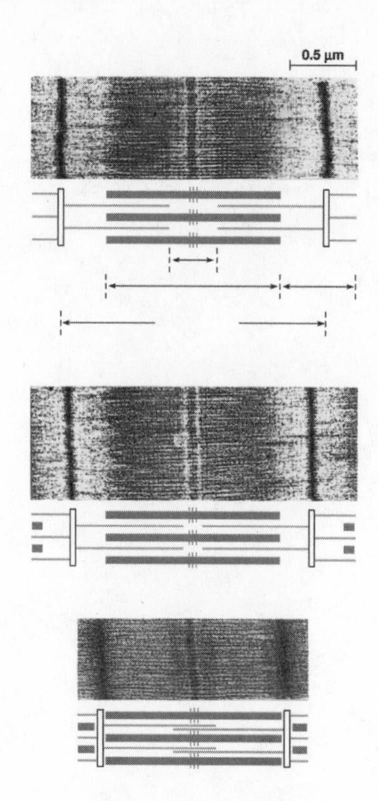

Figure 49.32 The sliding-filament model of muscle contraction, page 1081

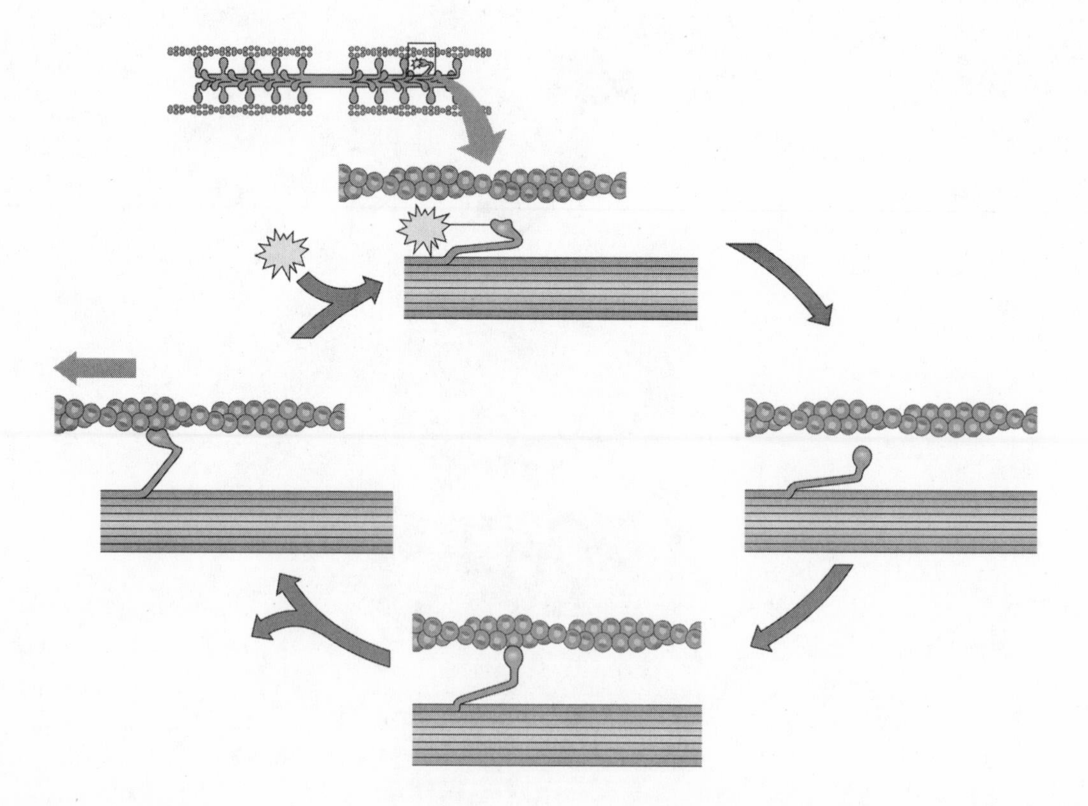

Figure 49.33 One hypothesis for how myosin-actin interactions generate the force for muscle contraction, page 1082

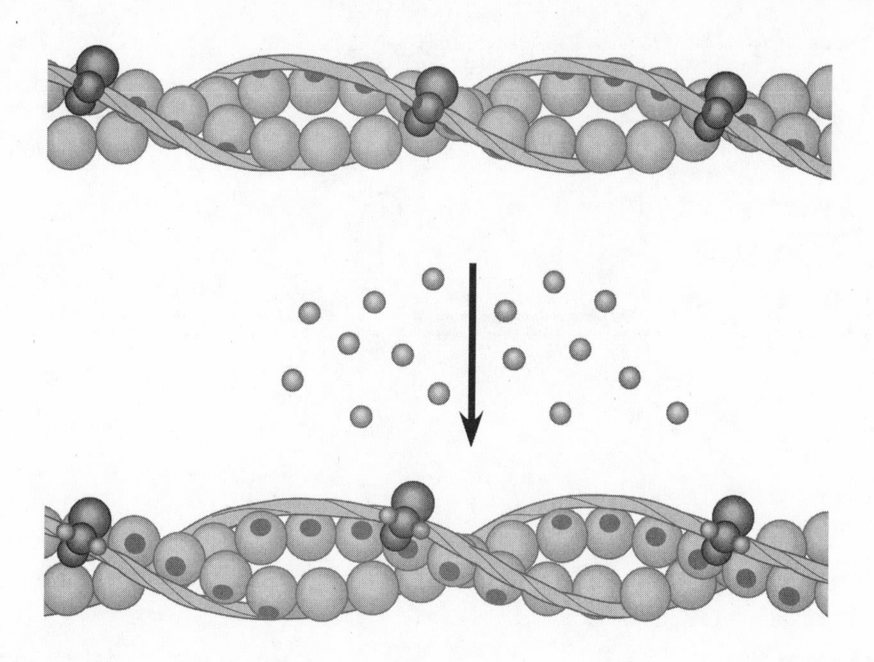

Figure 49.34 Hypothetical mechanism for the control of muscle contraction, page 1083

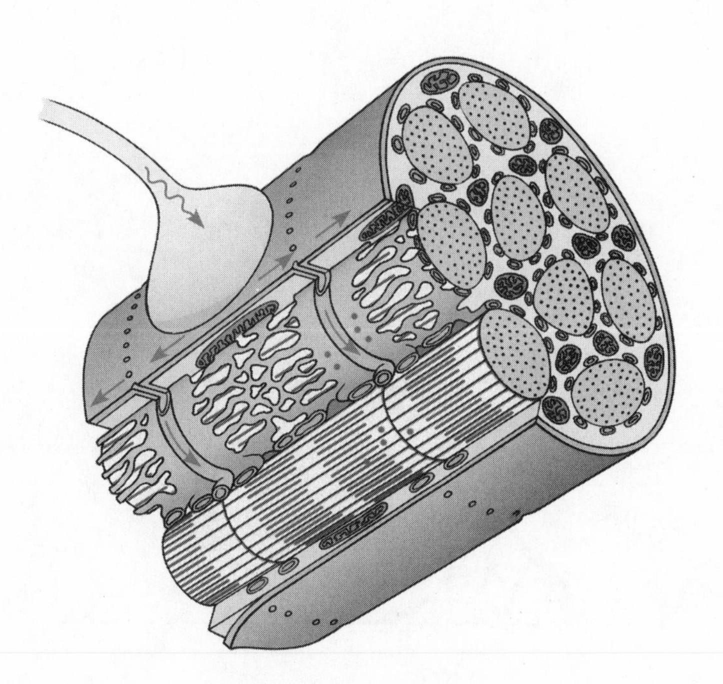

Figure 49.35 The roles of the muscle fiber's sarcoplasmic reticulum and T tubules in contraction, page 1083

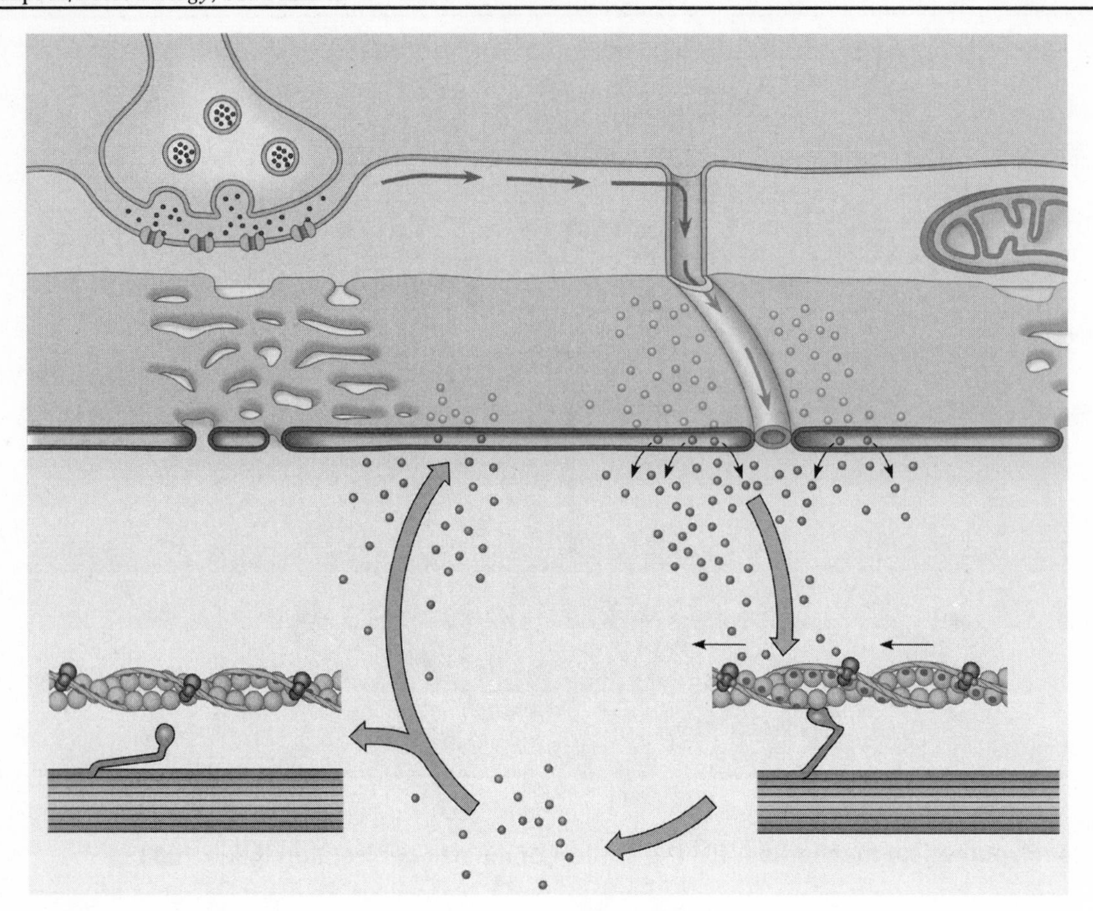

Figure 49.36 Review of skeletal muscle contraction, page 1084

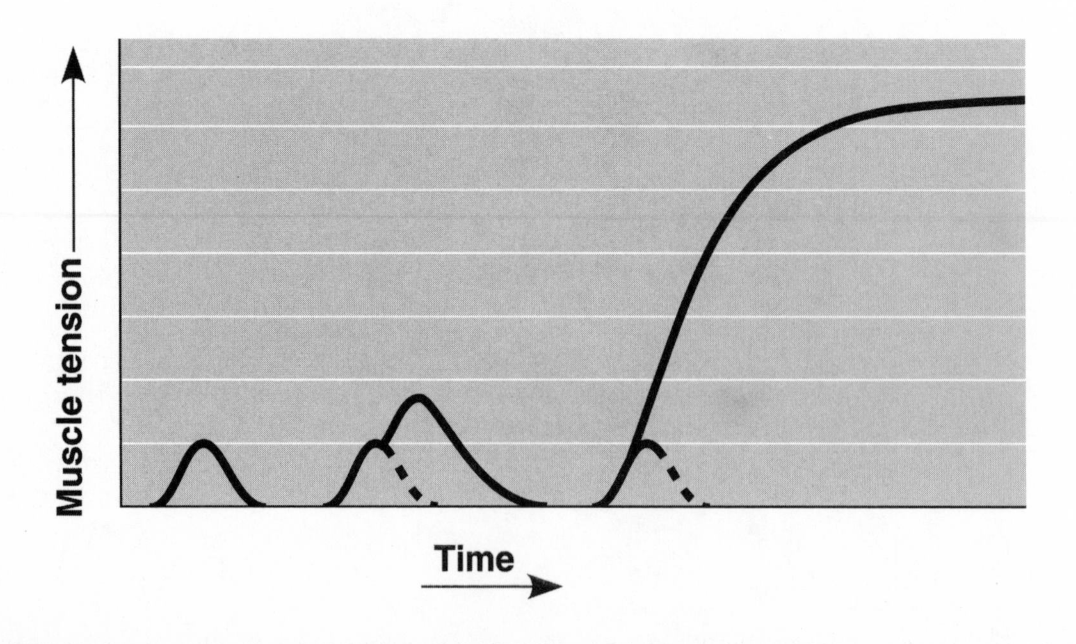

Figure 49.37 Temporal summation of muscle cell contractions, page 1085

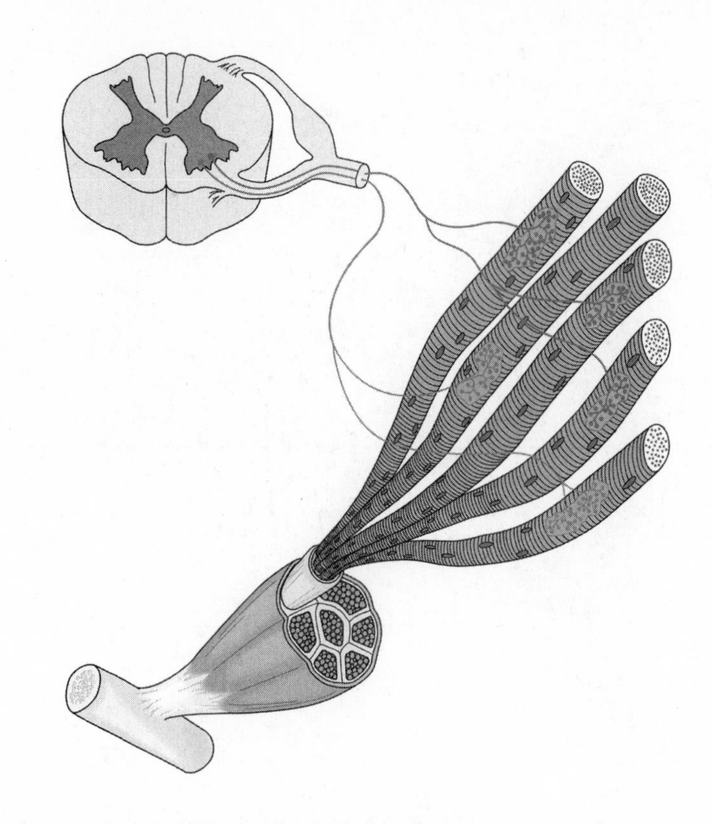

Figure 49.38 Motor units in a vertebrate muscle, page 1085

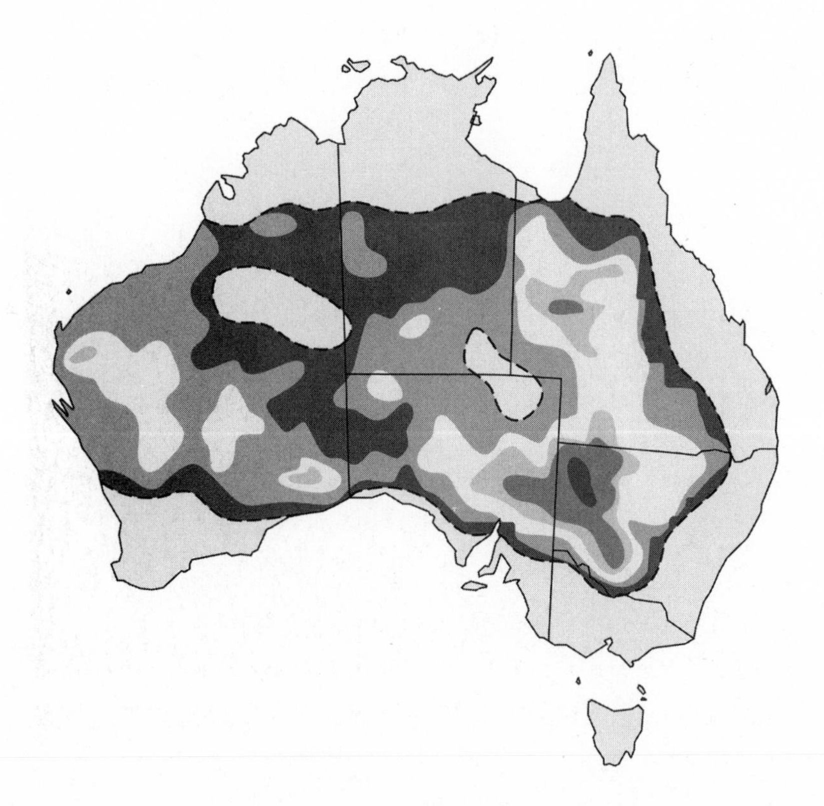

Figure 50.1 Distribution and abundance of the red kangaroo in Australia, based on aerial surveys, page 1093

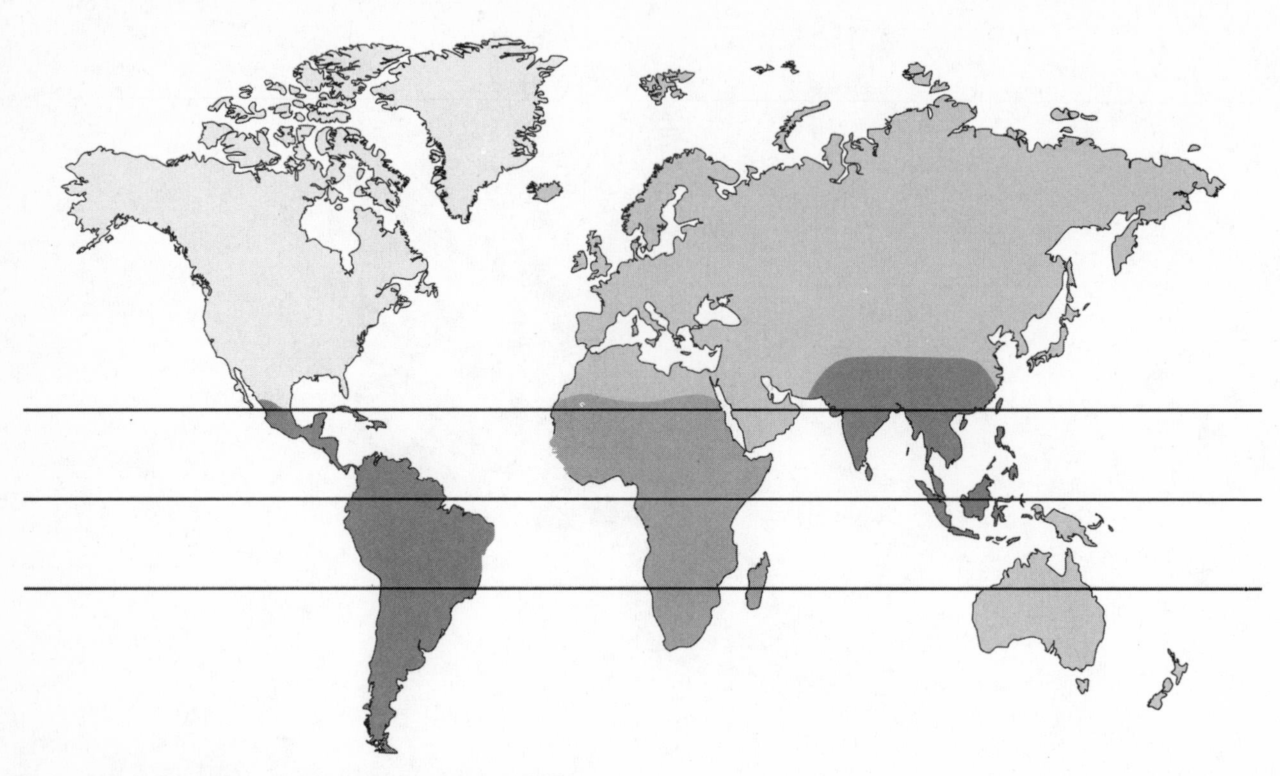

Figure 50.4 Biogeographic realms, page 1095

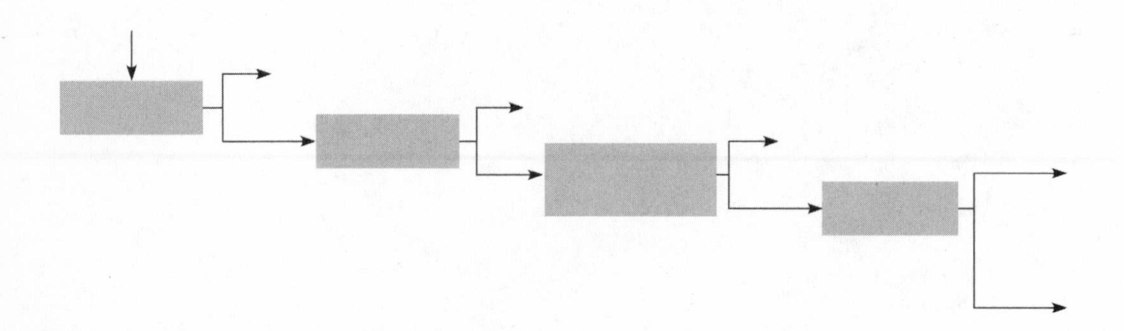

Figure 50.5 Flowchart of factors limiting geographic distribution, page 1096

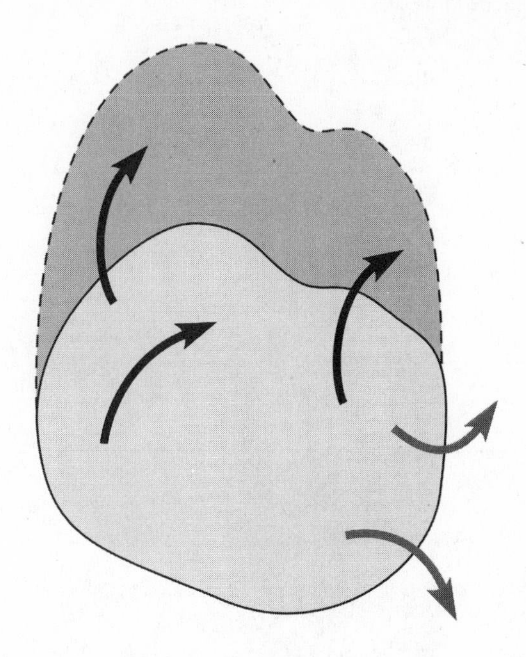

Figure 50.6 Set of transplant experiments for a hypothetical species. page 1096

Figure 50.7 Spread of the African honeybee in the Americas since 1956, page 1097

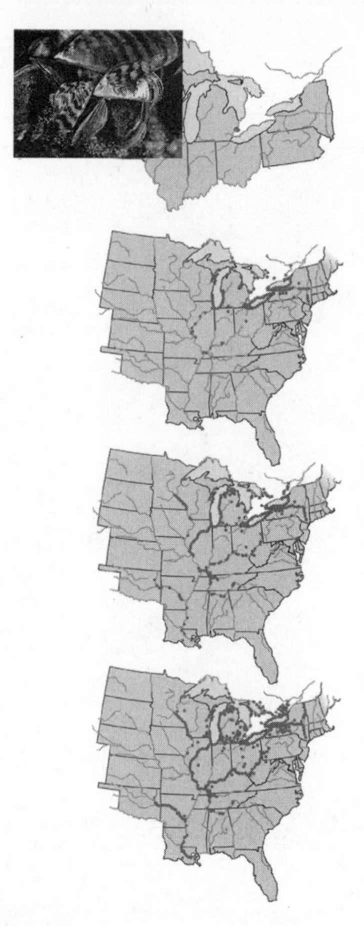

Figure 50.8 Expansion of the geographic range of the zebra mussel (*Dreissena polymorpha*) since its discovery near Detroit in 1988, page 1098

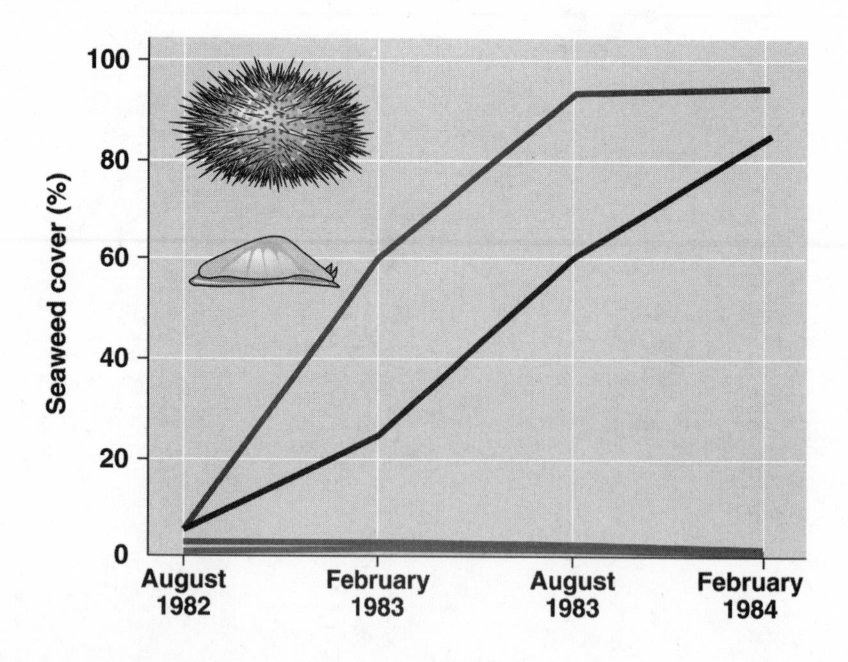

Figure 50.9 Predator-removal experiments, page 1099

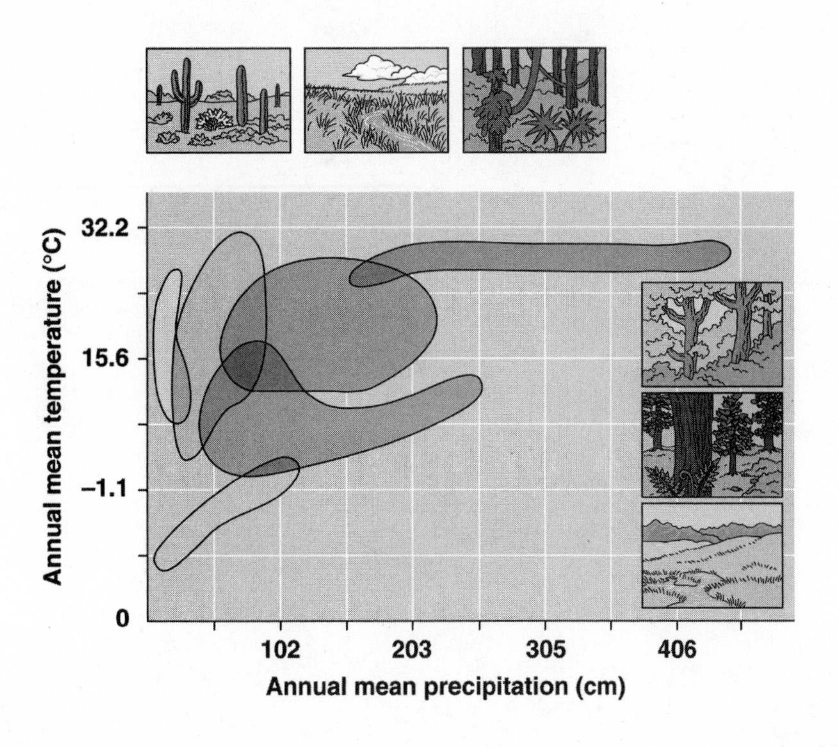

Figure 50.10 A climograph for some major kinds of ecosystems (biomes) in North America, page 1101

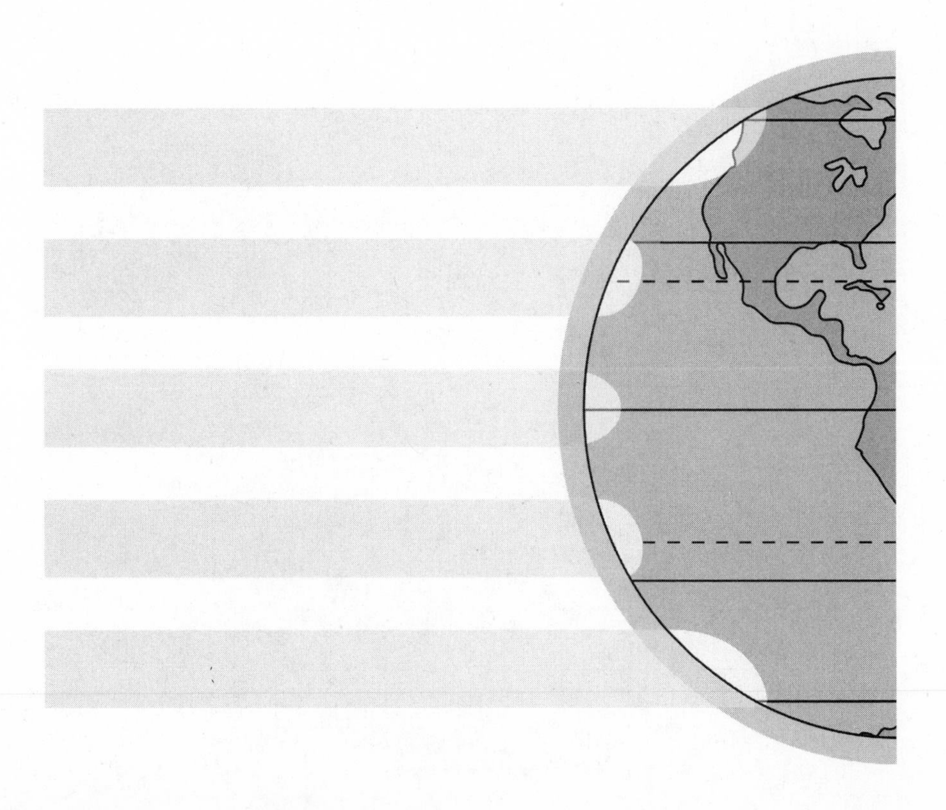

Figure 50.11 Solar radiation and latitude, page 1101

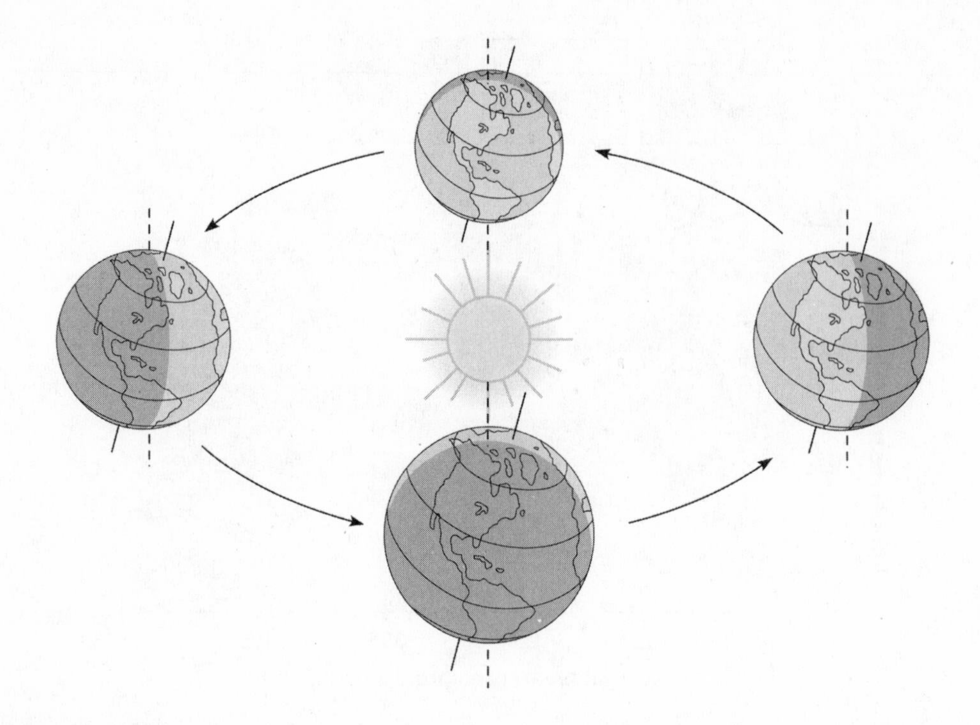

Figure 50.12 What causes the seasons?, page 1102

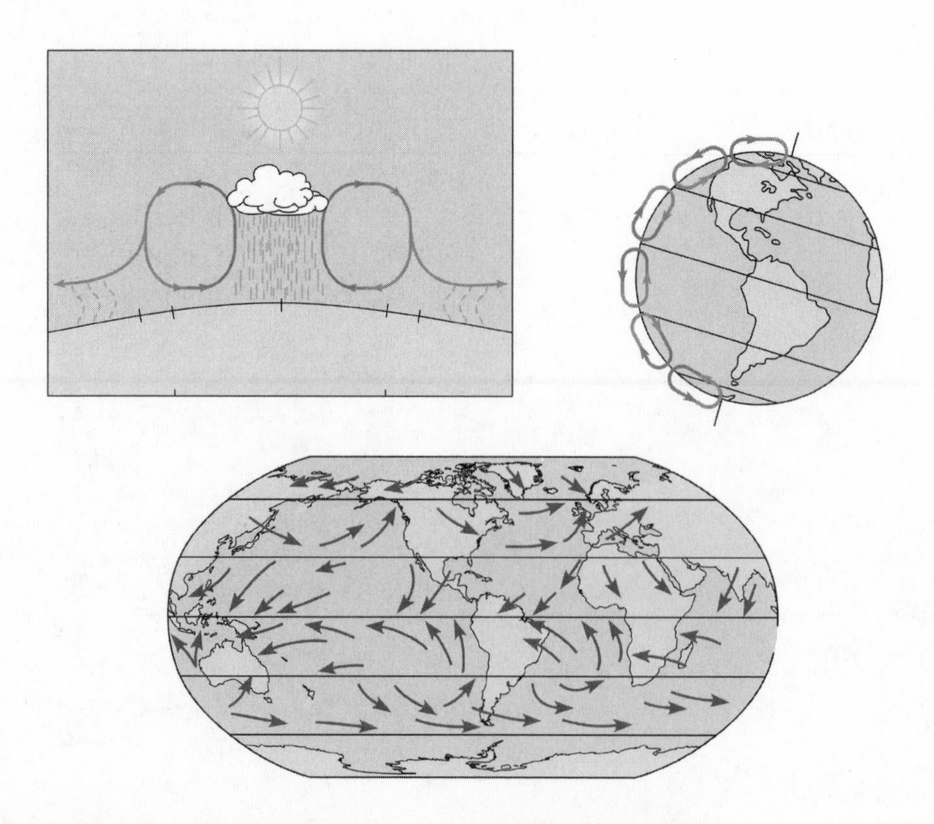

Figure 50.13 Global air circulation, precipitation, and winds, page 1103

Figure 50.14 How mountains affect rainfall, page 1104

Figure 50.15 Lake stratification and seasonal turnover, page 1104

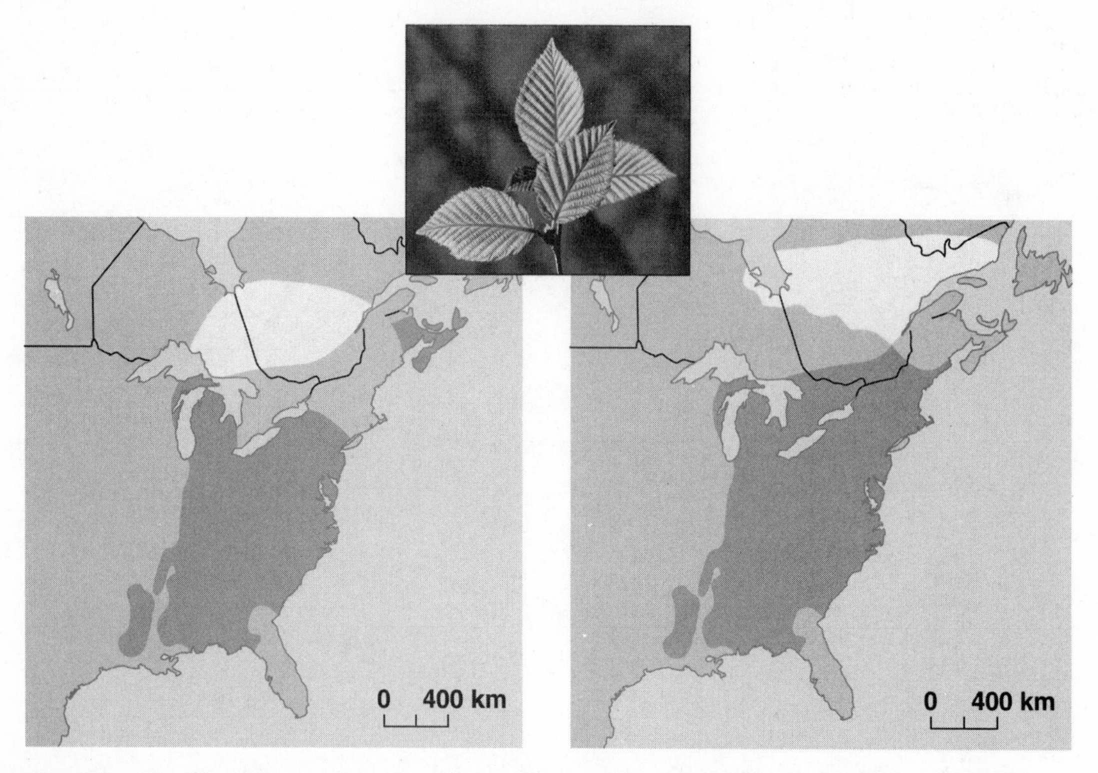

Figure 50.16 Current geographic range and predicted future range for the American beech (*Fagus grandifolia*) under two climate-change scenarios, page 1105

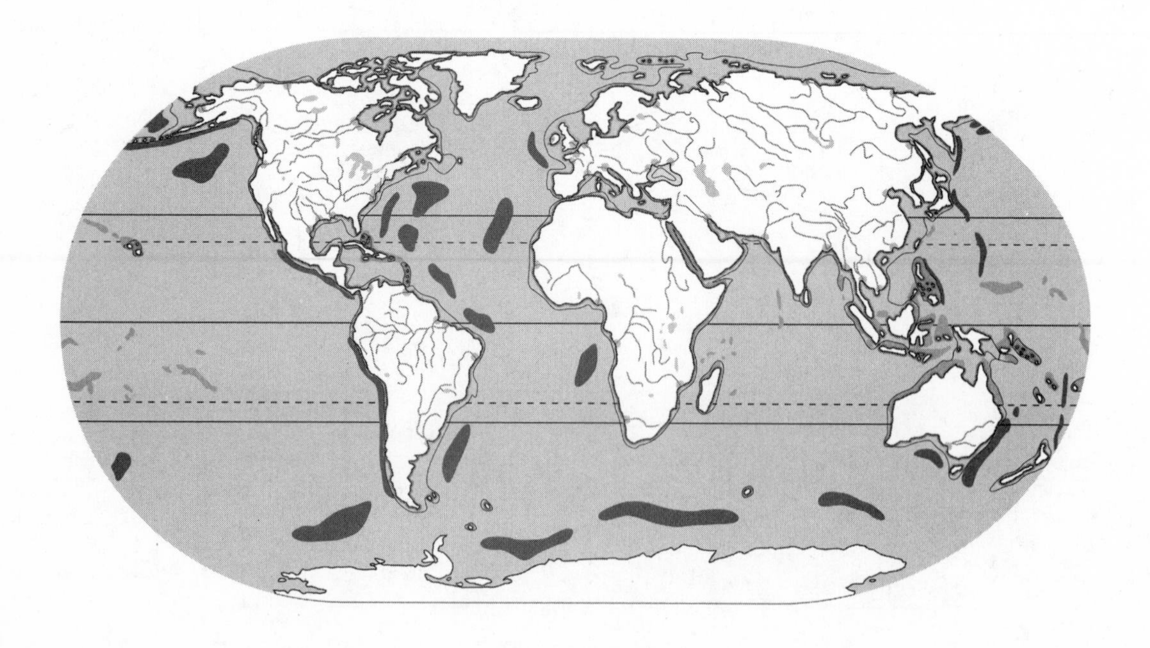

Figure 50.17 The distribution of major aquatic biomes, page 1106

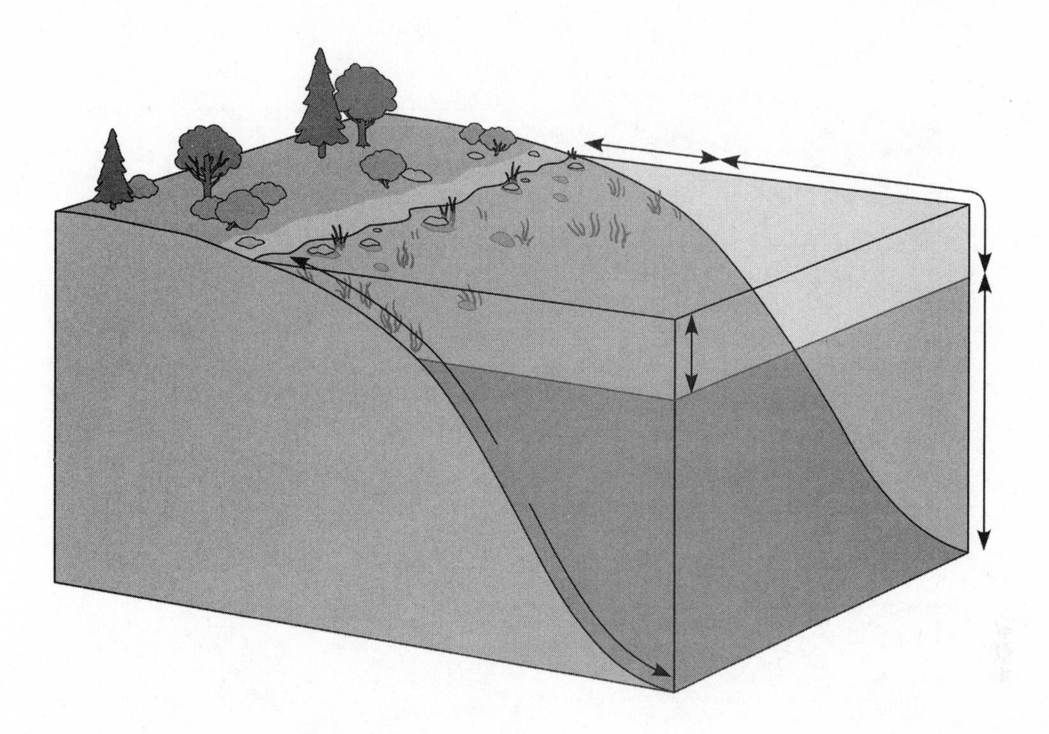

Figure 50.18 Zonation in a lake, page 1107

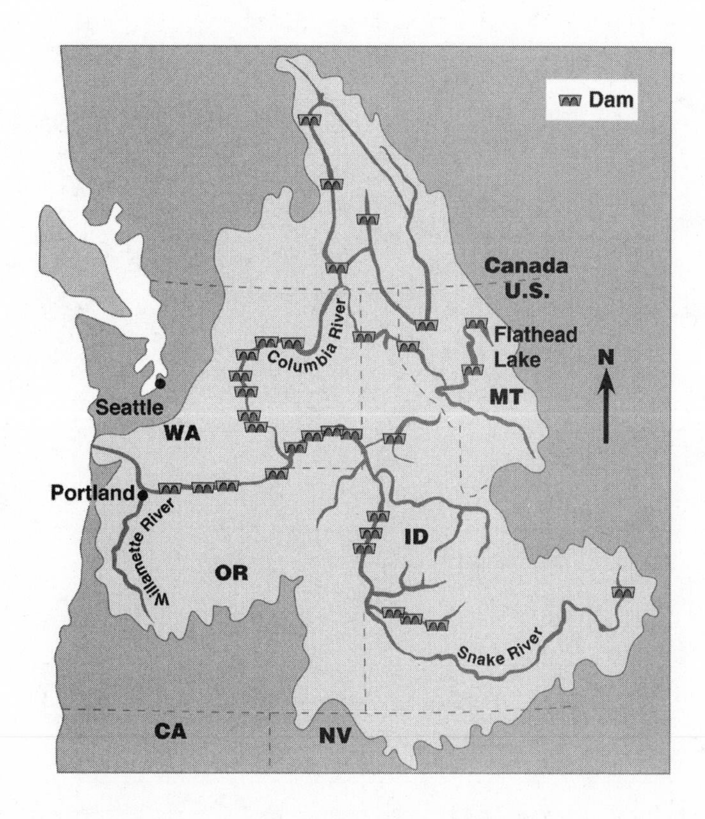

Figure 50.20 Damming the Columbia River Basin, page 1108

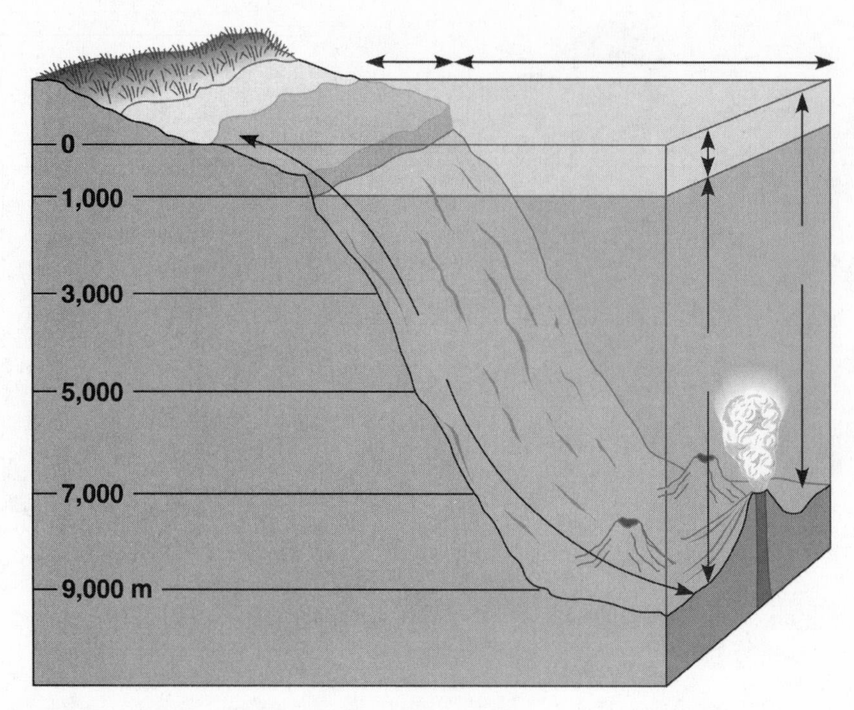

Figure 50.22 Zonation in the marine environment, page 1110

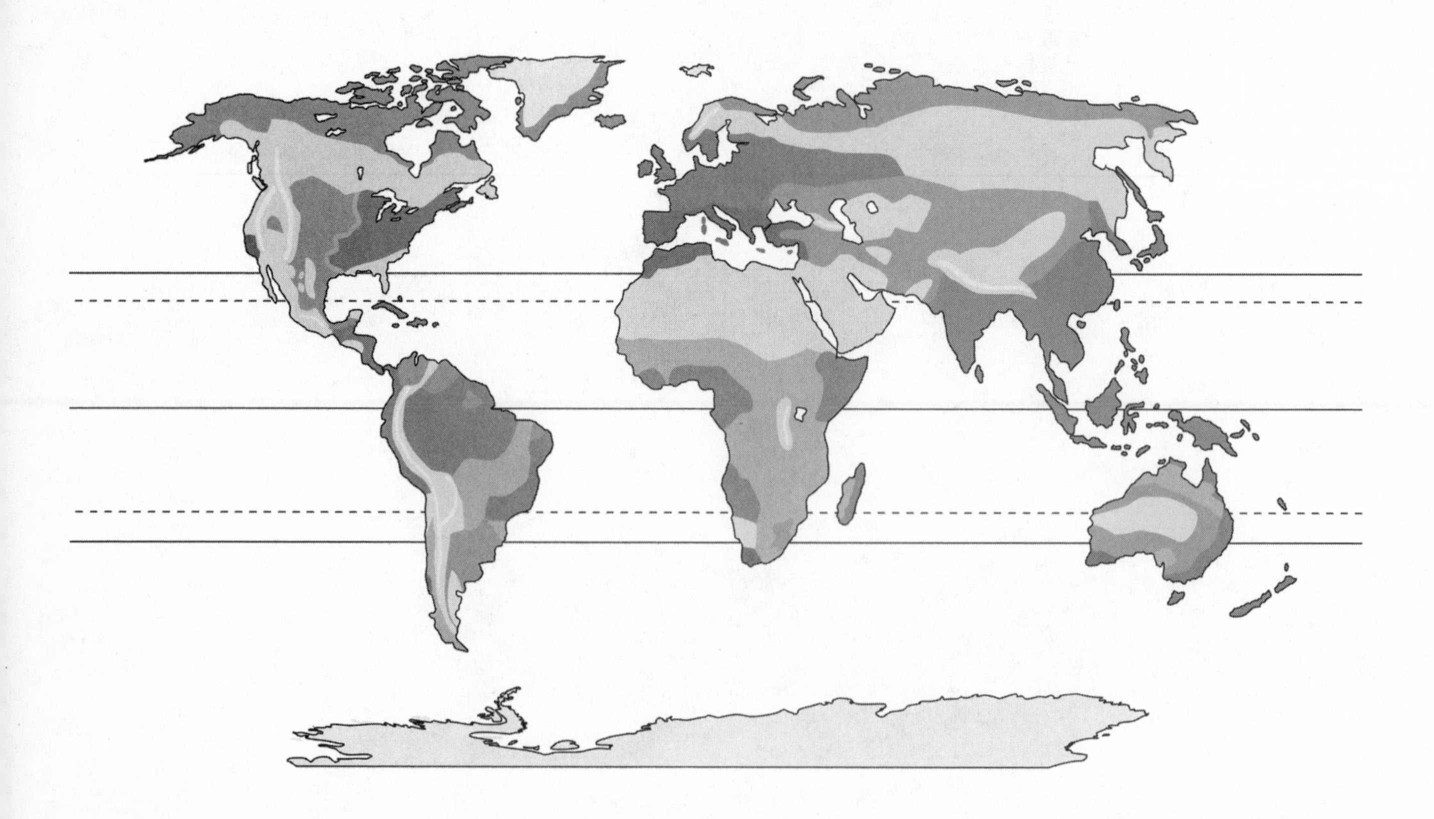

Figure 50.24 The distribution of major terrestrial biomes, age 1112

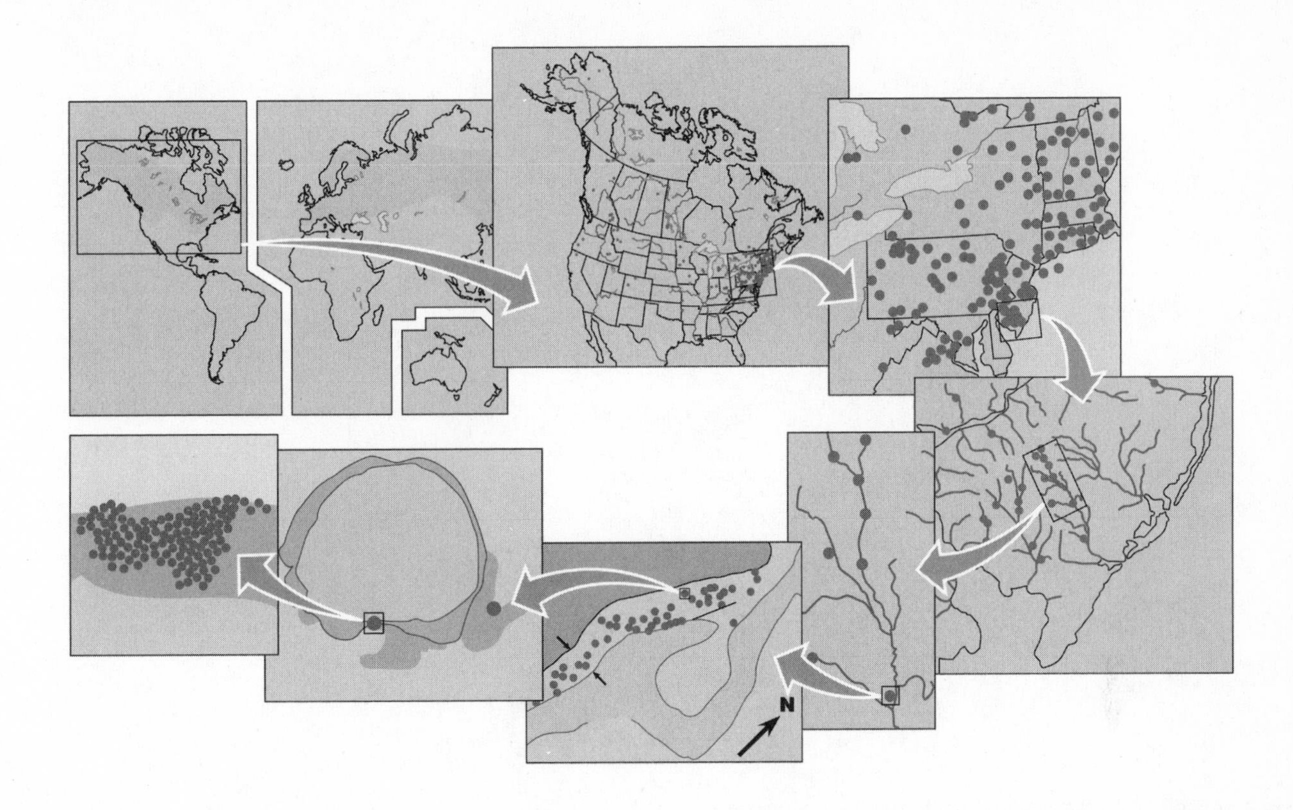

Figure 50.26 A hierarchy of scales for analyzing the geographic distribution of the moss *Tetraphis*, page 1118

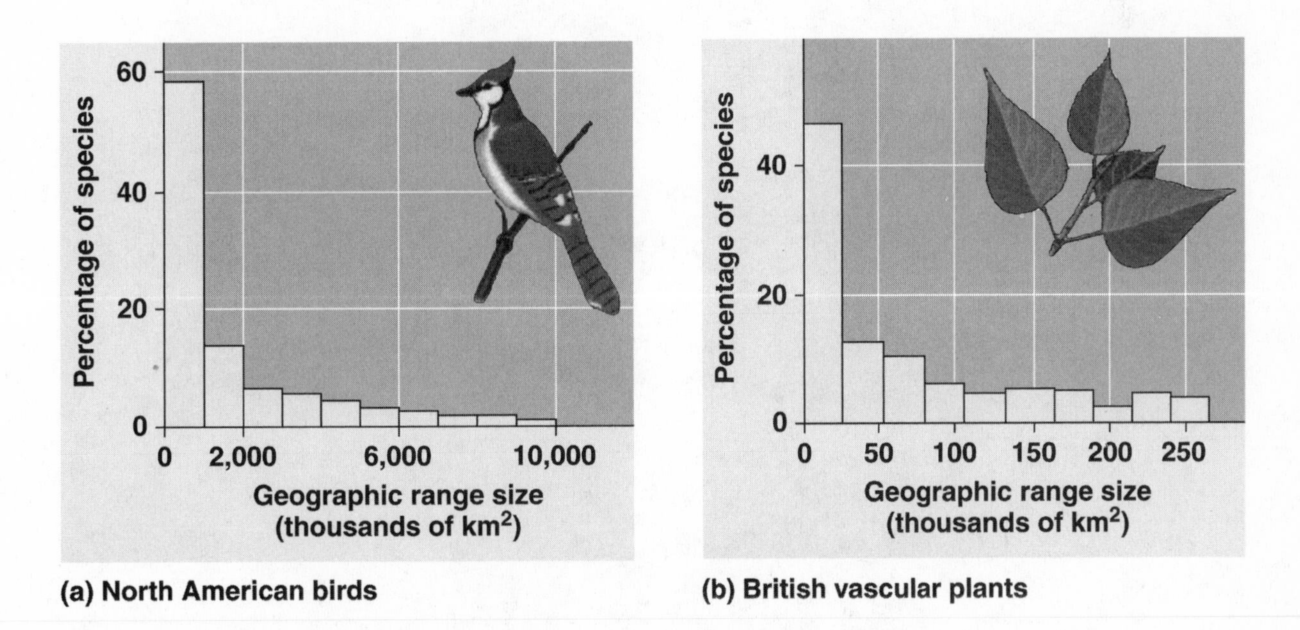

(a) North American birds

(b) British vascular plants

Figure 50.27 Most species have small geographic ranges, page 1118

Figure 51.1 Genetic and environmental components of behavior: a case study, page 1123

Figure 51.2 Niko Tinbergen's experiments on the digger wasp's nest-locating behavior, page 1124

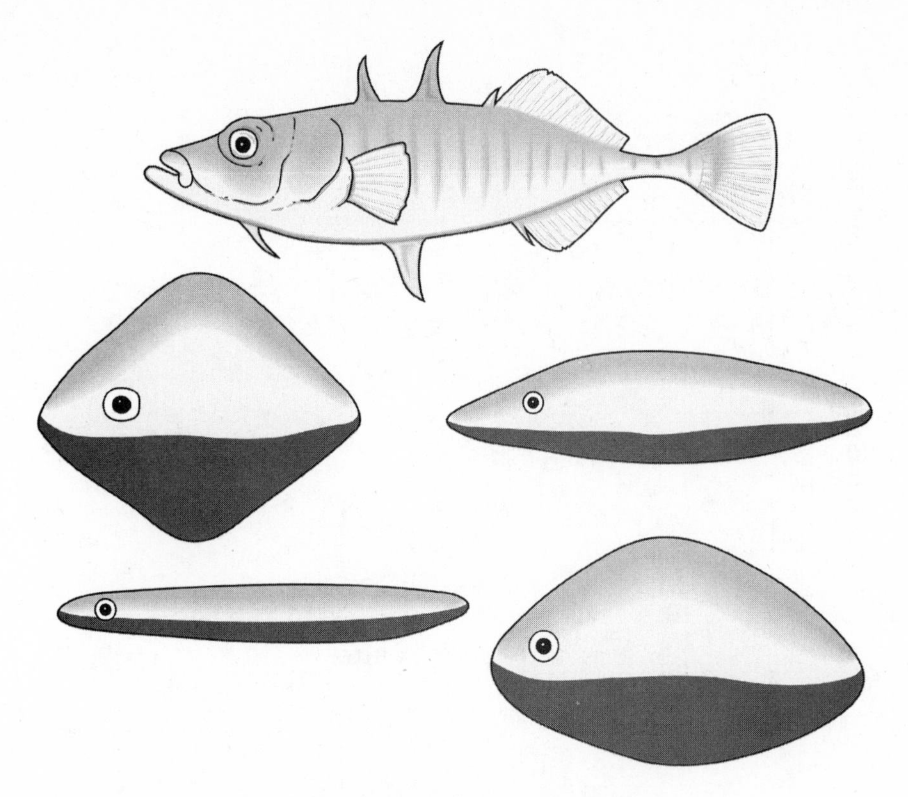

Figure 51.3 Classic demonstration of innate behavior, page 1125

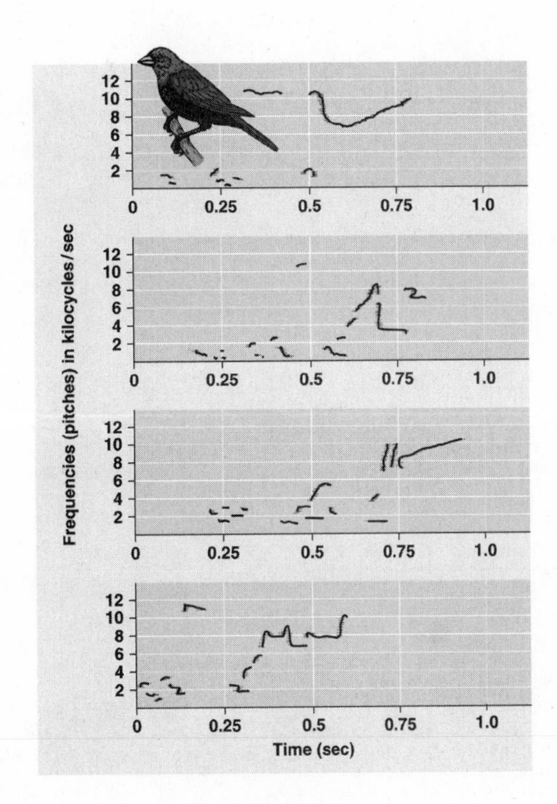

Figure 51.5 The repertoire of a songbird, page 1126

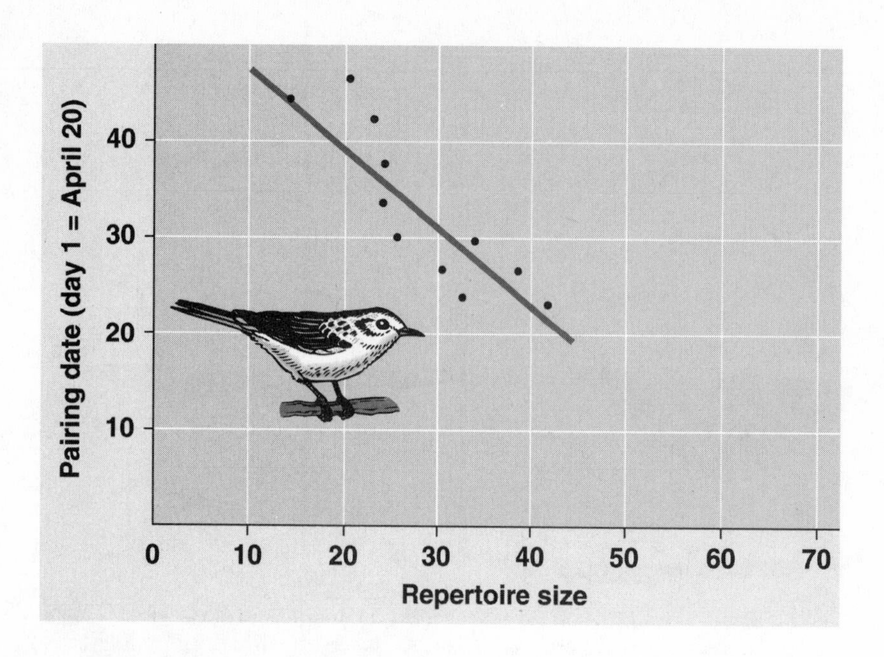

Figure 51.6 Female warblers prefer males with large song repertoires, page 1127

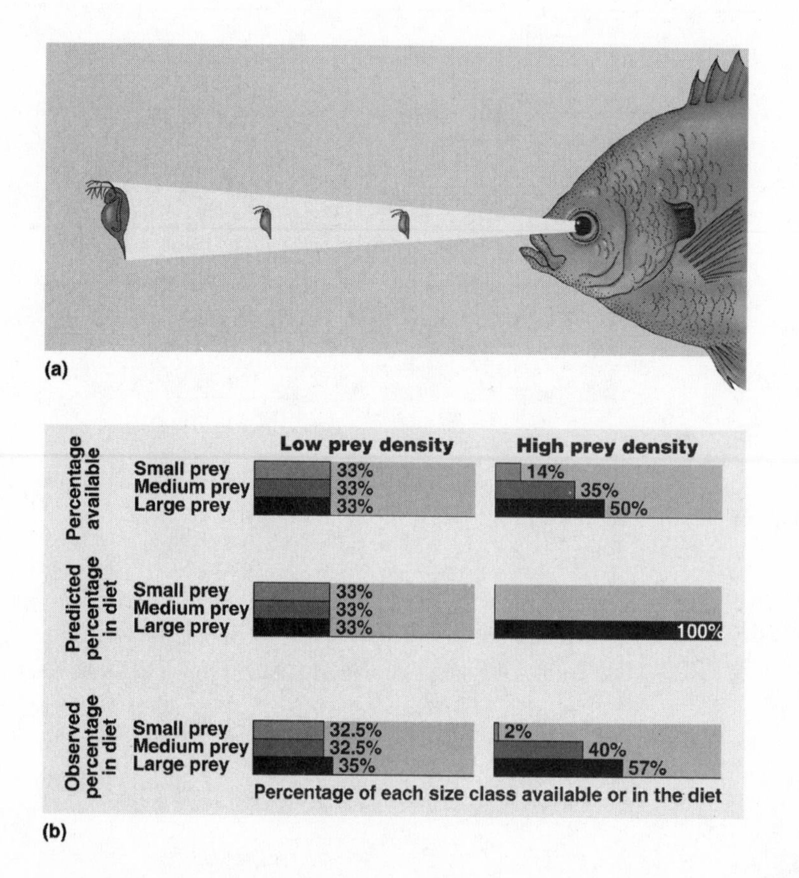

Figure 51.7 Feeding by young bluegill sunfish, page 1128

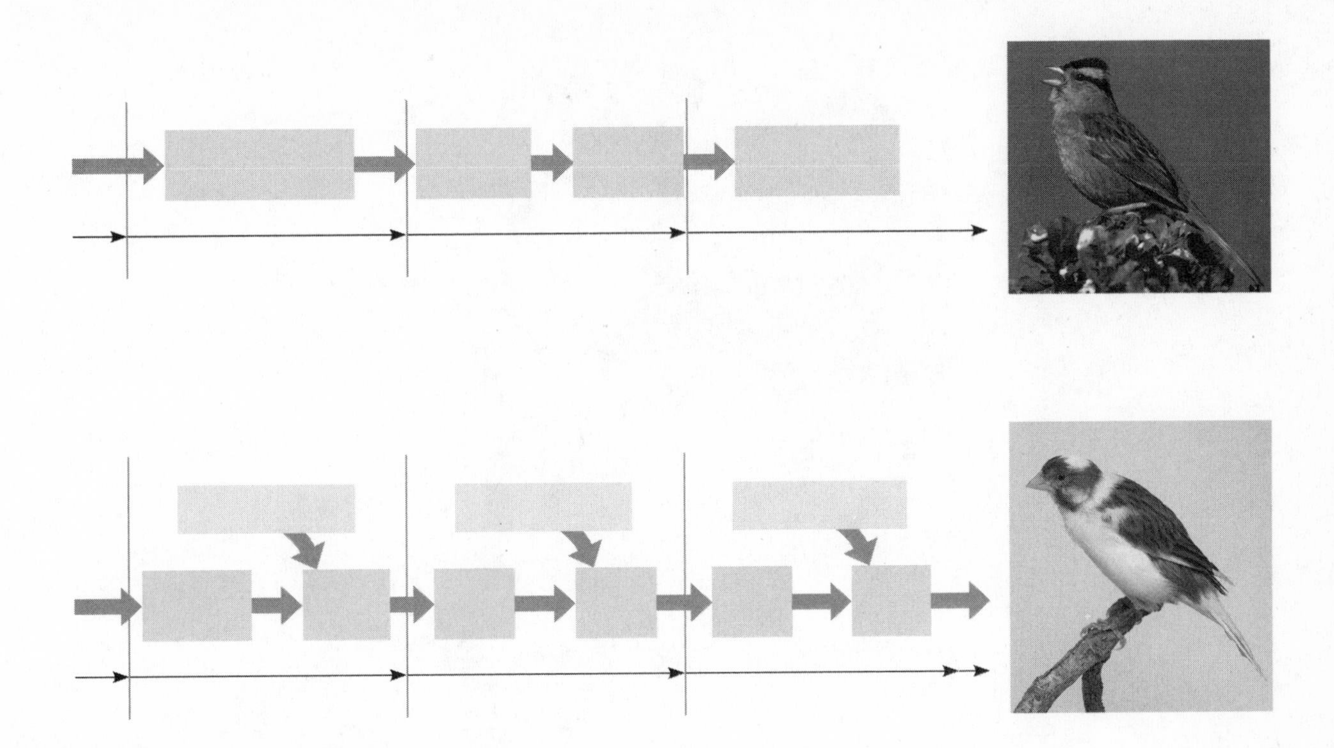

Figure 51.10 Two kinds of bird-song development, page 1131

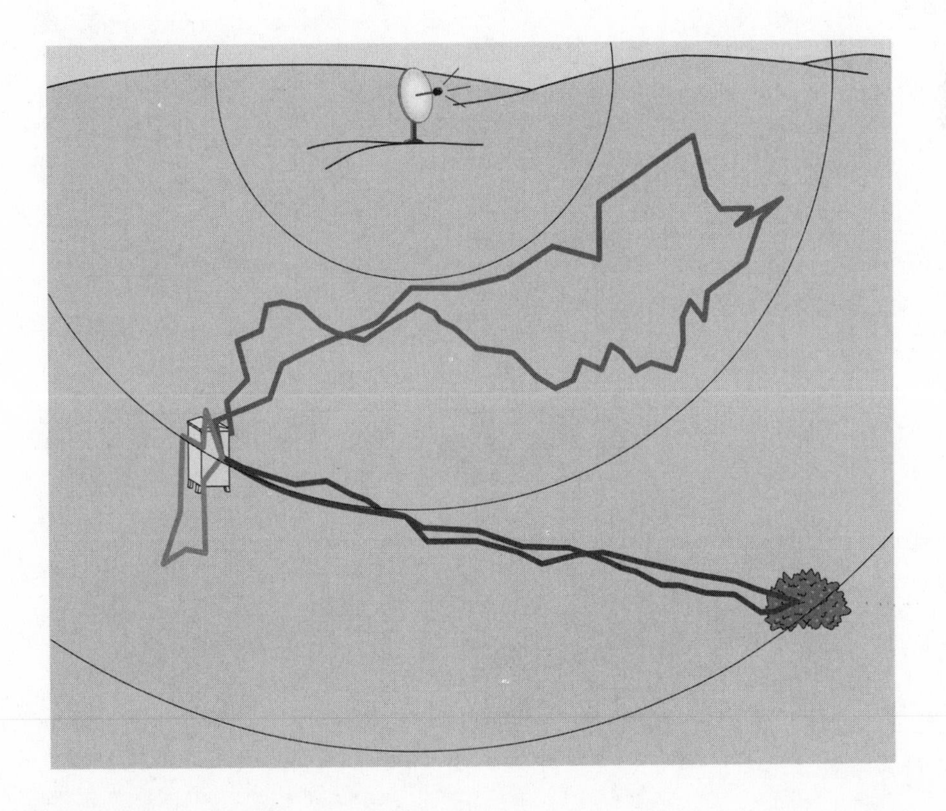

Figure 51.14b Electronic surveillance of honeybees, page 1135

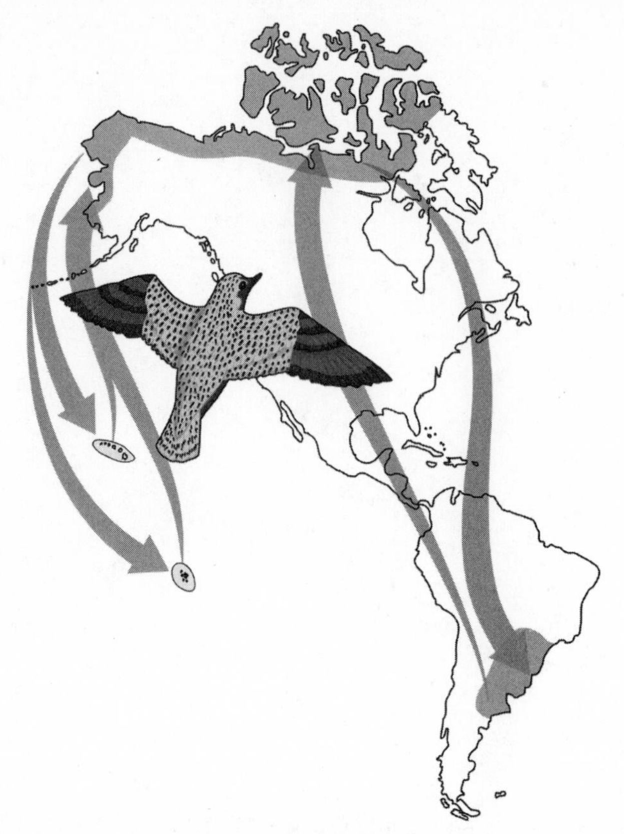

Figure 51.15 Migration routes of the golden plover, page 1135

Figure 51.16 Orientation versus navigation in juvenile and adult starlings, page 1136

Figure 51.23 Courtship behavior in the three-spined stickleback, page 1140

Figure 51.27 Communication in bees: one hypothesis, page 1144

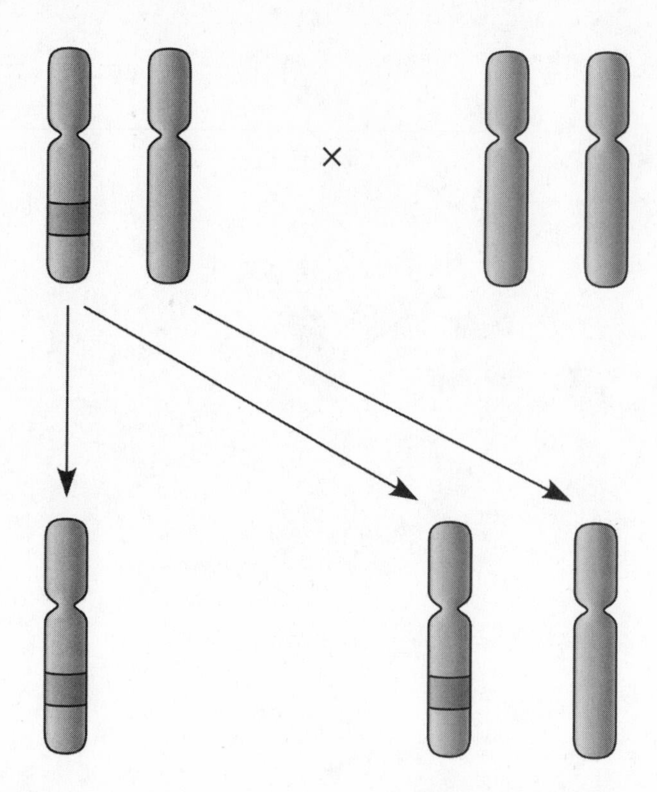

Figure 51.30 The coefficient of relatedness between siblings is 0.5, page 1146

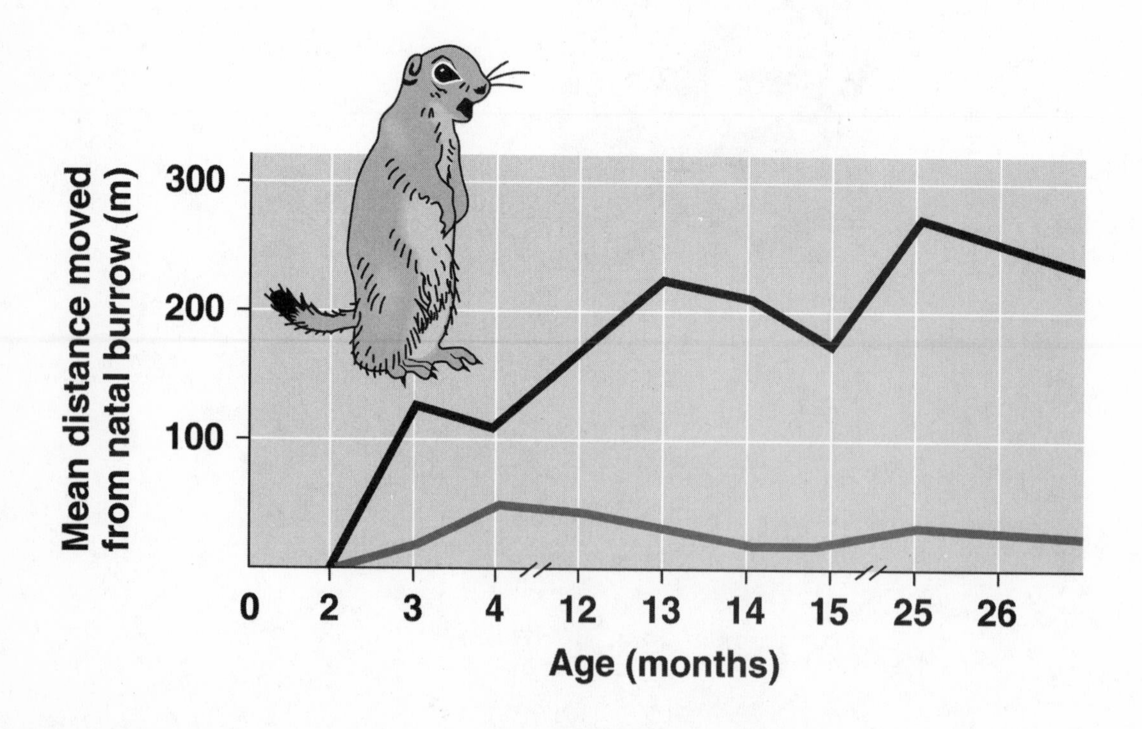

Figure 51.31 Kin selection and altruism in the Belding ground squirrel, page 1147

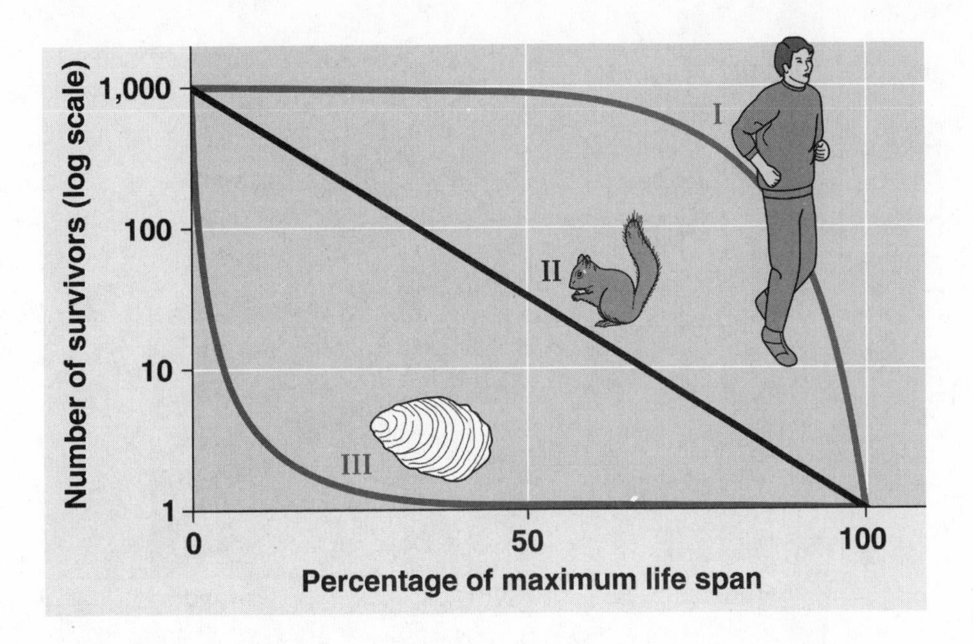

Figure 52.3 Idealized surviorship curves, page 1155

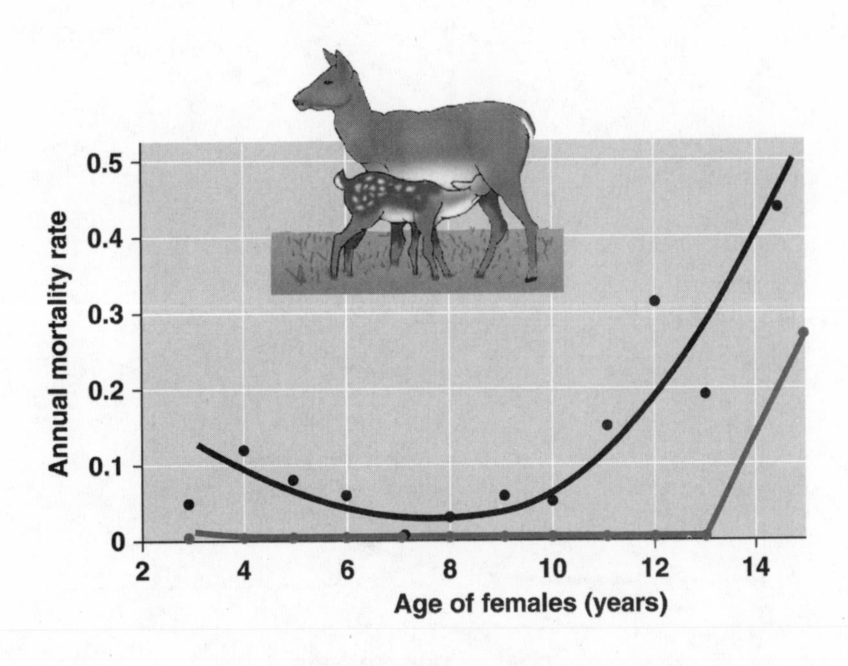

Figure 52.5 Cost of reproduction in female red deer on the island of Rhum, in Scotland, page 1157

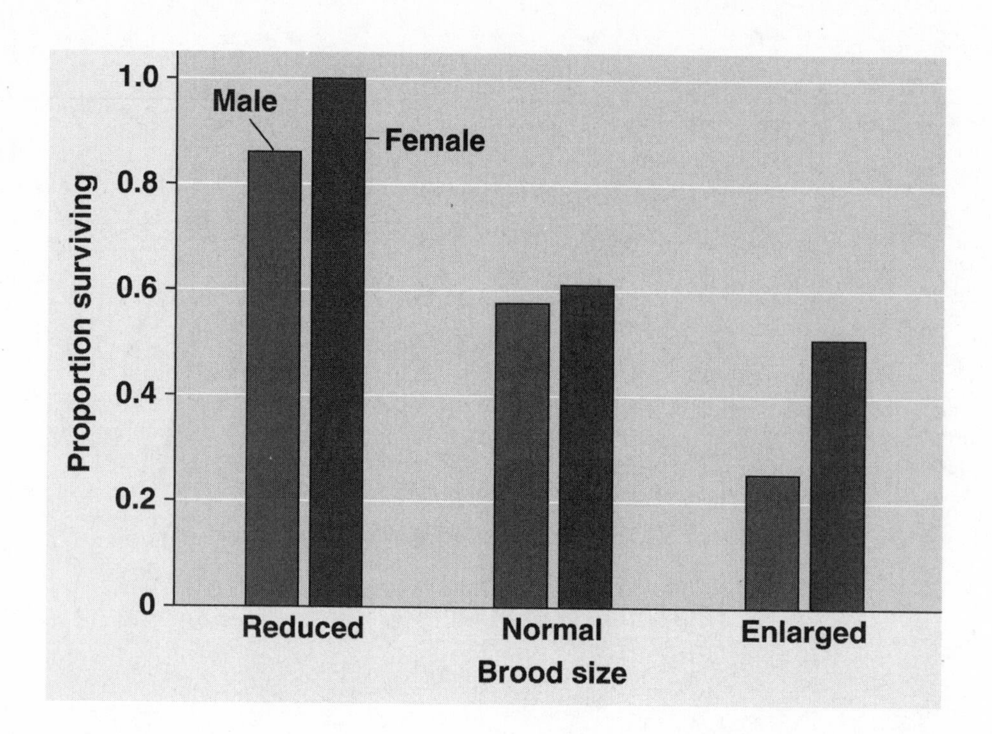

Figure 52.6 Probability of survival over the following year for European kestrels after raising a modified brood, page 1157

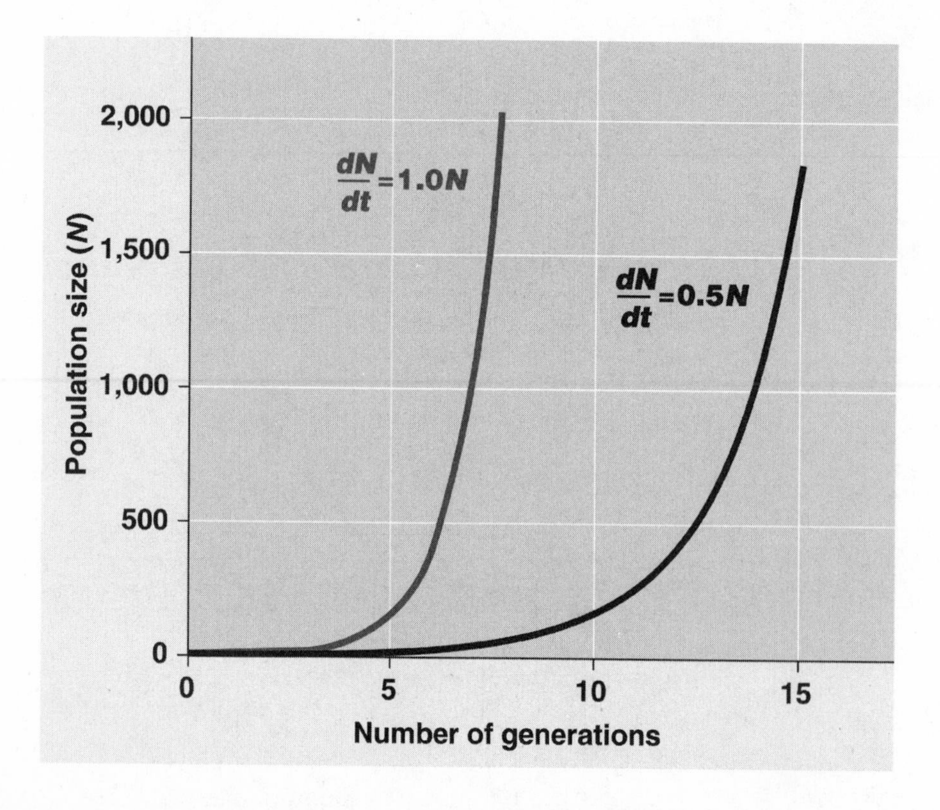

Figure 52.8 Population growth predicted by the exponential model, page 1160

Figure 52.9 Example of exponential population growth in nature, page 1160

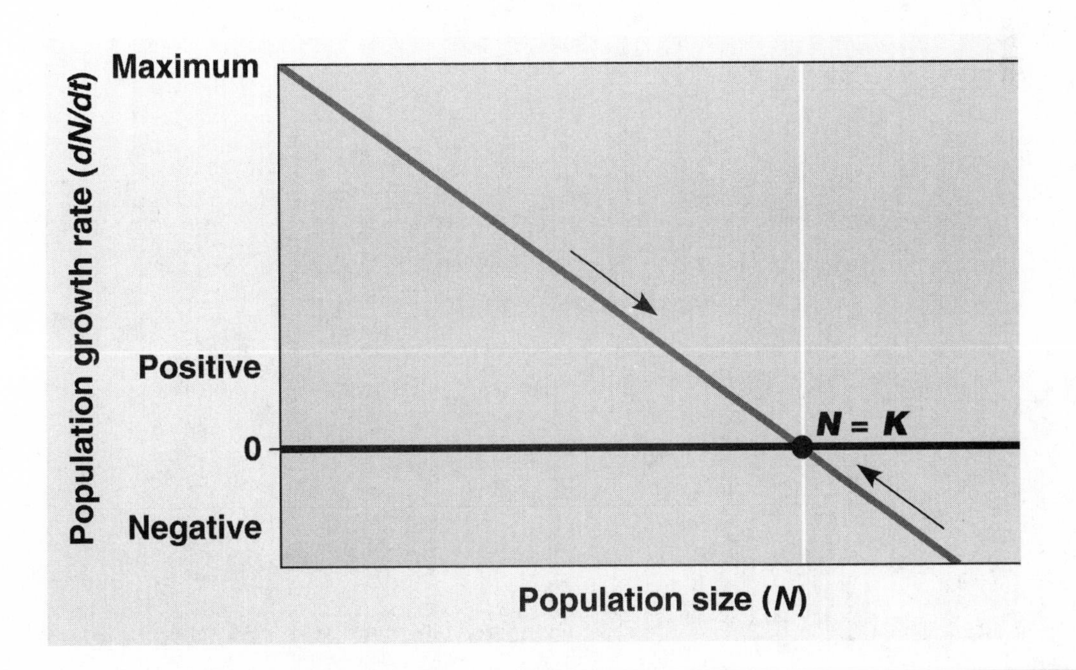

Figure 52.10 Reduction of population growth rate with increasing population size (N), page 1161

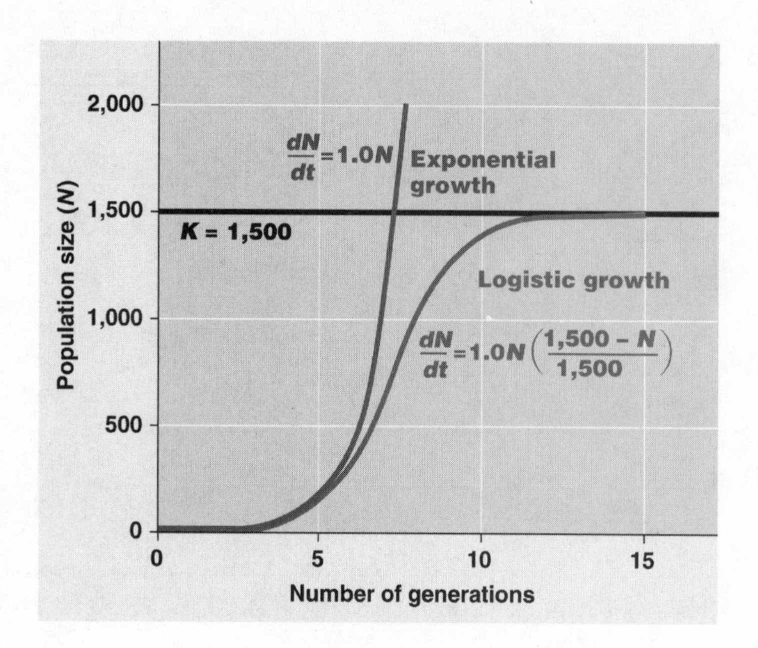

Figure 52.11 Population growth predicted by the logistic model, page 1162

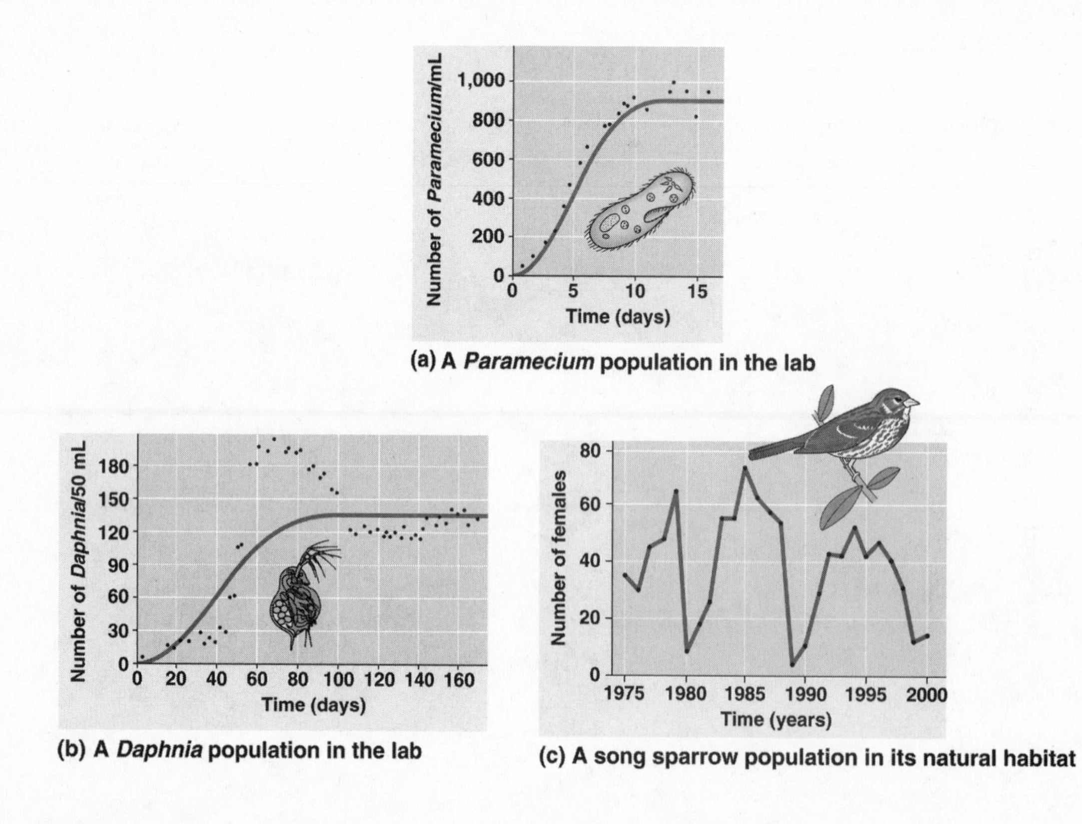

Figure 52.12 How well do these populations fit the logistic population growth model? page 1162

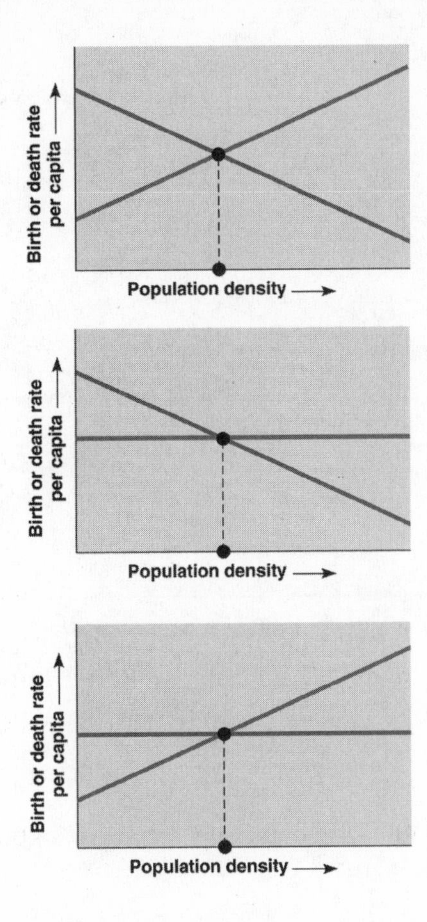

Figure 52.13 Graphic model showing how equilibrium may be determined for population density, page 1164

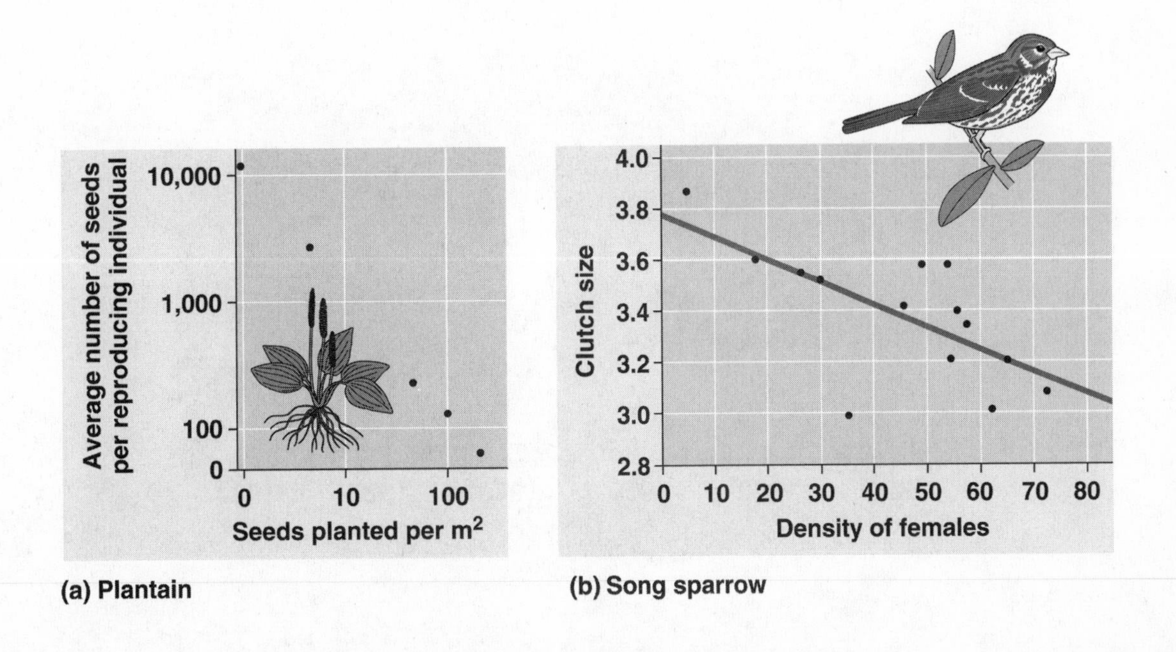

Figure 52.14 Decreased fecundity at high population densities, page 1164

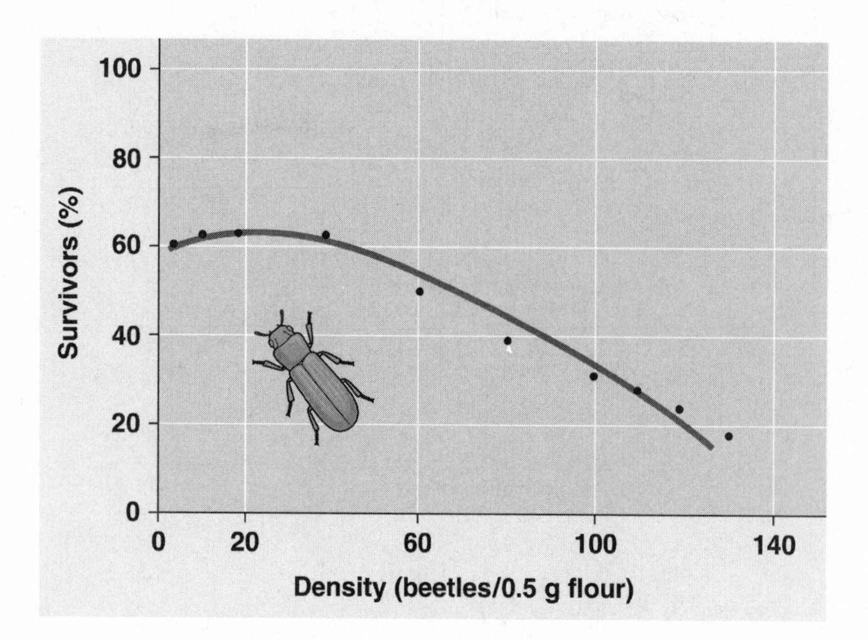

Figure 52.15 Decreased survivorship at high population densities. page 1165

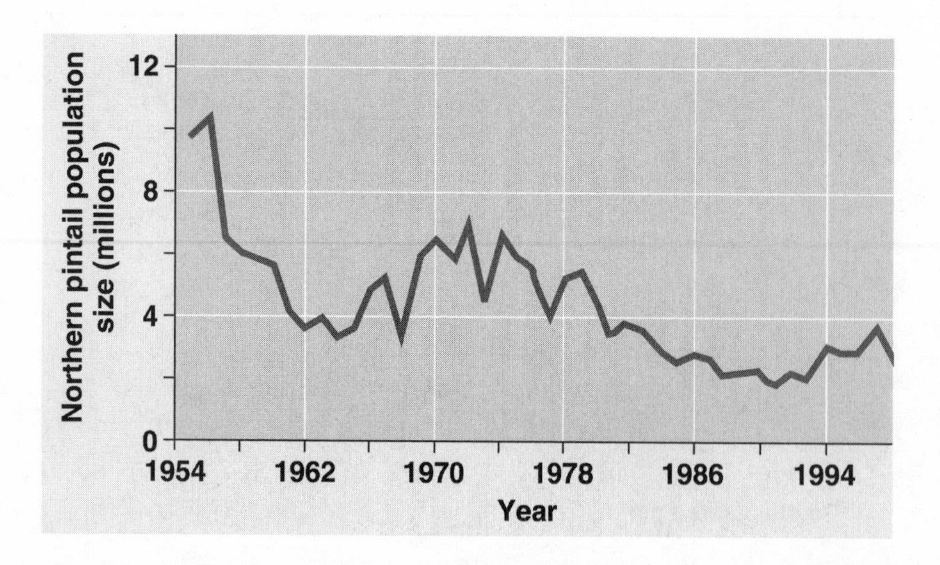

Figure 52.16 Decline in the breeding population of the northern pintail (*Anas actua*) from 1955 to 1998, page 1166

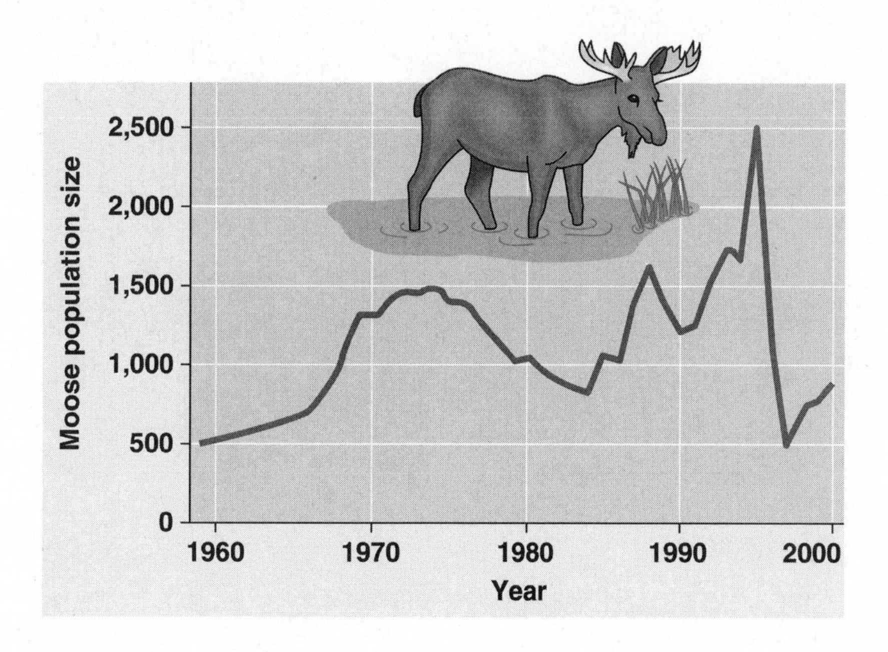

Figure 52.17 Long-term study of the moose (*Alces alces*) population of Isle Royale, Michigan, page 1166

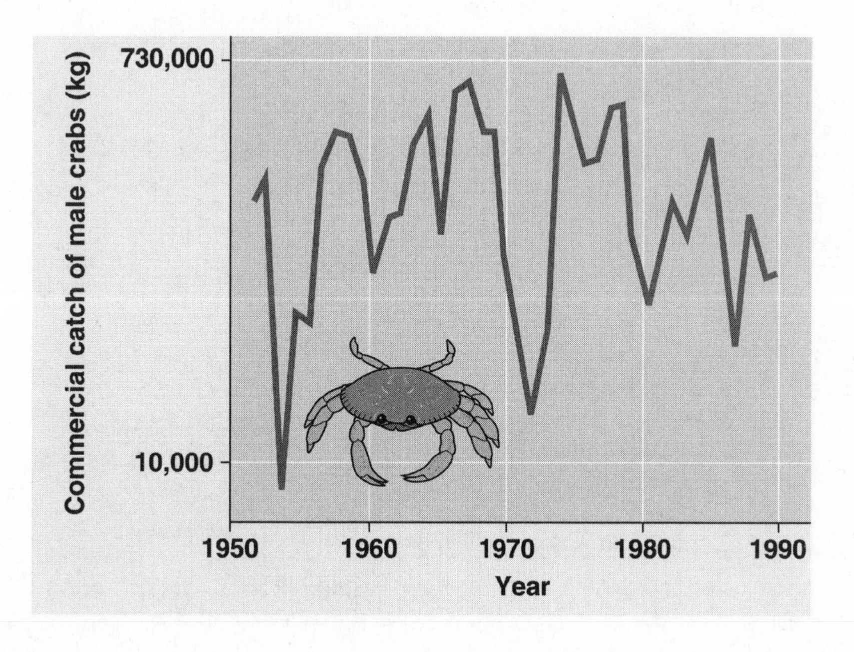

Figure 52.18 Extreme population fluctuations, page 1167

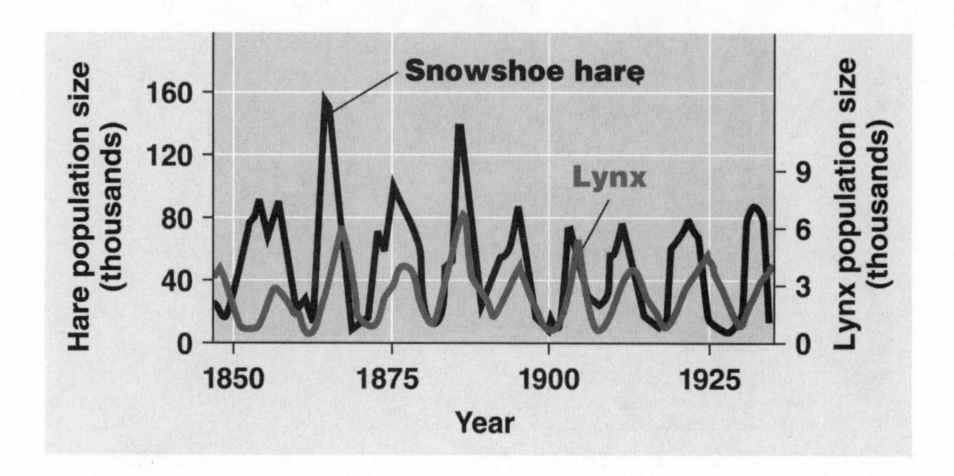

Figure 52.19 Population cycles in the snowshoe hare and lynx, page 1167

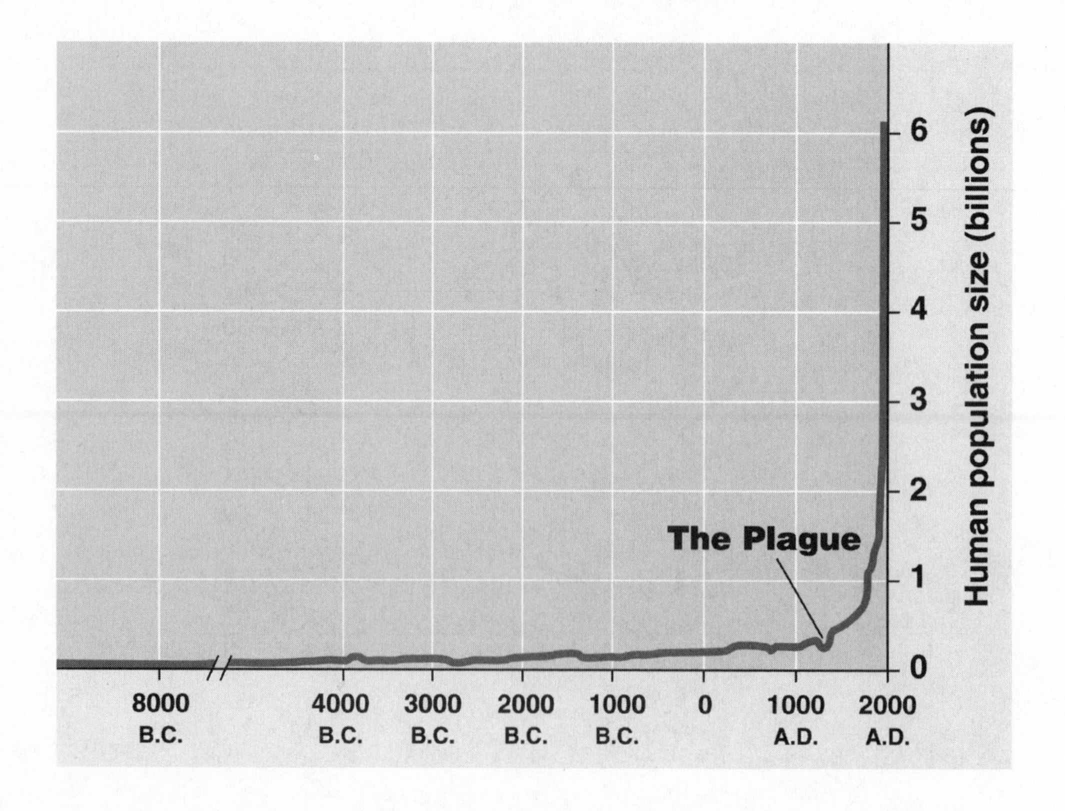

Figure 52.20 Human population growth, page 1168

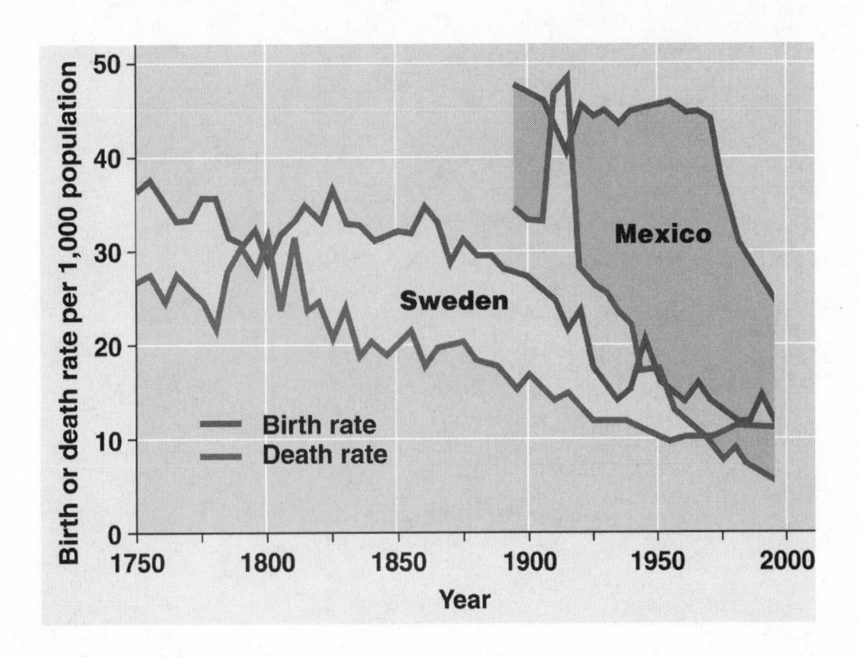

Figure 52.21 Demographic transition in Sweden and Mexico, 1750-1997, page 1169

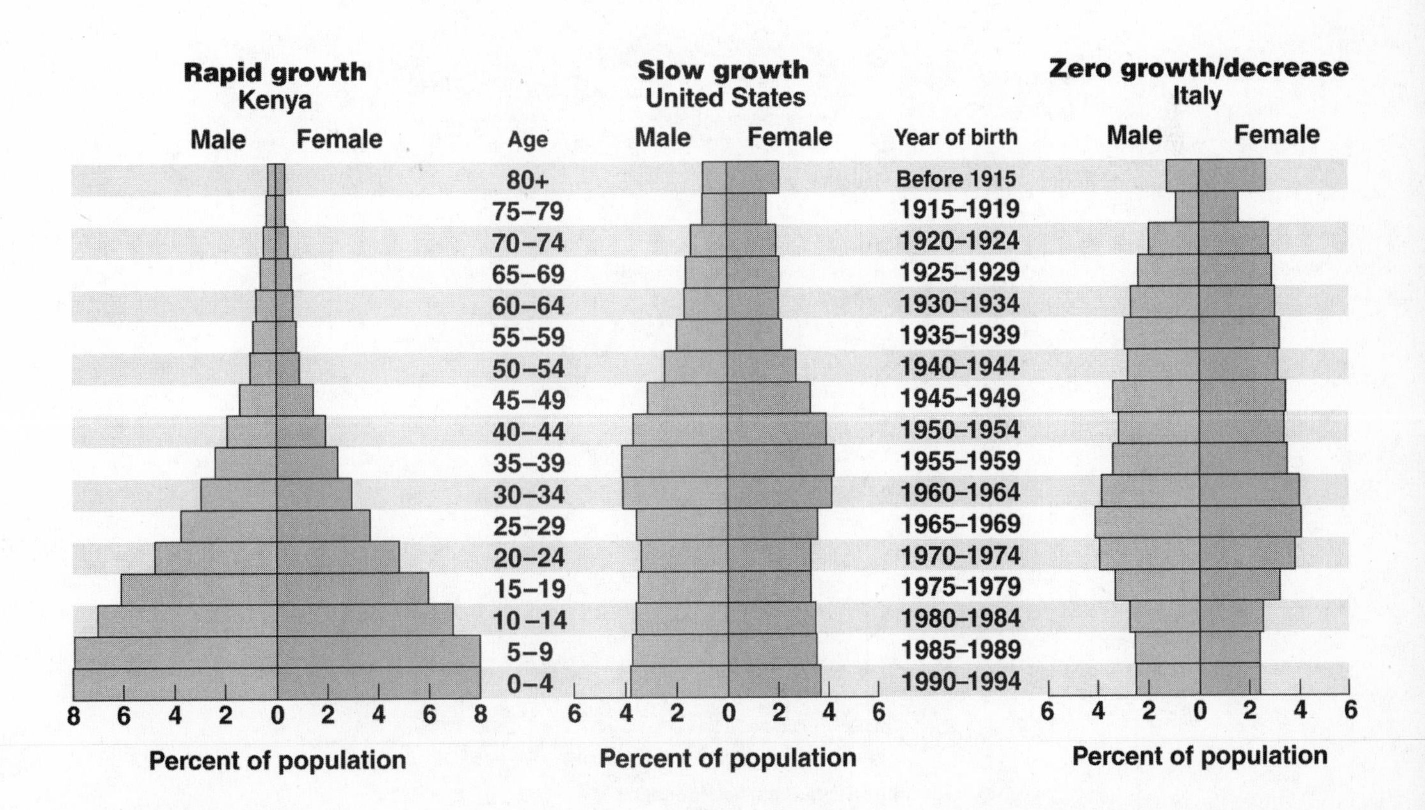

Figure 52.22 Age-structure pyramids for the human population of Kenya (growing at 2.1% per year), the United States (growing at 0.6% per year), and Italy (zero growth) for 1995, page 1170

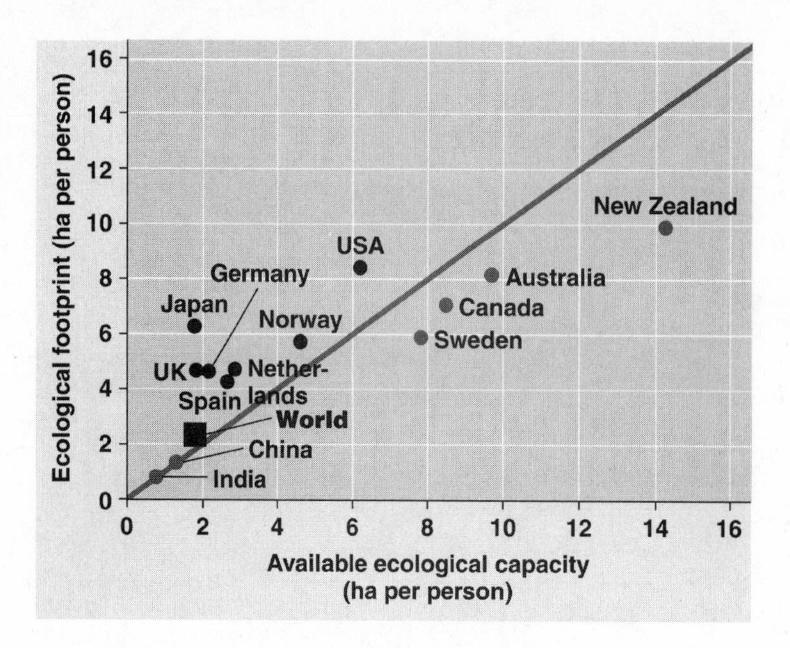

Figure 52.23 Ecological footprint in relation to available ecological capacity, page 1171

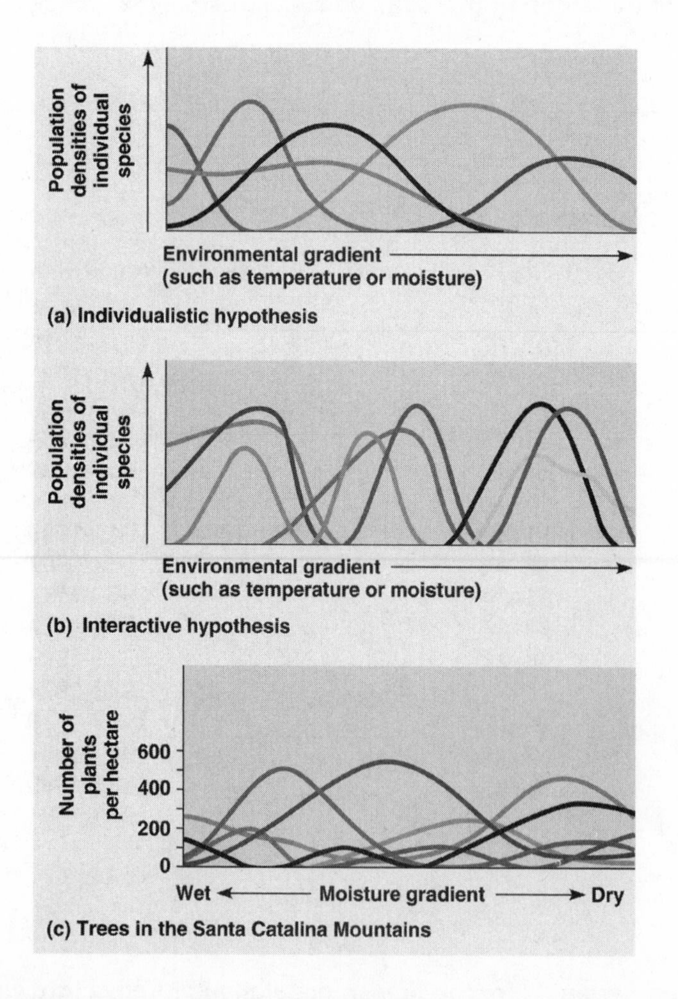

Figure 53.1 Testing the individualistic and interactive hypotheses of communities, page 1175

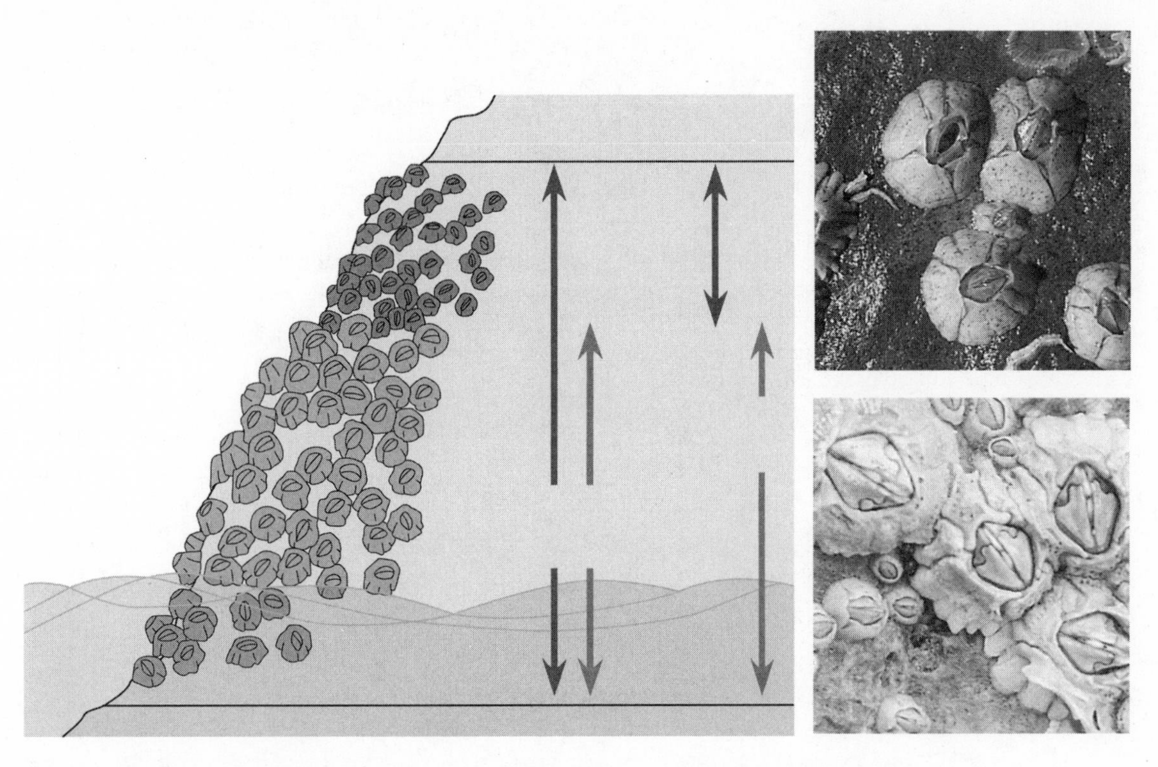

Figure 53.2 Testing a competitive exclusion hypothesis in the field, page 1177

Figure 53.3a Resource partitioning in a group of lizards, page 1178

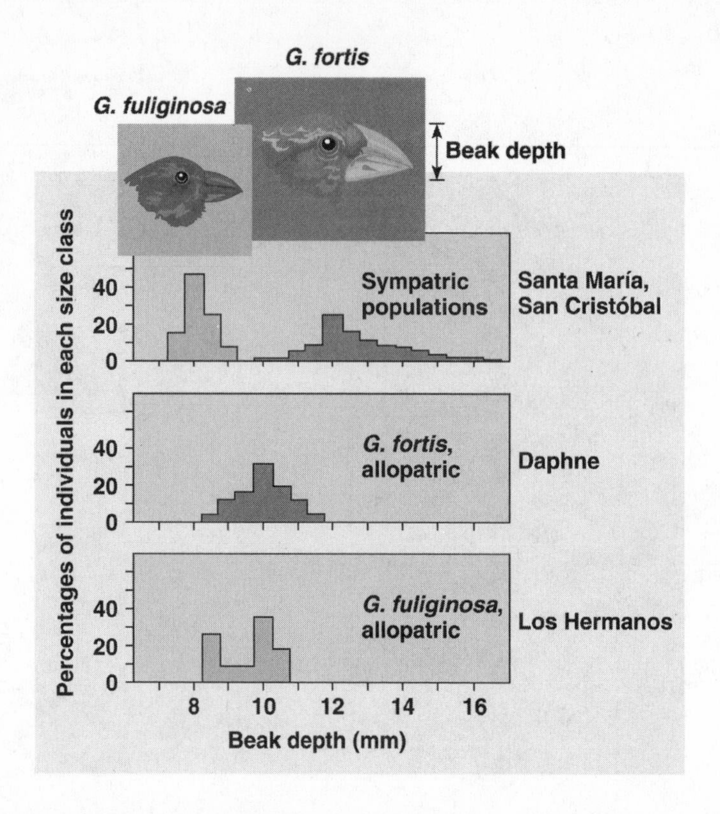

Figure 53.4 Character displacement: circumstantial evidence for competition in nature, paeg 1178

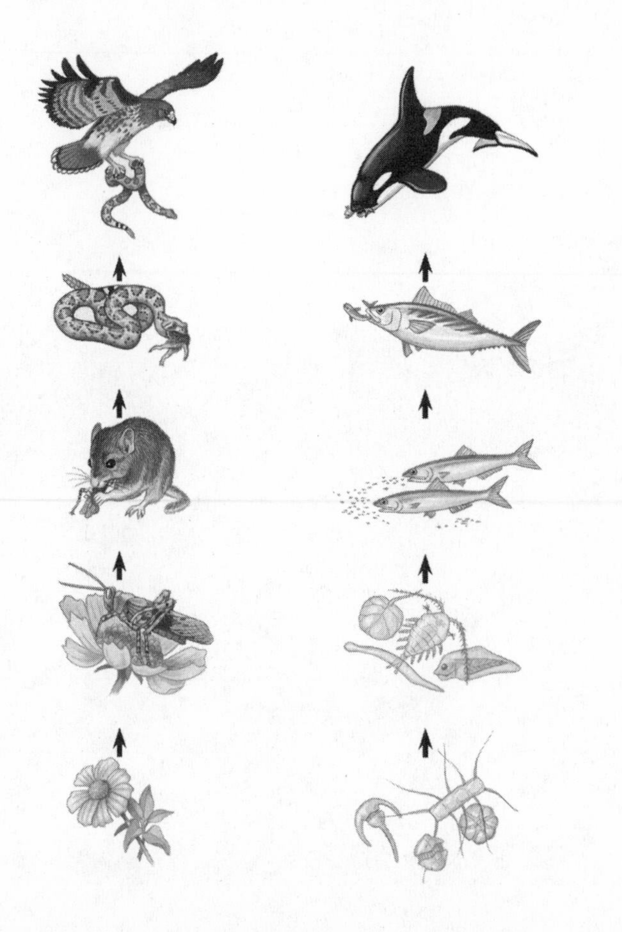

Figure 53.10 Examples of terrestrial and marine food chains, page 1181

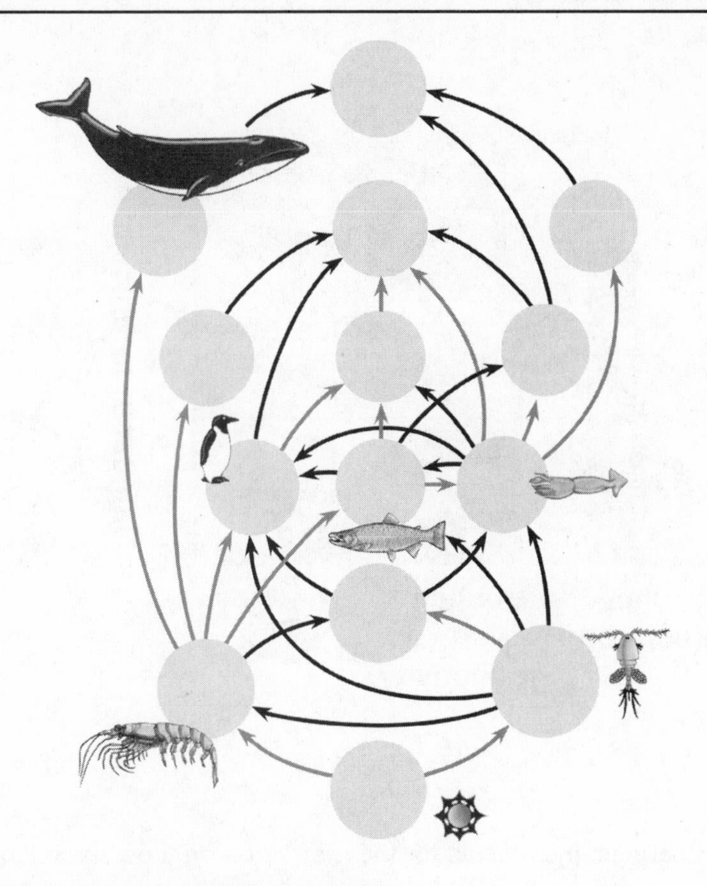

Figure 53.11 An antarctic marine food web, page 1182

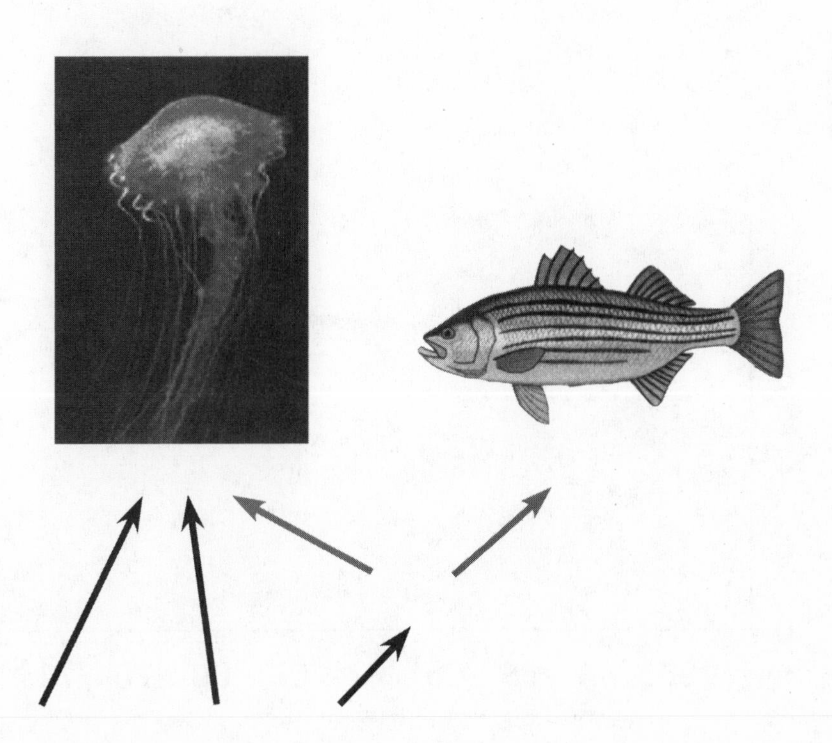

Figure 53.12 Partial food web for the Chesapeake Bay estuary on the U.S. Atlantic coast, page 1182

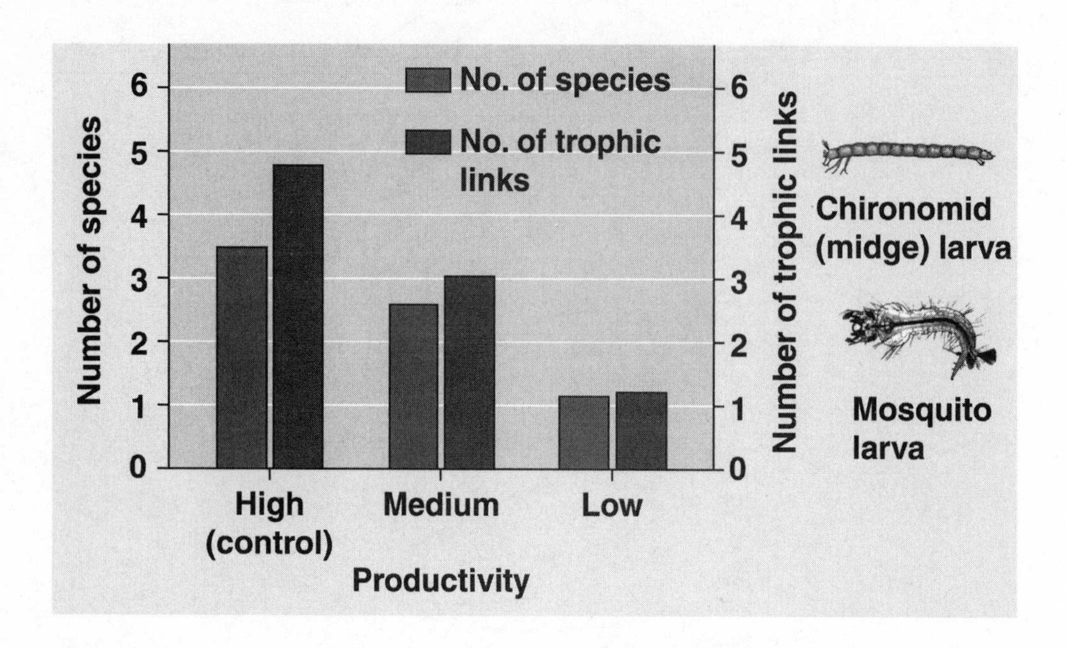

Figure 53.13 Test of the energetic hypothesis for the restriction on food chain length, paeg 1183

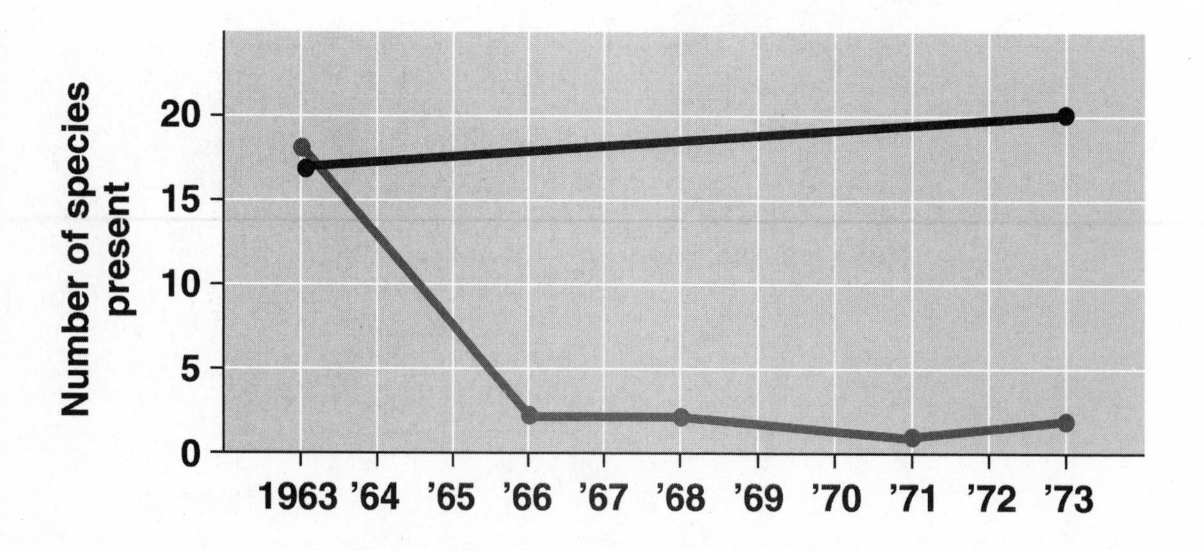

Figure 53.14b Testing a keystone predator hypothesis, page 1184

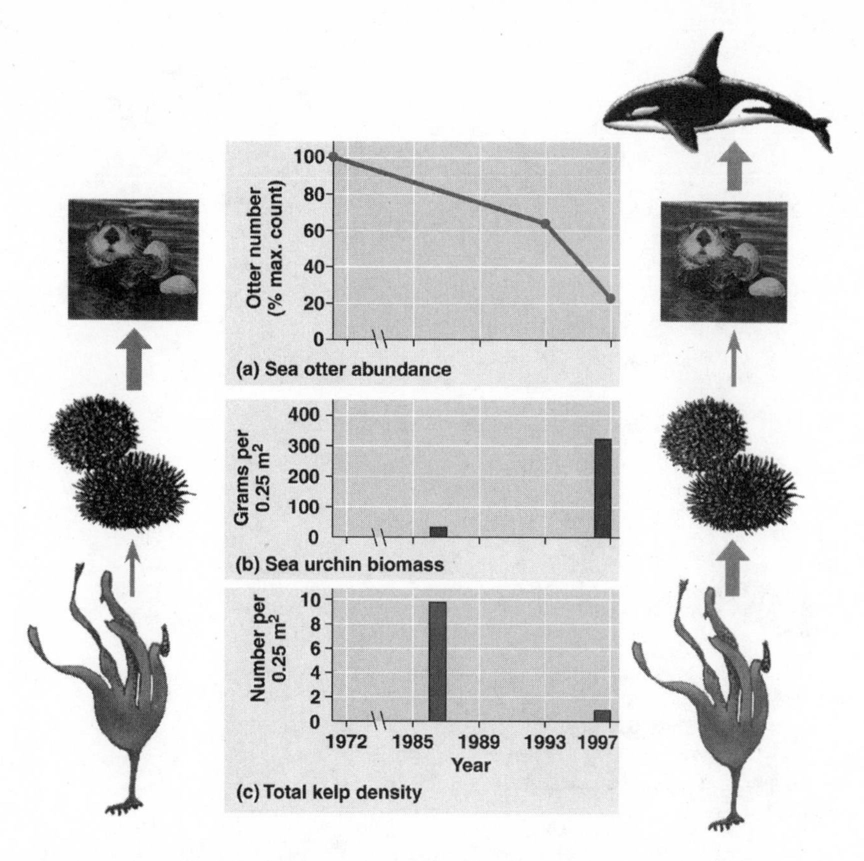

Figure 53.15 Sea otters as keystone predators in the North Pacific, page 1185

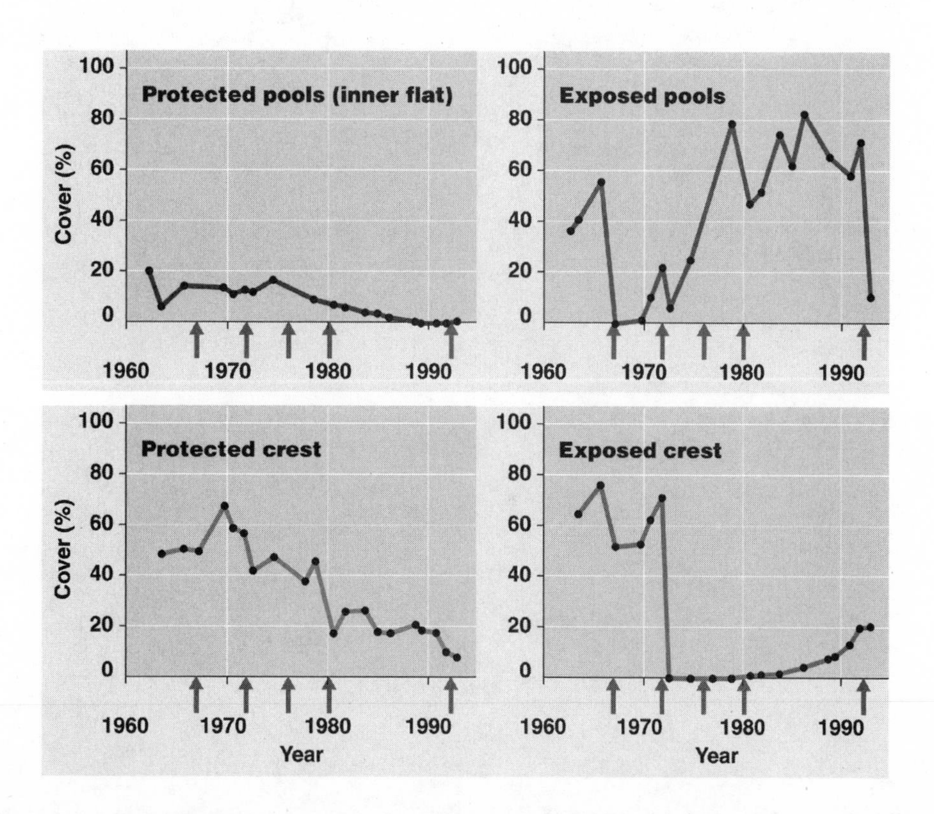

Figure 53.17 Storm disturbance to coral reef communities, page 1187

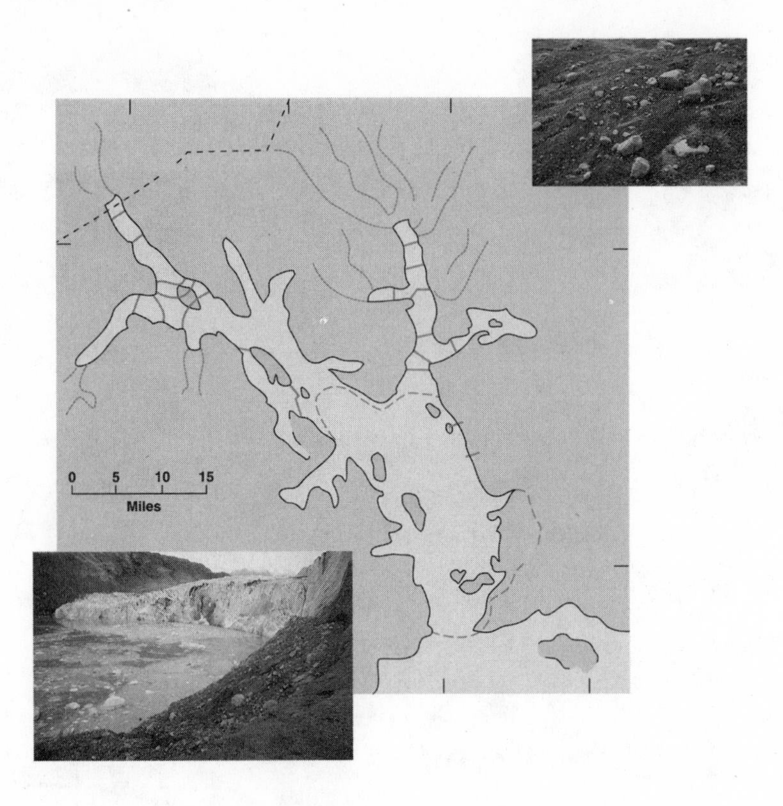

Figure 53.19 A glacial retreat in southeastern Alaska, page 1189

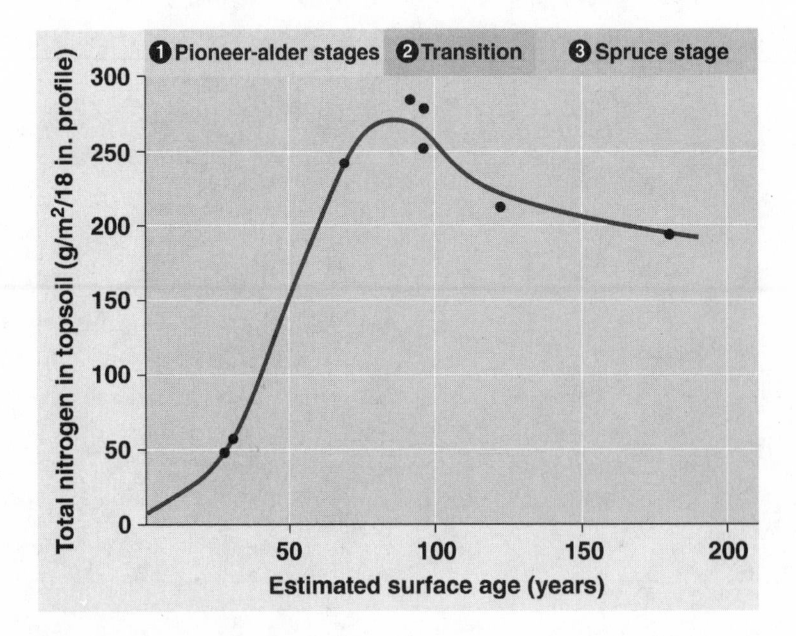

Figure 53.20 Change in soil nitrogen concentration during succession after glacial retreat in Glacier Bay, Alaska, page 1190

Figure 53.21 Which forest is more diverse? page 1191

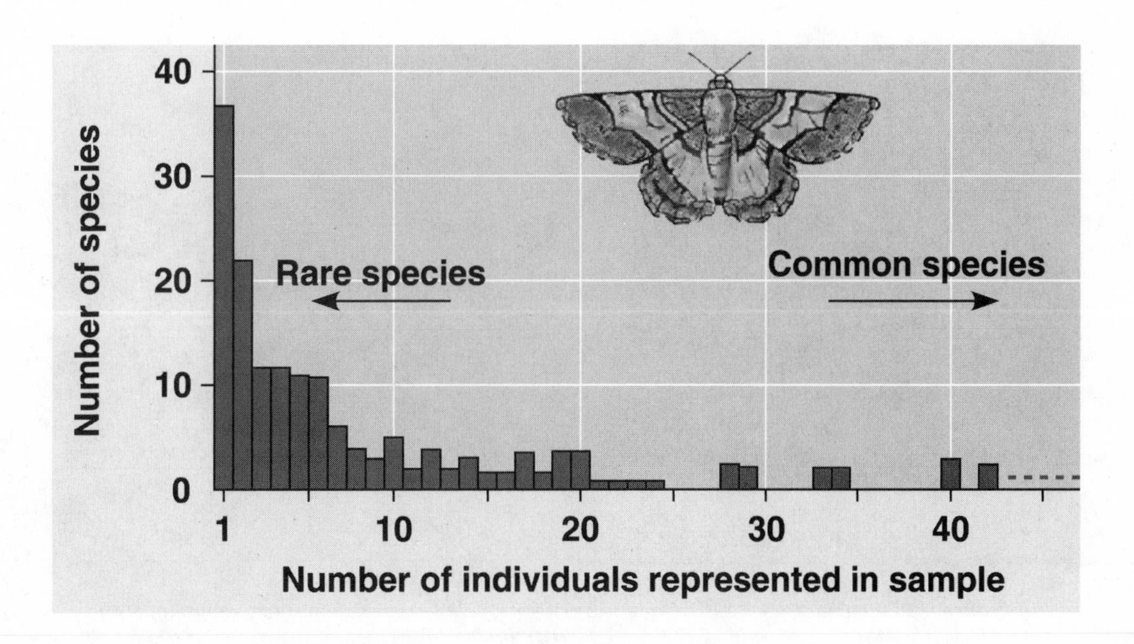

Figure 53.22 Relative abundance of Lepidoptera (butterflies and moths) captured in a light trap in Rothamsted, England, page 1192

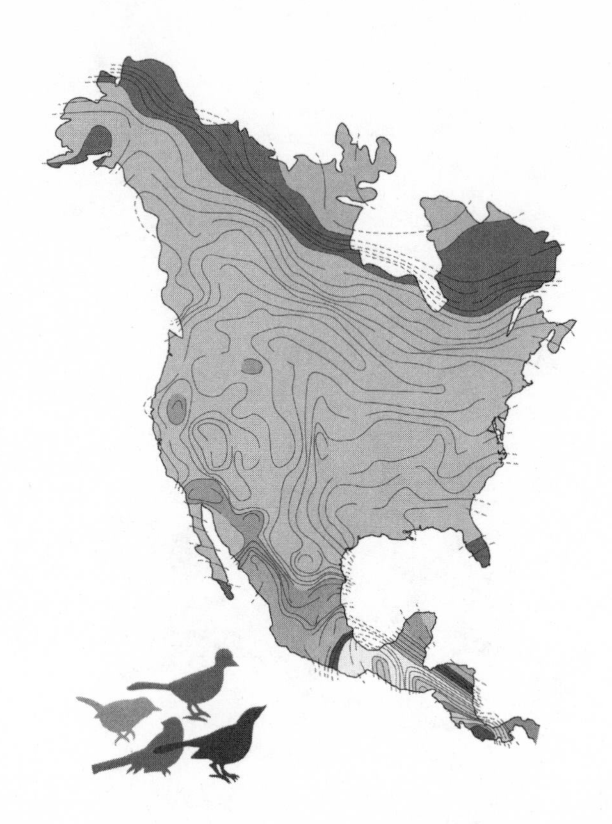

Figure 53.23 Geographic pattern of species richness in the land birds of North and Central America, page 1192

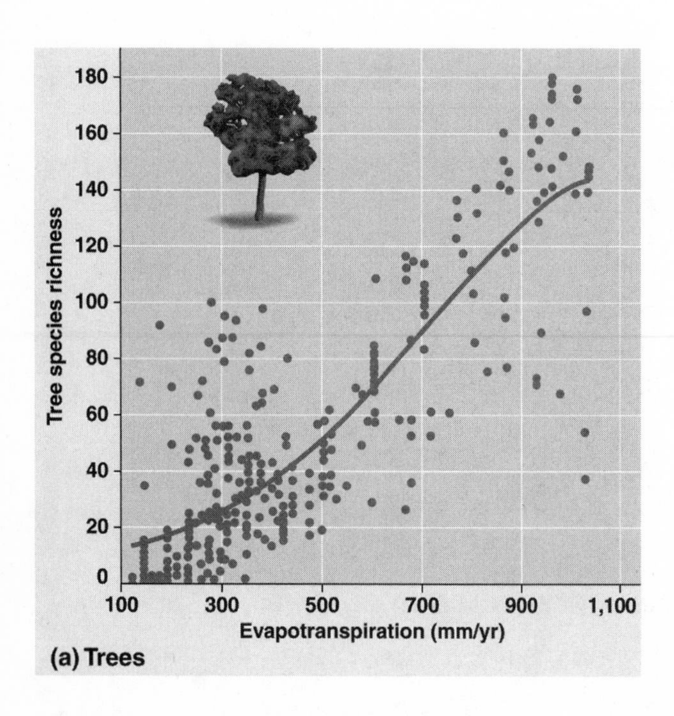

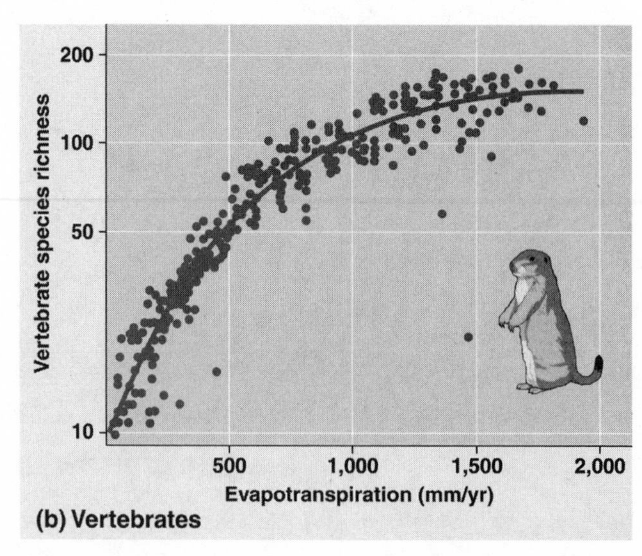

Figure 53.24 Energy and species richness, page 1193

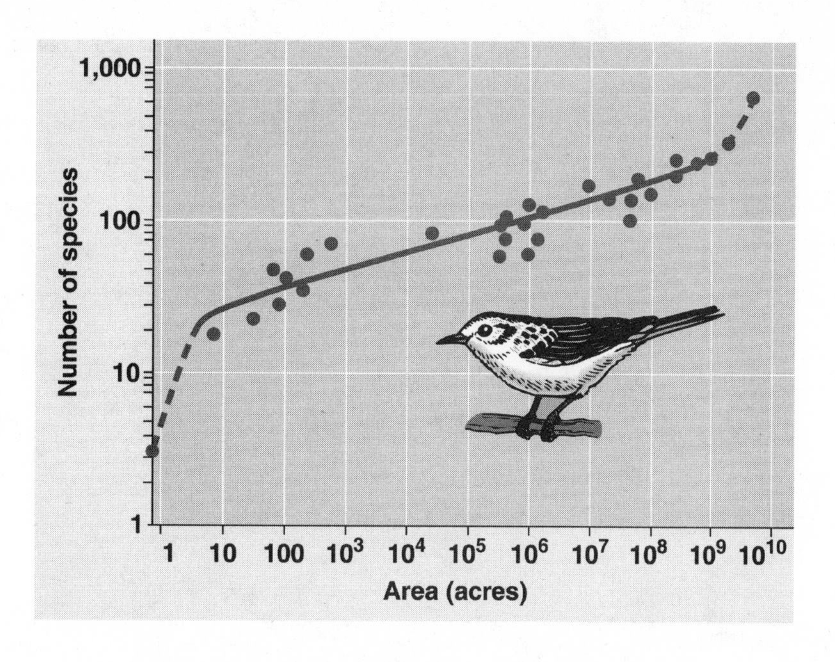

Figure 53.25 Species-area curve for North American birds, page 1194

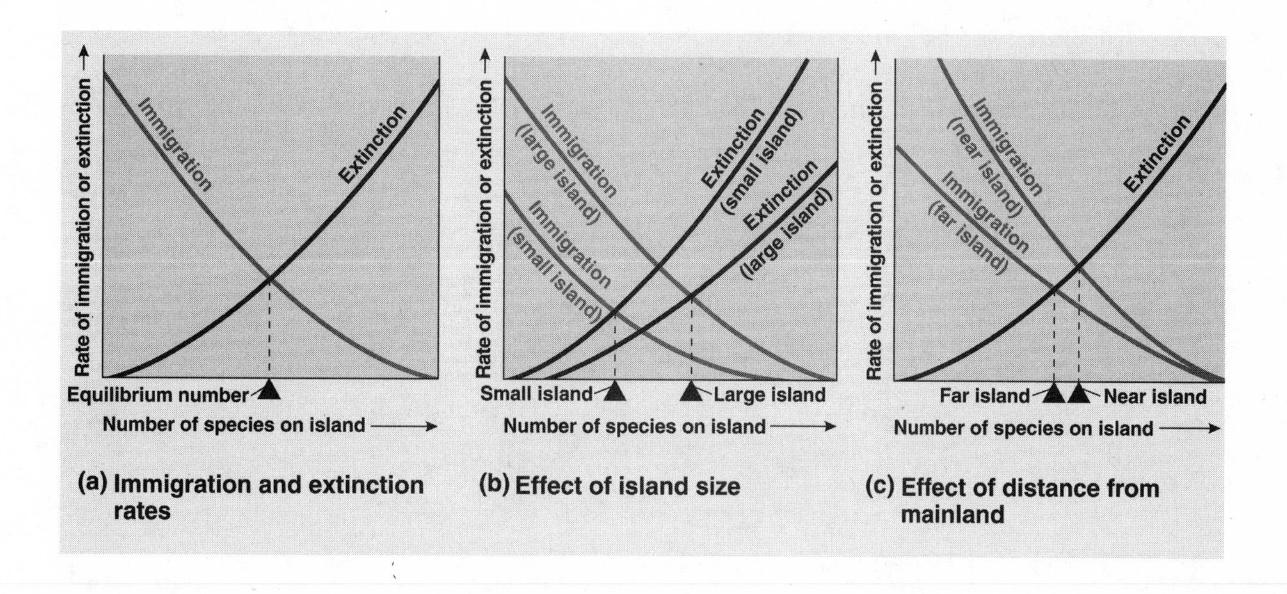

Figure 53.26 The hypothesis of island biogeography, page 1194

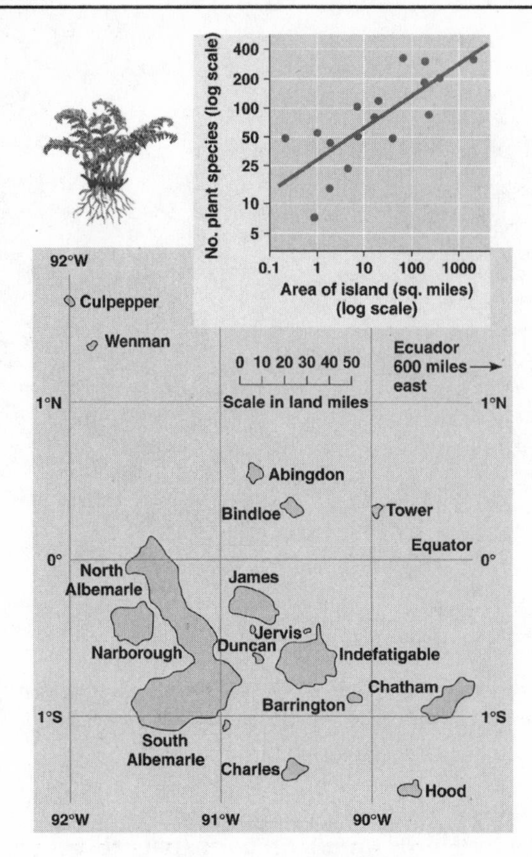

Figure 53.27 Number of plant species on the Galápagos Islands in relation to the area of the island, page 1195

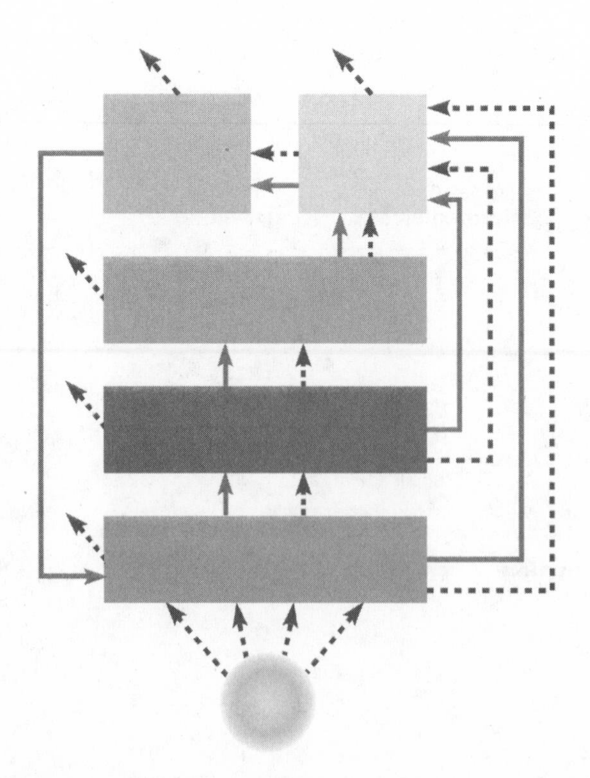

Figure 54.1 An overview of ecosystem dynamics, page 1199

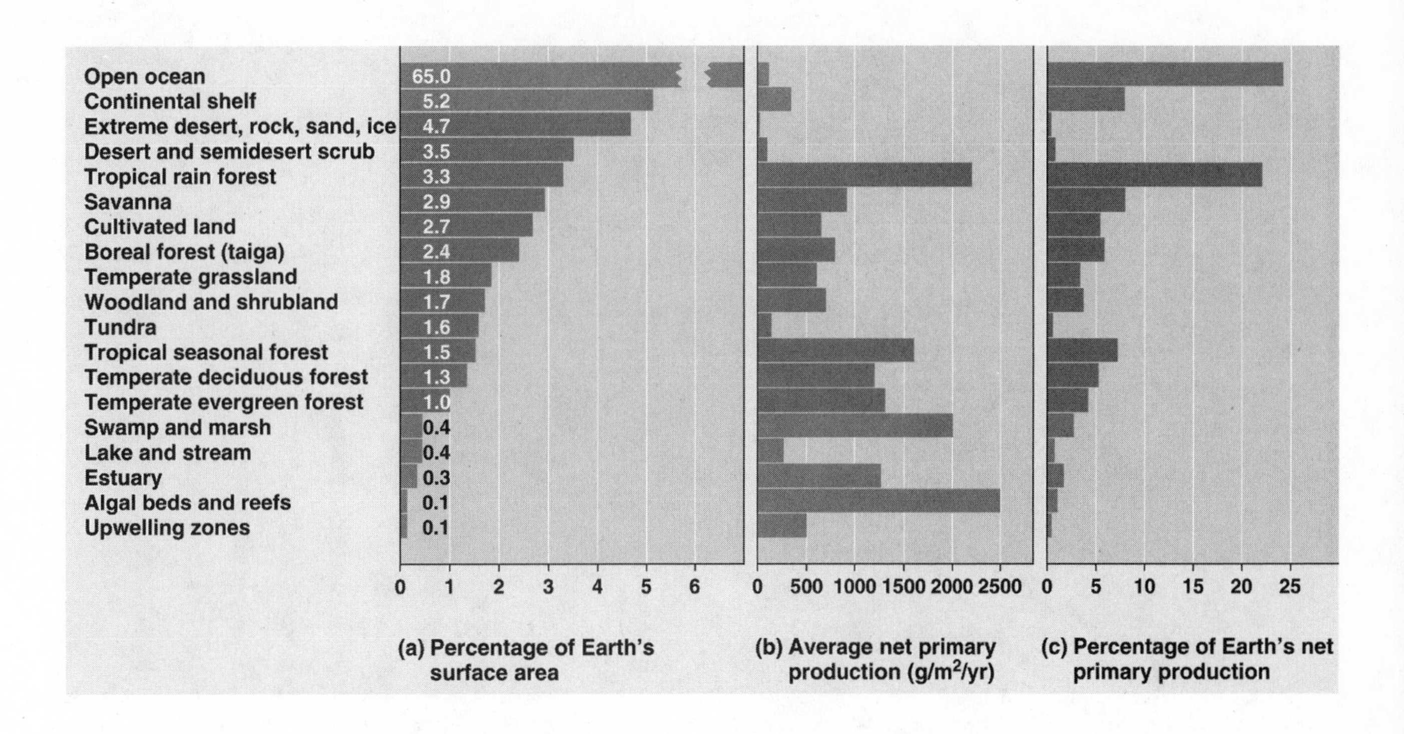

Figure 54.3 Primary production of different ecosystems, page 1201

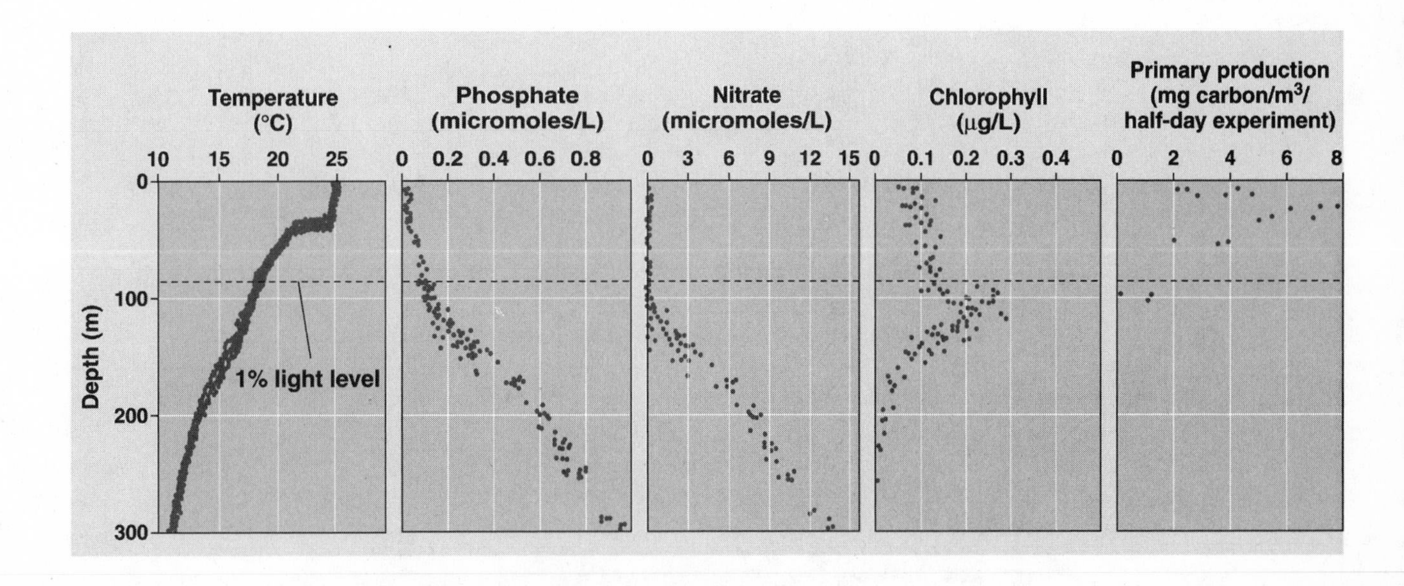

Figure 54.5 Vertical distribution of temperature, nutrients, and production in the upper layer of the central North Pacific during summer, page 1202

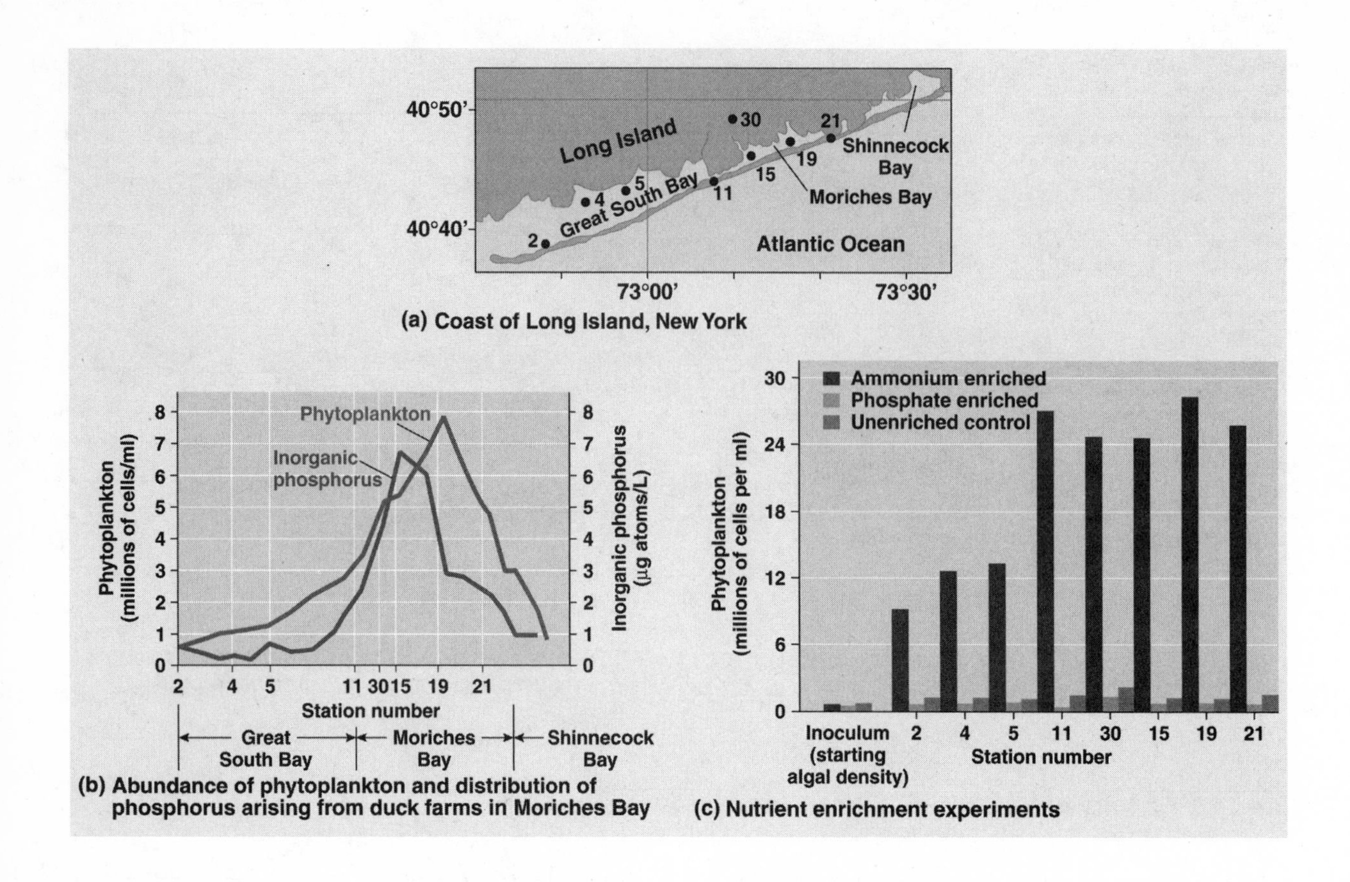

Figure 54.6 Experiments on nutrient limitations to phytoplankton production in coastal waters of Long Island, page 1203

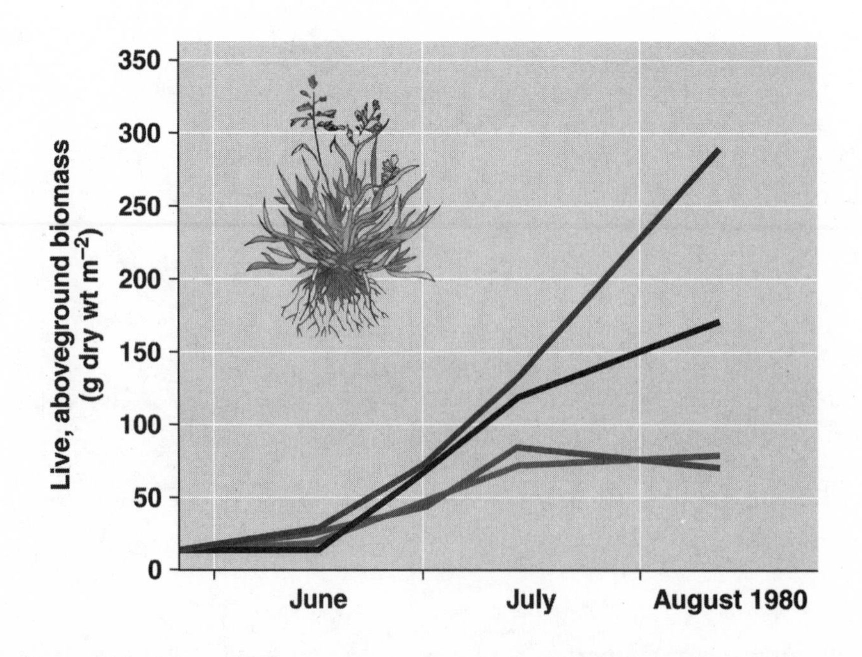

Figure 54.9 Nutrient addition experiments in a Hudson Bay salt marsh, page 1205

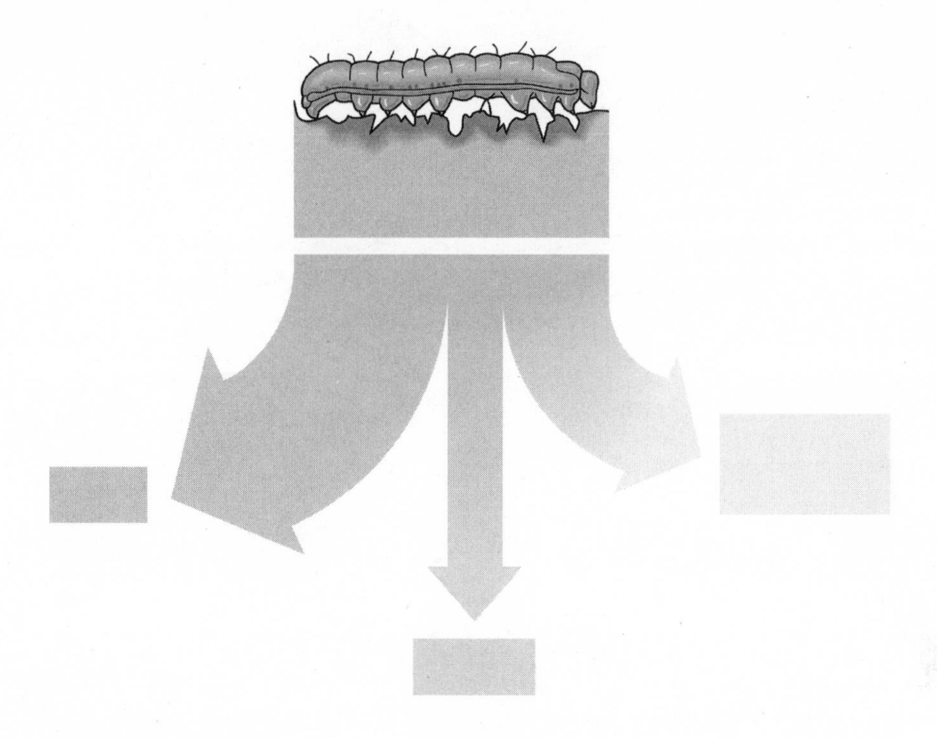

Figure 54.10 Energy partitioning within a link of the food chain, page 1206

Figure 54.11 An idealized pyramid of net production, page 1207

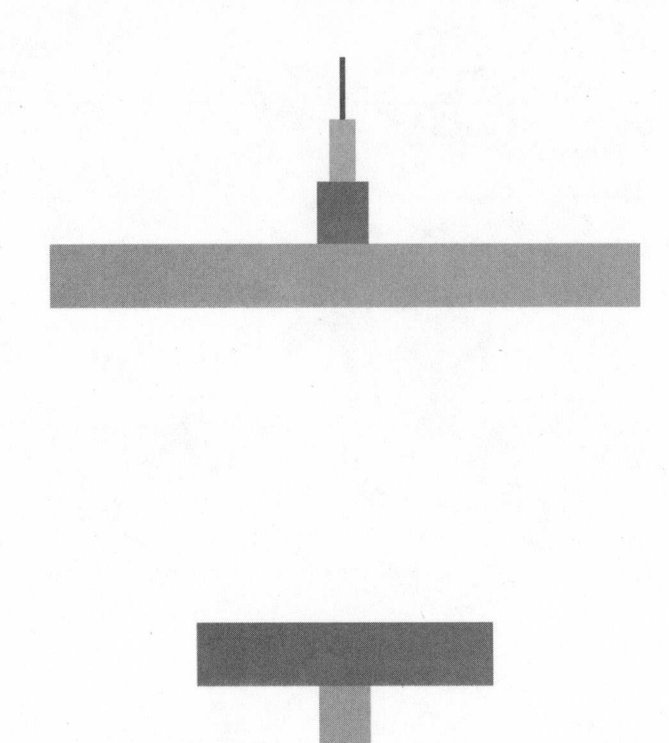

Figure 54.12 Pyramids of biomass (standing crop), page 1207

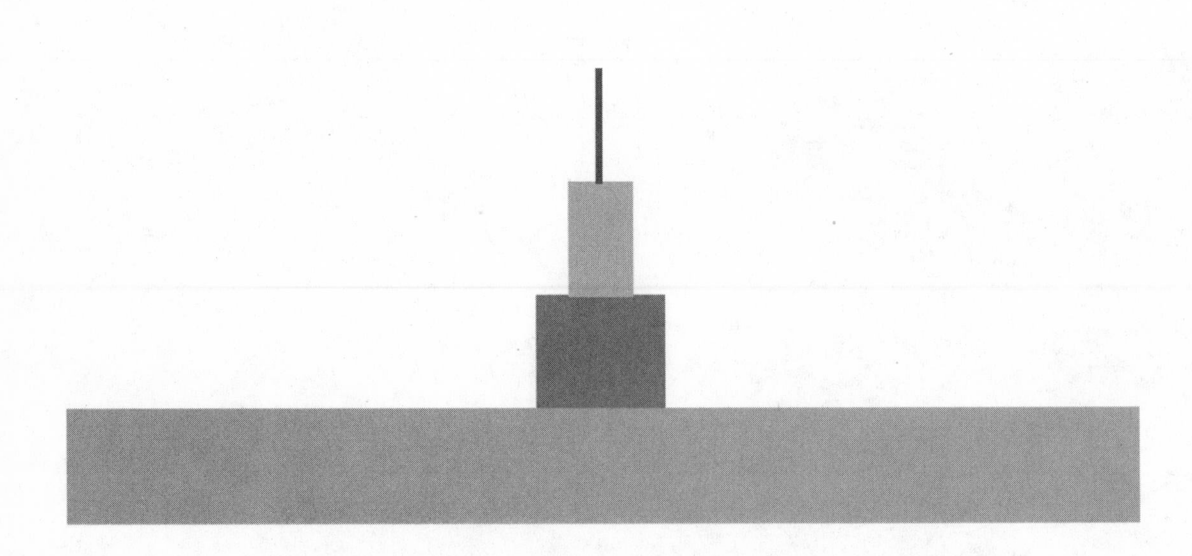

Figure 54.13 A pyramid of numbers, page 1207

Figure 54.14 Food energy available to the human population at different trophic levels, page 1208

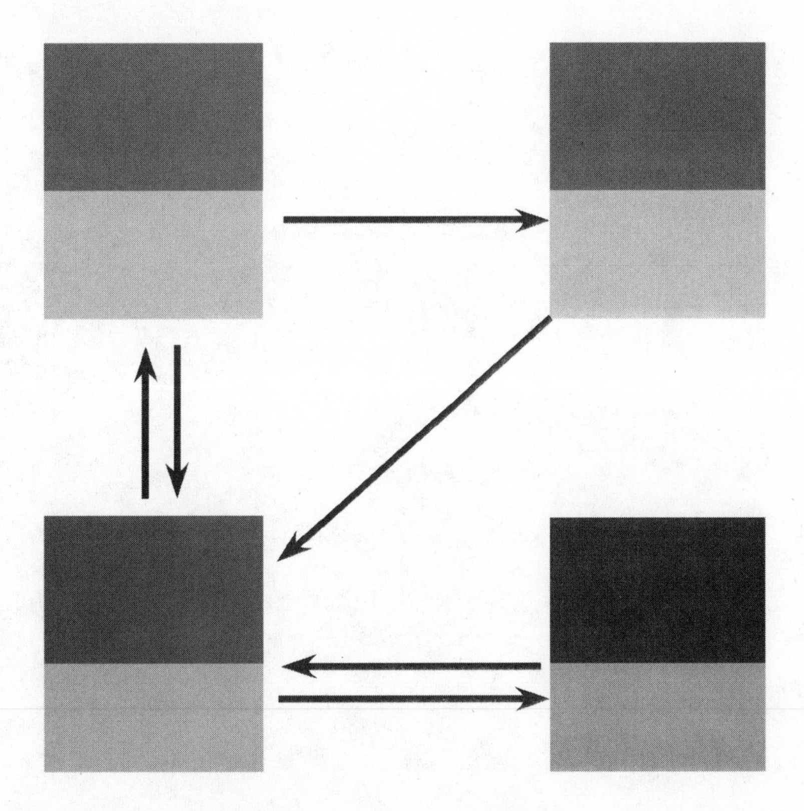

Figure 54.15 A general model of nutrient cycling, page 1209

Figure 54.16 The water cycle, page 1210

Figure 54.17 The carbon cycle, page 1211

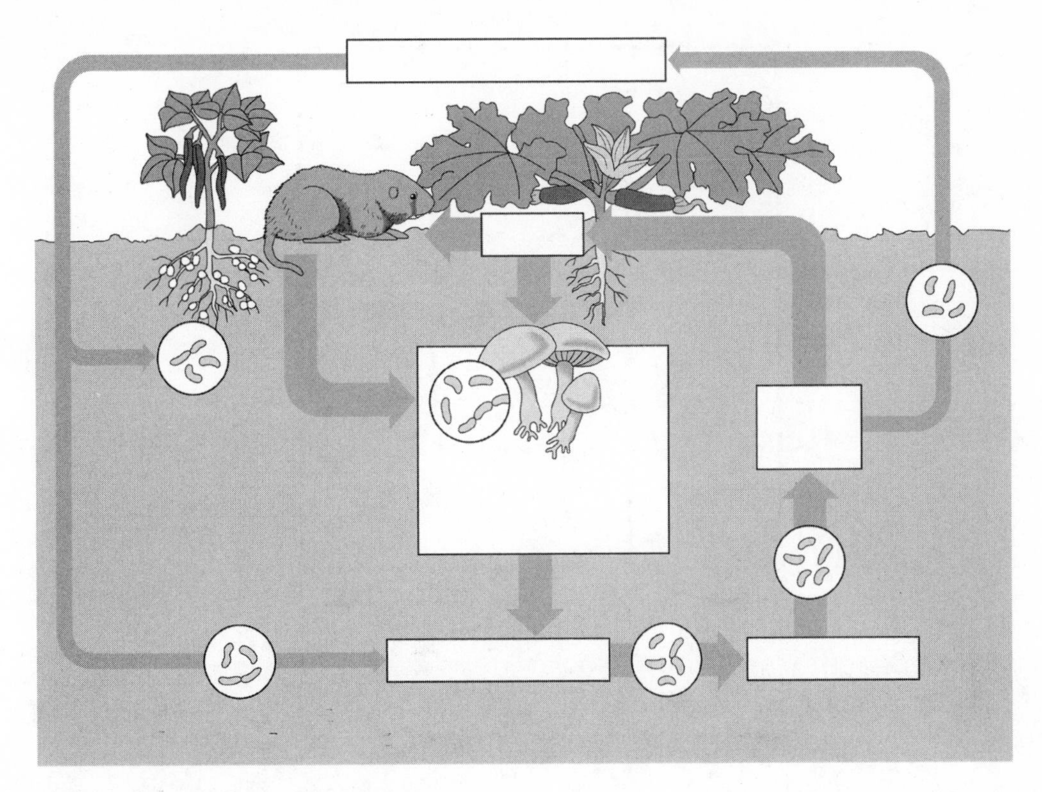

Figure 54.18 The nitrogen cycle, page 1211

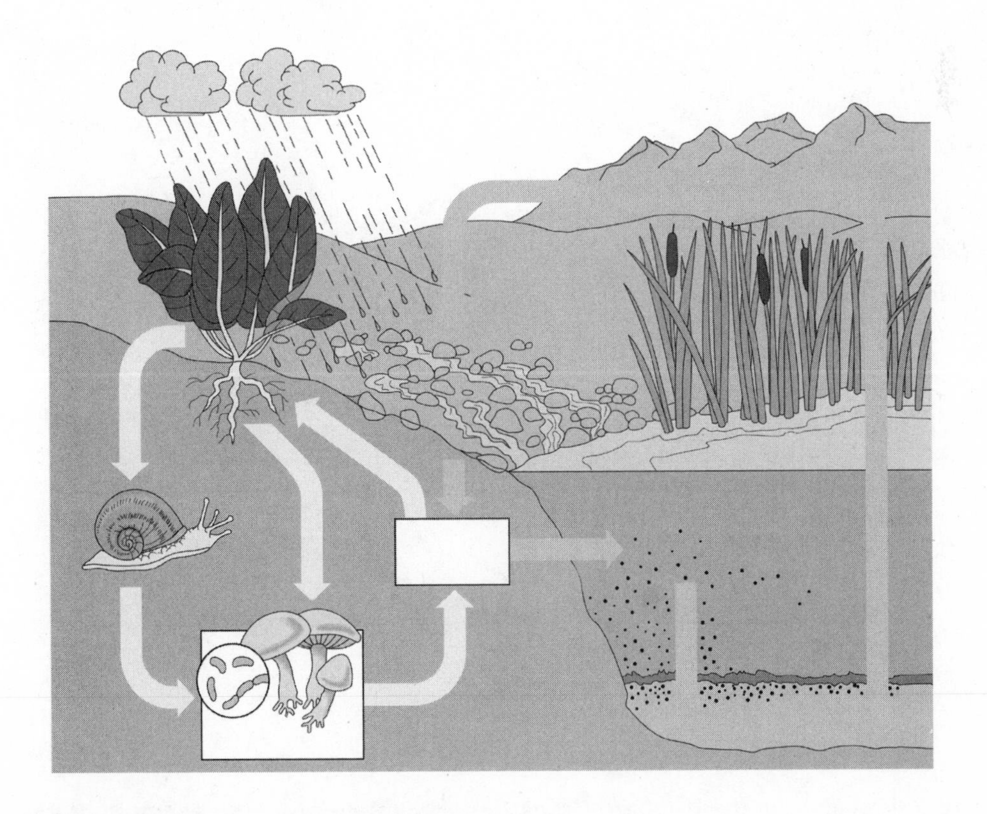

Figure 54.19 The phosphorous cycle, page 1212

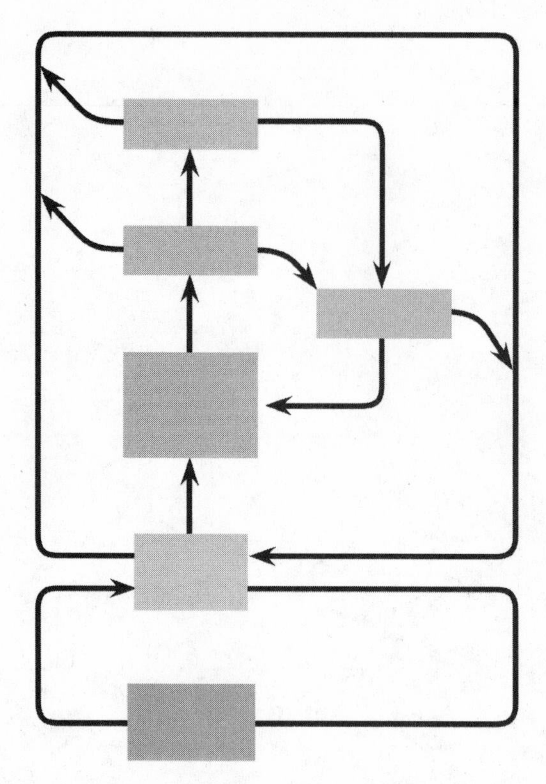

Figure 54.20 Review: Generalized scheme for biogeochemical cycles, page 1213

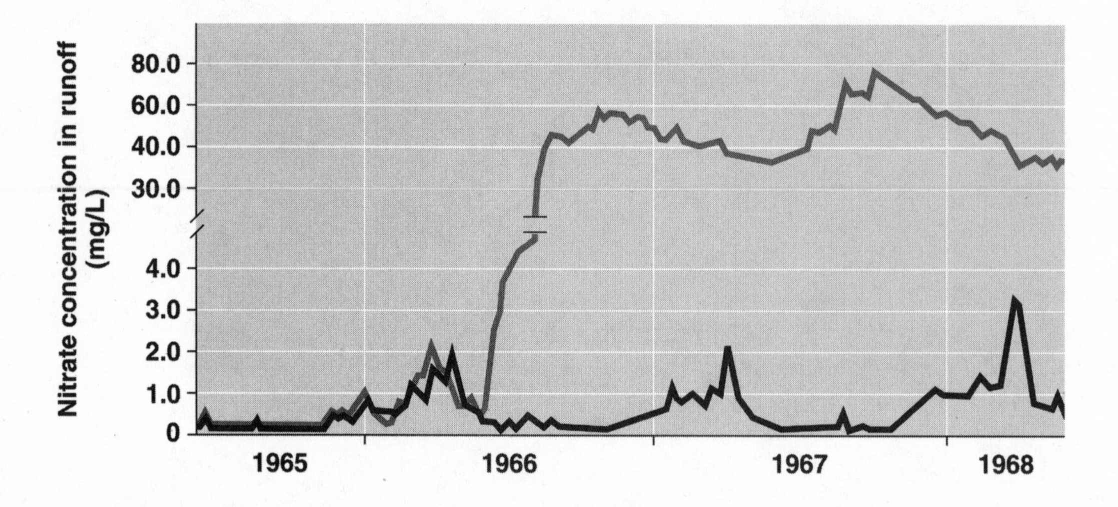

Figure 54.21 Nutrient cycling in the Hubbard Brook Experimental Forest: an example of long-term ecological research, page 1214

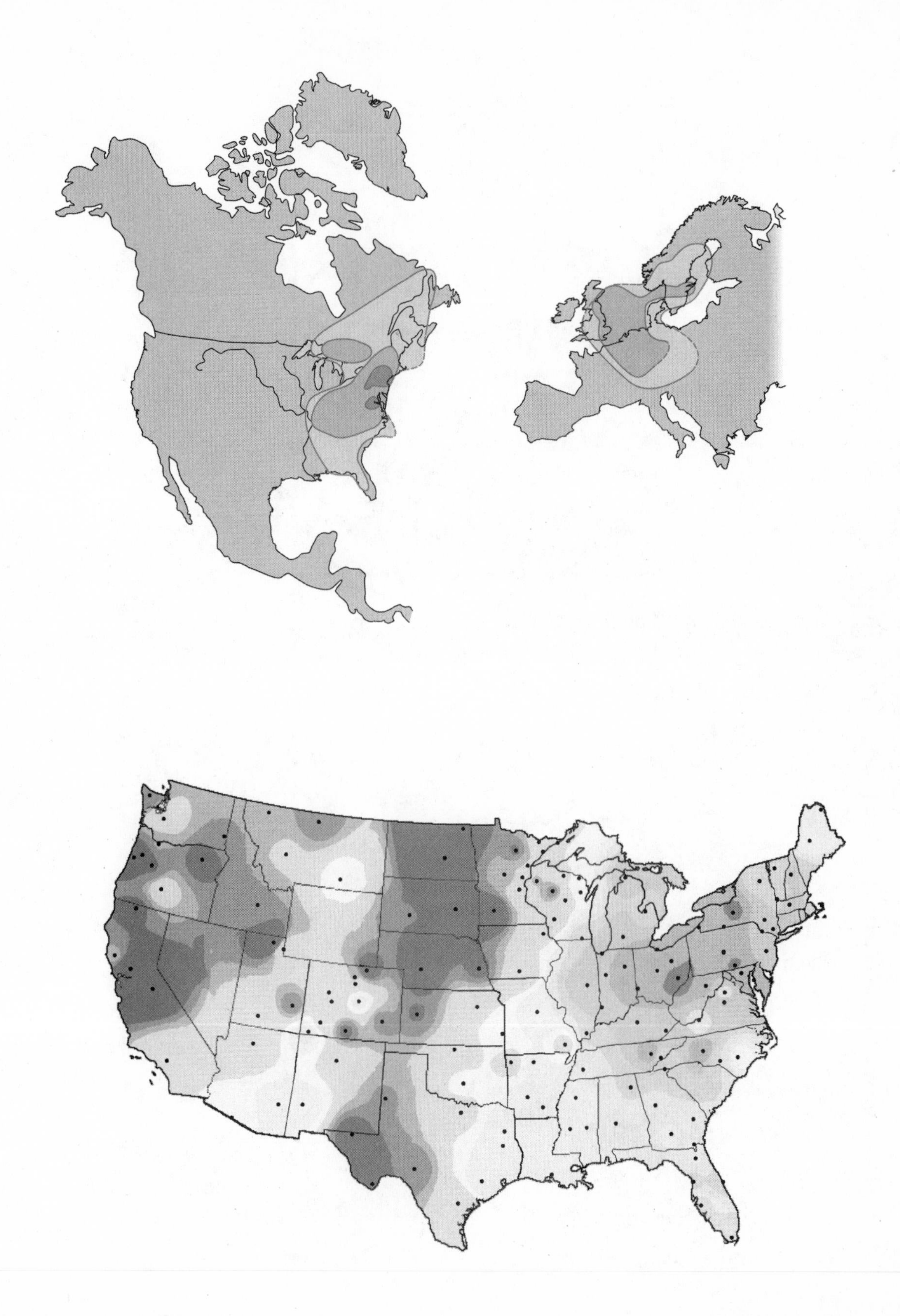

Figure 54.23 Distribution of acid precipitation in North America and Europe, page 1217

Figure 54.25 Biological magnification of DDT in a food chain, page 1218

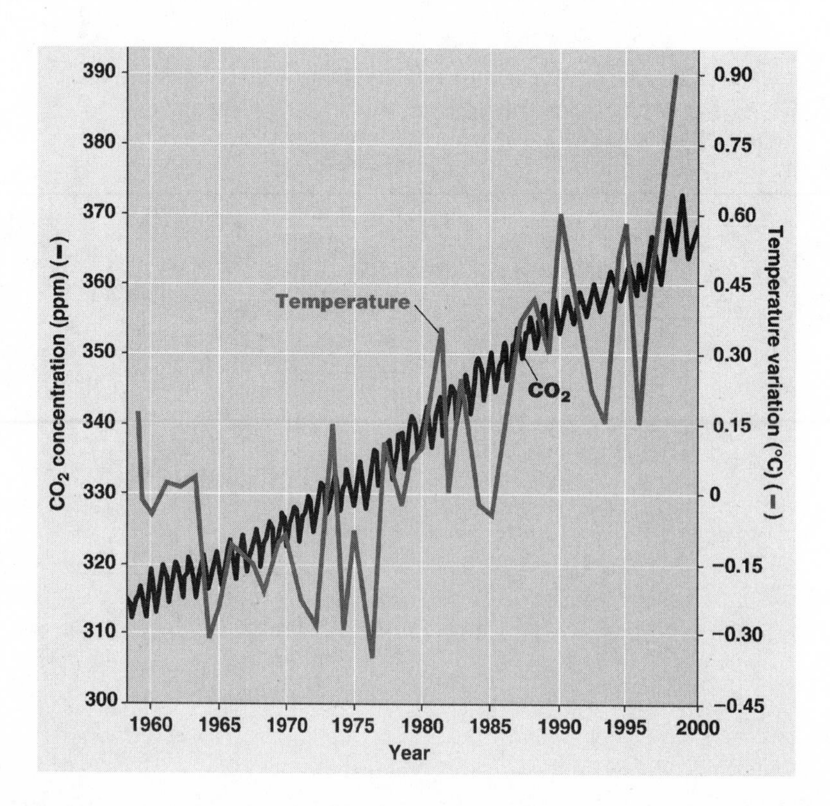

Figure 54.26 The increase in atmospheric carbon dioxide and average temperatures from 1958 to 2000, page 1219

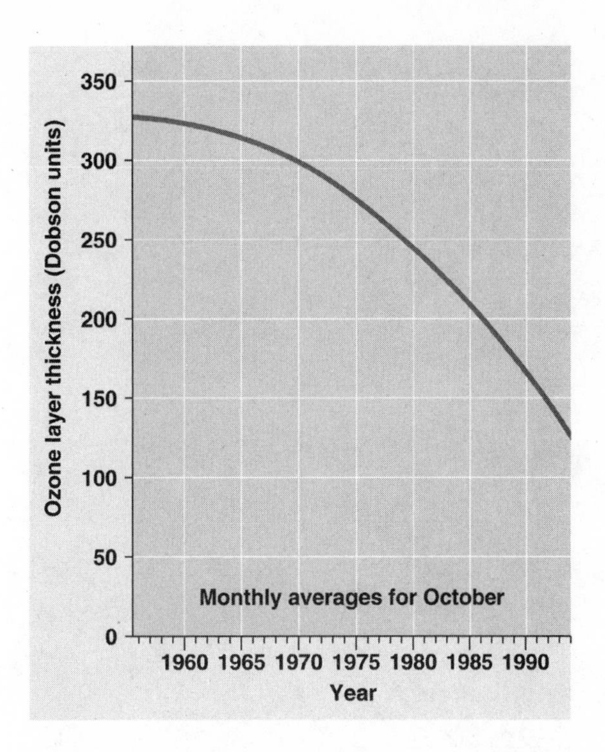

Figure 54.27b Erosion of Earth's ozone shield, page 1220

Figure 55.1 Three levels of biodiversity, page 1225

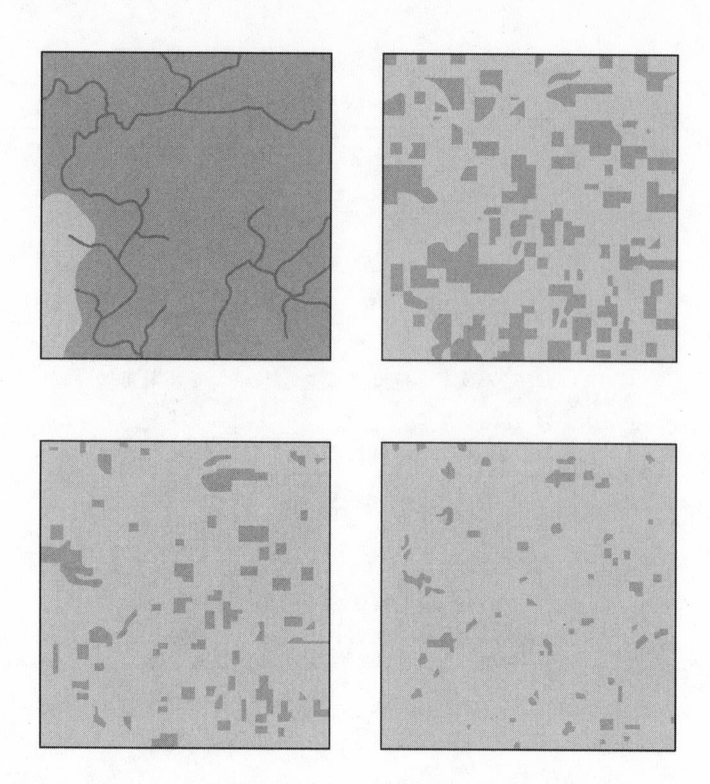

Figure 55.6 The history of habitat reduction and fragmentation in a Wisconsin forest, page 1229

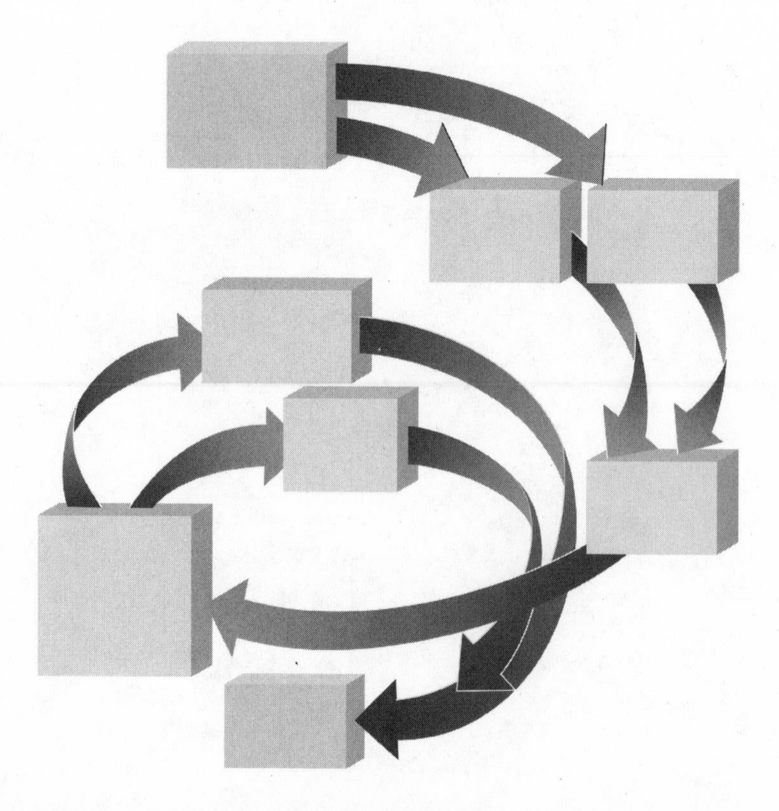

Figure 55.10 The extinction vortex of the small-population approach, page 1233

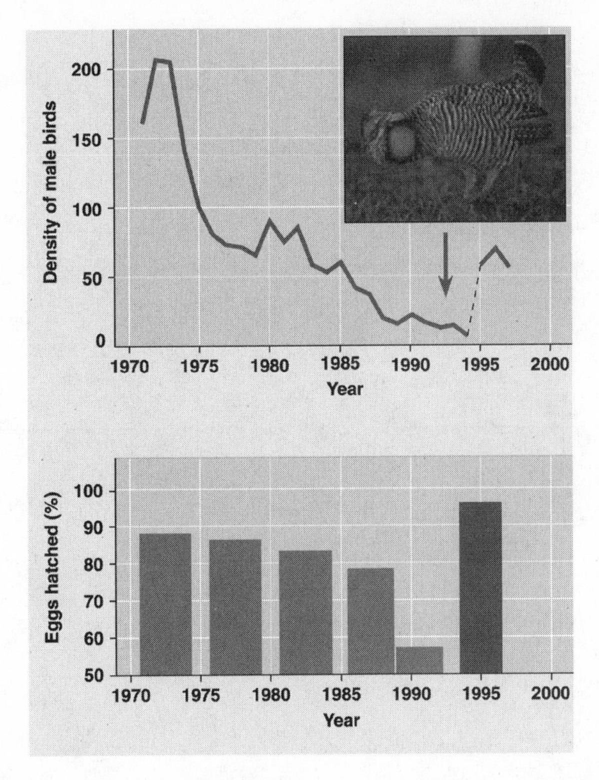

Figure 55.11 The decline of the greater prairie chicken (*Tympanuchus cupido*) in central Illinois from 1970 to 1997, page 1234

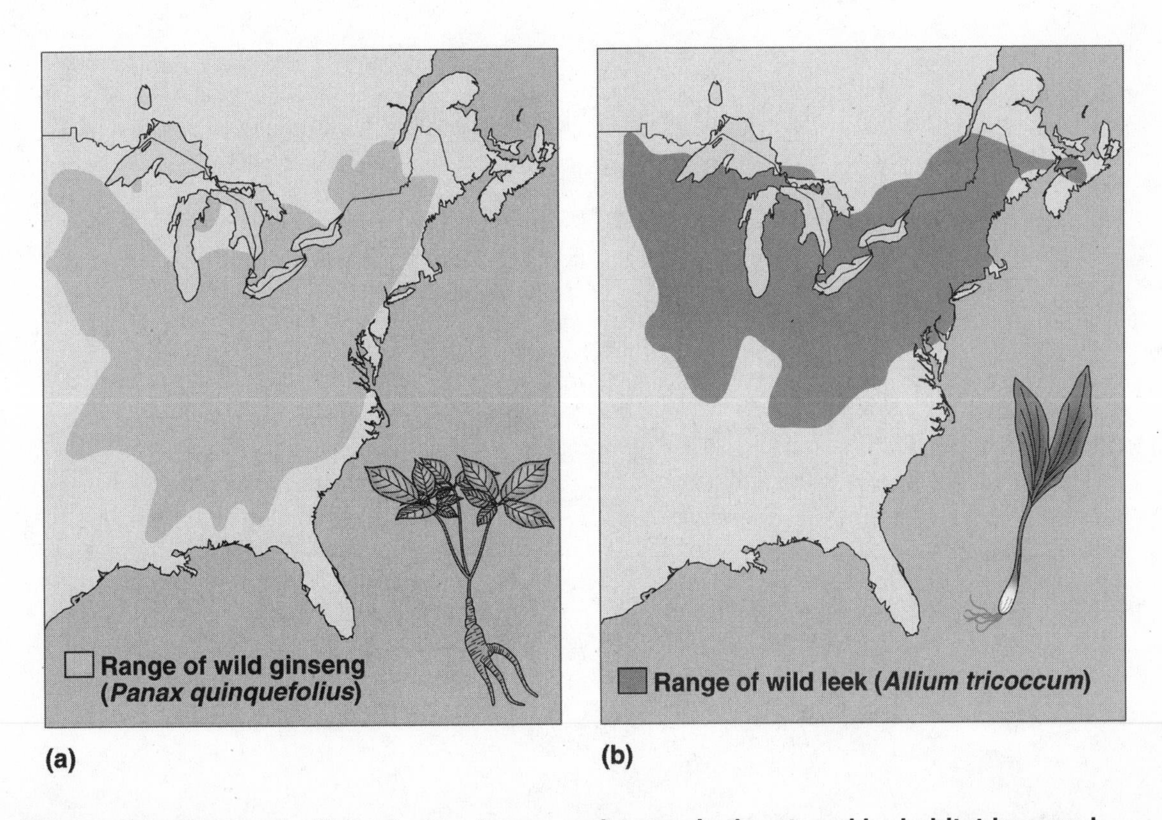

Figure 55.12 Two species of edible plants whose persistence is threatened by habitat loss and overharvesting, page 1235

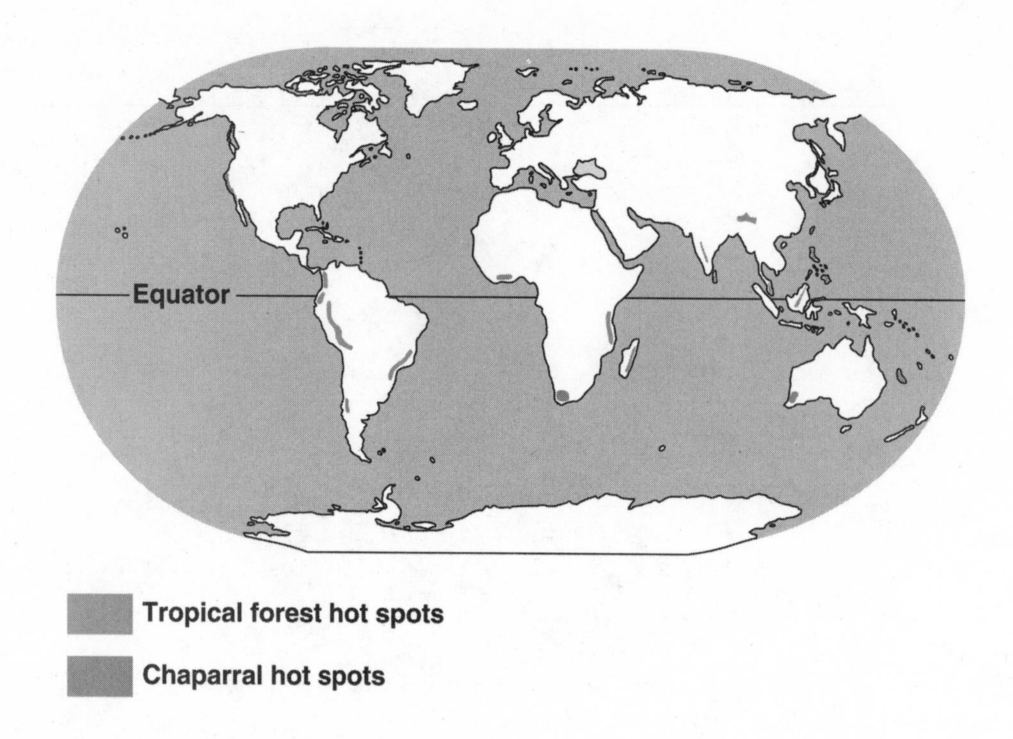

Figure 55.17 Some biodiversity hot spots, page 1240

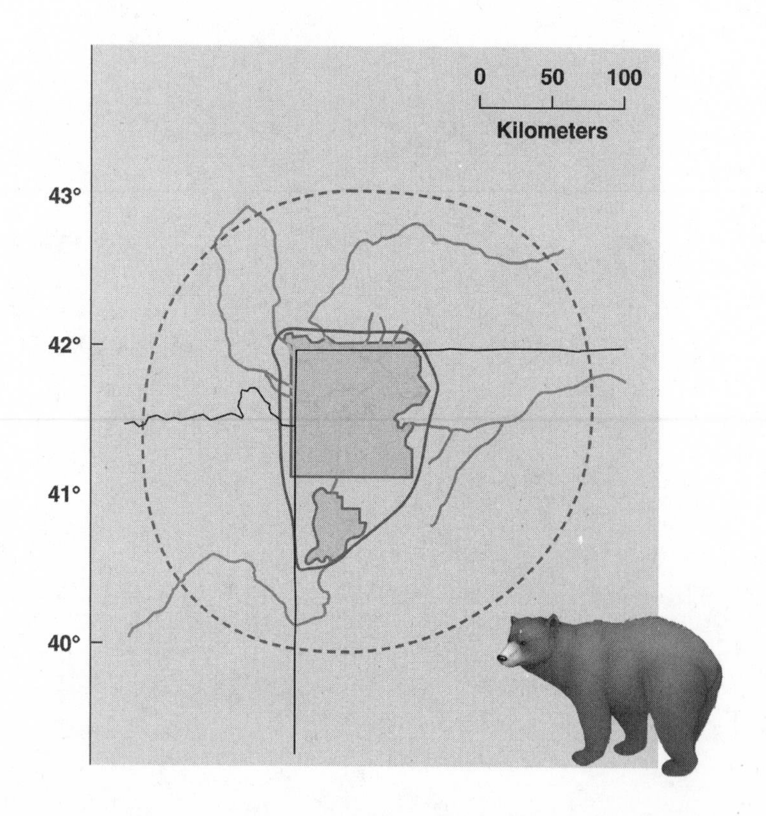

Figure 55.18 The legal and biotic boundaries for grizzly bears in Yellowstone and Grand Teton National Parks, page 1240

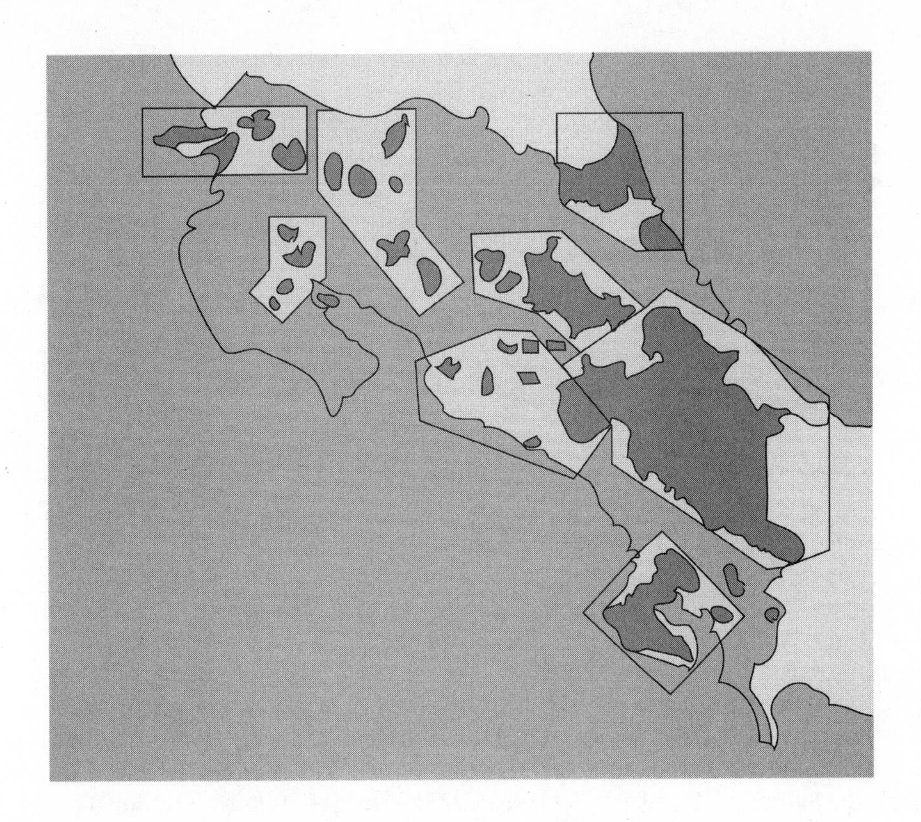

Figure 55.19 Zoned reserves in Costa Rica, page 1241

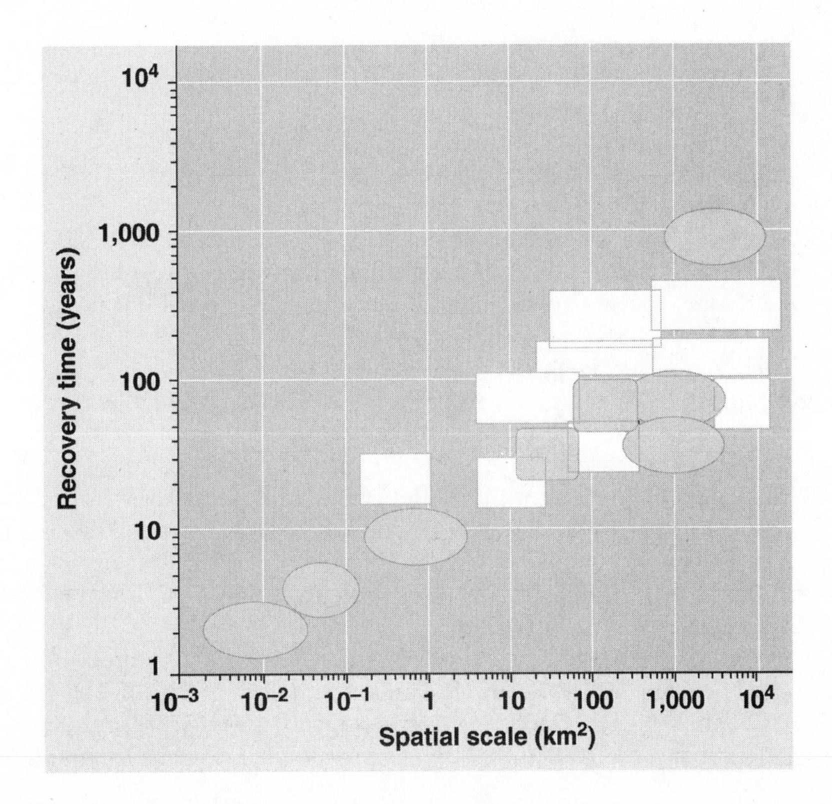

Figure 55.21 The size-time relationship for community recovery from natural (salmon-colored ellipses) and human-caused (white rectangles) disasters, page 1243

Photo Credits:

Chapter 1 1.5 Photodisc; **1.7** Photodisc; **1.12a** Manfred Kage/Peter Arnold, Inc.; **1.12b** Omikron/Photo Researchers, Inc.; **bottom** Frank Krahmer/Getty Images/Planet Earth Pictures, Ltd.
Chapter 2 2.6 left Terraphotographics/Biological Photo Service; **2.6 right** From M.C. Ratazzi et al., *Am J Human Genet* 28:143-154, 1976; **2.15** Stephen Frisch/Benjamin Cummings.
Chapter 4 4.5 Manfred Kage/Peter Arnold, Inc.; **4.8a and b** Digital Vision.
Chapter 5 5.6 top John N.A. Lott, McMaster University/Biological Photo Service; **5.6 bottom** H. Shio and P.B. Lazarow; **5.8** J. Litray/Visuals Unlimited; **5.11 left** The American Dairy Association; **5.11 right** Lara Hartley/Benjamin Cummings; **5.19a and b** Lawrence Berkeley National Laboratory; ; **5.26** P.B. Sigler from Z. Xu, A.L. Horwich, and P.B. Sigler, Nature (1997) 388:741-750. "1997 Macmillan Magazines, Ltd.; **5.27** Marie Green, University of California, Riverside.
Chapter 6 6.21 R. Rodewald, University of Virginia/Biological Photo Service.
Chapter 7 7.4 S.C. Holt, University of Texas Health Center/Biological Photo Service; **7.6** J. David Robertson; **7.9 top** From L. Orci and A. Perrelet, *Freeze-Etch Histology.* (Heidelberg: Springer-Verlag, 1975.) "1975 Springer-Verlag; **center** From A.C. Faberge, *Cell Tiss. Res.* 151 (1974): 403. " 1974 Springer-Verlag; **bottom** U. Aebi. et al. *Nature* 323 (1996): 560-564, figure 1a. Used by permission; **7.10** D.W. Fawcett/Photo Researchers, Inc.; **7.11** R. Bolender, D. Fawcett/Photo Researchers, Inc.; **7.12** Don Fawcett/Visuals Unlimited; **7.13 left** R. Rodewald University of Virginia/Biological Photo Service; **7.13 right** Daniel S. Friend, Harvard Medical School; **7.15** E.H. Newcomb; **7.17** Daniel S. Friend, Harvard Medical School; **7.18** WP Wergin and E.H. Newcomb, University of Wisconsin, Madison/Biological Photo Service; **7.19** From S.E. Fredrick and E.H. Newcomb, *The Journal of Cell Biology* 43 (1969): 343. Provided by E.H. Newcomb; **7.20** John E. Heuser, Washington University School of Medicine, St. Louis, MO; **7.22** Kent McDonald; **7.23 top** Richard Kessel/Visuals Unlimited; **7.23 bottom** Dennis Kunkel; **7.24 left** OMIKRON/Science Source/Photo Researchers, Inc.; **7.24 middle top** W.L. Dentler, University of Kansas/Biological Photo Service; **7.24 middle bottom** W.L. Dentler, University of Kansas/Biological Photo Service; **7.26** From Hirokawa Nobutaka *The Journal of Cell Biology* 94 (1982): 425 by copyright permission of The Rockefeller University Press; **7.28** G.F. Leedale/Photo Researchers, Inc.; **7.30 left** From Douglas J. Kelly, *The Journal of Cell Biology* 28 (1966): 51 by copyright permission of The Rockefeller University Press; **7.30 top right** L. Orci and A. Perrelet, *Freeze-Etch Histology,* Heidelberg: Springer-Verlag, 1975; **7.30 bottom right** From C. Peracchia and A.F. Dulhunty, *The Journal of Cell Biology* 70 (1976): 419 by copyright permission of The Rockefeller University Press.
Chapter 10 10.2 center M. Eichelberger/Visuals Unlimited; **bottom** Courtesy of W.P. Wergin and E.H. Newcomb, University of Wisconsin/Biological Photo Service; **10.10** Christine L. Case, Skyline College; **10.19 left** C.F. Miescke/Biological Photo Service; **right** Photodisc.
Chapter 12 12.3 Biophoto/Photo Researchers, Inc.; **12.5** Conly Rieder; **12.8 left** David M. Phillips/Visuals Unlimited; **12.8 right** Micrograph by B.A. Palevitz. Courtesy of E.H. Newcomb, University of Wisconsin; **12.15** Gunter Albrecht-Buehler, Northwestern University.
Chapter 13 13.3 left SIU/Visuals Unlimited; **13.3 right** CNRI/SPL/Photo Researchers, Inc.
Chapter 14 14.14 left and middle left Photodisc; **14.14 middle right and right** Anthony Loveday/Benjamin Cummings; **14.15 left** Tony Brain/Science Source/Photo Researchers, Inc.; **right** Bill Longcore/Photo Researchers, Inc.
Chapter 15 15.10 Grant Heilman/Grant Heilman Photography.
Chapter 16 16.5 Richard Wagner, UCSF Graphics; **16.10** From D.J. Burks and P.J. Stambrook, *The Journal of Cell Biology* 77 (1978): 762 by the copyright permission of The Rockefeller University Press. Photo provided by P.J. Stambrook.
Chapter 17 17.20 B. Hamkalo and O.L. Miller, Jr.; **17.22** Reprinted with permission from O.L. Miller, Jr., B.A. Hamkalo, and C.A. Thomas, Jr., *Science* 169 (1970): 392. Copyright "1970 American Association for the Advancement of Science.
Chapter 18 18.2 left, middle left and right Robley C. Williams, University of California, Berkeley/BPS; **18.2 middle right** John Cardamone Jr., University of Pittsburgh/BPS.
Chapter 19 19.1(1) S.C. Holt, University of Texas, Health Science Center, San Antonio/BPS; **19.1(2)** Courtesy of Victoria Foe; **19.1(3)** Barbara Hamkalo; **19.1(4)** From J.R. Paulsen and U.K. Laemmli, *Cell* 12 (1977): 817-828; **19.1(5) and (6)** G.F. Bahr/AFIP; **19.2** O.L. Miller Jr., Department of Biology, University of Virginia.
Chapter 20 20.09 Repligen Corporation; **20.17** Cellmark Diagnostics, Inc. Germantown, Maryland.

Chapter 21 **21.04** J.E. Sulston and H.R. Horvitz, Dev. Biol. 56 (1977):110-156; **21.12 top to bottom** Eric Wieschaus; Eric Wieschaus; Dr. Ruth Lahmann, The Whitehead Institution; Wolfgang Driever; **21.13 top to bottom** Jim Langeland, Steve Paddock, Sean Carroll, University of Wisconsin and The Howard Hughes Medical Institute; Jim Langeland, Steve Paddock, Sean Carroll, University of Wisconsin and The Howard Hughes Medical Institute; Jim Langeland, Steve Paddock, Sean Carroll, University of Wisconsin and The Howard Hughes Medical Institute; **21.20** Elliot Meyerowitz.

Chapter 22 **22.12** Jack Fields/Photo Researchers, Inc.; **22.16** Kenneth Kaneshiro; 22.17 Philip Gingerich 1991. Reprinted with permission of *Discover Magazine.*

Chapter 26 **26.12** F.M. Menger and Kurt Gabrielson, Emory University.

Chapter 27 **27.05** Christine Case.

Chapter 28 **28.03** Eric V. Grave, Photo Researchers, Inc.; **28.13** Masamichi Aikawa; **28.14(c)** M. Abbey/Visuals Unlimited; **28.16** Fred Rhoades/Mycena Consulting; **28.21** Courtesy of J.R. Waaland, University of Washington/BPS; **28.30** Robert Kay, MRC Cambridge.

Chapter 29 **29.20** Chip Clark.

Chapter 31 **31.01** Fred Rhoades/Mycena Consulting; **31.07** George Barrow; **31.07** Ed Reschkee/Peter Arnold, Inc.; **31.10** Fred Spiegel, University of Arkansas; **31.12** Biophoto Associates/Photo Researchers, Inc.; **31.17** V. Ahmadijian/Visuals Unlimited.

Chapter 33 **33.04 left** Ken Lucas/Planet Earth Pictures; **33.04 right** Claudia Mills/Friday Harbor Labs; **33.07** Robert Brons/BPS; **33.11** Center for Disease Control; **33.12** Stanley Fleger/Visuals Unlimited.

Chapter 34 **34.03** Robert Brons/Biological Photo Service; **34.25** Janice Sheldon.

Chapter 35 **35.08** R. Kessel-Shih/Visuals Unlimited; **35.09** Randy Moore/BioPhoto; **35.14** Carolina Biological Supply Phototake; **35.27** Courtesy of Susan Wick, University of Minnesota; **35.28** B. Wells and Kay Roberts.

Chapter 36 **36.14 left** William Cupples, Courtesty of Gary Tallman, Pepperdine University; **right** From T. D. Lamb, H.R. Matthews, and V. Torre, Journal of Physiology 372 (1986): 315-349. Reprinted by permission.

Chapter 38 **38.04 left** Graham Kent; **38.04 right** Ed Reschke; **38.17** Dr. John C. Sanford/Cornell University.

Chapter 39 **39.17** Malcolm Wilkins, University of Glasgow; **39.31** Barbara Baker, University of Berkeley.

Chapter 41 **41.21 left** Brian Milne/Animals Animals; **41.21 right** Hans and Judy Beste/Animals Animals.

Chapter 42 **42.01** Norbert Wu/Mo Young Productions; **42.22** Peng Chai, University of Texas and Hong Y. Yan, University of Kentucky; **42.25** CNRI/Photo Researchers, Inc.

Chapter 44 **44.05 top** Jeff Lepore/Photo Researchers, Inc.; **bottom** Dave B. Fleetham/Visuals Unlimited.

Chapter 47 **47.03** Reproduced from J.C. Rilkey, L.F. Jaffe, E.B. Ridgeway, and G.T. Reynolds, Journal of Cell Biology 76 (1978): 448-466, 1978; **47.09** Charles A Ettensohn, Carnegie Mellon University; **47.11 top** CABISCO/Visual Unlimited; **bottom** Thomas Poole, SUNY Health Science Center; **47.20** Hiroki Nishida, Developmental Biology 121 (1987): 526. Reprinted by permission of Academic Press.

Chapter 48 **48.02** Manfred Kage/Peter Arnold, Inc.

Chapter 49 **49.31** Clara Franzini-Armstrong, University of Pennsylvania; **49.32** Dr. H.E. Huxley.

Chapter 50 **50.08** Scott Camazine/The National Audubon Society Collection/Photo Researchers, Inc.; **50.16** L. Roberts. How fast can trees migrate? Science, Vol

Chapter 51 **51.10 top** Joe MacDonald.CORBIS; **bottom** Dorling Kindersley; **51.27** Kenneth Lorenzen, UC Davis.

Chapter 53 **53.02** Heather Angel/Natural Visions; **53.12** D.L. Breitburg, T. Loher, C.A. Pacey, and A. Gerstein. Varying effects of low dissolved oxygen on trophic interactions in an estuarine food web. *Ecological Monographs,* vol. 67, p.490. Copyright © 1997 Ecological Society of America. Reprinted with permission; **53.15** J.A. Lubena and S.A. Levin. The spread of a reinvading species: Expansion of the California sea otter. *American Naturalist,* vol. 131, fig. 1, p.529, fig. 2, p.535 Copyright © 1988 The University of Chicago Press, Chicago. Reprinted with permission; **53.19** Tom Bean/Tom & Susan Bean, Inc.

Chapter 55 **55.11** R.L. Westemeier, J.D. Brawn, S.A. Simpson, T.L. Esker, R.W. Jansen, J.W. Walk, E.L. Kershner, J.L. Bouzat, and K.N. Paige. Tracking the long-term decline and recovery of an isolated population. *Science,* vol.282, p.1696. Copyright © 1998 by the AAAS. Reprinted with permission.